# 2001 NATIONAL RENOVATION & INSURANCE REPAIR ESTIMATOR

**with data from the Rutlidge Institute**

**edited by Jonathan Russell**

---

## Includes inside the back cover:

- An estimating CD with all the costs in this book, plus,
- An estimating program that makes it easy to use these costs,
- An interactive video guide to the National Estimator program,
- A program that converts your estimates into invoices,
- A program that exports your estimates to QuickBooks Pro.

The Show Me video guide to National Estimator starts a few seconds after you insert the CD in your CD-ROM drive.

---

**Craftsman Book Company**
6058 Corte del Cedro / P.O. Box 6500 / Carlsbad, CA 92018

©2000 Craftsman Book Company    ISBN 1-57218-097-8    Published October 2000 for the year 2001.

# contents

# about this book

### NEW CHALLENGES IN 2001

Rising interest rates haven't been enough to significantly slow construction in most regions. Contractors still report difficulty finding skilled workers and spot material shortages still occur, especially during busy times of the year.

Training, accurate pricing, efficient crews, employee retention, and job management are growing increasingly important in a changing market place.

### A TOOL

This book is a tool and like all tools it can be misused. It is an excellent tool for the renovation and repair professional. It is not a substitute for experience, skill, and knowledge.

Prices in this book are based on research of actual jobs and successful estimates. They represent an average of the typical conditions.

Estimators should compare the conditions described in this book with actual conditions on site and adjust the price accordingly.

### UNIQUE TO RENOVATION AND REPAIR WORK

This book is compiled specifically for the unique problems and conditions found in renovation and repair work. *It is not a new construction cost book.*

Renovation and repair work involve different circumstances than those found in new construction.

For example, the renovation or repair professional must work around existing conditions including home contents, access problems, out-of-plumb or out-of-square buildings, outdated materials, and existing conditions that violate current building codes.

New-construction professionals have the luxury of placing items in a logical order, but the renovation, remodel, or repair professional must deal with conditions as they find them.

This means that joists have to be replaced in an existing floor system, paint has to be applied in a room where stain-grade base and carpeting are already installed, structures may have to be braced, contents have to be moved or worked around, and materials and installation techniques must be matched.

### DETERMINING COSTS

All costs in this book are based on typical conditions and typical problems found when remodeling or repairing a structure.

This means a door takes 10 to 15 minutes longer to install than it would in the ideal circumstances found in new construction.

Stairs are more difficult to install around pre-existing walls, wall framing takes longer when walls are typically splicing into existing work, and so on.

Some prices in this book will closely match prices used in new construction. Other prices will reflect the complex conditions found in renovation and repair and will be dramatically different.

For example, using this book's stair building prices to estimate stair work in a series of 150 tract homes will result in an estimate that is far too high.

### THE ART OF ESTIMATING

Estimating is part art, part science. Estimators must consider many factors, including access, crew productivity, special techniques, special abilities, temperament of the owner, and how busy the company is.

A contractor who is desperate for work will estimate much lower than a contractor who is swamped with work.

All of these factors—and many other similar ones—cannot be included in this or any other price book. They are part of the art of estimating.

The science of estimating, which includes prices, typical techniques, and materials, *is* included in this book.

This book is designed to make the *science* of estimating easier, which allows you to spend much more time focusing on the *art* of estimating, where your skill is crucial to the success of your company.

### GENERAL vs. SPECIFIC

It is important to note that the more specific the estimator is, the more accurate the final estimate will be.

For example, when an estimator calculates all electrical costs for a typical home using a square foot cost, it may not be as accurate as if the estimator priced each fixture, outlet, and appliance hook-up.

Since the square foot price is based on a typical installation, it will not be exact for a home that is atypical in any way–for example, one with special outdoor lighting or with an expensive crystal fixture in the entry.

The more specific the item, the more exact the prices. The more general an item, the more assumptions must be made.

## rounding

This book rounds hourly wage rates and the material, labor, and equipment components of a unit price.

These prices are rounded to "three significant digits." This means that prices under three digits (including two to the right of the decimal) are not rounded. Prices four digits and larger are rounded to the third digit from the left.

For example:

.23 is not rounded
2.33 is not rounded
23.33 is rounded to 23.30
233.33 is rounded to 233.00
2,333.33 is rounded to 2,330.00
23,333.33 is rounded to 23,300.00

To help ensure the accuracy of your estimates we describe any assumptions made when determining general items.

For example, the *Rough Carpentry* chapter contains a square foot price for estimating 2" by 4" wall framing. To help you make sure that this price will work for you, we describe our assumptions: the stud centers, the number of openings, headers, corners, plates, and so forth, that would typically be found in a wall.

In most cases the square foot price will apply, but you will always want to carefully consider items that are more general, and if needed, adjust them to fit the conditions.

In the case above, the estimator may want to use the square-foot price for average fixtures, then add an allowance for the crystal fixture and the outdoor lighting.

## TIME AND MATERIAL CHARTS

Almost all chapters include time and material charts at the end. These time and material charts are designed to show you the materials used, waste, labor rates, labor burden costs, and labor productivity.

When materials with a range of sizes appear, only the small and large size are usually listed.

When materials with a range of qualities appear, often only the low and high prices are listed.

These charts are designed to give you accurate detail on the exact prices used. When prices change, this book does not become obsolete. Compare current prices with those used and factor accordingly.

## MATERIAL COSTS

National average material costs are compiled from surveys of suppliers throughout the country.

Costs for some materials, such as clay tile, building stone and hardwood, will vary a great deal from region to region.

For example, clay tile plants are located near naturally occurring clay sources. Because clay tiles are heavy, the further the tiles have to be shipped, the more expensive the tiles will be. The user of this book must be aware of local price variations.

Materials commonly found in every city are priced based on local delivery. In most cases this will be delivery no greater than 20 miles away from a local source. However, many rural areas have lumber yards that will deliver to a wider area at no additional charge.

Materials that are not commonly available locally, like hand-carved moldings or historical wallpaper, include shipping costs anywhere in North America. Estimators in Hawaii, Alaska and remote areas of Canada should add for additional shipping costs when applicable.

Material waste is often indicated with the items, but it's always a good idea to check the time and material charts for the exact waste calculated for all the components of an item.

Waste indicates material that is discarded during installation. It does not include waste that occurs when materials are taken to storage and ruined, run over at the job site, spilled, improperly cut, or damaged due to mishandling.

These types of occurrences are kept to a minimum by every good contractor, but will still occur on any job site.

Another common waste issue in renovation and repair is when a contractor must buy a minimum quantity for a small repair. For example, to replace a six-inch section of base, it is necessary to buy a piece of base that is eight-feet long or longer. In these cases, use the minimum price.

Material prices may not be listed with the time and material charts in some chapters. In these chapters little new information would be provided by the materials chart so the space is saved for other information.

For example, a materials chart in the *Appliance* chapter will not provide an estimator with any new information.

The materials component of the unit price for an oven as listed in the main body of the chapter will tell the estimator how much the oven and connections cost.

Relisting these appliances in a materials chart wastes valuable space.

## LABOR COSTS

Labor costs are national average rates that usually are consistent with union labor wages.

See the time and material charts for specific costs and labor rates.

Crew labor rates are an average hourly rate for each member of the crew. For example, a masonry crew might consist of a mason, a mason's helper, and a hod carrier.

The hourly rate for this crew is the average cost of all three. In other words, the hourly rate is for 20 minutes work by the mason, 20 minutes work by the mason's helper, and 20 minutes work by the hod carrier.

Separation of labor in renovation and insurance repair work is much more difficult than is separation of labor on large commercial construction projects.

On a typical repair or renovation job a carpenter may participate in demolition, frame walls, set doors, set toilets, install electrical outlets and fixtures, and do a little painting.

In the jobs analyzed for this cost book, well over 40 percent of the demolition work was done by skilled workers. This is because demolition is often selective, requiring a skilled worker to ensure that additional damage does not occur.

Many renovation and repair companies are also relatively small, so skilled workers participate in all phases of construction.

These realities are reflected in the labor costs used in this book. This means that a demolition laborer's hourly rate may seem higher than is normal for an unskilled worker.

The time and material charts show all items that are built into each labor rate.

Some contractors may not provide health insurance or retirement plans to some or all of their workers. Estimators can "back-out" these expenses from the labor costs.

It is critical that estimators examine the Worker's Compensation costs calculated in the wage rates. Some states have Worker's Compensation rates that are double, triple, or even quadruple the national average rates used in this book.

Worker's Compensation rates should be adjusted to match local conditions.

Labor productivity is based on observation of work performed in renovation and repair conditions.

These conditions differ from new construction in many ways, but a few of the most common are:

❶ difficulty matching existing work, ❷ access problems, ❸ materials that must be more carefully shaped and attached than is typical in new construction, ❹ out-of-plumb or out-of-square structures, ❺ reinforcing, ❻ more trips and effort are required to find materials, ❼ much more travel time is required because most jobs will have a relatively small amount of work in some trades, ❽ more vehicles are required by the renovation or repair contractor because many tradespeople are often traveling between jobs, compared to new construction where crews may spend weeks or months on one job, and because crews tend to be smaller and each crew may need a vehicle, ❾ more unexpected problems, and ❿ more restrictions in established neighborhoods.

Labor productivity is based on a clean job site where tools are put away and secured at the end of each day.

Depending on the trade, 20 to 30 minutes per eight hours is allowed for cleanup and putting away tools. Normally skilled workers spend half as much time cleaning up as do unskilled workers.

As is typical in new construction, labor includes unpacking and in some cases unloading materials from a truck on site, some travel to pick up minor materials (e.g. a forgotten tube of caulk, or a forgotten tool), typical breaks, lay-out, planning, discussion, coordination, mobilization (many companies meet at a central location each morning to receive instructions), recording hours (including specific information needed for job costing), occasional correction of mistakes in installation, and so forth.

Supervision is not included in these costs but should not generally be required. This is because each crew includes a skilled tradesperson who normally would not require supervision beyond the normal dispatch and mobilization discussed previously.

## EQUIPMENT COSTS

Equipment costs are included only when equipment will be used that is not typically a part of the tools used by the majority of renovation or repair contractors.

For example, each carpenter should have a worm-drive saw, miter box, compressor, nail guns, and so forth. These types of tools are not included in the equipment costs.

However, equipment like cranes, backhoes, concrete saws, and jack hammers are not assumed to be part of the equipment and tools owned by a typical renovation or repair contractor. When these are needed, equipment rates are included in the unit price.

Equipment costs include the typical cost to rent the equipment from a local equipment rental shop. When applicable, they also include fuel or blade costs.

Check each item to determine if it includes delivery to the job site or operator labor. Also be careful to note minimum costs for work where rented equipment is needed.

## MARKUP

Prices in this book do not include markup. Insurance repair markup is almost always 20 percent: 10 percent for overhead and 10 percent for profit.

In renovation work on historical structures, markup may be as high as 30 percent, although markup over 20 percent may be "hidden" inside the unit cost. Typical remodeling work markup varies from 15 percent to 25 percent. The most common markup for all types of work is 20 percent.

## REGIONAL DIFFERENCES

Construction techniques vary from region to region. Different climates and local customs provide a variety of unique regional methods.

For example, in southern Florida it is common to build the first floor of a home from concrete block capped with a grade beam. This method won't be found in Colorado.

Similarly, coral stone walls aren't common in Denver, although they are often seen in Miami.

Slate roofs are common on historical homes and newer custom homes in Philadelphia but are virtually nonexistent in Rapid City.

Homes in the south often include screened porches which aren't nearly so common in the west.

A Georgia home is much more likely to include a series of architecturally-correct columns with Corinthian capitals than is a home in Minnesota.

A Hawaii home may be built entirely from treated wood, when an Arizona home only uses treated lumber when it contacts dirt or concrete.

Many regional materials and techniques are priced in this book. Keep in mind that you should not use these prices if the item is not common to your area.

# abbreviations

| | | |
|---|---|---|
| **ABS**....Acrylonitrile butadiene styrene | **lf** ...........................................lineal foot | **SBS**.................styrene butyl styrene |
| **ac** ...............................alternating current | **li** ..........................................lineal inch | **sf** ......................................square foot |
| **bf**...............................................board foot | **m** ....................................one thousand | **sh** .................................................sheet |
| **btu**.....................British thermal units | **mbf** ..........................1,000 board feet | **si** .....................................square inch |
| **CEC**.......California Earthquake Code | **mBtu**........1,000 British thermal units | **sq** .............................100 square feet |
| (also see page 83) | **mh** ..................................man hour | **st** ..................................................step |
| **cf**.............................................cubic foot | **mi** ...............................................mile | **sy** .................................square yard |
| **cfm** ............cubic foot per minute | **mlf**..........................1,000 lineal feet | **t&g** ............tongue-&-groove edge |
| **ci** ............................................cubic inch | **mm** ..............................millimeter(s) | **TV** .....................................television |
| **cy** .........................................cubic yard | **mo**...........................................month | **UBC**............Uniform Building Code |
| **ea** .................................................each | **mph** ........................miles per hour | **UL** .............Underwriters' Laboratory |
| **FUTA**............Federal Unemployment | **msf**........................1,000 square feet | **vlf** .........................vertical lineal foot |
| Compensation Act tax | **no.** .........................................number | **wk**...............................................week |
| **gal** ...........................................gallon | **oc**........................................on center | **w/** .................................................with |
| **GFCI** ..ground fault circuit interrupter | **oz**.............................................ounce | **x** ..........................................by or times |
| **gph** ...........................gallon(s) per hour | **pr**...............................................pair | |
| **gpm** .....................gallon(s) per minute | **psi** .............pounds per square inch | **SYMBOLS** |
| **hp** .......................................horsepower | **PVC**.....................polyvinyl chloride | **/** .....................................................per |
| **hr(s)** .........................................hour(s) | **qt** ...............................................quart | **-** ................................through or to |
| **IMC** ..........intermediate metal conduit | **R/L** ..........................random length(s) | **@** ...................................................at |
| **kd** ......................................kiln dried | **R/W/L** ......random widths and lengths | **%** ...........................................percent |
| **kv** .......................................kilovolt(s) | **RSC** ....................rigid steel conduit | **$** .............................U.S. dollars |
| **kva** ............................1,000 volt amps | **S1S2E**...........surfaced 1 side, 2 edges | **'** ..................................................feet |
| **kw**.....................................kilowatt(s) | **S2S** .............................surfaced 2 sides | **"** .............................................inches |
| **lb(s)** .........................................pound(s) | **S4S** .............................surfaced 4 sides | **#**.............................pound or number |

# acknowledgements

The editor wishes to gratefully acknowledge the contribution of the following: 18th Century Hardware Co., Inc. • A-Ball Plumbing Supply • A&Y Lumber • American Building Restoration Chemicals, Inc. • American Custom Millwork, Inc. • American Society for Testing and Materials (ASTM) • Anderson Windows • Anthony Lombardo Architectural Paneling Inc. • Anthony Wood Products Incorporated • The Antique Hardware Store • Architectural Components, Inc. • Architectural Woodwork Institute • The Balmer Architectural Art Studios • Bathroom Hardware, Inc. • Bathroom Machineries • Bendix Mouldings, Inc. • Brass Reproductions • Brick Institute of America • C & H Roofing, Inc. • C. G. Girolami & Sons • Caradco • Cataumet Sawmills • CertainTeed • Chadsworth Incorporated • Chelsea Decorative Metal Company • Classic Accents, Inc. • Classic Ceilings • CMW, Inc. • Conant Custom Brass • Conklin Metal Industries • Craftsman Lumber Company • Crown City Hardware Co. • Cumberland General Stores • Cumberland Woodcraft Co. Inc. • Designs in Tile • Dimension Hardwood • Donnell's Clapboard Mill • Driwood Moulding • Eisenhart Wallcoverings • Empire Wood Works • Raymond Enkeboll Designs • James Facenelli, *CGR #28* • Focal Point Architectural Products • Four Seasons Sun Rooms • Futurbilt • Garland • Gates Moore • General Electric Company • George Taylor Specialties Co. • Goodwin Heart Pine Company • Gougeon Brothers, Inc. • Grand Era, Inc. • Granville Manufacturing Company • Groff & Hearne Lumber • Hampton Decor • Harris-Tarkett, Inc. • Heatway • Heritage Vinyl Products • Michael Higuera • Italian Tile Center • J. G. Braun Company • Jeffries Wood Works, Inc. • Jennifer's Glass Works • JGR Enterprises • Johnson Paint Company, Inc. • Joseph Biunno Ltd • Kenmore Industries • King's Chandelier Company • Kraftmaid Cabinetry, Inc. • David Lawrence, illustrator • Lasting Impression Doors • Lehman's • Linoleum City, Inc. • Ludowici-Celadon, Inc. • MCA, Inc. • Millwork Specialties • The Millworks, Inc. • Mountain Lumber Co. • National Oak Flooring Manufacturers Association (NOFMA) • National Wood Flooring Association • Northwest Energy, Inc. • Oak Flooring Institute • The Old Fashioned Milk Paint Company, Inc. • Ole Fashion Things • Omega Too • Pagliacco Turning & Milling • Pella Corporation • Permaglaze • Piedmont Home Products, Inc. • Piedmont Mantel & Millwork Ltd • Pinecrest • Radiantec • The Readybuilt Products Company • Rejuvenation Lamp & Fixture, Co. • Runtal Radiators • The Saltbox • Salvage One Architectural Artifacts • Silverton Victorian Millworks • Stairways Inc. • Steptoe and Wife Antiques Ltd • Stromberg's Architectural Stone • The Structural Slate Co. • Sunbilt • Supradur Manufacturing Corporation • Taylor Door • Touchstone Woodworks • Turncraft • USG Company • Vande Hey's Roofing Tile Co., Inc. • Velux-America Inc. • Vixen Hill Manufacturing Co. • W. F. Norman Corporation • Watercolors, Inc. • WELco • Western Wood Products Association • Williamsburg Blacksmiths • Windy Hill Forge • Wolverine Technologies • The Wood Factory • Worthington Group Ltd •

# area modification factors

Construction costs are higher in some cities than in other cities. Use the factors on this and the following page to adapt the costs listed in this book to your job site. Increase or decrease your estimated total project cost by the percentage listed for the appropriate city in this table to find your estimated building cost.

These factors were compiled by comparing the actual construction cost of residential, institutional and commercial buildings in 740 communities throughout the United States. Because these factors are based on completed project costs, they consider all construction cost variables, including labor, equipment and material costs, labor productivity, climate, job conditions and markup.

Use the factor for the nearest or most comparable city. If the city you need is not listed in the table, use the factor for the appropriate state. Note that these location factors are composites of many costs and will not necessarily be accurate when estimating the cost of any particular part of a building. But when used to modify all estimated costs on a job, they should improve the accuracy of your estimates.

| ALABAMA | −1% |
| --- | --- |
| Anniston | −1% |
| Birmingham | 0% |
| Coosa | 0% |
| Dothan | −4% |
| Huntsville | 0% |
| Jasper | 0% |
| Mobile | 2% |
| Montgomery | 0% |
| Sheffield | −4% |
| Troy | −2% |

| ALASKA | 74% |
| --- | --- |
| Aleutian Islands | 90% |
| Anchorage | 70% |
| Barrow | 77% |
| Clear | 76% |
| Delta Junction | 73% |
| Fairbanks | 75% |
| Galena | 73% |
| Gambel | 73% |
| Goodnews Bay | 75% |
| Haines | 74% |
| Huslia | 74% |
| King Salmon | 86% |
| Nome | 73% |
| Whittier | 73% |

| ARIZONA | 2% |
| --- | --- |
| Douglas | 0% |
| Flagstaff | 5% |
| Gila Bend | 6% |
| Holbrook | 0% |
| Mesa | 0% |
| Phoenix | 0% |
| Sierra Vista | 2% |
| Tuba City | 5% |
| Tucson | 0% |
| Yuma | 1% |

| ARKANSAS | −2% |
| --- | --- |
| Arkadelphia | −2% |
| Blytheville | −2% |
| Camden | −2% |
| Conway | −2% |
| El Dorado | −2% |
| Fayetteville | 0% |
| Fort Smith | 1% |
| Harrison | −2% |
| Hot Springs | −2% |
| Jonesboro | −2% |
| Little Rock | −2% |
| Pine Bluff | −1% |

| CALIFORNIA | 17% |
| --- | --- |
| Alameda | 19% |
| Bakersfield | 18% |
| Barstow | 12% |
| Centerville | 15% |
| Concord | 24% |
| Coronado | 13% |
| Desert Area | 13% |
| El Centro | 12% |
| El Monte | 18% |
| El Toro | 13% |
| Forestville | 25% |
| Fresno | 18% |
| Hanford | 18% |
| Herlong | 19% |
| Jolon | 15% |
| Lathrop | 13% |
| Lawndale | 17% |
| Lompoc | 15% |
| Long Beach | 22% |
| Los Alamitos | 22% |
| Los Angeles | 26% |
| Marysville | 12% |
| Modesto | 13% |
| Mojave | 13% |

| CALIFORNIA | continued |
| --- | --- |
| Monterey | 16% |
| Novato | 25% |
| Oakland | 27% |
| Oceanside | 14% |
| Oxnard | 14% |
| Paso Robles | 18% |
| Rancho Cordova | 13% |
| Ridgecrest | 13% |
| Rio Vista | 20% |
| Riverbank | 13% |
| Riverside | 16% |
| Sacramento | 11% |
| Salinas | 17% |
| San Bernardino | 15% |
| San Bruno | 27% |
| San Diego | 17% |
| San Francisco | 88% |
| San Jose | 24% |
| San Leandro | 25% |
| San Mateo | 25% |
| San Pablo | 25% |
| Santa Rosa | 25% |
| Seal Beach | 18% |
| Stockton | 13% |
| Sunnyvale | 19% |
| Tracy | 20% |
| Tustin | 18% |
| Twentynine Palms | 13% |
| Ukiah | 20% |
| Upland | 18% |
| Vallejo | 19% |
| Victorville | 18% |

| COLORADO | 3% |
| --- | --- |
| Colorado Springs | 7% |
| Denver | 5% |
| Fort Carson | 4% |
| Grand Junction | 2% |

| COLORADO | continued |
| --- | --- |
| La Junta | 2% |
| Lakewood | 2% |
| Pueblo | −5% |
| Ski resorts | 32% |

| CONNECTICUT | 12% |
| --- | --- |
| Bridgeport | 13% |
| Cromwell | 12% |
| Fairfield | 12% |
| Hartford | 12% |
| Milford | 11% |
| New London | 11% |
| Stratford | 11% |
| West Hartford | 12% |

| DELAWARE | 5% |
| --- | --- |
| Dover | 4% |
| Kirkwood | 6% |
| Lewes | 6% |
| Milford | 4% |
| Wilmington | 7% |

| DISTRICT OF COLUMBIA | 4% |
| --- | --- |
| Washington | 4% |

| FLORIDA | 4% |
| --- | --- |
| Baldwin | 9% |
| Jacksonville | 9% |
| Key West | 22% |
| Lakeland | 2% |
| Lynn Haven | 0% |
| Melbourne | 10% |
| Miami | 6% |
| Milton | 0% |
| Ocala | 2% |
| Ocean City | −4% |
| Orlando | 10% |
| Palatka | 2% |

| FLORIDA | continued |
| --- | --- |
| Panama City | 2% |
| Pensacola | 0% |
| St Petersburg | 1% |
| Tampa | 1% |

| GEORGIA | 3% |
| --- | --- |
| Albany | −1% |
| Athens | 2% |
| Atlanta | 12% |
| Augusta | −5% |
| Chamblee | 2% |
| Columbus | −3% |
| Dublin | 2% |
| East Point | 2% |
| Forest Park | 13% |
| Fort Valley | 2% |
| Hinesville | 0% |
| Kings Bay | 2% |
| Macon | 2% |
| Marietta | 2% |
| Rome | 2% |
| Savannah | 0% |
| Tifton | 12% |
| Valdosta | 2% |

| HAWAII | 82% |
| --- | --- |
| Alimanu | 82% |
| Ewa | 82% |
| Halawa Heights | 82% |
| Hilo | 82% |
| Honolulu | 82% |
| Kailua | 90% |
| Lualualei | 82% |
| Mililani Town | 82% |
| Pearl City | 82% |
| Wahiawa | 82% |
| Waianae | 82% |
| Wailuku (Maui) | 82% |

| IDAHO | 0% |
|---|---|
| Boise | 4% |
| Coeur d'Alene | 2% |
| Idaho Falls | -1% |
| Mountain Home | -1% |
| Twin Falls | -2% |

| ILLINOIS | 5% |
|---|---|
| Addison | 5% |
| Arlington Heights | 5% |
| Aurora | 5% |
| Belleville | 3% |
| Bloomington | 5% |
| Champaign | 5% |
| Chicago | 16% |
| Decatur | 5% |
| Forest Park | 9% |
| Galesburg | 5% |
| Gibson City | 5% |
| Granite City | 5% |
| Green River | 5% |
| Hanover | 1% |
| Harvey | 5% |
| Highland Park | 5% |
| Homewood | 5% |
| Joliet | 5% |
| Kankakee | 5% |
| Mascoutah | 3% |
| North Chicago | 9% |
| North Park | 5% |
| Northfield | 5% |
| Orland Park | 5% |
| Peoria | 5% |
| Peru | 5% |
| Rantoul | 5% |
| Rock Island | 4% |
| Rockford | 5% |
| Springfield | 5% |
| Urbana | 5% |

| INDIANA | 0% |
|---|---|
| Bloomington | 1% |
| Crane | -2% |
| Fort Wayne | 1% |
| Gary | 1% |
| Indianapolis | -1% |
| Jeffersonville | 1% |
| Kokomo | 1% |
| Lafayette | 1% |

| INDIANA | ...continued |
|---|---|
| Lawrence | -1% |
| Logansport | 1% |
| New Albany | 1% |
| North Judson | 1% |
| Peru | 1% |
| Porter | 1% |
| Richmond | 1% |
| Rushville | 1% |
| South Bend | 1% |

| IOWA | -1% |
|---|---|
| Ames | 3% |
| Burlington | -2% |
| Cedar Rapids | -2% |
| Cherokee | -2% |
| Council Bluffs | -2% |
| Davenport | 0% |
| Decorah | -2% |
| Des Moines | 3% |
| Keokuk | -2% |
| Mason City | -2% |
| Pocahontas | -2% |
| Sac City | -2% |
| Sioux City | -2% |
| Washington | -2% |
| Waterloo | -2% |

| KANSAS | -1% |
|---|---|
| Atchison | -1% |
| Emporia | -1% |
| Hays | -1% |
| Independence | -1% |
| Junction City | -1% |
| Kansas City | -1% |
| Lawrence | -1% |
| Leavenworth | 7% |
| Manhattan | -4% |
| Olathe | -1% |
| Osage City | -1% |
| Parsons | -1% |
| Pittsburg | -1% |
| Topeka | -1% |
| Wichita | 3% |

| KENTUCKY | -3% |
|---|---|
| Ashland | -3% |
| Bardstown | -3% |
| Bowling Green | -3% |

| KENTUCKY | ...continued |
|---|---|
| Fort Thomas | -3% |
| Hopkinsville | -1% |
| Lexington | -5% |
| Louisville | -1% |
| Madisonville | -3% |
| Paducah | -3% |
| Radcliff | -1% |
| Richmond | -3% |
| Russell | -3% |

| LOUISIANA | -4% |
|---|---|
| Alexandria | -4% |
| Baton Rouge | -4% |
| Bogalusa | -4% |
| Bossier Base | -8% |
| Hammond | -4% |
| Leesville | -7% |
| Monroe | -4% |
| New Orleans | 11% |
| Shreveport | -4% |

| MAINE | 2% |
|---|---|
| Auburn | 1% |
| Bangor | -1% |
| Brunswick | 4% |
| Caribou | 1% |
| Cutler | 1% |
| Dexter | 1% |
| Northern Area | 1% |
| Portland | 3% |
| Winter Harbor | 1% |

| MARYLAND | 2% |
|---|---|
| Aberdeen | 0% |
| Annapolis | 2% |
| Baltimore | 1% |
| Bel Air, Hartford | 1% |
| Bethesda | 3% |
| Cascade | 0% |
| College Park | 1% |
| Cumberland | 1% |
| Curtis Bay | 1% |
| Edgewood | 1% |
| Frederick | 1% |
| Hagerstown | 1% |
| Hyattsville | 3% |
| Indian Head | 3% |
| Lexington Park | 3% |

| MARYLAND | ...continued |
|---|---|
| Olney | 1% |
| Patuxent River Area | 3% |
| Prince Georges | 3% |
| Westminster | 1% |
| White Oak | 1% |

| MASSACHUSETTS | 15% |
|---|---|
| Ayer | 15% |
| Bedford | 15% |
| Boston | 15% |
| Brockton | 15% |
| Chicopee | 15% |
| Fitchburg | 15% |
| Hingham | 15% |
| Lawrence | 15% |
| Natick | 15% |
| Pittsfield | 15% |
| Quincy | 15% |
| Roslindale | 15% |
| South Weymouth | 15% |
| Springfield | 15% |
| Taunton | 15% |
| Watertown | 15% |

| MICHIGAN | 4% |
|---|---|
| Ann Arbor | 5% |
| Bad Axe | 5% |
| Battle Creek | 5% |
| Bay City | 5% |
| Carleton | 5% |
| Detroit | 16% |
| Flint | 5% |
| Grand Rapids | 5% |
| Grayling | 5% |
| Inkster | 5% |
| Ishpeming | -1% |
| Lansing | 5% |
| Livonia | 5% |
| Marquette | -1% |
| Muskegon | 5% |
| Newport | 15% |
| Northern Area | 5% |
| Oscoda | -1% |
| Pontiac | 5% |
| Republic | -1% |
| Saginaw | 5% |
| Southfield | 5% |
| Traverse City | 6% |

| MICHIGAN | ...continued |
|---|---|
| Warren | 5% |

| MINNESOTA | 5% |
|---|---|
| Brainerd | 5% |
| Buffalo | 5% |
| Duluth | 2% |
| Fairbault | 5% |
| Fergus Falls | 5% |
| Fort Ripley | 5% |
| International Falls | 5% |
| Mankato | 5% |
| Minneapolis | 8% |
| New Brighton | 8% |
| Rochester | 5% |
| St Cloud | 5% |
| St Paul | 8% |
| Walker | 5% |
| Willmar | 5% |

| MISSISSIPPI | -4% |
|---|---|
| Bay St Louis | -5% |
| Biloxi | -5% |
| Clarksdale | -5% |
| Columbus | -7% |
| Greenville | 4% |
| Greenwood | -5% |
| Gulfport Area | -3% |
| Jackson | -5% |
| Laurel | -5% |
| Meridian | -5% |
| Pascagoula | -3% |
| Tupelo | -5% |
| Vicksburg | -5% |

| MISSOURI | 1% |
|---|---|
| Belton | 0% |
| Bolivar | 0% |
| Caruthersville | 0% |
| Farmington | 0% |
| Independence | 0% |
| Kansas City | 2% |
| Kirksville | 0% |
| Knob Noster | -1% |
| Lebanon | 2% |
| Portageville | 0% |
| St Louis | 4% |
| Washington | 4% |
| Weldon Springs | 4% |

| MONTANA ...........−1% | NEW JERSEY ...continued | NEW YORK .....continued | NORTH CAROLINA ...continued | OKLAHOMA ....continued |
|---|---|---|---|---|
| Billings ..................−1% | Browns Mills..............11% | Corning....................12% | Jacksonville..............−4% | Altus ......................−4% |
| Butte ......................−1% | Burlington................11% | Lockport...................12% | Kinston ...................−4% | Ardmore..................−2% |
| Cut Bank.................−1% | Camden....................11% | Long Island...............76% | New Bern ................−4% | Bartlesville ..............−2% |
| Fairview..................−1% | Earle........................11% | Malone ....................12% | Raleigh ...................−4% | Chickasha ...............−2% |
| Glasgow ..................−1% | Edison......................11% | Manhattan Beach.......32% | Salisbury.................−4% | Clinton....................−2% |
| Great Falls...............−1% | Freehold...................11% | Massena ..................12% | Southport ...............−4% | Durant....................−2% |
| Havre......................−1% | Highlands ................11% | Mattydale.................12% | Wilmington..............4% | El Reno...................−2% |
| Helena.....................−1% | Lakehurst .................11% | Montauk ..................12% | Wilson ....................−4% | Enid.......................−2% |
| Kalispell..................−1% | Lodi ........................11% | New York City ..........84% | Winston-Salem ........−4% | Lawton....................−2% |
| Lewistown ...............−1% | Long Branch.............11% | New York City (Manhattan).84% | | McAlester ...............−6% |
| Miles City................−1% | Middletown ..............11% | Newark-Arcadia ..........11% | | Miami......................−2% |
| Missoula .................−1% | Mount Hope.............12% | Newburgh ................11% | NORTH DAKOTA.−3% | Midwest City ...........−2% |
| | Newark ...................12% | Niagara Falls............10% | Bismarck.................−3% | Muskogee.................0% |
| NEBRASKA .........−1% | Pedricktown.............11% | Niskayuna................11% | Grand Forks............−4% | Norman ..................−2% |
| Ashland....................0% | Red Bank ................11% | Penn Yan.................11% | Minot .....................−1% | Oklahoma City..........0% |
| Bellevue....................0% | Trenton ...................11% | Plattsburgh ...............4% | Nekoma ..................−2% | Okmulgee.................−2% |
| Fremont ...................0% | Wallington...............11% | Rochester ................10% | Williston .................−2% | Ponca City..............−2% |
| Grand Island............−4% | Wrightstown.............11% | Rockaway.................12% | | Shawnee .................−2% |
| Lincoln....................−4% | | Rome ......................12% | OHIO.................3% | Stillwater.................−1% |
| Omaha.....................1% | NEW MEXICO ........2% | Schenectady .............11% | Akron .....................3% | Tulsa .....................−1% |
| | Alamogordo...............2% | Seneca Falls ..............5% | Chillicothe...............3% | |
| NEVADA.................4% | Albuquerque.............4% | Staten Island ...........77% | Cincinnati ...............3% | OREGON .............6% |
| Carson City..............5% | Clovis......................1% | Stewart ...................11% | Cleveland.................4% | Coos Bay................6% |
| Fallon.....................7% | Fort Sumner............3% | Syracuse..................12% | Columbus..................3% | Pendleton................6% |
| Hawthorne...............6% | Gallup .....................3% | Utica ......................12% | Dayton ...................2% | Portland .................5% |
| Las Vegas................14% | Las Cruces ...............2% | Watertown .................4% | Fairborn ..................2% | Salem.....................6% |
| North Las Vegas........14% | Sandia Base..............3% | Wayland ..................10% | Fremont ..................4% | Umatilla ..................7% |
| Reno ......................12% | Santa Fe ..................3% | West Point ...............12% | Lima ......................4% | |
| Yerington..................5% | | | Marietta ..................3% | PENNSYLVANIA ....3% |
| | NEW YORK .........17% | NORTH CAROLINA ..−3% | Newark ....................3% | Allentown ................4% |
| NEW HAMPSHIRE..1% | Albany ....................7% | Albemarle.................−4% | Sandusky.................4% | Altoona ...................4% |
| Claremont..................1% | Amherst ...................12% | Asheville ..................−4% | Springfield ...............3% | Annville...................4% |
| Concord....................1% | Amityville.................12% | Burlington ................−4% | Steubenville.............2% | Bristol.....................4% |
| Dover ......................1% | Auburn ....................12% | Camp Mackall...........−4% | Toledo.....................4% | Brookville ................4% |
| Manchester ...............1% | Batavia ....................12% | Charlotte..................−4% | Warren ...................3% | Butler......................4% |
| New Boston...............1% | Bellmore ..................12% | Cherry Point..............3% | Wooster...................3% | Carlisle ...................−2% |
| Portsmouth ...............1% | Brooklyn ..................12% | Durham ...................−4% | Youngstown..............3% | Chambersburg ..........−3% |
| | Buffalo ....................12% | Fayetteville...............4% | Zanesville ................3% | Clearfield .................4% |
| NEW JERSEY ........11% | Canandaigua .............11% | Goldsboro ................−4% | | Erie.........................4% |
| Bayonne....................11% | Canton.....................12% | Greensboro ..............−4% | OKLAHOMA.........−2% | Frankfort..................4% |
| | | | Ada ........................−2% | |

## PENNSYLVANIA ..continued
| | |
|---|---|
| Gettysburg | 4% |
| Johnstown | 4% |
| Kittanning | 4% |
| Lancaster | 4% |
| Meadville | 4% |
| Mechanicsburg Area | 4% |
| New Castle | 4% |
| New Cumberland | -2% |
| Oakdale | 1% |
| Philadelphia | 7% |
| Pittsburgh | 1% |
| Punxsutawney | 4% |
| Scranton | 4% |
| Tobyhanna | 3% |
| Valley Forge | 4% |
| Warminster Area | 7% |
| Wilkes Barre | 4% |
| Willow Grove | 4% |

## RHODE ISLAND ...9%
| | |
|---|---|
| Bristol | 9% |
| Coventry | 9% |
| Cranston | 9% |
| Davisville | 9% |
| Narragansett | 9% |
| Newport | 9% |
| Providence | 9% |
| Warwick | 9% |

## SOUTH CAROLINA ... -1%
| | |
|---|---|
| Anderson | -12% |
| Beaufort Area | 5% |
| Charleston | 1% |
| Clemson | -2% |
| Columbia | -2% |
| Greenville | -2% |
| Myrtle Beach | 1% |
| Rock Hill | -2% |
| Spartanburg | -2% |
| Sumter | -2% |

## SOUTH DAKOTA -2%
| | |
|---|---|
| Aberdeen | -3% |
| Box Elder | 1% |
| Hot Springs | -3% |
| Mitchell | -3% |
| Rapid City | 1% |
| Sioux Falls | -4% |

## TENNESSEE ......... 2%
| | |
|---|---|
| Chattanooga | 2% |
| Greeneville | 2% |
| Kingsport | 2% |
| Manchester | 0% |
| Memphis | 4% |
| Milan | 2% |
| Oak Ridge | 2% |

## TEXAS ......... 2%
| | |
|---|---|
| Abilene | 1% |
| Alice | 1% |
| Amarillo | 1% |
| Austin | 1% |
| Bay City | 1% |
| Beaumont | 1% |
| Beeville | 1% |
| Brownsville | 1% |
| Bryan | 1% |
| Corpus Chrsti | 1% |
| Dallas | 8% |
| Del Rio | 12% |
| Del Valle | 1% |
| El Paso | 1% |
| Ft Worth | 8% |
| Harlingen | 1% |
| Houston | 1% |
| Huntsville | 1% |
| Killeen | 1% |
| Kingsville | 1% |
| Laredo | 1% |
| Longview | 1% |
| Lubbock | 4% |

## TEXAS ............continued
| | |
|---|---|
| Marshall | 1% |
| McAllen | 1% |
| Mineral Wells | 1% |
| Paris | 1% |
| Pasadena | 1% |
| Port Arthur | 1% |
| Rio Grande City | 1% |
| San Angelo | -1% |
| San Antonio | 4% |
| San Marcos | 1% |
| Sinton | 1% |
| Texarkana | 6% |
| Victoria | 1% |
| Wichita Falls | 1% |
| Yoakum | 2% |

## UTAH ............ 4%
| | |
|---|---|
| Brigham City | 5% |
| Clearfield | -6% |
| Green River | -6% |
| Logan (Cache Valley) | 5% |
| Ogden | 5% |
| Price | -4% |
| Provo | 5% |
| Salt Lake City | 5% |
| St. George | 5% |
| Tooele | 4% |

## VERMONT ......... -1%
| | |
|---|---|
| Burlington | 0% |
| Chester | -1% |
| Montpelier | -1% |
| Rutland | -1% |

## VIRGINIA ............ 2%
| | |
|---|---|
| Abingdon | 1% |
| Alexandria | 15% |
| Arlington | 15% |
| Berryville (Winchester) | 1% |
| Blackstone | 3% |

## VIRGINA .........continued
| | |
|---|---|
| Bowling Green | 4% |
| Charlottesville | 1% |
| Chesapeake | 1% |
| Chincoteague | 1% |
| Churchland | 1% |
| Dahlgren | -3% |
| Dam Neck | 1% |
| Dublin (Radford) | 1% |
| Galax | 1% |
| Hampton | 3% |
| Herndon | 1% |
| Marion | 1% |
| Newport News | 3% |
| Norfolk | 3% |
| Petersburg | 2% |
| Quantico | -1% |
| Richmond | 1% |
| Vint Hill Farms | -1% |
| Virginia Beach | 3% |
| Warrenton | 1% |
| Williamsburg | 3% |
| Woodbridge | 1% |
| Yorktown | 1% |

## WASHINGTON ......... 7%
| | |
|---|---|
| Bangor | 7% |
| Bremerton | 10% |
| Keyport | 6% |
| Lakewood | 6% |
| Olympia | 6% |
| Pacific Beach | 6% |
| Pasco | 6% |
| Puget Sound Area | 6% |
| Seattle | 6% |
| Spokane | 9% |
| Tacoma | 6% |
| Trentwood | 7% |
| Vancouver | 6% |
| Whidbey Island | 6% |
| Yakima | 1% |

## WEST VIRGINIA .. -3%
| | |
|---|---|
| Bluefield | -5% |
| Charleston | -1% |
| Dawson | -3% |
| Fairmont | -3% |
| Grafton | -3% |
| Huntington | -3% |
| Martinsburg | -3% |
| New Martinsville | -3% |
| Parkersburg | -3% |
| Ripley | -3% |
| Romney | -3% |
| Sugar Grove | -5% |
| Weirton | -3% |
| Wheeling | -3% |

## WISCONSIN ............ 1%
| | |
|---|---|
| Clam Lake | 1% |
| Cornell | 1% |
| Dodgeville | 1% |
| Fond du Lac | 1% |
| Junction City | 1% |
| Kewaunee | 1% |
| La Crosse | 1% |
| Ladysmith | 1% |
| Madison | -5% |
| Milwaukee | 6% |
| Oshkosh | 1% |
| Wausau | 1% |

## WYOMING ......... -8%
| | |
|---|---|
| Casper | -4% |
| Cheyenne | -4% |
| Cody | 0% |
| Evanston | -6% |
| Gillette | -8% |
| Jackson | 6% |
| Laramie | -8% |
| Powell | -9% |
| Sheridan | 0% |
| Star Valley | 4% |

# unit price pages

The unit price pages have six columns. ❶ The column in the outside margin is the QuickFinder column. It contains headings and information designed to help you quickly find the item you need. ❷ The second column contains the item description along with applicable material, labor, and equipment prices and any necessary item information. ❸ The third column contains a two-letter abbreviation that indicates the unit of measure. ❹ The fourth column contains the price to tear out the item and place the debris in a dumpster on site. ❺ The fifth column contains the price to install the new item. ❻ The sixth column gives the total remove and replace cost.

Use the *QuickFinder* headings to quickly find items within a trade.

Use the *QuickFinder* sub-headings to quickly find items within a group.

Text below *QuickFinder* headings describe the item including installation techniques and waste.

Illustrated descriptions of an item are often most useful to determine if the item is the one you are looking for.

When needed, information about a specific item appears in the description column.

# time & material charts

**Material** charts show the material description, the material cost priced per typical unit purchased, the gross coverage, the typical waste, the net coverage after waste has been subtracted, and the resulting materials price including waste and often converted to a different unit of measure.

## TIME & MATERIAL CHARTS (selected items)

### Concrete Materials

| DESCRIPTION | MATERIAL PRICE | GROSS COVERAGE | WASTE | NET COVERAGE | UNIT PRICE |
|---|---|---|---|---|---|
| **Ready mix concrete delivered** | | | | | |
| 5 bag mix 2,500 psi, per cy | $83.60 cy | 1 | 6% | .94 | $88.90 cy |
| 5.5 bag mix 3,000 psi, per cy | $84.10 cy | 1 | 6% | .94 | $89.50 cy |
| 6 bag mix, 3,500 psi, per cy | $87.60 cy | 1 | 6% | .94 | $93.20 cy |
| 6.5 bag mix, 4,000 psi, per cy | $87.70 cy | 1 | 6% | .94 | $93.30 cy |
| 7 bag mix, 4,500 psi, per cy | $90.50 cy | 1 | 6% | .94 | $96.30 cy |
| 7.5 bag mix, 5,000 psi, per cy | $92.00 cy | 1 | 6% | .94 | $97.90 cy |
| add for synthetic fiber reinforcing | $10.30 cy | 1 | 0% | 1 | $10.30 cy |
| add for high early strength | $11.00 cy | 1 | 0% | 1 | $11.00 cy |
| minimum ready mix charge | $99.30 each | 1 | 0% | 1 | $99.30 ea |
| **Concrete form materials** | | | | | |
| form ties | $42.00 bar | 400 | 5% | 380 | $.11 sf |

### Concrete Rental Equipment

| DESCRIPTION | PRICE | COVERAGE | UNIT PRICE |
|---|---|---|---|
| **Forms** | | | |
| plywood wall forms (per sf of form) | $.17 per day | .25 per sf | $.68 sf |
| steel curb & gutter forms | $.84 per day | 1 lf | $.84 sf |
| **Tractor-mounted auger** | | | |
| hourly charge | $200.00 per hour | 90 lf | $2.22 lf |
| delivery and take-home charge | $422.00 each | 1 each | $422.00 ea |
| **Concrete pump truck** | | | |
| foundation wall | $122.00 hour | 450 sf of wall | $.27 sf |
| footings | $122.00 hour | 112 lf of footing | $1.09 lf |
| flatwork | $122.00 hour | 475 sf of flat. | $.26 sf |
| piers | $122.00 hour | 78 lf of pier. | $1.56 lf |
| grade beam | $122.00 hour | 146 lf of beam | $.84 lf |
| pressure grout | | 4 lf 2" pipe | $30.50 sf |

**Equipment** charts show the cost to rent equipment, the amount of work that can be done with the equipment per period of time, and the resulting unit price.

### Concrete Labor

| LABORER | BASE WAGE | PAID LEAVE | TRUE WAGE | FICA | FUTA | WORKER'S COMP. | UNEMPLOY. INSUR. | HEALTH INSUR. | RETIRE (401k) | LIABILITY INSUR. | COST PER HOUR |
|---|---|---|---|---|---|---|---|---|---|---|---|
| Concrete form installer | $22.10 | 1.72 | $23.82 | 1.82 | .19 | 5.49 | 2.07 | 2.54 | .71 | 3.10 | $39.70 |
| Concrete finisher | $22.00 | 1.72 | $23.72 | 1.81 | .19 | 5.47 | 2.06 | 2.54 | .71 | 2.51 | $39.60 |
| Concrete finisher's helper | $17.90 | 1.40 | $19.30 | 1.48 | .15 | 4.45 | 1.68 | 2.54 | .58 | 3.08 | $32.70 |
| Equipment operator | $28.70 | 2.24 | $30.94 | 2.37 | .25 | 5.36 | 2.06 | 2.54 | .93 | 4.02 | $49.10 |
| Plasterer | $22.00 | 1.72 | $23.72 | 1.81 | .19 | 6.54 | 2.06 | 2.54 | .71 | 3.08 | $40.70 |
| Concrete saw operator | $20.50 | 1.60 | $22.10 | 1.69 | .18 | 3.83 | 1.92 | 2.54 | .66 | 2.31 | $35.80 |
| Compaction grouter | $31.90 | 2.49 | $34.39 | 2.63 | .28 | 7.92 | 1.45 | 2.54 | 1.03 | 4.47 | $56.30 |
| Laborer | $15.50 | 1.21 | $16.71 | 1.28 | .13 | 3.85 | 2.99 | 2.54 | .50 | 2.17 | $28.60 |
| Demolition laborer | $13.40 | 1.05 | $14.45 | 1.11 | .12 | 4.44 | 1.26 | 2.54 | .43 | 1.88 | $26.20 |

**Labor** charts show the base wage, then add all additional costs that are based on wage. More information is always listed below this chart. It's important to note the "True" wage before adding labor related expenses. The true wage is the wage rate plus an allowance for vacation time. Since all the other costs must be paid even when an employee is on vacation, it is important that they become a component in the cost calculations when estimating work.

### Concrete Labor Productivity

| WORK DESCRIPTION | LABORER | COST PER HOUR | PRODUCTIVITY | UNIT PRICE |
|---|---|---|---|---|
| **Demolition** | | | | |
| remove footings including rebar | demolition laborer | $26.20 | 1.64 | $43.00 cy |
| remove footings including CEC rebar | demolition laborer | $26.20 | 1.96 | $51.40 cy |
| remove footings with rebar | demolition laborer | $26.20 | .121 | $3.17 lf |
| remove footings with CEC rebar | demolition laborer | $26.20 | .147 | $3.85 lf |
| remove foundation including rebar | demolition laborer | $26.20 | 2.44 | $63.90 cy |
| remove foundation including CEC rebar | demolition laborer | $26.20 | 2.94 | $77.00 cy |
| remove 5" or 6" foundation with rebar | demolition laborer | $26.20 | .073 | $1.91 sf |
| remove 5" or 6" foundation with CEC rebar | demolition laborer | $26.20 | .088 | $2.31 sf |
| remove 8" or 10" foundation with rebar | demolition laborer | $26.20 | .076 | $1.99 sf |
| remove 8" or 10" foundation with CEC rebar | demolition laborer | $26.20 | .092 | $2.41 sf |
| remove footing & foundation with rebar | demolition laborer | $26.20 | 1.96 | $51.40 cy |

**Labor productivity** charts show the description of the work, the laborer or crew who will do the work, the average cost per man hour, the productivity and the resulting cost per unit.

# crews

| Craft Code | Avg. Cost per Hour | Crew Composition |
|---|---|---|
| 1A | $31.20 | acoustic ceiling installer |
| 2A | $35.30 | appliance installer |
| 3A | $43.60 | appliance refinisher |
| 4A | $41.80 | awning installer |
| 5A | $29.20 | awning installer's helper |
| 6A | $35.50 | awning installer / awning installer's helper |
| 1B | $23.30 | cleaning laborer |
| 2B | $50.30 | post & beam carpenter |
| 3B | $35.50 | post & beam carpenter's helper |
| 4B | $42.90 | post & beam carpenter / post & beam carpenter's helper |
| 1C | $39.50 | carpenter |
| 5C | $29.20 | carpenter's helper |
| 6C | $34.40 | carpenter / carpenter's helper |
| 1D | $26.20 | demolition laborer |
| 2D | $34.40 | drywall hanger / drywall hanger's helper |
| 3D | $39.50 | drywall hanger |
| 4D | $29.20 | drywall hanger's helper |
| 5D | $39.80 | drywall taper |
| 6D | $36.20 | drywall hanger / drywall hanger's helper / drywall taper |
| 5E | $28.30 | excavation laborer |
| 6E | $38.70 | excavation laborer / equipment operator |
| 7E | $41.40 | electrician |
| 8E | $30.40 | electrician's helper |
| 9E | $35.90 | electrician / electrician's helper |
| 1F | $39.70 | concrete form installer |
| 2F | $28.60 | concrete laborer |
| 3F | $34.20 | concrete form installer / concrete laborer |
| 4F | $34.40 | carpenter (fence installer) / carpenter's helper |
| 5F | $40.70 | painter |
| 6F | $39.60 | concrete finisher |
| 7F | $32.70 | concrete finisher's helper |
| 8F | $36.20 | concrete finisher / concrete finisher's helper |
| 9F | $35.20 | concrete form installer / concrete laborer / concrete finisher / concrete finisher's helper |
| 1G | $56.30 | compaction grouting specialist |
| 2G | $42.50 | compaction grouting specialist / concrete laborer |
| 1H | $40.50 | hazardous materials laborer |

| Craft Code | Avg. Cost per Hour | Crew Composition |
|---|---|---|
| 2H | $44.20 | HVAC installer |
| 3H | $33.50 | wallpaper hanger |
| 1I | $28.80 | insulation installer |
| 2I | $32.70 | cabinet installer / laborer |
| 3I | $39.40 | flooring installer |
| 4I | $29.10 | flooring installer's helper |
| 5I | $34.30 | flooring installer / flooring installer's helper |
| 6I | $39.50 | paneling installer |
| 7I | $29.20 | paneling installer's helper |
| 2L | $25.80 | cabinet installer's helper |
| 3L | $25.00 | masking & moving laborer |
| 1M | $43.60 | mason |
| 2M | $39.90 | mason's helper |
| 3M | $30.50 | hod carrier |
| 4M | $38.00 | mason / mason's helper / hod carrier / laborer |
| 5M | $41.80 | mason / mason's helper |
| 6M | $102.30 | stone carver |
| 7M | $30.20 | mobile home repair specialist |
| 1O | $49.10 | equipment operator |
| 2O | $35.80 | concrete saw operator |
| 4P | $40.70 | plasterer |
| 5P | $34.80 | plasterer's helper |
| 6P | $37.80 | plasterer / plasterer's helper |
| 7P | $42.60 | plumber |
| 8P | $34.40 | paneling installer / paneling installer's helper |
| 9P | $36.20 | plumber's helper |
| 3R | $38.40 | retaining wall installer |
| 4R | $47.30 | roofer |
| 5R | $40.00 | roofer's helper |
| 6R | $43.70 | roofer / roofer's helper |
| 1S | $32.20 | susp. ceiling installer / susp. ceiling installer's helper |
| 2S | $36.90 | susp. ceiling installer |
| 3S | $27.40 | susp. ceiling installer's helper |
| 4S | $39.10 | siding installer |
| 5S | $28.90 | siding installer's helper |
| 6S | $34.00 | siding installer / siding installer's helper |
| 7S | $36.30 | security system installer |
| 8S | $48.30 | swimming pool installer |
| 9S | $33.80 | water extractor |
| 1T | $37.00 | tile layer |

# 1 ............................................ *Acoustic Ceilings*

| Item Description | Unit | Remove | Replace | Total | |
|---|---|---|---|---|---|
| **Minimum charge for acoustic ceiling tile work**<br>*Replace* Materials ......16.20      Labor ..........39.00 | ea | — | $55.20 | $55.20 | ◄ **MINIMUM** |
| **1/2" ceiling tiles on furring strips, smooth face**<br>*Replace* Materials ........ .96     Labor .............78<br>*Remove* ......................     Labor .............31 | sf | $.31 | $1.74 | $2.05 | ◄ **1/2" ON STRIPS**<br>*12" x 12" tiles stapled in place. Does not include furring strips. Includes 3% waste.* |
| **1/2" ceiling tiles on furring strips, fissured face**<br>*Replace* Materials .......1.27     Labor .............78<br>*Remove* ......................     Labor .............31 | sf | $.31 | $2.05 | $2.36 | |
| **1/2" ceiling tiles on furring strips, textured face**<br>*Replace* Materials .......1.48     Labor .............78<br>*Remove* ......................     Labor .............31 | sf | $.31 | $2.26 | $2.57 | |
| **1/2" ceiling tiles on furring strips, patterned face**<br>*Replace* Materials .......1.58     Labor .............78<br>*Remove* ......................     Labor .............31 | sf | $.31 | $2.36 | $2.67 | |
| **1/2" ceiling tiles on flat ceiling, smooth face**<br>*Replace* Materials ........ .96     Labor .............90<br>*Remove* ......................     Labor .............42 | sf | $.42 | $1.86 | $2.28 | ◄ **1/2" ON FLAT**<br>*12" x 12" tiles glued in place. Includes 3% waste.* |
| **1/2" ceiling tiles on flat ceiling, fissured face**<br>*Replace* Materials .......1.27     Labor .............90<br>*Remove* ......................     Labor .............42 | sf | $.42 | $2.17 | $2.59 | |
| **1/2" ceiling tiles on flat ceiling, textured face**<br>*Replace* Materials .......1.48     Labor .............90<br>*Remove* ......................     Labor .............42 | sf | $.42 | $2.38 | $2.80 | |
| **1/2" ceiling tiles on flat ceiling, patterned face**<br>*Replace* Materials .......1.58     Labor .............90<br>*Remove* ......................     Labor .............42 | sf | $.42 | $2.48 | $2.90 | |
| **5/8" ceiling tiles on furring strips, smooth face**<br>*Replace* Materials .......1.27     Labor .............78<br>*Remove* ......................     Labor .............31 | sf | $.31 | $2.05 | $2.36 | ◄ **5/8" ON STRIPS**<br>*12" x 12" tiles stapled in place. Does not include furring strips. Includes 3% waste.* |
| **5/8" ceiling tiles on furring strips, fissured face**<br>*Replace* Materials .......1.48     Labor .............78<br>*Remove* ......................     Labor .............31 | sf | $.31 | $2.26 | $2.57 | |
| **5/8" ceiling tiles on furring strips, textured face**<br>*Replace* Materials .......1.58     Labor .............78<br>*Remove* ......................     Labor .............31 | sf | $.31 | $2.36 | $2.67 | |
| **5/8" ceiling tiles on furring strips, patterned face**<br>*Replace* Materials .......1.79     Labor .............78<br>*Remove* ......................     Labor .............31 | sf | $.31 | $2.57 | $2.88 | **RELATED ITEMS**<br>Cleaning .....................55<br>Painting .....................333<br>Suspended Ceilings ......483 |
| **5/8" ceiling tiles on flat ceiling, smooth face**<br>*Replace* Materials .......1.27     Labor .............90<br>*Remove* ......................     Labor .............42 | sf | $.42 | $2.17 | $2.59 | ◄ **5/8" ON FLAT**<br>*12" x 12" tiles glued in place. Includes 3% waste.* |

| | Item Description | Unit | Remove | Replace | Total |
|---|---|---|---|---|---|
| **5/8" ON FLAT** ▶ *continued* | **5/8" ceiling tiles on flat ceiling, fissured face**<br>*Replace* Materials........1.48    Labor............90<br>*Remove* ......................    Labor............42 | sf | $.42 | $2.38 | $2.80 |
| | **5/8" ceiling tiles on flat ceiling, textured face**<br>*Replace* Materials........1.58    Labor............90<br>*Remove* ......................    Labor............42 | sf | $.42 | $2.48 | $2.90 |
| | **5/8" ceiling tiles on flat ceiling, patterned face**<br>*Replace* Materials........1.79    Labor............90<br>*Remove* ......................    Labor............42 | sf | $.42 | $2.69 | $3.11 |
| **3/4" ON STRIPS** ▶<br>*12" x 12" tiles stapled in place. Does not include furring strips. Includes 3% waste.* | **3/4" ceiling tiles on furring strips, smooth face**<br>*Replace* Materials........1.38    Labor............78<br>*Remove* ......................    Labor............31 | sf | $.31 | $2.16 | $2.47 |
| | **3/4" ceiling tiles on furring strips, fissured face**<br>*Replace* Materials........1.58    Labor............78<br>*Remove* ......................    Labor............31 | sf | $.31 | $2.36 | $2.67 |
| | **3/4" ceiling tiles on furring strips, textured face**<br>*Replace* Materials........1.70    Labor............78<br>*Remove* ......................    Labor............31 | sf | $.31 | $2.48 | $2.79 |
| | **3/4" ceiling tiles on furring strips, patterned face**<br>*Replace* Materials........1.85    Labor............78<br>*Remove* ......................    Labor............31 | sf | $.31 | $2.63 | $2.94 |
| **3/4" ON FLAT** ▶<br>*12" x 12" tiles glued in place. Includes 3% waste.* | **3/4" ceiling tiles on flat ceiling, smooth face**<br>*Replace* Materials........1.38    Labor............90<br>*Remove* ......................    Labor............42 | sf | $.42 | $2.28 | $2.70 |
| | **3/4" ceiling tiles on flat ceiling, fissured face**<br>*Replace* Materials........1.58    Labor............90<br>*Remove* ......................    Labor............42 | sf | $.42 | $2.48 | $2.90 |
| | **3/4" ceiling tiles on flat ceiling, textured face**<br>*Replace* Materials........1.70    Labor............90<br>*Remove* ......................    Labor............42 | sf | $.42 | $2.60 | $3.02 |
| | **3/4" ceiling tiles on flat ceiling, patterned face**<br>*Replace* Materials........1.85    Labor............90<br>*Remove* ......................    Labor............42 | sf | $.42 | $2.75 | $3.17 |
| **ADDITIONAL** ▶ **COSTS** | **Add for 3/4" tiles with fire rating**<br>*Replace* Materials ........ .27 | sf | — | $.27 | $.27 |
| | **Add for aluminum-coated tiles**<br>*Replace* Materials ........ .40 | sf | — | $.40 | $.40 |
| **FURRING STRIPS** ▶<br>*Nailed and glued to joists or flat ceiling. Includes 4% waste.* | **1" x 2" furring strips 12" on center**<br>*Replace* Materials ........ .23    Labor............22<br>*Remove* ......................    Labor............24 | sf | $.24 | $.45 | $.69 |
| **REPAIR** ▶ **LOOSE TILE** | **Repair loose acoustic tile**<br>*Replace* Materials ........ .13    Labor...........7.89 | ea | — | $8.02 | $8.02 |
| **ANGLED INSTALL** ▶ | **Add 24% for diagonal install** | | | | |
| | **Add 31% for chevron install** | | | | |
| | **Add 40% for herringbone install** | | | | |

# TIME & MATERIAL CHARTS (selected items)

## Acoustic Ceiling Materials

| DESCRIPTION | MATERIAL PRICE | | GROSS COVERAGE | WASTE | NET COVERAGE | UNIT PRICE |
|---|---|---|---|---|---|---|
| **1/2" thick acoustic tile (per 12" x 12" tile)** | | | | | | |
| smooth face | $.80 | each | 1 | 3% | .97 | $.82 sf |
| fissured face | $1.10 | each | 1 | 3% | .97 | $1.13 sf |
| textured face | $1.30 | each | 1 | 3% | .97 | $1.34 sf |
| patterned face | $1.40 | each | 1 | 3% | .97 | $1.44 sf |
| **5/8" thick acoustic tile (per 12" x 12" tile)** | | | | | | |
| smooth face | $1.10 | each | 1 | 3% | .97 | $1.13 sf |
| fissured face | $1.30 | each | 1 | 3% | .97 | $1.34 sf |
| textured face | $1.40 | each | 1 | 3% | .97 | $1.44 sf |
| patterned face | $1.60 | each | 1 | 3% | .97 | $1.65 sf |
| **3/4" thick acoustic tile (per 12" x 12" tile)** | | | | | | |
| smooth face | $1.20 | each | 1 | 3% | .97 | $1.24 sf |
| fissured face | $1.40 | each | 1 | 3% | .97 | $1.44 sf |
| textured face | $1.51 | each | 1 | 3% | .97 | $1.56 sf |
| patterned face | $1.66 | each | 1 | 3% | .97 | $1.71 sf |
| **Additional material costs** | | | | | | |
| add for fire rating | $.26 | per sf | 1 | 3% | .97 | $.28 sf |
| add for aluminum-coated face | $.39 | per sf | 1 | 3% | .97 | $.42 sf |
| add **5%** for diagonal installation | | | | | | |
| add **10%** for chevron installation | | | | | | |
| add **15%** for herringbone installation | | | | | | |
| **Tile adhesion** | | | | | | |
| adhesive | $12.80 | per gallon | 102 | 2% | 99.96 | $.13 sf |
| staples | $7.90 | per box | 1,200 | 4% | 1,152 | $.01 sf |
| 1" x 2" furring strips 12" on center | $.70 | per 8' strip | 6.77 | 4% | 6.5 | $.11 sf |
| construction adhesive (for furring strips) | $5.00 | per cartridge | 87 | 4% | 83.52 | $.06 sf |
| nails (for furring strips) | $50.00 | per box | 3,212 | 4% | 3,083.52 | $.02 sf |

## Acoustic Ceiling Labor

| LABORER | BASE WAGE | PAID LEAVE | TRUE WAGE | FICA | FUTA | WORKER'S COMP. | UNEMPLOY. INSUR. | HEALTH INSUR. | RETIRE (401k) | LIABILITY INSUR. | COST PER HOUR |
|---|---|---|---|---|---|---|---|---|---|---|---|
| Acoustic ceiling installer | $18.40 | 1.44 | $19.84 | 1.52 | .16 | 2.19 | 1.73 | 2.54 | .60 | 2.58 | $31.20 |
| Demolition laborer | $13.40 | 1.05 | $14.45 | 1.11 | .12 | 4.44 | 1.26 | 2.54 | .43 | 1.88 | $26.20 |

**Paid Leave** is calculated based on two weeks paid vacation, one week sick leave, and seven paid holidays. Employer's matching portion of **FICA** is 7.65 percent. **FUTA** (Federal Unemployment) is .8 percent. **Worker's compensation** for the acoustic ceiling trade was calculated using a national average of 11.03 percent. **Unemployment insurance** was calculated using a national average of 8.7 percent. **Health insurance** was calculated based on a projected national average for 2001 of $505 per employee (and family when applicable) per month. Employer pays 80 percent for a per month cost of $404 per employee. **Retirement** is based on a 401(k) retirement program with employer matching of 50 percent. Employee contributions to the 401(k) plan are an average of 6 percent of the true wage. **Liability insurance** is based on a national average of 12.9 percent.

## Acoustic Ceiling Labor Productivity

| WORK DESCRIPTION | LABORER | COST PER HOUR | PRODUCTIVITY | UNIT PRICE |
|---|---|---|---|---|
| **Demolition** | | | | |
| tiles attached with adhesive | demolition laborer | $26.20 | .016 | **$.42** *sf* |
| tiles attached with fasteners | demolition laborer | $26.20 | .012 | **$.31** *sf* |
| ceiling furring strips | demolition laborer | $26.20 | .009 | **$.24** *sf* |
| **Repair** | | | | |
| repair loose tile | installer | $31.20 | .253 | **$7.89** *ea* |
| **Installation** | | | | |
| tiles on furring strips | installer | $31.20 | .025 | **$.78** *sf* |
| tiles on flat ceiling | installer | $31.20 | .029 | **$.90** *sf* |
| furring strips | installer | $31.20 | .007 | **$.22** *sf* |
| **Additional labor costs** | | | | |
| minimum labor charge | installer | $31.20 | 1.25 | **$39.00** *ea* |
| add **55%** for diagonal installation | | | | |
| add **65%** for chevron installation | | | | |
| add **85%** for herringbone installation | | | | |

✎ *NOTES:* _____

_____

_____

_____

_____

_____

_____

_____

_____

_____

_____

_____

_____

_____

_____

_____

_____

_____

_____

_____

_____

_____ *end*

# 2 ............................................... *Appliances*

| Item Description | Unit | Remove | Replace | Total | |
|---|---|---|---|---|---|
| **Minimum charge for appliance work**<br>*Replace* Materials......32.00　　Labor..........68.80 | ea | — | $100.80 | $100.80 | ◄ MINIMUM |
| **Gas cook top, standard grade**<br>*Replace* Materials....400.00　　Labor..........84.80<br>*Remove* ........................　　Labor..........25.50<br>　► Baked enamel finish, standard burners, pilotless ignition. | ea | $25.50 | $484.80 | $510.30 | ◄ GAS COOK TOP |
| **Gas cook top, high grade**<br>*Replace* Materials.....510.00　　Labor..........84.80<br>*Remove* ........................　　Labor..........25.50<br>　► Tempered glass or brushed chrome finish, sealed burners, pilotless ignition,<br>　　automatic reignition.　May have retractable downdraft unit. | ea | $25.50 | $594.80 | $620.30 | |
| **Gas cook top with grill / griddle**<br>*Replace* Materials ....690.00　　Labor..........84.80<br>*Remove* ........................　　Labor..........25.50<br>　► Tempered glass or brushed chrome finish, two sealed burners, downdraft exhaust<br>　　unit, gas grill with griddle attachment, pilotless ignition, automatic reignition. | ea | $25.50 | $774.80 | $800.30 | |
| **Remove gas cook top for work, then reinstall**<br>*Replace* Materials........3.00　　Labor..........157.00 | ea | — | $160.00 | $160.00 | |
| **Gas range, economy grade**<br>*Replace* Materials....460.00　　Labor..........87.30<br>*Remove* ........................　　Labor..........27.00<br>　► Free-standing with standard-clean oven, chrome drip pans, analog clock and timer. | ea | $27.00 | $547.30 | $574.30 | ◄ GAS RANGE |
| **Gas range, standard grade**<br>*Replace* Materials ....620.00　　Labor..........87.30<br>*Remove* ........................　　Labor..........27.00<br>　► Free-standing with continuous-clean oven, chrome drip pans, digital clock and timer. | ea | $27.00 | $707.30 | $734.30 | |
| **Gas range, high grade**<br>*Replace* Materials....840.00　　Labor..........87.30<br>*Remove* ........................　　Labor..........27.00<br>　► Free-standing with self-clean oven, sealed burners, digital clock and timer. | ea | $27.00 | $927.30 | $954.30 | |
| **Gas range with grill / griddle**<br>*Replace* Materials ...1120.00　　Labor..........89.50<br>*Remove* ........................　　Labor..........27.00<br>　► Free-standing with self-clean oven, two sealed burners, grill, digital clock and timer. | ea | $27.00 | $1,209.50 | $1,236.50 | |
| **Space-saver gas range, standard grade**<br>*Replace* Materials....600.00　　Labor..........84.80<br>*Remove* ........................　　Labor..........27.00<br>　► 20" free-standing with continuous-clean oven, chrome drip pans, digital clock and<br>　　timer. | ea | $27.00 | $684.80 | $711.80 | ◄ SPACE SAVER<br>GAS RANGE |
| **Space-saver gas range, high grade**<br>*Replace* Materials....780.00　　Labor..........84.80<br>*Remove* ........................　　Labor..........27.00<br>　► 20" free-standing with self-clean oven, sealed burners, digital clock and timer. | ea | $27.00 | $864.80 | $891.80 | |

**RELATED ITEMS**

Electrical *(wiring)*
　gas oven or range..........143

| Item Description | Unit | Remove | Replace | Total |
|---|---|---|---|---|
| **HIGH-LOW GAS RANGE** | | | | |

| Item Description | Unit | Remove | Replace | Total |
|---|---|---|---|---|
| **High-low gas range with microwave high, standard grade**<br>*Replace* Materials ..1840.00    Labor ..........90.30<br>*Remove* .....................    Labor ..........30.90<br>▶ 1.4 cf microwave with touch-pad controls. Range with continuous-clean oven, chrome drip pans, digital clock and timer. | ea | $30.90 | $1,930.30 | $1,961.20 |
| **High-low gas range with microwave high, high grade**<br>*Replace* Materials ..2020.00    Labor ..........90.30<br>*Remove* .....................    Labor ..........30.90<br>▶ 1.4 cf microwave with touch-pad controls. Range with self-clean oven, chrome drip pans, digital clock and timer. | ea | $30.90 | $2,110.30 | $2,141.20 |
| **High-low gas range with microwave high, deluxe grade**<br>*Replace* Materials ..2280.00    Labor ..........90.30<br>*Remove* .....................    Labor ..........30.90<br>▶ 1.4 cf microwave with touch-pad controls. Range with self-clean oven, chrome drip pans, digital clock and timer, integrated hood and venting system. | ea | $30.90 | $2,370.30 | $2,401.20 |
| **Remove gas range for work, then reinstall**<br>*Replace* Materials ........3.00    Labor .........173.00 | ea | — | $176.00 | $176.00 |

**RESTAURANT GAS RANGE**

*Some common manufacturers are Viking, Thermador and Garland. Many of these manufacturers also deliver economy models starting at around $1,270. Also beware of "mimicked" restaurant styles from prominent manufacturers of standard ranges that sell from $810 to $2,050.*

| Item Description | Unit | Remove | Replace | Total |
|---|---|---|---|---|
| **Restaurant-style gas range, standard grade**<br>*Replace* Materials ..2520.00    Labor..........189.00<br>*Remove* .....................    Labor..........78.60<br>▶ Stainless-steel or black epoxy finish, zero clearance, insulated handles, stainless-steel upper shelf, electronic ignition, push-to-turn controls, six burners, single oven with in-oven infrared gas broiler. | ea | $78.60 | $2,709.00 | $2,787.60 |
| **Restaurant-style gas range, high grade**<br>*Replace* Materials ...5510.00    Labor..........189.00<br>*Remove* .....................    Labor..........78.60<br>▶ Stainless-steel or colored epoxy finish, zero clearance, insulated handles, stainless-steel upper shelf, electronic ignition, push-to-turn controls, four burners with griddle, and single oven. | ea | $78.60 | $5,699.00 | $5,777.60 |
| **Restaurant-style gas range, deluxe grade**<br>*Replace* Materials ..8700.00    Labor..........189.00<br>*Remove* .....................    Labor..........78.60<br>▶ Stainless-steel or colored epoxy finish, zero clearance, insulated handles, stainless-steel upper shelf, electronic ignition, push-to-turn controls, six burners with griddle, and convection oven. | ea | $78.60 | $8,889.00 | $8,967.60 |
| **Remove restaurant-style gas range for work, then reinstall**<br>*Replace* Materials ........5.00    Labor .........245.00 | ea | — | $250.00 | $250.00 |

**GAS WALL OVEN** ▶

| Item Description | Unit | Remove | Replace | Total |
|---|---|---|---|---|
| **Gas wall oven, economy grade**<br>*Replace* Materials .....513.00    Labor..........76.60<br>*Remove* .....................    Labor..........35.10<br>▶ Standard-clean oven, pilotless ignition. | ea | $35.10 | $589.60 | $624.70 |
| **Gas wall oven, standard grade**<br>*Replace* Materials .....591.00    Labor..........76.60<br>*Remove* .....................    Labor..........35.10<br>▶ Standard-clean oven, pilotless ignition, electronic pad controls. | ea | $35.10 | $667.60 | $702.70 |
| **Gas wall oven, high grade**<br>*Replace* Materials ....754.00    Labor..........76.60<br>*Remove* .....................    Labor..........35.10<br>▶ Continuous-clean oven, pilotless ignition, electronic pad controls with clock. | ea | $35.10 | $830.60 | $865.70 |

| Item Description | Unit | Remove | Replace | Total |
|---|---|---|---|---|
| **Gas wall oven, deluxe grade** | ea | $35.10 | $1,007.60 | $1,042.70 |
| *Replace* Materials ....931.00   Labor...........76.60 | | | | |
| *Remove* ...................   Labor...........35.10 | | | | |
| ▶ One self-clean oven, pilotless ignition, electronic pad controls with clock. | | | | |
| **Remove gas wall oven for work, then reinstall** | ea | — | $144.00 | $144.00 |
| *Replace* Materials........4.00   Labor.........140.00 | | | | |
| **Gas double wall oven, economy grade** | ea | $51.10 | $1,140.00 | $1,191.10 |
| *Replace* Materials ..1000.00   Labor.........140.00 | | | | |
| *Remove* ...................   Labor...........51.10 | | | | |
| ▶ Two standard-clean ovens with pilotless ignition. | | | | |
| **Gas double wall oven, standard grade** | ea | $51.10 | $1,290.00 | $1,341.10 |
| *Replace* Materials ...1150.00   Labor.........140.00 | | | | |
| *Remove* ...................   Labor...........51.10 | | | | |
| ▶ One standard-clean oven, one continuous-clean oven, pilotless ignition, electronic pad controls with clock. | | | | |
| **Gas double wall oven, high grade** | ea | $51.10 | $1,610.00 | $1,661.10 |
| *Replace* Materials ...1470.00   Labor.........140.00 | | | | |
| *Remove* ...................   Labor...........51.10 | | | | |
| ▶ One continuous-clean oven, one self-clean oven, pilotless ignition, electronic pad controls with clock. | | | | |
| **Gas double wall oven, deluxe grade** | ea | $51.10 | $1,960.00 | $2,011.10 |
| *Replace* Materials ..1820.00   Labor.........140.00 | | | | |
| *Remove* ...................   Labor...........51.10 | | | | |
| ▶ Two self-clean ovens, pilotless ignition, electronic pad controls with clock. | | | | |
| **Remove gas double wall oven for work, then reinstall** | ea | — | $260.00 | $260.00 |
| *Replace* Materials........5.00   Labor.........255.00 | | | | |
| **Electric cook top, standard grade** | ea | $27.00 | $423.30 | $450.30 |
| *Replace* Materials ....350.00   Labor...........73.30 | | | | |
| *Remove* ...................   Labor...........27.00 | | | | |
| ▶ Baked enamel finish with Calrod coil burners. | | | | |
| **Electric cook top, high grade** | ea | $27.00 | $513.30 | $540.30 |
| *Replace* Materials....440.00   Labor...........73.30 | | | | |
| *Remove* ...................   Labor...........27.00 | | | | |
| ▶ Brushed chrome finish with Calrod coil burners. | | | | |
| **Electric cook top with grill / griddle** | ea | $27.00 | $593.30 | $620.30 |
| *Replace* Materials ....520.00   Labor...........73.30 | | | | |
| *Remove* ...................   Labor...........27.00 | | | | |
| ▶ Tempered glass or brushed chrome finish, downdraft exhaust unit, two Calrod burners, grill with griddle attachment. | | | | |
| **Solid-disk electric cook top, standard grade** | ea | $27.00 | $623.30 | $650.30 |
| *Replace* Materials ....550.00   Labor...........73.30 | | | | |
| *Remove* ...................   Labor...........27.00 | | | | |
| ▶ Solid cast-iron burners, rotary heat controls. | | | | |
| **Solid-disk electric cook top, high grade** | ea | $27.00 | $693.30 | $720.30 |
| *Replace* Materials ....620.00   Labor...........73.30 | | | | |
| *Remove* ...................   Labor...........27.00 | | | | |
| ▶ Solid cast-iron burners, rotary heat controls, low profile, brushed chrome finish. | | | | |

**RELATED ITEMS**

**Electrical** *(wiring)*
gas oven or range...........143
electric appliance............142
cook top......................144
**Cleaning**......................55

◀ **GAS DOUBLE WALL OVEN**

◀ **ELECTRIC COOK TOP**

◀ **SOLID-DISK ELECTRIC COOK TOP**

| | Item Description | Unit | Remove | Replace | Total |
|---|---|---|---|---|---|
| **SOLID-DISK ▶ ELECTRIC COOK TOP** *continued* | **Solid-disk electric cook top with grill / griddle**<br>*Replace* Materials.....670.00　　　Labor...........73.30<br>*Remove* .......................　　　Labor...........27.00<br>▶ Downdraft exhaust unit, two solid cast-iron burners, grill with griddle attachment. | ea | $27.00 | $743.30 | $770.30 |
| **FLAT-SURFACE ▶ ELECTRIC COOK TOP** *For halogen instant-heat burners instead of radiant heat burners add $120 per burner.* | **Flat-surface radiant electric cook top, standard grade**<br>*Replace* Materials....660.00　　　Labor...........73.30<br>*Remove* .......................　　　Labor...........27.00<br>▶ White on white or almond on almond, 30" smooth surface, fingerprint and scratch resistant. | ea | $27.00 | $733.30 | $760.30 |
| | **Flat-surface radiant electric cook top, high grade**<br>*Replace* Materials....750.00　　　Labor...........73.30<br>*Remove* .......................　　　Labor...........27.00<br>▶ Black on black radiant cook top, 30" smooth surface, fingerprint and scratch resistant. | ea | $27.00 | $823.30 | $850.30 |
| | **Flat-surface radiant cook top with grill / griddle**<br>*Replace* Materials....800.00　　　Labor...........73.30<br>*Remove* .......................　　　Labor...........27.00<br>▶ Two flat radiant burners, center down draft unit, grill with griddle attachment. | ea | $27.00 | $873.30 | $900.30 |
| **MODULAR ▶ ELECTRIC COOK TOP UNIT** | **Modular electric cook top, two coil (Calrod) burners**<br>*Replace* Materials ....270.00　　　Labor...........26.00<br>*Remove* .......................　　　Labor...........13.40<br>▶ Two Calrod coil burners module. | ea | $13.40 | $296.00 | $309.40 |
| | **Modular electric cook top, two solid-disk burners**<br>*Replace* Materials ....320.00　　　Labor...........26.00<br>*Remove* .......................　　　Labor...........13.40<br>▶ Two solid-disk cast-iron burners module. | ea | $13.40 | $346.00 | $359.40 |
| | **Modular electric cook top, two flat-surface radiant burners**<br>*Replace* Materials ....370.00　　　Labor...........26.00<br>*Remove* .......................　　　Labor...........13.40<br>▶ Two smooth-surface radiant heat burners module. For halogen instant-heat burners instead of radiant heat burners add $120 per burner. | ea | $13.40 | $396.00 | $409.40 |
| | **Modular electric cook top, griddle**<br>*Replace* Materials....380.00　　　Labor...........26.00<br>*Remove* .......................　　　Labor...........13.40<br>▶ Griddle module. (See grill for units with a griddle attachment that fits on top of the grill module.) | ea | $13.40 | $406.00 | $419.40 |
| | **Modular electric cook top, grill**<br>*Replace* Materials....410.00　　　Labor...........26.00<br>*Remove* .......................　　　Labor...........13.40<br>▶ Grill module with one-piece grill and removable porcelain enamel reflector pan. Includes griddle accessory. | ea | $13.40 | $436.00 | $449.40 |
| | **Modular electric cook top, downdraft unit**<br>*Replace* Materials....200.00　　　Labor ..........20.20<br>*Remove* .......................　　　Labor...........13.40<br>▶ Two- to three-speed fan, 350 to 500 cfm. Add $140 for telescopic downdraft unit. | ea | $13.40 | $220.20 | $233.60 |
| **REMOVE & ▶ REINSTALL COOK TOP** | **Remove modular cooking unit for work, then reinstall**<br>*Replace* .......................　　　Labor ..........48.90 | ea | — | $48.90 | $48.90 |
| | **Remove modular downdraft unit for work, then reinstall**<br>*Replace* Materials........2.00　　　Labor ..........36.50 | ea | — | $38.50 | $38.50 |

| Item Description | Unit | Remove | Replace | Total |
|---|---|---|---|---|
| **Remove electric cook top for work, then reinstall**<br>*Replace* Materials........2.00          Labor .........135.00 | ea | — | $137.00 | $137.00 |
| **Electric range, standard grade**<br>*Replace* Materials ....520.00          Labor...........71.70<br>*Remove* .....................          Labor ..........25.50<br>▶ Free-standing range with standard-clean oven, four Calrod coil burners, chrome drip pans, analog clock and timer. | ea | $25.50 | $591.70 | $617.20 |
| **Electric range, high grade**<br>*Replace* Materials ....700.00          Labor...........71.70<br>*Remove* .....................          Labor ..........25.50<br>▶ Free-standing range with continuous-clean oven, four Calrod coil burners, chrome drip pans, digital clock and timer. | ea | $25.50 | $771.70 | $797.20 |
| **Electric range, deluxe grade**<br>*Replace* Materials.....910.00          Labor...........71.70<br>*Remove* .....................          Labor ..........25.50<br>▶ Free-standing range with self-clean oven, four Calrod coil burners, chrome drip pans, digital clock and timer. | ea | $25.50 | $981.70 | $1,007.20 |
| **Electric range with grill / griddle**<br>*Replace* Materials....1110.00          Labor...........71.70<br>*Remove* .....................          Labor ..........25.50<br>▶ Free-standing range with self-clean oven, two Calrod coil burners, grill with griddle accessory and cover, digital clock and timer. | ea | $25.50 | $1,181.70 | $1,207.20 |
| **Solid-disk electric range, standard grade**<br>*Replace* Materials ....720.00          Labor...........71.70<br>*Remove* .....................          Labor ..........25.50<br>▶ Free-standing range with standard-clean oven, four cast-iron solid-disk burners, chrome drip pans, analog clock and timer. | ea | $25.50 | $791.70 | $817.20 |
| **Solid-disk electric range, high grade**<br>*Replace* Materials ....770.00          Labor...........71.70<br>*Remove* .....................          Labor ..........25.50<br>▶ Free-standing range with continuous-clean oven, four cast-iron solid-disk burners, chrome drip pans, digital clock and timer. | ea | $25.50 | $841.70 | $867.20 |
| **Solid-disk electric range, deluxe grade**<br>*Replace* Materials ....940.00          Labor...........71.70<br>*Remove* .....................          Labor ..........25.50<br>▶ Free-standing range with self-clean oven, four cast-iron solid-disk burners, digital clock and timer. | ea | $25.50 | $1,011.70 | $1,037.20 |
| **Solid-disk electric range with grill / griddle**<br>*Replace* Materials....1170.00          Labor...........71.70<br>*Remove* .....................          Labor ..........25.50<br>▶ Free-standing range with self-clean oven, two cast-iron solid-disk burners, grill with griddle accessory and cover, digital clock and timer. | ea | $25.50 | $1,241.70 | $1,267.20 |
| **Flat-surface radiant electric range, standard grade**<br>*Replace* Materials ....870.00          Labor...........71.70<br>*Remove* .....................          Labor ..........25.50<br>▶ Free-standing range with standard-clean oven, four smooth-surface burners, chrome drip pans, analog clock and timer. | ea | $25.50 | $941.70 | $967.20 |
| **Flat-surface radiant electric range, high grade**<br>*Replace* Materials...1010.00          Labor...........71.70<br>*Remove* .....................          Labor ..........25.50<br>▶ Free-standing range with continuous-clean oven, four smooth-surface burners, chrome drip pans, digital clock and timer. | ea | $25.50 | $1,081.70 | $1,107.20 |

◀ **ELECTRIC RANGE**

◀ **SOLID-DISK ELECTRIC RANGE**

◀ **FLAT-SURFACE ELECTRIC RANGE**
*For halogen instant-heat burners instead of radiant heat burners add $120 per burner.*

**RELATED ITEMS**

| Item Description | Unit | Remove | Replace | Total |
|---|---|---|---|---|
| **FLAT-SURFACE ▶ ELECTRIC RANGE** *continued* | | | | |
| **Flat-surface radiant electric range, deluxe grade** | ea | $25.50 | $1,301.70 | $1,327.20 |
| *Replace* Materials...1230.00      Labor...........71.70 | | | | |
| *Remove* ........................      Labor ..........25.50 | | | | |
| ▶ Free-standing range with self-clean oven, four smooth-surface burners, digital clock and timer. | | | | |
| **Flat-surface radiant electric range with grill / griddle** | ea | $25.50 | $1,881.70 | $1,907.20 |
| *Replace* Materials...1810.00      Labor...........71.70 | | | | |
| *Remove* ........................      Labor ..........25.50 | | | | |
| ▶ Free-standing range with self-cleaning oven, two smooth-surface burners, grill with griddle accessory and cover, digital clock and timer. | | | | |
| **Remove electric range for work, then reinstall** | ea | — | $153.00 | $153.00 |
| *Replace* Materials........3.00      Labor.........150.00 | | | | |
| **DROP-IN OR ▶ SLIDE-IN ELECTRIC RANGE** | | | | |
| **Drop-in or slide-in electric range, standard grade** | ea | $32.00 | $746.10 | $778.10 |
| *Replace* Materials....660.00      Labor ..........86.10 | | | | |
| *Remove* ........................      Labor ..........32.00 | | | | |
| ▶ Drop-in or slide-in range with standard-clean oven, four Calrod coil burners, chrome drip pans, analog clock and timer. | | | | |
| **Drop-in or slide-in electric range, high grade** | ea | $32.00 | $956.10 | $988.10 |
| *Replace* Materials ....870.00      Labor ..........86.10 | | | | |
| *Remove* ........................      Labor ..........32.00 | | | | |
| ▶ Drop-in or slide-in range with continuous-clean oven, four solid-disk cast-iron burners, chrome drip pans, digital clock and timer. | | | | |
| **Drop-in or slide-in electric range, deluxe grade** | ea | $32.00 | $1,116.10 | $1,148.10 |
| *Replace* Materials ..1030.00      Labor ..........86.10 | | | | |
| *Remove* ........................      Labor ..........32.00 | | | | |
| ▶ Drop-in or slide-in range with self-clean oven, four smooth-surface burners, digital clock and timer. | | | | |
| **Drop-in or slide-in electric range with grill / griddle** | ea | $32.00 | $1,346.10 | $1,378.10 |
| *Replace* Materials...1260.00      Labor ..........86.10 | | | | |
| *Remove* ........................      Labor ..........32.00 | | | | |
| ▶ Drop-in or slide-in range with self-clean oven, two smooth-surface burners, grill with griddle accessory and cover, digital clock and timer. | | | | |
| **Remove drop-in or slide-in electric range, for work, then reinstall** | ea | — | $168.00 | $168.00 |
| *Replace* Materials........4.00      Labor.........164.00 | | | | |
| **SPACE-SAVER ▶ ELECTRIC RANGE** | | | | |
| **Space-saver electric range, standard grade** | ea | $25.50 | $949.50 | $975.00 |
| *Replace* Materials....880.00      Labor...........69.50 | | | | |
| *Remove* ........................      Labor ..........25.50 | | | | |
| ▶ 20" free-standing range with standard-clean oven, four Calrod coil burners, and chrome drip pans. | | | | |
| **Space-saver electric range, high grade** | ea | $25.50 | $1,009.50 | $1,035.00 |
| *Replace* Materials....940.00      Labor...........69.50 | | | | |
| *Remove* ........................      Labor ..........25.50 | | | | |
| ▶ 20" free-standing range with continuous-clean oven, four Calrod coil burners, and chrome drip pans. | | | | |
| **HIGH-LOW ▶ ELECTRIC RANGE** | | | | |
| **High-low electric range with microwave high, standard grade** | ea | $27.00 | $1,774.10 | $1,801.10 |
| *Replace* Materials...1700.00      Labor...........74.10 | | | | |
| *Remove* ........................      Labor...........27.00 | | | | |
| ▶ 1.4 cf microwave with touch-pad controls. Range with continuous-clean oven, four Calrod burners, chrome drip pans, digital clock and timer. | | | | |

| Item Description | Unit | Remove | Replace | Total |
|---|---|---|---|---|
| **High-low electric range with microwave high, high grade** | ea | $27.00 | $1,954.10 | $1,981.10 |
| *Replace* Materials ..1880.00          Labor............74.10 | | | | |
| *Remove* ........................          Labor............27.00 | | | | |
| ► 1.4 cf microwave with touch-pad controls. Range with self-clean oven, four Calrod burners, chrome drip pans, digital clock and timer. | | | | |
| **High-low electric range with microwave high, deluxe grade** | ea | $27.00 | $2,164.10 | $2,191.10 |
| *Replace* Materials ..2090.00          Labor............74.10 | | | | |
| *Remove* ........................          Labor............27.00 | | | | |
| ► 1.4 cf microwave with touch-pad controls. Range with self-clean oven, four Calrod burners, chrome drip pans, digital clock and timer, integrated hood and venting system. | | | | |
| **Electric wall oven, economy grade** | ea | $30.90 | $556.80 | $587.70 |
| *Replace* Materials ....488.00          Labor ..........68.80 | | | | |
| *Remove* ........................          Labor ..........30.90 | | | | |
| ► Standard-clean oven. | | | | |
| **Electric wall oven, standard grade** | ea | $30.90 | $632.80 | $663.70 |
| *Replace* Materials ....564.00          Labor ..........68.80 | | | | |
| *Remove* ........................          Labor ..........30.90 | | | | |
| ► Continuous-clean oven, electronic pad controls with clock. | | | | |
| **Electric wall oven, high grade** | ea | $30.90 | $784.80 | $815.70 |
| *Replace* Materials .....716.00          Labor ..........68.80 | | | | |
| *Remove* ........................          Labor ..........30.90 | | | | |
| ► Self-clean oven, electronic pad controls with clock. | | | | |
| **Electric wall oven, deluxe grade** | ea | $30.90 | $955.80 | $986.70 |
| *Replace* Materials ....887.00          Labor ..........68.80 | | | | |
| *Remove* ........................          Labor ..........30.90 | | | | |
| ► Convection oven, electronic pad controls with clock. | | | | |
| **Remove electric wall oven for work, then reinstall** | ea | — | $129.00 | $129.00 |
| *Replace* Materials ........2.00          Labor ..........127.00 | | | | |
| **Electric double wall oven, economy grade** | ea | $42.70 | $1,077.00 | $1,119.70 |
| *Replace* Materials ....950.00          Labor ..........127.00 | | | | |
| *Remove* ........................          Labor ...........42.70 | | | | |
| ► Two standard-clean ovens. | | | | |
| **Electric double wall oven, standard grade** | ea | $42.70 | $1,227.00 | $1,269.70 |
| *Replace* Materials ...1100.00          Labor ..........127.00 | | | | |
| *Remove* ........................          Labor ...........42.70 | | | | |
| ► One continuous-clean oven, one self-clean oven, electronic pad controls with clock. | | | | |
| **Electric double wall oven, high grade** | ea | $42.70 | $1,517.00 | $1,559.70 |
| *Replace* Materials ...1390.00          Labor ..........127.00 | | | | |
| *Remove* ........................          Labor ...........42.70 | | | | |
| ► Two self-clean ovens, electronic pad controls with clock. | | | | |
| **Electric double wall oven, deluxe grade** | ea | $42.70 | $1,857.00 | $1,899.70 |
| *Replace* Materials ...1730.00          Labor .........127.00 | | | | |
| *Remove* ........................          Labor ...........42.70 | | | | |
| ► One self-clean oven, one convection oven, electronic pad controls with clock. | | | | |
| **Remove electric double wall oven for work, then reinstall** | ea | — | $218.00 | $218.00 |
| *Replace* Materials ........3.00          Labor .........215.00 | | | | |

◄ **ELECTRIC WALL OVEN**

◄ **ELECTRIC DOUBLE WALL OVEN**

**RELATED ITEMS**

**Cleaning**........................55
**Electrical** (wiring)
*electric oven or range*......144

| | Item Description | Unit | Remove | Replace | Total |
|---|---|---|---|---|---|
| **RANGE HOOD ▶** | **Range hood, economy grade** | ea | $19.30 | $115.20 | $134.50 |
| | *Replace* Materials ......57.00  Labor ..........58.20 | | | | |
| | *Remove* ........................  Labor ..........19.30 | | | | |
| | ▶ 30" wide, two-speed fan, light, non-vented with disposable charcoal filter, baked enamel finish. | | | | |
| | **Range hood, standard grade** | ea | $19.30 | $153.20 | $172.50 |
| | *Replace* Materials ......95.00  Labor ..........58.20 | | | | |
| | *Remove* ........................  Labor ..........19.30 | | | | |
| | ▶ 30" or 36" wide, two-speed fan, light with night setting, vented with up to 16 lf duct, baked enamel finish. | | | | |
| | **Range hood, high grade** | ea | $19.30 | $172.20 | $191.50 |
| | *Replace* Materials .....114.00  Labor ..........58.20 | | | | |
| | *Remove* ........................  Labor ..........19.30 | | | | |
| | ▶ 30" or 36" wide, variable-speed fan, two lights, vented with up to 16 lf duct, baked enamel finish. | | | | |
| | **Range hood, deluxe grade** | ea | $19.30 | $197.20 | $216.50 |
| | *Replace* Materials .....139.00  Labor ..........58.20 | | | | |
| | *Remove* ........................  Labor ..........19.30 | | | | |
| | ▶ 30" or 36" wide, variable-speed fan, two lights, vented with up to 16 lf duct, brushed chrome finish. | | | | |
| | **Range hood, custom grade** | ea | $19.30 | $242.20 | $261.50 |
| | *Replace* Materials ....184.00  Labor ..........58.20 | | | | |
| | *Remove* ........................  Labor ..........19.30 | | | | |
| | ▶ 30" or 36" wide, variable-speed fan, two lights, vented with up to 16 lf duct, specialty deep design, copper finish. | | | | |
| **OVERSIZED ▶ RANGE HOOD** | **Oversized range hood, standard grade** | ea | $23.20 | $338.40 | $361.60 |
| | *Replace* Materials ....266.00  Labor..........72.40 | | | | |
| | *Remove* ........................  Labor ..........23.20 | | | | |
| | ▶ 42" wide, two-speed fan, light with night setting, vented with up to 16 lf duct, baked enamel finish. | | | | |
| | **Oversized range hood, high grade** | ea | $23.20 | $391.40 | $414.60 |
| | *Replace* Materials .....319.00  Labor..........72.40 | | | | |
| | *Remove* ........................  Labor ..........23.20 | | | | |
| | ▶ 42" wide, variable-speed fan, two lights, vented with up to 16 lf duct, baked enamel finish. | | | | |
| | **Oversized range hood, deluxe grade** | ea | $23.20 | $461.40 | $484.60 |
| | *Replace* Materials ....389.00  Labor..........72.40 | | | | |
| | *Remove* ........................  Labor ..........23.20 | | | | |
| | ▶ 42" wide, variable-speed fan, two lights, vented with up to 16 lf duct, brushed chrome finish. | | | | |
| | **Oversized range hood, custom grade** | ea | $23.20 | $587.40 | $610.60 |
| | *Replace* Materials .....515.00  Labor..........72.40 | | | | |
| | *Remove* ........................  Labor ..........23.20 | | | | |
| | ▶ 42" wide, variable-speed fan, two lights, vented with up to 16 lf duct, specialty deep design, copper finish. | | | | |
| | **Remove range hood for work, then reinstall** | ea | — | $124.00 | $124.00 |
| | *Replace* Materials ........2.00  Labor ........122.00 | | | | |
| **PUSH-BUTTON ▶ DISHWASHER** | **Push-button dishwasher, economy grade** | ea | $36.40 | $438.80 | $475.20 |
| | *Replace* Materials ....370.00  Labor ..........68.80 | | | | |
| | *Remove* ........................  Labor ..........36.40 | | | | |
| | ▶ Three cycles, five options, standard insulation package. | | | | |

| Item Description | Unit | Remove | Replace | Total |
|---|---|---|---|---|
| **Push-button dishwasher, standard grade** | ea | $36.40 | $558.80 | $595.20 |
| *Replace* Materials ....490.00    Labor ..........68.80 | | | | |
| *Remove* ........................    Labor ..........36.40 | | | | |
| ► Five cycles, eight options, standard insulation package. | | | | |
| **Push-button dishwasher, high grade** | ea | $36.40 | $678.80 | $715.20 |
| *Replace* Materials .....610.00    Labor ..........68.80 | | | | |
| *Remove* ........................    Labor ..........36.40 | | | | |
| ► Five cycles, fourteen options, deluxe insulation package. | | | | |
| **Push-button dishwasher, deluxe grade** | ea | $36.40 | $778.80 | $815.20 |
| *Replace* Materials ....710.00    Labor ..........68.80 | | | | |
| *Remove* ........................    Labor ..........36.40 | | | | |
| ► Six cycles, eighteen options, deluxe insulation package. | | | | |
| **Electronic dishwasher, economy grade** | ea | $36.40 | $818.80 | $855.20 |
| *Replace* Materials ....750.00    Labor ..........68.80 | | | | |
| *Remove* ........................    Labor ..........36.40 | | | | |
| ► Electronic touch-pad control, six cycles, twelve options, deluxe insulation package, specialty racks. | | | | |
| **Electronic dishwasher, standard grade** | ea | $36.40 | $898.80 | $935.20 |
| *Replace* Materials ....830.00    Labor ..........68.80 | | | | |
| *Remove* ........................    Labor ..........36.40 | | | | |
| ► Electronic touch-pad control, seven cycles, twenty-three options, deluxe "quiet" insulation package, water saver cycle, delayed start option, specialty racks. | | | | |
| **Electronic dishwasher, high grade** | ea | $36.40 | $1,068.80 | $1,105.20 |
| *Replace* Materials ..1000.00    Labor ..........68.80 | | | | |
| *Remove* ........................    Labor ..........36.40 | | | | |
| ► Electronic touch-pad control, seven cycles, twenty-three options, deluxe "quiet" insulation package, water saver cycle, delayed start option, specialty racks, self-cleaning filter system. | | | | |
| **Electronic dishwasher, deluxe grade** | ea | $36.40 | $1,128.80 | $1,165.20 |
| *Replace* Materials ..1060.00    Labor ..........68.80 | | | | |
| *Remove* ........................    Labor ..........36.40 | | | | |
| ► Electronic touch-pad control, seven cycles, twenty-three options, deluxe "quiet" insulation package, water saver cycle, delayed start option, specialty racks, self-cleaning filter system, smooth-surface exterior panels that can integrate with cabinet design. | | | | |
| **Convertible (portable) dishwasher, standard grade** | ea | $36.40 | $441.70 | $478.10 |
| *Replace* Materials ....400.00    Labor..........41.70 | | | | |
| *Remove* ........................    Labor ..........36.40 | | | | |
| ► Push-button control, four cycles, seven options, standard insulation package, plastic laminate top. | | | | |
| **Convertible (portable) dishwasher, high grade** | ea | $36.40 | $541.70 | $578.10 |
| *Replace* Materials ....500.00    Labor..........41.70 | | | | |
| *Remove* ........................    Labor ..........36.40 | | | | |
| ► Push-button control, four cycles, thirteen options, deluxe insulation package, specialty racks, wood veneer top. | | | | |
| **Convertible (portable) dishwasher, deluxe grade** | ea | $36.40 | $631.70 | $668.10 |
| *Replace* Materials ....590.00    Labor..........41.70 | | | | |
| *Remove* ........................    Labor ..........36.40 | | | | |
| ► Push-button control, four cycles, fourteen options, deluxe insulation package, specialty racks, solid wood top (often butcher block), delay start option. | | | | |

◄ **ELECTRONIC DISHWASHER**

◄ **CONVERTIBLE DISHWASHER**

| | Item Description | Unit | Remove | Replace | Total |
|---|---|---|---|---|---|
| **SPACE-SAVER ▶ UNDER-SINK DISHWASHER** | **Space-saver under-sink dishwasher, standard grade** | ea | $36.40 | $656.00 | $692.40 |
| | *Replace* Materials ....550.00    Labor.........106.00 | | | | |
| | *Remove* .......................    Labor.........36.40 | | | | |
| | ▶ Push-button control, four cycles, seven options, standard insulation package. | | | | |
| | **Space-saver under-sink dishwasher, high grade** | ea | $36.40 | $756.00 | $792.40 |
| | *Replace* Materials ....650.00    Labor.........106.00 | | | | |
| | *Remove* .......................    Labor.........36.40 | | | | |
| | ▶ Push-button control, five cycles, eight options, deluxe insulation package. | | | | |
| | **Remove dishwasher for work, then reinstall** | ea | — | $134.00 | $134.00 |
| | *Replace* Materials........4.00    Labor.........130.00 | | | | |
| **GARBAGE ▶ DISPOSAL** | **1/3 hp garbage disposal** | ea | $34.10 | $179.20 | $213.30 |
| | *Replace* Materials .....111.00    Labor .........68.20 | | | | |
| | *Remove* .......................    Labor .........34.10 | | | | |
| | ▶ Continuous feed. | | | | |
| | **1/2 hp garbage disposal** | ea | $34.10 | $201.20 | $235.30 |
| | *Replace* Materials.....133.00    Labor .........68.20 | | | | |
| | *Remove* .......................    Labor .........34.10 | | | | |
| | ▶ Continuous feed, sound shield. | | | | |
| | **1/2 hp stainless steel garbage disposal with auto-reverse** | ea | $34.10 | $378.20 | $412.30 |
| | *Replace* Materials.....310.00    Labor .........68.20 | | | | |
| | *Remove* .......................    Labor .........34.10 | | | | |
| | ▶ Continuous feed, sound shield, auto-reverse. | | | | |
| | **3/4 hp garbage disposal** | ea | $34.10 | $442.20 | $476.30 |
| | *Replace* Materials.....374.00    Labor .........68.20 | | | | |
| | *Remove* .......................    Labor .........34.10 | | | | |
| | ▶ Batch feed, deluxe "quiet" sound shield, non-corroding, glass-filled polyester drain housing and hopper. | | | | |
| | **3/4 hp stainless steel garbage disposal with auto-reverse** | ea | $34.10 | $511.20 | $545.30 |
| | *Replace* Materials....443.00    Labor .........68.20 | | | | |
| | *Remove* .......................    Labor .........34.10 | | | | |
| | ▶ Batch feed, deluxe "quiet" sound shield, non-corroding, glass-filled polyester drain housing and hopper, with auto-reverse. | | | | |
| | **1 hp garbage disposal** | ea | $34.10 | $714.20 | $748.30 |
| | *Replace* Materials....646.00    Labor .........68.20 | | | | |
| | *Remove* .......................    Labor .........34.10 | | | | |
| | ▶ Batch feed, deluxe "quiet" sound shield, non-corroding, glass-filled polyester drain housing and hopper. | | | | |
| | **1 hp stainless steel garbage disposal with auto-reverse** | ea | $34.10 | $771.20 | $805.30 |
| | *Replace* Materials....703.00    Labor .........68.20 | | | | |
| | *Remove* .......................    Labor .........34.10 | | | | |
| | ▶ Batch feed, deluxe "quiet" sound shield, non-corroding, glass-filled polyester drain housing and hopper, with auto-reverse. | | | | |
| | **Remove garbage disposal for work, then reinstall** | ea | — | $132.00 | $132.00 |
| | *Replace* Materials........4.00    Labor.........128.00 | | | | |
| **MICROWAVE ▶** | **Microwave oven, standard grade** | ea | $13.10 | $281.80 | $294.90 |
| | *Replace* Materials ....268.00    Labor...........13.80 | | | | |
| | *Remove* .......................    Labor...........13.10 | | | | |
| | ▶ To 800 watts, defrost, multiple power levels, time cook. | | | | |

| Item Description | Unit | Remove | Replace | Total |
|---|---|---|---|---|
| **Microwave oven, high grade** | ea | $13.10 | $387.80 | $400.90 |
| *Replace* Materials.....374.00    Labor..........13.80 | | | | |
| *Remove* ....................    Labor..........13.10 | | | | |
| ▶ To 800 watts, defrost, popcorn pad, 10 power levels, time cook, reheat pad. | | | | |
| **Microwave oven, deluxe grade** | ea | $13.10 | $526.80 | $539.90 |
| *Replace* Materials.....513.00    Labor..........13.80 | | | | |
| *Remove* ....................    Labor..........13.10 | | | | |
| ▶ To 800 watts, defrost, popcorn pad, 10 power levels, time cook, reheat pad, roasting and defrost automatic sensing controls. | | | | |
| **Microwave oven, custom grade** | ea | $13.10 | $646.80 | $659.90 |
| *Replace* Materials....633.00    Labor..........13.80 | | | | |
| *Remove* ....................    Labor..........13.10 | | | | |
| ▶ To 800 watts with convection heating, defrost, popcorn pad, 10 power levels, time cook, reheat pad, baking, defrost sensing controls. | | | | |
| **Microwave oven, under cabinet, standard grade** | ea | $13.10 | $657.80 | $670.90 |
| *Replace* Materials....589.00    Labor..........68.80 | | | | |
| *Remove* ....................    Labor..........13.10 | | | | |
| ▶ To 750 watts (many models around 550 to 600 watts), defrost, popcorn pad, 10 power levels, time cook, reheat pad, baking, defrost sensing controls, with high-capacity exhaust vent fan (includes up to 16 lf of duct). | | | | |
| **Microwave oven, under cabinet, high grade** | ea | $13.10 | $952.80 | $965.90 |
| *Replace* Materials....884.00    Labor..........68.80 | | | | |
| *Remove* ....................    Labor..........13.10 | | | | |
| ▶ To 750 watts (many models around 550 to 600 watts) with convection, defrost, popcorn pad, 10 power levels, time cook, reheat pad, baking, defrost sensing controls, with high-capacity exhaust vent fan (includes up to 16 lf of duct). | | | | |
| **Side-by-side refrigerator / freezer, 24 to 27 cf capacity, standard grade** | ea | $25.50 | $1,688.70 | $1,714.20 |
| *Replace* Materials...1660.00    Labor..........28.70 | | | | |
| *Remove* ....................    Labor..........25.50 | | | | |
| ▶ Standard-style shelves, energy efficient. | | | | |
| **Side-by-side refrigerator / freezer, 24 to 27 cf capacity, high grade** | ea | $25.50 | $2,118.70 | $2,144.20 |
| *Replace* Materials..2090.00    Labor..........28.70 | | | | |
| *Remove* ....................    Labor..........25.50 | | | | |
| ▶ Specialty-style shelves, deep doors, energy efficient. | | | | |
| **Side-by-side refrigerator / freezer, 24 to 27 cf capacity, deluxe grade** | ea | $25.50 | $2,538.70 | $2,564.20 |
| *Replace* Materials...2510.00    Labor..........28.70 | | | | |
| *Remove* ....................    Labor..........25.50 | | | | |
| ▶ Specialty-style shelves and doors, deep doors, highly energy efficient. | | | | |
| **Side-by-side refrigerator / freezer, 20 to 23 cf capacity, standard grade** | ea | $25.50 | $1,108.70 | $1,134.20 |
| *Replace* Materials..1080.00    Labor..........28.70 | | | | |
| *Remove* ....................    Labor..........25.50 | | | | |
| ▶ Standard-style shelves, energy efficient. | | | | |
| **Side-by-side refrigerator / freezer, 20 to 23 cf capacity, high grade** | ea | $25.50 | $1,578.70 | $1,604.20 |
| *Replace* Materials...1550.00    Labor..........28.70 | | | | |
| *Remove* ....................    Labor..........25.50 | | | | |
| ▶ Specialty-style shelves, deep doors, energy efficient. | | | | |
| **Side-by-side refrigerator / freezer, 20 to 23 cf capacity, deluxe grade** | ea | $25.50 | $1,838.70 | $1,864.20 |
| *Replace* Materials...1810.00    Labor..........28.70 | | | | |
| *Remove* ....................    Labor..........25.50 | | | | |
| ▶ Specialty-style shelves and doors, deep doors, highly energy efficient. | | | | |

◀ **UNDER CABINET MICROWAVE**

◀ **SIDE-BY-SIDE REFRIGERATOR / FREEZER**

| Item Description | Unit | Remove | Replace | Total |
|---|---|---|---|---|
| **SIDE-BY-SIDE ▶ CABINET MATCH**   **Add for side-by-side refrigerator / freezer with cabinet-matching doors** <br>     *Replace* Materials ....329.00 | ea | — | $329.00 | $329.00 |
| **OVER-UNDER ▶ REFRIGERATOR / FREEZER**   **Over-under refrigerator / freezer, 21 to 25 cf capacity, standard grade** <br>     *Replace* Materials ...1140.00     Labor ..........25.50 <br>     *Remove* ......................     Labor ..........22.20 <br>     ▶ Standard-style shelves, energy efficient. | ea | $22.20 | $1,165.50 | $1,187.70 |
| **Over-under refrigerator / freezer, 21 to 25 cf capacity, high grade** <br>     *Replace* Materials ..1300.00     Labor ..........25.50 <br>     *Remove* ......................     Labor ..........22.20 <br>     ▶ Specialty-style shelves, deep doors, energy efficient. | ea | $22.20 | $1,325.50 | $1,347.70 |
| **Over-under refrigerator / freezer, 21 to 25 cf capacity, deluxe grade** <br>     *Replace* Materials ...1620.00     Labor ..........25.50 <br>     *Remove* ......................     Labor ..........22.20 <br>     ▶ Specialty-style shelves and doors, deep doors, highly energy efficient. | ea | $22.20 | $1,645.50 | $1,667.70 |
| **Over-under refrigerator / freezer, 17 to 20 cf capacity, standard grade** <br>     *Replace* Materials ..1000.00     Labor ..........25.50 <br>     *Remove* ......................     Labor ..........22.20 <br>     ▶ Standard-style shelves, energy efficient. | ea | $22.20 | $1,025.50 | $1,047.70 |
| **Over-under refrigerator / freezer, 17 to 20 cf capacity, high grade** <br>     *Replace* Materials ...1140.00     Labor ..........25.50 <br>     *Remove* ......................     Labor ..........22.20 <br>     ▶ Specialty-style shelves, deep doors, energy efficient. | ea | $22.20 | $1,165.50 | $1,187.70 |
| **Over-under refrigerator / freezer, 17 to 20 cf capacity, deluxe grade** <br>     *Replace* Materials ..1380.00     Labor ..........25.50 <br>     *Remove* ......................     Labor ..........22.20 <br>     ▶ Specialty-style shelves and doors, deep doors, highly energy efficient. | ea | $22.20 | $1,405.50 | $1,427.70 |
| **Over-under refrigerator / freezer, 13 to 16 cf capacity, standard grade** <br>     *Replace* Materials ....855.00     Labor ..........25.50 <br>     *Remove* ......................     Labor ..........22.20 <br>     ▶ Standard-style shelves, energy efficient. | ea | $22.20 | $880.50 | $902.70 |
| **Over-under refrigerator / freezer, 13 to 16 cf capacity, high grade** <br>     *Replace* Materials ..1000.00     Labor ..........25.50 <br>     *Remove* ......................     Labor ..........22.20 <br>     ▶ Specialty-style shelves, deep doors, energy efficient. | ea | $22.20 | $1,025.50 | $1,047.70 |
| **Over-under refrigerator / freezer, 13 to 16 cf capacity, deluxe grade** <br>     *Replace* Materials ....1170.00     Labor ..........25.50 <br>     *Remove* ......................     Labor ..........22.20 <br>     ▶ Specialty-style shelves and doors, deep doors, highly energy efficient. | ea | $22.20 | $1,195.50 | $1,217.70 |
| **Over-under refrigerator / freezer, 10 to 12 cf capacity, standard grade** <br>     *Replace* Materials ....709.00     Labor ..........25.50 <br>     *Remove* ......................     Labor ..........22.20 <br>     ▶ Standard-style shelves, energy efficient. | ea | $22.20 | $734.50 | $756.70 |
| **Over-under refrigerator / freezer, 10 to 12 cf capacity, high grade** <br>     *Replace* Materials ....868.00     Labor ..........25.50 <br>     *Remove* ......................     Labor ..........22.20 <br>     ▶ Specialty-style shelves, deep doors, energy efficient. | ea | $22.20 | $893.50 | $915.70 |

| Item Description | Unit | Remove | Replace | Total |
|---|---|---|---|---|
| **Over-under refrigerator / freezer, 10 to 12 cf capacity, deluxe grade** | ea | $22.20 | $1,019.50 | $1,041.70 |
| *Replace* Materials ....994.00    Labor ..........25.50 | | | | |
| *Remove* .................    Labor ..........22.20 | | | | |
| ► Specialty-style shelves and doors, deep doors, highly energy efficient. | | | | |
| **Remove refrigerator for work, then reinstall** | ea | — | $53.20 | $53.20 |
| *Replace* .................    Labor ..........53.20 | | | | |
| **Add for refreshment center in refrigerator / freezer** | ea | — | $467.00 | $467.00 |
| *Replace* Materials .....361.00    Labor ........106.00 | | | | |
| **Disconnect refrigerator water line for work, then re-connect** | ea | — | $12.70 | $12.70 |
| *Replace* Materials ........ .60    Labor ..........12.10 | | | | |
| **Refreshment center plumbing hook-up in existing building** | ea | — | $302.00 | $302.00 |
| *Replace* Materials ......25.00    Labor ........277.00 | | | | |
| **Refreshment center plumbing hook-up, new construction** | ea | — | $161.00 | $161.00 |
| *Replace* Materials ......23.00    Labor ........138.00 | | | | |
| **Refinish refrigerator** | ea | — | $372.00 | $372.00 |
| *Replace* Materials ......38.00    Labor ........334.00 | | | | |
| **Refinish and recondition refrigerator** | ea | — | $441.00 | $441.00 |
| *Replace* Materials ......57.00    Labor ........384.00 | | | | |
| **Trash compactor, economy grade** | ea | $22.20 | $511.10 | $533.30 |
| *Replace* Materials ....462.00    Labor ..........49.10 | | | | |
| *Remove* .................    Labor ..........22.20 | | | | |
| ► Convertible or built-in, 12". | | | | |
| **Trash compactor, standard grade** | ea | $22.20 | $638.10 | $660.30 |
| *Replace* Materials ....589.00    Labor ..........49.10 | | | | |
| *Remove* .................    Labor ..........22.20 | | | | |
| ► Convertible or built-in, 12" to 15", key lock, automatic anti-jam, reversible panel. | | | | |
| **Trash compactor, high grade** | ea | $22.20 | $714.10 | $736.30 |
| *Replace* Materials ....665.00    Labor ..........49.10 | | | | |
| *Remove* .................    Labor ..........22.20 | | | | |
| ► Convertible or built-in, 12" to 15", key lock, automatic anti-jam, heavy gauge construction, reversible panel. | | | | |
| **Remove trash compactor for work, then reinstall** | ea | — | $103.60 | $103.60 |
| *Replace* Materials ........ .60    Labor ........103.00 | | | | |
| **Clothes washing machine, economy grade** | ea | $14.20 | $408.30 | $422.50 |
| *Replace* Materials ....393.00    Labor ..........15.30 | | | | |
| *Remove* .................    Labor ..........14.20 | | | | |
| ► Large capacity, five cycles, three water levels, bleach dispenser. | | | | |
| **Clothes washing machine, standard grade** | ea | $14.20 | $503.30 | $517.50 |
| *Replace* Materials ....488.00    Labor ..........15.30 | | | | |
| *Remove* .................    Labor ..........14.20 | | | | |
| ► Large capacity, six cycles, two speeds, two wash / spin combinations, three water levels, bleach dispenser. | | | | |
| **Clothes washing machine, high grade** | ea | $14.20 | $579.30 | $593.50 |
| *Replace* Materials ....564.00    Labor ..........15.30 | | | | |
| *Remove* .................    Labor ..........14.20 | | | | |
| ► Extra large capacity, nine cycles with pre-wash, three speeds, four wash / spin combinations, three water levels, bleach dispenser. | | | | |

### RELATED ITEMS

Cleaning.....................55
Electrical *(wiring)*
  trash compactor .............143
  clothes washer................142
Plumbing
  clothes washer .............368
  ice maker ...................368

◄ **REFRESHMENT CENTER**

◄ **REFRESHMENT CENTER PLUMBING**
With supply lines and hookup to appliances. For installation of supply lines only see Plumbing on page 368.

◄ **REFINISH REFRIGERATOR**

◄ **TRASH COMPACTOR**

◄ **WASHING MACHINE**

| Item Description | Unit | Remove | Replace | Total |
|---|---|---|---|---|
| **WASHING ►**<br>**MACHINE**<br>*continued*   **Clothes washing machine, deluxe grade** | ea | $14.20 | $762.30 | $776.50 |
| *Replace* Materials.....747.00    Labor...........15.30<br>*Remove* .....................    Labor...........14.20 | | | | |
| ► Extra large capacity, programmable, ten cycles with pre-wash, four programmable speeds, four programmable wash / spin combinations, variable water levels, bleach / fabric softener dispenser. | | | | |
| **Remove washing machine for work, then reinstall** | ea | — | $28.70 | $28.70 |
| *Replace* .....................    Labor ..........28.70 | | | | |
| **CLOTHES DRYER ►**   **Clothes dryer, electric, economy grade** | ea | $13.10 | $330.80 | $343.90 |
| *Replace* Materials....317.00    Labor...........13.80<br>*Remove* .....................    Labor...........13.10 | | | | |
| ► Large capacity, two cycles, three heat selections. | | | | |
| **Clothes dryer, electric, standard grade** | ea | $13.10 | $406.80 | $419.90 |
| *Replace* Materials....393.00    Labor...........13.80<br>*Remove* .....................    Labor...........13.10 | | | | |
| ► Large capacity with automatic drying control, six cycles, four heat selections. | | | | |
| **Clothes dryer, high grade** | ea | $13.10 | $520.80 | $533.90 |
| *Replace* Materials....507.00    Labor...........13.80<br>*Remove* .....................    Labor...........13.10 | | | | |
| ► Extra large capacity with electronic drying control, five cycles with delicate fabrics option, four heat selections, drum lamp. | | | | |
| **Clothes dryer, deluxe grade** | ea | $13.10 | $653.80 | $666.90 |
| *Replace* Materials....640.00    Labor...........13.80<br>*Remove* .....................    Labor...........13.10 | | | | |
| ► Extra large capacity with electronic drying control, six cycles with delicate fabrics option, four heat selections, drum lamp. | | | | |
| **Remove clothes dryer for work, then reinstall** | ea | — | $25.50 | $25.50 |
| *Replace* .....................    Labor ..........25.50 | | | | |

*Electric dryers with up to 20' of vent pipe. Add **$121** for gas dryer (includes additional cost of dryer and additional cost to install).*

✏ NOTES: _____

_____

_____

_____

_____

_____

_____

_____

_____

_____

_____

_____

_____

_____

_____ end

# TIME & MATERIAL CHARTS (selected items)

## Appliance Materials

See **Appliance** material prices with the line items and other information in the **QuickFinder** column.

## Appliance Labor

| LABORER | BASE WAGE | PAID LEAVE | TRUE WAGE | FICA | FUTA | WORKER'S COMP. | UNEMPLOY. INSUR. | HEALTH INSUR. | RETIRE (401K) | LIABILITY INSUR. | COST PER HOUR |
|---|---|---|---|---|---|---|---|---|---|---|---|
| Appliance installer | $20.90 | 1.63 | $22.53 | 1.72 | .18 | 2.73 | 1.96 | 2.54 | .68 | 2.93 | $35.30 |
| Appliance refinisher | $23.80 | 1.86 | $25.66 | 1.96 | .21 | 6.84 | 2.23 | 2.54 | .77 | 3.34 | $43.60 |
| Electrician | $25.10 | 1.96 | $27.06 | 2.07 | .22 | 2.80 | 2.35 | 2.54 | .81 | 3.52 | $41.40 |
| Plumber | $24.90 | 1.94 | $26.84 | 2.05 | .21 | 4.30 | 2.34 | 2.54 | .81 | 3.49 | $42.60 |
| Demolition laborer | $13.40 | 1.05 | $14.45 | 1.11 | .12 | 4.44 | 1.26 | 2.54 | .43 | 1.88 | $26.20 |

**Paid Leave** is calculated based on two weeks paid vacation, one week sick leave, and seven paid holidays. Employer's matching portion of **FICA** is 7.65 percent. **FUTA** (Federal Unemployment) is .8 percent. **Worker's compensation** was calculated using a national average of 12.12 percent for the appliance installer; 26.67 percent for the appliance refinisher; 10.35 percent for the electrician; 16.02 percent for the plumber; and 30.70 percent for the demolition laborer. **Unemployment insurance** was calculated using a national average of 8.7 percent. **Health insurance** was calculated based on a projected national average for 2001 of $505 per employee (and family when applicable) per month. Employer pays 80 percent for a per month cost of $404 per employee. **Retirement** is based on a 401(k) retirement program with employer matching of 50 percent. Employee contributions to the 401(k) plan are an average of 6 percent of the true wage. **Liability insurance** is based on a national average of 12.9 percent.

## Appliances Labor Productivity

| WORK DESCRIPTION | LABORER | COST PER HOUR | PRODUCTIVITY | UNIT PRICE |
|---|---|---|---|---|
| **Demolition** | | | | |
| remove gas cook top | demolition laborer | $26.20 | .975 | $25.50 ea |
| remove gas range | demolition laborer | $26.20 | 1.03 | $27.00 ea |
| remove high-low gas range | demolition laborer | $26.20 | 1.18 | $30.90 ea |
| remove restaurant-style gas range | demolition laborer | $26.20 | 3.00 | $78.60 ea |
| remove gas wall oven | demolition laborer | $26.20 | 1.34 | $35.10 ea |
| remove gas double wall oven | demolition laborer | $26.20 | 1.95 | $51.10 ea |
| remove electric cook top | demolition laborer | $26.20 | 1.03 | $27.00 ea |
| remove modular electric cook-top unit | demolition laborer | $26.20 | .510 | $13.40 ea |
| remove electric range | demolition laborer | $26.20 | .975 | $25.50 ea |
| remove drop-in or slide-in electric range | demolition laborer | $26.20 | 1.22 | $32.00 ea |
| remove high-low electric range | demolition laborer | $26.20 | 1.03 | $27.00 ea |
| remove electric wall oven | demolition laborer | $26.20 | 1.18 | $30.90 ea |
| remove electric double wall oven | demolition laborer | $26.20 | 1.63 | $42.70 ea |
| remove range hood | demolition laborer | $26.20 | .736 | $19.30 ea |
| remove over-sized range hood | demolition laborer | $26.20 | .886 | $23.20 ea |
| remove dishwasher | demolition laborer | $26.20 | 1.39 | $36.40 ea |
| remove garbage disposal | demolition laborer | $26.20 | 1.30 | $34.10 ea |
| remove microwave oven | demolition laborer | $26.20 | .500 | $13.10 ea |
| remove side-by-side refrigerator / freezer | demolition laborer | $26.20 | .975 | $25.50 ea |
| remove over-under refrigerator / freezer | demolition laborer | $26.20 | .848 | $22.20 ea |
| remove trash compactor | demolition laborer | $26.20 | .848 | $22.20 ea |
| remove clothes washing machine | demolition laborer | $26.20 | .542 | $14.20 ea |
| remove clothes dryer | demolition laborer | $26.20 | .500 | $13.10 ea |

... More ➤

## Appliances Labor Productivity *continued*

| WORK DESCRIPTION | LABORER | COST PER HOUR | PRODUCTIVITY | UNIT PRICE |
|---|---|---|---|---|
| **Install appliances** | | | | |
| gas cook top | plumber | $42.60 | 1.99 | $84.80 *ea* |
| gas range | plumber | $42.60 | 2.05 | $87.30 *ea* |
| gas range with grill / griddle | plumber | $42.60 | 2.10 | $89.50 *ea* |
| space-saver gas range | plumber | $42.60 | 1.99 | $84.80 *ea* |
| high-low gas range with microwave high | plumber | $42.60 | 2.12 | $90.30 *ea* |
| restaurant-style gas range | plumber | $42.60 | 4.43 | $189.00 *ea* |
| gas wall oven | installer | $35.30 | 2.17 | $76.60 *ea* |
| gas double wall oven | installer | $35.30 | 3.98 | $140.00 *ea* |
| electric cook top | electrician | $41.40 | 1.77 | $73.30 *ea* |
| modular cooking unit | electrician | $41.40 | .629 | $26.00 *ea* |
| modular electric cook top downdraft unit | electrician | $41.40 | .488 | $20.20 *ea* |
| electric range | installer | $35.30 | 2.03 | $71.70 *ea* |
| drop-in or slide-in electric range | installer | $35.30 | 2.44 | $86.10 *ea* |
| space-saver electric range | installer | $35.30 | 1.97 | $69.50 *ea* |
| high-low electric range with microwave high | installer | $35.30 | 2.10 | $74.10 *ea* |
| electric wall oven | installer | $35.30 | 1.95 | $68.80 *ea* |
| electric double wall oven | installer | $35.30 | 3.61 | $127.00 *ea* |
| range hood | installer | $35.30 | 1.65 | $58.20 *ea* |
| oversized range hood | installer | $35.30 | 2.05 | $72.40 *ea* |
| dishwasher | installer | $35.30 | 1.95 | $68.80 *ea* |
| convertible (portable) dishwasher | installer | $35.30 | 1.18 | $41.70 *ea* |
| space-saver under-sink dishwasher | installer | $35.30 | 3.00 | $106.00 *ea* |
| garbage disposal | plumber | $42.60 | 1.60 | $68.20 *ea* |
| microwave oven | installer | $35.30 | .390 | $13.80 *ea* |
| microwave oven under cabinet | installer | $35.30 | 1.95 | $68.80 *ea* |
| side-by-side refrigerator / freezer | installer | $35.30 | .813 | $28.70 *ea* |
| refreshment center in side-by-side refrigerator / freezer | installer | $35.30 | 3.00 | $106.00 *ea* |
| over-under refrigerator / freezer | installer | $35.30 | .722 | $25.50 *ea* |
| refreshment center in over-under refrigerator / freezer | installer | $35.30 | 3.00 | $106.00 *ea* |
| refreshment center plumbing hook-up in existing building | plumber | $42.60 | 6.50 | $277.00 *ea* |
| refreshment center plumbing hook-up, new construction | plumber | $42.60 | 3.25 | $138.00 *ea* |
| trash compactor | installer | $35.30 | 1.39 | $49.10 *ea* |
| clothes washing machine | installer | $35.30 | .433 | $15.30 *ea* |
| clothes dryer | installer | $35.30 | .390 | $13.80 *ea* |

✍ NOTES: _____

_____

_____

_____

_____

_____

_____

_____

_____

_____

_____

_____

_____

_____

_____

_____ end

# 3 ....................................... *Awnings*

| Item Description | Unit | Remove | Replace | Total | |
|---|---|---|---|---|---|
| **Free-standing aluminum carport, 150 sf or less**<br>*Replace* Materials........15.50    Labor ...........2.73<br>*Remove*.......................    Labor ...........1.31 | sf | $1.31 | $18.23 | $19.54 | ◄ **FREE-STANDING CARPORT** *40 psf. Aluminum with baked enamel finish. With 4 posts under 200 sf. With 6 posts over 200 sf.* |
| **Free-standing aluminum carport, 151 to 250 sf**<br>*Replace* Materials........13.50    Labor ...........2.73<br>*Remove*.......................    Labor ...........1.31 | sf | $1.31 | $16.23 | $17.54 | |
| **Free-standing aluminum carport, 251 to 480 sf**<br>*Replace* Materials ......12.90    Labor ...........2.73<br>*Remove*.......................    Labor ...........1.31 | sf | $1.31 | $15.63 | $16.94 | |
| **Remove free-standing aluminum carport for work, then reinstall**<br>*Replace* Materials ........ .40    Labor ...........5.72 | sf | — | $6.12 | $6.12 | |
| **Attached aluminum carport or patio cover, 150 sf or less**<br>*Replace* Materials ......14.10    Labor ...........2.52<br>*Remove*.......................    Labor ...........1.41 | sf | $1.41 | $16.62 | $18.03 | ◄ **ATTACHED CARPORT** *40 psf. Aluminum with baked enamel finish. With 3 posts under 200 sf. With 4 to 5 posts over 200 sf.* |
| **Attached aluminum carport or patio cover, 151 to 250 sf**<br>*Replace* Materials ......12.30    Labor ...........2.52<br>*Remove*.......................    Labor ...........1.41 | sf | $1.41 | $14.82 | $16.23 | |
| **Attached aluminum carport or patio cover, 251 to 480 sf**<br>*Replace* Materials......11.70    Labor ...........2.52<br>*Remove*.......................    Labor ...........1.41 | sf | $1.41 | $14.22 | $15.63 | |
| **Remove attached aluminum carport or patio cover for work, then reinstall**<br>*Replace* Materials ........ .40    Labor ...........5.33 | sf | — | $5.73 | $5.73 | |
| **Minimum charge for carport or patio cover work**<br>*Replace* Materials......46.00    Labor...........65.70 | ea | — | $111.70 | $111.70 | ◁ minimum |
| **Add for heavy gauge aluminum carport or patio cover**<br>*Replace* Materials........3.40 | sf | — | $3.40 | $3.40 | ◁ add for heavy gauge |
| **Carport or patio cover post**<br>*Replace* Materials......50.00    Labor ..........38.40<br>*Remove*.......................    Labor ...........7.46 | ea | $7.46 | $88.40 | $95.86 | ◁ post |
| **Remove carport or patio cover post for work, then reinstall**<br>*Replace* Materials........2.00    Labor...........62.20 | ea | — | $64.20 | $64.20 | |
| **Carport or patio cover post scroll**<br>*Replace* Materials......60.00    Labor...........14.40<br>*Remove*.......................    Labor ...........2.56 | ea | $2.56 | $74.40 | $76.96 | ◁ scroll |
| **Remove carport or patio cover post scroll for work, then reinstall**<br>*Replace* Materials........1.00    Labor ..........23.40 | ea | — | $24.40 | $24.40 | |
| **Carport or patio cover aluminum fascia**<br>*Replace* Materials.......13.00    Labor ...........4.40<br>*Remove*.......................    Labor ............ .74 | lf | $.74 | $17.40 | $18.14 | ◁ fascia |

| | Item Description | Unit | Remove | Replace | Total |
|---|---|---|---|---|---|
| | **Remove carport or patio cover aluminum fascia for work, then reinstall**<br>*Replace* Materials .......... Labor ...........7.30 | lf | — | $7.30 | $7.30 |
| roof panel ▷ | **Carport or patio cover roof panel**<br>*Replace* Materials ......75.00 Labor...........26.80<br>*Remove*...................... Labor...........13.00 | ea | $13.00 | $101.80 | $114.80 |
| | **Remove carport or patio cover roof panel for work, then reinstall**<br>*Replace* Materials........4.00 Labor...........42.90 | ea | — | $46.90 | $46.90 |
| downspout ▷ | **Carport or patio cover downspout**<br>*Replace* Materials......50.00 Labor ...........3.80<br>*Remove*...................... Labor ...........2.59 | ea | $2.59 | $53.80 | $56.39 |
| | **Remove carport or patio cover downspout for work, then reinstall**<br>*Replace* Materials .......... Labor ...........5.70 | ea | — | $5.70 | $5.70 |
| **42″ ALUMINUM ▶ DOOR AWNING**<br>*25 to 40 psf. Aluminum with baked enamel finish. Includes all hardware and adjustable supports.* | **Aluminum door awning with 42″ projection, 2 to 4 lf**<br>*Replace* Materials .....161.00 Labor...........16.40<br>*Remove*...................... Labor...........12.60 | lf | $12.60 | $177.40 | $190.00 |
| | **Aluminum door awning with 42″ projection, 5 to 8 lf**<br>*Replace* Materials .....136.00 Labor...........16.40<br>*Remove*...................... Labor...........12.60 | lf | $12.60 | $152.40 | $165.00 |
| | **Aluminum door awning with 42″ projection, 9 to 12 lf**<br>*Replace* Materials .....123.00 Labor...........16.40<br>*Remove*...................... Labor...........12.60 | lf | $12.60 | $139.40 | $152.00 |
| **54″ ALUMINUM ▶ DOOR AWNING**<br>*25 to 40 psf. Aluminum with baked enamel finish. Includes all hardware and adjustable supports.* | **Aluminum door awning with 54″ projection, 2 to 4 lf**<br>*Replace* Materials .....215.00 Labor...........17.20<br>*Remove*...................... Labor...........13.10 | lf | $13.10 | $232.20 | $245.30 |
| | **Aluminum door awning with 54″ projection, 5 to 8 lf**<br>*Replace* Materials .....181.00 Labor...........17.20<br>*Remove*...................... Labor...........13.10 | lf | $13.10 | $198.20 | $211.30 |
| | **Aluminum door awning with 54″ projection, 9 to 12 lf**<br>*Replace* Materials .....160.00 Labor...........17.20<br>*Remove*...................... Labor...........13.10 | lf | $13.10 | $177.20 | $190.30 |
| | **Remove aluminum door awning for work, then reinstall**<br>*Replace* Materials ........5.90 Labor ...........34.00 | lf | — | $39.90 | $39.90 |
| **3′ HIGH WINDOW ▶ AWNING**<br>*25 to 40 psf. Aluminum with baked enamel finish. Includes all hardware and adjustable supports.* | **3′ high aluminum window awning, 2 to 4 lf**<br>*Replace* Materials ......52.00 Labor...........12.30<br>*Remove*...................... Labor...........10.60 | lf | $10.60 | $64.30 | $74.90 |
| | **3′ high aluminum window awning, 5 to 8 lf**<br>*Replace* Materials .....40.70 Labor...........12.30<br>*Remove*...................... Labor...........10.60 | lf | $10.60 | $53.00 | $63.60 |
| | **3′ high aluminum window awning, 9 to 12 lf**<br>*Replace* Materials ......38.10 Labor...........12.30<br>*Remove*...................... Labor...........10.60 | lf | $10.60 | $50.40 | $61.00 |
| | **Remove 3′ high aluminum window awning for work, then reinstall**<br>*Replace* Materials........5.90 Labor ...........29.50 | lf | — | $35.40 | $35.40 |

| Item Description | Unit | Remove | Replace | Total | |
|---|---|---|---|---|---|
| **4' high aluminum window awning, 2 to 4 lf**<br>*Replace* Materials......60.90   Labor...........12.60<br>*Remove*........................   Labor...........10.90 | lf | $10.90 | $73.50 | $84.40 | ◄ **4' HIGH WINDOW AWNING**<br>*25 to 40 psf. Aluminum with baked enamel finish. Includes all hardware and adjustable supports.* |
| **4' high aluminum window awning, 5 to 8 lf**<br>*Replace* Materials......50.30   Labor...........12.60<br>*Remove*........................   Labor...........10.90 | lf | $10.90 | $62.90 | $73.80 | |
| **4' high aluminum window awning, 9 to 12 lf**<br>*Replace* Materials......46.90   Labor...........12.60<br>*Remove*........................   Labor...........10.90 | lf | $10.90 | $59.50 | $70.40 | |
| **Remove 4' high aluminum window awning for work, then reinstall**<br>*Replace* Materials........5.90   Labor..........30.00 | lf | — | $35.90 | $35.90 | |
| **5' high aluminum window awning, 2 to 4 lf**<br>*Replace* Materials......81.00   Labor...........12.80<br>*Remove*........................   Labor...........11.10 | lf | $11.10 | $93.80 | $104.90 | ◄ **5' HIGH WINDOW AWNING**<br>*25 to 40 psf. Aluminum with baked enamel finish. Includes all hardware and adjustable supports.* |
| **5' high aluminum window awning, 5 to 8 lf**<br>*Replace* Materials......73.40   Labor...........12.80<br>*Remove*........................   Labor...........11.10 | lf | $11.10 | $86.20 | $97.30 | |
| **5' high aluminum window awning, 9 to 12 lf**<br>*Replace* Materials......58.10   Labor...........12.80<br>*Remove*........................   Labor...........11.10 | lf | $11.10 | $70.90 | $82.00 | |
| **Remove 5' high aluminum window awning for work, then reinstall**<br>*Replace* Materials........5.90   Labor..........30.50 | lf | — | $36.40 | $36.40 | |
| **6' high aluminum window awning, 2 to 4 lf**<br>*Replace* Materials......93.70   Labor...........13.10<br>*Remove*........................   Labor...........11.20 | lf | $11.20 | $106.80 | $118.00 | ◄ **6' HIGH WINDOW AWNING**<br>*25 to 40 psf. Aluminum with baked enamel finish. Includes all hardware and adjustable supports.* |
| **6' high aluminum window awning, 5 to 8 lf**<br>*Replace* Materials......89.00   Labor...........13.10<br>*Remove*........................   Labor...........11.20 | lf | $11.20 | $102.10 | $113.30 | |
| **6' high aluminum window awning, 9 to 12 lf**<br>*Replace* Materials......68.40   Labor...........13.10<br>*Remove*........................   Labor...........11.20 | lf | $11.20 | $81.50 | $92.70 | |
| **Remove 6' high aluminum window awning for work, then reinstall**<br>*Replace* Materials........5.90   Labor..........31.10 | lf | — | $37.00 | $37.00 | |
| **Minimum charge for door or window awning work**<br>*Replace* Materials......46.00   Labor..........65.70 | ea | — | $111.70 | $111.70 | ◁ minimum |
| **Door or window awning slat**<br>*Replace* Materials......19.00   Labor...........13.20<br>*Remove*........................   Labor ...........6.18 | ea | $6.18 | $32.20 | $38.38 | |
| **Roll-up aluminum awning, 2 to 5 lf**<br>*Replace* Materials......58.40   Labor ...........9.73<br>*Remove*........................   Labor...........10.90 | lf | $10.90 | $68.13 | $79.03 | ◄ **ROLL-UP AWNING**<br>*Security awning that covers window. Aluminum with baked enamel finish. Includes all hardware and adjustable supports.* |
| **Roll-up aluminum awning, 6 to 12 lf**<br>*Replace* Materials......44.60   Labor ...........9.73<br>*Remove*........................   Labor...........10.90 | lf | $10.90 | $54.33 | $65.23 | |

| Item Description | Unit | Remove | Replace | Total |
|---|---|---|---|---|
| **Remove roll-up aluminum window awning for work, then reinstall**<br>*Replace* Materials........4.50        Labor...........21.60 | lf | — | $26.10 | $26.10 |
| **Canvas awning with 24" drop, 2 to 3 lf**<br>*Replace* Materials......82.50        Labor ...........17.50<br>*Remove*..........................        Labor ...........8.49 | lf | $8.49 | $100.00 | $108.49 |
| **Canvas awning with 24" drop, 4 to 5 lf**<br>*Replace* Materials ......76.90        Labor ...........17.50<br>*Remove*..........................        Labor ...........8.49 | lf | $8.49 | $94.40 | $102.89 |
| **Canvas awning with 30" drop, 2 to 3 lf**<br>*Replace* Materials ......96.70        Labor ...........18.70<br>*Remove*..........................        Labor ...........8.49 | lf | $8.49 | $115.40 | $123.89 |
| **Canvas awning with 30" drop, 4 to 5 lf**<br>*Replace* Materials......84.90        Labor ...........18.70<br>*Remove*..........................        Labor ...........8.49 | lf | $8.49 | $103.60 | $112.09 |
| **Canvas awning with 30" drop, 5 to 6 lf**<br>*Replace* Materials ......76.50        Labor ...........18.70<br>*Remove*..........................        Labor ...........8.49 | lf | $8.49 | $95.20 | $103.69 |
| **Canvas awning with 30" drop, 7 to 8 lf**<br>*Replace* Materials ......68.00        Labor ...........18.70<br>*Remove*..........................        Labor ...........8.49 | lf | $8.49 | $86.70 | $95.19 |
| **Canvas awning with 30" drop, 9 to 10 lf**<br>*Replace* Materials ......55.80        Labor ...........18.70<br>*Remove*..........................        Labor ...........8.49 | lf | $8.49 | $74.50 | $82.99 |
| **Canvas awning with 30" drop, 11 to 12 lf**<br>*Replace* Materials ......51.70        Labor ...........18.70<br>*Remove*..........................        Labor ...........8.49 | lf | $8.49 | $70.40 | $78.89 |
| **Remove canvas awning for work, then reinstall**<br>*Replace* Materials........4.80        Labor ...........40.80 | lf | — | $45.60 | $45.60 |
| **Minimum charge for canvas awning work**<br>*Replace* Materials......40.00        Labor ...........58.60 | ea | — | $98.60 | $98.60 |
| **Vinyl awning with 24" drop, 2 to 3 lf**<br>*Replace* Materials ......48.90        Labor ...........17.40<br>*Remove*..........................        Labor ...........8.49 | lf | $8.49 | $66.30 | $74.79 |
| **Vinyl awning with 24" drop, 4 to 5 lf**<br>*Replace* Materials......44.90        Labor ...........17.40<br>*Remove*..........................        Labor ...........8.49 | lf | $8.49 | $62.30 | $70.79 |
| **Vinyl awning with 30" drop, 2 to 3 lf**<br>*Replace* Materials ......57.20        Labor ...........18.50<br>*Remove*..........................        Labor ...........8.49 | lf | $8.49 | $75.70 | $84.19 |
| **Vinyl awning with 30" drop, 4 to 5 lf**<br>*Replace* Materials......50.20        Labor ...........18.50<br>*Remove*..........................        Labor ...........8.49 | lf | $8.49 | $68.70 | $77.19 |
| **Vinyl awning with 30" drop, 5 to 6 lf**<br>*Replace* Materials ......45.70        Labor ...........18.50<br>*Remove*..........................        Labor ...........8.49 | lf | $8.49 | $64.20 | $72.69 |

**CANVAS ► AWNING**
*Waterproof acrylic duck colorfast fabric with retractable metal frame and hardware.*

minimum ▷

**VINYL AWNING ►**
*Vinyl awning with acrylic coating. Includes metal frame and all hardware.*

| Item Description | Unit | Remove | Replace | Total |
|---|---|---|---|---|
| **Vinyl awning with 30" drop, 7 to 8 lf**<br>*Replace* Materials......36.50     Labor...........18.50<br>*Remove*..........................     Labor ...........8.49 | lf | $8.49 | $55.00 | $63.49 |
| **Vinyl awning with 30" drop, 9 to 10 lf**<br>*Replace* Materials......33.40     Labor...........18.50<br>*Remove*..........................     Labor ...........8.49 | lf | $8.49 | $51.90 | $60.39 |
| **Vinyl awning with 30" drop, 11 to 12 lf**<br>*Replace* Materials......32.50     Labor...........18.50<br>*Remove*..........................     Labor ...........8.49 | lf | $8.49 | $51.00 | $59.49 |
| **Remove vinyl awning for work, then reinstall**<br>*Replace* Materials......4.80     Labor ..........40.10 | lf | — | $44.90 | $44.90 |
| **Minimum charge for vinyl awning work**<br>*Replace* Materials......27.00     Labor...........52.20 | ea | — | $79.20 | $79.20   ◁ minimum |

🖎 NOTES: _____

_____

_____ end

# TIME & MATERIAL CHARTS (selected items)

## Awning Materials

| DESCRIPTION | UNIT PRICE |
|---|---|
| **Aluminum carport** | |
| free-standing, 151 to 250 sf............................................................ | **$13.50** *sf* |
| attached, 151 to 250 sf................................................................... | **$12.30** *sf* |
| **Aluminum door awning** | |
| with 42" projection, 5 to 8 lf........................................................... | **$136.00** *lf* |
| with 54" projection, 5 to 8 lf........................................................... | **$181.00** *lf* |
| **Aluminum window awning** | |
| 3' high, 5 to 8 lf............................................................................ | **$40.70** *lf* |
| 4' high, 5 to 8 lf............................................................................ | **$50.30** *lf* |
| 5' high, 5 to 8 lf............................................................................ | **$73.40** *lf* |
| 6' high, 5 to 8 lf............................................................................ | **$89.00** *lf* |
| **Roll-up aluminum awning** | |
| 2 to 5 lf....................................................................................... | **$58.40** *lf* |
| 6 to 12 lf..................................................................................... | **$44.60** *lf* |
| **Canvas awning** | |
| 24" drop, 2 to 3 lf......................................................................... | **$82.50** *lf* |
| 24" drop, 4 to 5 lf......................................................................... | **$76.90** *lf* |
| 30" drop, 2 to 3 lf......................................................................... | **$96.70** *lf* |
| 30" drop, 7 to 8 lf......................................................................... | **$68.00** *lf* |
| 30" drop, 11 to 12 lf...................................................................... | **$51.70** *lf* |
| **Vinyl awning** | |
| 24" drop, 2 to 3 lf......................................................................... | **$48.90** *lf* |
| 24" drop, 4 to 5 lf......................................................................... | **$44.90** *lf* |
| 30" drop, 2 to 3 lf......................................................................... | **$57.20** *lf* |
| 30" drop, 7 to 8 lf......................................................................... | **$36.50** *lf* |
| 30" drop, 11 to 12 lf...................................................................... | **$32.50** *lf* |

## Awning Labor

| LABORER | BASE WAGE | PAID LEAVE | TRUE WAGE | FICA | FUTA | WORKER'S COMP. | UNEMPLOY. INSUR. | HEALTH INSUR. | RETIRE (401K) | LIABILITY INSUR. | COST PER HOUR |
|---|---|---|---|---|---|---|---|---|---|---|---|
| Awning installer | $23.90 | 1.86 | $25.76 | 1.97 | .21 | 4.97 | 2.24 | 2.54 | .77 | 3.35 | $41.80 |
| Awning installer's helper | $16.20 | 1.26 | $17.46 | 1.34 | .14 | 3.37 | 1.52 | 2.54 | .52 | 2.27 | $29.20 |
| Demolition laborer | $13.40 | 1.05 | $14.45 | 1.11 | .12 | 4.44 | 1.26 | 2.54 | .43 | 1.88 | $26.20 |

**Paid Leave** is calculated based on two weeks paid vacation, one week sick leave, and seven paid holidays. Employer's matching portion of **FICA** is 7.65 percent. **FUTA** (Federal Unemployment) is .8 percent. **Worker's Compensation** for the awning trade was calculated using a national average of 19.28 percent. **Unemployment insurance** was calculated using a national average of 8.7 percent. **Health insurance** was calculated based on a projected national average for 2001 of $505 per employee (and family when applicable) per month. Employer pays 80 percent for a per month cost of $404 per employee. **Retirement** is based on a 401(k) retirement program with employer matching of 50 percent. Employee contributions to the 401(k) plan are an average of 6 percent of the true wage. **Liability insurance** is based on a national average of 12.9 percent.

## Awning Labor Productivity

| WORK DESCRIPTION | LABORER | COST PER HOUR | PRODUCTIVITY | UNIT PRICE |
|---|---|---|---|---|
| **Demolition** | | | | |
| remove free-standing aluminum carport | demolition laborer | $26.20 | .050 | $1.31 sf |
| remove attached aluminum carport or patio cover | demolition laborer | $26.20 | .054 | $1.41 sf |
| remove 42" projection aluminum door awning | demolition laborer | $26.20 | .481 | $12.60 sf |
| remove 54" projection aluminum door awning | demolition laborer | $26.20 | .500 | $13.10 sf |
| remove 3' high aluminum window awning | demolition laborer | $26.20 | .403 | $10.60 lf |
| remove 4' high aluminum window awning | demolition laborer | $26.20 | .415 | $10.90 lf |
| remove 5' high aluminum window awning | demolition laborer | $26.20 | .423 | $11.10 lf |
| remove 6' high aluminum window awning | demolition laborer | $26.20 | .429 | $11.20 lf |
| remove roll-up aluminum window awning | demolition laborer | $26.20 | .417 | $10.90 lf |
| remove canvas or vinyl window awning | demolition laborer | $26.20 | .324 | $8.49 lf |
| **Awning Installation Crew** | | | | |
| install, awnings and patio covers | awning installer | $41.80 | | |
| install, awnings and patio covers | awning installer's helper | $29.20 | | |
| **awning installation crew** | **awning installation crew** | $35.50 | | |
| **Install aluminum carport or patio cover** | | | | |
| free-standing carport | awning installation crew | $35.50 | .077 | $2.73 sf |
| attached carport or patio cover | awning installation crew | $35.50 | .071 | $2.52 sf |
| **Install aluminum door awning** | | | | |
| 42" projection | awning installation crew | $35.50 | .463 | $16.40 lf |
| 54" projection | awning installation crew | $35.50 | .484 | $17.20 lf |
| **Install aluminum window awning** | | | | |
| 3' high | awning installation crew | $35.50 | .346 | $12.30 lf |
| 4' high | awning installation crew | $35.50 | .354 | $12.60 lf |
| 5' high | awning installation crew | $35.50 | .361 | $12.80 lf |
| 6' high | awning installation crew | $35.50 | .368 | $13.10 lf |
| **Install roll-up aluminum awning** | | | | |
| per lf | awning installation crew | $35.50 | .274 | $9.73 lf |
| **Install canvas awning** | | | | |
| 24" drop | awning installation crew | $35.50 | .493 | $17.50 lf |
| 30" drop | awning installation crew | $35.50 | .526 | $18.70 lf |
| **Install vinyl awning** | | | | |
| 24" drop | awning installation crew | $35.50 | .491 | $17.40 lf |
| 30" drop | awning installation crew | $35.50 | .520 | $18.50 lf |

NOTES: _____

_____

_____ end

# 4 .................................... *Bathroom Hardware*

| Item Description | Unit | Remove | Replace | Total | |
|---|---|---|---|---|---|
| **Minimum charge for bathroom hardware work**<br>*Replace* Materials......20.00    Labor..........22.20 | ea | — | $42.20 | $42.20 | ◄ **MINIMUM** |
| **Bath hardware for complete bathroom, economy grade**<br>*Replace* Materials....103.00    Labor..........159.00<br>*Remove* ......................    Labor..........58.20 | ea | $58.20 | $262.00 | $320.20 | ◄ **COMPLETE BATH**<br>*Bathroom with toilet, sink, and bathtub / shower. Includes towel bar, wash cloth bar, door-mount robe hook, toilet paper dispenser, and cup / toothbrush holder.* |
| **Bath hardware for complete bathroom, standard grade**<br>*Replace* Materials.....193.00    Labor..........159.00<br>*Remove* ......................    Labor..........58.20 | ea | $58.20 | $352.00 | $410.20 | |
| **Bath hardware for complete bathroom, high grade**<br>*Replace* Materials....281.00    Labor..........159.00<br>*Remove* ......................    Labor..........58.20 | ea | $58.20 | $440.00 | $498.20 | **HARDWARE QUALITY**<br>Some "rules of thumb" for determining bathroom hardware quality: |
| **Bath hardware for complete bathroom, deluxe grade**<br>*Replace* Materials....380.00    Labor..........159.00<br>*Remove* ......................    Labor..........58.20 | ea | $58.20 | $539.00 | $597.20 | **Economy:** Light-gauge metal, chrome plated. May have some plastic components. Little or no pattern. |
| **Bath hardware for complete bathroom, custom grade**<br>*Replace* Materials....433.00    Labor..........159.00<br>*Remove* ......................    Labor..........58.20 | ea | $58.20 | $592.00 | $650.20 | **Standard:** Heavier gauge metal, chrome or brass plated with little or no pattern or wood hardware made of ash or oak. |
| **Bath hardware for complete bathroom, antique reproduction**<br>*Replace* Materials....709.00    Labor..........159.00<br>*Remove* ......................    Labor..........58.20 | ea | $58.20 | $868.00 | $926.20 | |
| **1/2 bath hardware for complete bathroom, economy grade**<br>*Replace* Materials......34.00    Labor...........85.70<br>*Remove* ......................    Labor...........41.90 | ea | $41.90 | $119.70 | $161.60 | ◄ **1/2 BATH**<br>*Bathroom with toilet, and sink. Includes wash cloth bar, towel ring, and toilet paper dispenser.* |
| **1/2 bath hardware for complete bathroom, standard grade**<br>*Replace* Materials......66.00    Labor...........85.70<br>*Remove* ......................    Labor...........41.90 | ea | $41.90 | $151.70 | $193.60 | |
| **1/2 bath hardware for complete bathroom, high grade**<br>*Replace* Materials......95.00    Labor...........85.70<br>*Remove* ......................    Labor...........41.90 | ea | $41.90 | $180.70 | $222.60 | **QUALITY** *continued*<br>**High:** Brass, chrome over brass, or nickel over brass with minimal detail, or plated hardware with ornate detail, or European style curved plastic, or hardware with porcelain components, or wood hardware made of walnut, cherry, or similar wood. |
| **1/2 bath hardware for complete bathroom, deluxe grade**<br>*Replace* Materials....129.00    Labor...........85.70<br>*Remove* ......................    Labor...........41.90 | ea | $41.90 | $214.70 | $256.60 | |
| **1/2 bath hardware for complete bathroom, custom grade**<br>*Replace* Materials.....147.00    Labor...........85.70<br>*Remove* ......................    Labor...........41.90 | ea | $41.90 | $232.70 | $274.60 | **Deluxe:** Brass, chrome over brass, or nickel over brass with ornate detail. |
| **1/2 bath hardware for complete bathroom, antique reproduction**<br>*Replace* Materials....251.00    Labor...........85.70<br>*Remove* ......................    Labor...........41.90 | ea | $41.90 | $336.70 | $378.60 | **Antique Reproduction / Custom:** Brass, chrome over brass, or nickel over brass with ornate and/or antique style detail. |
| **Glass bathroom shelf**<br>*Replace* Materials......72.00    Labor...........11.10<br>*Remove* ......................    Labor...........8.52<br>► With plated chrome hardware. | ea | $8.52 | $83.10 | $91.62 | ◄ **GLASS SHELF**<br>*21" x 5-1/2" glass shelf.* |

| | Item Description | Unit | Remove | Replace | Total |
|---|---|---|---|---|---|
| **GLASS SHELF** ▶ continued | **Glass & brass bathroom shelf**<br>*Replace* Materials ....105.00    Labor ..........11.10<br>*Remove* .....................    Labor ..........8.52<br>▶ With solid brass or chrome-plated brass hardware. | ea | $8.52 | $116.10 | $124.62 |
| | **Remove glass bathroom shelf for work, then reinstall**<br>*Replace* .....................    Labor ..........13.10 | ea | — | $13.10 | $13.10 |
| **CUP & TOOTH-** ▶ **BRUSH HOLDER** *For quality indicators see page 41.* | **Cup & toothbrush holder, standard grade**<br>*Replace* Materials ......10.00    Labor ..........6.68<br>*Remove* .....................    Labor ..........4.27 | ea | $4.27 | $16.68 | $20.95 |
| | **Cup & toothbrush holder, high grade**<br>*Replace* Materials ......16.10    Labor ..........6.68<br>*Remove* .....................    Labor ..........4.27 | ea | $4.27 | $22.78 | $27.05 |
| | **Remove cup & toothbrush holder for work, then reinstall**<br>*Replace* .....................    Labor ..........8.57 | ea | — | $8.57 | $8.57 |
| **DOOR CLOTHES** ▶ **HANGER** *For quality indicators see page 41.* | **Door-mounted clothes hanger, standard grade**<br>*Replace* Materials ........9.00    Labor ..........5.57<br>*Remove* .....................    Labor ..........3.64 | ea | $3.64 | $14.57 | $18.21 |
| | **Door-mounted clothes hanger, high grade**<br>*Replace* Materials ......14.60    Labor ..........5.57<br>*Remove* .....................    Labor ..........3.64 | ea | $3.64 | $20.17 | $23.81 |
| | **Remove door-mounted clothes hanger for work, then reinstall**<br>*Replace* .....................    Labor ..........6.91 | ea | — | $6.91 | $6.91 |
| **ROBE HOOK** ▶ *For quality indicators see page 41.* | **Robe hook, standard grade**<br>*Replace* Materials ......10.00    Labor ..........5.57<br>*Remove* .....................    Labor ..........3.64 | ea | $3.64 | $15.57 | $19.21 |
| | **Robe hook, high grade**<br>*Replace* Materials .......17.00    Labor ..........5.57<br>*Remove* .....................    Labor ..........3.64 | ea | $3.64 | $22.57 | $26.21 |
| | **Remove robe hook for work, then reinstall**<br>*Replace* .....................    Labor ..........6.91 | ea | — | $6.91 | $6.91 |
| **SOAP HOLDER** ▶ *For quality indicators see page 41.* | **Soap holder, standard grade**<br>*Replace* Materials ......36.00    Labor ..........6.68<br>*Remove* .....................    Labor ..........4.27 | ea | $4.27 | $42.68 | $46.95 |
| | **Soap holder, high grade**<br>*Replace* Materials ......58.00    Labor ..........6.68<br>*Remove* .....................    Labor ..........4.27 | ea | $4.27 | $64.68 | $68.95 |
| | **Remove soap holder for work, then reinstall**<br>*Replace* .....................    Labor ..........8.57 | ea | — | $8.57 | $8.57 |
| **RECESSED** ▶ **SOAP HOLDER** *For quality indicators see page 41.* | **Recessed soap holder, standard grade**<br>*Replace* Materials .......19.00    Labor ..........7.94<br>*Remove* .....................    Labor ..........4.27 | ea | $4.27 | $26.94 | $31.21 |
| | **Recessed soap holder, high grade**<br>*Replace* Materials ......48.00    Labor ..........7.94<br>*Remove* .....................    Labor ..........4.27 | ea | $4.27 | $55.94 | $60.21 |

| Item Description | Unit | Remove | Replace | Total | |
|---|---|---|---|---|---|
| **Remove recessed soap holder for work, then reinstall** | ea | — | $10.50 | $10.50 | |
| *Replace* ...................... Labor...........10.50 | | | | | |
| **Soap dispenser, standard grade** | ea | $4.27 | $23.19 | $27.46 | ◄ **SOAP DISPENSER** |
| *Replace* Materials ......16.00 Labor ...........7.19 | | | | | For quality indicators |
| *Remove* ...................... Labor ...........4.27 | | | | | see page 41. |
| **Soap dispenser, high grade** | ea | $4.27 | $44.19 | $48.46 | |
| *Replace* Materials ......37.00 Labor ...........7.19 | | | | | |
| *Remove* ...................... Labor ...........4.27 | | | | | |
| **Remove soap dispenser for work, then reinstall** | ea | — | $8.85 | $8.85 | |
| *Replace* ...................... Labor ...........8.85 | | | | | |
| **Recessed tissue holder, standard grade** | ea | $3.64 | $43.75 | $47.39 | ◄ **RECESSED** |
| *Replace* Materials ......37.00 Labor ...........6.75 | | | | | **TISSUE HOLDER** |
| *Remove* ...................... Labor ...........3.64 | | | | | For quality indicators |
| **Recessed tissue holder, high grade** | ea | $3.64 | $64.75 | $68.39 | see page 41. |
| *Replace* Materials ......58.00 Labor ...........6.75 | | | | | |
| *Remove* ...................... Labor ...........3.64 | | | | | |
| **Remove recessed tissue holder for work, then reinstall** | ea | — | $9.84 | $9.84 | |
| *Replace* ...................... Labor ...........9.84 | | | | | |
| **Shower curtain rod** | ea | $2.33 | $41.46 | $43.79 | ◄ **SHOWER ROD** |
| *Replace* Materials ......37.00 Labor ...........4.46 | | | | | For quality indicators |
| *Remove* ...................... Labor ...........2.33 | | | | | see page 41. |
| **Remove shower curtain rod for work, then reinstall** | ea | — | $5.14 | $5.14 | |
| *Replace* ...................... Labor ...........5.14 | | | | | |
| **Towel bar, economy grade** | ea | $8.52 | $30.50 | $39.02 | ◄ **TOWEL BAR** |
| *Replace* Materials ......15.00 Labor ...........15.50 | | | | | For quality indicators |
| *Remove* ...................... Labor ...........8.52 | | | | | see page 41. |
| **Towel bar, standard grade** | ea | $8.52 | $37.50 | $46.02 | |
| *Replace* Materials ......22.00 Labor ...........15.50 | | | | | |
| *Remove* ...................... Labor ...........8.52 | | | | | |
| **Towel bar, high grade** | ea | $8.52 | $50.50 | $59.02 | |
| *Replace* Materials ......35.00 Labor ...........15.50 | | | | | |
| *Remove* ...................... Labor ...........8.52 | | | | | |
| **Towel bar, deluxe grade** | ea | $8.52 | $68.50 | $77.02 | |
| *Replace* Materials ......53.00 Labor ...........15.50 | | | | | |
| *Remove* ...................... Labor ...........8.52 | | | | | |
| **Remove towel bar for work, then reinstall** | ea | — | $22.20 | $22.20 | |
| *Replace* ...................... Labor ...........22.20 | | | | | |
| **Toilet paper dispenser, economy grade** | ea | $8.52 | $35.43 | $43.95 | ◄ **TOILET PAPER** |
| *Replace* Materials ......28.00 Labor ...........7.43 | | | | | **DISPENSER** |
| *Remove* ...................... Labor ...........8.52 | | | | | For quality indicators |
| **Toilet paper dispenser, standard grade** | ea | $8.52 | $43.43 | $51.95 | see page 41. |
| *Replace* Materials ......36.00 Labor ...........7.43 | | | | | |
| *Remove* ...................... Labor ...........8.52 | | | | | |

**RELATED ITEMS**

Cleaning ......................56

| Item Description | Unit | Remove | Replace | Total |
|---|---|---|---|---|
| **TOILET PAPER ▶ DISPENSER** *continued* | | | | |
| **Toilet paper dispenser, high grade** | ea | $8.52 | $56.43 | $64.95 |
| *Replace* Materials ......49.00    Labor ............7.43 | | | | |
| *Remove* ........................    Labor ............8.52 | | | | |
| **Toilet paper dispenser, deluxe grade** | ea | $8.52 | $64.43 | $72.95 |
| *Replace* Materials ......57.00    Labor ............7.43 | | | | |
| *Remove* ........................    Labor ............8.52 | | | | |
| **Remove toilet paper dispenser for work, then reinstall** | ea | — | $9.68 | $9.68 |
| *Replace* ........................    Labor ............9.68 | | | | |
| **TOWEL RING ▶** *For quality indicators see page 41.* **Towel ring, economy grade** | • ea | $8.52 | $24.40 | $32.92 |
| *Replace* Materials.......15.00    Labor ............9.40 | | | | |
| *Remove* ........................    Labor ............8.52 | | | | |
| **Towel ring, standard grade** | ea | $8.52 | $28.40 | $36.92 |
| *Replace* Materials.......19.00    Labor ............9.40 | | | | |
| *Remove* ........................    Labor ............8.52 | | | | |
| **Towel ring, high grade** | ea | $8.52 | $31.40 | $39.92 |
| *Replace* Materials ......22.00    Labor ............9.40 | | | | |
| *Remove* ........................    Labor ............8.52 | | | | |
| **Towel ring, deluxe grade** | ea | $8.52 | $34.40 | $42.92 |
| *Replace* Materials ......25.00    Labor ............9.40 | | | | |
| *Remove* ........................    Labor ............8.52 | | | | |
| **Remove towel ring for work, then reinstall** | ea | — | $11.80 | $11.80 |
| *Replace* ........................    Labor ............11.80 | | | | |
| **WASH CLOTH BAR ▶** *For quality indicators see page 41.* **Wash cloth bar, economy grade** | ea | $8.52 | $28.50 | $37.02 |
| *Replace* Materials.......13.00    Labor ............15.50 | | | | |
| *Remove* ........................    Labor ............8.52 | | | | |
| **Wash cloth bar, standard grade** | ea | $8.52 | $32.50 | $41.02 |
| *Replace* Materials.......17.00    Labor ............15.50 | | | | |
| *Remove* ........................    Labor .............. | | | | |
| **Wash cloth bar, high grade** | ea | $8.52 | $37.50 | $46.02 |
| *Replace* Materials ......22.00    Labor ............15.50 | | | | |
| *Remove* ........................    Labor ............8.52 | | | | |
| **Wash cloth bar, deluxe grade** | ea | $8.52 | $45.50 | $54.02 |
| *Replace* Materials ......30.00    Labor ............15.50 | | | | |
| *Remove* ........................    Labor ............8.52 | | | | |
| **Remove wash cloth bar for work, then reinstall** | ea | — | $22.20 | $22.20 |
| *Replace* ........................    Labor ............22.20 | | | | |
| **RECESSED ▶ MEDICINE CABINET** **Recessed medicine cabinet, economy grade** | ea | $16.00 | $100.70 | $116.70 |
| *Replace* Materials ......49.00    Labor............51.70 | | | | |
| *Remove* ........................    Labor............16.00 | | | | |
| ▶ Plastic or polystyrene box with two to three shelves.  Up to 16" wide and up to 25" tall.  Mirror doors with chrome-plated trim. | | | | |
| **Recessed medicine cabinet, standard grade** | ea | $16.00 | $111.70 | $127.70 |
| *Replace* Materials ......60.00    Labor............51.70 | | | | |
| *Remove* ........................    Labor............16.00 | | | | |
| ▶ Plastic or polystyrene box with two to three shelves.  Up to 16" wide and up to 25" tall.  Mirror door with brass-plated or wood trim or vinyl shutter door. | | | | |

| Item Description | Unit | Remove | Replace | Total |
|---|---|---|---|---|
| **Recessed medicine cabinet, high grade** | ea | $16.00 | $137.70 | $153.70 |

*Replace* Materials......86.00     Labor.........51.70
*Remove* .......................     Labor.........16.00

▶ Steel box with adjustable shelves. Up to 16" wide and up to 25" tall. Mirror door with chrome-plated or wood trim; or real wood door (includes stain & varnish). May have beveled mirror with no trim.

| | | | | |
|---|---|---|---|---|
| **Recessed medicine cabinet, deluxe grade** | ea | $16.00 | $152.70 | $168.70 |

*Replace* Materials.....101.00     Labor.........51.70
*Remove* .......................     Labor.........16.00

▶ Steel box with adjustable shelves. Up to 20" wide and up to 32" tall. Arched mirror door with brass or wood trim; or real wood door (includes stain & varnish). May have beveled mirror with no trim.

| | | | | |
|---|---|---|---|---|
| **Recessed medicine cabinet, custom grade** | ea | $16.00 | $176.70 | $192.70 |

*Replace* Materials.....125.00     Labor.........51.70
*Remove* .......................     Labor.........16.00

▶ Steel box with adjustable shelves. Up to 20" wide and up to 32" tall. Arched or oval mirror door brass or wood trim; or real wood door (includes stain & varnish). May have beveled mirror with no trim.

| | | | | |
|---|---|---|---|---|
| **Remove recessed medicine cabinet for work, then reinstall** | ea | — | $74.30 | $74.30 |

*Replace* .......................     Labor.........74.30

| | | | | |
|---|---|---|---|---|
| **Surface-mounted medicine cabinet, economy grade** | ea | $17.00 | $119.60 | $136.60 |

*Replace* Materials......60.00     Labor.........59.60
*Remove* .......................     Labor.........17.00

▶ Plastic or polystyrene box with two to three shelves. Up to 16" wide and up to 25" tall. Hinged mirror doors with chrome-plated trim; or vinyl shutter door. Also larger mirror styles with small sliding door cabinet below mirror.

| | | | | |
|---|---|---|---|---|
| **Surface-mounted medicine cabinet, standard grade** | ea | $17.00 | $145.60 | $162.60 |

*Replace* Materials......86.00     Labor.........59.60
*Remove* .......................     Labor.........17.00

▶ Metal box with adjustable shelves. Up to 16" wide and up to 25" tall. Hinged mirror doors with chrome-plated trim or wood trim; or wood shutter door (includes stain & varnish).

| | | | | |
|---|---|---|---|---|
| **Surface-mounted medicine cabinet, high grade** | ea | $17.00 | $205.60 | $222.60 |

*Replace* Materials ....146.00     Labor.........59.60
*Remove* .......................     Labor.........17.00

▶ Metal box with two to three shelves. Up to 16" wide and up to 25" tall. Hinged mirror doors with chrome-plated trim or wood trim; or wood shutter door (includes stain & varnish). Also up to 30" by 30" cabinets with bypassing mirror doors.

| | | | | |
|---|---|---|---|---|
| **Surface-mounted medicine cabinet, deluxe grade** | ea | $17.00 | $307.60 | $324.60 |

*Replace* Materials ....248.00     Labor.........59.60
*Remove* .......................     Labor.........17.00

▶ Wood plastic laminate coated box with two to three shelves. Up to 30" wide and up to 30" tall. 3 door hinged doors usually with oak trim.

| | | | | |
|---|---|---|---|---|
| **Surface-mounted medicine cabinet, custom grade** | ea | $17.00 | $413.60 | $430.60 |

*Replace* Materials ....354.00     Labor.........59.60
*Remove* .......................     Labor.........17.00

▶ Metal box (may be chrome) with two to three shelves. Up to 38" wide and up to 32" tall. 3 hinged doors usually with oak trim.

| | | | | |
|---|---|---|---|---|
| **Remove surface-mounted medicine cabinet for work, then reinstall** | ea | — | $77.80 | $77.80 |

*Replace* .......................     Labor .........77.80

| | | | | |
|---|---|---|---|---|
| **Bathroom mirror with stainless-steel trim** | sf | $1.07 | $21.19 | $22.26 |

*Replace* Materials.......17.00     Labor .........4.19
*Remove* .......................     Labor .........1.07

◀ **SURFACE-MOUNT MEDICINE CABINET**

**RELATED ITEMS**
Cleaning ....................56

◀ **BATHROOM MIRROR**

| Item Description | Unit | Remove | Replace | Total |
|---|---|---|---|---|
| **Bathroom mirror with brass-finished trim** | sf | $1.07 | $22.19 | $23.26 |
| *Replace* Materials ......18.00    Labor ...........4.19 | | | | |
| *Remove* .....................    Labor ...........1.07 | | | | |
| **Bathroom mirror with wood frame** | sf | $1.07 | $22.19 | $23.26 |
| *Replace* Materials ......18.00    Labor ...........4.19 | | | | |
| *Remove* .....................    Labor ...........1.07 | | | | |
| **Bathroom mirror beveled glass** | sf | $1.07 | $22.19 | $23.26 |
| *Replace* Materials ......18.00    Labor ...........4.19 | | | | |
| *Remove* .....................    Labor ...........1.07 | | | | |
| **Remove bathroom mirror for work, then reinstall** | sf | — | $6.68 | $6.68 |
| *Replace* .....................    Labor ...........6.68 | | | | |

**BATHROOM ▶ MIRROR** *continued*

# TIME & MATERIAL CHARTS *(selected items)*

## Bathroom Hardware Materials

See **Bathroom Hardware** material prices with the line items and other information in the **QuickFinder** column.

## Bathroom Hardware Labor

| LABORER | BASE WAGE | PAID LEAVE | TRUE WAGE | FICA | FUTA | WORKER'S COMP. | UNEMPLOY. INSUR. | HEALTH INSUR. | RETIRE (401K) | LIABILITY INSUR. | COST PER HOUR |
|---|---|---|---|---|---|---|---|---|---|---|---|
| Carpenter (installer) | $22.60 | 1.76 | $24.36 | 1.86 | .19 | 4.56 | 2.12 | 2.54 | .73 | 3.17 | $39.50 |
| Demolition laborer | $13.40 | 1.05 | $14.45 | 1.11 | .12 | 4.44 | 1.26 | 2.54 | .43 | 1.88 | $26.20 |

**Paid Leave** is calculated based on two weeks paid vacation, one week sick leave, and seven paid holidays. Employer's matching portion of **FICA** is 7.65 percent. **FUTA** (Federal Unemployment) is .8 percent. **Worker's compensation** for the bathroom hardware trade was calculated using a national average of 18.71 percent. **Unemployment insurance** was calculated using a national average of 8.7 percent. **Health insurance** was calculated based on a projected national average for 2001 of $505 per employee (and family when applicable) per month. Employer pays 80 percent for a per month cost of $404 per employee. **Retirement** is based on a 401(k) retirement program with employer matching of 50 percent. Employee contributions to the 401(k) plan are an average of 6 percent of the true wage. **Liability insurance** is based on a national average of 12.9 percent.

## Bathroom Hardware Labor Productivity

| WORK DESCRIPTION | LABORER | COST PER HOUR | PRODUCTIVITY | UNIT PRICE |
|---|---|---|---|---|
| **Demolition** | | | | |
| hardware for complete bathroom | demolition laborer | $26.20 | 2.22 | $58.20 ea |
| hardware for complete 1/2 bathroom | demolition laborer | $26.20 | 1.60 | $41.90 ea |
| recessed medicine cabinet | demolition laborer | $26.20 | .609 | $16.00 ea |
| surface-mounted medicine cabinet | demolition laborer | $26.20 | .650 | $17.00 ea |
| bathroom mirror attached with glue | demolition laborer | $26.20 | .041 | $1.07 sf |
| **Install complete bathroom hardware** | | | | |
| full bathroom | carpenter | $39.50 | 4.02 | $159.00 ea |
| 1/2 bathroom | carpenter | $39.50 | 2.17 | $85.70 ea |
| **Install hardware** | | | | |
| soap holder | carpenter | $39.50 | .169 | $6.68 ea |
| recessed tissue holder | carpenter | $39.50 | .171 | $6.75 ea |
| towel bar | carpenter | $39.50 | .393 | $15.50 ea |
| toilet paper dispenser | carpenter | $39.50 | .188 | $7.43 ea |
| towel ring | carpenter | $39.50 | .238 | $9.40 ea |
| wash cloth bar | carpenter | $39.50 | .393 | $15.50 ea |
| recessed medicine cabinet | carpenter | $39.50 | 1.31 | $51.70 ea |
| surface-mounted medicine cabinet | carpenter | $39.50 | 1.51 | $59.60 ea |
| bathroom mirror | carpenter | $39.50 | .106 | $4.19 sf |

# 5 .......................................................................... *Cabinets*

| Item Description | Unit | Remove | Replace | Total | |
|---|---|---|---|---|---|
| **Minimum charge for cabinet work**<br>*Replace* Materials ......42.00　　　　Labor...........87.30 | ea | — | $129.30 | $129.30 | ◄ **MINIMUM** |
| **Lower kitchen cabinets, standard grade**<br>*Replace* Materials ......83.00　　Labor ............11.80<br>*Remove* ........................　　Labor ............6.86 | lf | $6.86 | $94.80 | $101.66 | ◄ **LOWER CABINETS** |
| **Lower kitchen cabinets, high grade**<br>*Replace* Materials ....106.00　　Labor ............11.80<br>*Remove* ........................　　Labor ............6.86 | lf | $6.86 | $117.80 | $124.66 | |
| **Lower kitchen cabinets, deluxe grade**<br>*Replace* Materials ....150.00　　Labor ............11.80<br>*Remove* ........................　　Labor ............6.86 | lf | $6.86 | $161.80 | $168.66 | |
| **Lower kitchen cabinets, custom grade**<br>*Replace* Materials .....214.00　　Labor ............11.80<br>*Remove* ........................　　Labor ............6.86 | lf | $6.86 | $225.80 | $232.66 | |
| **Lower kitchen cabinets, custom deluxe grade**<br>*Replace* Materials ....277.00　　Labor ............11.80<br>*Remove* ........................　　Labor ............6.86 | lf | $6.86 | $288.80 | $295.66 | |
| **Remove lower kitchen cabinets for work, then reinstall**<br>*Replace* ........................　　Labor ...........20.80 | lf | — | $20.80 | $20.80 | |
| **Upper kitchen cabinets, economy grade**<br>*Replace* Materials ......58.00　　Labor ............11.40<br>*Remove* ........................　　Labor ............6.18 | lf | $6.18 | $69.40 | $75.58 | ◄ **UPPER CABINETS** |
| **Upper kitchen cabinets, standard grade**<br>*Replace* Materials ......77.00　　Labor ............11.40<br>*Remove* ........................　　Labor ............6.18 | lf | $6.18 | $88.40 | $94.58 | |
| **Upper kitchen cabinets, high grade**<br>*Replace* Materials ......95.00　　Labor ............11.40<br>*Remove* ........................　　Labor ............6.18 | lf | $6.18 | $106.40 | $112.58 | |
| **Upper kitchen cabinets, deluxe grade**<br>*Replace* Materials .....139.00　　Labor ............11.40<br>*Remove* ........................　　Labor ............6.18 | lf | $6.18 | $150.40 | $156.58 | |
| **Upper kitchen cabinets, custom grade**<br>*Replace* Materials .....199.00　　Labor ............11.40<br>*Remove* ........................　　Labor ............6.18 | lf | $6.18 | $210.40 | $216.58 | |
| **Upper kitchen cabinets, custom deluxe grade**<br>*Replace* Materials ....254.00　　Labor ............11.40<br>*Remove* ........................　　Labor ............6.18 | lf | $6.18 | $265.40 | $271.58 | |
| **Remove upper kitchen cabinets for work, then reinstall**<br>*Replace* ........................　　Labor ..........20.00 | lf | — | $20.00 | $20.00 | |

### CABINET CONSTRUCTION

**STOCK CABINETS** Stock-grade cabinets are manufactured in standard sizes and warehoused until sold.

**SEMI-CUSTOM CABINETS** Semi-custom grade cabinets are available in a wide variety of styles and shapes. Within limits, the manufacturer builds the cabinets to match the kitchen.

**CUSTOM CABINETS** Custom-grade cabinets are built specifically for the kitchen and include specialty doors, woods and construction.

### CABINET GRADES

**ECONOMY GRADE** Stock-grade cabinets with flush-face doors. Doors made from veneered particle board.

**STANDARD GRADE** Stock-grade cabinets with raised panel or cathedral doors. Interior panel may be plywood. Lower grade plastic-laminate face cabinets.

**HIGH GRADE** Semi-custom cabinets with raised panel or cathedral doors. Higher grade plastic-laminate face and foil-face cabinets.

*continued on next page*

### RELATED ITEMS
Cleaning ......................56

| | Item Description | Unit | Remove | Replace | Total |
|---|---|---|---|---|---|
| **LOWER ISLAND ▶ CABINETS** | **Lower kitchen island cabinets, economy grade**<br>*Replace* Materials......68.00    Labor..........12.10<br>*Remove* ......................    Labor...........6.63 | lf | $6.63 | $80.10 | $86.73 |
| | **Lower kitchen island cabinets, standard grade**<br>*Replace* Materials......86.00    Labor..........12.10<br>*Remove* ......................    Labor...........6.63 | lf | $6.63 | $98.10 | $104.73 |
| | **Lower kitchen island cabinets, high grade**<br>*Replace* Materials.....110.00    Labor..........12.10<br>*Remove* ......................    Labor...........6.63 | lf | $6.63 | $122.10 | $128.73 |
| | **Lower kitchen island cabinets, deluxe grade**<br>*Replace* Materials.....156.00    Labor..........12.10<br>*Remove* ......................    Labor...........6.63 | lf | $6.63 | $168.10 | $174.73 |
| | **Lower kitchen island cabinets, custom grade**<br>*Replace* Materials....223.00    Labor..........12.10<br>*Remove* ......................    Labor...........6.63 | lf | $6.63 | $235.10 | $241.73 |
| | **Lower kitchen island cabinets, custom deluxe grade**<br>*Replace* Materials....288.00    Labor..........12.10<br>*Remove* ......................    Labor...........6.63 | lf | $6.63 | $300.10 | $306.73 |
| | **Remove lower kitchen island cabinets for work, then reinstall**<br>*Replace* ......................    Labor..........21.40 | lf | — | $21.40 | $21.40 |
| **UPPER ISLAND ▶ CABINETS** | **Upper kitchen island cabinets, economy grade**<br>*Replace* Materials......60.00    Labor..........11.70<br>*Remove* ......................    Labor...........6.24 | lf | $6.24 | $71.70 | $77.94 |
| | **Upper kitchen island cabinets, standard grade**<br>*Replace* Materials......80.00    Labor..........11.70<br>*Remove* ......................    Labor...........6.24 | lf | $6.24 | $91.70 | $97.94 |
| | **Upper kitchen island cabinets, high grade**<br>*Replace* Materials......99.00    Labor..........11.70<br>*Remove* ......................    Labor...........6.24 | lf | $6.24 | $110.70 | $116.94 |
| | **Upper kitchen island cabinets, deluxe grade**<br>*Replace* Materials.....145.00    Labor..........11.70<br>*Remove* ......................    Labor...........6.24 | lf | $6.24 | $156.70 | $162.94 |
| | **Upper kitchen island cabinets, custom grade**<br>*Replace* Materials....207.00    Labor..........11.70<br>*Remove* ......................    Labor...........6.24 | lf | $6.24 | $218.70 | $224.94 |
| | **Upper kitchen island cabinets, custom deluxe grade**<br>*Replace* Materials....264.00    Labor..........11.70<br>*Remove* ......................    Labor...........6.24 | lf | $6.24 | $275.70 | $281.94 |
| | **Remove upper kitchen island cabinets for work, then reinstall**<br>*Replace* ......................    Labor..........20.70 | lf | — | $20.70 | $20.70 |
| **FULL-HEIGHT ▶ UTILITY CABINET** | **Full-height utility cabinet, economy grade**<br>*Replace* Materials.....157.00    Labor..........19.40<br>*Remove* ......................    Labor...........8.67 | lf | $8.67 | $176.40 | $185.07 |
| | **Full-height utility cabinet, standard grade**<br>*Replace* Materials.....198.00    Labor..........19.40<br>*Remove* ......................    Labor...........8.67 | lf | $8.67 | $217.40 | $226.07 |

**CABINET GRADES**

*continued from prior page*

**DELUXE GRADE** Semi-custom cabinets with raised panel or cathedral doors. May include special slide-out drawers, pull-out baskets, glass doors, foil-face, cherry, pecan, or Shaker style maple or pine.

**CUSTOM GRADE** Custom cabinets with raised panel or cathedral doors. May include specialty slide-out drawers, pull-out baskets, glass mullion or leaded glass doors, cherry, pecan, or Shaker style maple or pine.

**CUSTOM DELUXE GRADE** Same as Custom Grade may have some curved wood cabinets and more custom features.

| Item Description | Unit | Remove | Replace | Total |
|---|---|---|---|---|
| **Full-height utility cabinet, high grade** | lf | $8.67 | $261.40 | $270.07 |
| *Replace* Materials.....242.00  Labor...........19.40 | | | | |
| *Remove* .....................  Labor ............8.67 | | | | |
| **Full-height utility cabinet, deluxe grade** | lf | $8.67 | $328.40 | $337.07 |
| *Replace* Materials....309.00  Labor...........19.40 | | | | |
| *Remove* .....................  Labor ............8.67 | | | | |
| **Full-height utility cabinet, custom grade** | lf | $8.67 | $357.40 | $366.07 |
| *Replace* Materials....338.00  Labor...........19.40 | | | | |
| *Remove* .....................  Labor ............8.67 | | | | |
| **Full-height utility cabinet custom, deluxe grade** | lf | $8.67 | $398.40 | $407.07 |
| *Replace* Materials ....379.00  Labor...........19.40 | | | | |
| *Remove* .....................  Labor ............8.67 | | | | |
| **Remove full-height kitchen cabinets for work, then reinstall** | lf | — | $23.10 | $23.10 |
| *Replace* .....................  Labor ..........23.10 | | | | |
| **Full-height built-in oven cabinet, economy grade** | lf | $8.67 | $168.40 | $177.07 |
| *Replace* Materials.....149.00  Labor...........19.40 | | | | |
| *Remove* .....................  Labor ............8.67 | | | | |
| **Full-height built-in oven cabinet, standard grade** | lf | $8.67 | $207.40 | $216.07 |
| *Replace* Materials ....188.00  Labor...........19.40 | | | | |
| *Remove* .....................  Labor ............8.67 | | | | |
| **Full-height built-in oven cabinet, high grade** | lf | $8.67 | $249.40 | $258.07 |
| *Replace* Materials ....230.00  Labor...........19.40 | | | | |
| *Remove* .....................  Labor ............8.67 | | | | |
| **Full-height built-in oven cabinet, deluxe grade** | lf | $8.67 | $313.40 | $322.07 |
| *Replace* Materials ....294.00  Labor...........19.40 | | | | |
| *Remove* .....................  Labor ............8.67 | | | | |
| **Full-height built-in oven cabinet, custom grade** | lf | $8.67 | $340.40 | $349.07 |
| *Replace* Materials ....321.00  Labor...........19.40 | | | | |
| *Remove* .....................  Labor ............8.67 | | | | |
| **Full-height built-in oven cabinet, custom deluxe grade** | lf | $8.67 | $379.40 | $388.07 |
| *Replace* Materials ....360.00  Labor...........19.40 | | | | |
| *Remove* .....................  Labor ............8.67 | | | | |
| **Remove full-height built-in oven cabinets for work, then reinstall** | lf | — | $23.10 | $23.10 |
| *Replace* .....................  Labor ..........23.10 | | | | |
| **Full-height built-in double oven cabinet, economy grade** | lf | $8.67 | $163.40 | $172.07 |
| *Replace* Materials ....144.00  Labor...........19.40 | | | | |
| *Remove* .....................  Labor ............8.67 | | | | |
| **Full-height built-in double oven cabinet, standard grade** | lf | $8.67 | $201.40 | $210.07 |
| *Replace* Materials ....182.00  Labor...........19.40 | | | | |
| *Remove* .....................  Labor ............8.67 | | | | |
| **Full-height built-in double oven cabinet, high grade** | lf | $8.67 | $242.40 | $251.07 |
| *Replace* Materials ....223.00  Labor...........19.40 | | | | |
| *Remove* .....................  Labor ............8.67 | | | | |
| **Full-height built-in double oven cabinet, deluxe grade** | lf | $8.67 | $303.40 | $312.07 |
| *Replace* Materials ....284.00  Labor...........19.40 | | | | |
| *Remove* .....................  Labor ............8.67 | | | | |

◄ **FULL-HEIGHT OVEN CABINET**

### FOIL-FACE CABINETS

Foil-faced cabinets (also called thermo foil) are coated with rigid polyvinyl chloride (PVC) that has been heated and pressed. The interior core is usually medium density particle board.

Currently, there is no good way to repair scratched or dented foil-face cabinets. Although colors do not fade from foil-faces, it is almost impossible to replace doors or other parts with colors that will match.

Foil-face cabinets are high to custom deluxe quality depending on the interior features and the complexity of the design.

◄ **FULL-HEIGHT DOUBLE OVEN CABINET**

**RELATED ITEMS**
Cleaning ....................56

| Item Description | Unit | Remove | Replace | Total |
|---|---|---|---|---|
| **FULL-HEIGHT ▶** **DOUBLE OVEN** **CABINET** *continued* | | | | |
| **Full-height built-in double oven cabinet, custom grade** | lf | $8.67 | $330.40 | $339.07 |
| *Replace* Materials.....311.00    Labor..........19.40 | | | | |
| *Remove* .......................    Labor...........8.67 | | | | |
| **Full-height built-in double oven cabinet, custom deluxe grade** | lf | $8.67 | $368.40 | $377.07 |
| *Replace* Materials....349.00    Labor..........19.40 | | | | |
| *Remove* .......................    Labor...........8.67 | | | | |
| **Remove full-height built-in double oven cabinets for work, then reinstall** | lf | — | $23.10 | $23.10 |
| *Replace* ......................    Labor..........23.10 | | | | |
| **CABINET ▶** **DRAWER FRONT** **Cabinet drawer front** | ea | $3.77 | $16.86 | $20.63 |
| *Replace* Materials.......13.00    Labor...........3.86 | | | | |
| *Remove* .......................    Labor...........3.77 | | | | |
| **CABINET DOOR ▶** **Flush-face cabinet door** | ea | $7.00 | $24.24 | $31.24 |
| *Replace* Materials ......16.00    Labor...........8.24 | | | | |
| *Remove* .......................    Labor...........7.00 | | | | |
| *flat panel* **Flat panel cabinet door** | ea | $7.00 | $31.24 | $38.24 |
| *Replace* Materials ......23.00    Labor...........8.24 | | | | |
| *Remove* .......................    Labor...........7.00 | | | | |
| *raised panel* **Raised panel cabinet door** | ea | $7.00 | $41.24 | $48.24 |
| *Replace* Materials ......33.00    Labor...........8.24 | | | | |
| *Remove* .......................    Labor...........7.00 | | | | |
| *raised panel cathedral* **Raised panel cathedral cabinet door** | ea | $7.00 | $50.24 | $57.24 |
| *Replace* Materials ......42.00    Labor...........8.24 | | | | |
| *Remove* .......................    Labor...........7.00 | | | | |
| **Cabinet door with glass** | ea | $7.00 | $60.24 | $67.24 |
| *Replace* Materials ......52.00    Labor...........8.24 | | | | |
| *Remove* .......................    Labor...........7.00 | | | | |
| *with leaded glass* **Cabinet door with leaded glass per door** | ea | $7.00 | $111.24 | $118.24 |
| *Replace* Materials ....103.00    Labor...........8.24 | | | | |
| *Remove* .......................    Labor...........7.00 | | | | |
| **REFINISH CABINET ▶** *Cabinets are stripped and restained. Edge surfaces that are finished with 1/4" hardwood plywood are replaced.* **Refinish cabinet drawer front** | ea | — | $10.41 | $10.41 |
| *Replace* Materials........1.50    Labor............8.91 | | | | |
| **Refinish cabinet door** | ea | — | $24.20 | $24.20 |
| *Replace* Materials........3.30    Labor..........20.90 | | | | |
| **Refinish cabinet door with glass** | ea | — | $22.60 | $22.60 |
| *Replace* Materials........1.60    Labor..........21.00 | | | | |
| **Refinish cabinets & doors, re-face plywood ends** | lf | — | $58.00 | $58.00 |
| *Replace* Materials ......12.00    Labor..........46.00 | | | | |
| **Refinish island cabinets & doors, re-face plywood ends & faces** | lf | — | $72.80 | $72.80 |
| *Replace* Materials.......13.00    Labor..........59.80 | | | | |
| *repair gouge or hole ▷* **Repair gouge or hole in cabinet, grain patch to match finish** | ea | — | $55.40 | $55.40 |
| *Replace* Materials........7.00    Labor..........48.40 | | | | |
| ▶ Gouge or hole is filled, then "grained" by the painter to look like natural wood grain, matched to the finish of the cabinets. | | | | |

| Item Description | Unit | Remove | Replace | Total | |
|---|---|---|---|---|---|
| **Post-formed plastic laminate countertop** | sf | $3.46 | $12.95 | $16.41 | ◄ **PLASTIC** |
| *Replace* Materials........3.60    Labor .........9.35 | | | | | **LAMINATE** |
| *Remove* .....................    Labor .........3.46 | | | | | **COUNTERTOP** |
| ► Backsplash is integrated into countertop with a rounded cove transition. | | | | | *Most commonly known by the trade name "Formica." Add 6% for installation on bathroom vanity.* |
| **Flat-laid plastic laminate countertop** | sf | $3.46 | $13.60 | $17.06 | |
| *Replace* Materials........3.50    Labor..........10.10 | | | | | |
| *Remove* .....................    Labor .........3.46 | | | | | |
| ► Countertop butts into wall with flat edge. | | | | | |
| **Cultured marble countertop** | sf | $3.46 | $26.30 | $29.76 | ◄ **CULTURED** |
| *Replace* Materials ......16.00    Labor..........10.30 | | | | | **MARBLE** |
| *Remove* .....................    Labor .........3.46 | | | | | **COUNTERTOP** |
| **Add for integrated sink in cultured marble countertop** | ea | — | $144.00 | $144.00 | *Add 6% for installation on bathroom vanity.* |
| *Replace* Materials ....144.00 | | | | | |
| **Cultured granite countertop** | sf | $3.46 | $32.30 | $35.76 | ◄ **CULTURED** |
| *Replace* Materials......22.00    Labor..........10.30 | | | | | **GRANITE** |
| *Remove* .....................    Labor .........3.46 | | | | | **COUNTERTOP** |
| **Add for integrated sink in cultured granite countertop** | ea | — | $181.00 | $181.00 | *Add 6% for installation on bathroom vanity.* |
| *Replace* Materials.....181.00 | | | | | |
| **Onyx countertop** | sf | $3.46 | $32.30 | $35.76 | ◄ **CULTURED ONYX** |
| *Replace* Materials......22.00    Labor..........10.30 | | | | | **COUNTERTOP** |
| *Remove* .....................    Labor .........3.46 | | | | | *Add 6% for installation on bathroom vanity.* |
| **Add for integrated sink in onyx countertop** | ea | — | $176.00 | $176.00 | |
| *Replace* Materials.....176.00 | | | | | |
| **Solid-surface countertop, economy grade** | sf | $3.46 | $110.80 | $114.26 | ◄ **SOLID-SURFACE** |
| *Replace* Materials ....100.00    Labor..........10.80 | | | | | **COUNTERTOP** |
| *Remove* .....................    Labor .........3.46 | | | | | *Commonly known by the trade name Corian. Other* |
| ► Off-white colors, bull-nose edge. | | | | | *trade names include Avonite, Surell, Gibraltar, and Fountainhead. Add* |
| **Solid-surface countertop, standard grade** | sf | $3.46 | $154.80 | $158.26 | *9% for installation on* |
| *Replace* Materials ....144.00    Labor..........10.80 | | | | | *bathroom vanity.* |
| *Remove* .....................    Labor .........3.46 | | | | | |
| ► All standard colors, patterned edge detail, with thin strip inlay. | | | | | |
| **Solid-surface countertop, high grade** | sf | $3.46 | $210.80 | $214.26 | |
| *Replace* Materials....200.00    Labor..........10.80 | | | | | |
| *Remove* .....................    Labor .........3.46 | | | | | |
| ► All standard colors, patterned edge detail, with wood or strip inlay. | | | | | |
| **Solid-surface countertop, deluxe grade** | sf | $3.46 | $252.80 | $256.26 | |
| *Replace* Materials.....242.00    Labor..........10.80 | | | | | |
| *Remove* .....................    Labor .........3.46 | | | | | |
| ► Layered with alternating colored layers, wood strip inlays, custom edge detailing. | | | | | |
| **Solid-surface countertop, custom grade** | sf | $3.46 | $280.80 | $284.26 | |
| *Replace* Materials ....270.00    Labor..........10.80 | | | | | |
| *Remove* .....................    Labor .........3.46 | | | | | |
| ► Layered with alternating colored layers, wood strip inlays, custom edge detailing, inlaid patterns in countertop. | | | | | |
| **Granite countertop** | sf | $3.46 | $165.60 | $169.06 | ◄ **GRANITE** |
| *Replace* Materials.....152.00    Labor ..........13.60 | | | | | **COUNTERTOP** |
| *Remove* .....................    Labor .........3.46 | | | | | *Add 6% for installation on bathroom vanity.* |

| | Item Description | Unit | Remove | Replace | Total |
|---|---|---|---|---|---|
| **STAINLESS STEEL ▶ COUNTERTOP** | **Stainless steel countertop** *Replace* Materials ......24.00　Labor..........12.30 *Remove* ................　Labor ..........3.46 | sf | $3.46 | $36.30 | $39.76 |
| **BUTCHER-BLOCK ▶ COUNTERTOP** Add **6%** for installation on bathroom vanity. | **Butcher-block countertop** *Replace* Materials ......21.00　Labor..........10.30 *Remove* ................　Labor ..........3.46 | sf | $3.46 | $31.30 | $34.76 |
| **SOLID WOOD ▶ COUNTERTOP** Add **6%** for installation on bathroom vanity. | **Solid wood countertop** *Replace* Materials........7.40　Labor ..........9.55 *Remove* ................　Labor ..........3.46 ▶ Maple or oak. | sf | $3.46 | $16.95 | $20.41 |
| | **Remove countertop for work, then reinstall** *Replace* ................　Labor..........14.60 | sf | — | $14.60 | $14.60 |
| **TILE ▶ COUNTERTOP** Add **6%** for installation on bathroom vanity. | **Tile countertop, economy grade tile** *Replace* Materials ......12.00　Labor..........8.21 *Remove* ................　Labor ..........6.00 ▶ Average priced tile set in thinset mortar bed over cement backer board. | sf | $6.00 | $20.21 | $26.21 |
| | **Tile countertop, standard grade tile** *Replace* Materials.......17.00　Labor ..........8.21 *Remove* ................　Labor ..........6.00 ▶ Average priced tile set in mortar bed or higher priced tile set in thinset mortar over cement backer board. | sf | $6.00 | $25.21 | $31.21 |
| | **Tile countertop, high grade tile** *Replace* Materials ......22.00　Labor ..........8.21 *Remove* ................　Labor ..........6.00 ▶ Higher priced tile set in mortar bed or deluxe priced tile set in thinset mortar over cement backer board. | sf | $6.00 | $30.21 | $36.21 |
| | **Tile countertop, deluxe grade tile** *Replace* Materials ......34.00　Labor ..........8.21 *Remove* ................　Labor ..........6.00 ▶ Deluxe priced tile set in mortar bed. | sf | $6.00 | $42.21 | $48.21 |
| **REPAIR TILE ▶ COUNTERTOP** | **Replace tile in tile countertop to match** *Replace* Materials ......28.00　Labor ..........30.10 | ea | — | $58.10 | $58.10 |
| | **Re-affix loose tile in tile countertop** *Replace* Materials ......18.00　Labor ..........20.50 | ea | — | $38.50 | $38.50 |
| | **Minimum charge for tile countertop work** *Replace* Materials.......19.00　Labor..........72.60 | ea | — | $91.60 | $91.60 |
| **BATHROOM ▶ VANITY CABINET** | **Bathroom vanity cabinet, economy grade** *Replace* Materials ......67.00　Labor..........12.10 *Remove* ................　Labor ..........7.07 | lf | $7.07 | $79.10 | $86.17 |
| | **Bathroom vanity cabinets, standard grade** *Replace* Materials ......85.00　Labor..........12.10 *Remove* ................　Labor ..........7.07 | lf | $7.07 | $97.10 | $104.17 |
| | **Bathroom vanity cabinets, high grade** *Replace* Materials ....109.00　Labor..........12.10 *Remove* ................　Labor ..........7.07 | lf | $7.07 | $121.10 | $128.17 |
| | **Bathroom vanity cabinets, deluxe grade** *Replace* Materials......155.00　Labor..........12.10 *Remove* ................　Labor ..........7.07 | lf | $7.07 | $167.10 | $174.17 |

| Item Description | Unit | Remove | Replace | Total |
|---|---|---|---|---|
| **Bathroom vanity cabinets, custom grade** | lf | $7.07 | $232.10 | $239.17 |
| *Replace* Materials ....220.00    Labor...........12.10 | | | | |
| **Remove** .....................    Labor............7.07 | | | | |
| **Bathroom vanity cabinets, custom deluxe grade** | lf | $7.07 | $297.10 | $304.17 |
| *Replace* Materials ....285.00    Labor...........12.10 | | | | |
| **Remove** .....................    Labor............7.07 | | | | |
| **Remove bathroom vanity cabinet for work, then reinstall** | lf | — | $21.40 | $21.40 |
| *Replace* .....................    Labor...........21.40 | | | | |

**RELATED ITEMS**
Cleaning .....................56

✎ NOTES: _____

_____

_____ end

# TIME & MATERIAL CHARTS *(selected items)*

## Cabinets Materials

*See **Cabinets** material prices with the line items and other information in the **QuickFinder** column.*

## Cabinets Labor

| LABORER | BASE WAGE | PAID LEAVE | TRUE WAGE | FICA | FUTA | WORKER'S COMP. | UNEMPLOY. INSUR. | HEALTH INSUR. | RETIRE (401K) | LIABILITY INSUR. | COST PER HOUR |
|---|---|---|---|---|---|---|---|---|---|---|---|
| Cabinet installer | $22.60 | 1.76 | $24.36 | 1.86 | .19 | 4.56 | 2.12 | 2.54 | .73 | 3.17 | $39.50 |
| Painter | $22.30 | 1.74 | $24.04 | 1.84 | .19 | 6.14 | 2.09 | 2.54 | .72 | 3.13 | $40.70 |
| Tile layer | $21.20 | 1.65 | $22.85 | 1.75 | .18 | 3.98 | 1.99 | 2.54 | .69 | 2.97 | $37.00 |
| Laborer | $14.20 | 1.11 | $15.31 | 1.17 | .12 | 2.86 | 1.33 | 2.54 | .46 | 1.99 | $25.80 |
| Demolition laborer | $13.40 | 1.05 | $14.45 | 1.11 | .12 | 4.44 | 1.26 | 2.54 | .43 | 1.88 | $26.20 |

**Paid Leave** is calculated based on two weeks paid vacation, one week sick leave, and seven paid holidays. Employer's matching portion of **FICA** is 7.65 percent. **FUTA** (Federal Unemployment) is .8 percent. **Worker's Compensation** was calculated using a national average of 18.71 percent for the cabinet installer and helper; 25.52 percent for the painter; and 17.41 percent for the tile layer. **Unemployment insurance** was calculated using a national average of 8.7 percent. **Health insurance** was calculated based on a projected national average for 2001 of $505 per employee (and family when applicable) per month. Employer pays 80 percent for a per month cost of $404 per employee. **Retirement** is based on a 401(k) retirement program with employer matching of 50 percent. Employee contributions to the 401(k) plan are an average of 6 percent of the true wage. **Liability insurance** is based on a national average of 12.9 percent.

## Cabinets Labor Productivity

| WORK DESCRIPTION | LABORER | COST PER HOUR | PRODUCTIVITY | UNIT PRICE |
|---|---|---|---|---|
| **Demolition** | | | | |
| remove lower kitchen cabinets | demolition laborer | $26.20 | .262 | $6.86 lf |
| remove lower island kitchen cabinets | demolition laborer | $26.20 | .253 | $6.63 lf |
| remove upper kitchen cabinets | demolition laborer | $26.20 | .236 | $6.18 lf |
| remove upper island kitchen cabinets | demolition laborer | $26.20 | .238 | $6.24 lf |
| remove full-height kitchen cabinets | demolition laborer | $26.20 | .331 | $8.67 lf |
| remove bathroom vanity cabinet | demolition laborer | $26.20 | .270 | $7.07 lf |

*. . . More ➤*

## Cabinets Labor Productivity *continued*

| WORK DESCRIPTION | LABORER | COST PER HOUR | PRODUCTIVITY | UNIT PRICE |
|---|---|---|---|---|
| remove countertop | demolition laborer | $26.20 | .132 | $3.46 *sf* |
| remove tile countertop | demolition laborer | $26.20 | .229 | $6.00 *sf* |
| remove cabinet door | demolition laborer | $26.20 | .267 | $7.00 *ea* |
| remove cabinet drawer front | demolition laborer | $26.20 | .144 | $3.77 *ea* |
| **Cabinet crew** | | | | |
| install cabinets & countertop | cabinet installer | $39.50 | | |
| install cabinets & countertop | laborer | $25.80 | | |
| *cabinet installation* | *installation crew* | *$32.70* | | |
| **Install kitchen cabinets** | | | | |
| lower kitchen cabinets | installation crew | $32.70 | .360 | $11.80 *lf* |
| upper kitchen cabinets | installation crew | $32.70 | .349 | $11.40 *lf* |
| lower kitchen island cabinets | installation crew | $32.70 | .371 | $12.10 *lf* |
| upper kitchen island cabinets | installation crew | $32.70 | .359 | $11.70 *lf* |
| full-height cabinet | installation crew | $32.70 | .593 | $19.40 *lf* |
| **Install cabinet drawer fronts & doors** | | | | |
| drawer front | installation crew | $32.70 | .118 | $3.86 *ea* |
| door | installation crew | $32.70 | .252 | $8.24 *ea* |
| **Refinish cabinets** | | | | |
| cabinet drawer front | painter | $40.70 | .219 | $8.91 *ea* |
| cabinet door | painter | $40.70 | .513 | $20.90 *ea* |
| cabinet door with glass | painter | $40.70 | .515 | $21.00 *ea* |
| cabinets & doors, re-face plywood ends | painter | $40.70 | 1.13 | $46.00 *lf* |
| island cabinets & doors, re-face plywood ends & faces | painter | $40.70 | 1.47 | $59.80 *lf* |
| **Cabinet repair** | | | | |
| repair gouge or hole in cabinet, grain to match | painter | $40.70 | 1.19 | $48.40 *ea* |
| **Install countertop** | | | | |
| post-formed plastic laminate | installation crew | $32.70 | .286 | $9.35 *sf* |
| flat-laid plastic laminate | installation crew | $32.70 | .309 | $10.10 *sf* |
| cultured material | installation crew | $32.70 | .314 | $10.30 *sf* |
| solid-surface | installation crew | $32.70 | .330 | $10.80 *sf* |
| granite | installation crew | $32.70 | .415 | $13.60 *sf* |
| stainless steel | installation crew | $32.70 | .377 | $12.30 *sf* |
| butcher block | installation crew | $32.70 | .314 | $10.30 *sf* |
| solid wood | installation crew | $32.70 | .292 | $9.55 *sf* |
| tile | installation crew | $32.70 | .251 | $8.21 *sf* |
| **Install bathroom vanity cabinet** | | | | |
| bathroom vanity cabinet | installation crew | $32.70 | .371 | $12.10 *lf* |

NOTES: _____

_____

_____

_____

_____

_____

_____

_____

_____

_____

_____

_____ end

# 6

# *Cleaning*

| Item Description | Unit | | | Total | |
|---|---|---|---|---|---|
| **Minimum charge for cleaning work**<br>*Clean* Materials............2.00   Labor............41.90 | ea | — | — | $43.90 | ◄ Minimum |
| **Clean acoustic ceiling tiles**<br>*Clean* Materials............ .02   Labor............. .33 | sf | — | — | $.35 | ◄ Acoustic tile |
| **Clean cook top**<br>*Clean* Materials............ .80   Labor..........20.40 | ea | — | — | $21.20 | ◄ Appliances |
| **Clean range**<br>*Clean* Materials............1.40   Labor..........35.90 | ea | — | — | $37.30 | |
| **Clean space-saver range**<br>*Clean* Materials............1.40   Labor..........33.80 | ea | — | — | $35.20 | |
| **Clean high-low range**<br>*Clean* Materials............1.90   Labor..........47.10 | ea | — | — | $49.00 | |
| **Clean restaurant-style gas range**<br>*Clean* Materials............2.00   Labor..........49.20 | ea | — | — | $51.20 | |
| **Clean wall oven**<br>*Clean* Materials............1.20   Labor..........29.60 | ea | — | — | $30.80 | |
| **Clean double wall oven**<br>*Clean* Materials............2.00   Labor..........49.20 | ea | — | — | $51.20 | |
| **Clean modular electric cook top unit**<br>*Clean* Materials............ .40   Labor..........10.25 | ea | — | — | $10.65 | |
| **Clean drop-in or slide-in range**<br>*Clean* Materials............1.30   Labor..........32.60 | ea | — | — | $33.90 | |
| **Clean range hood**<br>*Clean* Materials............ .40   Labor.............9.97 | ea | — | — | $10.37 | |
| **Clean oversize range hood**<br>*Clean* Materials............ .40   Labor..........10.60 | ea | — | — | $11.00 | |
| **Clean dishwasher**<br>*Clean* Materials............ .90   Labor..........23.30 | ea | — | — | $24.20 | |
| **Clean microwave**<br>*Clean* Materials............ .50   Labor..........11.30 | ea | — | — | $11.80 | |
| **Clean side-by-side refrigerator**<br>*Clean* Materials............1.70   Labor..........41.90 | ea | — | — | $43.60 | |
| **Clean over-under refrigerator**<br>*Clean* Materials............1.50   Labor..........37.70 | ea | — | — | $39.20 | |
| **Clean trash compactor**<br>*Clean* Materials............ .50   Labor..........13.10 | ea | — | — | $13.60 | |

### CLEANING

Unless otherwise noted, all cleaning prices are for items typically smoke stained. For lightly stained items deduct **10%**.
For heavily stained items add **15%**.

### RELATED ITEMS

| | Item Description | Unit | | | Total |
|---|---|---|---|---|---|
| **APPLIANCES ▶** continued | **Clean clothes washing machine** *Clean* Materials ........... .60   Labor........... 15.00 | ea | — | — | $15.60 |
| | **Clean clothes dryer** *Clean* Materials ........... .40   Labor........... 11.00 | ea | — | — | $11.40 |
| **AWNINGS ▶** | **Clean aluminum or steel carport or patio** *Clean* Materials ........... .02   Labor........... .44 | sf | — | — | $.46 |
| | **Clean aluminum or steel door or window awning** *Clean* Materials ........... .18   Labor........... 4.50 | lf | — | — | $4.68 |
| **BATHROOM ▶** HARDWARE | **Clean complete bathroom fixtures and hardware** *Clean* Materials ........... 3.70   Labor........... 93.00 | ea | — | — | $96.70 |
| | **Clean complete 1/2 bathroom fixtures and hardware** *Clean* Materials ........... 2.40   Labor........... 59.90 | ea | — | — | $62.30 |
| | **Clean bathroom hardware (per piece)** *Clean* Materials ........... .23   Labor........... 5.73 | ea | — | — | $5.96 |
| | **Clean medicine cabinet** *Clean* Materials ........... .53   Labor........... 13.30 | ea | — | — | $13.83 |
| | **Clean bathroom mirror** *Clean* Materials ........... .02   Labor........... .61 | sf | — | — | $.63 |
| **CABINETS ▶** | **Clean lower cabinets** *Clean* Materials ........... .42   Labor........... 10.39 | lf | — | — | $10.81 |
| | **Clean upper cabinets** *Clean* Materials ........... .39   Labor........... 9.74 | lf | — | — | $10.13 |
| | **Clean lower island cabinets** *Clean* Materials ........... .42   Labor........... 10.60 | lf | — | — | $11.02 |
| | **Clean upper island cabinets** *Clean* Materials ........... .48   Labor........... 12.00 | lf | — | — | $12.48 |
| | **Clean full-height cabinets** *Clean* Materials ........... .70   Labor........... 17.50 | lf | — | — | $18.20 |
| countertop ▷ | **Clean plastic laminate countertop** *Clean* Materials ........... .03   Labor........... .82 | sf | — | — | $.85 |
| | **Clean cultured stone countertop** *Clean* Materials ........... .04   Labor........... .89 | sf | — | — | $.93 |
| | **Clean solid-surface countertop** *Clean* Materials ........... .04   Labor........... .91 | sf | — | — | $.95 |
| | **Clean granite countertop** *Clean* Materials ........... .04   Labor........... 1.00 | sf | — | — | $1.04 |
| | **Clean stainless steel countertop** *Clean* Materials ........... .04   Labor........... .93 | sf | — | — | $.97 |
| | **Clean wood countertop (butcher block or solid wood)** *Clean* Materials ........... .04   Labor........... 1.05 | sf | — | — | $1.09 |

| Item Description | Unit | | | Total | |
|---|---|---|---|---|---|
| **Clean tile countertop**<br>*Clean* Materials ............ .06          Labor ............1.44 | sf | — | — | **$1.50** | |
| **Clean bathroom vanity cabinet**<br>*Clean* Materials ............ .32          Labor ............8.06 | lf | — | — | **$8.38** | |
| **Clean column**<br>*Clean* Materials ............ .15          Labor ............3.68 | lf | — | — | **$3.83** | ◄ **COLUMNS** |
| **Clean pilaster**<br>*Clean* Materials ............ .08          Labor ............2.03 | lf | — | — | **$2.11** | |
| **Clean capital**<br>*Clean* Materials............1.29          Labor ............32.20 | ea | — | — | **$33.49** | |
| **Clean ornate capital (Corinthian)**<br>*Clean* Materials............2.29          Labor............57.30 | ea | — | — | **$59.59** | |
| **Clean column base**<br>*Clean* Materials ............ .80          Labor............19.90 | ea | — | — | **$20.70** | |
| **Clean pilaster base**<br>*Clean* Materials ............ .43          Labor............10.70 | ea | — | — | **$11.13** | |
| **Clean concrete wall**<br>*Clean* Materials ............ .02          Labor ............ .33 | sf | — | — | **$.35** | ◄ **CONCRETE** |
| **Clean concrete floor**<br>*Clean* Materials ............ .01          Labor ............ .28 | sf | — | — | **$.29** | |
| **Clean concrete step (per step)**<br>*Clean* Materials ............ .21          Labor ............5.17 | lf | — | — | **$5.38** | |
| **Clean door jamb and casing (per lf)**<br>*Clean* Materials ............ .02          Labor ............ .47 | lf | — | — | **$.49** | ◄ **DOORS** |
| **Clean door jamb and casing (per door)**<br>*Clean* Materials ............ .33          Labor ............8.13 | ea | — | — | **$8.46** | |
| **Clean folding door**<br>*Clean* Materials ............ .24          Labor ............6.06 | ea | — | — | **$6.30** | |
| **Clean louvered folding door**<br>*Clean* Materials ............ .41          Labor............10.21 | ea | — | — | **$10.62** | |
| **Clean bypassing door**<br>*Clean* Materials ............ .43          Labor............10.80 | ea | — | — | **$11.23** | |
| **Clean louvered bypassing door**<br>*Clean* Materials ............ .58          Labor............14.50 | ea | — | — | **$15.08** | |
| **Clean French door**<br>*Clean* Materials ............ .76          Labor............19.00 | ea | — | — | **$19.76** | |
| **Clean standard flush door**<br>*Clean* Materials ............ .41          Labor............10.21 | ea | — | — | **$10.62** | |
| **Clean pocket door**<br>*Clean* Materials ............ .42          Labor............10.46 | ea | — | — | **$10.88** | |

| Item Description | | | Unit | | | Total |
|---|---|---|---|---|---|---|
| **Doors ▶** continued | **Clean panel door** | | ea | — | — | **$11.13** |
| | *Clean* Materials .............. .43 | Labor ............10.70 | | | | |
| | **Clean transom** | | ea | — | — | **$5.57** |
| | *Clean* Materials .............. .21 | Labor .............5.36 | | | | |
| | **Clean batten door** | | ea | — | — | **$11.54** |
| | *Clean* Materials .............. .44 | Labor ............11.10 | | | | |
| | **Clean storm door** | | ea | — | — | **$11.02** |
| | *Clean* Materials .............. .42 | Labor ............10.60 | | | | |
| | **Clean exterior door side lite** | | ea | — | — | **$8.96** |
| | *Clean* Materials .............. .34 | Labor .............8.62 | | | | |
| | **Clean Dutch door** | | ea | — | — | **$11.23** |
| | *Clean* Materials .............. .43 | Labor ............10.80 | | | | |
| | **Clean fan lite** | | ea | — | — | **$8.22** |
| | *Clean* Materials .............. .32 | Labor .............7.90 | | | | |
| | **Clean cafe doors** | | ea | — | — | **$8.53** |
| | *Clean* Materials .............. .33 | Labor .............8.20 | | | | |
| sliding patio door ▷ | **Clean 6' wide sliding patio door** | | ea | — | — | **$25.70** |
| | *Clean* Materials .......... 1.00 | Labor ............24.70 | | | | |
| | **Clean 8' wide sliding patio door** | | ea | — | — | **$29.10** |
| | *Clean* Materials ...........1.10 | Labor ..........28.00 | | | | |
| | **Clean 12' wide sliding patio door** | | ea | — | — | **$33.50** |
| | *Clean* Materials ...........1.30 | Labor ..........32.20 | | | | |
| garage door ▷ | **Clean 8' wide garage door** | | ea | — | — | **$37.80** |
| | *Clean* Materials ...........1.50 | Labor ............36.30 | | | | |
| | **Clean 9' wide garage door** | | ea | — | — | **$39.90** |
| | *Clean* Materials ...........1.50 | Labor ...........38.40 | | | | |
| | **Clean 10' wide garage door** | | ea | — | — | **$42.10** |
| | *Clean* Materials ...........1.60 | Labor ...........40.50 | | | | |
| | **Clean 12' wide garage door** | | ea | — | — | **$44.30** |
| | *Clean* Materials ...........1.70 | Labor ............42.60 | | | | |
| | **Clean 14' wide garage door** | | ea | — | — | **$46.80** |
| | *Clean* Materials ...........1.80 | Labor ...........45.00 | | | | |
| | **Clean 16' wide garage door** | | ea | — | — | **$49.40** |
| | *Clean* Materials ...........1.90 | Labor ............47.50 | | | | |
| | **Clean 18' wide garage door** | | ea | — | — | **$52.30** |
| | *Clean* Materials ...........2.00 | Labor ..........50.30 | | | | |
| | **Clean garage door opener** | | ea | — | — | **$23.40** |
| | *Clean* Materials .............. .90 | Labor .........22.50 | | | | |
| **Drywall or ▶ Plaster** | **Clean wall** | | sf | — | — | **$.32** |
| | *Clean* Materials .............. .02 | Labor ............. .30 | | | | |

| Item Description | Unit | | | Total | |
|---|---|---|---|---|---|
| **Clean ceiling**<br>*Clean* Materials ............ .01          Labor ............ .33 | sf | — | — | $.34 | |
| **Clean ceiling acoustic texture**<br>*Clean* Materials ............ .02          Labor ............ .40 | sf | — | — | $.42 | |
| **Clean outlet or switch**<br>*Clean* Materials ............ .08          Labor ............1.96 | ea | — | — | $2.04 | ◀ ELECTRICAL |
| **Clean breaker panel**<br>*Clean* Materials ............ .64          Labor ............16.10 | ea | — | — | $16.74 | |
| **Clean circuit breaker**<br>*Clean* Materials ............ .21          Labor ............5.29 | ea | — | — | $5.50 | |
| **Clean door bell or chime button**<br>*Clean* Materials ............ .03          Labor ............ .79 | ea | — | — | $.82 | |
| **Clean bathroom exhaust fan**<br>*Clean* Materials ............ .27          Labor ............6.76 | ea | — | — | $7.03 | |
| **Clean bathroom exhaust fan with heat lamp**<br>*Clean* Materials ............ .30          Labor ............7.48 | ea | — | — | $7.78 | |
| **Clean kitchen exhaust fan**<br>*Clean* Materials ............ .28          Labor ............6.97 | ea | — | — | $7.25 | |
| **Clean whole-house exhaust fan**<br>*Clean* Materials ............ .33          Labor ............8.20 | ea | — | — | $8.53 | |
| **Clean intercom system station**<br>*Clean* Materials ............ .18          Labor ............4.50 | ea | — | — | $4.68 | |
| **Clean detector**<br>*Clean* Materials ............ .17          Labor ............4.31 | ea | — | — | $4.48 | |
| **Clean thermostat**<br>*Clean* Materials ............ .20          Labor ............4.92 | ea | — | — | $5.12 | |
| **Clean light fixture**<br>*Clean* Materials ............ .42          Labor ............10.46 | ea | — | — | $10.88 | ◁ light fixtures |
| **Clean bathroom light bar (per light)**<br>*Clean* Materials ............ .15          Labor ............3.73 | ea | — | — | $3.88 | |
| **Clean chandelier, typical detail**<br>*Clean* Materials ............1.20          Labor ............29.80 | ea | — | — | $31.00 | |
| **Clean chandelier, ornate detail**<br>*Clean* Materials ............1.85          Labor ............46.60 | ea | — | — | $48.45 | |
| **Clean chandelier, very ornate detail**<br>*Clean* Materials ............2.80          Labor ............69.70 | ea | — | — | $72.50 | |
| **Clean crystal chandelier, typical detail**<br>*Clean* Materials ............4.20          Labor ............104.60 | ea | — | — | $108.80 | |
| **Clean crystal chandelier, ornate detail**<br>*Clean* Materials ............5.40          Labor ............135.00 | ea | — | — | $140.40 | |

**RELATED ITEMS**
Drywall ............133
Plaster & Stucco ............353
Electrical ............139
*light fixtures* ............153

| Item Description | Unit | | | Total |
|---|---|---|---|---|
| **ELECTRICAL ▶** (light fixtures) *continued* | | | | |
| **Clean crystal chandelier, very ornate detail**<br>*Clean* Materials............7.30     Labor.........182.00 | ea | — | — | **$189.30** |
| **Clean fluorescent light fixture**<br>*Clean* Materials............ .50     Labor............12.10 | ea | — | — | **$12.60** |
| **Clean ceiling fan**<br>*Clean* Materials............ .55     Labor............13.50 | ea | — | — | **$14.05** |
| **Clean ceiling fan with light**<br>*Clean* Materials............ .65     Labor............16.00 | ea | — | — | **$16.65** |
| **Clean recessed spot light fixture**<br>*Clean* Materials............ .35     Labor ............9.13 | ea | — | — | **$9.48** |
| **Clean strip light (per spot)**<br>*Clean* Materials............ .18     Labor ............4.54 | ea | — | — | **$4.72** |
| **Clean exterior flood light fixture (per spot)**<br>*Clean* Materials............ .19     Labor ............4.82 | ea | — | — | **$5.01** |
| **Clean exterior light fixture**<br>*Clean* Materials............ .45     Labor ..........11.30 | ea | — | — | **$11.75** |
| **Clean exterior post light fixture**<br>*Clean* Materials............ .54     Labor ..........13.50 | ea | — | — | **$14.04** |
| **FENCES ▶** **Clean 4' high wood fence**<br>*Clean* Materials............ .06     Labor ............1.49 | lf | — | — | **$1.55** |
| **Clean 6' high wood fence**<br>*Clean* Materials............ .07     Labor ............1.82 | lf | — | — | **$1.89** |
| **Clean 8' high wood fence**<br>*Clean* Materials............ .09     Labor ............2.33 | lf | — | — | **$2.42** |
| **Clean 4' high chain-link fence**<br>*Clean* Materials............ .04     Labor............ 1.03 | lf | — | — | **$1.07** |
| **Clean 6' high chain-link fence**<br>*Clean* Materials............ .05     Labor ............1.17 | lf | — | — | **$1.22** |
| **Clean 8' high chain-link fence**<br>*Clean* Materials............ .05     Labor ............1.35 | lf | — | — | **$1.40** |
| **Clean 4' high vinyl fence**<br>*Clean* Materials............ .05     Labor ............1.30 | lf | — | — | **$1.35** |
| **Clean 6' high vinyl fence**<br>*Clean* Materials............ .06     Labor ............1.56 | lf | — | — | **$1.62** |
| **Clean 8' high vinyl fence**<br>*Clean* Materials............ .08     Labor ............1.91 | lf | — | — | **$1.99** |
| **Clean 60" high ornamental iron fence**<br>*Clean* Materials............ .07     Labor ............1.82 | lf | — | — | **$1.89** |
| **Clean 72" high ornamental iron fence**<br>*Clean* Materials............ .06     Labor ............1.61 | lf | — | — | **$1.67** |

| Item Description | Unit | | | Total |
|---|---|---|---|---|
| **Clean molding**<br>*Clean* Materials ............ .01    Labor............. .35 | lf | — | — | $.36 ◀ **FINISH CARPENTRY** |
| **Clean interior wood architrave**<br>*Clean* Materials ............ .03    Labor............. .86 | lf | — | — | $.89 |
| **Clean exterior wood architrave**<br>*Clean* Materials ............ .04    Labor............. .98 | lf | — | — | $1.02 |
| **Clean exterior door surround**<br>*Clean* Materials ............ .08    Labor.............1.91 | lf | — | — | $1.99 |
| **Clean exterior window surround**<br>*Clean* Materials ............ .07    Labor.............1.68 | lf | — | — | $1.75 |
| **Clean closet shelf and brackets**<br>*Clean* Materials ............ .04    Labor............. .89 | lf | — | — | $.93 |
| **Clean closet organizer**<br>*Clean* Materials ............ .03    Labor............. .70 | sf | — | — | $.73 |
| **Clean linen closet shelves**<br>*Clean* Materials ............ .03    Labor............. .84 | sf | — | — | $.87 |
| **Clean closet rod**<br>*Clean* Materials ............ .02    Labor............. .47 | lf | — | — | $.49 |
| **Clean bookcase**<br>*Clean* Materials ............ .03    Labor............. .68 | sf | — | — | $.71 |
| **Clean fireplace mantel**<br>*Clean* Materials ............ .91    Labor .........22.70 | ea | — | — | $23.61 |
| **Clean ceiling with exposed beams**<br>*Clean* Materials ............ .03    Labor............. .65 | sf | — | — | $.68 |
| **Clean coffered ceiling**<br>*Clean* Materials ............ .03    Labor............. .86 | sf | — | — | $.89 |
| **Clean wall niche**<br>*Clean* Materials ............ .21    Labor .............5.29 | ea | — | — | $5.50 |
| **Clean gingerbread trim**<br>*Clean* Materials ............ .02    Labor............. .58 | lf | — | — | $.60 |
| **Clean gingerbread bracket**<br>*Clean* Materials ............ .18    Labor .............4.50 | ea | — | — | $4.68 |
| **Clean gingerbread corbel**<br>*Clean* Materials ............ .20    Labor .............4.99 | ea | — | — | $5.19 |
| **Clean gingerbread spandrel**<br>*Clean* Materials ............ .18    Labor .............4.50 | lf | — | — | $4.68 |
| **Clean gingerbread cornice**<br>*Clean* Materials ............ .16    Labor .............3.98 | lf | — | — | $4.14 |
| **Clean gingerbread gable ornament**<br>*Clean* Materials ............ .41    Labor...........10.21 | ea | — | — | $10.62 |

| | Item Description | | Unit | | | Total |
|---|---|---|---|---|---|---|
| **FINISH CARPENTRY ▶** *continued* | **Clean gingerbread finial** | | ea | — | — | $8.69 |
| | *Clean* Materials ............ .33 | Labor ............8.36 | | | | |
| | **Clean porch post** | | lf | — | — | $1.02 |
| | *Clean* Materials ............ .04 | Labor............ .98 | | | | |
| **FIREPLACES ▶** | **Clean fireplace screen** | | ea | — | — | $27.15 |
| | *Clean* Materials............1.05 | Labor............26.10 | | | | |
| | **Clean fireplace door** | | ea | — | — | $25.69 |
| | *Clean* Materials ............ .99 | Labor............24.70 | | | | |
| | **Clean marble fireplace face** | | sf | — | — | $1.14 |
| | *Clean* Materials ............ .04 | Labor ............1.10 | | | | |
| | **Clean brick fireplace face** | | sf | — | — | $1.31 |
| | *Clean* Materials ............ .05 | Labor ............1.26 | | | | |
| | **Clean stone fireplace face** | | sf | — | — | $1.40 |
| | *Clean* Materials ............ .05 | Labor ............1.35 | | | | |
| | **Clean tile fireplace face** | | sf | — | — | $1.35 |
| | *Clean* Materials ............ .05 | Labor ............1.30 | | | | |
| | **Clean marble fireplace hearth** | | lf | — | — | $2.30 |
| | *Clean* Materials ............ .09 | Labor ............2.21 | | | | |
| | **Clean brick fireplace hearth** | | lf | — | — | $2.57 |
| | *Clean* Materials ............ .10 | Labor ............2.47 | | | | |
| | **Clean stone fireplace hearth** | | lf | — | — | $2.71 |
| | *Clean* Materials ............ .10 | Labor ............2.61 | | | | |
| | **Clean tile fireplace hearth** | | lf | — | — | $2.57 |
| | *Clean* Materials ............ .10 | Labor ............2.47 | | | | |
| **FLOORING ▶** | **Clean carpet** | | sf | — | — | $.56 |
| | *Clean* Materials ............ .02 | Labor............ .54 | | | | |
| | **Clean wool carpet** | | sf | — | — | $.80 |
| | *Clean* Materials ............ .03 | Labor............ .77 | | | | |
| | **Clean carpet cove** | | lf | — | — | $.51 |
| | *Clean* Materials ............ .02 | Labor............ .49 | | | | |
| | **Add per step for carpet cleaning** | | ea | — | — | $3.75 |
| | *Clean* Materials ............ .14 | Labor ............3.61 | | | | |
| | **Clean stone floor** | | sf | — | — | $.60 |
| | *Clean* Materials ............ .02 | Labor............ .58 | | | | |
| | **Clean tile floor** | | sf | — | — | $.82 |
| | *Clean* Materials ............ .03 | Labor............ .79 | | | | |
| | **Clean tile base** | | lf | — | — | $.38 |
| | *Clean* Materials ............ .01 | Labor............ .37 | | | | |
| | **Clean and wax vinyl floor** | | sf | — | — | $.68 |
| | *Clean* Materials ............ .03 | Labor............ .65 | | | | |

| Item Description | Unit | | | Total | |
|---|---|---|---|---|---|
| **Clean vinyl cove**<br>*Clean* Materials ............ .01    Labor ............ .37 | lf | — | — | **$.38** | |
| **Clean and wax wood floor**<br>*Clean* Materials ............ .03    Labor ............ .82 | sf | — | — | **$.85** | |
| **Clean and deodorize ducts (per lf of duct)**<br>*Clean* Materials ............ .15    Labor ............ 3.63 | lf | — | — | **$3.78** | ◄ **HVAC** |
| **Clean furnace**<br>*Clean* Materials ............ 2.75    Labor ............ 68.70 | ea | — | — | **$71.45** | |
| **Clean heat pump**<br>*Clean* Materials ............ 1.20    Labor ............ 29.80 | ea | — | — | **$31.00** | |
| **Clean humidifier**<br>*Clean* Materials ............ .90    Labor ............ 22.00 | ea | — | — | **$22.90** | |
| **Clean through-wall AC unit**<br>*Clean* Materials ............ 1.05    Labor ............ 26.10 | ea | — | — | **$27.15** | |
| **Clean evaporative cooler**<br>*Clean* Materials ............ 1.30    Labor ............ 32.20 | ea | — | — | **$33.50** | |
| **Clean evaporative cooler grille**<br>*Clean* Materials ............ .23    Labor ............ 5.83 | ea | — | — | **$6.06** | |
| **Clean heat register**<br>*Clean* Materials ............ .22    Labor ............ 5.59 | ea | — | — | **$5.81** | |
| **Clean cold-air return cover**<br>*Clean* Materials ............ .23    Labor ............ 5.66 | ea | — | — | **$5.89** | |
| **Clean brick wall**<br>*Clean* Materials ............ .02    Labor ............ .58 | sf | — | — | **$.60** | ◄ **MASONRY** |
| **Clean block wall**<br>*Clean* Materials ............ .02    Labor ............ .54 | sf | — | — | **$.56** | |
| **Clean slump block wall**<br>*Clean* Materials ............ .02    Labor ............ .58 | sf | — | — | **$.60** | |
| **Clean fluted block wall**<br>*Clean* Materials ............ .03    Labor ............ .68 | sf | — | — | **$.71** | |
| **Clean glazed block wall**<br>*Clean* Materials ............ .03    Labor ............ .65 | sf | — | — | **$.68** | |
| **Clean split-face block wall**<br>*Clean* Materials ............ .03    Labor ............ .75 | sf | — | — | **$.78** | |
| **Clean split-rib block wall**<br>*Clean* Materials ............ .03    Labor ............ .70 | sf | — | — | **$.73** | |
| **Clean stone wall**<br>*Clean* Materials ............ .03    Labor ............ .77 | sf | — | — | **$.80** | |
| **Clean glazed structural tile wall**<br>*Clean* Materials ............ .02    Labor ............ .56 | sf | — | — | **$.58** | |

| Item Description | Unit | | | Total |
|---|---|---|---|---|
| **MASONRY** ▶ **Clean glass block wall** | sf | — | — | $.58 |
| *continued*   *Clean* Materials ............ .02    Labor ............ .56 | | | | |
| **Clean pavers** | sf | — | — | $.60 |
| *Clean* Materials ............ .02    Labor ............ .58 | | | | |
| **Clean stone veneer panels** | sf | — | — | $.60 |
| *Clean* Materials ............ .02    Labor ............ .58 | | | | |
| **Clean cultured stone veneer panels** | sf | — | — | $.60 |
| *Clean* Materials ............ .02    Labor ............ .58 | | | | |
| **Clean stone architrave** | lf | — | — | $1.09 |
| *Clean* Materials ............ .04    Labor ............ 1.05 | | | | |
| **Clean stone trim stones** | lf | — | — | $.97 |
| *Clean* Materials ............ .04    Labor ............ .93 | | | | |
| **PANELING** ▶ **Clean wood paneling** | sf | — | — | $.42 |
| *Clean* Materials ............ .02    Labor ............ .40 | | | | |
| **Clean wood paneling with moldings or onlays** | sf | — | — | $.51 |
| *Clean* Materials ............ .02    Labor ............ .49 | | | | |
| **Clean panel wall** | sf | — | — | $.85 |
| *Clean* Materials ............ .03    Labor ............ .82 | | | | |
| **Clean pegboard** | sf | — | — | $.44 |
| *Clean* Materials ............ .02    Labor ............ .42 | | | | |
| **Clean rough-sawn wood paneling** | sf | — | — | $.56 |
| *Clean* Materials ............ .02    Labor ............ .54 | | | | |
| **Clean tongue-and-groove paneling** | sf | — | — | $.49 |
| *Clean* Materials ............ .02    Labor ............ .47 | | | | |
| **STUCCO** ▶ **Clean stucco** | sf | — | — | $.58 |
| *Clean* Materials ............ .02    Labor ............ .56 | | | | |
| **Clean stucco architrave** | lf | — | — | $1.11 |
| *Clean* Materials ............ .04    Labor ............ 1.07 | | | | |
| **PLASTER** ▶ **Clean plaster molding** | lf | — | — | $.85 |
| *See* **Drywall** *heading in*   *Clean* Materials ............ .03    Labor ............ .82 | | | | |
| *this chapter for prices to* | | | | |
| *clean interior plaster* **Clean plaster architrave** | lf | — | — | $1.02 |
| *walls.*   *Clean* Materials ............ .04    Labor ............ .98 | | | | |
| **Clean ceiling medallion** | ea | — | — | $13.42 |
| *Clean* Materials ............ .52    Labor ............ 12.90 | | | | |
| **Clean ceiling rose** | ea | — | — | $22.88 |
| *Clean* Materials ............ .88    Labor ............ 22.00 | | | | |
| **PLUMBING** ▶ **Clean sink faucet** | ea | — | — | $11.44 |
| *Clean* Materials ............ .44    Labor ............ 11.00 | | | | |
| **Clean shower faucet and head** | ea | — | — | $14.04 |
| *Clean* Materials ............ .54    Labor ............ 13.50 | | | | |

| Item Description | Unit | | | Total |
|---|---|---|---|---|
| **Clean tub faucet** | ea | — | — | $12.06 |
| *Clean* Materials ............ .46    Labor ...........11.60 | | | | |
| **Clean tub faucet and shower head** | ea | — | — | $14.98 |
| *Clean* Materials ............ .58    Labor ...........14.40 | | | | |
| **Clean wet bar sink** | ea | — | — | $9.47 |
| *Clean* Materials ............ .36    Labor ...........9.11 | | | | |
| **Clean bathroom sink** | ea | — | — | $10.13 |
| *Clean* Materials ............ .39    Labor ...........9.74 | | | | |
| **Clean kitchen sink, per bowl** | ea | — | — | $10.37 |
| *Clean* Materials ............ .40    Labor ...........9.97 | | | | |
| **Clean laundry sink, per bowl** | ea | — | — | $10.88 |
| *Clean* Materials ............ .42    Labor ...........10.46 | | | | |
| **Clean visible sink supply lines** | ea | — | — | $6.23 |
| *Clean* Materials ............ .24    Labor ...........5.99 | | | | |
| **Clean toilet** | ea | — | — | $16.12 |
| *Clean* Materials ............ .62    Labor ...........15.50 | | | | |
| **Clean bidet** | ea | — | — | $16.74 |
| *Clean* Materials ............ .64    Labor ...........16.10 | | | | |
| **Clean toilet seat** | ea | — | — | $4.36 |
| *Clean* Materials ............ .17    Labor ...........4.19 | | | | |
| **Clean porcelain enamel finish tub** | ea | — | — | $24.23 |
| *Clean* Materials ............ .93    Labor ...........23.30 | | | | |
| **Clean porcelain enamel finish tub with whirlpool jets** | ea | — | — | $31.00 |
| *Clean* Materials ............1.20    Labor ...........29.80 | | | | |
| **Clean fiberglass finish tub** | ea | — | — | $29.10 |
| *Clean* Materials ............1.10    Labor ...........28.00 | | | | |
| **Clean fiberglass finish tub with whirlpool jets** | ea | — | — | $39.50 |
| *Clean* Materials ............1.50    Labor ...........38.00 | | | | |
| **Clean tub and shower combination** | ea | — | — | $39.50 |
| *Clean* Materials ............1.50    Labor ...........38.00 | | | | |
| **Clean fiberglass or metal shower stall** | ea | — | — | $28.40 |
| *Clean* Materials ............1.10    Labor ...........27.30 | | | | |
| **Clean glass shower stall** | ea | — | — | $35.65 |
| *Clean* Materials ............1.35    Labor ...........34.30 | | | | |
| **Clean tub surround** | ea | — | — | $13.20 |
| *Clean* Materials ............ .50    Labor ...........12.70 | | | | |
| **Clean shower door** | ea | — | — | $21.30 |
| *Clean* Materials ............ .80    Labor ...........20.50 | | | | |
| **Clean sliding glass tub door** | ea | — | — | $28.60 |
| *Clean* Materials ............1.10    Labor ...........27.50 | | | | |

| Item Description | Unit | | | Total |
|---|---|---|---|---|
| **PLUMBING ▶** *continued* **Clean folding plastic tub door** <br> *Clean* Materials............1.10     Labor .........28.00 | ea | — | — | $29.10 |
| **Clean water heater** <br> *Clean* Materials ........... .90     Labor .........22.00 | ea | — | — | $22.90 |
| **Clean claw-foot tub faucet** <br> *Clean* Materials ........... .45     Labor .........11.60 | ea | — | — | $12.05 |
| **Clean claw-foot tub faucet and shower conversion** <br> *Clean* Materials ........... .65     Labor .........15.90 | ea | — | — | $16.55 |
| **Clean freestanding water feeds** <br> *Clean* Materials ........... .25     Labor .........6.60 | ea | — | — | $6.85 |
| **Clean pedestal sink** <br> *Clean* Materials ........... .50     Labor .........12.00 | ea | — | — | $12.50 |
| **Clean pill-box toilet** <br> *Clean* Materials ........... .75     Labor .........19.00 | ea | — | — | $19.75 |
| **Clean low-tank toilet** <br> *Clean* Materials ........... 1.00     Labor .........24.70 | ea | — | — | $25.70 |
| **Clean high-tank toilet** <br> *Clean* Materials ............1.30     Labor .........32.20 | ea | — | — | $33.50 |
| **Clean antique tub** <br> *Clean* Materials ............1.10     Labor .........27.30 | ea | — | — | $28.40 |
| **SIDING ▶** **Clean fiberglass corrugated siding** <br> *Clean* Materials ........... .02     Labor ........... .33 | sf | — | — | $.35 |
| **Clean metal or vinyl siding** <br> *Clean* Materials ........... .01     Labor ........... .35 | sf | — | — | $.36 |
| **Clean wood lap siding** <br> *Clean* Materials ........... .01     Labor ........... .35 | sf | — | — | $.36 |
| **Clean vertical wood siding (board on board, etc.)** <br> *Clean* Materials ........... .01     Labor ........... .35 | sf | — | — | $.36 |
| **Clean cement fiber shingle siding** <br> *Clean* Materials ........... .02     Labor ........... .40 | sf | — | — | $.42 |
| **Clean shake or wood shingle siding** <br> *Clean* Materials ........... .02     Labor ........... .44 | sf | — | — | $.46 |
| **Clean hardboard or plywood siding** <br> *Clean* Materials ........... .35     Labor ........... .35 | sf | — | — | $.36 |
| **Clean tongue-and-groove siding** <br> *Clean* Materials ........... .01     Labor ........... .37 | sf | — | — | $.38 |
| **Clean metal or vinyl fascia** <br> *Clean* Materials ........... .01     Labor ........... .37 | sf | — | — | $.38 |
| **Clean wood fascia** <br> *Clean* Materials ........... .01     Labor ........... .37 | sf | — | — | $.38 |

| Item Description | Unit | | | Total | |
|---|---|---|---|---|---|
| **Clean metal or vinyl soffit**<br>*Clean* Materials ............ .01  Labor............ .33 | sf | — | — | $.34 | |
| **Clean wood soffit**<br>*Clean* Materials ............ .01  Labor............ .35 | sf | — | — | $.36 | |
| **Clean rough-sawn wood soffit**<br>*Clean* Materials ............ .02  Labor............ .42 | sf | — | — | $.44 | |
| **Clean shutter**<br>*Clean* Materials ............ .33  Labor ............8.36 | ea | — | — | $8.69 | |
| **Clean wood stair tread**<br>*Clean* Materials ............ .15  Labor............3.80 | ea | — | — | $3.95 | ◄ STAIRS |
| **Clean spiral stair balustrade**<br>*Clean* Materials ............ .11  Labor............2.63 | lf | — | — | $2.74 | |
| **Clean stair balustrade**<br>*Clean* Materials ............ .11  Labor............2.66 | lf | — | — | $2.77 | |
| **Clean disappearing attic stair**<br>*Clean* Materials............2.25  Labor............55.90 | ea | — | — | $58.15 | |
| **Clean stair bracket**<br>*Clean* Materials ............ .29  Labor ............7.22 | ea | — | — | $7.51 | |
| **Clean suspended ceiling grid**<br>*Clean* Materials ............ .01  Labor............ .23 | sf | — | — | $.24 | ◄ SUSPENDED CEILING |
| **Clean tile shower**<br>*Clean* Materials............1.30  Labor ..........32.20 | ea | — | — | $33.50 | ◄ TILE<br>See **Cabinet** heading in this chapter for prices to clean tile countertops and **Flooring** for prices to clean tile floors and base. |
| **Clean tile tub surround**<br>*Clean* Materials............1.70  Labor..........41.90 | ea | — | — | $43.60 | |
| **Clean vinyl wallpaper**<br>*Clean* Materials ............ .01  Labor............ .35 | sf | — | — | $.36 | ◄ WALLPAPER |
| **Clean paper wallpaper**<br>*Clean* Materials ............ .02  Labor............ .40 | sf | — | — | $.42 | |
| **Clean grass or rice cloth wallpaper**<br>*Clean* Materials ............ .02  Labor............ .58 | sf | — | — | $.60 | |
| **Clean window up to 8 sf**<br>*Clean* Materials ............ .38  Labor............9.51 | ea | — | — | $9.89 | ◄ WINDOWS |
| **Clean window 9 to 14 sf**<br>*Clean* Materials ............ .44  Labor............11.00 | ea | — | — | $11.44 | |
| **Clean window 15 to 20 sf**<br>*Clean* Materials ............ .54  Labor............13.50 | ea | — | — | $14.04 | |
| **Clean window 21 to 30 sf**<br>*Clean* Materials ............ .80  Labor............19.90 | ea | — | — | $20.70 | |
| **Clean window, per sf**<br>*Clean* Materials ............ .03  Labor............ .70 | sf | — | — | $.73 | |

| | Item Description | Unit | | | Total |
|---|---|---|---|---|---|
| **WINDOWS** *continued* | **Clean skylight up to 8 sf** | ea | — | — | $10.37 |
| | *Clean* Materials ........... .40        Labor .......9.97 | | | | |
| | **Clean skylight 9 to 14 sf** | ea | — | — | $12.06 |
| | *Clean* Materials ........... .46        Labor ........11.60 | | | | |
| | **Clean skylight 15 to 20 sf** | ea | — | — | $14.98 |
| | *Clean* Materials ........... .58        Labor ........14.40 | | | | |
| | **Clean skylight 21 to 30 sf** | ea | — | — | $21.74 |
| | *Clean* Materials ........... .84        Labor ........20.90 | | | | |
| | **Clean skylight per sf** | sf | — | — | $.78 |
| | *Clean* Materials ........... .03        Labor ........... .75 | | | | |
| | **Add 15% to clean windows with multiple, small panes** | | | | |
| **MIRROR ▶** *Also see* **Bathroom Hardware** *heading.* | **Clean wall mirror** | sf | — | — | $.66 |
| | *Clean* Materials ........... .03        Labor ........... .63 | | | | |
| **FINAL CLEAN ▶** | **Final construction clean-up to broom clean** | sf | — | — | $.29 |
| | *Clean* Materials ........... .01        Labor ........... .28 | | | | |

✍ NOTES: _____

_____ end

# TIME & MATERIAL CHARTS (selected items)

## Cleaning Materials

See **Cleaning** material prices with the line items and other information in the **QuickFinder** column.

## Cleaning Labor

| LABORER | BASE WAGE | PAID LEAVE | TRUE WAGE | FICA | FUTA | WORKER'S COMP. | UNEMPLOY. INSUR. | HEALTH INSUR. | RETIRE (401K) | LIABILITY INSUR. | COST PER HOUR |
|---|---|---|---|---|---|---|---|---|---|---|---|
| Cleaning laborer | $13.20 | 1.03 | $14.23 | 1.09 | .11 | 1.85 | 1.24 | 2.54 | .43 | 1.85 | $23.30 |

**Paid Leave** is calculated based on two weeks paid vacation, one week sick leave, and seven paid holidays. Employer's matching portion of **FICA** is 7.65 percent. **FUTA** (Federal Unemployment) is .8 percent. **Worker's compensation** for the cleaning trade was calculated using a national average of 12.98 percent. **Unemployment insurance** was calculated using a national average of 8.7 percent. **Health insurance** was calculated based on a projected national average for 2001 of $505 per employee (and family when applicable) per month. Employer pays 80 percent for a per month cost of $404 per employee. **Retirement** is based on a 401(k) retirement program with employer matching of 50 percent. Employee contributions to the 401(k) plan are an average of 6 percent of the true wage. **Liability insurance** is based on a national average of 12.9 percent.

## Cleaning Labor Productivity

| WORK DESCRIPTION | LABORER | COST PER HOUR | PRODUCTIVITY | UNIT PRICE |
|---|---|---|---|---|
| **Clean appliances** | | | | |
| cook top | cleaning laborer | $23.30 | .876 | $20.40 ea |
| range | cleaning laborer | $23.30 | 1.54 | $35.90 ea |
| wall oven | cleaning laborer | $23.30 | 1.27 | $29.60 ea |

*... More ≫*

## Cleaning Labor Productivity continued

| WORK DESCRIPTION | LABORER | COST PER HOUR | PRODUCTIVITY | UNIT PRICE |
|---|---|---|---|---|
| **Clean appliances** continued | | | | |
| range hood | cleaning laborer | $23.30 | .428 | $9.97 ea |
| dishwasher | cleaning laborer | $23.30 | 1.00 | $23.30 ea |
| microwave | cleaning laborer | $23.30 | .486 | $11.30 ea |
| side-by-side refrigerator | cleaning laborer | $23.30 | 1.80 | $41.90 ea |
| over-under refrigerator | cleaning laborer | $23.30 | 1.62 | $37.70 ea |
| trash compactor | cleaning laborer | $23.30 | .561 | $13.10 ea |
| **Clean awnings** | | | | |
| aluminum or steel carport or patio | cleaning laborer | $23.30 | .019 | $.44 sf |
| aluminum or steel door or window awning | cleaning laborer | $23.30 | .193 | $4.50 lf |
| **Clean bathroom hardware** | | | | |
| bathroom hardware (per piece) | cleaning laborer | $23.30 | .246 | $5.73 ea |
| medicine cabinet | cleaning laborer | $23.30 | .570 | $13.30 ea |
| **Clean cabinets** | | | | |
| lower cabinets | cleaning laborer | $23.30 | .446 | $10.40 lf |
| upper cabinets | cleaning laborer | $23.30 | .418 | $9.74 lf |
| full-height cabinets | cleaning laborer | $23.30 | .749 | $17.50 lf |
| plastic laminate countertop | cleaning laborer | $23.30 | .035 | $.82 sf |
| tile countertop | cleaning laborer | $23.30 | .062 | $1.44 sf |
| **Clean concrete** | | | | |
| wall | cleaning laborer | $23.30 | .014 | $.33 sf |
| floor | cleaning laborer | $23.30 | .012 | $.28 sf |
| **Clean door** | | | | |
| folding door (per section) | cleaning laborer | $23.30 | .260 | $6.06 ea |
| bypassing door | cleaning laborer | $23.30 | .462 | $10.80 ea |
| door | cleaning laborer | $23.30 | .438 | $10.20 ea |
| storm door | cleaning laborer | $23.30 | .454 | $10.60 ea |
| **Clean drywall or plaster** | | | | |
| wall | cleaning laborer | $23.30 | .013 | $.30 sf |
| ceiling | cleaning laborer | $23.30 | .014 | $.33 sf |
| ceiling acoustic texture | cleaning laborer | $23.30 | .017 | $.40 sf |
| **Clean electrical** | | | | |
| light fixture | cleaning laborer | $23.30 | .449 | $10.50 ea |
| bathroom light bar (per light) | cleaning laborer | $23.30 | .160 | $3.73 ea |
| chandelier, typical detail | cleaning laborer | $23.30 | 1.28 | $29.80 ea |
| fluorescent light fixture | cleaning laborer | $23.30 | .519 | $12.10 ea |
| ceiling fan | cleaning laborer | $23.30 | .580 | $13.50 ea |
| ceiling fan with light | cleaning laborer | $23.30 | .686 | $16.00 ea |
| **Clean fence** | | | | |
| 4' high wood | cleaning laborer | $23.30 | .064 | $1.49 lf |
| 4' high chain-link | cleaning laborer | $23.30 | .044 | $1.03 lf |
| 4' high vinyl | cleaning laborer | $23.30 | .056 | $1.30 lf |
| 60" high ornamental iron | cleaning laborer | $23.30 | .078 | $1.82 lf |
| **Clean finish carpentry** | | | | |
| molding | cleaning laborer | $23.30 | .015 | $.35 lf |
| **Clean fireplace** | | | | |
| screen | cleaning laborer | $23.30 | 1.12 | $26.10 ea |
| door | cleaning laborer | $23.30 | 1.06 | $24.70 ea |
| **Clean flooring** | | | | |
| carpet | cleaning laborer | $23.30 | .023 | $.54 sf |
| stone floor | cleaning laborer | $23.30 | .025 | $.58 sf |
| tile floor | cleaning laborer | $23.30 | .034 | $.79 sf |
| vinyl floor and wax | cleaning laborer | $23.30 | .028 | $.65 sf |
| wood floor and wax | cleaning laborer | $23.30 | .035 | $.82 sf |
| **Clean HVAC** | | | | |
| furnace | cleaning laborer | $23.30 | 2.95 | $68.70 ea |
| through-wall AC unit | cleaning laborer | $23.30 | 1.12 | $26.10 ea |
| evaporative cooler | cleaning laborer | $23.30 | 1.38 | $32.20 ea |

. . . More ➤

## Cleaning Labor Productivity *continued*

| WORK DESCRIPTION | LABORER | COST PER HOUR | PRODUCTIVITY | UNIT PRICE |
|---|---|---|---|---|
| **Clean masonry** | | | | |
| brick wall | cleaning laborer | $23.30 | .025 | $.58 sf |
| block wall | cleaning laborer | $23.30 | .023 | $.54 sf |
| stone wall | cleaning laborer | $23.30 | .033 | $.77 sf |
| glass block wall | cleaning laborer | $23.30 | .024 | $.56 sf |
| stone veneer panels | cleaning laborer | $23.30 | .025 | $.58 sf |
| **Clean paneling** | | | | |
| wood paneling | cleaning laborer | $23.30 | .017 | $.40 sf |
| wood paneling with moldings or onlays | cleaning laborer | $23.30 | .021 | $.49 sf |
| panel wall | cleaning laborer | $23.30 | .035 | $.82 sf |
| rough-sawn wood paneling | cleaning laborer | $23.30 | .023 | $.54 sf |
| tongue-and-groove paneling | cleaning laborer | $23.30 | .020 | $.47 sf |
| **Clean plaster** *(also see clean drywall)* | | | | |
| stucco | cleaning laborer | $23.30 | .024 | $.56 sf |
| **Clean plumbing** | | | | |
| sink faucet | cleaning laborer | $23.30 | .473 | $11.00 ea |
| tub faucet | cleaning laborer | $23.30 | .499 | $11.60 ea |
| tub faucet and shower head | cleaning laborer | $23.30 | .620 | $14.40 ea |
| bathroom sink | cleaning laborer | $23.30 | .418 | $9.74 ea |
| kitchen sink, per bowl | cleaning laborer | $23.30 | .428 | $9.97 ea |
| laundry sink, per bowl | cleaning laborer | $23.30 | .449 | $10.50 ea |
| toilet | cleaning laborer | $23.30 | .665 | $15.50 ea |
| bidet | cleaning laborer | $23.30 | .691 | $16.10 ea |
| porcelain enamel finish tub | cleaning laborer | $23.30 | 1.00 | $23.30 ea |
| fiberglass finish tub | cleaning laborer | $23.30 | 1.20 | $28.00 ea |
| tub and shower combination | cleaning laborer | $23.30 | 1.63 | $38.00 ea |
| fiberglass or metal shower stall | cleaning laborer | $23.30 | 1.17 | $27.30 ea |
| glass shower stall | cleaning laborer | $23.30 | 1.47 | $34.30 ea |
| tub surround | cleaning laborer | $23.30 | .544 | $12.70 ea |
| shower door | cleaning laborer | $23.30 | .881 | $20.50 ea |
| sliding glass tub door | cleaning laborer | $23.30 | 1.18 | $27.50 ea |
| pedestal sink | cleaning laborer | $23.30 | .513 | $12.00 ea |
| pill-box toilet | cleaning laborer | $23.30 | .817 | $19.00 ea |
| **Clean siding** | | | | |
| fiberglass corrugated | cleaning laborer | $23.30 | .014 | $.33 sf |
| metal or vinyl siding | cleaning laborer | $23.30 | .015 | $.35 sf |
| wood lap siding | cleaning laborer | $23.30 | .015 | $.35 sf |
| vertical wood siding (board on board, etc.) | cleaning laborer | $23.30 | .015 | $.35 sf |
| cement fiber shingle siding | cleaning laborer | $23.30 | .017 | $.40 sf |
| shake or wood shingle siding | cleaning laborer | $23.30 | .019 | $.44 sf |
| plywood siding | cleaning laborer | $23.30 | .015 | $.35 sf |
| tongue-and-groove siding | cleaning laborer | $23.30 | .016 | $.37 sf |
| **Clean stairs** | | | | |
| wood stair tread | cleaning laborer | $23.30 | .163 | $3.80 ea |
| stair balustrade | cleaning laborer | $23.30 | .114 | $2.66 lf |
| disappearing attic stair | cleaning laborer | $23.30 | 2.40 | $55.90 ea |
| **Clean tile** | | | | |
| tile shower | cleaning laborer | $23.30 | 1.38 | $32.20 ea |
| tile tub surround | cleaning laborer | $23.30 | 1.80 | $41.90 ea |
| **Clean wallpaper** | | | | |
| vinyl wallpaper | cleaning laborer | $23.30 | .015 | $.35 sf |
| paper wallpaper | cleaning laborer | $23.30 | .017 | $.40 sf |
| grass or rice cloth wallpaper | cleaning laborer | $23.30 | .025 | $.58 sf |
| **Clean window** | | | | |
| window up to 8 sf | cleaning laborer | $23.30 | .408 | $9.51 ea |
| window 21 to 30 sf | cleaning laborer | $23.30 | .856 | $19.90 ea |
| window, per sf | cleaning laborer | $23.30 | .030 | $.70 sf |
| skylight up to 8 sf | cleaning laborer | $23.30 | .428 | $9.97 ea |
| skylight 21 to 30 sf | cleaning laborer | $23.30 | .898 | $20.90 ea |
| skylight per sf | cleaning laborer | $23.30 | .032 | $.75 ea |

# 7 ............................................................. *Columns*

| Item Description | Unit | Remove | Replace | Total | |
|---|---|---|---|---|---|
| **Minimum charge for column or pilaster work** | lf | — | $109.00 | $109.00 | ◀ **MINIMUM** |
| *Replace* Materials......30.00  Labor...........79.00 | | | | | |
| **12" round column made from composite materials** | lf | $5.55 | $51.00 | $56.55 | ◀ **12" COLUMN** |
| *Replace* Materials......37.80  Labor...........13.20 | | | | | Round columns with no |
| *Remove*........................ Labor ...........5.55 | | | | | taper. See page 72 to |
| **12" round pine column** | lf | $5.55 | $51.70 | $57.25 | add for taper, fluting, and |
| *Replace* Materials......38.50  Labor...........13.20 | | | | | architecturally correct taper. |
| *Remove*........................ Labor ...........5.55 | | | | | |
| **12" round redwood column** | lf | $5.55 | $58.60 | $64.15 | |
| *Replace* Materials......45.40  Labor...........13.20 | | | | | |
| *Remove*........................ Labor ...........5.55 | | | | | **COLUMN MATERIALS** |
| **12" round oak column** | lf | $5.55 | $63.60 | $69.15 | **Composite materials:** A combination of marble (or similar material) poly- |
| *Replace* Materials......50.40  Labor...........13.20 | | | | | mers, and fiberglass or |
| *Remove*........................ Labor ...........5.55 | | | | | columns made from high- |
| **12" round stone column** | lf | $5.55 | $83.20 | $88.75 | density polyurethane. |
| *Replace* Materials......70.00  Labor...........13.20 | | | | | **Pine:** Made from lami- |
| *Remove*........................ Labor ...........5.55 | | | | | nated staves of Douglas |
| **12" round synthetic stone column** | lf | $5.55 | $79.10 | $84.65 | fir or Ponderosa pine. |
| *Replace* Materials......65.90  Labor...........13.20 | | | | | **Redwood:** Made from |
| *Remove*........................ Labor ...........5.55 | | | | | laminated staves of red- |
| **12" round aluminum column** | lf | $5.55 | $53.10 | $58.65 | wood. |
| *Replace* Materials......39.90  Labor...........13.20 | | | | | **Oak:** Made from lami- |
| *Remove*........................ Labor ...........5.55 | | | | | nated staves of red oak. |
| **12" round interior plaster column** | lf | $5.55 | $49.80 | $55.35 | **Stone:** Crushed and reconstructed limestone |
| *Replace* Materials......36.60  Labor...........13.20 | | | | | reinforced with glass |
| *Remove*........................ Labor ...........5.55 | | | | | fibers. |
| **12" round exterior stucco column** | lf | $5.55 | $49.10 | $54.65 | **Synthetic stone:** Light- weight simulated stone |
| *Replace* Materials......35.90  Labor...........13.20 | | | | | which are either cement |
| *Remove*........................ Labor ...........5.55 | | | | | or gypsum-based fiber- glass. |
| **12" round pilaster made from composite materials** | lf | $3.51 | $35.50 | $39.01 | **Aluminum:** Cast alu- minum. |
| *Replace* Materials ......24.00  Labor...........11.50 | | | | | |
| *Remove*........................ Labor ...........3.51 | | | | | *continued on next page* |
| **12" round pine pilaster** | lf | $3.51 | $36.10 | $39.61 | ◀ **12" PILASTER** |
| *Replace* Materials ......24.60  Labor...........11.50 | | | | | Half-round pilaster with no |
| *Remove*........................ Labor ...........3.51 | | | | | taper. See page 72 to |
| **12" round redwood pilaster** | lf | $3.51 | $40.50 | $44.01 | add for taper, fluting, and |
| *Replace* Materials......29.00  Labor...........11.50 | | | | | architecturally correct taper. |
| *Remove*........................ Labor ...........3.51 | | | | | |
| **12" round oak pilaster** | lf | $3.51 | $43.60 | $47.11 | **RELATED ITEMS** |
| *Replace* Materials......32.10  Labor...........11.50 | | | | | Cleaning.....................57 |
| *Remove*........................ Labor ...........3.51 | | | | | Finish Carpentry...........199 |
| | | | | | Painting .....................333 |

| Item Description | Unit | Remove | Replace | Total |
|---|---|---|---|---|
| **12" round stone pilaster** | lf | $3.51 | $56.30 | $59.81 |
| *Replace* Materials......44.80     Labor...........11.50 | | | | |
| *Remove*............     Labor............3.51 | | | | |
| **12" round synthetic stone pilaster** | lf | $3.51 | $53.60 | $57.11 |
| *Replace* Materials......42.10     Labor...........11.50 | | | | |
| *Remove*............     Labor............3.51 | | | | |
| **12" round aluminum pilaster** | lf | $3.51 | $37.00 | $40.51 |
| *Replace* Materials......25.50     Labor...........11.50 | | | | |
| *Remove*............     Labor............3.51 | | | | |
| **12" round interior plaster pilaster** | lf | $3.51 | $34.90 | $38.41 |
| *Replace* Materials......23.40     Labor...........11.50 | | | | |
| *Remove*............     Labor............3.51 | | | | |
| **12" round exterior stucco pilaster** | lf | $3.51 | $34.40 | $37.91 |
| *Replace* Materials......22.90     Labor...........11.50 | | | | |
| *Remove*............     Labor............3.51 | | | | |

**12" PILASTER ▶** *continued*

---

**COLUMN MATERIALS**

*continued from prior page*

**Plaster:** Made from fibrous plaster and gypsum products reinforced with fiberglass or jute, or steel or sisal for use on interior of structure.

**Stucco:** Made from fibrous plaster products reinforced with fiberglass or jute or steel or sisal for use on exterior of structure.

---

**ADDITIONAL ▶ COLUMN COSTS**

**Add 18% for round fluted column or pilaster**

**Add 13% for tapered column or pilaster**
  ▶ Consistent taper from bottom to top.

**Add 65% for architecturally correct tapered column or pilaster**
  ▶ Columns that taper according to the classic Greek or Roman styles.

**12" SQUARE ▶ COLUMN**

| Item Description | Unit | Remove | Replace | Total |
|---|---|---|---|---|
| **12" square column made from composite materials** | lf | $5.55 | $62.00 | $67.55 |
| *Replace* Materials......49.80     Labor...........12.20 | | | | |
| *Remove*............     Labor............5.55 | | | | |
| **12" square pine column** | lf | $5.55 | $63.00 | $68.55 |
| *Replace* Materials......50.80     Labor...........12.20 | | | | |
| *Remove*............     Labor............5.55 | | | | |
| **12" square redwood column** | lf | $5.55 | $72.00 | $77.55 |
| *Replace* Materials......59.80     Labor...........12.20 | | | | |
| *Remove*............     Labor............5.55 | | | | |
| **12" square oak column** | lf | $5.55 | $78.80 | $84.35 |
| *Replace* Materials......66.60     Labor...........12.20 | | | | |
| *Remove*............     Labor............5.55 | | | | |
| **12" square stone column** | lf | $5.55 | $104.60 | $110.15 |
| *Replace* Materials......92.40     Labor...........12.20 | | | | |
| *Remove*............     Labor............5.55 | | | | |
| **12" square synthetic stone column** | lf | $5.55 | $99.20 | $104.75 |
| *Replace* Materials......87.00     Labor...........12.20 | | | | |
| *Remove*............     Labor............5.55 | | | | |
| **12" square aluminum column** | lf | $5.55 | $64.80 | $70.35 |
| *Replace* Materials......52.60     Labor...........12.20 | | | | |
| *Remove*............     Labor............5.55 | | | | |
| **12" square interior plaster column** | lf | $5.55 | $60.60 | $66.15 |
| *Replace* Materials......48.40     Labor...........12.20 | | | | |
| *Remove*............     Labor............5.55 | | | | |

| Item Description | Unit | Remove | Replace | Total | |
|---|---|---|---|---|---|
| **12" square exterior stucco column**<br>*Replace* Materials ......47.30    Labor...........12.20<br>*Remove*........................    Labor ............5.55 | lf | $5.55 | $59.50 | $65.05 | |
| **12" square pilaster made from composite materials**<br>*Replace* Materials ......31.80    Labor...........10.70<br>*Remove*........................    Labor ............3.51 | lf | $3.51 | $42.50 | $46.01 | ◄ 12" SQUARE PILASTER |
| **12" square pine pilaster**<br>*Replace* Materials ......32.50    Labor...........10.70<br>*Remove*........................    Labor ............3.51 | lf | $3.51 | $43.20 | $46.71 | |
| **12" square redwood pilaster**<br>*Replace* Materials ......38.30    Labor...........10.70<br>*Remove*........................    Labor ............3.51 | lf | $3.51 | $49.00 | $52.51 | |
| **12" square oak pilaster**<br>*Replace* Materials ......42.50    Labor...........10.70<br>*Remove*........................    Labor ............3.51 | lf | $3.51 | $53.20 | $56.71 | |
| **12" square stone pilaster**<br>*Replace* Materials ......59.00    Labor...........10.70<br>*Remove*........................    Labor ............3.51 | lf | $3.51 | $69.70 | $73.21 | |
| **12" square synthetic stone pilaster**<br>*Replace* Materials ......55.80    Labor...........10.70<br>*Remove*........................    Labor ............3.51 | lf | $3.51 | $66.50 | $70.01 | |
| **12" square aluminum pilaster**<br>*Replace* Materials ......33.60    Labor...........10.70<br>*Remove*........................    Labor ............3.51 | lf | $3.51 | $44.30 | $47.81 | |
| **12" square interior plaster pilaster**<br>*Replace* Materials ......30.80    Labor...........10.70<br>*Remove*........................    Labor ............3.51 | lf | $3.51 | $41.50 | $45.01 | |
| **12" square exterior stucco pilaster**<br>*Replace* Materials ......30.10    Labor...........10.70<br>*Remove*........................    Labor ............3.51 | lf | $3.51 | $40.80 | $44.31 | |
| **Repair wood column or pilaster with wood patch**<br>*Replace* Materials ........3.20    Labor ..........25.60 | ea | — | $28.80 | $28.80 | ◄ COLUMN REPAIR |
| **Repair fluted wood column or pilaster with wood patch**<br>*Replace* Materials ........3.20    Labor...........31.70 | ea | — | $34.90 | $34.90 | |
| **Repair wood column or pilaster by replacing section**<br>*Replace* Materials ........5.70    Labor...........70.70 | ea | — | $76.40 | $76.40 | |
| **Repair fluted wood column or pilaster by replacing section**<br>*Replace* Materials ........7.10    Labor ..........92.00 | ea | — | $99.10 | $99.10 | |
| **Repair dry rot in column or pilaster with epoxy**<br>*Replace* Materials ........5.70    Labor.........102.00 | ea | — | $107.70 | $107.70 | |
| **Repair dry rot in fluted column or pilaster with epoxy**<br>*Replace* Materials ........5.70    Labor..........115.00 | ea | — | $120.70 | $120.70 | |
| **Add for column repair if column is removed from structure**<br>*Replace* Materials ......57.00    Labor ......368.00<br>► Additional cost to build temporary brace wall and remove column from structure. | ea | — | $425.00 | $425.00 | |

**RELATED ITEMS**

| Item Description | Unit | Remove | Replace | Total |
|---|---|---|---|---|
| **COLUMN REPAIR ▶** *continued* | | | | |
| **Minimum charge for column or pilaster repair** | ea | — | $108.00 | $108.00 |
| *Replace* Materials ......16.00    Labor .........92.00 | | | | |
| **CONTEMPORARY ▶ CAPITAL** *Capital up to 4" high. Includes load-bearing plug.* | | | | |
| **Contemporary capital made from composite materials** | ea | $22.30 | $166.40 | $188.70 |
| *Replace* Materials ....144.00    Labor .........22.40    *Remove* .................    Labor .........22.30 | | | | |
| **Contemporary capital made from pine** | ea | $22.30 | $183.40 | $205.70 |
| *Replace* Materials .....161.00    Labor .........22.40    *Remove* .................    Labor .........22.30 | | | | |
| **Contemporary capital made from redwood** | ea | $22.30 | $205.40 | $227.70 |
| *Replace* Materials ....183.00    Labor .........22.40    *Remove* .................    Labor .........22.30 | | | | |
| **Contemporary capital made from oak** | ea | $22.30 | $233.40 | $255.70 |
| *Replace* Materials .....211.00    Labor .........22.40    *Remove* .................    Labor .........22.30 | | | | |
| **Contemporary capital made from stone** | ea | $22.30 | $313.40 | $335.70 |
| *Replace* Materials ....291.00    Labor .........22.40    *Remove* .................    Labor .........22.30 | | | | |
| **Contemporary capital made from synthetic stone** | ea | $22.30 | $294.40 | $316.70 |
| *Replace* Materials ....272.00    Labor .........22.40    *Remove* .................    Labor .........22.30 | | | | |
| **Contemporary capital made from aluminum** | ea | $22.30 | $186.40 | $208.70 |
| *Replace* Materials ....164.00    Labor .........22.40    *Remove* .................    Labor .........22.30 | | | | |
| **Contemporary capital made from interior plaster** | ea | $22.30 | $173.40 | $195.70 |
| *Replace* Materials ......151.00    Labor .........22.40    *Remove* .................    Labor .........22.30 | | | | |
| **Contemporary capital made from exterior stucco** | ea | $22.30 | $170.40 | $192.70 |
| *Replace* Materials ....148.00    Labor .........22.40    *Remove* .................    Labor .........22.30 | | | | |
| **CORINTHIAN ▶ CAPITAL** *Capital up to 14" high. Includes load-bearing plug.* | | | | |
| **Corinthian capital made from composite materials** | ea | $22.30 | $463.40 | $485.70 |
| *Replace* Materials ....441.00    Labor .........22.40    *Remove* .................    Labor .........22.30 | | | | |
| **Corinthian capital made from pine** | ea | $22.30 | $781.40 | $803.70 |
| *Replace* Materials ....759.00    Labor .........22.40    *Remove* .................    Labor .........22.30 | | | | |
| **Corinthian capital made from redwood** | ea | $22.30 | $885.40 | $907.70 |
| *Replace* Materials ....863.00    Labor .........22.40    *Remove* .................    Labor .........22.30 | | | | |
| **Corinthian capital made from oak** | ea | $22.30 | $1,017.40 | $1,039.70 |
| *Replace* Materials ....995.00    Labor .........22.40    *Remove* .................    Labor .........22.30 | | | | |
| **Corinthian capital made from stone** | ea | $22.30 | $608.40 | $630.70 |
| *Replace* Materials ....586.00    Labor .........22.40    *Remove* .................    Labor .........22.30 | | | | |
| **Corinthian capital made from synthetic stone** | ea | $22.30 | $570.40 | $592.70 |
| *Replace* Materials ....548.00    Labor .........22.40    *Remove* .................    Labor .........22.30 | | | | |

| Item Description | Unit | Remove | Replace | Total |
|---|---|---|---|---|
| **Corinthian capital made from aluminum**<br>*Replace* Materials....330.00  Labor..........22.40<br>*Remove*.....................  Labor..........22.30 | ea | $22.30 | $352.40 | $374.70 |
| **Corinthian capital made from interior plaster**<br>*Replace* Materials....304.00  Labor..........22.40<br>*Remove*.....................  Labor..........22.30 | ea | $22.30 | $326.40 | $348.70 |
| **Corinthian capital made from exterior stucco**<br>*Replace* Materials....298.00  Labor..........22.40<br>*Remove*.....................  Labor..........22.30 | ea | $22.30 | $320.40 | $342.70 |
| **Doric or Tuscan capital made from composite materials**<br>*Replace* Materials....150.00  Labor..........22.40<br>*Remove*.....................  Labor..........22.30 | ea | $22.30 | $172.40 | $194.70 |
| **Doric or Tuscan capital made from pine**<br>*Replace* Materials.....167.00  Labor..........22.40<br>*Remove*.....................  Labor..........22.30 | ea | $22.30 | $189.40 | $211.70 |
| **Doric or Tuscan capital made from redwood**<br>*Replace* Materials.....190.00  Labor..........22.40<br>*Remove*.....................  Labor..........22.30 | ea | $22.30 | $212.40 | $234.70 |
| **Doric or Tuscan capital made from oak**<br>*Replace* Materials.....219.00  Labor..........22.40<br>*Remove*.....................  Labor..........22.30 | ea | $22.30 | $241.40 | $263.70 |
| **Doric or Tuscan capital made from stone**<br>*Replace* Materials....302.00  Labor..........22.40<br>*Remove*.....................  Labor..........22.30 | ea | $22.30 | $324.40 | $346.70 |
| **Doric or Tuscan capital made from synthetic stone**<br>*Replace* Materials....282.00  Labor..........22.40<br>*Remove*.....................  Labor..........22.30 | ea | $22.30 | $304.40 | $326.70 |
| **Doric or Tuscan capital made from aluminum**<br>*Replace* Materials.....169.00  Labor..........22.40<br>*Remove*.....................  Labor..........22.30 | ea | $22.30 | $191.40 | $213.70 |
| **Doric or Tuscan capital made from interior plaster**<br>*Replace* Materials.....156.00  Labor..........22.40<br>*Remove*.....................  Labor..........22.30 | ea | $22.30 | $178.40 | $200.70 |
| **Doric or Tuscan capital made from exterior stucco**<br>*Replace* Materials.....152.00  Labor..........22.40<br>*Remove*.....................  Labor..........22.30 | ea | $22.30 | $174.40 | $196.70 |
| **Empire capital made from composite materials**<br>*Replace* Materials....281.00  Labor..........22.40<br>*Remove*.....................  Labor..........22.30 | ea | $22.30 | $303.40 | $325.70 |
| **Empire capital made from pine**<br>*Replace* Materials....483.00  Labor..........22.40<br>*Remove*.....................  Labor..........22.30 | ea | $22.30 | $505.40 | $527.70 |
| **Empire capital made from redwood**<br>*Replace* Materials....551.00  Labor..........22.40<br>*Remove*.....................  Labor..........22.30 | ea | $22.30 | $573.40 | $595.70 |

◀ **DORIC OR TUSCAN CAPITAL**
*Capital up to 4" high.*
*Includes load-bearing plug.*

◀ **EMPIRE CAPITAL**
*Capital up to 7" high.*
*Includes load-bearing plug.*

**RELATED ITEMS**
Cleaning.....................57
Finish Carpentry...........199
Painting.....................333

| Item Description | Unit | Remove | Replace | Total |
|---|---|---|---|---|
| **Empire capital made from oak**<br>*Replace* Materials....634.00  Labor .........22.40<br>*Remove*.......................  Labor .........22.30 | ea | $22.30 | $656.40 | $678.70 |
| **Empire capital made from stone**<br>*Replace* Materials.....374.00  Labor .........22.40<br>*Remove*.......................  Labor .........22.30 | ea | $22.30 | $396.40 | $418.70 |
| **Empire capital made from synthetic stone**<br>*Replace* Materials....348.00  Labor .........22.40<br>*Remove*.......................  Labor .........22.30 | ea | $22.30 | $370.40 | $392.70 |
| **Empire capital made from aluminum**<br>*Replace* Materials.....210.00  Labor .........22.40<br>*Remove*.......................  Labor .........22.30 | ea | $22.30 | $232.40 | $254.70 |
| **Empire capital made from interior plaster**<br>*Replace* Materials.....193.00  Labor .........22.40<br>*Remove*.......................  Labor .........22.30 | ea | $22.30 | $215.40 | $237.70 |
| **Empire capital made from exterior stucco**<br>*Replace* Materials ....189.00  Labor .........22.40<br>*Remove*.......................  Labor .........22.30 | ea | $22.30 | $211.40 | $233.70 |
| **Erechtheum capital made from composite materials**<br>*Replace* Materials ....272.00  Labor .........22.40<br>*Remove*.......................  Labor .........22.30 | ea | $22.30 | $294.40 | $316.70 |
| **Erechtheum capital made from pine**<br>*Replace* Materials.....470.00  Labor .........22.40<br>*Remove*.......................  Labor .........22.30 | ea | $22.30 | $492.40 | $514.70 |
| **Erechtheum capital made from redwood**<br>*Replace* Materials ....533.00  Labor .........22.40<br>*Remove*.......................  Labor .........22.30 | ea | $22.30 | $555.40 | $577.70 |
| **Erechtheum capital made from oak**<br>*Replace* Materials.....614.00  Labor .........22.40<br>*Remove*.......................  Labor .........22.30 | ea | $22.30 | $636.40 | $658.70 |
| **Erechtheum capital made from stone**<br>*Replace* Materials.....361.00  Labor .........22.40<br>*Remove*.......................  Labor .........22.30 | ea | $22.30 | $383.40 | $405.70 |
| **Erechtheum capital made from synthetic stone**<br>*Replace* Materials ....339.00  Labor .........22.40<br>*Remove*.......................  Labor .........22.30 | ea | $22.30 | $361.40 | $383.70 |
| **Erechtheum capital made from aluminum**<br>*Replace* Materials ....204.00  Labor .........22.40<br>*Remove*.......................  Labor .........22.30 | ea | $22.30 | $226.40 | $248.70 |
| **Erechtheum capital made from interior plaster**<br>*Replace* Materials ....188.00  Labor .........22.40<br>*Remove*.......................  Labor .........22.30 | ea | $22.30 | $210.40 | $232.70 |
| **Erechtheum capital made from exterior stucco**<br>*Replace* Materials ....184.00  Labor .........22.40<br>*Remove*.......................  Labor .........22.30 | ea | $22.30 | $206.40 | $228.70 |

**EMPIRE CAPITAL** ▶
*continued.*

**ERECHTHEUM** ▶
**CAPITAL**
*Capital up to 7" high.
Add **50%** for necking.
Includes load-bearing
plug.*

| Item Description | Unit | Remove | Replace | Total |
|---|---|---|---|---|
| **Roman Ionic capital made from composite materials**<br>*Replace* Materials ....284.00    Labor .........22.40<br>*Remove*.........................    Labor .........22.30 | ea | $22.30 | $306.40 | $328.70 |
| **Roman Ionic capital made from pine**<br>*Replace* Materials ....488.00    Labor .........22.40<br>*Remove*.........................    Labor .........22.30 | ea | $22.30 | $510.40 | $532.70 |
| **Roman Ionic capital made from redwood**<br>*Replace* Materials ....556.00    Labor .........22.40<br>*Remove*.........................    Labor .........22.30 | ea | $22.30 | $578.40 | $600.70 |
| **Roman Ionic capital made from oak**<br>*Replace* Materials ....641.00    Labor .........22.40<br>*Remove*.........................    Labor .........22.30 | ea | $22.30 | $663.40 | $685.70 |
| **Roman Ionic capital made from stone**<br>*Replace* Materials ....378.00    Labor .........22.40<br>*Remove*.........................    Labor .........22.30 | ea | $22.30 | $400.40 | $422.70 |
| **Roman Ionic capital made from synthetic stone**<br>*Replace* Materials ....352.00    Labor .........22.40<br>*Remove*.........................    Labor .........22.30 | ea | $22.30 | $374.40 | $396.70 |
| **Roman Ionic capital made from aluminum**<br>*Replace* Materials .....213.00    Labor .........22.40<br>*Remove*.........................    Labor .........22.30 | ea | $22.30 | $235.40 | $257.70 |
| **Roman Ionic capital made from interior plaster**<br>*Replace* Materials .....195.00    Labor .........22.40<br>*Remove*.........................    Labor .........22.30 | ea | $22.30 | $217.40 | $239.70 |
| **Roman Ionic capital made from exterior stucco**<br>*Replace* Materials .....192.00    Labor .........22.40<br>*Remove*.........................    Labor .........22.30 | ea | $22.30 | $214.40 | $236.70 |
| **Scamozzi capital made from composite materials**<br>*Replace* Materials ....298.00    Labor .........22.40<br>*Remove*.........................    Labor .........22.30 | ea | $22.30 | $320.40 | $342.70 |
| **Scamozzi capital made from pine**<br>*Replace* Materials .....513.00    Labor .........22.40<br>*Remove*.........................    Labor .........22.30 | ea | $22.30 | $535.40 | $557.70 |
| **Scamozzi capital made from redwood**<br>*Replace* Materials .....584.00    Labor .........22.40<br>*Remove*.........................    Labor .........22.30 | ea | $22.30 | $606.40 | $628.70 |
| **Scamozzi capital made from oak**<br>*Replace* Materials ....672.00    Labor .........22.40<br>*Remove*.........................    Labor .........22.30 | ea | $22.30 | $694.40 | $716.70 |
| **Scamozzi capital made from stone**<br>*Replace* Materials ....396.00    Labor .........22.40<br>*Remove*.........................    Labor .........22.30 | ea | $22.30 | $418.40 | $440.70 |
| **Scamozzi capital made from synthetic stone**<br>*Replace* Materials ....371.00    Labor .........22.40<br>*Remove*.........................    Labor .........22.30 | ea | $22.30 | $393.40 | $415.70 |

◀ **ROMAN IONIC CAPITAL**
*Capital up to 5" high. Includes load-bearing plug.*

◀ **SCAMOZZI CAPITAL**
*Capital up to 5" high. Includes load-bearing plug.*

**RELATED ITEMS**

| Item Description | Unit | Remove | Replace | Total |
|---|---|---|---|---|
| **SCAMOZZI CAPITAL** continued. | | | | |
| **Scamozzi capital made from aluminum** | ea | $22.30 | $244.40 | $266.70 |
| *Replace* Materials....222.00   Labor..........22.40 | | | | |
| *Remove*........................   Labor..........22.30 | | | | |
| **Scamozzi capital made from interior plaster** | ea | $22.30 | $227.40 | $249.70 |
| *Replace* Materials....205.00   Labor..........22.40 | | | | |
| *Remove*........................   Labor..........22.30 | | | | |
| **Scamozzi capital made from exterior stucco** | ea | $22.30 | $223.40 | $245.70 |
| *Replace* Materials....201.00   Labor..........22.40 | | | | |
| *Remove*........................   Labor..........22.30 | | | | |
| **TEMPLE-OF-THE-WINDS CAPITAL** Capital up to 12" high. Includes load-bearing plug. | | | | |
| **Temple-of-the-Winds capital made from composite materials** | ea | $22.30 | $363.40 | $385.70 |
| *Replace* Materials....341.00   Labor..........22.40 | | | | |
| *Remove*........................   Labor..........22.30 | | | | |
| **Temple-of-the-Winds capital made from pine** | ea | $22.30 | $609.40 | $631.70 |
| *Replace* Materials....587.00   Labor..........22.40 | | | | |
| *Remove*........................   Labor..........22.30 | | | | |
| **Temple-of-the-Winds capital made from redwood** | ea | $22.30 | $690.40 | $712.70 |
| *Replace* Materials....668.00   Labor..........22.40 | | | | |
| *Remove*........................   Labor..........22.30 | | | | |
| **Temple-of-the-Winds capital made from oak** | ea | $22.30 | $791.40 | $813.70 |
| *Replace* Materials....769.00   Labor..........22.40 | | | | |
| *Remove*........................   Labor..........22.30 | | | | |
| **Temple-of-the-Winds capital made from stone** | ea | $22.30 | $474.40 | $496.70 |
| *Replace* Materials....452.00   Labor..........22.40 | | | | |
| *Remove*........................   Labor..........22.30 | | | | |
| **Temple-of-the-Winds capital made from synthetic stone** | ea | $22.30 | $445.40 | $467.70 |
| *Replace* Materials....423.00   Labor..........22.40 | | | | |
| *Remove*........................   Labor..........22.30 | | | | |
| **Temple-of-the-Winds capital made from aluminum** | ea | $22.30 | $277.40 | $299.70 |
| *Replace* Materials....255.00   Labor..........22.40 | | | | |
| *Remove*........................   Labor..........22.30 | | | | |
| **Temple-of-the-Winds capital made from interior plaster** | ea | $22.30 | $257.40 | $279.70 |
| *Replace* Materials....235.00   Labor..........22.40 | | | | |
| *Remove*........................   Labor..........22.30 | | | | |
| **Temple-of-the-Winds capital made from exterior stucco** | ea | $22.30 | $252.40 | $274.70 |
| *Replace* Materials....230.00   Labor..........22.40 | | | | |
| *Remove*........................   Labor..........22.30 | | | | |
| **CAPITAL REPAIR** | | | | |
| **Repair wood capital with wood patch (each patch)** | ea | — | $44.40 | $44.40 |
| *Replace* Materials........2.50   Labor..........41.90 | | | | |
| **Repair wood capital by replacing section** | ea | — | $176.00 | $176.00 |
| *Replace* Materials......23.00   Labor..........153.00 | | | | |
| **Repair dry rot in capital with epoxy** | ea | — | $84.70 | $84.70 |
| *Replace* Materials........2.50   Labor..........82.20 | | | | |
| **Minimum charge for capital repair** | ea | — | $143.00 | $143.00 |
| *Replace* Materials......28.00   Labor..........115.00 | | | | |

| Item Description | Unit | Remove | Replace | Total | |
|---|---|---|---|---|---|
| **Add 78% for spiral column or pilaster** | | | | | ◄ **ADDITIONAL COLUMN SIZES** |
| **Deduct 45% for 6″ column, pilaster, capital, or base** | | | | | *Add or deduct from the costs for 12″ columns, pilasters, capitals and bases. (Bases are built to hold columns of the size indicated.)* |
| **Deduct 35% for 8″ column, pilaster, capital, or base** | | | | | |
| **Deduct 17% for 10″ column, pilaster, capital, or base** | | | | | |
| **Add 59% for 14″ column, pilaster, capital, or base** | | | | | |
| **Add 81% for 16″ column, pilaster, capital, or base** | | | | | |
| **Add 115% for 18″ column, pilaster, capital, or base** | | | | | |
| **Add 185% for 20″ column, pilaster, capital, or base** | | | | | |
| **Column base made from composite materials** | ea | $20.60 | $66.40 | $87.00 | ◄ **COLUMN BASE** |
| *Replace* Materials......44.00      Labor ..........22.40<br>*Remove*..........................      Labor ..........20.60 | | | | | |
| **Column base made from pine** | ea | $20.60 | $67.40 | $88.00 | |
| *Replace* Materials ......45.00      Labor ..........22.40<br>*Remove*..........................      Labor ..........20.60 | | | | | |
| **Column base made from redwood** | ea | $20.60 | $75.40 | $96.00 | |
| *Replace* Materials......53.00      Labor ..........22.40<br>*Remove*..........................      Labor ..........20.60 | | | | | |
| **Column base made from oak** | ea | $20.60 | $81.40 | $102.00 | |
| *Replace* Materials ......59.00      Labor ..........22.40<br>*Remove*..........................      Labor ..........20.60 | | | | | |
| **Column base made from stone** | ea | $20.60 | $104.40 | $125.00 | |
| *Replace* Materials......82.00      Labor ..........22.40<br>*Remove*..........................      Labor ..........20.60 | | | | | |
| **Column base made from synthetic stone** | ea | $20.60 | $99.40 | $120.00 | |
| *Replace* Materials......77.00      Labor ..........22.40<br>*Remove*..........................      Labor ..........20.60 | | | | | |
| **Column base made from aluminum** | ea | $20.60 | $69.40 | $90.00 | |
| *Replace* Materials ......47.00      Labor ..........22.40<br>*Remove*..........................      Labor ..........20.60 | | | | | |
| **Column base made from interior plaster** | ea | $20.60 | $65.40 | $86.00 | |
| *Replace* Materials......43.00      Labor ..........22.40<br>*Remove*..........................      Labor ..........20.60 | | | | | |
| **Column base made from exterior stucco** | ea | $20.60 | $64.40 | $85.00 | |
| *Replace* Materials......42.00      Labor ..........22.40<br>*Remove*..........................      Labor ..........20.60 | | | | | |
| **Column pedestal, standard grade** | ea | $10.70 | $496.00 | $506.70 | ◄ **COLUMN PEDESTAL** |
| *Replace* Materials......161.00      Labor..........335.00<br>*Remove*..........................      Labor..........10.70 | | | | | |
| ► Pedestal framed with 2″ x 4″ up to 3′ high. Outside trimmed with paint-grade pine or poplar. Moldings around top of pedestal and bottom. | | | | | |

| | Item Description | Unit | Remove | Replace | Total |
|---|---|---|---|---|---|
| **COLUMN ▶ PEDESTAL** *continued* | **Column pedestal, high grade** | ea | $10.70 | $584.00 | $594.70 |
| | *Replace* Materials.....212.00 Labor.........372.00 | | | | |
| | *Remove*.................... Labor..........10.70 | | | | |
| | ▶ Pedestal framed with 2" x 4" up to 3' high. Outside trimmed with paint-grade pine or poplar. Moldings around top of pedestal and bottom. Each of the four sides also includes panel molding. Or standard grade from stain-grade fir. | | | | |
| | **Column pedestal, deluxe grade** | ea | $10.70 | $733.00 | $743.70 |
| | *Replace* Materials.....314.00 Labor.........419.00 | | | | |
| | *Remove*.................... Labor..........10.70 | | | | |
| | ▶ Pedestal framed with 2" x 4" up to 3' high. Outside trimmed with paint-grade pine or poplar. Moldings around top of pedestal and bottom. Each of the four sides includes a recessed raised panel. Or standard grade from red oak or mahogany. | | | | |
| | **Column pedestal, custom grade** | ea | $10.70 | $832.00 | $842.70 |
| | *Replace* Materials ....370.00 Labor.........462.00 | | | | |
| | *Remove*.................... Labor..........10.70 | | | | |
| | ▶ Pedestal framed with 2" x 4" up to 3' high. Outside trimmed with paint-grade pine or poplar. Moldings around top of pedestal and bottom. Each of the four sides includes a recessed raised cathedral panel. Or deluxe grade from red oak or mahogany. | | | | |
| **PILASTER ▶ PEDESTAL** | **Pilaster pedestal, standard grade** | ea | $8.75 | $335.00 | $343.75 |
| | *Replace* Materials ......98.00 Labor.....237.00 | | | | |
| | *Remove*.................... Labor .........8.75 | | | | |
| | ▶ Pedestal framed with 2" x 4" up to 3' high. Outside trimmed with paint-grade pine or poplar. Moldings around top of pedestal and bottom. | | | | |
| | **Pilaster pedestal, high grade** | ea | $8.75 | $391.00 | $399.75 |
| | *Replace* Materials.....128.00 Labor.........263.00 | | | | |
| | *Remove*.................... Labor .........8.75 | | | | |
| | ▶ Pedestal framed with 2" x 4" up to 3' high. Outside trimmed with paint-grade pine or poplar. Moldings around top of pedestal and bottom. Each of the three sides also includes panel molding. Or standard grade from stain-grade fir. | | | | |
| | **Pilaster pedestal, deluxe grade** | ea | $8.75 | $484.00 | $492.75 |
| | *Replace* Materials ....189.00 Labor.........295.00 | | | | |
| | *Remove*.................... Labor ...........8.75 | | | | |
| | ▶ Pedestal framed with 2" x 4" up to 3' high. Outside trimmed with paint-grade pine or poplar. Moldings around top of pedestal and bottom. Each of the three sides includes a recessed raised panel. Or standard grade from red oak or mahogany. | | | | |
| | **Pilaster pedestal, custom grade** | ea | $8.75 | $552.00 | $560.75 |
| | *Replace* Materials ....223.00 Labor ........329.00 | | | | |
| | *Remove*.................... Labor ...........8.75 | | | | |
| | ▶ Pedestal framed with 2" x 4" up to 3' high. Outside trimmed with paint-grade pine or poplar. Moldings around top of pedestal and bottom. Each of the three sides includes a recessed raised cathedral panel. Or deluxe grade from red oak or mahogany. | | | | |
| **ADD FOR OTHER ▶ WOOD SPECIES** | **Add 12% for stain-grade redwood materials** | | | | |
| | ▶ Add to the cost of any redwood item listed above. | | | | |
| | **Add 16% for mahogany materials** | | | | |
| | ▶ Add to the cost of any redwood item listed above. | | | | |

*standard △*    *△ high*

*deluxe △*    *△ custom*

✎ NOTES: _____

_____

_____ end

# TIME & MATERIAL CHARTS *(selected items)*

## Columns Materials

| DESCRIPTION | MATERIAL PRICE | GROSS COVERAGE | WASTE | NET COVERAGE | UNIT PRICE |
|---|---|---|---|---|---|
| **Minimum materials charge for column or pilaster work** | | | | | |
| minimum | $30.00 ea | | | | $30.00 ea |
| **12" round column** | | | | | |
| composite materials | $302.00 8' | 8 | 0% | 8 | $37.80 lf |
| pine | $308.00 8' | 8 | 0% | 8 | $38.50 lf |
| **12" round pilaster** | | | | | |
| composite materials | $192.00 8' | 8 | 0% | 8 | $24.00 lf |
| pine | $197.00 8' | 8 | 0% | 8 | $24.60 lf |
| **12" square column** | | | | | |
| composite materials | $398.00 8' | 8 | 0% | 8 | $49.80 lf |
| pine | $406.00 8' | 8 | 0% | 8 | $50.80 lf |
| **12" square pilaster** | | | | | |
| composite materials | $254.00 8' | 8 | 0% | 8 | $31.80 lf |
| pine pilaster | $260.00 8' | 8 | 0% | 8 | $32.50 lf |
| **Contemporary capital** | | | | | |
| composite materials | $144.00 ea | | | | $144.00 ea |
| pine | $161.00 ea | | | | $161.00 ea |
| **Corinthian capital** | | | | | |
| composite materials | $441.00 ea | | | | $441.00 ea |
| pine | $759.00 ea | | | | $759.00 ea |
| **Doric or Tuscan capital** | | | | | |
| composite materials | $150.00 ea | | | | $150.00 ea |
| pine | $167.00 ea | | | | $167.00 ea |
| **Empire capital** | | | | | |
| composite materials | $281.00 ea | | | | $281.00 ea |
| pine | $483.00 ea | | | | $483.00 ea |
| **Erechtheum capital** | | | | | |
| composite materials | $272.00 ea | | | | $272.00 ea |
| pine | $470.00 ea | | | | $470.00 ea |
| **Roman Ionic capital** | | | | | |
| composite materials | $284.00 ea | | | | $284.00 ea |
| pine | $488.00 ea | | | | $488.00 ea |
| **Scamozzi capital** | | | | | |
| composite materials | $298.00 ea | | | | $298.00 ea |
| pine | $513.00 ea | | | | $513.00 ea |
| **Temple-of-the-Winds capital** | | | | | |
| composite materials | $341.00 ea | | | | $341.00 ea |
| pine | $587.00 ea | | | | $587.00 ea |
| **Column base** | | | | | |
| composite materials | $44.00 ea | | | | $44.00 ea |
| pine | $45.00 ea | | | | $45.00 ea |
| **Column pedestal** | | | | | |
| standard grade | $161.00 ea | | | | $161.00 ea |
| custom grade | $370.00 ea | | | | $370.00 ea |
| **Pilaster pedestal** | | | | | |
| standard grade | $98.00 ea | | | | $98.00 ea |
| custom grade | $223.00 ea | | | | $223.00 ea |

## Columns Labor

| LABORER | BASE WAGE | PAID LEAVE | TRUE WAGE | FICA | FUTA | WORKER'S COMP. | UNEMPLOY. INSUR. | HEALTH INSUR. | RETIRE (401K) | LIABILITY INSUR. | COST PER HOUR |
|---|---|---|---|---|---|---|---|---|---|---|---|
| Carpenter | $22.60 | 1.76 | $24.36 | 1.86 | .19 | 4.56 | 2.12 | 2.54 | .73 | 3.17 | $39.50 |
| Demolition laborer | $13.40 | 1.05 | $14.45 | 1.11 | .12 | 4.44 | 1.26 | 2.54 | .43 | 1.88 | $26.20 |

**Paid Leave** is calculated based on two weeks paid vacation, one week sick leave, and seven paid holidays. Employer's matching portion of **FICA** is 7.65 percent. **FUTA** (Federal Unemployment) is .8 percent. **Worker's compensation** for columns was calculated using a national average of 18.71 percent. **Unemployment insurance** was calculated using a national average of 8.7 percent. **Health insurance** was calculated based on a projected national average for 2001 of $505 per employee (and family when applicable) per month. Employer pays 80 percent for a per month cost of $404 per employee. **Retirement** is based on a 401(k) retirement program with employer matching of 50 percent. Employee contributions to the 401(k) plan are an average of 6 percent of the true wage. **Liability insurance** is based on a national average of 12.9 percent.

## Columns Labor Productivity

| WORK DESCRIPTION | LABORER | COST PER HOUR | PRODUCTIVITY | UNIT PRICE |
|---|---|---|---|---|
| **Demolition** | | | | |
| remove column | demolition laborer | $26.20 | .212 | $5.55 lf |
| remove pilaster | demolition laborer | $26.20 | .134 | $3.51 lf |
| remove column or pilaster capital | demolition laborer | $26.20 | .850 | $22.30 ea |
| remove column or pilaster base | demolition laborer | $26.20 | .785 | $20.60 ea |
| remove column pedestal | demolition laborer | $26.20 | .410 | $10.70 ea |
| remove pilaster pedestal | demolition laborer | $26.20 | .334 | $8.75 ea |
| **Install column** | | | | |
| round | finish carpenter | $39.50 | .333 | $13.20 lf |
| square | finish carpenter | $39.50 | .308 | $12.20 lf |
| **Install pilaster** | | | | |
| round | finish carpenter | $39.50 | .292 | $11.50 lf |
| square | finish carpenter | $39.50 | .270 | $10.70 lf |
| **Install capital** | | | | |
| column or pilaster capital | finish carpenter | $39.50 | .566 | $22.40 ea |
| **Install column or pilaster base** | | | | |
| column or pilaster base | finish carpenter | $39.50 | .566 | $22.40 ea |
| **Repair column or pilaster** | | | | |
| round with wood patch | finish carpenter | $39.50 | .706 | $27.90 ea |
| fluted with wood patch | finish carpenter | $39.50 | .863 | $34.10 ea |
| round by replacing section | finish carpenter | $39.50 | 1.94 | $76.60 ea |
| fluted by replacing section | finish carpenter | $39.50 | 2.59 | $102.00 ea |
| round dry rot with epoxy | finish carpenter | $39.50 | 2.74 | $108.00 ea |
| fluted dry rot with epoxy | finish carpenter | $39.50 | 3.24 | $128.00 ea |
| minimum charge | finish carpenter | $39.50 | 2.33 | $92.00 ea |
| **Repair wood capital** | | | | |
| with wood patch | finish carpenter | $39.50 | 1.06 | $41.90 ea |
| by replacing section | finish carpenter | $39.50 | 3.88 | $153.00 ea |
| dry rot with epoxy | finish carpenter | $39.50 | 2.08 | $82.20 ea |
| minimum charge | finish carpenter | $39.50 | 2.91 | $115.00 ea |
| **Build and install column pedestal** | | | | |
| standard grade | finish carpenter | $39.50 | 8.49 | $335.00 ea |
| custom grade | finish carpenter | $39.50 | 11.7 | $462.00 ea |
| **Build and install pilaster pedestal** | | | | |
| standard grade | finish carpenter | $39.50 | 6.01 | $237.00 ea |
| custom grade | finish carpenter | $39.50 | 8.33 | $329.00 ea |

# 8 ........................................................ *Concrete*

| Item Description | Unit | Remove | Replace | Total | |
|---|---|---|---|---|---|
| **Minimum charge for concrete repair** | ea | — | $374.00 | $374.00 | ◀ **MINIMUM** |
| *Replace* Materials ......57.00          Labor .........317.00 | | | | | |
| **Concrete crack repair with pressurized epoxy injection** | lf | — | $6.49 | $6.49 | ◀ **EPOXY REPAIR** |
| *Replace* Materials ........ .67          Labor ...........4.40          Equipment...........1.42 | | | | | |
| ► A pressure pot is used to inject pressurized epoxy into a concrete crack.  Care is taken to fill and plug areas where the epoxy could escape. | | | | | |
| **Minimum charge for pressurized epoxy injection concrete crack repair** | ea | — | $267.00 | $267.00 | |
| *Replace* Materials ......63.00          Labor..........116.00          Equipment..........88.00 | | | | | |
| **Concrete hole repair with epoxy system per cubic inch of hole** | ci | — | $2.13 | $2.13 | |
| *Replace* Materials ........ .03          Labor ............2.10 | | | | | |
| ► Epoxy is poured or injected into a hole.  Priced per cubic inch of the hole. | | | | | |
| **Minimum charge for concrete hole repair with epoxy system** | ea | — | $76.80 | $76.80 | |
| *Replace* Materials ......57.00          Labor...........19.80 | | | | | |
| **Concrete crack repair with caulking gun epoxy injection** | lf | — | $1.38 | $1.38 | |
| *Replace* Materials ........ .39          Labor ............. .99 | | | | | |
| **Minimum charge for concrete crack repair with epoxy injection** | ea | — | $82.80 | $82.80 | |
| *Replace* Materials ......63.00          Labor...........19.80 | | | | | |
| **Repair spalled concrete with concrete resurfacer** | sf | — | $1.14 | $1.14 | |
| *Replace* Materials ........ .78          Labor ............. .36 | | | | | |
| **Minimum charge to repair spalled concrete** | ea | — | $77.50 | $77.50 | |
| *Replace* Materials ......37.90          Labor .........39.60 | | | | | |
| **Concrete footings including rebar package & forming** | cy | $96.80 | $192.90 | $289.70 | ◀ **FOOTING** |
| *Replace* Materials .....107.00          Labor..........85.90 | | | | | |
| *Remove*.......................          Labor ..........43.00          Equipment..........53.80 | | | | | |
| **Concrete footings including CEC rebar package & forming** | cy | $141.30 | $234.00 | $375.30 | |
| *Replace* Materials .....131.00          Labor..........103.00 | | | | | |
| *Remove*.......................          Labor..........51.40          Equipment..........89.90 | | | | | |
| **16" wide by 10" deep concrete footings with rebar** | lf | $5.94 | $9.95 | $15.89 | |
| *Replace* Materials.....4.66          Labor ...........5.29 | | | | | |
| *Remove*.......................          Labor ...........3.17          Equipment...........2.77 | | | | | |
| **16" wide by 10" deep concrete footings with CEC rebar** | lf | $7.20 | $12.38 | $19.58 | |
| *Replace* Materials.....6.03          Labor ...........6.35 | | | | | |
| *Remove*.......................          Labor ...........3.85          Equipment...........3.35 | | | | | |
| **20" wide by 10" deep concrete footings with rebar** | lf | $5.94 | $11.20 | $17.14 | |
| *Replace* Materials.......5.58          Labor ...........5.62 | | | | | |
| *Remove*.......................          Labor ...........3.17          Equipment...........2.77 | | | | | |
| **20" wide by 10" deep concrete footings with CEC rebar** | lf | $7.20 | $13.77 | $20.97 | |
| *Replace* Materials.......7.09          Labor ............6.68 | | | | | |
| *Remove*.......................          Labor ............3.85          Equipment...........3.35 | | | | | |

**CALIFORNIA EARTHQUAKE CODE**

Items that include "CEC" in the description are priced according to California earthquake code requirements.

Although these *Universal Building Code* or similar standards are also required in other areas of the country, they are most commonly associated with efforts initiated in the State of California to improve the construction and engineering of structures in quake zones.

◀ **FOOTING**
*Standard 16", 20", and 24" footings include 3 horizontal lengths of #4 rebar.  Standard 32" footing includes 4 horizontal lengths of #4 rebar.  CEC 16" and 20" footings include 3 horizontal lengths of #5 rebar.  CEC 24" and 32" footings include 4 horizontal lengths of #5 rebar.  Tie-in rebar from foundation wall bent continuously into the footing is included in the foundation wall prices.*

*CEC = California Earthquake Code.*

| Item Description | Unit | Remove | Replace | Total |
|---|---|---|---|---|
| **FOOTINGS ▶** *continued* | | | | |
| **24" wide by 12" deep concrete footings with rebar** | lf | $5.94 | $13.80 | $19.74 |
| *Replace* Materials........7.93    Labor ............5.87 | | | | |
| *Remove* ........................    Labor ............3.17    Equipment............2.77 | | | | |
| **24" wide by 12" deep concrete footings with CEC rebar** | lf | $7.20 | $16.53 | $23.73 |
| *Replace* Materials........9.60    Labor ............6.93 | | | | |
| *Remove* ........................    Labor ............3.85    Equipment............3.35 | | | | |
| **32" wide by 14" deep concrete footings with rebar** | lf | $5.94 | $17.93 | $23.87 |
| *Replace* Materials.......11.70    Labor ............6.23 | | | | |
| *Remove* ........................    Labor ............3.17    Equipment............2.77 | | | | |
| **32" wide by 14" deep concrete footings with CEC rebar** | lf | $7.20 | $20.69 | $27.89 |
| *Replace* Materials.......13.40    Labor ............7.29 | | | | |
| *Remove* ........................    Labor ............3.85    Equipment............3.35 | | | | |
| **minimum ▷ Minimum charge for concrete footing work** | ea | — | $78.40 | $78.40 |
| *Replace* Materials ......42.20    Labor ..........36.20 | | | | |
| **FOUNDATION ▶ Concrete foundation wall including rebar package & forming** | cy | $131.10 | $224.70 | $355.80 |
| *Replace* Materials ....102.20    Labor.........95.00    Equipment ..........27.50 | | | | |
| *Remove* ........................    Labor.........63.90    Equipment ..........67.20 | | | | |
| **Concrete foundation wall including CEC rebar package & forming** | cy | $166.60 | $259.50 | $426.10 |
| *Replace* Materials ....122.00    Labor.........110.00    Equipment ..........27.50 | | | | |
| *Remove* ........................    Labor.........77.00    Equipment ..........89.60 | | | | |
| **5" wide concrete foundation wall** | sf | $3.57 | $4.18 | $7.75 |
| *Replace* Materials........1.43    Labor ............2.07    Equipment ...........68 | | | | |
| *Remove* ........................    Labor ............1.91    Equipment............1.66 | | | | |
| **Rebar package for 5" wide concrete foundation wall** | sf | — | $1.48 | $1.48 |
| *Replace* Materials ........ .21    Labor ............1.27 | | | | |
| **CEC rebar package for 5" wide concrete foundation wall** | sf | — | $2.97 | $2.97 |
| *Replace* Materials ........ .68    Labor ............2.29 | | | | |
| **6" wide concrete foundation wall** | sf | $3.57 | $4.66 | $8.23 |
| *Replace* Materials........1.73    Labor ............2.25    Equipment ........... .68 | | | | |
| *Remove* ........................    Labor ............1.91    Equipment............1.66 | | | | |
| **Rebar package for 6" wide concrete foundation wall** | sf | — | $1.48 | $1.48 |
| *Replace* Materials ........ .21    Labor ............1.27 | | | | |
| **CEC rebar package for 6" wide concrete foundation wall** | sf | — | $2.97 | $2.97 |
| *Replace* Materials ........ .68    Labor ............2.29 | | | | |
| **8" wide concrete foundation wall** | sf | $3.90 | $5.59 | $9.49 |
| *Replace* Materials........2.30    Labor ............2.61    Equipment ........... .68 | | | | |
| *Remove* ........................    Labor ............1.99    Equipment............1.91 | | | | |
| **Rebar package for 8" wide concrete foundation wall** | sf | — | $1.48 | $1.48 |
| *Replace* Materials ........ .21    Labor ............1.27 | | | | |
| **CEC rebar package for 8" wide concrete foundation wall** | sf | — | $2.97 | $2.97 |
| *Replace* Materials ........ .68    Labor ............2.29 | | | | |
| **10" wide concrete foundation wall** | sf | $3.90 | $6.53 | $10.43 |
| *Replace* Materials........2.88    Labor ............2.97    Equipment ........... .68 | | | | |
| *Remove* ........................    Labor ............1.99    Equipment............1.91 | | | | |

*Standard foundation walls include horizontal and vertical lengths of #4 rebar 24" on center. Vertical rebar is bent continuously into footing. CEC foundations include horizontal and vertical lengths of #5 rebar 12" on center. Vertical rebar is bent continuously into footing.*

*CEC = California Earthquake Code.*

| Item Description | Unit | Remove | Replace | Total | |
|---|---|---|---|---|---|
| **Rebar package for 10" wide concrete foundation wall** | sf | — | **$1.48** | **$1.48** | |
| *Replace* Materials ........ .21       Labor ...........1.27 | | | | | |
| **CEC rebar package for 10" wide concrete foundation wall** | sf | — | **$2.97** | **$2.97** | |
| *Replace* Materials ........ .68       Labor ...........2.29 | | | | | |
| **Add for insulating foam stay-in-place foundation wall forms** | sf | — | **$2.88** | **$2.88** | |
| *Replace* Materials ...... 1.34       Labor ...........1.54 | | | | | |
| **Minimum charge for concrete foundation wall work** | ea | — | **$291.00** | **$291.00** | ◁ minimum |
| *Replace* Materials ......55.00       Labor .........141.00       Equipment ..........95.00 | | | | | |
| **Single-pour footing and foundation wall with rebar package** | cy | $111.80 | $149.60 | $261.40 | ◀ **SINGLE-POUR** |
| *Replace* Materials ......94.80       Labor ..........20.70       Equipment ..........34.10 | | | | | **FOOTING &** |
| *Remove*.......................       Labor...........51.40       Equipment..........60.40 | | | | | **FOUNDATION** |
| **Single-pour footing and foundation wall with CEC rebar package** | cy | $126.10 | $156.20 | $282.30 | *Single-pour footing and* |
| *Replace* Materials ......97.00       Labor ..........25.10       Equipment ..........34.10 | | | | | *foundation wall. See* |
| *Remove*.......................       Labor...........61.00       Equipment..........65.10 | | | | | *footings on page 83 and* |
| **Single-pour footing with 6" wide by 3' stem wall** | lf | $17.57 | $26.25 | $43.82 | *foundations on 84 for* |
| *Replace* Materials........9.97       Labor ...........12.20       Equipment ..........4.08 | | | | | *explanations about the* |
| *Remove*.......................       Labor ............9.07       Equipment ............8.50 | | | | | *rebar included in each* |
| **Single-pour footing with 8" wide by 3' stem wall** | lf | $17.57 | $27.98 | $45.55 | *system.* |
| *Replace* Materials.......11.70       Labor ...........12.20       Equipment ..........4.08 | | | | | |
| *Remove*.......................       Labor ............9.07       Equipment ............8.50 | | | | | |
| **Single-pour footing with 10" wide by 3' stem wall** | lf | $17.57 | $28.28 | $45.85 | |
| *Replace* Materials ......12.00       Labor ...........12.20       Equipment ..........4.08 | | | | | |
| *Remove*.......................       Labor ............9.07       Equipment ............8.50 | | | | | |
| **Rebar package for single-pour footing & 3' stem wall** | lf | — | $6.32 | $6.32 | |
| *Replace* Materials........1.57       Labor ............4.75 | | | | | |
| **CEC rebar package for single-pour footing & 3' stem wall** | lf | — | $12.06 | $12.06 | |
| *Replace* Materials........3.75       Labor ............8.31 | | | | | |
| **Single-pour footing with 6" wide by 4' stem wall** | lf | $19.60 | $32.64 | $52.24 | |
| *Replace* Materials.......11.70       Labor ...........15.50       Equipment .............5.44 | | | | | |
| *Remove*.......................       Labor ...........11.10       Equipment ............8.50 | | | | | |
| **Single-pour footing with 8" wide by 4' stem wall** | lf | $19.60 | $34.94 | $54.54 | |
| *Replace* Materials ......14.00       Labor ...........15.50       Equipment .............5.44 | | | | | |
| *Remove*.......................       Labor ...........11.10       Equipment ............8.50 | | | | | |
| **Single-pour footing with 10" wide by 4' stem wall** | lf | $19.60 | $37.24 | $56.84 | |
| *Replace* Materials ......16.30       Labor ...........15.50       Equipment .............5.44 | | | | | |
| *Remove*.......................       Labor ...........11.10       Equipment ............8.50 | | | | | |
| **Rebar package for 6" wide by 4' single-pour footing & stem wall** | lf | — | $7.00 | $7.00 | |
| *Replace* Materials........1.80       Labor ............5.20 | | | | | |
| **CEC rebar package for 6" wide by 4' single-pour footing & stem wall** | lf | — | $12.91 | $12.91 | |
| *Replace* Materials........4.19       Labor ............8.72 | | | | | |
| **Minimum charge for single-pour footing & stem wall work** | ea | — | $258.00 | $258.00 | ◁ minimum |
| *Replace* Materials......22.00       Labor .........141.00       Equipment ..........95.00 | | | | | |

*CEC = California Earthquake Code.*

| | Item Description | Unit | Remove | Replace | Total |
|---|---|---|---|---|---|
| **DRILL PIER HOLE ▶** *Pier hole from 12" to 24" in diameter. (Most common sizes are 16" and 18".)* | **Delivery & take home charge for tractor-mounted auger (mobilization)** | ea | — | $729.00 | $729.00 |
| | *Replace* .......................... Labor.........307.00 Equipment ........422.00 | | | | |
| | **Drill concrete pier hole for hillside home construction** | lf | — | $6.30 | $6.30 |
| | *Replace* .......................... Labor............4.08 Equipment............2.22 | | | | |
| | **Minimum charge to drill concrete pier** | ea | — | $744.00 | $744.00 |
| | *Replace* .......................... Labor........244.00 Equipment........500.00 | | | | |
| **PIER ▶** *Pier from 12" to 24" in diameter. (Most common sizes are 16" and 18".) In most cases piers are not removed. When removed they are pulled from the ground with a crane or trackhoe. An engineer should be consulted when piers are removed and a new structure will be built on the same site.* | **Concrete pier including rebar cage** | cy | $69.20 | $925.00 | $994.20 |
| | *Replace* Materials ....401.00 Labor .........524.00 | | | | |
| | *Remove* ................... Labor...........18.30 Equipment..........50.90 | | | | |
| | **Concrete pier with up to 36" fiber tube wrapped cap** | lf | $8.07 | $76.70 | $84.77 |
| | *Replace* Materials .......14.80 Labor .........61.90 | | | | |
| | *Remove* ................... Labor...........2.15 Equipment...........5.92 | | | | |
| | **Above-grade concrete pier with fiber tube wrap** | lf | $8.07 | $101.50 | $109.57 |
| | *Replace* Materials .......37.60 Labor .........63.90 | | | | |
| | *Remove* ................... Labor...........2.15 Equipment...........5.92 | | | | |
| | **Rebar cage for concrete pier (meets CEC requirements)** | lf | — | $39.11 | $39.11 |
| | *Replace* Materials ......36.00 Labor ............3.11 | | | | |
| | **Minimum charge for concrete pier work** | ea | — | $746.00 | $746.00 |
| | *Replace* Materials ....305.00 Labor.........441.00 | | | | |
| **JACKET PIER ▶** | **Jacket concrete pier with new concrete and rebar ties** | ea | — | $241.40 | $241.40 |
| | *Replace* Materials ......34.70 Labor .........174.00 Equipment..........32.70 | | | | |
| | ▶ Existing pier is jackhammered. Holes are drilled for rebar. Rebar is secured with epoxy. Pier is formed and concrete jacket poured. | | | | |
| **minimum ▷** | **Minimum charge to jacket a concrete pier with concrete and rebar** | ea | — | $481.00 | $481.00 |
| | *Replace* Materials ......86.00 Labor.........282.00 Equipment ..........113.00 | | | | |
| **SHALLOW PIER ▶** *Usually poured in hand-dug holes for light structures or decks.* | **Shallow concrete pier (less than 3' deep) for deck or light structure** | ea | $29.90 | $121.40 | $151.30 |
| | *Replace* Materials ........17.70 Labor..........103.70 | | | | |
| | *Remove*........................ Labor ...........29.90 | | | | |
| | **Pre-cast concrete pier for deck or light structure** | ea | $6.10 | $29.18 | $35.28 |
| | *Replace* Materials .......20.00 Labor ..........9.18 | | | | |
| | *Remove*........................ Labor ............6.10 | | | | |
| **GRADE BEAM ▶** *Grade beams include pre-fabricated rebar cage. All rebar cages are to CEC standards. When removed, grade beams are detached from piers with a jackhammer or concrete saw. The beams are broken into manageable chunks and loaded by crane or backhoe into a truck. (Does not include hauling or dump fees.)* | **Grade beam with rebar cage per cy** | cy | $98.20 | $715.00 | $813.20 |
| | *Replace* Materials....574.00 Labor .........141.00 | | | | |
| | *Remove*........................ Labor ...........61.00 Equipment ...........37.20 | | | | |
| | **12" wide by 18" deep grade beam with rebar cage** | lf | $8.54 | $53.19 | $61.73 |
| | *Replace* Materials .......41.20 Labor ...........9.27 Equipment............2.72 | | | | |
| | *Remove*........................ Labor ...........4.56 Equipment............3.98 | | | | |
| | **12" wide by 20" deep grade beam with rebar cage** | lf | $8.54 | $54.70 | $63.24 |
| | *Replace* Materials .......41.80 Labor...........10.18 Equipment............2.72 | | | | |
| | *Remove*........................ Labor ...........4.56 Equipment............3.98 | | | | |
| | **12" wide by 22" deep grade beam with rebar cage** | lf | $9.70 | $57.02 | $66.72 |
| | *Replace* Materials ......42.30 Labor ..........12.00 Equipment............2.72 | | | | |
| | *Remove*........................ Labor ...........5.11 Equipment............4.59 | | | | |

*CEC = California Earthquake Code.*

| Item Description | Unit | Remove | Replace | Total |
|---|---|---|---|---|
| **12" wide by 24" deep grade beam with rebar cage** | lf | $9.70 | $55.44 | $65.14 |
| *Replace* Materials ......42.90   Labor ...........9.82   Equipment............2.72 | | | | |
| *Remove*......................   Labor ...........5.11   Equipment............4.59 | | | | |
| **14" wide by 18" deep grade beam with rebar cage** | lf | $8.54 | $55.62 | $64.16 |
| *Replace* Materials ......42.00   Labor ...........10.90   Equipment............2.72 | | | | |
| *Remove*......................   Labor ...........4.56   Equipment............3.98 | | | | |
| **14" wide by 20" deep grade beam with rebar cage** | lf | $8.54 | $58.42 | $66.96 |
| *Replace* Materials ......42.70   Labor ...........13.00   Equipment............2.72 | | | | |
| *Remove*......................   Labor ...........4.56   Equipment............3.98 | | | | |
| **14" wide by 22" deep grade beam with rebar cage** | lf | $9.89 | $59.12 | $69.01 |
| *Replace* Materials ......43.40   Labor ...........13.00   Equipment............2.72 | | | | |
| *Remove*......................   Labor ...........5.21   Equipment............4.68 | | | | |
| **14" wide by 24" deep grade beam with rebar cage** | lf | $9.89 | $61.92 | $71.81 |
| *Replace* Materials ......44.10   Labor ...........15.10   Equipment............2.72 | | | | |
| *Remove*......................   Labor ...........5.21   Equipment............4.68 | | | | |
| **16" wide by 18" deep grade beam with rebar cage** | lf | $10.74 | $65.02 | $75.76 |
| *Replace* Materials ......42.90   Labor ...........19.40   Equipment............2.72 | | | | |
| *Remove*......................   Labor ...........5.66   Equipment............5.08 | | | | |
| **16" wide by 20" deep grade beam with rebar cage** | lf | $10.74 | $70.02 | $80.76 |
| *Replace* Materials ......43.70   Labor ...........23.60   Equipment............2.72 | | | | |
| *Remove*......................   Labor ...........5.66   Equipment............5.08 | | | | |
| **16" wide by 22" deep grade beam with rebar cage** | lf | $11.08 | $66.52 | $77.60 |
| *Replace* Materials ......44.40   Labor ...........19.40   Equipment............2.72 | | | | |
| *Remove*......................   Labor ...........5.84   Equipment............5.24 | | | | |
| **16" wide by 24" deep grade beam with rebar cage** | lf | $11.08 | $71.52 | $82.60 |
| *Replace* Materials ......45.20   Labor ...........23.60   Equipment............2.72 | | | | |
| *Remove*......................   Labor ...........5.84   Equipment............5.24 | | | | |
| **18" wide by 18" deep grade beam with rebar cage** | lf | $10.74 | $57.42 | $68.16 |
| *Replace* Materials ......43.80   Labor ...........10.90   Equipment............2.72 | | | | |
| *Remove*......................   Labor ...........5.66   Equipment............5.08 | | | | |
| **18" wide by 20" deep grade beam with rebar cage** | lf | $10.74 | $60.32 | $71.06 |
| *Replace* Materials ......44.60   Labor ...........13.00   Equipment............2.72 | | | | |
| *Remove*......................   Labor ...........5.66   Equipment............5.08 | | | | |
| **18" wide by 22" deep grade beam with rebar cage** | lf | $11.08 | $61.22 | $72.30 |
| *Replace* Materials ......45.50   Labor ...........13.00   Equipment............2.72 | | | | |
| *Remove*......................   Labor ...........5.84   Equipment............5.24 | | | | |
| **18" wide by 24" deep grade beam with rebar cage** | lf | $11.08 | $64.22 | $75.30 |
| *Replace* Materials ......46.40   Labor ...........15.10   Equipment............2.72 | | | | |
| *Remove*......................   Labor ...........5.84   Equipment............5.24 | | | | |
| **Minimum charge for concrete grade beam work** | ea | — | $427.20 | $427.20 |
| *Replace* Materials ....296.00   Labor ...........36.20   Equipment...........95.00 | | | | |
| **Jacket concrete grade beam with new concrete and rebar ties** | lf | — | $34.06 | $34.06 |
| *Replace* Materials ......10.70   Labor ...........19.00   Equipment............4.36 | | | | |

► Existing grade beam is jackhammered. Holes are drilled for rebar. Rebar is secured with epoxy. Grade beam is formed and concrete jacket poured.

**RELATED ITEMS**
Cleaning.........................57
Masonry
  *grade beam wall cap* ......303
Painting .....................333

◁ minimum

◄ JACKET GRADE BEAM

| Item Description | Unit | Remove | Replace | Total |
|---|---|---|---|---|
| **JACKET ▶ GRADE BEAM** *continued* | | | | |
| **Minimum charge to jacket grade beam with concrete and rebar** | ea | — | $445.00 | $445.00 |
| *Replace* Materials......50.00    Labor.........282.00    Equipment .........113.00 | | | | |
| **LIGHTWEIGHT ▶ FLATWORK** | | | | |
| **Lightweight concrete flatwork per cy (no rebar)** | cy | $107.70 | $188.80 | $296.50 |
| *Replace* Materials .....117.00    Labor.........71.80 | | | | |
| *Remove*.....................    Labor.........61.60    Equipment .........46.10 | | | | |
| **2" lightweight concrete slab** | sf | $1.30 | $1.53 | $2.83 |
| *Replace* Materials ........ .72    Labor........... .81 | | | | |
| *Remove*.....................    Labor........... .68    Equipment ........... .62 | | | | |
| **4" lightweight concrete slab** | sf | $1.30 | $2.29 | $3.59 |
| *Replace* Materials.......1.44    Labor........... .85 | | | | |
| *Remove*.....................    Labor........... .68    Equipment ........... .62 | | | | |
| **6" lightweight concrete slab** | sf | $1.30 | $3.09 | $4.39 |
| *Replace* Materials.......2.17    Labor........... .92 | | | | |
| *Remove*.....................    Labor........... .68    Equipment ........... .62 | | | | |
| *minimum ▷* **Minimum charge for lightweight concrete slab work** | ea | — | $197.00 | $197.00 |
| *Replace* Materials......56.00    Labor.........141.00 | | | | |
| **FLATWORK ▶** | | | | |
| **Concrete flatwork by cy (no rebar)** | cy | $109.10 | $165.00 | $274.10 |
| *Replace* Materials......93.20    Labor.........71.80 | | | | |
| *Remove*.....................    Labor.........62.60    Equipment .........46.50 | | | | |
| **4" concrete slab** | sf | $1.33 | $2.40 | $3.73 |
| *Replace* Materials........1.15    Labor ...........1.25 | | | | |
| *Remove*.....................    Labor........... .71    Equipment ........... .62 | | | | |
| **6" concrete slab** | sf | $1.33 | $3.41 | $4.74 |
| *Replace* Materials........1.73    Labor ...........1.68 | | | | |
| *Remove*.....................    Labor........... .71    Equipment ........... .62 | | | | |
| **8" concrete slab** | sf | $1.33 | $3.98 | $5.31 |
| *Replace* Materials........2.30    Labor ...........1.68 | | | | |
| *Remove*.....................    Labor........... .71    Equipment ........... .62 | | | | |
| *minimum ▷* **Minimum charge for concrete slab work** | ea | — | $185.00 | $185.00 |
| *Replace* Materials......44.00    Labor.........141.00 | | | | |
| **UTILITY ▶ FLATWORK** | | | | |
| **Concrete footing for chimney** | sf | $1.48 | $4.08 | $5.56 |
| *Replace* Materials........2.52    Labor ...........1.56 | | | | |
| *Remove*.....................    Labor........... .79    Equipment ........... .69 | | | | |
| **Concrete slab for exterior heat pump, condenser, etc.** | sf | $1.33 | $2.93 | $4.26 |
| *Replace* Materials........1.37    Labor ...........1.56 | | | | |
| *Remove*.....................    Labor........... .71    Equipment ........... .62 | | | | |
| **REBAR FOR ▶ FLATWORK** | | | | |
| **Rebar for concrete slab, #4 24" on center** | sf | — | $1.72 | $1.72 |
| *Replace* Materials ........ .49    Labor ...........1.23 | | | | |
| **Rebar for concrete slab, #4 12" on center** | sf | — | $3.74 | $3.74 |
| *Replace* Materials ...... 1.00    Labor ...........2.74 | | | | |
| **Wire mesh for concrete slab, 6" x 6" #10** | sf | — | $.67 | $.67 |
| *Replace* Materials ........ .16    Labor ........... .51 | | | | |
| **FLATWORK ▶ BASE** | | | | |
| **2" aggregate slab base** | sf | — | $.62 | $.62 |
| *Replace* Materials ........ .04    Labor........... .47    Equipment ........... .11 | | | | |

| Item Description | Unit | Remove | Replace | Total |
|---|---|---|---|---|
| **4" aggregate slab base** | sf | — | $.72 | $.72 |
| *Replace* Materials ........ .08    Labor............ .53    Equipment ............ .11 | | | | |
| **2" sand slab base** | sf | — | $.54 | $.54 |
| *Replace* Materials ........ .04    Labor............ .39    Equipment ............ .11 | | | | |
| **4" sand slab base** | sf | — | $.64 | $.64 |
| *Replace* Materials ........ .08    Labor............ .45    Equipment ............ .11 | | | | |
| **6 mil slab membrane** | sf | — | $.10 | $.10 |
| *Replace* Materials ........ .04    Labor............ .06 | | | | |
| **5 mil slab membrane** | sf | — | $.10 | $.10 |
| *Replace* Materials ........ .04    Labor............ .06 | | | | |
| **Concrete sidewalk per cy** | cy | $109.10 | $250.50 | $359.60 |
| *Replace* Materials ....103.50    Labor ........147.00 | | | | |
| *Remove*.....................    Labor........62.60    Equipment..........46.50 | | | | |
| ► Sidewalks 4" to 6" thick. | | | | |
| **3" concrete sidewalk** | sf | $1.51 | $2.34 | $3.85 |
| *Replace* Materials ........ .86    Labor ............1.48 | | | | |
| *Remove*.....................    Labor............ .89    Equipment ............ .62 | | | | |
| **4" concrete sidewalk** | sf | $1.51 | $2.88 | $4.39 |
| *Replace* Materials........1.15    Labor ............1.73 | | | | |
| *Remove*.....................    Labor............ .89    Equipment ............ .62 | | | | |
| **6" concrete sidewalk** | sf | $1.51 | $3.93 | $5.44 |
| *Replace* Materials........1.73    Labor ............2.20 | | | | |
| *Remove*.....................    Labor............ .89    Equipment ............ .62 | | | | |
| **Minimum charge for concrete sidewalk work** | ea | — | $211.00 | $211.00 |
| *Replace* Materials ....105.00    Labor........106.00 | | | | |
| **Add for troweled-in concrete dye in flatwork** | sf | — | $1.71 | $1.71 |
| *Replace* Materials........1.38    Labor............. .33 | | | | |
| **Add for concrete dye in flatwork per 1" deep layer, blacks and grays** | sf | — | $.07 | $.07 |
| *Replace* Materials ........ .07 | | | | |
| **Add for concrete dye in flatwork per 1" deep layer, blues** | sf | — | $.30 | $.30 |
| *Replace* Materials ........ .30 | | | | |
| **Add for concrete dye in flatwork per 1" deep layer, browns & terra cotta reds** | sf | — | $.29 | $.29 |
| *Replace* Materials ........ .29 | | | | |
| **Add for concrete dye in flatwork per 1" deep layer, bright reds** | sf | — | $.30 | $.30 |
| *Replace* Materials ........ .30 | | | | |
| **Add for concrete dye in flatwork per 1" deep layer, greens** | sf | — | $.61 | $.61 |
| *Replace* Materials ........ .61 | | | | |
| **Add for concrete stamping of slab or sidewalk** | sf | — | $1.92 | $1.92 |
| *Replace* .......................    Labor ............1.92 | | | | |
| **Add for paver-pattern concrete stamping of slab or sidewalk** | sf | — | $1.63 | $1.63 |
| *Replace* .......................    Labor ............1.63 | | | | |

**RELATED ITEMS**

Cleaning.........................57
Painting ......................333

◄ **FLATWORK VAPOR BARRIER**

◄ **SIDEWALK**
*Sidewalk to 3' wide.*

◁ **minimum**

◄ **CONCRETE DYE**
*For concrete quantities under 350 sf add $28 per truck for wash-out. This charge does not apply to troweled-in dyes.*

◄ **STAMPING**

| | Item Description | Unit | Remove | Replace | Total |
|---|---|---|---|---|---|
| **STAMPING** ▶ continued | **Add for paver stamped slab or sidewalk with grouted joints** *Replace* Materials ......... .31  Labor ............2.46 | sf | — | $2.77 | $2.77 |
| **EXPOSED** ▶ **AGGREGATE** | **Add for exposed aggregate finish on slab or sidewalk** *Replace* Materials ......... .15  Labor............. .69  ▶ Where required, add for disposal of slurry. | sf | — | $.84 | $.84 |
| **CURB & GUTTER** ▶ | **Concrete curb & gutter** *Replace* Materials ........4.75  Labor ............9.64  Equipment .......... .84 *Remove*.........................  Labor ............3.80  Equipment............1.26 | lf | $5.06 | $15.23 | $20.29 |
| | **Minimum charge for concrete curb & gutter work** *Replace* Materials ......35.00  Labor ............129.00  Equipment ..........87.00 | ea | — | $251.00 | $251.00 |
| **CONCRETE STEP** ▶ *Includes rebar reinforcement: 2 horizontal pieces on each step with vertical tie-ins.* | **Concrete step per cy** *Replace* Materials ....257.00  Labor............271.00 *Remove*.........................  Labor ............81.70  Equipment ..........51.40 | cy | $133.40 | $528.00 | $661.40 |
| | **Concrete step per lf of step** *Replace* Materials ........2.84  Labor ............8.17 *Remove*.........................  Labor ............1.23  Equipment ............ .68 | lf | $1.91 | $11.01 | $12.92 |
| | **Concrete step landing per sf of landing** *Replace* Materials ........7.19  Labor ............2.41 *Remove*.........................  Labor ............1.21  Equipment ............ .82 | sf | $2.03 | $9.60 | $11.63 |
| minimum ▷ | **Minimum charge for a concrete step** *Replace* Materials ......68.00  Labor ............211.00 | ea | — | $279.00 | $279.00 |
| **PARGETING** ▶ *Break ties, prep, and plaster above grade exterior foundation wall.* | **Foundation wall pargeting (break ties if necessary)** *Replace* Materials ........ .32  Labor............. .90 | sf | — | $1.22 | $1.22 |
| | **Minimum charge for foundation wall pargeting** *Replace* Materials ......23.00  Labor ..........40.70 | ea | — | $63.70 | $63.70 |
| **CONCRETE** ▶ **SAWING** *Includes blade wear.* | **Saw concrete wall with standard rebar package per lf of cut, 1" deep** *Replace* .........................  Labor ............3.97  Equipment............1.59 | lf | — | $5.56 | $5.56 |
| | **Saw concrete wall with CEC rebar package per lf of cut, 1" deep** *Replace* .........................  Labor ............4.48  Equipment............2.31 | lf | — | $6.79 | $6.79 |
| | **Saw concrete floor (no rebar) per lf of cut, 1" deep** *Replace* .........................  Labor ............1.79  Equipment ............ .60 | lf | — | $2.39 | $2.39 |
| | **Saw concrete floor with rebar package** *Replace*.........................  Labor ............1.93  Equipment ............ .71 | lf | — | $2.64 | $2.64 |
| | **Saw concrete floor with wire mesh reinforcement** *Replace*.........................  Labor ............1.86  Equipment ............ .83 | lf | — | $2.69 | $2.69 |
| | **Saw expansion joint in "green" concrete pad** *Replace*.........................  Labor ............6.77  Equipment............2.40 | lf | — | $9.17 | $9.17 |
| minimum ▷ | **Minimum charge for concrete wall sawing** *Replace*.........................  Labor ..........107.00  Equipment ........101.20 | ea | — | $208.20 | $208.20 |
| | **Minimum charge for concrete slab sawing** *Replace*.........................  Labor ..........80.60  Equipment..........88.00 | ea | — | $168.60 | $168.60 |

*CEC = California Earthquake Code.*

| Item Description | Unit | Remove | Replace | Total | |
|---|---|---|---|---|---|
| **Core drill 2″ concrete wall per inch of depth** | li | — | $3.06 | $3.06 | ◄ **CONCRETE CORE DRILLING** *Includes drill bit wear.* |
| *Replace* Labor ....2.36  Equipment ....70 | | | | | |
| **Core drill 4″ concrete wall per inch of depth** | li | — | $3.42 | $3.42 | |
| *Replace* Labor ....2.61  Equipment ....81 | | | | | |
| **Core drill 2″ concrete floor per inch of depth** | li | — | $2.94 | $2.94 | **RELATED ITEMS** |
| *Replace* Labor ....2.29  Equipment ....65 | | | | | Cleaning ....57  Excavation ....177  Painting ....333 |
| **Core drill 4″ concrete floor per inch of depth** | li | — | $3.16 | $3.16 | |
| *Replace* Labor ....2.40  Equipment ....76 | | | | | |
| **Add for pumping footing concrete with pump truck** | lf | — | $1.09 | $1.09 | ◄ **PUMP TRUCK** *When pumping concrete 50 feet or less and no more than three stories high.* |
| *Replace* Equipment ....1.09 | | | | | |
| **Add for pumping foundation wall concrete with pump truck** | sf | — | $.27 | $.27 | |
| *Replace* Equipment ....27 | | | | | |
| **Add for pumping pier concrete with pump truck** | lf | — | $1.56 | $1.56 | |
| *Replace* Equipment ....1.56 | | | | | |
| **Add for pumping grade-beam concrete with pump truck** | lf | — | $.84 | $.84 | |
| *Replace* Equipment ....84 | | | | | |
| **Add for pumping slab or sidewalk concrete with pump truck** | sf | — | $.26 | $.26 | |
| *Replace* Equipment ....26 | | | | | |
| **Minimum charge for pump truck** | ea | — | $370.00 | $370.00 | ◁ minimum |
| *Replace* Equipment ....370.00 | | | | | |
| **#3 rebar (3/8″)** | lf | — | $.65 | $.65 | ◄ **REBAR** *Tied and bent into place.* |
| *Replace* Materials ....17  Labor ....48 | | | | | |
| **#4 rebar (1/2″)** | lf | — | $.70 | $.70 | |
| *Replace* Materials ....22  Labor ....48 | | | | | |
| **#5 rebar (5/8″)** | lf | — | $.82 | $.82 | |
| *Replace* Materials ....34  Labor ....48 | | | | | |
| **#6 rebar (3/4″)** | lf | — | $1.00 | $1.00 | |
| *Replace* Materials ....52  Labor ....48 | | | | | |
| **#7 rebar (7/8″)** | lf | — | $1.22 | $1.22 | |
| *Replace* Materials ....71  Labor ....51 | | | | | |
| **#8 rebar (1″)** | lf | — | $1.44 | $1.44 | |
| *Replace* Materials ....93  Labor ....51 | | | | | |
| **Foundation coating** | sf | — | $.51 | $.51 | ◄ **FOUNDATION COATING** |
| *Replace* Materials ....04  Labor ....47 | | | | | |
| **Excavate exterior of foundation** | sf | — | $7.33 | $7.33 | ◄ **BUTTRESS FOUNDATION** *Excavation, forming, pouring, and finishing of concrete buttress over existing foundation. Does not include shoring.* |
| *Replace* Labor ....5.93  Equipment ....1.40 | | | | | |
| **Hand excavate interior of foundation in crawl space** | sf | — | $13.10 | $13.10 | |
| *Replace* Labor ....13.10 | | | | | |
| **Hand excavate interior of footing in basement** | sf | — | $5.83 | $5.83 | |
| *Replace* Labor ....5.83 | | | | | |

| Item Description | Unit | Remove | Replace | Total |
|---|---|---|---|---|
| **BUTTRESS FOUNDATION** *continued* — **Backfill foundation when work is complete** | sf | — | $1.49 | $1.49 |
| *Replace* .................. Labor ........1.37 Equipment .......... .12 | | | | |
| **Buttress exterior of existing foundation wall** | sf | — | $6.00 | $6.00 |
| *Replace* Materials ........3.72 Labor ..........2.28 | | | | |
| **Buttress interior of existing foundation with crawl space** | sf | — | $6.94 | $6.94 |
| *Replace* Materials ........3.72 Labor ..........3.22 | | | | |
| **Buttress interior of existing foundation with basement** | sf | — | $11.06 | $11.06 |
| *Replace* Materials ........3.72 Labor ..........7.34 | | | | |
| **Minimum charge to buttress existing foundation with concrete** | ea | — | $632.00 | $632.00 |
| *Replace* Materials ....150.00 Labor ........482.00 | | | | |
| **COMPACTION GROUTING** — **2" core drill through footings for compaction grouting** | ea | — | $24.50 | $24.50 |
| *Replace* .................. Labor ..........16.10 Equipment..........8.40 | | | | |
| ► When footings and foundation walls are exposed, 2" holes are core drilled through footings around all corners and approximately 10' on center. | | | | |
| **Insert 2" compaction grouting pipes into ground beneath footings** | lf | — | $6.08 | $6.08 |
| *Replace* .................. Labor ..........6.08 | | | | |
| ► 2" pipes are inserted into the ground through holes in the footing (usually much deeper than is shown in the illustration to the left). | | | | |
| **Pump pressurized concrete grout through pipes** | lf | — | $45.02 | $45.02 |
| *Replace* Materials ........3.92 Labor ..........10.60 Equipment..........30.50 | | | | |
| ► Pressurized grout is pumped into the ground as the pipe is slowly withdrawn. | | | | |
| **ASPHALT GRADED BASE** — **4" graded base for asphalt** | sf | — | $.19 | $.19 |
| *Replace* Materials ........ .04 Labor ............ .04 Equipment .......... .11 | | | | |
| **6" graded base for asphalt** | sf | — | $.22 | $.22 |
| *Replace* Materials ..........05 Labor ..............04 Equipment..............13 | | | | |
| **Minimum grading charge** | sf | — | $375.40 | $375.40 |
| *Replace* Materials .....55.00 Labor ........70.40 Equipment.......250.00 | | | | |
| **ASPHALT DRIVEWAY** — **2" asphalt driveway** | sf | $.21 | $1.39 | $1.60 |
| *Replace* Materials ........ .52 Labor ............42 Equipment .......... .45 | | | | |
| *Remove* .................. Labor ............21 | | | | |
| **3" asphalt driveway** | sf | $.24 | $1.77 | $2.01 |
| *Replace* Materials ........ .78 Labor ............49 Equipment .......... .50 | | | | |
| *Remove* .................. Labor ............24 | | | | |
| **4" asphalt driveway** | sf | $.26 | $2.17 | $2.43 |
| *Replace* Materials ...... 1.05 Labor ............56 Equipment .......... .56 | | | | |
| *Remove* .................. Labor ............26 | | | | |
| **ASPHALT OVERLAY** — **1" asphalt overlay** | sf | $.24 | $1.26 | $1.50 |
| *Replace* Materials ........ .26 Labor ............53 Equipment .......... .47 | | | | |
| *Remove* .................. Labor ............24 | | | | |
| **2" asphalt overlay** | sf | $.24 | $1.63 | $1.87 |
| *Replace* Materials ........ .52 Labor ............60 Equipment .......... .51 | | | | |
| *Remove* .................. Labor ............24 | | | | |

**COMPACTION GROUTING** *Does not include excavation. (See excavation under concrete buttress above.) The process can form a "pier" for the foundation and compacts the destabilized soil. An engineer is required to supervise and dictate specifications.*

| Item Description | Unit | Remove | Replace | Total | |
|---|---|---|---|---|---|
| **3" asphalt overlay** | sf | $.24 | $2.02 | $2.26 | |
| *Replace* Materials ........ .78    Labor............ .67    Equipment ............ .57 | | | | | |
| *Remove* ....................... Labor............ .24 | | | | | |
| **Fill pothole in asphalt driveway** | ea | — | $20.40 | $20.40 | ◄ FILL ASPHALT POTHOLE |
| *Replace* Materials ....... 4.30    Labor........... 16.10 | | | | | |
| **Seal crack in asphalt driveway** | lf | — | $.75 | $.75 | ◄ SEAL ASPHALT CRACK |
| *Replace* Materials ........ .25    Labor............ .50 | | | | | |
| **Minimum charge for asphalt paving work** | ea | — | $1,272.00 | $1,272.00 | ◄ MINIMUM ASPAHLT |
| *Replace* Materials .... 130.00    Labor........ 422.00    Equipment ....... 720.00 | | | | | |
| **Seal asphalt** | sf | — | $.12 | $.12 | ◄ SEAL ASPAHLT |
| *Replace* Materials ........ .05    Labor............ .07 | | | | | |
| **Seal and sand asphalt** | sf | — | $.19 | $.19 | |
| *Replace* Materials ........ .08    Labor............ .11 | | | | | |

✍ NOTES: _____

_____ end

# TIME & MATERIAL CHARTS *(selected items)*

## Concrete Materials

| DESCRIPTION | MATERIAL PRICE | GROSS COVERAGE | WASTE | NET COVERAGE | UNIT PRICE |
|---|---|---|---|---|---|
| **Ready mix concrete delivered** | | | | | |
| 5 bag mix 2,500 psi, per cy | $83.60 cy | 1 | 6% | .94 | $88.90 cy |
| 5.5 bag mix 3,000 psi, per cy | $84.10 cy | 1 | 6% | .94 | $89.50 cy |
| 6 bag mix, 3,500 psi, per cy | $87.60 cy | 1 | 6% | .94 | $93.20 cy |
| 6.5 bag mix, 4,000 psi, per cy | $87.70 cy | 1 | 6% | .94 | $93.30 cy |
| 7 bag mix, 4,500 psi, per cy | $90.50 cy | 1 | 6% | .94 | $96.30 cy |
| 7.5 bag mix, 5,000 psi, per cy | $92.00 cy | 1 | 6% | .94 | $97.90 cy |
| add for synthetic fiber reinforcing | $10.30 cy | 1 | 0% | 1 | $10.30 cy |
| add for high early strength | $11.00 cy | 1 | 0% | 1 | $11.00 cy |
| minimum ready mix charge | $99.30 each | 1 | 0% | 1 | $99.30 ea |
| **Concrete form materials** | | | | | |
| form ties | $42.00 box | 400 | 5% | 380 | $.11 sf |
| footing forms (2 x lumber, use 6 times, use key 3 times) | $.30 lf | 1 | 0% | 1 | $.30 lf |
| **Concrete footings** | | | | | |
| with rebar per cy | $101.00 cy | 1 | 6% | .94 | $107.00 cy |
| with CEC rebar per cy | $123.00 cy | 1 | 6% | .94 | $131.00 cy |
| 16" wide by 10" deep | $87.60 lf | 24.3 | 6% | 22.84 | $3.84 lf |
| rebar package for 16" by 10" | $.36 pound | .7 | 6% | .69 | $.52 lf |
| CEC rebar package for 16" by 10" | $.36 pound | .2 | 6% | .19 | $1.89 lf |
| 20" wide by 10" deep | $87.60 lf | 19.44 | 6% | 18.27 | $4.79 lf |
| rebar package for 20" by 10" | $.36 pound | .74 | 2% | .73 | $.49 lf |
| CEC rebar package for 20" by 10" | $.36 pound | .19 | 4% | .18 | $2.00 lf |
| 24" wide by 12" deep | $87.60 lf | 13.5 | 6% | 12.69 | $6.90 lf |
| rebar package for 24" by 12" | $.36 pound | .5 | 2% | .49 | $.73 lf |
| CEC rebar package for 24" by 10" | $.36 pound | .16 | 4% | .15 | $2.40 lf |
| 32" wide by 14" deep | $87.60 lf | 8.68 | 6% | 8.16 | $10.70 lf |
| rebar package for 32" by 14" | $.36 pound | .5 | 2% | .49 | $.73 lf |
| CEC rebar package for 32" by 14" | $.36 pound | .16 | 4% | .15 | $2.40 lf |

*. . . More ➤*

CEC = California Earthquake Code.

## Concrete Materials *continued*

| DESCRIPTION | MATERIAL PRICE | GROSS COVERAGE | WASTE | NET COVERAGE | UNIT PRICE |
|---|---|---|---|---|---|
| **Foundation wall** | | | | | |
| including rebar package per cy | $96.10 cy | 1 | 6% | .94 | $102.20 cy |
| including CEC rebar package per cy | $115.00 cy | 1 | 6% | .94 | $122.00 cy |
| 5" wide wall | $87.60 cy | 65.06 | 6% | 61.16 | $1.43 ea |
| rebar package for 5" wide | $.36 pound | 1.71 | 2% | 1.68 | $.21 sf |
| CEC rebar package for 5" wide | $.36 pound | .55 | 4% | .53 | $.68 sf |
| 6" wide wall | $87.60 cy | 54 | 6% | 50.76 | $1.73 ea |
| rebar package for 6" wide wall | $.36 pound | 1.71 | 2% | 1.68 | $.21 sf |
| CEC rebar package for 6" wide wall | $.36 pound | .55 | 4% | .53 | $.68 sf |
| concrete for 8" wide wall | $87.60 cy | 40.5 | 6% | 38.07 | $2.30 ea |
| rebar package for 8" wide wall | $.36 sf | 1.71 | 2% | 1.68 | $.21 sf |
| CEC rebar package for 8" wide wall | $.36 sf | .55 | 4% | .53 | $.68 sf |
| concrete for 10" wide wall | $87.60 cy | 32.4 | 6% | 30.46 | $2.88 ea |
| rebar package for 10" wide wall | $.36 sf | 1.71 | 2% | 1.68 | $.21 sf |
| CEC rebar package for 10" wide wall | $.36 sf | .55 | 4% | .53 | $.68 sf |
| insulating foam stay-in-place foundation wall forms | $1.34 sf | 1 | 0% | 1 | $1.34 sf |
| **Pier** | | | | | |
| concrete | $87.60 cy | 8.6 | 6% | 8.08 | $10.80 lf |
| fiber tube with bracing | $87.50 10' tube | 3.33 | 2% | 3.26 | $26.80 ea |
| prefabricated rebar cage | $.36 pound | .01 | 0% | .01 | $36.00 lf |
| **Grade beam** | | | | | |
| concrete for 12" by 18" | $87.60 cy | 18 | 6% | 16.92 | $5.18 lf |
| concrete for 12" by 24" | $87.60 cy | 13.5 | 6% | 12.69 | $6.90 lf |
| concrete for 14" by 18" | $87.60 cy | 15.43 | 6% | 14.50 | $6.04 lf |
| concrete for 14" by 24" | $87.60 cy | 11.57 | 6% | 10.88 | $8.05 lf |
| concrete for 16" by 18" | $87.60 cy | 13.5 | 6% | 12.69 | $6.90 lf |
| concrete for 16" by 24" | $87.60 cy | 10.13 | 6% | 9.52 | $9.20 lf |
| concrete for 18" by 18" | $87.60 cy | 12 | 6% | 11.28 | $7.77 lf |
| concrete for 18" by 24" | $87.60 cy | 9 | 6% | 8.46 | $10.35 lf |
| rebar cage | $.36 pound | .01 | 0% | .01 | $36.00 lf |
| **Lightweight concrete flatwork** | | | | | |
| per cy | $110.00 cy | 1 | 6% | .94 | $117.00 cy |
| 2" slab | $110.00 cy | 162 | 6% | 152.28 | $.72 sf |
| 4" slab | $110.00 cy | 81 | 6% | 76.14 | $1.44 sf |
| 6" slab | $110.00 cy | 54 | 6% | 50.76 | $2.17 sf |
| **Concrete flatwork** | | | | | |
| per cy | $87.60 cy | 1 | 6% | .94 | $93.20 cy |
| 4" slab | $87.60 cy | 81 | 6% | 76.14 | $1.15 sf |
| 6" slab | $87.60 cy | 54 | 6% | 50.76 | $1.73 sf |
| 8" slab | $87.60 cy | 40.5 | 6% | 38.07 | $2.30 sf |
| rebar #4, 24" on center | $.36 pound | .75 | 2% | .74 | $.49 sf |
| rebar #4, 12" on center | $.36 pound | .37 | 2% | .36 | $1.00 sf |
| wire mesh (6" x 6" #10) | $114.00 roll | 750 | 2% | 735 | $.16 sf |
| aggregate for 2" slab base | $6.60 cy | 162 | 0% | 162 | $.04 sf |
| aggregate for 4" slab base | $6.60 cy | 81 | 0% | 81 | $.08 sf |
| sand for 2" slab base | $6.60 cy | 162 | 0% | 162 | $.04 sf |
| sand for 4" slab base | $6.60 cy | 81 | 0% | 81 | $.08 sf |
| **Sidewalk** | | | | | |
| 3" sidewalk | $87.60 cy | 108 | 6% | 101.52 | $.86 sf |
| 4" sidewalk | $87.60 cy | 81 | 6% | 76.14 | $1.15 sf |
| 6" sidewalk | $87.60 cy | 54 | 6% | 50.76 | $1.73 sf |
| **Rebar** | | | | | |
| #3 (3/8" .376 pound per lf) | $3.32 20' bar | 20 | 4% | 19.2 | $.17 lf |
| #4 (1/2" .668 pounds per lf) | $4.24 20' bar | 20 | 4% | 19.2 | $.22 lf |
| #5 (5/8" 1.043 pounds per lf) | $6.59 20' bar | 20 | 4% | 19.2 | $.34 lf |
| #6 (3/4" 1.502 pounds per lf) | $9.99 20' bar | 20 | 4% | 19.2 | $.52 lf |
| #7 (7/8" 2.044 pounds per lf) | $13.60 20' bar | 20 | 4% | 19.2 | $.71 lf |
| #8 (1" 2.670 pounds per lf) | $17.80 20' bar | 20 | 4% | 19.2 | $.93 lf |

*CEC = California Earthquake Code.*

## Concrete Rental Equipment

| DESCRIPTION | PRICE | COVERAGE | UNIT PRICE |
|---|---|---|---|
| **Forms** | | | |
| plywood wall forms (per sf of form) | $.17 per day | .25 per sf | **$.68** sf |
| steel curb & gutter forms | $.84 per day | 1 lf | **$.84** lf |
| **Tractor-mounted auger** | | | |
| hourly charge | $200.00 per hour | .90 lf | **$2.22** lf |
| delivery and take-home charge | $422.00 each | 1 each | **$422.00** ea |
| **Concrete pump truck** | | | |
| foundation wall | $122.00 hour | 450 sf of wall | **$.27** sf |
| footings | $122.00 hour | 112 lf of footing | **$1.09** lf |
| flatwork | $122.00 hour | 475 sf of flat | **$.26** sf |
| piers | $122.00 hour | .78 lf or pier | **$1.56** lf |
| grade beam | $122.00 hour | 146 lf of beam | **$.84** lf |
| pressure grout | $122.00 hour | 4 lf 2" pipe | **$30.50** sf |
| **Dump truck** | | | |
| 5 cy, average aggregate base haul | $61.00 day | 540 sf | **$.11** sf |
| **Jackhammer with compressor** | | | |
| foundation wall demo | $183.00 day | 110 sf | **$1.66** sf |
| footing demo | $183.00 day | .66 lf | **$2.77** lf |
| flatwork demo | $183.00 day | 295 sf | **$.62** sf |
| grade beam demo | $183.00 day | .46 lf | **$3.98** lf |
| jacket grade beam | $183.00 day | .42 lf | **$4.36** lf |
| jacket pier | $183.00 day | 5.6 each | **$32.70** ea |
| curb & gutter | $183.00 day | 145 lf | **$1.26** lf |
| **Portable concrete saw** | | | |
| wall sawing | $124.00 day | .78 1" x 1' | **$1.59** lf |
| floor sawing | $96.00 day | 160 1" x 1' | **$.60** lf |
| **Concrete core drill** | | | |
| per day | $87.00 day | 125 1" x 1' | **$.70** lf |
| **Crane** | | | |
| concrete pier removal | $580.00 day | .98 day | **$5.92** lf |
| **Pressure pot** | | | |
| for pressurized epoxy injection | $170.00 day | 120 day | **$1.42** lf |
| **Backhoe** | | | |
| per day | $451.00 day | 322 day | **$1.40** cy |

## Concrete Labor

| LABORER | BASE WAGE | PAID LEAVE | TRUE WAGE | FICA | FUTA | WORKER'S COMP. | UNEMPLOY. INSUR. | HEALTH INSUR. | RETIRE (401k) | LIABILITY INSUR. | COST PER HOUR |
|---|---|---|---|---|---|---|---|---|---|---|---|
| Concrete form installer | $22.10 | 1.72 | $23.82 | 1.82 | .19 | 5.49 | 2.07 | 2.54 | .71 | 3.10 | **$39.70** |
| Concrete finisher | $22.00 | 1.72 | $23.72 | 1.81 | .19 | 5.47 | 2.06 | 2.54 | .71 | 3.08 | **$39.60** |
| Concrete finisher's helper | $17.90 | 1.40 | $19.30 | 1.48 | .15 | 4.45 | 1.68 | 2.54 | .58 | 2.51 | **$32.70** |
| Equipment operator | $28.70 | 2.24 | $30.94 | 2.37 | .25 | 5.36 | 2.69 | 2.54 | .93 | 4.02 | **$49.10** |
| Plasterer | $22.00 | 1.72 | $23.72 | 1.81 | .19 | 6.54 | 2.06 | 2.54 | .71 | 3.08 | **$40.70** |
| Concrete saw operator | $20.50 | 1.60 | $22.10 | 1.69 | .18 | 3.83 | 1.92 | 2.54 | .66 | 2.87 | **$35.80** |
| Compaction grouter | $31.90 | 2.49 | $34.39 | 2.63 | .28 | 7.92 | 2.99 | 2.54 | 1.03 | 4.47 | **$56.30** |
| Laborer | $15.50 | 1.21 | $16.71 | 1.28 | .13 | 3.85 | 1.45 | 2.54 | .50 | 2.17 | **$28.60** |
| Demolition laborer | $13.40 | 1.05 | $14.45 | 1.11 | 12 | 4.44 | 1.26 | 2.54 | .43 | 1.88 | **$26.20** |

**Paid Leave** is calculated based on two weeks paid vacation, one week sick leave, and seven paid holidays. Employer's matching portion of **FICA** is 7.65 percent. **FUTA** (Federal Unemployment) is .8 percent. **Worker's Compensation** was calculated using a national average of 23.04 percent for the concrete trade; 17.31 percent for the equipment operator, 17.31 percent for the concrete saw operator; 27.58 percent for the plastering trade; 23.04 percent for the compaction grouting specialist; and 30.70 percent for the demolition laborer. **Unemployment insurance** was calculated using a national average of 8.7 percent. **Health insurance** was calculated based on a projected national average for 2001 of $505 per employee (and family when applicable) per month. Employer pays 80 percent for a per month cost of $404 per employee. **Retirement** is based on a 401(k) retirement program with employer matching of 50 percent. Employee contributions to the 401(k) plan are an average of 6 percent of the true wage. **Liability insurance** is based on a national average of 12.9 percent.

## Concrete Labor Productivity

| WORK DESCRIPTION | LABORER | COST PER HOUR | PRODUCTIVITY | UNIT PRICE |
|---|---|---|---|---|
| **Demolition** | | | | |
| remove footings including rebar | demolition laborer | $26.20 | 1.64 | $43.00 cy |
| remove footings including CEC rebar | demolition laborer | $26.20 | 1.96 | $51.40 cy |
| remove footings with rebar | demolition laborer | $26.20 | .121 | $3.17 lf |
| remove footings with CEC rebar | demolition laborer | $26.20 | .147 | $3.85 lf |
| remove foundation including rebar | demolition laborer | $26.20 | 2.44 | $63.90 cy |
| remove foundation including CEC rebar | demolition laborer | $26.20 | 2.94 | $77.00 cy |
| remove 5" or 6" foundation with rebar | demolition laborer | $26.20 | .073 | $1.91 sf |
| remove 5" or 6" foundation with CEC rebar | demolition laborer | $26.20 | .088 | $2.31 sf |
| remove 8" or 10" foundation with rebar | demolition laborer | $26.20 | .076 | $1.99 sf |
| remove 8" or 10" foundation with CEC rebar | demolition laborer | $26.20 | .092 | $2.41 sf |
| remove footing & foundation with rebar | demolition laborer | $26.20 | 1.96 | $51.40 cy |
| remove footing & foundation with CEC rebar | demolition laborer | $26.20 | 2.33 | $61.00 cy |
| remove footing & 3' foundation | demolition laborer | $26.20 | .346 | $9.07 lf |
| remove footing & 3' foundation with CEC rebar | demolition laborer | $26.20 | .418 | $11.00 lf |
| remove footing & 4' foundation | demolition laborer | $26.20 | .422 | $11.10 lf |
| remove footing & 4' foundation with CEC rebar | demolition laborer | $26.20 | .510 | $13.40 lf |
| remove pier per cy | demolition laborer | $26.20 | .699 | $18.30 cy |
| remove pier | demolition laborer | $26.20 | .082 | $2.15 lf |
| remove grade beam per cy | demolition laborer | $26.20 | 2.33 | $61.00 cy |
| remove grade beam | demolition laborer | $26.20 | .174 | $4.56 lf |
| remove lightweight slab | demolition laborer | $26.20 | .026 | $.68 sf |
| remove lightweight slab with rebar | demolition laborer | $26.20 | .029 | $.76 sf |
| remove lightweight slab with wire mesh | demolition laborer | $26.20 | .031 | $.81 sf |
| remove slab | demolition laborer | $26.20 | .027 | $.71 sf |
| remove slab with rebar | demolition laborer | $26.20 | .030 | $.79 sf |
| remove slab with wire mesh | demolition laborer | $26.20 | .033 | $.86 sf |
| remove sidewalk | demolition laborer | $26.20 | .034 | $.89 sf |
| remove curb & gutter | demolition laborer | $26.20 | .145 | $3.80 lf |
| remove step | demolition laborer | $26.20 | .047 | $1.23 lf |
| remove step landing | demolition laborer | $26.20 | .046 | $1.21 sf |
| **Forming and rebar setting crew** | | | | |
| form and set rebar | concrete form installer | $39.70 | | |
| form and set rebar | laborer | $28.60 | | |
| form and set rebar | **forming crew** | $34.20 | | |
| **Pouring and finishing crew** | | | | |
| pour & finish concrete | concrete finisher | $39.60 | | |
| pour & finish concrete | concrete finisher's helper | $32.70 | | |
| pour and finish concrete | **finishing crew** | $36.20 | | |
| **Concrete footings** | | | | |
| form, set rebar, pour, & finish per cy | forming & finishing crews | $35.20 | 2.44 | $85.90 cy |
| form, set CEC rebar, pour, & finish per cy | forming & finishing crews | $35.20 | 2.94 | $103.00 cy |
| set forms for concrete footings | forming crew | $34.20 | .041 | $1.40 lf |
| strip forms from concrete footings & clean | forming crew | $34.20 | .009 | $.31 lf |
| set rebar in forms for concrete footings | forming crew | $34.20 | .036 | $1.23 lf |
| set CEC rebar in forms for concrete footings | forming crew | $34.20 | .067 | $2.29 lf |
| pour and finish 16" by 10" footings | finishing crew | $36.20 | .065 | $2.35 lf |
| pour and finish 20" by 10" footings | finishing crew | $36.20 | .074 | $2.68 lf |
| pour and finish 24" by 12" footings | finishing crew | $36.20 | .081 | $2.93 lf |
| pour and finish 32" by 14" footings | finishing crew | $36.20 | .091 | $3.29 lf |
| **Concrete foundation wall** | | | | |
| form, set rebar, pour, & finish per cy | forming & finishing crews | $35.20 | 2.70 | $95.00 cy |
| form, set CEC rebar, pour, & finish per cy | forming & finishing crews | $35.20 | 3.13 | $110.00 cy |
| set forms | forming crew | $34.20 | .029 | $.99 sf |
| strip forms & clean | forming crew | $34.20 | .006 | $.21 sf |
| set rebar package | forming crew | $34.20 | .037 | $1.27 sf |
| set CEC rebar package | forming crew | $34.20 | .067 | $2.29 sf |
| pour and finish 5" wide wall | finishing crew | $36.20 | .024 | $.87 sf |
| pour and finish 6" wide wall | finishing crew | $36.20 | .029 | $1.05 sf |
| pour and finish 8" wide wall | finishing crew | $36.20 | .039 | $1.41 sf |
| pour and finish 10" wide wall | finishing crew | $36.20 | .049 | $1.77 sf |

. . . More ➤

CEC = California Earthquake Code.

## Concrete Labor Productivity *continued*

| WORK DESCRIPTION | LABORER | COST | PRODUCTIVITY | UNIT PRICE |
|---|---|---|---|---|
| **Tractor-mounted auger (hole drilling for pier)** | | | | |
| delivery and take home charges (mobilization) | equipment operator | $49.10 | 6.25 | $307.00 ea |
| drill pier hole | equipment operator | $49.10 | .083 | $4.08 sf |
| **Concrete pier** | | | | |
| form, set rebar cage, pour and finish per cy | forming & finishing crews | $35.20 | 14.9 | $524.00 cy |
| set and brace fiber tube cap | forming crew | $34.20 | .125 | $4.28 lf |
| pour concrete pier | finishing crew | $36.20 | 1.54 | $55.70 lf |
| set and brace fiber tube for above-grade pier | forming crew | $34.20 | .183 | $6.26 lf |
| strip fiber tube | forming crew | $34.20 | .056 | $1.92 lf |
| pour above-grade concrete pier | finishing crew | $36.20 | .185 | $6.70 sf |
| set rebar cage for concrete pier | forming crew | $34.20 | .091 | $3.11 lf |
| **Jacket pier** | | | | |
| jackhammer for jacket, drill for new rebar | demolition laborer | $26.20 | 2.32 | $60.80 ea |
| set forms | forming crew | $34.20 | 1.09 | $37.30 ea |
| set rebar, secure with epoxy | forming crew | $34.20 | .833 | $28.50 ea |
| pour concrete jacket | finishing crew | $36.20 | 1.30 | $47.10 ea |
| **Grade beam** | | | | |
| form, set rebar cage, pour, and finish per cy | forming & finishing crews | $35.20 | 4.00 | $141.00 cy |
| set forms | forming crew | $34.20 | .127 | $4.34 lf |
| set rebar cage | forming crew | $34.20 | .067 | $2.29 lf |
| pour and finish 12" by 18" | finishing crew | $36.20 | .073 | $2.64 lf |
| pour and finish 12" by 24" | finishing crew | $36.20 | .088 | $3.19 lf |
| pour and finish 14" by 18" | finishing crew | $36.20 | .118 | $4.27 lf |
| pour and finish 14" by 24" | finishing crew | $36.20 | .235 | $8.51 lf |
| pour and finish 16" by 18" | finishing crew | $36.20 | .353 | $12.80 lf |
| pour and finish 16" by 24" | finishing crew | $36.20 | .470 | $17.00 lf |
| pour and finish 18" by 18" | finishing crew | $36.20 | .118 | $4.27 lf |
| pour and finish 18" by 24" | finishing crew | $36.20 | .235 | $8.51 lf |
| **Jacket grade beam** | | | | |
| jackhammer for jacket | demolition laborer | $26.20 | .088 | $2.31 lf |
| set forms | forming crew | $34.20 | .150 | $5.13 lf |
| set rebar, secure with epoxy | forming crew | $34.20 | .083 | $2.84 lf |
| pour concrete | finishing crew | $36.20 | .240 | $8.69 lf |
| **Lightweight concrete flatwork** | | | | |
| form, pour, and finish per cy | forming & finishing crews | $35.20 | 2.04 | $71.80 cy |
| pour and finish 2" slab | finishing crew | $36.20 | .012 | $.43 sf |
| pour and finish 4" slab | finishing crew | $36.20 | .013 | $.47 sf |
| pour and finish 6" slab | finishing crew | $36.20 | .015 | $.54 sf |
| **Concrete flatwork** | | | | |
| form, pour, and finish per cy | forming & finishing crews | $35.20 | 2.04 | $71.80 cy |
| set forms for concrete slab | forming crew | $34.20 | .011 | $.38 sf |
| set rebar 24" on center | forming crew | $34.20 | .036 | $1.23 sf |
| set rebar 12" on center | forming crew | $34.20 | .080 | $2.74 sf |
| set wire mesh | forming crew | $34.20 | .015 | $.51 sf |
| pour and finish 4" slab | finishing crew | $36.20 | .024 | $.87 sf |
| pour and finish 6" slab | finishing crew | $36.20 | .036 | $1.30 sf |
| pour and finish 8" slab | finishing crew | $36.20 | .036 | $1.30 sf |
| haul aggregate for slab base to job site | equipment operator | $49.10 | .002 | $.10 sf |
| spread 2" aggregate slab base | laborer | $28.60 | .013 | $.37 sf |
| spread 4" aggregate slab base | laborer | $28.60 | .015 | $.43 sf |
| haul sand for slab base to job site | equipment operator | $49.10 | .001 | $.05 sf |
| spread 2" sand slab base | laborer | $28.60 | .012 | $.34 sf |
| spread 4" sand slab base | laborer | $28.60 | .014 | $.40 sf |
| **Sidewalk** | | | | |
| form, pour, and finish per cy | forming & finishing crews | $35.20 | 4.17 | $147.00 cy |
| set forms | forming crew | $34.20 | .023 | $.79 sf |
| pour and finish 3" sidewalk | finishing crew | $36.20 | .019 | $.69 sf |
| pour and finish 4" sidewalk | finishing crew | $36.20 | .026 | $.94 sf |
| pour and finish 6" sidewalk | finishing crew | $36.20 | .039 | $1.41 sf |

*. . . More ➢*

*CEC = California Earthquake Code.*

## Concrete Labor Productivity *continued*

| WORK DESCRIPTION | LABORER | COST | PRODUCTIVITY | UNIT PRICE |
|---|---|---|---|---|
| **Concrete dye** | | | | |
| trowel into wet concrete | finishing crew | $36.20 | .009 | $.33 sf |
| **Stamp concrete** | | | | |
| slab or sidewalk | finishing crew | $36.20 | .053 | $1.92 sf |
| with paver pattern | finishing crew | $36.20 | .045 | $1.63 sf |
| grout stamped paver pattern joints | finishing crew | $36.20 | .023 | $.83 sf |
| **Exposed aggregate** | | | | |
| Finish with exposed aggregate finish | finishing crew | $36.20 | .019 | $.69 sf |
| **Curb & gutter** | | | | |
| set forms | forming crew | $34.20 | .123 | $4.21 lf |
| pour and finish | finishing crew | $36.20 | .150 | $5.43 lf |
| **Concrete step** | | | | |
| form, set rebar, pour, and finish per cy | forming & finishing crews | $35.20 | 7.69 | $271.00 cy |
| set forms and rebar per lf of step | forming crew | $34.20 | .133 | $4.55 lf |
| pour and finish per lf of step | finishing crew | $36.20 | .100 | $3.62 lf |
| set forms and rebar for landing per cubic foot | forming crew | $34.20 | .011 | $.38 cf |
| pour and finish landing per cubic foot | finishing crew | $36.20 | .056 | $2.03 cf |
| **Saw concrete** | | | | |
| wall with rebar per lf, 1" deep | saw operator | $35.80 | .111 | $3.97 lf |
| wall with CEC rebar per lf, 1" deep | saw operator | $35.80 | .125 | $4.48 lf |
| floor per lf, 1" deep | saw operator | $35.80 | .050 | $1.79 lf |
| floor with rebar per lf, 1" deep | saw operator | $35.80 | .054 | $1.93 lf |
| floor with wire mesh per lf, 1" deep | saw operator | $35.80 | .052 | $1.86 lf |
| expansion joint in "green" slab | saw operator | $35.80 | .189 | $6.77 lf |
| **Core drill concrete** | | | | |
| 2" wall per inch of depth | saw operator | $35.80 | .066 | $2.36 li |
| 4" wall per inch of depth | saw operator | $35.80 | .073 | $2.61 li |
| 2" floor per inch of depth | saw operator | $35.80 | .064 | $2.29 li |
| 4" floor per inch of depth | saw operator | $35.80 | .067 | $2.40 li |
| **Set rebar** | | | | |
| #3 (3/8") | forming crew | $34.20 | .014 | $.48 lf |
| #4 (1/2") | forming crew | $34.20 | .014 | $.48 lf |
| #5 (5/8") | forming crew | $34.20 | .014 | $.48 lf |
| #6 (3/4") | forming crew | $34.20 | .014 | $.48 lf |
| #7 (7/8") | forming crew | $34.20 | .015 | $.51 lf |
| #8 (1") | forming crew | $34.20 | .015 | $.51 lf |
| **Buttress foundation** | | | | |
| machine excavate to 12" to 24" of ext. foundation | equipment operator | $49.10 | .027 | $1.33 sf |
| hand excavate exterior of foundation | laborer | $28.60 | .161 | $4.60 sf |
| backfill buttressed foundation | laborer | $28.60 | .048 | $1.37 sf |
| set forms for exterior buttress | forming crew | $34.20 | .021 | $.72 sf |
| set rebar for exterior buttress | forming crew | $34.20 | .017 | $.58 sf |
| pour and finish exterior buttress | finishing crew | $36.20 | .027 | $.98 sf |
| hand excavate interior crawl space for buttress | laborer | $28.60 | .457 | $13.10 sf |
| set forms for interior buttress in crawl space | forming crew | $34.20 | .032 | $1.09 sf |
| set rebar for interior buttress in crawl space | forming crew | $34.20 | .023 | $.79 sf |
| pour and finish interior buttress in crawl space | finishing crew | $36.20 | .037 | $1.34 sf |
| hand excavate interior foundation in basement | laborer | $28.60 | .204 | $5.83 sf |
| set forms for interior buttress in basement | forming crew | $34.20 | .025 | $.86 sf |
| set rebar for interior buttress in basement | forming crew | $34.20 | .019 | $.65 sf |
| pour and finish interior buttress in basement | finishing crew | $36.20 | .032 | $1.16 sf |
| **Compaction grouting crew** | | | | |
| core drill, insert pipes, pump grout | compaction grouting specialist | $56.30 | | |
| core drill, insert pipes, pump grout | laborer | $28.60 | | |
| core drill, insert pipes, pump grout | compaction grouting crew | $42.50 | | |
| **Foundation & footing stabilization with pressurized grout** | | | | |
| 2" core drill through footings | compaction grouting crew | $42.50 | .379 | $16.10 ea |
| insert 2" pipes into ground beneath footings | compaction grouting crew | $42.50 | .143 | $6.08 lf |
| pump pressurized grout through pipes | compaction grouting crew | $42.50 | .250 | $10.60 lf |

*CEC = California Earthquake Code.*

# 9 .................................................. *Demolition & Hauling*

| Item Description | Unit | | | Total | |
|---|---|---|---|---|---|
| **Minimum demolition charge**<br>*Demo* ..................... Labor..........78.60 Equipment ........100.00 | ea | — | — | **$178.60** | ◄ MINIMUM |
| **Dump charge per cy**<br>*Demo Fee* .................41.60 | cy | — | — | **$41.60** | ◄ DUMP FEE<br>*Typical metro area landfill fees. Will be up to 60% higher in major metro areas and 30% to 60% lower in rural areas.* |
| **Dump charge per ton**<br>*Demo Fee* .................78.20 | tn | — | — | **$78.20** | |
| **3 cy dumpster rental per week**<br>*Demo* ..................... .............. Equipment ........100.00 | ea | — | — | **$100.00** | ◄ DUMPSTER<br>*Includes up to two dumps per week.* |
| **5 cy dumpster rental per week**<br>*Demo* ..................... .............. Equipment ........180.00 | ea | — | — | **$180.00** | |
| **10 cy dumpster rental per week**<br>*Demo* ..................... .............. Equipment ........220.00 | ea | — | — | **$220.00** | |
| **30 cy dumpster rental per week**<br>*Demo* ..................... .............. Equipment........310.00 | ea | — | — | **$310.00** | |
| **Minimum dumpster charge**<br>*Demo* ..................... .............. Equipment ........150.00 | ea | — | — | **$150.00** | |
| **Plywood refuse chute**<br>*Demo* Materials ..........11.90 Labor..........42.70 | lf | — | — | **$54.60** | ◄ REFUSE CHUTE |
| **Minimum charge for plywood refuse chute**<br>*Demo* Materials .........63.00 Labor..........96.20 | ea | — | — | **$159.20** | |
| **18" prefabricated circular steel refuse chute**<br>*Demo* Materials ..........13.40 Labor ..........30.90 | lf | — | — | **$44.30** | |
| **36" prefabricated circular steel refuse chute**<br>*Demo* Materials..........24.50 Labor..........41.90 | lf | — | — | **$66.40** | |
| **Minimum charge for circular steel refuse chute**<br>*Demo* Materials..........71.00 Labor ..........86.50 | ea | — | — | **$157.50** | |
| **Debris hauling (by trailer or dump truck) per cy**<br>*Demo* ..................... .............. Equipment ..........19.30 | cy | — | — | **$19.30** | ◄ DEBRIS HAULING |
| **Debris hauling (by trailer or dump truck) per ton**<br>*Demo* ..................... .............. Equipment ..........52.60 | tn | — | — | **$52.60** | |
| **Debris hauling per pick-up truck load**<br>*Demo* ..................... .............. Equipment ..........19.40 | ea | — | — | **$19.40** | |
| **Strip typical room to bare walls and sub-floor**<br>*Demo* ..................... Labor ..........1.94 | sf | — | — | **$1.94** | ◄ STRIP ROOM<br>*Remove all wall and floor coverings, doors, trim, and underlayment. Stud walls and plywood subfloor remain. Per sf of floor.* |
| **Strip bathroom to bare walls and sub-floor**<br>*Demo* ..................... Labor ..........3.93 | sf | — | — | **$3.93** | |

|---|---|---|---|---|
| **STRIP ROOM ▶** *continued* | **Strip kitchen to bare walls and sub-floor** | sf | — | — | $3.01 |

| | Item Description | Unit | | | Total |
|---|---|---|---|---|---|
| **STRIP ROOM ▶**<br>*continued*<br>For rooms with<br>contents add 4%. | **Strip kitchen to bare walls and sub-floor**<br>Demo .......... Labor ......3.01 | sf | — | — | $3.01 |
| | **Strip utility room to bare walls and sub-floor**<br>Demo .......... Labor ......2.25 | sf | — | — | $2.25 |
| | **Strip laundry room to bare walls and sub-floor**<br>Demo .......... Labor ......2.49 | sf | — | — | $2.49 |

# TIME & MATERIAL CHARTS *(selected items)*

## Demolition & Hauling Materials

| DESCRIPTION | MATERIAL PRICE | GROSS COVERAGE | WASTE | NET COVERAGE | UNIT PRICE |
|---|---|---|---|---|---|
| **Refuse chute** | | | | | |
| plywood | | | | | $11.90 lf |
| 18" prefabricated circular steel | | | | | $13.40 lf |
| 36" prefabricated circular steel | | | | | $24.50 lf |

## Demolition & Hauling Rental Equipment

| DESCRIPTION | PRICE | COVERAGE | UNIT PRICE |
|---|---|---|---|
| **Dumpster rental per week** | | | |
| 3 cy | $100.00 week | | $100.00 ea |
| 5 cy | $180.00 week | | $180.00 ea |
| 10 cy | $220.00 week | | $220.00 ea |
| 30 cy | $310.00 week | | $310.00 ea |
| **Truck rental with driver** | | | |
| 3 cy dump truck | $425.00 day | 22 cy | $19.30 cy |
| 3 cy dump truck | $425.00 day | 8.08 ton | $52.60 ton |
| pick-up truck | $175.00 day | 9 load | $19.40 ea |

## Demolition & Hauling Labor

| LABORER | BASE WAGE | PAID LEAVE | TRUE WAGE | FICA | FUTA | WORKER'S COMP. | UNEMPLOY. INSUR. | HEALTH INSUR. | RETIRE (401K) | LIABILITY INSUR. | COST PER HOUR |
|---|---|---|---|---|---|---|---|---|---|---|---|
| Demolition laborer | $13.40 | 1.05 | $14.45 | 1.11 | .12 | 4.44 | 1.26 | 2.54 | .43 | 1.88 | $26.20 |

**Paid Leave** is calculated based on two weeks paid vacation, one week sick leave, and seven paid holidays. Employer's matching portion of **FICA** is 7.65 percent. **FUTA** (Federal Unemployment) is .8 percent. **Worker's Compensation** for Demolition was calculated using a national average of 30.7 percent. **Unemployment insurance** was calculated using a national average of 8.7 percent. **Health insurance** was calculated based on a projected national average for 2001 of $505 per employee (and family when applicable) per month. Employer pays 80 percent for a per month cost of $404 per employee. **Retirement** is based on a 401(k) retirement program with employer matching of 50 percent. Employee contributions to the 401(k) plan are an average of 6 percent of the true wage. **Liability insurance** is based on a national average of 12.9 percent.

## Demolition & Hauling Labor Productivity

| WORK DESCRIPTION | LABORER | COST PER HOUR | PRODUCTIVITY | UNIT PRICE |
|---|---|---|---|---|
| **Build / install refuse chute** | | | | |
| plywood | demolition laborer | $26.20 | 1.63 | $42.70 lf |
| 18" prefabricated circular steel | demolition laborer | $26.20 | 1.18 | $30.90 lf |
| 36" prefabricated circular steel | demolition laborer | $26.20 | 1.60 | $41.90 lf |
| **Strip room to bare walls and sub-floor** | | | | |
| typical | demolition laborer | $26.20 | .074 | $1.94 sf |
| bathroom | demolition laborer | $26.20 | .150 | $3.93 sf |
| kitchen | demolition laborer | $26.20 | .115 | $3.01 sf |
| utility | demolition laborer | $26.20 | .086 | $2.25 sf |
| laundry | demolition laborer | $26.20 | .095 | $2.49 sf |

# 10 ............................................................ *Doors*

| Item Description | Unit | Remove | Replace | Total | |
|---|---|---|---|---|---|
| **Minimum charge for door work**<br>*Replace* Materials......32.00     Labor...........98.80 | ea | — | $130.80 | $130.80 | ◄ **MINIMUM** |
| **Hardboard smooth or wood-textured folding door (per section)**<br>*Replace* Materials......26.50     Labor...........15.60<br>*Remove*.......................     Labor ............2.99 | ea | $2.99 | $42.10 | $45.09 | ◄ **FOLDING DOOR**<br>*Folding doors usually used in closets.* **Priced per section.** *For jamb & casing see page 102.* |
| **Hardboard wood-textured & embossed folding door (per section)**<br>*Replace* Materials......30.30     Labor...........15.60<br>*Remove*.......................     Labor ............2.99<br>► Referred to by the brand name "Colonist" in many areas of the country. | ea | $2.99 | $45.90 | $48.89 | |
| **Mahogany (lauan) or birch veneer folding door (per section)**<br>*Replace* Materials......28.40     Labor...........15.60<br>*Remove*.......................     Labor ............2.99 | ea | $2.992 | $44.00 | $46.99 | |
| **Ash or oak veneer folding door (per section)**<br>*Replace* Materials......30.90     Labor...........15.60<br>*Remove*.......................     Labor ............2.99 | ea | $2.99 | $46.50 | $49.49 | |
| **Walnut or cherry veneer folding door (per section)**<br>*Replace* Materials......35.30     Labor...........15.60<br>*Remove*.......................     Labor ............2.99 | ea | $2.99 | $50.90 | $53.89 | |
| **Paint-grade pine panel folding door (per section)**<br>*Replace* Materials......46.10     Labor...........15.60<br>*Remove*.......................     Labor ............2.99 | ea | $2.99 | $61.70 | $64.69 | |
| **Stain-grade pine panel folding door (per section)**<br>*Replace* Materials......56.80     Labor...........15.60<br>*Remove*.......................     Labor ............2.99 | ea | $2.99 | $72.40 | $75.39 | |
| **Paint-grade pine full-louvered folding door (per section)**<br>*Replace* Materials......54.30     Labor...........15.60<br>*Remove*.......................     Labor ............2.99 | ea | $2.99 | $69.90 | $72.89 | |
| **Stain-grade pine full-louvered folding door (per section)**<br>*Replace* Materials......63.10     Labor...........15.60<br>*Remove*.......................     Labor ............2.99 | ea | $2.99 | $78.70 | $81.69 | |
| **Paint-grade pine half-louvered folding door (per section)**<br>*Replace* Materials ......51.70     Labor...........15.60<br>*Remove*.......................     Labor ............2.99 | ea | $2.99 | $67.30 | $70.29 | |
| **Stain-grade pine half-louvered folding door (per section)**<br>*Replace* Materials ......59.90     Labor...........15.60<br>*Remove*.......................     Labor ............2.99 | ea | $2.99 | $75.50 | $78.49 | |
| **Red oak folding panel door (per section)**<br>*Replace* Materials ......69.40     Labor...........15.60<br>*Remove*.......................     Labor ............2.99 | ea | $2.99 | $85.00 | $87.99 | |
| **Folding mirrored door (per section)**<br>*Replace* Materials......79.50     Labor...........15.60<br>*Remove*.......................     Labor ............2.99 | ea | $2.99 | $95.10 | $98.09 | |

**USING DOOR ITEMS**

When replacing a door, select the door type, then the jamb type, and add the two together.

Door prices are for the door slab only and include routing and drilling for standard hardware and hinges. Door tear-out is for the door slab only. Use this tear-out price when removing the slab and leaving the jamb and casing intact.

Jamb & casing prices include the cost to pre-hang the door in the jamb and the cost of hinges (but not the door lockset). Tear-out includes removal of the entire door. Use this tear-out price when removing the door, jamb and casing.

standard △      △ full-louver

half-louver △      △ panel

101

| Item Description | Unit | Remove | Replace | Total |
|---|---|---|---|---|
| **FOLDING DOOR ▶** *continued* **Remove folding doors for work, then reinstall (per section)** | ea | — | $5.85 | $5.85 |
|    *Replace* ........................ Labor ............5.85 | | | | |
| **BYPASSING ▶ DOOR** **Hardboard smooth or wood-textured bypassing door (per section)** | ea | $3.64 | $82.20 | $85.84 |
|    *Replace* Materials ......52.40 Labor ..........29.80 | | | | |
|    *Remove* ........................ Labor ............3.64 | | | | |
| **Hardboard wood-textured & embossed bypassing door (per section)** | ea | $3.64 | $88.50 | $92.14 |
|    *Replace* Materials ......58.70 Labor ..........29.80 | | | | |
|    *Remove* ........................ Labor ............3.64 | | | | |
|    ▶ Referred to by the brand name "Colonist" in many areas of the country. | | | | |
| **Mahogany (lauan) or birch veneer bypassing door (per section)** | ea | $3.64 | $86.60 | $90.24 |
|    *Replace* Materials ......56.80 Labor ..........29.80 | | | | |
|    *Remove* ........................ Labor ............3.64 | | | | |
| **Ash or oak veneer bypassing door (per section)** | ea | $3.64 | $89.10 | $92.74 |
|    *Replace* Materials ......59.30 Labor ..........29.80 | | | | |
|    *Remove* ........................ Labor ............3.64 | | | | |
| **Walnut or cherry veneer bypassing door (per section)** | ea | $3.64 | $103.60 | $107.24 |
|    *Replace* Materials ......73.80 Labor ..........29.80 | | | | |
|    *Remove* ........................ Labor ............3.64 | | | | |
| **Paint-grade pine panel bypassing door (per section)** | ea | $3.64 | $121.30 | $124.94 |
|    *Replace* Materials ......91.50 Labor ..........29.80 | | | | |
|    *Remove* ........................ Labor ............3.64 | | | | |
| **Stain-grade pine panel bypassing door (per section)** | ea | $3.64 | $138.80 | $142.44 |
|    *Replace* Materials ....109.00 Labor ..........29.80 | | | | |
|    *Remove* ........................ Labor ............3.64 | | | | |
| **Red oak bypassing panel door (per section)** | ea | $3.64 | $169.80 | $173.44 |
|    *Replace* Materials ....140.00 Labor ..........29.80 | | | | |
|    *Remove* ........................ Labor ............3.64 | | | | |
| **Paint-grade pine full-louvered bypassing door (per section)** | ea | $3.64 | $135.80 | $139.44 |
|    *Replace* Materials ....106.00 Labor ..........29.80 | | | | |
|    *Remove* ........................ Labor ............3.64 | | | | |
| **Stain-grade pine full-louvered bypassing door (per section)** | ea | $3.64 | $153.80 | $157.44 |
|    *Replace* Materials .....124.00 Labor ..........29.80 | | | | |
|    *Remove* ........................ Labor ............3.64 | | | | |
| **Paint-grade pine half-louvered bypassing door (per section)** | ea | $3.64 | $130.80 | $134.44 |
|    *Replace* Materials .....101.00 Labor ..........29.80 | | | | |
|    *Remove* ........................ Labor ............3.64 | | | | |
| **Stain-grade pine half-louvered bypassing door (per section)** | ea | $3.64 | $147.80 | $151.44 |
|    *Replace* Materials .....118.00 Labor ..........29.80 | | | | |
|    *Remove* ........................ Labor ............3.64 | | | | |
| **Mirrored bypassing door (per section)** | ea | $3.64 | $184.80 | $188.44 |
|    *Replace* Materials .....155.00 Labor ..........29.80 | | | | |
|    *Remove* ........................ Labor ............3.64 | | | | |
| **Remove bypassing sliding doors for work, then reinstall (per section)** | ea | — | $8.69 | $8.69 |
|    *Replace* ........................ Labor ............8.69 | | | | |
| **JAMB & CASING ▶ FOR CLOSET DOOR** *Per lf around opening.* **Paint-grade jamb & casing for folding or bypassing door opening** | lf | $.68 | $5.24 | $5.92 |
|    *Replace* Materials ........ .93 Labor ............4.31 | | | | |
|    *Remove* ........................ Labor ............ .68 | | | | |

*Usually used in closets.* **Priced per door section.** *Includes track and hardware. For jamb & casing see below.*

△ standard

△ panel

△ full-louver

△ half-louver

| Item Description | Unit | Remove | Replace | Total |
|---|---|---|---|---|
| **Stain-grade pine jamb & casing for folding or bypassing door opening** | lf | $.68 | $5.34 | $6.02 |
| *Replace* Materials ...... 1.03     Labor ...........4.31 | | | | |
| *Remove* .........................     Labor ............. .68 | | | | |
| **Birch jamb & casing for folding or bypassing door opening** | lf | $.68 | $5.32 | $6.00 |
| *Replace* Materials ...... 1.01     Labor ...........4.31 | | | | |
| *Remove* .........................     Labor ............. .68 | | | | |
| **Mahogany jamb & casing for folding or bypassing door opening** | lf | $.68 | $5.75 | $6.43 |
| *Replace* Materials ........1.44     Labor ...........4.31 | | | | |
| *Remove* .........................     Labor ............. .68 | | | | |
| ► Deduct **$.16** for mahogany veneer jamb & casing. | | | | |
| **Ash or oak jamb & casing for folding or bypassing door opening** | lf | $.68 | $5.87 | $6.55 |
| *Replace* Materials ........1.56     Labor ...........4.31 | | | | |
| *Remove* .........................     Labor ............. .68 | | | | |
| ► Deduct **$.14** for ash or oak veneer jamb & casing. | | | | |
| **Walnut or cherry jamb & casing for folding or bypassing door opening** | lf | $.68 | $6.39 | $7.07 |
| *Replace* Materials ........2.08     Labor ...........4.31 | | | | |
| *Remove* .........................     Labor ............. .68 | | | | |
| ► Deduct **$.11** for walnut or cherry veneer jamb & casing. | | | | |
| **Hardboard smooth or wood-textured interior door** | ea | $5.69 | $79.19 | $84.88 |
| *Replace* Materials ......70.700     Labor ...........8.49 | | | | |
| *Remove* .........................     Labor ...........5.69 | | | | |
| **Hardboard wood-textured and embossed interior door** | ea | $5.69 | $106.89 | $112.58 |
| *Replace* Materials ......98.40     Labor ...........8.49 | | | | |
| *Remove* .........................     Labor ...........5.69 | | | | |
| ► Called "colonist" style in many areas of the country. | | | | |
| **Mahogany or birch veneer interior door** | ea | $5.69 | $86.69 | $92.38 |
| *Replace* Materials ......78.20     Labor ...........8.49 | | | | |
| *Remove* .........................     Labor ...........5.69 | | | | |
| **Ash or oak veneer interior door** | ea | $5.69 | $93.69 | $99.38 |
| *Replace* Materials ......85.20     Labor ...........8.49 | | | | |
| *Remove* .........................     Labor ...........5.69 | | | | |
| **Walnut or cherry veneer interior door** | ea | $5.69 | $119.49 | $125.18 |
| *Replace* Materials .....111.00     Labor ...........8.49 | | | | |
| *Remove* .........................     Labor ...........5.69 | | | | |
| **Mirrored interior door** | ea | $5.69 | $191.49 | $197.18 |
| *Replace* Materials ....183.00     Labor ...........8.49 | | | | |
| *Remove* .........................     Labor ...........5.69 | | | | |
| **Plastic laminate faced interior door** | ea | $5.69 | $292.49 | $298.18 |
| *Replace* Materials ....284.00     Labor ...........8.49 | | | | |
| *Remove* .........................     Labor ...........5.69 | | | | |
| **Add for solid-core, fire-rated interior door** | ea | — | $101.00 | $101.00 |
| *Replace* Materials .....101.00 | | | | |
| ► 1 hour fire rating. | | | | |
| **Paint-grade wood French door** | ea | $5.69 | $191.49 | $197.18 |
| *Replace* Materials ....183.00     Labor ...........8.49 | | | | |
| *Remove* .........................     Labor ...........5.69 | | | | |

**RELATED ITEMS**

◄ **INTERIOR DOOR**
*Hollow-core interior doors. Pre-drilled and routed for hardware and hinges. For jamb & casing see page 104.*

◁ add for fire-rated

◄ **FRENCH DOOR**
*For interior French doors Pre-drilled and routed for hardware and hinges. For jamb & casing see page 104.*

| Item Description | Unit | Remove | Replace | Total |
|---|---|---|---|---|
| **FRENCH DOOR** ▶ *continued* **Stain-grade fir French door** Replace Materials ....221.00    Labor ...........8.49  Remove ......................    Labor ...........5.69 | ea | $5.69 | $229.49 | $235.18 |
| **Metal French door** Replace Materials ....189.00    Labor ...........8.49  Remove ......................    Labor ...........5.69 | ea | $5.69 | $197.49 | $203.18 |
| **Full-lite door with simulated French door grid** Replace Materials ....164.00    Labor ...........8.49  Remove ......................    Labor ...........5.69 | ea | $5.69 | $172.49 | $178.18 |
| add for double-glazed ▷ **Add for double-glazed insulated glass in French door** Replace Materials ......71.30 | ea | — | $71.30 | $71.30 |
| add for fire-rated ▷ **Add for fire-rated glass in French door** Replace Materials ......82.00    ▶ 1 hour fire rating. | ea | — | $82.00 | $82.00 |
| **FULL-LOUVERED** ▶ **DOOR** **Paint-grade full-louvered door** Replace Materials ....154.00    Labor ...........8.49  Remove ......................    Labor ...........5.69 | ea | $5.69 | $162.49 | $168.18 |
| **Stain-grade pine full-louvered door** Replace Materials ....189.00    Labor ...........8.49  Remove ......................    Labor ...........5.69 | ea | $5.69 | $197.49 | $203.18 |
| **HALF-LOUVERED** ▶ **DOOR** **Paint-grade pine half-louvered door** Replace Materials .....139.00    Labor ...........8.49  Remove ......................    Labor ...........5.69 | ea | $5.69 | $147.49 | $153.18 |
| **Stain-grade pine half-louvered door** Replace Materials ....182.00    Labor ...........8.49  Remove ......................    Labor ...........5.69 | ea | $5.69 | $190.49 | $196.18 |
| **REMOVE** ▶ **INTERIOR DOOR & REINSTALL** **Remove door slab for work, then reinstall** Replace ......................    Labor ...........5.96 | ea | — | $5.96 | $5.96 |
| **Remove door, jamb & casing for work, then reinstall** Replace ......................    Labor ..........64.40 | ea | — | $64.40 | $64.40 |
| **Remove double door slabs for work, then reinstall** Replace ......................    Labor ..........11.60 | ea | — | $11.60 | $11.60 |
| **Remove double doors, jamb & casing for work, then reinstall** Replace ......................    Labor.........105.00 | ea | — | $105.00 | $105.00 |
| **JAMB & CASING** ▶ **FOR INTERIOR DOOR** *Per door.* **Paint-grade jamb & casing for interior door** Replace Materials ......16.70    Labor ..........56.50  Remove......................    Labor ..........10.20 | ea | $10.20 | $73.20 | $83.40 |
| **Paint-grade jamb & casing for double interior door** Replace Materials ......31.10    Labor ..........56.50  Remove......................    Labor ..........10.20 | ea | $10.20 | $87.60 | $97.80 |
| **Stain-grade pine jamb & casing for interior door** Replace Materials .......19.10    Labor ..........56.50  Remove......................    Labor ..........10.20 | ea | $10.20 | $75.60 | $85.80 |

| Item Description | Unit | Remove | Replace | Total | RELATED ITEMS |
|---|---|---|---|---|---|
| **Stain-grade pine jamb & casing for double interior door** | ea | $10.20 | $91.40 | $101.60 | Cleaning....................57 |
| *Replace* Materials......34.90    Labor..........56.50 | | | | | Door Hardware..........127 |
| *Remove*........................    Labor..........10.20 | | | | | Finish Carpentry........201 |
| **Birch jamb & casing for interior door** | ea | $10.20 | $77.10 | $87.30 | Painting.....................334 |
| *Replace* Materials......20.60    Labor..........56.50 | | | | | |
| *Remove*........................    Labor..........10.20 | | | | | |
| **Birch jamb & casing for double interior door** | ea | $10.20 | $94.20 | $104.40 | |
| *Replace* Materials......37.70    Labor..........56.50 | | | | | |
| *Remove*........................    Labor..........10.20 | | | | | |
| **Mahogany jamb & casing for interior door** | ea | $10.20 | $81.10 | $91.30 | |
| *Replace* Materials......24.60    Labor..........56.50 | | | | | |
| *Remove*........................    Labor..........10.20 | | | | | |
| ▶ Deduct **$1.60** for mahogany veneer jamb & casing. | | | | | |
| **Mahogany jamb & casing for double interior door** | ea | $10.20 | $104.00 | $114.20 | |
| *Replace* Materials......47.50    Labor..........56.50 | | | | | |
| *Remove*........................    Labor..........10.20 | | | | | |
| ▶ Deduct **$.69** for mahogany veneer jamb & casing. | | | | | |
| **Ash or oak jamb & casing for interior door** | ea | $10.20 | $86.20 | $96.40 | |
| *Replace* Materials......29.70    Labor..........56.50 | | | | | |
| *Remove*........................    Labor..........10.20 | | | | | |
| ▶ Deduct **$2.80** for ash or oak veneer jamb & casing. | | | | | |
| **Ash or oak jamb & casing for double interior door** | ea | $10.20 | $109.50 | $119.70 | |
| *Replace* Materials......53.00    Labor..........56.50 | | | | | |
| *Remove*........................    Labor..........10.20 | | | | | |
| ▶ Deduct **$2.30** for ash or oak veneer jamb & casing. | | | | | |
| **Walnut or cherry jamb & casing for interior door** | ea | $10.20 | $99.40 | $109.60 | |
| *Replace* Materials......42.90    Labor..........56.50 | | | | | |
| *Remove*........................    Labor..........10.20 | | | | | |
| ▶ Deduct **$2.20** for walnut or cherry veneer jamb & casing. | | | | | |
| **Walnut or cherry jamb & casing for double interior door** | ea | $10.20 | $136.00 | $146.20 | |
| *Replace* Materials......79.50    Labor..........56.50 | | | | | |
| *Remove*........................    Labor..........10.20 | | | | | |
| ▶ Deduct **$3.90** for walnut or cherry veneer jamb & casing. | | | | | |
| **Steel jamb & casing for interior door** | ea | $10.20 | $170.50 | $180.70 | ◁ steel jamb & casing |
| *Replace* Materials.....114.00    Labor..........56.50 | | | | | |
| *Remove*........................    Labor..........10.20 | | | | | |
| **Steel jamb & casing for double interior door** | ea | $12.70 | $277.50 | $290.20 | |
| *Replace* Materials....221.00    Labor..........56.50 | | | | | |
| *Remove*........................    Labor..........12.70 | | | | | |
| **Add for jamb & casing installed for pocket door** | ea | — | $26.90 | $26.90 | ◁ add for pocket door |
| *Replace* Materials......14.20    Labor..........12.70 | | | | | |
| ▶ Add to price above when jamb is installed for a pocket door. | | | | | |
| **Add for jamb & casing installed for double pocket door** | ea | — | $58.40 | $58.40 | |
| *Replace* Materials......24.00    Labor..........34.40 | | | | | |
| ▶ Add to price above when jamb is installed for a double pocket door. | | | | | |
| **Rough framing package for pocket door in 2" x 4" wall** | ea | — | $82.60 | $82.60 | ◀ ROUGH FRAMING FOR POCKET DOOR |
| *Replace* Materials......23.30    Labor..........59.30 | | | | | |

*continued on next page*

| Item Description | Unit | Remove | Replace | Total |
|---|---|---|---|---|
| **ROUGH FRAMING** ▶ **FOR POCKET DOOR** *continued* | | | | |
| **Rough framing package for double pocket doors in 2" x 4" wall** | ea | — | $151.40 | $151.40 |
| *Replace* Materials ......37.40    Labor..........114.00 | | | | |
| **Rough framing package for pocket door in 2" x 6" wall** | ea | — | $85.20 | $85.20 |
| *Replace* Materials ......25.20    Labor..........60.00 | | | | |
| **Rough framing package for double pocket doors in 2" x 6" wall** | ea | — | $162.00 | $162.00 |
| *Replace* Materials ......45.00    Labor..........117.00 | | | | |
| **Rough framing package for pocket door in 2" x 8" wall** | ea | — | $87.90 | $87.90 |
| *Replace* Materials ......27.10    Labor..........60.80 | | | | |
| **Rough framing package for double pocket doors in 2" x 8" wall** | ea | — | $168.00 | $168.00 |
| *Replace* Materials ......48.00    Labor..........120.00 | | | | |
| **Rough framing package for antique pocket door** | ea | — | $178.80 | $178.80 |
| *Replace* Materials ......82.00    Labor..........96.80 | | | | |
| **Rough framing package for antique double pocket doors** | ea | — | $348.00 | $348.00 |
| *Replace* Materials ....146.00    Labor........202.00 | | | | |
| **POCKET DOOR** ▶ **TRACK** | | | | |
| **Overhead pocket door track for antique pocket door system** | ea | $19.70 | $99.40 | $119.10 |
| *Replace* Materials ......48.00    Labor..........51.40 | | | | |
| *Remove*........................    Labor..........19.70 | | | | |
| **Overhead pocket door track for antique double pocket door system** | ea | $33.50 | $158.00 | $191.50 |
| *Replace* Materials ......65.60    Labor..........92.40 | | | | |
| *Remove*........................    Labor..........33.50 | | | | |
| **Clean and realign overhead pocket door track** | ea | — | $77.40 | $77.40 |
| *Replace* ........................    Labor ..........77.40 | | | | |
| **Floor track for antique pocket door system** | ea | $19.70 | $100.80 | $120.50 |
| *Replace* Materials ......53.00    Labor..........47.80 | | | | |
| *Remove*........................    Labor..........19.70 | | | | |
| **Floor track for antique double pocket door system** | ea | $33.50 | $158.20 | $191.70 |
| *Replace* Materials ......71.30    Labor ..........86.90 | | | | |
| *Remove*........................    Labor ..........33.50 | | | | |
| **Clean and realign pocket door floor track** | ea | — | $104.00 | $104.00 |
| *Replace* ........................    Labor..........104.00 | | | | |
| **REMOVE** ▶ **POCKET DOOR & REINSTALL** | | | | |
| **Remove pocket door and trim for work, then reinstall** | ea | — | $45.40 | $45.40 |
| *Replace* ........................    Labor..........45.40 | | | | |
| **Remove pocket door, jamb & casing for work, then reinstall** | ea | — | $128.00 | $128.00 |
| *Replace* ........................    Labor..........128.00 | | | | |
| **Remove double pocket doors & trim for work, then reinstall** | ea | — | $62.40 | $62.40 |
| *Replace* ........................    Labor..........62.40 | | | | |
| **Remove double pocket doors, jamb & casing for work, then reinstall** | ea | — | $134.00 | $134.00 |
| *Replace* ........................    Labor..........134.00 | | | | |
| **PANEL DOOR** ▶ | | | | |
| **Paint-grade panel door** | ea | $5.69 | $493.03 | $498.72 |
| *Replace* Materials ....486.00    Labor ..........7.03 | | | | |
| *Remove* ........................    Labor ..........5.69 | | | | |
| ▶ Add **67%** for panel door custom milled to match. | | | | |

**ROUGH FRAMING FOR POCKET DOOR** *continued*

*Includes track, hardware, and side framing kit. Antique systems include framing for walls on each side of the pocket door.*

**POCKET DOOR TRACK**

**REMOVE POCKET DOOR & REINSTALL**

**PANEL DOOR**
continued on next page

| Item Description | Unit | Remove | Replace | Total |
|---|---|---|---|---|
| **Reconditioned painted antique panel door** | ea | $5.69 | $398.03 | $403.72 |
| *Replace* Materials ....391.00    Labor ..........7.03 | | | | |
| *Remove* ......................    Labor ..........5.69 | | | | |
| **Reconditioned grained antique panel door** | ea | $5.69 | $575.03 | $580.72 |
| *Replace* Materials ....568.00    Labor ..........7.03 | | | | |
| *Remove* ......................    Labor ..........5.69 | | | | |

> ► "Graining" is a method of painting wood to make it look like the grain of another wood. This process was used extensively in the 19th century, most often to paint pine to appear like quartersawn oak.

| Item Description | Unit | Remove | Replace | Total |
|---|---|---|---|---|
| **Stain-grade fir panel door** | ea | $5.69 | $651.03 | $656.72 |
| *Replace* Materials ....644.00    Labor ..........7.03 | | | | |
| *Remove* ......................    Labor ..........5.69 | | | | |

► Add **35%** for panel door custom milled to match.

| Item Description | Unit | Remove | Replace | Total |
|---|---|---|---|---|
| **Reconditioned stained fir antique panel door** | ea | $5.69 | $596.03 | $601.72 |
| *Replace* Materials ....589.00    Labor ..........7.03 | | | | |
| *Remove* ......................    Labor ..........5.69 | | | | |
| **Redwood panel door** | ea | $5.69 | $701.03 | $706.72 |
| *Replace* Materials .....694.00    Labor ..........7.03 | | | | |
| *Remove* ......................    Labor ..........5.69 | | | | |

► Add **26%** for panel door custom milled to match.

| Item Description | Unit | Remove | Replace | Total |
|---|---|---|---|---|
| **Reconditioned redwood antique panel door** | ea | $5.69 | $676.03 | $681.72 |
| *Replace* Materials ....669.00    Labor ..........7.03 | | | | |
| *Remove* ......................    Labor ..........5.69 | | | | |
| **Cypress panel door** | ea | $5.69 | $666.03 | $671.72 |
| *Replace* Materials ....659.00    Labor ..........7.03 | | | | |
| *Remove* ......................    Labor ..........5.69 | | | | |

► Add **17%** for panel door custom milled to match.

| Item Description | Unit | Remove | Replace | Total |
|---|---|---|---|---|
| **Reconditioned cypress antique panel door** | ea | $5.69 | $619.03 | $624.72 |
| *Replace* Materials .....612.00    Labor ..........7.03 | | | | |
| *Remove* ......................    Labor ..........5.69 | | | | |
| **Oak panel door** | ea | $5.69 | $594.03 | $599.72 |
| *Replace* Materials ....587.00    Labor ..........7.03 | | | | |
| *Remove* ......................    Labor ..........5.69 | | | | |

► Add **35%** for panel door custom milled to match.

| Item Description | Unit | Remove | Replace | Total |
|---|---|---|---|---|
| **Reconditioned painted oak antique panel door** | ea | $5.69 | $442.03 | $447.72 |
| *Replace* Materials ....435.00    Labor ..........7.03 | | | | |
| *Remove* ......................    Labor ..........5.69 | | | | |
| **Reconditioned stained oak antique panel door** | ea | $5.69 | $512.03 | $517.72 |
| *Replace* Materials ....505.00    Labor ..........7.03 | | | | |
| *Remove* ......................    Labor ..........5.69 | | | | |
| **Mahogany panel door** | ea | $5.69 | $682.03 | $687.72 |
| *Replace* Materials ....675.00    Labor ..........7.03 | | | | |
| *Remove* ......................    Labor ..........5.69 | | | | |

► Add **29%** for panel door custom milled to match.

| Item Description | Unit | Remove | Replace | Total |
|---|---|---|---|---|
| **Reconditioned mahogany antique panel door** | ea | $5.69 | $632.03 | $637.72 |
| *Replace* Materials .....625.00    Labor ..........7.03 | | | | |
| *Remove* ......................    Labor ..........5.69 | | | | |

◄ **PANEL DOOR** *continued*

*6 to 9 panels. Each wood species includes line items for a new door, a reconditioned door, and a door that is custom milled to match a specific pattern. For more see below.*

*For interior jamb & casing see page 104. For exterior jamb and casing see page 116.*

**RECONDITIONED DOOR**

Reconditioned panel doors have been removed from a historical structure and reconditioned by an architectural salvage company.

These doors will have some scratches, dents, patching and may have been stripped of paint.

**CUSTOM-MILLED DOOR**

Custom-milled doors include the additional costs for panel doors that are milled to match an existing door pattern.

For these doors it is necessary to cut custom shaper knives for the panels and custom molder (or shaper) knives for the stiles and rails. Add **60%** if milling two or less doors.

**RELATED ITEMS**

| Item Description | Unit | Remove | Replace | Total |
|---|---|---|---|---|
| **PANEL DOOR ▶** *continued* **Walnut panel door** *Replace* Materials ..1020.00    Labor ............7.03 *Remove* .......................    Labor ............5.69 ▶ Add **17%** for panel door custom milled to match. | ea | $5.69 | $1,027.03 | $1,032.72 |
| **Reconditioned walnut antique panel door** *Replace* Materials ....902.00    Labor ............7.03 *Remove* .......................    Labor ............5.69 | ea | $5.69 | $909.03 | $914.72 |
| **ADDITIONAL ▶ PANEL DOOR COSTS** **Add for panel door with tempered glass lite** *Replace* Materials ....240.00 | ea | — | $240.00 | $240.00 |
| **Add for panel door with beveled or edged glass lite** *Replace* Materials ....449.00 | ea | — | $449.00 | $449.00 |
| **Add for panel door with leaded or colored glass lite** *Replace* Materials ....520.00 | ea | — | $520.00 | $520.00 |
| **Add for panel door with round or elliptical top** *Replace* Materials ....587.00    Labor .........180.00 | ea | — | $767.00 | $767.00 |
| **REMOVE & ▶ REINSTALL PANEL DOOR** **Remove panel door slab only for work, then reinstall** *Replace* .......................    Labor ............6.00 | ea | — | $6.00 | $6.00 |
| **Remove panel door, jamb, & casing for work, then reinstall** *Replace* .......................    Labor ............64.40 | ea | — | $64.40 | $64.40 |
| **PANEL DOOR ▶ REPAIR** **Replace antique panel door panel (not including custom knife charges)** *Replace* Materials ......98.00    Labor .........108.00 | ea | — | $206.00 | $206.00 |
| **Replace antique panel door stile (not including custom knife charges)** *Replace* Materials ......72.00    Labor ...........98.40 | ea | — | $170.40 | $170.40 |
| **Minimum charge to repair antique panel door (no custom milling)** *Replace* Materials .....114.00    Labor ...........98.40 | ea | — | $212.40 | $212.40 |
| **Minimum charge to repair antique panel door (custom milling)** *Replace* Materials ....391.00    Labor .........139.00 | ea | — | $530.00 | $530.00 |
| **Custom work shaper or molder knife charge** *Replace* Materials ....309.00 | ea | — | $309.00 | $309.00 |
| **Custom work shaper or molder setup charge** *Replace* Materials .....145.00 | ea | — | $145.00 | $145.00 |
| **Minimum custom work shaper or molder charge** *Replace* Materials ....573.00 | ea | — | $573.00 | $573.00 |
| **Repair cracks & dry rot in antique door with epoxy, tighten stiles** *Replace* Materials .....141.00    Labor .........177.00 | ea | — | $318.00 | $318.00 |
| **Repair cracks & dry rot in antique door jamb with epoxy** *Replace* Materials ......82.00    Labor .........134.00 | ea | — | $216.00 | $216.00 |
| **Repair cracks & dry rot in antique door casing with epoxy** *Replace* Materials ......63.10    Labor .........134.00 | ea | — | $197.10 | $197.10 |
| **Remove antique door casing, re-plumb door, & reinstall casing** *Replace* .......................    Labor ..........117.00 | ea | — | $117.00 | $117.00 |

**BATTEN DOORS**
*(on facing page)*

Batten doors are built from vertical boards (usually tongue and groove) held in place by horizontal battens and diagonal braces.

**STANDARD GRADE** Boards held in place by horizontal battens that are braced diagonally. (Sometimes called ledged-and-braced doors.)

**HIGH GRADE** Boards held in place by a stile frame and a single horizontal batten. Frame is joined with mortise and tenon joints. Also includes diagonal braces. (Sometimes called framed ledged-and-braced doors.)

| Item Description | Unit | Remove | Replace | Total |
|---|---|---|---|---|
| **Add 38% for antique panel door transom** ▶ Includes hinges, jamb, casing and brass opening hardware. For newer style transoms see page 118. | | | | |
| **Paint-grade batten door, standard grade** *Replace* Materials....366.00   Labor..........7.03   *Remove*   Labor..........5.69 | ea | $5.69 | $373.03 | $378.72 |
| **Paint-grade batten door, high grade** *Replace* Materials....530.00   Labor..........7.03   *Remove*   Labor..........5.69 | ea | $5.69 | $537.03 | $542.72 |
| **Stain-grade batten door, standard grade** *Replace* Materials....669.00   Labor..........7.03   *Remove*   Labor..........5.69 | ea | $5.69 | $676.03 | $681.72 |
| **Stain-grade batten door, high grade** *Replace* Materials....934.00   Labor..........7.03   *Remove*   Labor..........5.69 | ea | $5.69 | $941.03 | $946.72 |
| **Metal storm/screen door, economy grade** *Replace* Materials....124.00   Labor..........47.80   *Remove*   Labor..........5.95 | ea | $5.95 | $171.80 | $177.75 |
| **Metal storm/screen door, standard grade** *Replace* Materials....182.00   Labor..........47.80   *Remove*   Labor..........5.95 | ea | $5.95 | $229.80 | $235.75 |
| **Metal storm/screen door, high grade** *Replace* Materials....264.00   Labor..........47.80   *Remove*   Labor..........5.95 | ea | $5.95 | $311.80 | $317.75 |
| **Metal storm/screen door, deluxe grade** *Replace* Materials....334.00   Labor..........47.80   *Remove*   Labor..........5.95 | ea | $5.95 | $381.80 | $387.75 |
| **Wood storm/screen door, economy grade** *Replace* Materials....140.00   Labor..........47.80   *Remove*   Labor..........5.95 | ea | $5.95 | $187.80 | $193.75 |
| **Wood storm/screen door, standard grade** *Replace* Materials....227.00   Labor..........47.80   *Remove*   Labor..........5.95 | ea | $5.95 | $274.80 | $280.75 |
| **Wood storm/screen door, high grade** *Replace* Materials....270.00   Labor..........47.80   *Remove*   Labor..........5.95 | ea | $5.95 | $317.80 | $323.75 |
| **Wood storm/screen door, deluxe grade** *Replace* Materials....334.00   Labor..........47.80   *Remove*   Labor..........5.95 | ea | $5.95 | $381.80 | $387.75 |
| **Victorian style wood storm/screen door, standard grade** *Replace* Materials....366.00   Labor..........47.80   *Remove*   Labor..........5.95 | ea | $5.95 | $413.80 | $419.75 |
| **Victorian style wood storm/screen door, high grade** *Replace* Materials....435.00   Labor..........47.80   *Remove*   Labor..........5.95 | ea | $5.95 | $482.80 | $488.75 |
| **Victorian style wood storm/screen door, deluxe grade** *Replace* Materials....612.00   Labor..........47.80   *Remove*   Labor..........5.95 | ea | $5.95 | $659.80 | $665.75 |

◀ **BATTEN DOOR** For interior jamb & casing see page 104. For exterior jamb and casing see page 116. See "Batten Doors" on facing page.

△ standard   △ high

◀ **STORM DOOR**

**METAL . . .**

△ economy   △ standard

△ high   △ deluxe

**VICTORIAN WOOD . . .**

△ standard   △ standard

△ high   △ deluxe

| Item Description | Unit | Remove | Replace | Total |
|---|---|---|---|---|
| **STORM DOOR ▶**<br>*continued* | **Remove storm/screen door for work, then reinstall**<br>*Replace* ........................ Labor..........67.20 | ea | — | $67.20 | $67.20 |
| **EXTERIOR ▶**<br>**FRENCH DOOR**<br>*For exterior jamb &*<br>*casing see page 116.* | **Exterior paint-grade wood French door**<br>*Replace* Materials....366.00    Labor ............8.37<br>*Remove* ........................    Labor ............7.41 | ea | $7.41 | $374.37 | $381.78 |
| | **Exterior stain-grade fir French door**<br>*Replace* Materials.....416.00    Labor ............8.37<br>*Remove* ........................    Labor ............7.41 | ea | $7.41 | $424.37 | $431.78 |
| | **Exterior metal French door**<br>*Replace* Materials....406.00    Labor ............8.37<br>*Remove* ........................    Labor ............7.41 | ea | $7.41 | $414.37 | $421.78 |
| | **Exterior full-lite insulated door with simulated French door grid**<br>*Replace* Materials....348.00    Labor ............8.37<br>*Remove* ........................    Labor ............7.41 | ea | $7.41 | $356.37 | $363.78 |
| **EXTERIOR ▶**<br>**VENEER DOOR**<br>*For exterior jamb &*<br>*casing see page 116.* | **Mahogany (lauan) or birch veneer exterior door**<br>*Replace* Materials.....174.00    Labor ............8.37<br>*Remove* ........................    Labor ............7.41 | ea | $7.41 | $182.37 | $189.78 |
| | **Ash or red oak veneer exterior door**<br>*Replace* Materials ....189.00    Labor ............8.37<br>*Remove* ........................    Labor ............7.41 | ea | $7.41 | $197.37 | $204.78 |
| | **Walnut or cherry veneer exterior door**<br>*Replace* Materials....208.00    Labor ............8.37<br>*Remove* ........................    Labor ............7.41 | ea | $7.41 | $216.37 | $223.78 |
| | **Insulated steel exterior door**<br>*Replace* Materials.....174.00    Labor ............8.37<br>*Remove* ........................    Labor ............7.41 | ea | $7.41 | $182.37 | $189.78 |
| **ADDITIONAL ▶**<br>**EXTERIOR DOOR**<br>**COSTS** | **Add for full-lite in exterior door**<br>*Replace* Materials....233.00 | ea | — | $233.00 | $233.00 |
| | **Add for leaded or colored glass full-lite in exterior door**<br>*Replace* Materials ....520.00 | ea | — | $520.00 | $520.00 |
| | **Add for half-lite in exterior door**<br>*Replace* Materials.....101.00 | ea | — | $101.00 | $101.00 |
| | **Add for leaded or colored glass half-lite in exterior wood door**<br>*Replace* Materials....290.00 | ea | — | $290.00 | $290.00 |
| | **Add for 1' by 1' lite in exterior door**<br>*Replace* Materials......30.90 | ea | — | $30.90 | $30.90 |
| **DUTCH DOOR ▶**<br>*See jambs and casing*<br>*for Dutch doors on*<br>*pages 116 and 117.* | **Bottom Dutch door section, flush**<br>*Replace* Materials.....172.00    Labor...........12.80<br>*Remove* ........................    Labor...........10.20 | ea | $10.20 | $184.80 | $195.00 |
| **BOTTOM . . .** | **Bottom Dutch door section, raised panel**<br>*Replace* Materials ....257.00    Labor...........12.80<br>*Remove* ........................    Labor...........10.20 | ea | $10.20 | $269.80 | $280.00 |
| △ flush    raised panel △ | **Bottom Dutch door section, cross buck**<br>*Replace* Materials....333.00    Labor...........12.80<br>*Remove* ........................    Labor...........10.20 | ea | $10.20 | $345.80 | $356.00 |

| Item Description | Unit | Remove | Replace | Total |
|---|---|---|---|---|
| **Add for shelf on bottom Dutch door section**<br>*Replace* Materials ......55.50 | ea | — | $55.50 | $55.50 |
| **Top Dutch door section with full lite**<br>*Replace* Materials ....227.00  Labor ..........12.80<br>*Remove* ....................  Labor ..........10.20 | ea | $10.20 | $239.80 | $250.00 |
| **Top Dutch door section with four lites**<br>*Replace* Materials ....273.00  Labor ..........12.80<br>*Remove* ....................  Labor ..........10.20 | ea | $10.20 | $285.80 | $296.00 |
| **Top Dutch door section with six lites**<br>*Replace* Materials ....290.00  Labor ..........12.80<br>*Remove* ....................  Labor ..........10.20 | ea | $10.20 | $302.80 | $313.00 |
| **Top Dutch door section with nine lites**<br>*Replace* Materials .....314.00  Labor ..........12.80<br>*Remove* ....................  Labor ..........10.20 | ea | $10.20 | $326.80 | $337.00 |
| **Remove exterior Dutch door, jamb, & casing for work, then reinstall**<br>*Replace* ....................  Labor ......108.00 | ea | — | $108.00 | $108.00 |
| **Remove exterior Dutch door slabs for work, then reinstall**<br>*Replace* ....................  Labor ..........15.60 | ea | — | $15.60 | $15.60 |
| **Steel entry door, standard grade**<br>*Replace* Materials ....208.00  Labor ............8.37<br>*Remove* ....................  Labor ............7.41 | ea | $7.41 | $216.37 | $223.78 |
| **Steel entry door, high grade**<br>*Replace* Materials ....279.00  Labor ............8.37<br>*Remove* ....................  Labor ............7.41 | ea | $7.41 | $287.37 | $294.78 |
| **Steel entry door side-lite, standard grade**<br>*Replace* Materials .....107.00  Labor ..........45.00<br>*Remove* ....................  Labor ..........13.30 | ea | $13.30 | $152.00 | $165.30 |
| **Steel entry door side-lite, high grade**<br>*Replace* Materials .....139.00  Labor ..........45.00<br>*Remove* ....................  Labor ..........13.30 | ea | $13.30 | $184.00 | $197.30 |
| **Paint-grade wood entry door, standard grade**<br>*Replace* Materials ....225.00  Labor ............8.37<br>*Remove* ....................  Labor ............7.41 | ea | $7.41 | $233.37 | $240.78 |
| **Paint-grade wood entry door, high grade**<br>*Replace* Materials ....321.00  Labor ............8.37<br>*Remove* ....................  Labor ............7.41 | ea | $7.41 | $329.37 | $336.78 |
| **Paint-grade wood entry door, deluxe grade**<br>*Replace* Materials ....433.00  Labor ............8.37<br>*Remove* ....................  Labor ............7.41 | ea | $7.41 | $441.37 | $448.78 |
| **Paint-grade wood entry door, custom grade**<br>*Replace* Materials ....625.00  Labor ............8.37<br>*Remove* ....................  Labor ............7.41 | ea | $7.41 | $633.37 | $640.78 |
| **Paint-grade wood entry door, custom deluxe grade**<br>*Replace* Materials ....726.00  Labor ............8.37<br>*Remove* ....................  Labor ............7.41 | ea | $7.41 | $734.37 | $741.78 |

BOTTOM ... △ crossbuck  △ shelf

TOP ... △ full lite  △ four lite  △ six lite  △ nine lite

◄ **STEEL ENTRY DOOR**
For exterior jamb & casing see page 116. Standard grade is flush face and high grade is embossed.

◄ **STEEL ENTRY DOOR SIDE-LITE**
Includes jamb & casing.

◄ **PAINT-GRADE WOOD ENTRY DOOR**
For exterior jamb & casing see page 116. Also see quality indicators on page 112.

**ENTRY DOORS**
All entry doors are solid wood with occasional veneered wood components in the lower grades.

Entry door prices do not include jamb & casing. See page 116 for exterior jambs.

See quality indicators on page 112.

| Item Description | Unit | Remove | Replace | Total |
|---|---|---|---|---|
| **Paint-grade wood entry door side-lite, standard grade** | ea | $13.30 | $198.00 | $211.30 |
| *Replace* Materials......153.00    Labor...........45.00 | | | | |
| *Remove* .......................    Labor............13.30 | | | | |
| **Paint-grade wood entry door side-lite, high grade** | ea | $13.30 | $254.00 | $267.30 |
| *Replace* Materials....209.00    Labor...........45.00 | | | | |
| *Remove* .......................    Labor............13.30 | | | | |
| **Paint-grade wood entry door side-lite, deluxe grade** | ea | $13.30 | $349.00 | $362.30 |
| *Replace* Materials....304.00    Labor...........45.00 | | | | |
| *Remove* .......................    Labor............13.30 | | | | |
| **Paint-grade wood entry door side-lite, custom grade** | ea | $13.30 | $465.00 | $478.30 |
| *Replace* Materials ....420.00    Labor...........45.00 | | | | |
| *Remove* .......................    Labor............13.30 | | | | |
| **Paint-grade wood entry door side-lite, custom deluxe grade** | ea | $13.30 | $552.00 | $565.30 |
| *Replace* Materials ....507.00    Labor...........45.00 | | | | |
| *Remove* .......................    Labor............13.30 | | | | |
| **Stain-grade fir entry door, standard grade** | ea | $7.41 | $506.37 | $513.78 |
| *Replace* Materials ....498.00    Labor ...........8.37 | | | | |
| *Remove* .......................    Labor ............7.41 | | | | |
| **Stain-grade fir entry door, high grade** | ea | $7.41 | $614.37 | $621.78 |
| *Replace* Materials ....606.00    Labor ...........8.37 | | | | |
| *Remove* .......................    Labor ............7.41 | | | | |
| **Stain-grade fir entry door, deluxe grade** | ea | $7.41 | $784.37 | $791.78 |
| *Replace* Materials ....776.00    Labor ...........8.37 | | | | |
| *Remove* .......................    Labor ............7.41 | | | | |
| **Stain-grade fir entry door, custom grade** | ea | $7.41 | $1,148.37 | $1,155.78 |
| *Replace* Materials ...1140.00    Labor ...........8.37 | | | | |
| *Remove* .......................    Labor ............7.41 | | | | |
| **Stain-grade fir entry door, custom deluxe grade** | ea | $7.41 | $1,518.37 | $1,525.78 |
| *Replace* Materials ...1510.00    Labor ...........8.37 | | | | |
| *Remove* .......................    Labor ............7.41 | | | | |
| **Stain-grade fir entry door side-lite, standard grade** | ea | $13.30 | $368.00 | $381.30 |
| *Replace* Materials ....323.00    Labor...........45.00 | | | | |
| *Remove* .......................    Labor............13.30 | | | | |
| **Stain-grade fir entry door side-lite, high grade** | ea | $13.30 | $461.00 | $474.30 |
| *Replace* Materials......416.00    Labor...........45.00 | | | | |
| *Remove* .......................    Labor............13.30 | | | | |
| **Stain-grade fir entry door side-lite, deluxe grade** | ea | $13.30 | $562.00 | $575.30 |
| *Replace* Materials......517.00    Labor...........45.00 | | | | |
| *Remove* .......................    Labor............13.30 | | | | |
| **Stain-grade fir entry door side-lite, custom grade** | ea | $13.30 | $836.00 | $849.30 |
| *Replace* Materials ....791.00    Labor...........45.00 | | | | |
| *Remove* .......................    Labor............13.30 | | | | |
| **Stain-grade fir entry door side-lite, custom deluxe grade** | ea | $13.30 | $1,105.00 | $1,118.30 |
| *Replace* Materials ..1060.00    Labor...........45.00 | | | | |
| *Remove* .......................    Labor............13.30 | | | | |

**PAINT-GRADE ►**
**WOOD ENTRY**
**DOOR SIDE-LITE**
*Includes jamb & casing.*
*Also see quality grades*
*below.*

**FIR ENTRY DOOR ►**
*For exterior jamb &*
*casing see page 116. Also*
*see quality grades below.*

**ENTRY DOOR GRADES**

**STANDARD GRADE**
Multiple panel doors
(nine and more) with
some embossed compo-
nents. May have lites in
place of panels.

**HIGH GRADE** Same as
Standard grade with
some embossed and
carved components. Also
may have carved on-lays.

**FIR ENTRY ►**
**DOOR SIDE-LITE**
*Includes jamb & casing.*
*Also see quality grades*
*above and below.*

**ENTRY DOOR GRADES**

**DELUXE GRADE** Door
components have moder-
ate carvings. May have
exotic wood compo-
nents.

**CUSTOM GRADE** Door
components have exten-
sive carvings. May have
exotic wood compo-
nents, leaded glass or
beveled glass.

**CUSTOM DELUXE GRADE**
Same as Custom grade
with oval or elliptical-top
windows.

| Item Description | Unit | Remove | Replace | Total |
|---|---|---|---|---|
| **Mahogany entry door, standard grade** | ea | $7.41 | $439.30 | $446.71 |
| *Replace* Materials....423.00    Labor..........16.30 | | | | |
| *Remove* .....................    Labor...........7.41 | | | | |
| **Mahogany entry door, high grade** | ea | $7.41 | $660.30 | $667.71 |
| *Replace* Materials....644.00    Labor..........16.30 | | | | |
| *Remove* .....................    Labor...........7.41 | | | | |
| **Mahogany entry door, deluxe grade** | ea | $7.41 | $1,016.30 | $1,023.71 |
| *Replace* Materials...1000.00    Labor..........16.30 | | | | |
| *Remove* .....................    Labor...........7.41 | | | | |
| **Mahogany entry door, custom grade** | ea | $7.41 | $1,346.30 | $1,353.71 |
| *Replace* Materials...1330.00    Labor..........16.30 | | | | |
| *Remove* .....................    Labor...........7.41 | | | | |
| **Mahogany entry door, custom deluxe grade** | ea | $7.41 | $1,696.30 | $1,703.71 |
| *Replace* Materials...1680.00    Labor..........16.30 | | | | |
| *Remove* .....................    Labor...........7.41 | | | | |
| **Mahogany entry door side-lite, standard grade** | ea | $13.30 | $337.00 | $350.30 |
| *Replace* Materials....292.00    Labor..........45.00 | | | | |
| *Remove* .....................    Labor..........13.30 | | | | |
| **Mahogany entry door side-lite, high grade** | ea | $13.30 | $484.00 | $497.30 |
| *Replace* Materials....439.00    Labor..........45.00 | | | | |
| *Remove* .....................    Labor..........13.30 | | | | |
| **Mahogany entry door side-lite, deluxe grade** | ea | $13.30 | $742.00 | $755.30 |
| *Replace* Materials....697.00    Labor..........45.00 | | | | |
| *Remove* .....................    Labor..........13.30 | | | | |
| **Mahogany entry door side-lite, custom grade** | ea | $13.30 | $975.00 | $988.30 |
| *Replace* Materials....930.00    Labor..........45.00 | | | | |
| *Remove* .....................    Labor..........13.30 | | | | |
| **Mahogany entry door side-lite, custom deluxe grade** | ea | $13.30 | $1,245.00 | $1,258.30 |
| *Replace* Materials..1200.00    Labor..........45.00 | | | | |
| *Remove* .....................    Labor..........13.30 | | | | |
| **Ash or oak entry door, standard grade** | ea | $7.41 | $420.30 | $427.71 |
| *Replace* Materials....404.00    Labor..........16.30 | | | | |
| *Remove* .....................    Labor...........7.41 | | | | |
| **Ash or oak entry door, high grade** | ea | $7.41 | $641.30 | $648.71 |
| *Replace* Materials....625.00    Labor..........16.30 | | | | |
| *Remove* .....................    Labor...........7.41 | | | | |
| **Ash or oak entry door, deluxe grade** | ea | $7.41 | $849.30 | $856.71 |
| *Replace* Materials....833.00    Labor..........16.30 | | | | |
| *Remove* .....................    Labor...........7.41 | | | | |
| **Ash or oak entry door, custom grade** | ea | $7.41 | $1,416.30 | $1,423.71 |
| *Replace* Materials..1400.00    Labor..........16.30 | | | | |
| *Remove* .....................    Labor...........7.41 | | | | |
| **Ash or red entry door, custom deluxe grade** | ea | $7.41 | $1,786.30 | $1,793.71 |
| *Replace* Materials...1770.00    Labor..........16.30 | | | | |
| *Remove* .....................    Labor...........7.41 | | | | |

◄ **MAHOGANY ENTRY DOOR**
For exterior jamb & casing see page 116. Also see quality indicators on facing page.

**WOOD EMBOSSING**

Wood is often embossed to appear like it has been carved. Embossing stamps a pattern onto the wood.

Embossing is far less expensive than carving and can only be used for relatively shallow patterns.

◄ **MAHOGANY DOOR SIDE-LITE**
Includes jamb & casing. Also see quality indicators on facing page.

**WOOD ONLAYS**

Wood onlays are mass-produced carved wood components that are nailed and glued on doors to give a hand-carved look.

◄ **ASH OR OAK ENTRY DOOR**
See exterior jamb & casing on page 116. Also see quality indicators on facing page.

| Item Description | Unit | Remove | Replace | Total |
|---|---|---|---|---|
| **ASH OR OAK ▶ ENTRY DOOR SIDE-LITE** *Includes jamb & casing. Also see quality indicators on page 112.* | | | | |
| **Ash or oak entry door side-lite, standard grade** | ea | $13.30 | $318.00 | $331.30 |
| *Replace* Materials ....273.00     Labor..........45.00 | | | | |
| *Remove* .....................     Labor..........13.30 | | | | |
| **Ash or oak entry door side-lite, high grade** | ea | $13.30 | $487.00 | $500.30 |
| *Replace* Materials ....442.00     Labor..........45.00 | | | | |
| *Remove* .....................     Labor..........13.30 | | | | |
| **Ash or oak entry door side-lite, deluxe grade** | ea | $13.30 | $590.00 | $603.30 |
| *Replace* Materials ....545.00     Labor..........45.00 | | | | |
| *Remove* .....................     Labor..........13.30 | | | | |
| **Ash or oak entry door side-lite, custom grade** | ea | $13.30 | $1,042.00 | $1,055.30 |
| *Replace* Materials ....997.00     Labor..........45.00 | | | | |
| *Remove* .....................     Labor..........13.30 | | | | |
| **Ash or oak entry door side-lite, custom deluxe grade** | ea | $13.30 | $1,295.00 | $1,308.30 |
| *Replace* Materials ..1250.00     Labor..........45.00 | | | | |
| *Remove* .....................     Labor..........13.30 | | | | |
| **REDWOOD ▶ ENTRY DOOR** *For exterior jamb & casing see page 116. Also see quality indicators on page 112.* | | | | |
| **Redwood entry door, standard grade** | ea | $7.41 | $533.30 | $540.71 |
| *Replace* Materials .....517.00     Labor..........16.30 | | | | |
| *Remove* .....................     Labor ...........7.41 | | | | |
| **Redwood entry door, high grade** | ea | $7.41 | $862.30 | $869.71 |
| *Replace* Materials ....846.00     Labor..........16.30 | | | | |
| *Remove* .....................     Labor ...........7.41 | | | | |
| **Redwood entry door, deluxe grade** | ea | $7.41 | $1,086.30 | $1,093.71 |
| *Replace* Materials ...1070.00     Labor..........16.30 | | | | |
| *Remove* .....................     Labor ...........7.41 | | | | |
| **Redwood entry door, custom grade** | ea | $7.41 | $1,476.30 | $1,483.71 |
| *Replace* Materials ...1460.00     Labor..........16.30 | | | | |
| *Remove* .....................     Labor ...........7.41 | | | | |
| **Redwood entry door, custom deluxe grade** | ea | $7.41 | $1,686.30 | $1,693.71 |
| *Replace* Materials ...1670.00     Labor..........16.30 | | | | |
| *Remove* .....................     Labor ...........7.41 | | | | |
| **REDWOOD ▶ ENTRY DOOR SIDE-LITE** *Includes jamb & casing. Also see quality indicators on page 112.* | | | | |
| **Redwood entry door side-lite, standard grade** | ea | $13.30 | $386.00 | $399.30 |
| *Replace* Materials ....341.00     Labor..........45.00 | | | | |
| *Remove* .....................     Labor..........13.30 | | | | |
| **Redwood entry door side-lite, high grade** | ea | $13.30 | $632.00 | $645.30 |
| *Replace* Materials ....587.00     Labor..........45.00 | | | | |
| *Remove* .....................     Labor..........13.30 | | | | |
| **Redwood entry door side-lite, deluxe grade** | ea | $13.30 | $803.00 | $816.30 |
| *Replace* Materials ....758.00     Labor..........45.00 | | | | |
| *Remove* .....................     Labor..........13.30 | | | | |
| **Redwood entry door side-lite, custom grade** | ea | $13.30 | $1,075.00 | $1,088.30 |
| *Replace* Materials ..1030.00     Labor..........45.00 | | | | |
| *Remove* .....................     Labor..........13.30 | | | | |
| **Redwood entry door side-lite, custom deluxe grade** | ea | $13.30 | $1,235.00 | $1,248.30 |
| *Replace* Materials ..1190.00     Labor..........45.00 | | | | |
| *Remove* .....................     Labor..........13.30 | | | | |

| Item Description | Unit | Remove | Replace | Total | |
|---|---|---|---|---|---|
| **Cypress entry door, standard grade**<br>*Replace* Materials ....472.00     Labor...........16.30<br>*Remove* ......................     Labor ...........7.41 | ea | $7.41 | $488.30 | $495.71 | ◄ **CYPRESS ENTRY DOOR** *For exterior jamb & casing see page 116. Also see quality indicators on page 112.* |
| **Cypress entry door, high grade**<br>*Replace* Materials ....631.00     Labor...........16.30<br>*Remove* ......................     Labor ...........7.41 | ea | $7.41 | $7.41 | $654.71 | |
| **Cypress entry door, deluxe grade**<br>*Replace* Materials ...799.00     Labor...........16.30<br>*Remove* ......................     Labor ...........7.41 | ea | $7.41 | $815.30 | $822.71 | |
| **Cypress entry door, custom grade**<br>*Replace* Materials ...1150.00     Labor...........16.30<br>*Remove* ......................     Labor ...........7.41 | ea | $7.41 | $1,166.30 | $1,173.71 | |
| **Cypress entry door, custom deluxe grade**<br>*Replace* Materials ..1500.00     Labor...........16.30<br>*Remove* ......................     Labor ...........7.41 | ea | $7.41 | $1,516.30 | $1,523.71 | |
| **Cypress entry door side-lite, standard grade**<br>*Replace* Materials ....322.00     Labor...........45.00<br>*Remove* ......................     Labor...........13.30 | ea | $13.30 | $367.00 | $380.30 | ◄ **CYPRESS DOOR SIDE-LITE** *Includes jamb & casing. Also see quality indicators on page 112.* |
| **Cypress entry door side-lite, high grade**<br>*Replace* Materials ....432.00     Labor...........45.00<br>*Remove* ......................     Labor...........13.30 | ea | $13.30 | $477.00 | $490.30 | |
| **Cypress entry door side-lite, deluxe grade**<br>*Replace* Materials ....557.00     Labor...........45.00<br>*Remove* ......................     Labor...........13.30 | ea | $13.30 | $602.00 | $615.30 | |
| **Cypress entry door side-lite, custom grade**<br>*Replace* Materials.....814.00     Labor...........45.00<br>*Remove* ......................     Labor...........13.30 | ea | $13.30 | $859.00 | $872.30 | |
| **Cypress entry door side-lite, custom deluxe grade**<br>*Replace* Materials ..1060.00     Labor...........45.00<br>*Remove* ......................     Labor...........13.30 | ea | $13.30 | $1,105.00 | $1,118.30 | |
| **Walnut or cherry entry door, standard grade**<br>*Replace* Materials ....663.00     Labor...........16.30<br>*Remove* ......................     Labor ...........7.41 | ea | $7.41 | $679.30 | $686.71 | ◄ **WALNUT OR CHERRY ENTRY DOOR** *For exterior jamb & casing see page 116. Also see quality indicators on page 112.* |
| **Walnut or cherry entry door, high grade**<br>*Replace* Materials ....997.00     Labor...........16.30<br>*Remove* ......................     Labor ...........7.41 | ea | $7.41 | $1,013.30 | $1,020.71 | |
| **Walnut or cherry entry door, deluxe grade**<br>*Replace* Materials ..1250.00     Labor...........16.30<br>*Remove* ......................     Labor ...........7.41 | ea | $7.41 | $1,266.30 | $1,273.71 | |
| **Walnut or cherry entry door, custom grade**<br>*Replace* Materials ..1860.00     Labor...........16.30<br>*Remove* ......................     Labor ...........7.41 | ea | $7.41 | $1,876.30 | $1,883.71 | |
| **Walnut or cherry entry door, custom deluxe grade**<br>*Replace* Materials ..2410.00     Labor...........16.30<br>*Remove* ......................     Labor ...........7.41 | ea | $7.41 | $2,426.30 | $2,433.71 | |

**RELATED ITEMS**

| Item Description | Unit | Remove | Replace | Total |
|---|---|---|---|---|
| **WALNUT OR ▶ CHERRY ENTRY DOOR SIDE-LITE** *Includes jamb & casing. Also see quality indicators on page 112.* | | | | |
| **Walnut or cherry entry door side-lite, standard grade** *Replace* Materials....430.00     Labor..........45.00 *Remove* .................     Labor..........13.30 | ea | $13.30 | $475.00 | $488.30 |
| **Walnut or cherry entry door side-lite, high grade** *Replace* Materials....680.00     Labor..........45.00 *Remove* .................     Labor..........13.30 | ea | $13.30 | $725.00 | $738.30 |
| **Walnut or cherry entry door side-lite, deluxe grade** *Replace* Materials....868.00     Labor..........45.00 *Remove* .................     Labor..........13.30 | ea | $13.30 | $913.00 | $926.30 |
| **Walnut or cherry entry door side-lite, custom grade** *Replace* Materials...1330.00     Labor..........45.00 *Remove* .................     Labor..........13.30 | ea | $13.30 | $1,375.00 | $1,388.30 |
| **Walnut or cherry entry door side-lite, custom deluxe grade** *Replace* Materials...1730.00     Labor..........45.00 *Remove* .................     Labor..........13.30 | ea | $13.30 | $1,775.00 | $1,788.30 |
| **REMOVE ▶ EXTERIOR DOOR & REINSTALL** | | | | |
| **Remove exterior door, jamb, & casing for work, then reinstall** *Replace* .................     Labor..........86.90 | ea | — | $86.90 | $86.90 |
| **Remove exterior door slab for work, then reinstall** *Replace* .................     Labor..........11.50 | ea | — | $11.50 | $11.50 |
| **Remove exterior double door, jamb, & casing for work, then reinstall** *Replace* .................     Labor..........123.00 | ea | — | $123.00 | $123.00 |
| **Remove exterior double door slab for work, then reinstall** *Replace* .................     Labor..........14.50 | ea | — | $14.50 | $14.50 |
| **EXTERIOR DOOR ▶ JAMB & CASING** **Paint-grade jamb & casing for exterior door** *Replace* Materials......42.90     Labor..........69.10 *Remove* .................     Labor..........13.00 | ea | $13.00 | $112.00 | $125.00 |
| **Paint-grade jamb & casing for double exterior door** *Replace* Materials......77.00     Labor..........123.00 *Remove* .................     Labor..........13.00 | ea | $13.00 | $200.00 | $213.00 |
| **Stain-grade pine jamb & casing for exterior door** *Replace* Materials......50.50     Labor..........69.10 *Remove* .................     Labor..........13.00 | ea | $13.00 | $119.60 | $132.60 |
| **Stain-grade pine jamb & casing for double exterior door** *Replace* Materials......92.10     Labor..........123.00 *Remove* .................     Labor..........13.00 | ea | $13.00 | $215.10 | $228.10 |
| **Birch jamb & casing for exterior door** *Replace* Materials......48.00     Labor..........69.10 *Remove* .................     Labor..........13.00 | ea | $13.00 | $117.10 | $130.10 |
| **Birch jamb & casing for double exterior door** *Replace* Materials......85.20     Labor..........123.00 *Remove* .................     Labor..........13.00 | ea | $13.00 | $208.20 | $221.20 |
| **Mahogany jamb & casing for exterior door** *Replace* Materials......56.80     Labor..........69.10 *Remove* .................     Labor..........13.00 ▶ Deduct **$5.30** for mahogany veneer jamb and casing. | ea | $13.00 | $125.90 | $138.90 |

| Item Description | Unit | Remove | Replace | Total |
|---|---|---|---|---|
| **Mahogany jamb & casing for double exterior door**<br>*Replace* Materials ....102.00  Labor.........123.00<br>*Remove* ..................... Labor...........13.00<br>▶ Deduct **$7.90** for mahogany veneer jamb and casing. | ea | $13.00 | $225.00 | $238.00 |
| **Ash or oak jamb & casing for exterior door**<br>*Replace* Materials ......59.90  Labor.........69.10<br>*Remove* ..................... Labor...........13.00<br>▶ Deduct **$4.80** for ash or oak veneer jamb and casing. | ea | $13.00 | $129.00 | $142.00 |
| **Ash or oak jamb & casing for double exterior door**<br>*Replace* Materials ....107.00  Labor.........123.00<br>*Remove* ..................... Labor...........13.00<br>▶ Deduct **$6.30** for ash or oak veneer jamb and casing. | ea | $13.00 | $230.00 | $243.00 |
| **Redwood jamb & casing for exterior door**<br>*Replace* Materials ......53.60  Labor.........69.10<br>*Remove* ..................... Labor...........13.00 | ea | $13.00 | $122.70 | $135.70 |
| **Redwood jamb & casing for double exterior door**<br>*Replace* Materials ......95.90  Labor.........123.00<br>*Remove* ..................... Labor...........13.00 | ea | $13.00 | $218.90 | $231.90 |
| **Cypress jamb & casing for exterior door**<br>*Replace* Materials ......49.80  Labor.........69.10<br>*Remove* ..................... Labor...........13.00 | ea | $13.00 | $118.90 | $131.90 |
| **Cypress jamb & casing for double exterior door**<br>*Replace* Materials ......91.50  Labor.........123.00<br>*Remove* ..................... Labor...........13.00 | ea | $13.00 | $214.50 | $227.50 |
| **Walnut or cherry jamb & casing for exterior door**<br>*Replace* Materials ......70.70  Labor.........69.10<br>*Remove* ..................... Labor...........13.00<br>▶ Deduct **$5.30** for walnut or cherry veneer jamb and casing. | ea | $13.00 | $139.80 | $152.80 |
| **Walnut or cherry jamb & casing for double exterior door**<br>*Replace* Materials ....121.00  Labor.........123.00<br>*Remove* ..................... Labor...........13.00<br>▶ Deduct **$6.30** for walnut or cherry veneer jamb and casing. | ea | $13.00 | $244.00 | $257.00 |
| **Steel jamb & casing for exterior door**<br>*Replace* Materials ......69.40  Labor.........69.10<br>*Remove* ..................... Labor...........13.00 | ea | $13.00 | $138.50 | $151.50 |
| **Steel jamb & casing for double exterior door**<br>*Replace* Materials ....101.00  Labor.........123.00<br>*Remove* ..................... Labor...........13.00 | ea | $13.00 | $224.00 | $237.00 |
| **Add for hanging exterior Dutch door**<br>*Replace* Labor...........69.10 | ea | — | $69.10 | $69.10 |
| **Add for jamb & casing for a round- or elliptical-top door**<br>*Replace* Materials .....145.00 | ea | — | $145.00 | $145.00 |
| **Fanlite for single entry door, standard grade**<br>*Replace* Materials .....179.00  Labor...........73.10<br>*Remove* ..................... Labor...........19.60 | ea | $19.60 | $252.10 | $271.70 |

**RELATED ITEMS**
Cleaning.......................55
Door Hardware ..........125
Finish Carpentry..........201
Painting ....................336

◀ **ADDITIONAL EXTERIOR JAMB & CASING COSTS**

◀ **ENTRY DOOR FANLITE** *For more info about fanlites see the following page.*

| Item Description | Unit | Remove | Replace | Total |
|---|---|---|---|---|
| **Fanlite for single entry door, high grade** | ea | $19.60 | $376.10 | $395.70 |
| *Replace* Materials....303.00    Labor............73.10 | | | | |
| *Remove* ......................    Labor............19.60 | | | | |
| **Fanlite for single entry door, deluxe grade** | ea | $19.60 | $493.10 | $512.70 |
| *Replace* Materials....420.00    Labor............73.10 | | | | |
| *Remove* ......................    Labor............19.60 | | | | |
| **Fanlite for single entry door, custom grade** | ea | $19.60 | $655.10 | $674.70 |
| *Replace* Materials....582.00    Labor............73.10 | | | | |
| *Remove* ......................    Labor............19.60 | | | | |
| **Fanlite for single entry door, custom deluxe grade** | ea | $19.60 | $838.10 | $857.70 |
| *Replace* Materials.....765.00    Labor............73.10 | | | | |
| *Remove* ......................    Labor............19.60 | | | | |
| **Remove entry door fanlite & casing for work, then reinstall** | ea | — | $123.00 | $123.00 |
| *Replace* ......................    Labor.........123.00 | | | | |
| **Add 34% for fanlite for single door with side-lite** | | | | |
| **Add 85% for fanlite for single door with two side-lites** | | | | |
| **Add 99% for fanlite for double doors** | | | | |
| **Add 147% for fanlite for double doors with two side-lites** | | | | |
| **Fixed transom for entry door, standard grade** | ea | $24.20 | $159.50 | $183.70 |
| *Replace* Materials.....120.00    Labor ..........39.50 | | | | |
| *Remove* ......................    Labor...........24.20 | | | | |
| **Fixed transom for entry door, high grade** | ea | $24.20 | $241.50 | $265.70 |
| *Replace* Materials....202.00    Labor ..........39.50 | | | | |
| *Remove* ......................    Labor...........24.20 | | | | |
| **Fixed transom for entry door, deluxe grade** | ea | $24.20 | $376.50 | $400.70 |
| *Replace* Materials....337.00    Labor ..........39.50 | | | | |
| *Remove* ......................    Labor...........24.20 | | | | |
| **Fixed transom for entry door, custom grade** | ea | $24.20 | $529.50 | $553.70 |
| *Replace* Materials....490.00    Labor ..........39.50 | | | | |
| *Remove* ......................    Labor...........24.20 | | | | |
| **Fixed transom for entry door, custom deluxe grade** | ea | $24.20 | $736.50 | $760.70 |
| *Replace* Materials....697.00    Labor ..........39.50 | | | | |
| *Remove* ......................    Labor...........24.20 | | | | |
| **Remove fixed transom & casing for work, then reinstall** | ea | — | $108.00 | $108.00 |
| *Replace* ......................    Labor.........108.00 | | | | |
| **Add 42% for fixed transom for single door with side-lite** | | | | |
| **Add 65% for fixed transom for single door with two side-lites** | | | | |
| **Add 89% for fixed transom for double doors** | | | | |
| **Add 106% for fixed transom for double doors with two side-lites** | | | | |
| **Cafe doors (bar doors) louvered paint-grade** | ea | $6.65 | $115.20 | $121.85 |
| *Replace* Materials......88.30    Labor............26.90 | | | | |
| *Remove* ......................    Labor............6.65 | | | | |

**FANLITE ▶**
*continued*

**FANLITE QUALITY**

Fanlites are semi-circular or half-elliptical windows that appear above doors. True fanlites have mullions that fan out from the bottom center of the lite. Lower grades will have a simulated fan grid.

All fanlites include jamb and casing. Grades match entry door grades found on page 112.

**ADDITIONAL ▶ FANLITE SIZES**
*Includes jamb & casing.*

**ENTRY DOOR ▶ FIXED TRANSOM**
*Includes jamb & casing.*

**FIXED TRANSOMS**

Fixed transoms are rectangular windows that appear above doors. Transoms may have circular, semi-circular, or elliptical components, but the unit fits in a rectangular jamb.

All transoms include jamb and casing. Grades match exterior door grades found on page 112.

**ADDITIONAL ▶ TRANSOM SIZES**
*Includes jamb & casing.*

**CAFE DOORS ▶**
*Includes hardware.*

| Item Description | Unit | Remove | Replace | Total |
|---|---|---|---|---|
| **Cafe doors (bar doors) louvered stain-grade** | ea | $6.65 | $137.90 | $144.55 |
| *Replace* Materials .....111.00   Labor..........26.90 | | | | |
| *Remove* .....................   Labor ............6.65 | | | | |
| **Cafe doors (bar doors) Victorian spindle & raised-panel paint-grade** | ea | $6.65 | $140.90 | $147.55 |
| *Replace* Materials .....114.00   Labor..........26.90 | | | | |
| *Remove* .....................   Labor ............6.65 | | | | |
| **Cafe doors (bar doors) Victorian spindle & raised-panel stain-grade** | ea | $6.65 | $167.90 | $174.55 |
| *Replace* Materials.....141.00   Labor..........26.90 | | | | |
| *Remove* .....................   Labor ............6.65 | | | | |
| **Remove cafe doors for work, then reinstall** | ea | — | $40.30 | $40.30 |
| *Replace* .....................   Labor ..........40.30 | | | | |
| **6' wide by 6'8" tall bronze finish sliding patio door single-glazed** | ea | $49.00 | $602.00 | $651.00 |
| *Replace* Materials ....429.00   Labor ......173.00 | | | | |
| *Remove* .....................   Labor..........49.00 | | | | |
| **6' wide by 6'8" tall mill finish sliding patio door double-glazed** | ea | $49.00 | $754.00 | $803.00 |
| *Replace* Materials ....581.00   Labor ......173.00 | | | | |
| *Remove* .....................   Labor..........49.00 | | | | |
| **8' wide by 6'8" tall bronze finish sliding patio door single-glazed** | ea | $49.00 | $693.00 | $742.00 |
| *Replace* Materials ....520.00   Labor ......173.00 | | | | |
| *Remove* .....................   Labor..........49.00 | | | | |
| **8' wide by 6'8" tall mill finish sliding patio door double-glazed** | ea | $49.00 | $854.00 | $903.00 |
| *Replace* Materials ....681.00   Labor ......173.00 | | | | |
| *Remove* .....................   Labor..........49.00 | | | | |
| **12' wide by 6'8" tall bronze finish sliding patio door single-glazed** | ea | $73.60 | $1,004.00 | $1,077.60 |
| *Replace* Materials ....777.00   Labor.......227.00 | | | | |
| *Remove* .....................   Labor..........73.60 | | | | |
| ► 3 lites | | | | |
| **12' by 6'8" mill finish sliding patio door double-glazed** | ea | $73.60 | $1,317.00 | $1,390.60 |
| *Replace* Materials ..1090.00   Labor.......227.00 | | | | |
| *Remove* .....................   Labor..........73.60 | | | | |
| ► 3 lites. | | | | |
| **6' by 6'8" wood sliding patio door single-glazed** | ea | $49.00 | $1,094.00 | $1,143.00 |
| *Replace* Materials ....921.00   Labor ......173.00 | | | | |
| *Remove* .....................   Labor..........49.00 | | | | |
| **6' by 6'8" wood sliding patio door double-glazed** | ea | $49.00 | $1,203.00 | $1,252.00 |
| *Replace* Materials ..1030.00   Labor ......173.00 | | | | |
| *Remove* .....................   Labor..........49.00 | | | | |
| **8' by 6'8" wood sliding patio door single-glazed** | ea | $49.00 | $1,273.00 | $1,322.00 |
| *Replace* Materials...1100.00   Labor ......173.00 | | | | |
| *Remove* .....................   Labor..........49.00 | | | | |
| **8' by 6'8" wood sliding patio door double-glazed** | ea | $49.00 | $1,413.00 | $1,462.00 |
| *Replace* Materials...1240.00   Labor ......173.00 | | | | |
| *Remove* .....................   Labor..........49.00 | | | | |
| **12' by 6'8" wood sliding patio door single-glazed (3 lites)** | ea | $73.60 | $1,897.00 | $1,970.60 |
| *Replace* Materials...1670.00   Labor.......227.00 | | | | |
| *Remove* .....................   Labor..........73.60 | | | | |

◄ **SLIDING PATIO DOOR**

△ *two lite patio door*

△ *three lite patio door*

| | Item Description | Unit | Remove | Replace | Total |
|---|---|---|---|---|---|
| **SLIDING PATIO ▶ DOOR** *continued* | **12' by 6'8" wood sliding patio door double-glazed (3 lites)**<br>*Replace* Materials ..1830.00    Labor........227.00<br>*Remove* ..................    Labor..........73.60 | ea | $73.60 | $2,057.00 | $2,130.60 |
| | **6' by 6'8" wood sliding patio door single-glazed clad exterior**<br>*Replace* Materials ....934.00    Labor........173.00<br>*Remove* ..................    Labor..........49.00 | ea | $49.00 | $1,107.00 | $1,156.00 |
| | **6' by 6'8" wood sliding patio door double-glazed clad exterior**<br>*Replace* Materials ...1140.00    Labor........173.00<br>*Remove* ..................    Labor..........49.00 | ea | $49.00 | $1,313.00 | $1,362.00 |
| | **8' by 6'8" wood sliding patio door single-glazed clad exterior**<br>*Replace* Materials ..1090.00    Labor........227.00<br>*Remove* ..................    Labor..........49.00 | ea | $49.00 | $1,317.00 | $1,366.00 |
| | **8' by 6'8" wood sliding patio door double-glazed clad exterior**<br>*Replace* Materials...1330.00    Labor........227.00<br>*Remove* ..................    Labor..........49.00 | ea | $49.00 | $1,557.00 | $1,606.00 |
| | **12' by 6'8" wood sliding patio door single-glazed clad exterior**<br>*Replace* Materials...1700.00    Labor........227.00<br>*Remove* ..................    Labor..........73.60<br>▶ 3 lites. | ea | $73.60 | $1,927.00 | $2,000.60 |
| | **12' by 6'8" wood sliding patio door double-glazed clad exterior**<br>*Replace* Materials ..2220.00    Labor........227.00<br>*Remove* ..................    Labor..........73.60 | ea | $73.60 | $2,447.00 | $2,520.60 |
| **ADDITIONAL ▶ SLIDING PATIO DOOR COSTS** | **Add for sliding patio door tinted glass (per lite)**<br>*Replace* Materials ......211.00 | ea | — | $211.00 | $211.00 |
| | **Remove sliding patio door, jamb, & casing for work, then reinstall**<br>*Replace* ..................    Labor ..........219.00 | ea | — | $219.00 | $219.00 |
| | **Remove sliding patio door lites for work, then reinstall**<br>*Replace* ..................    Labor..........65.20 | ea | — | $65.20 | $65.20 |
| | **Minimum charge for sliding glass patio door work**<br>*Replace* Materials ......25.00    Labor ..........128.00 | ea | — | $153.00 | $153.00 |
| | **Recondition sliding glass patio door, replace hardware**<br>*Replace* Materials ......57.00    Labor ..........92.00 | ea | — | $149.00 | $149.00 |
| **SLIDING PATIO ▶ DOOR SCREEN** | **36" sliding patio door screen**<br>*Replace* Materials ......56.80    Labor ..........4.94<br>*Remove* ..................    Labor ..........3.28 | ea | $3.28 | $61.74 | $65.02 |
| | **48" sliding patio door screen**<br>*Replace* Materials ......70.70    Labor ..........4.94<br>*Remove* ..................    Labor ..........3.28 | ea | $3.28 | $75.64 | $78.92 |
| **PET DOOR ▶** *Includes lock, aluminum frame, and PVC door.* | **Pet door for small dogs, cats**<br>*Replace* Materials ......50.50    Labor ..........33.30<br>*Remove* ..................    Labor ..........7.60 | ea | $7.60 | $83.80 | $91.40 |
| | **Pet door for average size dogs**<br>*Replace* Materials ......88.30    Labor ..........33.30<br>*Remove* ..................    Labor ..........7.60 | ea | $7.60 | $121.60 | $129.20 |

| Item Description | Unit | Remove | Replace | Total |
|---|---|---|---|---|
| **Pet door for large dogs** | ea | $7.60 | $172.30 | $179.90 |
| *Replace* Materials.....139.00        Labor .........33.30 | | | | |
| *Remove* ......................        Labor ...........7.60 | | | | |
| **Remove pet door for work, then reinstall** | ea | — | $57.30 | $57.30 |
| *Replace* Materials........6.30        Labor...........51.00 | | | | |
| **8′ garage door with hardware, economy grade** | ea | $96.00 | $607.00 | $703.00 |
| *Replace* Materials ....360.00        Labor ......247.00 | | | | |
| *Remove* ......................        Labor...........96.00 | | | | |
| **8′ garage door with hardware, standard grade** | ea | $96.00 | $663.00 | $759.00 |
| *Replace* Materials .....416.00        Labor ......247.00 | | | | |
| *Remove* ......................        Labor...........96.00 | | | | |
| **8′ garage door with hardware, high grade** | ea | $96.00 | $821.00 | $917.00 |
| *Replace* Materials....574.00        Labor ......247.00 | | | | |
| *Remove* ......................        Labor...........96.00 | | | | |
| **8′ garage door with hardware, deluxe grade** | ea | $96.00 | $891.00 | $987.00 |
| *Replace* Materials....644.00        Labor ......247.00 | | | | |
| *Remove* ......................        Labor...........96.00 | | | | |
| **9′ garage door with hardware, economy grade** | ea | $96.00 | $638.00 | $734.00 |
| *Replace* Materials ....391.00        Labor ......247.00 | | | | |
| *Remove* ......................        Labor...........96.00 | | | | |
| **9′ garage door with hardware, standard grade** | ea | $96.00 | $780.00 | $876.00 |
| *Replace* Materials ....533.00        Labor .........247.00 | | | | |
| *Remove* ......................        Labor...........96.00 | | | | |
| **9′ garage door with hardware, high grade** | ea | $96.00 | $872.00 | $968.00 |
| *Replace* Materials ....625.00        Labor .........247.00 | | | | |
| *Remove* ......................        Labor...........96.00 | | | | |
| **9′ garage door with hardware, deluxe grade** | ea | $96.00 | $954.00 | $1,050.00 |
| *Replace* Materials ....707.00        Labor .........247.00 | | | | |
| *Remove* ......................        Labor...........96.00 | | | | |
| **10′ garage door with hardware, economy grade** | ea | $96.00 | $695.00 | $791.00 |
| *Replace* Materials....448.00        Labor .........247.00 | | | | |
| *Remove* ......................        Labor...........96.00 | | | | |
| **10′ garage door with hardware, standard grade** | ea | $96.00 | $802.00 | $898.00 |
| *Replace* Materials ....555.00        Labor .........247.00 | | | | |
| *Remove* ......................        Labor...........96.00 | | | | |
| **10′ garage door with hardware, high grade** | ea | $96.00 | $935.00 | $1,031.00 |
| *Replace* Materials ....688.00        Labor .........247.00 | | | | |
| *Remove* ......................        Labor...........96.00 | | | | |
| **10′ garage door with hardware, deluxe grade** | ea | $96.00 | $1,029.00 | $1,125.00 |
| *Replace* Materials ....782.00        Labor .........247.00 | | | | |
| *Remove* ......................        Labor...........96.00 | | | | |
| **12′ garage door with hardware, economy grade** | ea | $96.00 | $752.00 | $848.00 |
| *Replace* Materials....505.00        Labor .........247.00 | | | | |
| *Remove* ......................        Labor...........96.00 | | | | |
| **12′ garage door with hardware, standard grade** | ea | $96.00 | $872.00 | $968.00 |
| *Replace* Materials ....625.00        Labor .........247.00 | | | | |
| *Remove* ......................        Labor...........96.00 | | | | |

◀ **GARAGE DOOR**

**GARAGE DOOR GRADES**

**ECONOMY GRADE**
Overhead doors that are plastic-faced polystyrene or flush steel or uninsulated fiberglass. Single-piece doors with flush surface or tongue-and-groove boards in herringbone or chevron patterns.

**STANDARD GRADE**
Overhead doors that are textured or embossed steel, aluminum or fiberglass, usually insulated. Single-piece doors same as economy grade with lites, and paneled patterns.

**HIGH GRADE**
Overhead doors are same as standard grade with lites. Single-piece stain-grade wood doors with lites and carvings.

**DELUXE GRADE**
Overhead doors are stain-grade wood doors, specialty patterns, designed carvings or embossing, fan-tops, and so forth.

△ *economy*

△ *standard*

△ *high*

| | Item Description | Unit | Remove | Replace | Total |
|---|---|---|---|---|---|
| **GARAGE DOOR ▶** *continued* | **12' garage door with hardware, high grade**<br>*Replace* Materials ....789.00        Labor .........247.00<br>*Remove* .......................        Labor...........96.00 | ea | $96.00 | $1,036.00 | $1,132.00 |
|  | **12' garage door with hardware, deluxe grade**<br>*Replace* Materials ....940.00        Labor .........247.00<br>*Remove* .......................        Labor...........96.00 | ea | $96.00 | $1,187.00 | $1,283.00 |
| △ *deluxe* | **14' garage door with hardware, economy grade**<br>*Replace* Materials....540.00        Labor .........247.00<br>*Remove* .......................        Labor...........96.00 | ea | $96.00 | $787.00 | $883.00 |
|  | **14' garage door with hardware, standard grade**<br>*Replace* Materials....644.00        Labor .........247.00<br>*Remove* .......................        Labor...........96.00 | ea | $96.00 | $891.00 | $987.00 |
| △ *deluxe (fanlite)* | **14' garage door with hardware, high grade**<br>*Replace* Materials ....789.00        Labor .........247.00<br>*Remove* .......................        Labor...........96.00 | ea | $96.00 | $1,036.00 | $1,132.00 |
| | **14' garage door with hardware, deluxe grade**<br>*Replace* Materials ....959.00        Labor .........247.00<br>*Remove* .......................        Labor...........96.00 | ea | $96.00 | $1,206.00 | $1,302.00 |
| | **16' garage door with hardware, economy grade**<br>*Replace* Materials ....587.00        Labor .........247.00<br>*Remove* .......................        Labor...........96.00 | ea | $96.00 | $834.00 | $930.00 |
| | **16' garage door with hardware, standard grade**<br>*Replace* Materials.....745.00        Labor .........247.00<br>*Remove* .......................        Labor...........96.00 | ea | $96.00 | $992.00 | $1,088.00 |
| | **16' garage door with hardware, high grade**<br>*Replace* Materials....883.00        Labor .........247.00<br>*Remove* .......................        Labor...........96.00 | ea | $96.00 | $1,130.00 | $1,226.00 |
| | **16' garage door with hardware, deluxe grade**<br>*Replace* Materials ..1020.00        Labor .........247.00<br>*Remove* .......................        Labor...........96.00 | ea | $96.00 | $1,267.00 | $1,363.00 |
| | **18' garage door with hardware, economy grade**<br>*Replace* Materials....644.00        Labor .........247.00<br>*Remove* .......................        Labor...........96.00 | ea | $96.00 | $891.00 | $987.00 |
| | **18' garage door with hardware, standard grade**<br>*Replace* Materials ....789.00        Labor .........247.00<br>*Remove* .......................        Labor...........96.00 | ea | $96.00 | $1,036.00 | $1,132.00 |
| | **18' garage door with hardware, high grade**<br>*Replace* Materials ....921.00        Labor .........247.00<br>*Remove* .......................        Labor...........96.00 | ea | $96.00 | $1,168.00 | $1,264.00 |
| | **18' garage door with hardware, deluxe grade**<br>*Replace* Materials ..1090.00        Labor .........247.00<br>*Remove* .......................        Labor...........96.00 | ea | $96.00 | $1,337.00 | $1,433.00 |
| **GARAGE DOOR ▶ OPENER**  | **Garage door opener, standard grade**<br>*Replace* Materials....290.00        Labor...........96.80<br>*Remove* .......................        Labor .........20.00 | ea | $20.00 | $386.80 | $406.80 |

| Item Description | Unit | Remove | Replace | Total | |
|---|---|---|---|---|---|
| **Garage door opener, high grade** | ea | $20.00 | $412.80 | $432.80 | **RELATED ITEMS** |
| *Replace* Materials.....316.00 Labor...........96.80 | | | | | Cleaning......................57 |
| *Remove* ...................... Labor ..........20.00 | | | | | Door Hardware ..........127 |
| | | | | | Finish Carpentry..........201 |
| **Garage door opener, deluxe grade** | ea | $20.00 | $443.80 | $463.80 | Painting .....................334 |
| *Replace* Materials ....347.00 Labor...........96.80 | | | | | |
| *Remove* ...................... Labor ..........20.00 | | | | | |
| **Remove radio transmitter for overhead door opener** | ea | — | $37.00 | $37.00 | |
| *Replace* Materials ......37.00 | | | | | |
| **Remove garage door opener for work, then reinstall** | ea | — | $138.00 | $138.00 | |
| *Replace* ...................... Labor.........138.00 | | | | | |
| **Replace garage door spring** | ea | — | $131.00 | $131.00 | ◁ garage door spring |
| *Replace* Materials ......52.00 Labor...........79.00 | | | | | |
| **Remove single-car garage door for work, then reinstall** | ea | — | $304.00 | $304.00 | ◁ remove and reinstall |
| *Replace* ...................... Labor .......304.00 | | | | | |
| **Remove two-car garage door for work, then reinstall** | ea | — | $365.00 | $365.00 | |
| *Replace* ...................... Labor.........365.00 | | | | | |
| **Minimum charge for garage door work** | ea | — | $130.80 | $130.80 | |
| *Replace* Materials ......32.00 Labor...........98.80 | | | | | |
| **Add 14% for 7' tall doors** | | | | | ◀ **ADD FOR** |
| | | | | | **TALL DOOR** |
| **Add 22% for 8' tall doors** | | | | | *All door types.* |

✐ NOTES: _____

_____

_____

_____

_____

_____

_____

_____

_____

_____

_____

_____

_____

_____

_____

_____ end

# TIME & MATERIAL CHARTS *(selected items)*

## Doors Materials

See **Doors** material prices with the line items and other information in the **QuickFinder** column.

## Doors Labor

| LABORER | BASE WAGE | PAID LEAVE | TRUE WAGE | FICA | FUTA | WORKER'S COMP. | UNEMPLOY. INSUR. | HEALTH INSUR. | RETIRE (401K) | LIABILITY INSUR. | COST PER HOUR |
|---|---|---|---|---|---|---|---|---|---|---|---|
| Finish carpenter | $22.60 | 1.76 | $24.36 | 1.86 | .19 | 4.56 | 2.12 | 2.54 | .73 | 3.17 | $39.50 |
| Demolition laborer | $13.40 | 1.05 | $14.45 | 1.11 | .12 | 4.44 | 1.26 | 2.54 | .43 | 1.88 | $26.20 |

**Paid Leave** is calculated based on two weeks paid vacation, one week sick leave, and seven paid holidays. Employer's matching portion of **FICA** is 7.65 percent. **FUTA** (Federal Unemployment) is .8 percent. **Worker's compensation** for the doors trade was calculated using a national average of 18.71 percent. **Unemployment insurance** was calculated using a national average of 8.7 percent. **Health insurance** was calculated based on a projected national average for 2001 of $505 per employee (and family when applicable) per month. Employer pays 80 percent for a per month cost of $404 per employee. **Retirement** is based on a 401(k) retirement program with employer matching of 50 percent. Employee contributions to the 401(k) plan are an average of 6 percent of the true wage. **Liability insurance** is based on a national average of 12.9 percent.

## Doors Labor Productivity

| WORK DESCRIPTION | LABORER | COST PER HOUR | PRODUCTIVITY | UNIT PRICE |
|---|---|---|---|---|
| **Demolition** | | | | |
| folding door | demolition laborer | $26.20 | .114 | $2.99 ea |
| bypassing door | demolition laborer | $26.20 | .139 | $3.64 ea |
| bypassing or folding door jamb & casing | demolition laborer | $26.20 | .026 | $.68 lf |
| pre-hung interior door, jamb, & casing | demolition laborer | $26.20 | .388 | $10.20 ea |
| pre-hung interior door slab only | demolition laborer | $26.20 | .217 | $5.69 ea |
| double pre-hung interior door, jamb, & casing | demolition laborer | $26.20 | .585 | $15.30 ea |
| double pre-hung interior door slabs only | demolition laborer | $26.20 | .321 | $8.40 ea |
| garage door, overhead tracks, jamb, & casing | demolition laborer | $26.20 | 3.65 | $96.00 ea |
| garage door, hardware, jamb, & casing | demolition laborer | $26.20 | 2.90 | $76.00 ea |
| garage door only | demolition laborer | $26.20 | 1.82 | $47.70 ea |
| garage door opener | demolition laborer | $26.20 | .765 | $20.00 ea |
| pocket door, jamb, & casing | demolition laborer | $26.20 | 1.02 | $26.70 ea |
| pocket door slab only | demolition laborer | $26.20 | .491 | $12.90 ea |
| double pocket door, jamb, & casing | demolition laborer | $26.20 | 1.86 | $48.70 ea |
| double pocket door slab only | demolition laborer | $26.20 | .913 | $23.90 ea |
| pocket door hardware | demolition laborer | $26.20 | .496 | $13.00 ea |
| double pocket door hardware | demolition laborer | $26.20 | .733 | $19.20 ea |
| panel door, jamb, & casing | demolition laborer | $26.20 | .477 | $12.50 ea |
| panel door slab only | demolition laborer | $26.20 | .217 | $5.69 ea |
| transom | demolition laborer | $26.20 | .451 | $11.80 ea |
| entry door fanlite & casing | demolition laborer | $26.20 | .749 | $19.60 ea |
| double entry door fanlite & casing | demolition laborer | $26.20 | 1.71 | $44.80 ea |
| storm door | demolition laborer | $26.20 | .227 | $5.95 ea |
| entry door, jamb, casing, & threshold | demolition laborer | $26.20 | .496 | $13.00 ea |
| entry door slab only | demolition laborer | $26.20 | .283 | $7.41 ea |
| double entry door, jamb, casing, & threshold | demolition laborer | $26.20 | .842 | $22.10 ea |
| double entry door slabs only | demolition laborer | $26.20 | .492 | $12.90 ea |
| entry door side-lite | demolition laborer | $26.20 | .508 | $13.30 ea |
| Dutch door slabs, jamb, & casing | demolition laborer | $26.20 | .883 | $23.10 ea |
| Dutch door slabs only | demolition laborer | $26.20 | .321 | $8.40 ea |
| cafe door | demolition laborer | $26.20 | .254 | $6.65 ea |
| sliding glass patio door (per lite) | demolition laborer | $26.20 | .427 | $11.20 ea |
| pet door | demolition laborer | $26.20 | .290 | $7.60 ea |

*. . . More ➤*

## Doors Labor Productivity *continued*

| WORK DESCRIPTION | LABORER | COST PER HOUR | PRODUCTIVITY | UNIT PRICE |
|---|---|---|---|---|
| **Minimum labor charge for door work** | | | | |
| minimum charge | finish carpenter | $39.50 | 2.50 | $98.80 ea |
| **Install interior doors** | | | | |
| folding door per section | finish carpenter | $39.50 | .394 | $15.60 ea |
| bypassing door per section | finish carpenter | $39.50 | .755 | $29.80 ea |
| bypassing or folding door jamb & casing | finish carpenter | $39.50 | .109 | $4.31 lf |
| pre-hung interior door & casing | finish carpenter | $39.50 | 1.43 | $56.50 ea |
| pre-hung interior door slab only | finish carpenter | $39.50 | .215 | $8.49 ea |
| double pre-hung interior door & casing | finish carpenter | $39.50 | 2.45 | $96.80 ea |
| double pre-hung interior door slabs only | finish carpenter | $39.50 | .412 | $16.30 ea |
| **Install garage door** | | | | |
| with overhead tracks, jamb, & casing | finish carpenter | $39.50 | 6.25 | $247.00 ea |
| with hardware, jamb, & casing | finish carpenter | $39.50 | 5.21 | $206.00 ea |
| door only | finish carpenter | $39.50 | 3.15 | $124.00 ea |
| opener | finish carpenter | $39.50 | 2.45 | $96.80 ea |
| **Install pocket door** | | | | |
| door slabs | finish carpenter | $39.50 | .850 | $33.60 ea |
| door, jamb, trim, & casing | finish carpenter | $39.50 | 1.35 | $53.30 ea |
| double doors | finish carpenter | $39.50 | 2.34 | $92.40 ea |
| double door, jamb, trim, & casing | finish carpenter | $39.50 | 3.12 | $123.00 ea |
| **Install pocket door rough framing package including track and hardware** | | | | |
| single door in 2" x 4" wall | finish carpenter | $39.50 | 1.50 | $59.30 ea |
| double doors in 2" x 4" wall | finish carpenter | $39.50 | 2.88 | $114.00 ea |
| single door in 2" x 6" wall | finish carpenter | $39.50 | 1.52 | $60.00 ea |
| double doors in 2" x 6" wall | finish carpenter | $39.50 | 2.95 | $117.00 ea |
| single door in 2" x 8" wall | finish carpenter | $39.50 | 1.54 | $60.80 ea |
| double doors in 2" x 8" wall | finish carpenter | $39.50 | 3.03 | $120.00 ea |
| rough framing for antique door | finish carpenter | $39.50 | 2.45 | $96.80 ea |
| rough framing for antique double doors | finish carpenter | $39.50 | 5.12 | $202.00 ea |
| **Install pocket door track** | | | | |
| overhead track for antique door | finish carpenter | $39.50 | 1.30 | $51.40 ea |
| overhead track for antique double door | finish carpenter | $39.50 | 2.34 | $92.40 ea |
| clean and realign overhead antique door track | finish carpenter | $39.50 | 1.96 | $77.40 ea |
| floor track for antique door | finish carpenter | $39.50 | 1.21 | $47.80 ea |
| floor track for antique double door | finish carpenter | $39.50 | 2.20 | $86.90 ea |
| clean and realign floor antique doors | finish carpenter | $39.50 | 2.64 | $104.00 ea |
| **Install panel door** | | | | |
| hang door & install casing | finish carpenter | $39.50 | 1.23 | $48.60 ea |
| slab only | finish carpenter | $39.50 | .178 | $7.03 ea |
| **Install entry door, fanlite, transom** | | | | |
| fanlite & casing | finish carpenter | $39.50 | 1.85 | $73.10 ea |
| transom & casing | finish carpenter | $39.50 | 1.00 | $39.50 ea |
| hang entry door & install casing | finish carpenter | $39.50 | 1.75 | $69.10 ea |
| slab only | finish carpenter | $39.50 | .212 | $8.37 ea |
| hang double-entry door & casing | finish carpenter | $39.50 | 3.11 | $123.00 ea |
| double door slabs only | finish carpenter | $39.50 | .330 | $13.00 ea |
| side-lite | finish carpenter | $39.50 | 1.14 | $45.00 ea |
| **Install Dutch door** | | | | |
| hang door & install casing | finish carpenter | $39.50 | 1.70 | $67.20 ea |
| slabs only | finish carpenter | $39.50 | .325 | $12.80 ea |
| **Install door lite** | | | | |
| cut hole in door and install | finish carpenter | $39.50 | 1.12 | $44.20 ea |
| **Install cafe door** | | | | |
| per set | finish carpenter | $39.50 | .681 | $26.90 ea |
| **Install sliding glass patio doors** | | | | |
| with two lites | finish carpenter | $39.50 | 4.39 | $173.00 ea |
| **Install pet door** | | | | |
| per door | finish carpenter | $39.50 | .844 | $33.30 ea |

. . . More ➤

## Doors Labor Productivity *continued*

| WORK DESCRIPTION | LABORER | COST PER HOUR | PRODUCTIVITY | UNIT PRICE |
|---|---|---|---|---|
| **Assemble & install storm door** | | | | |
| per door | finish carpenter | $39.50 | 1.70 | $67.20 ea |
| **Remove for work, then reinstall** | | | | |
| folding doors per section | finish carpenter | $39.50 | .148 | $5.85 ea |
| bypass sliding doors per section | finish carpenter | $39.50 | .220 | $8.69 ea |
| door slab | finish carpenter | $39.50 | .151 | $5.96 ea |
| door slab, jamb & casing | finish carpenter | $39.50 | 1.63 | $64.40 ea |
| double door slabs | finish carpenter | $39.50 | .293 | $11.60 ea |
| double door slabs, jamb & casing | finish carpenter | $39.50 | 2.67 | $105.00 ea |
| pocket door & casing | finish carpenter | $39.50 | 1.15 | $45.40 ea |
| pocket door, jamb & casing | finish carpenter | $39.50 | 3.23 | $128.00 ea |
| double pocket doors & casing | finish carpenter | $39.50 | 1.58 | $62.40 ea |
| double pocket doors, jamb & casing | finish carpenter | $39.50 | 3.39 | $134.00 ea |
| panel door slab | finish carpenter | $39.50 | .152 | $6.00 ea |
| panel door, jamb, & casing | finish carpenter | $39.50 | 1.63 | $64.40 ea |
| antique door casing & re-plumb door | finish carpenter | $39.50 | 2.95 | $117.00 ea |
| transom | finish carpenter | $39.50 | 1.12 | $44.20 ea |
| storm door | finish carpenter | $39.50 | 1.70 | $67.20 ea |
| Dutch door, jamb, & casing | finish carpenter | $39.50 | 2.74 | $108.00 ea |
| Dutch door slabs | finish carpenter | $39.50 | .394 | $15.60 ea |
| exterior door, jamb, & casing | finish carpenter | $39.50 | 2.20 | $86.90 ea |
| exterior door slab | finish carpenter | $39.50 | .292 | $11.50 ea |
| exterior double door, jamb, & casing | finish carpenter | $39.50 | 3.12 | $123.00 ea |
| exterior double door slabs | finish carpenter | $39.50 | .366 | $14.50 ea |
| entry door fanlite & casing | finish carpenter | $39.50 | 3.12 | $123.00 ea |
| entry door fixed transom & casing | finish carpenter | $39.50 | 2.74 | $108.00 ea |
| cafe door | finish carpenter | $39.50 | 1.02 | $40.30 ea |
| sliding patio door, jamb, & casing | finish carpenter | $39.50 | 5.55 | $219.00 ea |
| sliding patio door lites | finish carpenter | $39.50 | 1.65 | $65.20 ea |
| pet door | finish carpenter | $39.50 | 1.29 | $51.00 ea |
| garage door opener | finish carpenter | $39.50 | 3.50 | $138.00 ea |
| single-car garage door | finish carpenter | $39.50 | 7.70 | $304.00 ea |
| two-car garage door | finish carpenter | $39.50 | 9.25 | $365.00 ea |
| **Door repair** | | | | |
| minimum labor to repair antique panel door (no custom milling) | finish carpenter | $39.50 | 2.49 | $98.40 ea |
| minimum labor charge to repair antique panel door when custom milling is required | finish carpenter | $39.50 | 3.51 | $139.00 ea |
| replace antique panel door panel (not including custom knife charges) | finish carpenter | $39.50 | 2.74 | $108.00 ea |
| replace antique panel door stile (not including custom knife charges) | finish carpenter | $39.50 | 2.49 | $98.40 ea |
| repair cracks & dry rot in antique door with epoxy, tighten stiles | finish carpenter | $39.50 | 4.49 | $177.00 ea |
| repair cracks & dry rot in antique door jamb with epoxy | finish carpenter | $39.50 | 3.40 | $134.00 ea |
| repair cracks & dry rot in antique door casing with epoxy | finish carpenter | $39.50 | 3.40 | $134.00 ea |
| **Additional door labor charges** | | | | |
| add for installation of full-lite in exterior door | finish carpenter | $39.50 | 1.39 | $54.90 ea |
| add for installation of half-lite in exterior door | finish carpenter | $39.50 | 1.07 | $42.30 ea |
| add for installation of 1' by 1' lite in exterior door | finish carpenter | $39.50 | .594 | $23.50 ea |
| recondition sliding glass door, replace hardware | finish carpenter | $39.50 | 2.33 | $92.00 ea |
| minimum labor for garage door work | finish carpenter | $39.50 | 2.50 | $98.80 ea |
| minimum labor for sliding glass door work | finish carpenter | $39.50 | 3.25 | $128.00 ea |

# 11 ............................................................ *Door Hardware*

| Item Description | Unit | Remove | Replace | Total | |
|---|---|---|---|---|---|
| **Deadbolt, standard grade** | ea | $7.23 | $48.80 | $56.03 | ◄ DEADBOLT |
| *Replace* Material ........22.00   Labor...........26.80 | | | | | |
| *Remove* ....................... Labor ...........7.23l; | | | | | |
| **Deadbolt, high grade** | ea | $7.23 | $59.80 | $67.03 | |
| *Replace* Material ........33.00   Labor...........26.80 | | | | | |
| *Remove* ....................... Labor ...........7.23 | | | | | |
| **Deadbolt, deluxe grade** | ea | $7.23 | $67.80 | $75.03 | |
| *Replace* Material ........39.00   Labor...........26.80 | | | | | |
| *Remove* ....................... Labor ...........7.23 | | | | | |
| **Remove deadbolt for work, then reinstall** | ea | — | $43.50 | $43.50 | |
| *Replace* ....................... Labor ...........43.50 | | | | | |
| **Exterior door keyed lockset, standard grade** | ea | $8.23 | $40.20 | $48.43 | ◄ EXTERIOR LOCKSET |
| *Replace* Material ........22.00   Labor...........18.20 | | | | | |
| *Remove* ....................... Labor ...........8.23 | | | | | |
| **Exterior door keyed lockset, high grade** | ea | $8.23 | $54.20 | $62.43 | |
| *Replace* Material ........36.00   Labor...........18.20 | | | | | |
| *Remove* ....................... Labor ...........8.23 | | | | | |
| **Exterior door keyed lockset, deluxe grade** | ea | $8.23 | $65.20 | $73.43 | |
| *Replace* Material........47.00   Labor...........18.20 | | | | | |
| *Remove* ....................... Labor ...........8.23 | | | | | |
| **Remove exterior lockset for work, then reinstall** | ea | — | $40.70 | $40.70 | |
| *Replace* ....................... Labor ...........40.70 | | | | | |
| **Entry door keyed lockset, standard grade** | ea | $18.20 | $137.30 | $155.50 | ◄ ENTRY LOCKSET |
| *Replace* Material ........80.00   Labor...........57.30 | | | | | |
| *Remove* ....................... Labor...........18.20 | | | | | |
| **Entry door keyed lockset, high grade** | ea | $18.20 | $266.30 | $284.50 | |
| *Replace* Material .....209.00   Labor...........57.30 | | | | | |
| *Remove* ....................... Labor...........18.20 | | | | | |
| **Entry door keyed lockset, deluxe grade** | ea | $18.20 | $410.30 | $428.50 | |
| *Replace* Material .....353.00   Labor...........57.30 | | | | | |
| *Remove* ....................... Labor...........18.20 | | | | | |
| **Entry door keyed lockset, custom grade** | ea | $18.20 | $547.30 | $565.50 | |
| *Replace* Material......490.00   Labor...........57.30 | | | | | |
| *Remove* ....................... Labor...........18.20 | | | | | |
| **Remove entry door lockset for work, then reinstall** | ea | — | $108.00 | $108.00 | |
| *Replace* ....................... Labor..........108.00 | | | | | |
| **Antique style door thumb latch, standard grade** | ea | $13.50 | $284.30 | $297.80 | ◄ THUMB LATCH |
| *Replace* Material ......216.00   Labor ..........68.30 | | | | | |
| *Remove* ....................... Labor ..........13.50 | | | | | |

### HARDWARE QUALITY

*Some rules of thumb:*

**Standard:** Light gauge metal, chrome or brass plated with little or no pattern.

**High:** Brass, chrome over brass, or nickel over brass with minimal detail, or plated with ornate detail.

**Deluxe:** Brass, chrome over brass, or nickel over brass with moderate detail.

**Custom:** Brass, chrome over brass, or nickel over brass with ornate detail.

### RELATED ITEMS

| | Item Description | Unit | Remove | Replace | Total |
|---|---|---|---|---|---|
| **THUMB LATCH ▶**<br>*continued* | **Antique style door thumb latch, high grade**<br>*Replace* Material .....263.00    Labor ..........68.30<br>*Remove* ......................    Labor ..........13.50 | ea | $13.50 | $331.30 | $344.80 |
| **INTERIOR ▶**<br>**DOOR LOCKSET**<br>*See quality indicators*<br>*on previous page.* | **Interior door lockset, standard grade**<br>*Replace* Material ........17.00    Labor ..........16.00<br>*Remove* ......................    Labor ..........7.36 | ea | $7.36 | $33.00 | $40.36 |
| | **Interior door lockset, high grade**<br>*Replace* Material ........42.00    Labor ..........16.00<br>*Remove* ......................    Labor ..........7.36 | ea | $7.36 | $58.00 | $65.36 |
| | **Interior door lockset, deluxe grade**<br>*Replace* Material ........67.00    Labor ..........16.00<br>*Remove* ......................    Labor ..........7.36 | ea | $7.36 | $83.00 | $90.36 |
| | **Remove interior door lockset for work, then reinstall**<br>*Replace* ......................    Labor ..........28.00 | ea | — | $28.00 | $28.00 |
| **DOOR CLOSER ▶**<br>*See quality indicators*<br>*on previous page.* | **Spring hinge door closer**<br>*Replace* Material ........16.00    Labor ..........10.20<br>*Remove* ......................    Labor ..........2.36 | ea | $2.36 | $26.20 | $28.56 |
| | **Door closer, standard grade**<br>*Replace* Material ........42.00    Labor ..........17.00<br>*Remove* ......................    Labor ..........7.62 | ea | $7.62 | $59.00 | $66.62 |
| | **Door closer, high grade**<br>*Replace* Material .......73.00    Labor ..........17.00<br>*Remove* ......................    Labor ..........7.62 | ea | $7.62 | $90.00 | $97.62 |
| | **Remove door closer for work, then reinstall**<br>*Replace* ......................    Labor ..........29.30 | ea | — | $29.30 | $29.30 |
| **SECURITY CHAIN ▶**<br>*See quality indicators*<br>*on previous page.* | **Security chain**<br>*Replace* Material ........12.00    Labor ..........10.30<br>*Remove* ......................    Labor ..........6.76 | ea | $6.76 | $22.30 | $29.06 |
| | **Remove security chain for work, then reinstall**<br>*Replace* ......................    Labor ..........17.60 | ea | — | $17.60 | $17.60 |
| **DOOR HINGES ▶**<br>*See quality indicators*<br>*on previous page.*<br>*Deluxe grade hinges*<br>*include embossed*<br>*antique patterns.* | **Door hinges, standard grade**<br>*Replace* Material ........11.00    Labor ..........17.30<br>*Remove* ......................    Labor ..........12.70 | ea | $12.70 | $28.30 | $41.00 |
| | **Door hinges, high grade**<br>*Replace* Material .......23.00    Labor ..........17.30<br>*Remove* ......................    Labor ..........12.70 | ea | $12.70 | $40.30 | $53.00 |
| | **Door hinges, deluxe grade**<br>*Replace* Material ........37.00    Labor ..........17.30<br>*Remove* ......................    Labor ..........12.70 | ea | $12.70 | $54.30 | $67.00 |
| *deluxe grade △* | **Batten door hinges**<br>*Replace* Material ........55.00    Labor ..........19.60<br>*Remove* ......................    Labor ..........12.70 | ea | $12.70 | $74.60 | $87.30 |
| *deluxe grade △* | **Remove door hinges for work, then reinstall**<br>*Replace* ......................    Labor ..........31.00 | ea | — | $31.00 | $31.00 |

| Item Description | Unit | Remove | Replace | Total | |
|---|---|---|---|---|---|
| **Door knocker, standard grade** | ea | $6.55 | $30.90 | $37.45 | ◄ **DOOR KNOCKER** |
| *Replace* Material........17.00          Labor...........13.90 | | | | | See quality indicators |
| *Remove* .....................          Labor............6.55 | | | | | on page 127. |
| **Door knocker, high grade** | ea | $6.55 | $51.90 | $58.45 | |
| *Replace* Material .......38.00          Labor...........13.90 | | | | | |
| *Remove* .....................          Labor............6.55 | | | | | |
| **Door knocker, deluxe grade** | ea | $6.55 | $87.90 | $94.45 | |
| *Replace* Material........74.00          Labor...........13.90 | | | | | |
| *Remove* .....................          Labor ...........6.55 | | | | | |
| **Remove door knocker for work, then reinstall** | ea | — | $25.10 | $25.10 | |
| *Replace* .....................          Labor ..........25.10 | | | | | |
| **Storm door hinges** | ea | $12.00 | $31.50 | $43.50 | ◄ **STORM DOOR** |
| *Replace* Material........18.00          Labor ..........13.50 | | | | | **HINGES** |
| *Remove* .....................          Labor...........12.00 | | | | | |
| **Remove storm door hinges for work, then reinstall** | ea | — | $24.00 | $24.00 | |
| *Replace* .....................          Labor...........24.00 | | | | | |
| **Storm door lockset, standard grade** | ea | $8.57 | $39.30 | $47.87 | ◄ **STORM DOOR** |
| *Replace* Material........24.00          Labor ..........15.30 | | | | | **LOCKSET** |
| *Remove* .....................          Labor ............8.57 | | | | | |
| **Storm door lockset, high grade** | ea | $8.57 | $50.30 | $58.87 | |
| *Replace* Material .......35.00          Labor ..........15.30 | | | | | |
| *Remove* .....................          Labor ............8.57 | | | | | |
| **Remove storm door lockset for work, then reinstall** | ea | — | $27.10 | $27.10 | |
| *Replace* .....................          Labor...........27.10 | | | | | |
| **Hinge door stop** | ea | $2.20 | $9.56 | $11.76 | ◄ **DOOR STOP** |
| *Replace* Material.........4.50          Labor ...........5.06 | | | | | See quality indicators |
| *Remove* .....................          Labor ...........2.20 | | | | | on page 127. |
| **Flexible spring baseboard door stop** | ea | $2.20 | $10.95 | $13.15 | |
| *Replace* Material.........5.50          Labor ...........5.45 | | | | | |
| *Remove* .....................          Labor ...........2.20 | | | | | *flexible spring △* |
| **Rigid baseboard door stop** | ea | $2.20 | $11.95 | $14.15 | |
| *Replace* Material ........6.50          Labor ...........5.45 | | | | | |
| *Remove* .....................          Labor ...........2.20 | | | | | *rigid △* |
| **Remove door stop for work, then reinstall** | ea | — | $9.95 | $9.95 | |
| *Replace* .....................          Labor ............9.95 | | | | | |
| **Door push plate, standard grade** | ea | $4.19 | $35.50 | $39.69 | ◄ **PUSH PLATE** |
| *Replace* Material........19.00          Labor ..........16.50 | | | | | See quality indicators |
| *Remove* .....................          Labor ............4.19 | | | | | on page 127. |
| **Door push plate, high grade** | ea | $4.19 | $52.50 | $56.69 | |
| *Replace* Material .......36.00          Labor ..........16.50 | | | | | |
| *Remove* .....................          Labor ............4.19 | | | | | |
| **Remove door push plate for work, then reinstall** | ea | — | $29.30 | $29.30 | △ *high grade* △ |
| *Replace* .....................          Labor ..........29.30 | | | | | |

**RELATED ITEMS**

| | Item Description | Unit | Remove | Replace | Total |
|---|---|---|---|---|---|
| **KICK PLATE** ▶<br>See quality indicators<br>on page 127. | **Door kick plate, standard grade**<br>*Replace* Material .......33.00    Labor ..........17.60<br>*Remove* ................    Labor ..........5.58 | ea | $5.58 | $50.60 | $56.18 |
| | **Door kick plate, high grade**<br>*Replace* Material .......48.00    Labor ..........17.60<br>*Remove* ................    Labor ..........5.58 | ea | $5.58 | $65.60 | $71.18 |
| | **Remove door kick plate for work, then reinstall**<br>*Replace* ................    Labor ..........32.00 | ea | — | $32.00 | $32.00 |
| **LETTER PLATE** ▶<br>See quality indicators<br>on page 127. | **Letter plate, standard grade**<br>*Replace* Material .......27.00    Labor ..........19.80<br>*Remove* ................    Labor ..........5.66 | ea | $5.66 | $46.80 | $52.46 |
| | **Letter plate, high grade**<br>*Replace* Material .......53.00    Labor ..........19.80<br>*Remove* ................    Labor ..........5.66 | ea | $5.66 | $72.80 | $78.46 |
| | **Remove letter plate for work, then reinstall**<br>*Replace* ................    Labor ..........35.60 | ea | — | $35.60 | $35.60 |
| **PEEP HOLE** ▶ | **Door peep hole**<br>*Replace* Material .......18.00    Labor ..........19.10<br>*Remove* ................    Labor ..........5.37 | ea | $5.37 | $37.10 | $42.47 |
| | **Remove door peep hole for work, then reinstall**<br>*Replace* ................    Labor ..........34.70 | ea | — | $34.70 | $34.70 |
| **DOOR SWEEP** ▶ | **Door sweep**<br>*Replace* Material .......27.00    Labor ..........17.00<br>*Remove* ................    Labor ..........6.26 | ea | $6.26 | $44.00 | $50.26 |
| | **Remove door sweep for work, then reinstall**<br>*Replace* ................    Labor ..........30.10 | ea | — | $30.10 | $30.10 |
| **THRESHOLD** ▶<br>Standard grade is<br>aluminum or flat wood. | **Door threshold, standard grade**<br>*Replace* Material .......15.00    Labor ..........18.80<br>*Remove* ................    Labor ..........6.86 | ea | $6.86 | $33.80 | $40.66 |
| | **Door threshold, high grade**<br>*Replace* Material .......28.0000    Labor ..........18.80<br>*Remove* ................    Labor ..........6.86 | ea | $6.86 | $46.80 | $53.66 |
| | **Remove door threshold for work, then reinstall**<br>*Replace* ................    Labor ..........34.00 | ea | — | $34.00 | $34.00 |
| **WEATHERSTRIP** ▶ | **Door weatherstripping**<br>*Replace* Material .......18.00    Labor ..........16.50<br>*Remove* ................    Labor ..........5.11 | ea | $5.11 | $34.50 | $39.61 |
| **GARAGE DOOR** ▶<br>**HARDWARE** | **Garage door hardware, standard grade**<br>*Replace* Material .......73.00    Labor ..........90.90<br>*Remove* ................    Labor ..........20.00 | ea | $20.00 | $163.90 | $183.90 |
| | **Garage door hardware, high grade**<br>*Replace* Material .......99.00    Labor ..........90.90<br>*Remove* ................    Labor ..........20.00 | ea | $20.00 | $189.90 | $209.90 |
| | **Remove garage door hardware for work, then reinstall**<br>*Replace* ................    Labor ..........160.00 | ea | — | $160.00 | $160.00 |

# TIME & MATERIAL CHARTS (selected items)

## Door Hardware Materials

See **Door Hardware** material prices with the line items and other information in the **QuickFinder** column.

## Door Hardware Labor

| LABORER | BASE WAGE | PAID LEAVE | TRUE WAGE | FICA | FUTA | WORKER'S COMP. | UNEMPLOY. INSUR. | HEALTH INSUR. | RETIRE (401K) | LIABILITY INSUR. | COST PER HOUR |
|---|---|---|---|---|---|---|---|---|---|---|---|
| Finish carpenter | $22.60 | 1.76 | $24.36 | 1.86 | .19 | 4.56 | 2.12 | 2.54 | .73 | 3.17 | $39.50 |
| Demolition laborer | $13.40 | 1.05 | $14.45 | 1.11 | .12 | 4.44 | 1.26 | 2.54 | .43 | 1.88 | $26.20 |

**Paid Leave** is calculated based on two weeks paid vacation, one week sick leave, and seven paid holidays. Employer's matching portion of **FICA** is 7.65 percent. **FUTA** (Federal Unemployment) is .8 percent. **Worker's compensation** for the door hardware trade was calculated using a national average of 18.71 percent. **Unemployment insurance** was calculated using a national average of 8.7 percent. **Health insurance** was calculated based on a projected national average for 2001 of $505 per employee (and family when applicable) per month. Employer pays 80 percent for a per month cost of $404 per employee. **Retirement** is based on a 401(k) retirement program with employer matching of 50 percent. Employee contributions to the 401(k) plan are an average of 6 percent of the true wage. **Liability insurance** is based on a national average of 12.9 percent.

## Door Hardware Labor Productivity

| WORK DESCRIPTION | LABORER | COST PER HOUR | PRODUCTIVITY | UNIT PRICE |
|---|---|---|---|---|
| **Demolition** | | | | |
| deadbolt | demolition laborer | $26.20 | .276 | $7.23 ea |
| exterior door keyed lockset | demolition laborer | $26.20 | .314 | $8.23 ea |
| entry door keyed lockset | demolition laborer | $26.20 | .696 | $18.20 ea |
| antique-style door thumb latch | demolition laborer | $26.20 | .516 | $13.50 ea |
| interior door lockset | demolition laborer | $26.20 | .281 | $7.36 ea |
| door closer | demolition laborer | $26.20 | .291 | $7.62 ea |
| security chain | demolition laborer | $26.20 | .258 | $6.76 ea |
| hinges | demolition laborer | $26.20 | .485 | $12.70 ea |
| door knocker | demolition laborer | $26.20 | .250 | $6.55 ea |
| storm door hinges | demolition laborer | $26.20 | .457 | $12.00 ea |
| storm door lockset | demolition laborer | $26.20 | .327 | $8.57 ea |
| door stop | demolition laborer | $26.20 | .084 | $2.20 ea |
| door push plate | demolition laborer | $26.20 | .160 | $4.19 ea |
| door kick plate | demolition laborer | $26.20 | .213 | $5.58 ea |
| door letter plate | demolition laborer | $26.20 | .216 | $5.66 ea |
| door peep hole | demolition laborer | $26.20 | .205 | $5.37 ea |
| door sweep | demolition laborer | $26.20 | .239 | $6.26 ea |
| door threshold | demolition laborer | $26.20 | .262 | $6.86 ea |
| door weatherstripping | demolition laborer | $26.20 | .195 | $5.11 ea |
| garage door hardware | demolition laborer | $26.20 | .762 | $20.00 ea |
| **Install deadbolt** | | | | |
| install | finish carpenter | $39.50 | .678 | $26.80 ea |
| remove for work, then reinstall | finish carpenter | $39.50 | 1.10 | $43.50 ea |
| **Install exterior door keyed lockset** | | | | |
| install | finish carpenter | $39.50 | .461 | $18.20 ea |
| remove for work, then reinstall | finish carpenter | $39.50 | 1.03 | $40.70 ea |
| **Install entry door keyed lockset** | | | | |
| install | finish carpenter | $39.50 | 1.45 | $57.30 ea |
| remove for work, then reinstall | finish carpenter | $39.50 | 2.73 | $108.00 ea |
| **Install antique style door thumb latch** | | | | |
| install | finish carpenter | $39.50 | 1.73 | $68.30 ea |

. . . More ➤

## Door Hardware Labor Productivity *continued*

| WORK DESCRIPTION | LABORER | COST PER HOUR | PRODUCTIVITY | UNIT PRICE |
|---|---|---|---|---|
| **Install interior door lockset** | | | | |
| install | finish carpenter | $39.50 | .405 | $16.00 ea |
| remove for work, then reinstall | finish carpenter | $39.50 | .710 | $28.00 ea |
| **Install door closer** | | | | |
| spring hinge | finish carpenter | $39.50 | .257 | $10.20 ea |
| typical | finish carpenter | $39.50 | .431 | $17.00 ea |
| remove for work, then reinstall | finish carpenter | $39.50 | .742 | $29.30 ea |
| **Install security chain** | | | | |
| install | finish carpenter | $39.50 | .262 | $10.30 ea |
| remove for work, then reinstall | finish carpenter | $39.50 | .445 | $17.60 ea |
| **Install door hinges** | | | | |
| typical | finish carpenter | $39.50 | .438 | $17.30 ea |
| for batten door | finish carpenter | $39.50 | .495 | $19.60 ea |
| remove for work, then reinstall | finish carpenter | $39.50 | .786 | $31.00 ea |
| **Install door knocker** | | | | |
| install | finish carpenter | $39.50 | .351 | $13.90 ea |
| remove for work, then reinstall | finish carpenter | $39.50 | .636 | $25.10 ea |
| **Install storm door hinges** | | | | |
| install | finish carpenter | $39.50 | .342 | $13.50 ea |
| remove for work, then reinstall | finish carpenter | $39.50 | .607 | $24.00 ea |
| **Install storm door lockset** | | | | |
| install | finish carpenter | $39.50 | .387 | $15.30 ea |
| remove for work, then reinstall | finish carpenter | $39.50 | .685 | $27.10 ea |
| **Install door stop** | | | | |
| hinge | finish carpenter | $39.50 | .128 | $5.06 ea |
| baseboard | finish carpenter | $39.50 | .138 | $5.45 ea |
| remove for work, then reinstall | finish carpenter | $39.50 | .252 | $9.95 ea |
| **Install door push plate** | | | | |
| install | finish carpenter | $39.50 | .417 | $16.50 ea |
| remove for work, then reinstall | finish carpenter | $39.50 | .742 | $29.30 ea |
| **Install door kick plate** | | | | |
| install | finish carpenter | $39.50 | .445 | $17.60 ea |
| remove for work, then reinstall | finish carpenter | $39.50 | .809 | $32.00 ea |
| **Install letter plate** | | | | |
| install | finish carpenter | $39.50 | .500 | $19.80 ea |
| remove for work, then reinstall | finish carpenter | $39.50 | .902 | $35.60 ea |
| **Install door peep hole** | | | | |
| install | finish carpenter | $39.50 | .484 | $19.10 ea |
| remove for work, then reinstall | finish carpenter | $39.50 | .879 | $34.70 ea |
| **Install door sweep** | | | | |
| install | finish carpenter | $39.50 | .431 | $17.00 ea |
| remove for work, then reinstall | finish carpenter | $39.50 | .763 | $30.10 ea |
| **Install door threshold** | | | | |
| install | finish carpenter | $39.50 | .477 | $18.80 ea |
| remove for work, then reinstall | finish carpenter | $39.50 | .862 | $34.00 ea |
| **Install door weatherstripping** | | | | |
| install | finish carpenter | $39.50 | .417 | $16.50 ea |
| **Install garage door hardware** | | | | |
| install | finish carpenter | $39.50 | 2.30 | $90.90 ea |
| remove for work, then reinstall | finish carpenter | $39.50 | 4.05 | $160.00 ea |

NOTES: _____

_____

_____

_____ end

# 12 ............................................................ *Drywall*

| Item Description | Unit | Remove | Replace | Total |
|---|---|---|---|---|
| **Remove drywall & prep walls for new installation**<br>*Remove*........................  Labor.............21 | sf | **$.21** | — | **$.21** |
| **Scrape (remove) acoustic ceiling texture**<br>*Remove*........................  Labor.............29 | sf | **$.29** | — | **$.29** |
| **Scrape (remove) painted acoustic ceiling texture**<br>*Remove*........................  Labor.............50 | sf | **$.50** | — | **$.50** |
| **Remove furring strips attached to wood, 16" on center**<br>*Remove*........................  Labor.............26 | sf | **$.26** | — | **$.26** |
| **Remove furring strips attached to concrete or masonry, 16" on center**<br>*Remove*........................  Labor.............29 | sf | **$.29** | — | **$.29** |
| **Remove furring strips attached to wood, 24" on center**<br>*Remove*........................  Labor.............24 | sf | **$.24** | — | **$.24** |
| **Remove furring strips attached to concrete or masonry, 24" on center**<br>*Remove*........................  Labor.............26 | sf | **$.26** | — | **$.26** |
| **3/8" drywall installed with machine texture**<br>*Replace* Materials .........47   Labor ...........1.14<br>*Remove*........................  Labor.............21 | sf | **$.21** | **$1.61** | **$1.82** |
| **3/8" drywall installed with knock-down machine texture**<br>*Replace* Materials .........47   Labor ...........1.18<br>*Remove*........................  Labor.............21 | sf | **$.21** | **$1.65** | **$1.86** |
| **3/8" drywall installed with light texture**<br>*Replace* Materials .........48   Labor ...........1.22<br>*Remove*........................  Labor.............21 | sf | **$.21** | **$1.70** | **$1.91** |
| **3/8" drywall installed with medium texture**<br>*Replace* Materials .........52   Labor ...........1.26<br>*Remove*........................  Labor.............21 | sf | **$.21** | **$1.78** | **$1.99** |
| **3/8" drywall installed heavy texture**<br>*Replace* Materials .........56   Labor ...........1.30<br>*Remove*........................  Labor.............21 | sf | **$.21** | **$1.86** | **$2.07** |
| **3/8" drywall installed with smooth-wall finish**<br>*Replace* Materials .........50   Labor ...........1.49<br>*Remove*........................  Labor.............21 | sf | **$.21** | **$1.99** | **$2.20** |
| **3/8" drywall installed (all coats, no texture)**<br>*Replace* Materials .........38   Labor...........1.02<br>*Remove*........................  Labor.............21 | sf | **$.21** | **$1.40** | **$1.61** |
| **3/8" drywall, hung & fire taped only**<br>*Replace* Materials .........36   Labor.............74<br>*Remove*........................  Labor.............21 | sf | **$.21** | **$1.10** | **$1.31** |

◄ **DEMOLITION**
*Tear-out and debris removal to a truck or dumpster on site. Does not include hauling, dumpster, or dump fees. No salvage value is assumed.*

◄ **3/8" DRYWALL**

**DRYWALL INSTALLATION**

Drywall is hung and taped according to industry standards. Drywall is attached with nails when hung, then permanently affixed with screws. Perfatape and three coats of mud are applied plus texture.

One lf of corner bead is calculated for every 24 sf of installed drywall.

Productivity is based on repair installations.

| Item Description | Unit | Remove | Replace | Total |
|---|---|---|---|---|
| **3/8″ drywall, hung only (no tape, coating or texture)** | sf | $.21 | $.73 | $.94 |
| *Replace* Materials ........ .34     Labor............ .39 | | | | |
| *Remove*....................     Labor............ .21 | | | | |
| **Add for installation of 3/8″ drywall over existing plaster wall** | sf | — | $.12 | $.12 |
| *Replace* ................     Labor............ ..12 | | | | |
| **Add for 3/8″ foil-backed drywall** | sf | — | $.10 | $.10 |
| *Replace* Materials ........ .10 | | | | |
| **1/2″ drywall installed with machine texture** | sf | $.21 | $1.59 | $1.80 |
| *Replace* Materials ........ .45     Labor............1.14 | | | | |
| *Remove*....................     Labor............ .21 | | | | |
| **1/2″ drywall installed with knock-down machine texture** | sf | $.21 | $1.63 | $1.84 |
| *Replace* Materials ........ .45     Labor............1.18 | | | | |
| *Remove*....................     Labor............ .21 | | | | |
| **1/2″ drywall installed with light texture** | sf | $.21 | $1.68 | $1.89 |
| *Replace* Materials ........ .46     Labor............1.22 | | | | |
| *Remove*....................     Labor............ .21 | | | | |
| **1/2″ drywall installed with medium texture** | sf | $.21 | $1.76 | $1.97 |
| *Replace* Materials ........ .50     Labor............1.26 | | | | |
| *Remove*....................     Labor............ .21 | | | | |
| **1/2″ drywall installed heavy texture** | sf | $.21 | $1.84 | $2.05 |
| *Replace* Materials ........ .54     Labor............1.30 | | | | |
| *Remove*....................     Labor............ .21 | | | | |
| **1/2″ drywall installed with smooth-wall finish** | sf | $.21 | $1.97 | $2.18 |
| *Replace* Materials ........ .48     Labor............1.49 | | | | |
| *Remove*....................     Labor............ .21 | | | | |
| **1/2″ drywall installed (all coats, no texture)** | sf | $.21 | $1.38 | $1.59 |
| *Replace* Materials ........ .36     Labor............ 1.02 | | | | |
| *Remove*....................     Labor............ .21 | | | | |
| **1/2″ drywall, hung & fire taped only** | sf | $.21 | $1.08 | $1.29 |
| *Replace* Materials ........ .34     Labor............ .74 | | | | |
| *Remove*....................     Labor............ .21 | | | | |
| **1/2″ drywall, hung only (no tape, coating or texture)** | sf | $.21 | $.71 | $.92 |
| *Replace* Materials ........ .32     Labor............ .39 | | | | |
| *Remove*....................     Labor............ .21 | | | | |
| **Add for installation of 1/2″ drywall over existing plaster wall** | sf | — | $.12 | $.12 |
| *Replace* ................     Labor............ .12 | | | | |
| **Add for 1/2″ moisture-resistant drywall** | sf | — | $.11 | $.11 |
| *Replace* Materials ........ .11 | | | | |
| **Add for 1/2″ type X fire-rated drywall** | sf | — | $.09 | $.09 |
| *Replace* Materials ........ .09 | | | | |
| **Add for 1/2″ foil-backed drywall** | sf | — | $.15 | $.15 |
| *Replace* Materials ........ .15 | | | | |
| **Add for 1/2″ type X fire-rated, foil-backed drywall** | sf | — | $.22 | $.22 |
| *Replace* Materials ........ .22 | | | | |

**3/8″ DRYWALL** ▶ *continued*

**1/2″ DRYWALL** ▶

| Item Description | Unit | Remove | Replace | Total | |
|---|---|---|---|---|---|
| **5/8" drywall installed with machine texture**<br>*Replace* Materials ......... .52  Labor ............1.14<br>*Remove*...................  Labor............ .21 | sf | $.21 | $1.66 | $1.87 | ◄ **5/8" DRYWALL** |
| **5/8" drywall installed with knock-down machine texture**<br>*Replace* Materials ........ .52  Labor ............1.18<br>*Remove*...................  Labor............ .21 | sf | $.21 | $1.70 | $1.91 | |
| **5/8" drywall installed with light texture**<br>*Replace* Materials ........ .53  Labor ............1.22<br>*Remove*...................  Labor............ .21 | sf | $.21 | $1.75 | $1.96 | |
| **5/8" drywall installed with medium texture**<br>*Replace* Materials ........ .57  Labor ............1.26<br>*Remove*...................  Labor............ .21 | sf | $.21 | $1.83 | $2.04 | |
| **5/8" drywall installed heavy texture**<br>*Replace* Materials ........ .61  Labor ............1.30<br>*Remove*...................  Labor............ .21 | sf | $.21 | $1.91 | $2.12 | |
| **5/8" drywall installed with smooth-wall finish**<br>*Replace* Materials ........ .55  Labor ............1.49<br>*Remove*...................  Labor............ .21 | sf | $.21 | $2.04 | $2.25 | |
| **5/8" drywall installed (all coats, no texture)**<br>*Replace* Materials ........ .43  Labor ............ 1.02<br>*Remove*...................  Labor............ .21 | sf | $.21 | $1.45 | $1.66 | |
| **5/8" drywall, hung & fire taped only**<br>*Replace* Materials ........ .41  Labor ............ .74<br>*Remove*...................  Labor............ .21 | sf | $.21 | $1.15 | $1.36 | |
| **5/8" drywall, hung only (no tape, coating or texture)**<br>*Replace* Materials ........ .39  Labor ............ .39<br>*Remove*...................  Labor............ .21 | sf | $.21 | $.78 | $.99 | |
| **Add for installation of 5/8" drywall over existing plaster wall**<br>*Replace* ...................  Labor ............. | sf | — | $.12 | $.12 | |
| **Add for 5/8" moisture-resistant drywall**<br>*Replace* Materials ........ .10 | sf | — | $.10 | $.10 | |
| **Add for 5/8" foil-backed drywall**<br>*Replace* Materials ........ .18 | sf | — | $.18 | $.18 | |
| **Acoustic ceiling (cottage cheese) texture, light coverage**<br>*Replace* Materials ........ .14  Labor............ .32<br>*Remove*...................  Labor............ .29 | sf | $.29 | $.46 | $.75 | ◄ **ACOUSTIC CEILING** |
| **Acoustic ceiling (cottage cheese) texture, medium coverage**<br>*Replace* Materials ........ .18  Labor............ .44<br>*Remove*...................  Labor............ .29 | sf | $.29 | $.62 | $.91 | |
| **Acoustic ceiling (cottage cheese) texture, heavy coverage**<br>*Replace* Materials ........ .20  Labor............ .64<br>*Remove*...................  Labor............ .29 | sf | $.29 | $.84 | $1.13 | |
| **Glitter application to acoustic-ceiling texture**<br>*Replace* Materials ........ .01  Labor............ .08 | sf | — | $.09 | $.09 | |

**RELATED ITEMS**

| | Item Description | Unit | Remove | Replace | Total |
|---|---|---|---|---|---|
| **MINIMUM ▶**<br>**ACOUSTIC CHARGE** | **Minimum charge for acoustic-ceiling texture**<br>*Replace* Materials......90.00    Labor..........62.90 | ea | — | $152.90 | $152.90 |
| **DRYWALL PATCH ▶** | **Drywall patch (match existing texture or finish)**<br>*Replace* Materials......25.00    Labor..........56.50 | ea | — | $81.50 | $81.50 |
| **MINIMUM ▶**<br>**DRYWALL CHARGE** | **Minimum charge for drywall repair**<br>*Replace* Materials......35.00    Labor........231.00 | ea | — | $266.00 | $266.00 |
| **TEXTURE ▶** | **Texture drywall with light hand texture**<br>*Replace* Materials........10    Labor............20 | sf | — | $.30 | $.30 |
| | **Texture drywall with medium hand texture**<br>*Replace* Materials........14    Labor............24 | sf | — | $.38 | $.38 |
| | **Texture drywall with heavy hand texture**<br>*Replace* Materials........18    Labor............24 | sf | — | $.42 | $.42 |
| | **Texture drywall with thin-coat smooth-wall**<br>*Replace* Materials........12    Labor............48 | sf | — | $.60 | $.60 |
| | **Texture drywall, machine applied**<br>*Replace* Materials........09    Labor............16 | sf | — | $.25 | $.25 |
| | **Texture drywall, machine applied and knocked down with trowel**<br>*Replace* Materials........09    Labor............20 | sf | — | $.29 | $.29 |
| **METAL FURRING ▶**<br>*See Rough Carpentry,*<br>*page 430 for wood*<br>*furring strips.* | **Metal hat-shaped furring channel, 16" on center on wood**<br>*Replace* Materials........16    Labor............38<br>*Remove*.....................    Labor............26 | sf | $.26 | $.54 | $.80 |
| | **Metal hat-shaped furring channel, 24" on center on wood**<br>*Replace* Materials........12    Labor............28<br>*Remove*.....................    Labor............24 | sf | $.24 | $.40 | $.64 |
| | **Metal sound-resistant furring channel, 16" on center on wood**<br>*Replace* Materials........18    Labor............38<br>*Remove*.....................    Labor............26 | sf | $.26 | $.56 | $.82 |
| △ *hat-shaped channel* | **Metal sound-resistant furring channel, 24" on center on wood**<br>*Replace* Materials........14    Labor............28<br>*Remove*.....................    Labor............24 | sf | $.24 | $.42 | $.66 |
| | **Metal hat-shaped furring channel, 16" on center on concrete or masonry**<br>*Replace* Materials........16    Labor............41<br>*Remove*.....................    Labor............29 | sf | $.29 | $.57 | $.86 |
| △ *sound-resistant channel* | **Metal hat-shaped furring channel, 24" on center on concrete or masonry**<br>*Replace* Materials........12    Labor............28<br>*Remove*.....................    Labor............26 | sf | $.26 | $.40 | $.66 |
| | **Metal sound-resistant furring channel, 16" on center on concrete or masonry**<br>*Replace* Materials........18    Labor............41<br>*Remove*.....................    Labor............29 | sf | $.29 | $.59 | $.88 |
| △ *Z channel* | **Metal sound-resistant furring channel, 24" on center on concrete or masonry**<br>*Replace* Materials........14    Labor............28<br>*Remove*.....................    Labor............26 | sf | $.26 | $.42 | $.68 |

| Item Description | Unit | Remove | Replace | Total |
|---|---|---|---|---|
| **Metal Z channel, 16" on center on concrete or masonry** | sf | $.29 | $.54 | $.83 |
| *Replace* Materials ........ .13    Labor............ .41 | | | | |
| *Remove*................ Labor............ .29 | | | | |
| **Metal Z channel, 24" on center on concrete or masonry** | sf | $.26 | $.37 | $.63 |
| *Replace* Materials ........ .09    Labor............ .28 | | | | |
| *Remove*................ Labor............ .26 | | | | |

**RELATED ITEMS**

Cleaning .....................58
Painting ....................333
Paneling ...................347
Plaster......................353
**Rough Carpentry**
   *furring strips*................430
Wallpaper ..................495

NOTES: _____

_____

_____ end

# TIME & MATERIAL CHARTS *(selected items)*

## Drywall Materials

| DESCRIPTION | MATERIAL PRICE | GROSS COVERAGE | WASTE | NET COVERAGE | UNIT PRICE |
|---|---|---|---|---|---|
| **3/8" drywall board** | | | | | |
| standard | $292.00 per 1,000 | 1,000 | 8% | 920 | $.32 sf |
| foil-backed | $388.00 per 1,000 | 1,000 | 8% | 920 | $.42 sf |
| **1/2" drywall board** | | | | | |
| standard | $279.00 per 1,000 | 1,000 | 7% | 930 | $.30 sf |
| moisture-resistant | $384.00 per 1,000 | 1,000 | 7% | 930 | $.41 sf |
| foil-backed | $400.00 per 1,000 | 1,000 | 7% | 930 | $.43 sf |
| fire-rated type X | $344.00 per 1,000 | 1,000 | 7% | 930 | $.37 sf |
| fire-rated type X foil-backed | $486.00 per 1,000 | 1,000 | 7% | 930 | $.52 sf |
| **5/8" drywall board** | | | | | |
| type X | $342.00 per 1,000 | 1,000 | 7% | 930 | $.37 sf |
| moisture-resistant | $440.00 per 1,000 | 1,000 | 7% | 930 | $.47 sf |
| **Fasteners** | | | | | |
| drywall nails, used to secure when hanging | $47.00 per box | 32,000 | 4% | 30,720 | $.01 sf |
| drywall screws, used to attach after hung | $93.00 per box | 8,534 | 3% | 8,278 | $.01 sf |
| **Drywall taping materials** | | | | | |
| perfatape (per 500' roll) | $6.00 per roll | 1,111 | 6% | 1,044 | $.01 sf |
| corner bead | $1.00 per stick | 204 | 4% | 196 | $.01 sf |
| joint compound | $13.40 per 50 lb box | 965 | 16% | 811 | $.02 sf |
| **Drywall texture compound** | | | | | |
| machine-sprayed | $14.60 per 50 lb box | 190 | 13% | 165 | $.09 sf |
| light hand texture | $14.60 per 50 lb box | 175 | 13% | 152 | $.10 sf |
| medium hand texture | $14.60 per 50 lb box | 120 | 13% | 104 | $.14 sf |
| heavy hand texture | $14.60 per 50 lb box | 93 | 14% | 80 | $.18 sf |
| heavy trowel texture | $14.60 per 50 lb box | 77 | 15% | 65 | $.22 sf |
| smooth wall | $14.60 per 50 lb box | 142 | 14% | 122 | $.12 sf |
| **Acoustic ceiling (cottage cheese) texture compound** | | | | | |
| light texture | $25.50 per 50 lb bag | 220 | 17% | 183 | $.14 sf |
| medium texture | $25.50 per 50 lb box | 170 | 17% | 141 | $.18 sf |
| heavy texture | $25.50 per 50 lb box | 153 | 17% | 127 | $.20 sf |
| **Acoustic ceiling glitter (per pound)** | | | | | |
| light to heavy application | $3.10 per pound | 2,350 | 22% | 1,833 | $.01 sf |
| **Metal furring strips** | | | | | |
| hat-shaped channel installed 24" on center | $2.40 per 12' stick | 21 | 3% | 20 | $.12 sf |
| sound-resistant channel installed 24" on center | $2.70 per 12' stick | 21 | 3% | 20 | $.14 sf |
| Z channel installed 24" on center | $1.30 per 8' stick | 15 | 3% | 15 | $.09 sf |

## Drywall Rental Equipment

| DESCRIPTION | PRICE | COVERAGE | UNIT PRICE |
|---|---|---|---|
| Ames taping tools | $10.00 per day | 416 per day | $.02 sf |
| texture equipment (gun with hopper & compressor) | $60.00 per day | 1,536 per day | $.04 sf |
| glitter blower for acoustic ceilings | $5.00 per day | 5,000 per day | $.001 sf |
| drywall lifter (for one-person hanging) | $15.00 per day | 102 per day | $.15 sf |
| minimum charge | $40.00 minimum | 1 minimum | $40.00 each |

## Drywall Labor

| LABORER | BASE WAGE | PAID LEAVE | TRUE WAGE | FICA | FUTA | WORKER'S COMP. | UNEMPLOY. INSUR. | HEALTH INSUR. | RETIRE (401K) | LIABILITY INSUR. | COST PER HOUR |
|---|---|---|---|---|---|---|---|---|---|---|---|
| Drywall hanger | $21.70 | 1.69 | $23.39 | 1.79 | .19 | 5.77 | 2.03 | 2.54 | .70 | 3.04 | $39.50 |
| Drywall hanger's helper | $15.70 | 1.22 | $16.92 | 1.29 | .14 | 4.17 | 1.47 | 2.54 | .51 | 2.20 | $29.20 |
| Drywall taper | $21.90 | 1.71 | $23.61 | 1.81 | .19 | 5.82 | 2.05 | 2.54 | .71 | 3.07 | $39.80 |
| Demolition laborer | $13.40 | 1.05 | $14.45 | 1.11 | 12 | 4.44 | 1.26 | 2.54 | .43 | 1.88 | $26.20 |

**Paid Leave** is calculated based on two weeks paid vacation, one week sick leave, and seven paid holidays. Employer's matching portion of **FICA** is 7.65 percent. **FUTA** (Federal Unemployment) is .8 percent. **Worker's compensation** for the drywall trade was calculated using a national average of 24.66 percent. **Unemployment insurance** was calculated using a national average of 8.7 percent. **Health insurance** was calculated based on a projected national average for 2001 of $505 per employee (and family when applicable) per month. Employer pays 80 percent for a per month cost of $404 per employee. **Retirement** is based on a 401(k) retirement program with employer matching of 50 percent. Employee contributions to the 401(k) plan are an average of 6 percent of the true wage. **Liability insurance** is based on a national average of 12.9 percent.

## Drywall Labor Productivity

| WORK DESCRIPTION | LABORER | COST PER HOUR | PRODUCTIVITY | UNIT PRICE |
|---|---|---|---|---|
| **Demolition** | | | | |
| remove drywall and prep walls | demolition laborer | $26.20 | .008 | $.21 sf |
| scrape and prep acoustical ceiling | demolition laborer | $26.20 | .011 | $.29 sf |
| scrape and prep painted acoustical ceiling | demolition laborer | $26.20 | .019 | $.50 sf |
| remove furring strips on wood, 16" oc | demolition laborer | $26.20 | .010 | $.26 sf |
| remove furring strips on conc. or masonry, 16" oc | demolition laborer | $26.20 | .011 | $.29 sf |
| remove furring strips on wood, 24" oc | demolition laborer | $26.20 | .009 | $.24 sf |
| remove furring strips on conc. or masonry, 24" oc | demolition laborer | $26.20 | .010 | $.26 sf |
| **Hang drywall** | | | | |
| hang drywall | drywall hanger | $39.50 | | |
| hang drywall | drywall hanger's helper | $29.20 | | |
| hang drywall | drywall hanging crew | $34.40 | | |
| **Tape and coat drywall** | | | | |
| to finish (no texture) | drywall taper | $39.80 | .017 | $.68 sf |
| tape coat only | drywall taper | $39.80 | .010 | $.40 sf |
| tape coat and one additional coat only | drywall taper | $39.80 | .012 | $.48 sf |
| to finish, apply machine-sprayed texture | drywall taper | $39.80 | .020 | $.80 sf |
| to finish, apply machine-sprayed, knock-down texture | drywall taper | $39.80 | .021 | $.84 sf |
| to finish, apply light hand texture | drywall taper | $39.80 | .022 | $.88 sf |
| to finish, apply heavy hand texture | drywall taper | $39.80 | .024 | $.96 sf |
| to finish, apply smooth-wall texture | drywall taper | $39.80 | .029 | $1.15 sf |
| **Apply texture** | | | | |
| with compressor and spray gun | drywall taper | $39.80 | .004 | $.16 sf |
| with spray gun, then knock down with trowel | drywall taper | $39.80 | .005 | $.20 sf |
| light hand texture | drywall taper | $39.80 | .005 | $.20 sf |
| heavy hand texture | drywall taper | $39.80 | .006 | $.24 sf |
| thin coat smooth-wall finish | drywall taper | $39.80 | .012 | $.48 sf |
| **Apply acoustical ceiling texture** | | | | |
| light | drywall taper | $39.80 | .008 | $.32 sf |
| heavy | drywall taper | $39.80 | .016 | $.64 sf |
| apply glitter to freshly sprayed ceiling | drywall taper | $39.80 | .002 | $.08 sf |

# 13 ........................ Electrical

| Item Description | Unit | Remove | Replace | Total | |
|---|---|---|---|---|---|
| **Minimum charge for electrical work** <br> *Replace* Materials......20.00     Labor..........48.10 | ea | — | $68.10 | $68.10 | ◀ **MINIMUM** |
| **Complete house wiring, outlets, switches & light fixtures, economy grade** <br> *Replace* Materials........1.52     Labor............1.90 | sf | — | $3.42 | $3.42 | ◀ **COMPLETE HOUSE** <br> *Complete house wiring, boxes, switches, outlets and fixtures to code for a house that is not electrically heated. (Electrical hookups for furnace, AC unit, and/or heat pump included.) Does not include breaker panel, main disconnect or service drop. Grades refer to quality of light fixtures (see pages 154-155).* |
| **Complete house wiring, outlets, switches & light fixtures, standard grade** <br> *Replace* Materials........1.73     Labor............3.23 | sf | — | $4.96 | $4.96 | |
| **Complete house wiring, outlets, switches & light fixtures, high grade** <br> *Replace* Materials........1.99     Labor............3.73 | sf | — | $5.72 | $5.72 | |
| **Complete house wiring, outlets, switches & light fixtures, deluxe grade** <br> *Replace* Materials........2.10     Labor............3.91 | sf | — | $6.01 | $6.01 | |
| **Complete house wiring, outlets, switches & light fixtures, low-voltage system** <br> *Replace* Materials........1.92     Labor............3.59 | sf | — | $5.51 | $5.51 | |
| **Add for complete house electrical with wiring in conduit** <br> *Replace* Materials........1.93     Labor............1.97 <br> ▶ EMT conduit with 4.4 terminations, 7 bends, and 4 clamps per 100 lf. | sf | — | $3.90 | $3.90 | |
| **Complete house rough electrical (no light fixtures), standard** <br> *Replace* Materials........ .89     Labor............2.51 | sf | — | $3.40 | $3.40 | ◀ **COMPLETE HOUSE WIRING** <br> *Same as above but does not include fixtures.* |
| **Complete house rough electrical (no light fixtures), in conduit** <br> *Replace* Materials........1.97     Labor............5.53 <br> ▶ EMT conduit with 4.4 terminations, 7 bends, and 4 clamps per 100 lf. | sf | — | $7.50 | $7.50 | |
| **Complete house rough electrical (no light fixtures), low-voltage system** <br> *Replace* Materials........ .97     Labor............2.69 | sf | — | $3.66 | $3.66 | |
| **Complete house light fixtures, economy grade** <br> *Replace* Materials........ .98     Labor............. .54 | sf | — | $1.52 | $1.52 | ◀ **COMPLETE HOUSE FIXTURES** <br> *See pages 154-155 for info about fixture grades.* |
| **Complete house light fixtures, standard grade** <br> *Replace* Materials........1.27     Labor............. .57 | sf | — | $1.84 | $1.84 | |
| **Complete house light fixtures, high grade** <br> *Replace* Materials........1.77     Labor............. .57 | sf | — | $2.34 | $2.34 | |
| **Complete house light fixtures, deluxe grade** <br> *Replace* Materials........2.33     Labor............. .61 | sf | — | $2.94 | $2.94 | |
| **Complete house light fixtures for low-voltage system** <br> *Replace* Materials........1.69     Labor............. .61 | sf | — | $2.16 | $2.16 | |
| **120 volt outlet with wiring run & box** <br> *Replace* Materials........15.00     Labor........35.10 <br> ▶ General-purpose use, average of 6 outlets per single-pole breaker (breaker not included). Includes up to 15 lf of #12/2 wire. | ea | — | $50.10 | $50.10 | ◀ **WIRE, OUTLETS & SWITCHES** <br> *Unless otherwise indicated, includes outlet or switch, box, and up to 26 lf of wire.* |

**VOLTAGE**

Voltage listed as "120 volt" applies to 110, 115, 120, and 125 volt applications.

Voltage listed as "240 volt" applies to 220, 240, or 250 volt applications.

| | Item Description | Unit | Remove | Replace | Total |
|---|---|---|---|---|---|
| **WIRE, OUTLETS & SWITCHES** *continued* | **120 volt GFCI outlet with wiring run & box**<br>*Replace* Materials ......45.00   Labor..........35.10<br>► Average of 3 outlets per single–pole breaker. Includes up to 26 lf of #12/2 wire. | ea | — | $80.10 | $80.10 |
| | **120 volt exterior waterproof outlet with wiring run & box**<br>*Replace* Materials ......20.00   Labor..........35.10<br>► General-purpose use, average of 3 outlets per single–pole breaker (breaker not included). Includes up to 26 lf of #12/2 wire. | ea | — | $55.10 | $55.10 |
| | **120 volt switch with wiring run & box**<br>*Replace* Materials ......20.00   Labor..........35.10<br>► Includes up to 15 lf of #12/2 wire. | ea | — | $55.10 | $55.10 |
| | **120 volt 3-way switch with wiring run & box**<br>*Replace* Materials ......30.00   Labor..........70.00<br>► Includes up to 20 lf of #12/2 wire. | ea | — | $100.00 | $100.00 |
| | **120 volt exterior waterproof switch with wiring run & box**<br>*Replace* Materials ......20.00   Labor..........35.10<br>► Includes up to 26 lf of #12/2 wire. | ea | — | $55.10 | $55.10 |
| **240 volt** | **240 volt outlet with wiring run & box (30 amp)**<br>*Replace* Materials ......65.00   Labor ..........48.10<br>► Includes up to 30 lf of #10/3 wire and a 30 amp double-pole breaker. Common uses: small clothes dryers, through-wall AC / heat units, and baseboard heaters. | ea | — | $113.10 | $113.10 |
| | **240 volt outlet with wiring run & box (40 amp)**<br>*Replace* Materials ......70.00   Labor ..........48.10<br>► Includes up to 30 lf of #8/3 wire and a 40 amp double-pole breaker. Common uses: clothes dryers, kitchen ranges. | ea | — | $118.10 | $118.10 |
| | **240 volt outlet with wiring run & box (50 amp)**<br>*Replace* Materials ......80.00   Labor ..........48.10<br>► Includes up to 30 lf of #6/3 wire and a 50 amp double-pole breaker. Common use: air conditioning hookup. | ea | — | $128.10 | $128.10 |
| | **240 volt switch with wiring run & box**<br>*Replace* Materials ......70.00   Labor ..........48.10<br>► Includes up to 15 lf of #10/2 wire. | ea | — | $118.10 | $118.10 |
| **low-voltage** | **Low-voltage switch wiring run & box**<br>*Replace* Materials ......20.00   Labor ..........33.40<br>► Includes up to 18 lf of #18/2 wire. | ea | — | $53.40 | $53.40 |
| **OUTLETS & SWITCHES** *Includes outlet or switch and cover only (no wire or box).* | **120 volt outlet with cover**<br>*Replace* Materials ........9.00   Labor ............8.11<br>*Remove* ......................   Labor ............3.93 | ea | $3.93 | $17.11 | $21.04 |
| | **120 volt GFCI outlet with cover**<br>*Replace* Materials ......28.00   Labor ............8.11<br>*Remove* ......................   Labor ............3.93 | ea | $3.93 | $36.11 | $40.04 |
| | **120 volt exterior waterproof outlet with cover**<br>*Replace* Materials ......14.00   Labor ............8.11<br>*Remove* ......................   Labor ............3.93 | ea | $3.93 | $22.11 | $26.04 |
| | **120 volt switch with cover**<br>*Replace* Materials ........5.50   Labor ............8.11<br>*Remove* ......................   Labor ............3.93 | ea | $3.93 | $13.61 | $17.54 |

| Item Description | Unit | Remove | Replace | Total |
|---|---|---|---|---|
| **120 volt lighted switch with cover** | ea | $3.93 | $16.11 | $20.04 |
| *Replace* Materials........8.00    Labor .........8.11 | | | | |
| *Remove* .....................    Labor .........3.93 | | | | |
| **120 volt push-button switch with cover** | ea | $3.93 | $25.61 | $29.54 |
| *Replace* Materials....17.50    Labor .........8.11 | | | | |
| *Remove* .....................    Labor .........3.93 | | | | |
| ▶ Antique reproduction style, also use this price when replacing an antique rotary snap switch (used between 1900 and 1925). | | | | |
| **120 volt rotary dimmer switch with cover** | ea | $3.93 | $31.11 | $35.04 |
| *Replace* Materials......23.00    Labor .........8.11 | | | | |
| *Remove* .....................    Labor .........3.93 | | | | |
| **120 volt touch dimmer switch with cover** | ea | $3.93 | $36.11 | $40.04 |
| *Replace* Materials......28.00    Labor .........8.11 | | | | |
| *Remove* .....................    Labor .........3.93 | | | | |
| **120 volt exterior waterproof switch with cover** | ea | $3.93 | $22.61 | $26.54 |
| *Replace* Materials ......14.50    Labor .........8.11 | | | | |
| *Remove* .....................    Labor .........3.93 | | | | |
| **240 volt outlet with cover** | ea | $5.24 | $23.90 | $29.14 |
| *Replace* Materials......13.50    Labor .........10.40 | | | | |
| *Remove* .....................    Labor .........5.24 | | | | |
| ▶ 15, 30, or 50 amp style. | | | | |
| **240 volt switch with cover** | ea | $5.24 | $24.90 | $30.14 |
| *Replace* Materials ......14.50    Labor .........10.40 | | | | |
| *Remove* .....................    Labor .........5.24 | | | | |
| **Low-voltage computer network outlet** | ea | $3.93 | $40.10 | $44.03 |
| *Replace* Materials......28.00    Labor .........12.10 | | | | |
| *Remove* .....................    Labor .........3.93 | | | | |
| **Low-voltage sound system speaker outlet** | ea | — | $17.19 | $17.19 |
| *Replace* Materials......8.00    Labor .........9.19 | | | | |
| ▶ Use only when speaker wiring terminates at an outlet for connection to an external speaker.  See page 145 for wiring speakers that are mounted in the wall. | | | | |
| **Low-voltage TV outlet** | ea | $3.93 | $16.69 | $20.62 |
| *Replace* Materials........7.50    Labor .........9.19 | | | | |
| *Remove* .....................    Labor .........3.93 | | | | |
| **Low-voltage phone outlet** | ea | $3.93 | $14.69 | $18.62 |
| *Replace* Materials........5.50    Labor .........9.19 | | | | |
| *Remove* .....................    Labor .........3.93 | | | | |
| **Low-voltage switch with cover** | ea | $3.93 | $18.11 | $22.04 |
| *Replace* Materials ......10.00    Labor .........8.11 | | | | |
| *Remove* .....................    Labor .........3.93 | | | | |
| **Add for high grade outlet or switch cover** | ea | — | $1.00 | $1.00 |
| *Replace* Materials........1.00 | | | | |
| ▶ Decorative plastic, over-size plastic, and coated plastic covers. | | | | |
| **Add for deluxe grade outlet or switch cover** | ea | — | $3.00 | $3.00 |
| *Replace* Materials........3.00 | | | | |
| ▶ Brass, chrome, hardwood, or porcelain covers. | | | | |

△ *push-button switch*

◁ **240 volt**

◁ **low-voltage**

◁ **additional outlet covers**

| | Item Description | Unit | Remove | Replace | Total |
|---|---|---|---|---|---|
| **OUTLET / SWITCH ▶ COVERS** | **Outlet or switch cover, standard grade** | ea | $.92 | $1.72 | $2.64 |
| | *Replace* Materials........1.00        Labor............. .72 | | | | |
| | *Remove* .....................        Labor............. .92 | | | | |
| | ▶ Standard plastic cover style as is provided with typical switch. | | | | |
| | **Outlet or switch cover, high grade** | ea | $.92 | $3.72 | $4.64 |
| | *Replace* Materials........3.00        Labor............. .72 | | | | |
| | *Remove* .....................        Labor............. .92 | | | | |
| | ▶ Decorative plastic, wide plastic, and coated plastic covers. | | | | |
| | **Outlet or switch cover, deluxe grade** | ea | $.92 | $6.75 | $7.67 |
| | *Replace* Materials........6.00        Labor............. .75 | | | | |
| | *Remove* .....................        Labor............. .92 | | | | |
| | ▶ Brass, chrome, hardwood, or porcelain covers. | | | | |
| **WIRING RUN ▶** | **120 volt wiring for typical 120 volt appliance** | ea | — | $76.60 | $76.60 |
| | *Replace* Materials......40.00        Labor .........36.60 | | | | |
| | ▶ One direct-wired run per appliance. Includes up to 26 lf of #12/2 wire and box. Does not include breaker or outlet. | | | | |
| | **120 volt wiring for through-wall air conditioner and/or heater** | ea | — | $75.40 | $75.40 |
| | *Replace* Materials......30.50        Labor .........44.90 | | | | |
| | ▶ One direct-wired run per unit. Includes up to 26 lf of #12/2 wire and box. Does not include breaker or outlet. | | | | |
| | **120 volt wiring for bathroom fan** | ea | — | $44.00 | $44.00 |
| | *Replace* Materials......16.00        Labor .........28.00 | | | | |
| | ▶ General-purpose circuit. Includes up to 20 lf of #12/2 wire. Does not include fan or vent hose. | | | | |
| | **120 volt wiring with GFCI for bathroom ceiling heater** | ea | — | $72.50 | $72.50 |
| | *Replace* Materials......43.00        Labor .........29.50 | | | | |
| | ▶ Includes up to 24 lf of #12/2 wire. | | | | |
| | **120 volt wiring for clothes washer** | ea | — | $56.00 | $56.00 |
| | *Replace* Materials......28.00        Labor .........28.00 | | | | |
| | ▶ Laundry room outlet includes up to 20 lf of #12/2 wire. 1 to 2 outlets per circuit. Does not include breaker. | | | | |
| | **120 volt wiring for dishwasher** | ea | — | $45.50 | $45.50 |
| | *Replace* Materials.......17.50        Labor .........28.00 | | | | |
| | ▶ 1 direct-wired run. Includes up to 26 lf of #13/2 wire. Does not include breaker. | | | | |
| | **120 volt wiring for door bell or chime** | ea | — | $55.00 | $55.00 |
| | *Replace* Materials......27.00        Labor .........28.00 | | | | |
| | ▶ General-purpose circuit. Includes up to 15 lf of #12/2 wire, up to 30 lf of #18 low-voltage wiring, and box. Does not include breaker, transformer, or chime. | | | | |
| | **120 volt wiring for electric baseboard heater** | ea | — | $48.50 | $48.50 |
| | *Replace* Materials.......19.00        Labor .........29.50 | | | | |
| | ▶ 1 direct-wired run per 9 lf of baseboard heater or per location. Includes up to 30 lf of #12/2 wire. Does not include breaker. For 240 volt wiring see page 144. | | | | |
| | **120 volt wiring for electrical-resistance radiant heating system** | ea | — | $58.70 | $58.70 |
| | *Replace* Materials......26.50        Labor .........32.20 | | | | |
| | ▶ Direct-wired run. Includes up to 30 lf of #12/2 wire and single-pole breaker. Does not include electrical resistance wiring. For 240 volt wiring see page 144. | | | | |
| | **120 volt wiring for furnace** | ea | — | $39.00 | $39.00 |
| | *Replace* Materials.......11.00        Labor .........28.00 | | | | |
| | ▶ 1 direct-wired run. Includes up to 30 lf of #12/2 wire. Does not include breaker. | | | | |

| Item Description | Unit | Remove | Replace | Total |
|---|---|---|---|---|
| **120 volt wiring for garage door opener** | ea | — | $44.50 | $44.50 |
| *Replace* Materials.......15.00      Labor ..........29.50 | | | | |
| ▶ Garage circuit. Includes up to 30 lf of #12/2 wire. Does not include breaker. | | | | |
| **120 volt wiring for garbage disposal** | ea | — | $59.90 | $59.90 |
| *Replace* Materials ......24.00      Labor...........35.90 | | | | |
| ▶ 1 direct-wired run. Includes up to 30 lf of #12/2 wire, outlet with box, and switch with box. Does not include breaker. | | | | |
| **120 volt wiring for gas oven or range** | ea | — | $44.00 | $44.00 |
| *Replace* Materials ......16.00      Labor ..........28.00 | | | | |
| ▶ Light appliance circuit. 2 to 3 outlets per circuit. Includes up to 20 lf of #12/2 wire. Does not include breaker. | | | | |
| **120 volt wiring for humidifier** | ea | — | $43.00 | $43.00 |
| *Replace* Materials.......15.00      Labor ..........28.00 | | | | |
| ▶ With no more than 1 to 3 fixtures or outlets per run. Includes up to 30 lf of #12/2 wire. Does not include breaker. | | | | |
| **120 volt wiring for in-sink hot water dispenser** | ea | — | $43.00 | $43.00 |
| *Replace* Materials.......15.00      Labor ..........28.00 | | | | |
| ▶ Direct-wired run. Includes up to 30 lf of #12/2 wire. Does not include breaker. | | | | |
| **120 volt wiring for intercom master station** | ea | — | $56.30 | $56.30 |
| *Replace* Materials ......24.00      Labor ..........32.30 | | | | |
| ▶ Up to 20 lf of #12/2 wire. Does not include breaker. | | | | |
| **120 volt wiring for kitchen fan** | ea | — | $45.00 | $45.00 |
| *Replace* Materials.......17.00      Labor ..........28.00 | | | | |
| ▶ Includes up to 20 lf of #12/2 wire. Does not include fan or breaker. | | | | |
| **120 volt wiring for light fixture** | ea | — | $53.50 | $53.50 |
| *Replace* Materials ......25.50      Labor ..........28.00 | | | | |
| ▶ General-purpose circuit, average of 6 outlets or lights per single-pole breaker. Includes up to 15 lf of #12/2 wire and box  Does not include breaker or fixture. | | | | |
| **120 volt wiring for range hood fan and light** | ea | — | $44.50 | $44.50 |
| *Replace* Materials ......16.50      Labor ..........28.00 | | | | |
| ▶ General-purpose circuit. Includes up to 20 lf of #12/2 wire. Does not include breaker. | | | | |
| **120 volt wiring for security system** | ea | — | $56.00 | $56.00 |
| *Replace* Materials ......28.00      Labor ..........28.00 | | | | |
| ▶ General-purpose circuit. Includes up to 15 lf of #12/2 wire and box. Does not include breaker or security system. | | | | |
| **120 volt wiring for smoke or carbon monoxide detector** | ea | — | $51.00 | $51.00 |
| *Replace* Materials ......23.00      Labor ..........28.00 | | | | |
| ▶ General-purpose circuit. Includes up to 15 lf of #12/2 wire and box. Does not include breaker or detector. (Also use for direct-wired radon and carbon monoxide detectors.) | | | | |
| **120 volt wiring for sump / water pump** | ea | — | $210.50 | $210.50 |
| *Replace* Materials.......17.50      Labor .........193.00 | | | | |
| ▶ Direct-wired run. Includes up to 50 lf of #12/2 wire, up to 13 lf liquid-tight flexible conduit, remote switch with box, and single-pole breaker. | | | | |
| **120 volt wiring for trash compactor** | ea | — | $58.10 | $58.10 |
| *Replace* Materials ......23.00      Labor...........35.10 | | | | |
| ▶ On garbage disposal run. Includes up to 15 lf of #12/2 wire. Does not include breaker. | | | | |

| Item Description | Unit | Remove | Replace | Total |
|---|---|---|---|---|
| **WIRING RUN ▶** *continued*    **120 volt wiring for built-in vacuum system** <br> *Replace* Materials.......15.00    Labor..........29.50 <br> ▶ Up to 30 lf of #12/2 wire. Does not include breaker. | ea | — | $44.50 | $44.50 |
| **120 volt wiring run for typical outlet** <br> *Replace* Materials......30.00    Labor..........28.80 <br> ▶ General-purpose circuit, average of 6 outlets or lights per single-pole breaker. Includes up to 15 lf of #12/2 wire, box, and outlet. Does not include breaker. | ea | — | $58.80 | $58.80 |
| **120 volt wiring for water heater** <br> *Replace* Materials ......18.00    Labor..........75.70 <br> ▶ Direct-wired run. Includes up to 30 lf of #12/2 wire and single-pole breaker. | ea | — | $93.70 | $93.70 |
| **120 volt wiring for whole-house fan** <br> *Replace* Materials......20.50    Labor..........29.50 <br> ▶ Up to 36 lf of #12/2 wire and remote switch with box. Does not include fan or breaker. For bathroom fan wiring see page 142. For kitchen fan wiring see page 143. | ea | — | $50.00 | $50.00 |
| **240 volt ▷**    **240 volt wiring for air conditioner** <br> *Replace* Materials ....140.00    Labor..........107.00 <br> ▶ Includes up to 36 lf of #6/3 wire, up to 32 lf of #3/2 wire, box, 60 amp disconnect switch, 40 amp 2 pole breaker, up to 6 lf of liquid-tight flexible conduit. | ea | — | $247.00 | $247.00 |
| **240 volt wiring, box, & outlet for clothes dryer (30 amp)** <br> *Replace* Materials......63.50    Labor..........48.10 <br> ▶ Includes up to 30 lf of #8/3 wire and a 30 amp double-pole breaker. | ea | — | $111.60 | $111.60 |
| **240 volt wiring, box, & outlet for clothes dryer (40 amp)** <br> *Replace* Materials......71.00    Labor..........48.10 <br> ▶ Includes up to 30 lf of #8/3 wire and a 40 amp double-pole breaker. | ea | — | $119.10 | $119.10 |
| **240 volt wiring for electric cook top** <br> *Replace* Materials......76.00    Labor..........48.10 <br> ▶ Includes up to 38 lf of #8/3 wire and a 40 amp double-pole breaker. | ea | — | $124.10 | $124.10 |
| **240 volt wiring for electric baseboard heater** <br> *Replace* Materials......23.00    Labor..........48.10 <br> ▶ 1 direct-wired run per 9 lf of baseboard heater or per location. Includes up to 30 lf of #10/2 wire. Does not include breaker. For 120 volt wiring see page 142. | ea | — | $71.10 | $71.10 |
| **240 volt wiring for electrical-resistance radiant heating system** <br> *Replace* Materials....350.00    Labor..........43.80 <br> ▶ Direct-wired run. Includes up to 30 lf of #8/2 wire and double-pole breaker. Does not include electrical resistance wiring. For 120 volt wiring see page 142. | ea | — | $393.80 | $393.80 |
| **240 volt wiring, box & outlet for electric oven or range (40 amp)** <br> *Replace* Materials......63.50    Labor..........48.10 <br> ▶ Includes up to 30 lf of #8/3 wire and a 40 amp double-pole breaker. | ea | — | $111.60 | $111.60 |
| **240 volt wiring, box & outlet for electric oven or range (50 amp)** <br> *Replace* Materials......81.00    Labor..........48.10 <br> ▶ Includes up to 30 lf of #6/3 wire and a 50 amp double-pole breaker. | ea | — | $129.10 | $129.10 |
| **240 volt wiring for heat pump** <br> *Replace* Materials.....310.00    Labor..........276.00 <br> ▶ Includes up to 42 lf of #6/3 wire, up to 36 lf of #3/2 wire, box, 60 amp disconnect switch, 100 amp 2 pole breaker, 40 amp 2 pole breaker, up to 6 lf of liquid-tight flexible conduit. | ea | — | $586.00 | $586.00 |

| Item Description | Unit | Remove | Replace | Total | |
|---|---|---|---|---|---|
| **240 volt wiring for water heater** | ea | — | $116.60 | $116.60 | |
| *Replace* Materials......68.50          Labor..........48.10 | | | | | |
| ▶ Direct-wired run. Includes up to 30 lf of #10/2 wire and double-pole breaker. | | | | | |
| **Low-voltage computer network wiring (per outlet)** | ea | — | $36.90 | $36.90 | ◁ **low-voltage** |
| *Replace* Materials ......24.00          Labor..........12.90 | | | | | |
| ▶ Up to 28 lf computer network cable. | | | | | |
| **Low-voltage wiring for door bell or chime (per button)** | ea | — | $23.40 | $23.40 | |
| *Replace* Materials........3.20          Labor..........20.20 | | | | | |
| ▶ Up to 32 lf #18/2 wire. | | | | | |
| **Low-voltage wiring for door or gate latch release** | ea | — | $39.20 | $39.20 | |
| *Replace* Materials.......13.50          Labor..........25.70 | | | | | |
| ▶ Up to 40 lf of #18/2 low-voltage wire. Does not include transformer or breaker. | | | | | |
| **Low-voltage wiring for intercom (per station)** | ea | — | $34.30 | $34.30 | |
| *Replace* Materials ......12.00          Labor..........22.30 | | | | | |
| ▶ Up to 32 lf #18/2 wire. | | | | | |
| **Low-voltage wiring for light fixture** | ea | — | $56.00 | $56.00 | |
| *Replace* Materials......28.00          Labor..........28.00 | | | | | |
| ▶ Average of 6 lights per circuit. Includes up to 24 lf of #18/2 wire and box. Also includes allowance for transformer. Does not include breaker or fixture. | | | | | |
| **Low-voltage phone wiring (per outlet)** | ea | — | $17.40 | $17.40 | |
| *Replace* Materials........4.50          Labor..........12.90 | | | | | |
| ▶ Up to 30 lf of 4 or 8 wire bell wire. | | | | | |
| **Low-voltage sound system speaker wiring (per speaker)** | ea | — | $19.40 | $19.40 | |
| *Replace* Materials........6.50          Labor..........12.90 | | | | | |
| ▶ Up to 30 lf of #20/2 wire. | | | | | |
| **Low-voltage wiring for thermostat** | ea | — | $30.80 | $30.80 | |
| *Replace* Materials.......11.50          Labor..........19.30 | | | | | |
| ▶ Up to 28 lf of #18/2 low-voltage wire. | | | | | |
| **Low-voltage TV wiring (per outlet)** | ea | — | $18.90 | $18.90 | |
| *Replace* Materials........6.00          Labor..........12.90 | | | | | |
| ▶ Up to 30 lf shielded coaxial television cable. | | | | | |
| **Electric metallic tubing (EMT) conduit, average installation** | sf | — | $3.46 | $3.46 | ◀ **CONDUIT** *Based on typical home or light commercial installation. Per sf of floor.* |
| *Replace* Materials ........ .70          Labor..........2.76 | | | | | |
| ▶ Typical house and light commercial installation per sf of floor, various diameters: 94% 1/2"; 3% 3/4"; 2% misc. flexible and larger IMC and RMC conduit. | | | | | |
| **Flexible metal conduit, average installation** | sf | — | $3.17 | $3.17 | |
| *Replace* Materials........1.70          Labor..........1.47 | | | | | |
| ▶ Typical house and light commercial installation per sf of floor, various diameters: 72% 1/2"; 13% 3/4"; 15% misc. EMT, IMC and RMC conduit. | | | | | |
| **PVC conduit, average installation** | sf | — | $2.12 | $2.12 | |
| *Replace* Materials ........ .50          Labor..........1.62 | | | | | |
| ▶ Typical house and light commercial installation per sf of floor, various diameters: 94% 1/2"; 3% 3/4"; 2% misc. larger sizes. | | | | | |
| **Intermediate conduit (IMC), average installation** | sf | — | $5.66 | $5.66 | |
| *Replace* Materials.......1.60          Labor..........4.06 | | | | | |
| ▶ Commercial and light industrial installation per sf of floor, various diameters: 44% 1/2"; 35% 3/4" or 1"; 22% misc. larger sizes. | | | | | |

| Item Description | Unit | Remove | Replace | Total |
|---|---|---|---|---|
| **CONDUIT ▶** *continued*    **Rigid metal conduit (RMC), average installation** | sf | — | **$7.41** | **$7.41** |
| *Replace* Materials........5.00     Labor............2.41 | | | | |
| ▶ Commercial, industrial and exposed installation per sf of floor, various diameters: 44% 1/2"; 35% 3/4" or 1"; 22% misc. larger sizes. | | | | |
| **WIRE ▶** *Average installation and conditions for single family housing and light commercial construction. Per lf of installed wire.*    **#10 2 wire with ground non-metallic sheathed cable (Romex)** | lf | — | **$2.38** | **$2.38** |
| *Replace* Materials........ .55     Labor............1.83 | | | | |
| ▶ Typical house or light commercial installation per lf of run. | | | | |
| **#12 2 wire with ground non-metallic sheathed cable (Romex)** | lf | — | **$1.99** | **$1.99** |
| *Replace* Materials........ .30     Labor............1.69 | | | | |
| ▶ Typical house or light commercial installation per lf of run. | | | | |
| **#14 2 wire with ground non-metallic sheathed cable (Romex)** | lf | — | **$1.64** | **$1.64** |
| *Replace* Materials........ .20     Labor............1.44 | | | | |
| ▶ Typical house installation per lf of run. | | | | |
| **BREAKER PANEL ▶**    **100 amp exterior breaker panel** | ea | $161.00 | $527.00 | $688.00 |
| *Replace* Materials....325.00     Labor........202.00 | | | | |
| *Remove* ..........................     Labor..........161.00 | | | | |
| ▶ 20 breaker capacity, 5 breakers installed. | | | | |
| **100 amp interior breaker panel** | ea | $161.00 | $483.00 | $644.00 |
| *Replace* Materials....305.00     Labor..........178.00 | | | | |
| *Remove* ..........................     Labor..........161.00 | | | | |
| ▶ 20 breaker capacity, 5 breakers installed. | | | | |
| **150 amp exterior breaker panel** | ea | $161.00 | $733.00 | $894.00 |
| *Replace* Materials.....415.00     Labor..........318.00 | | | | |
| *Remove* ..........................     Labor..........161.00 | | | | |
| ▶ 20 breaker capacity, 10 breakers installed. | | | | |
| **150 amp interior breaker panel** | ea | $161.00 | $692.00 | $853.00 |
| *Replace* Materials....395.00     Labor..........297.00 | | | | |
| *Remove* ..........................     Labor..........161.00 | | | | |
| ▶ 20 breaker capacity, 10 breakers installed. | | | | |
| **200 amp exterior breaker panel** | ea | $161.00 | $982.00 | $1,143.00 |
| *Replace* Materials....535.00     Labor..........447.00 | | | | |
| *Remove* ..........................     Labor..........161.00 | | | | |
| ▶ 40 breaker capacity, 15 breakers installed. | | | | |
| **200 amp interior breaker panel** | ea | $161.00 | $909.00 | $1,070.00 |
| *Replace* Materials....505.00     Labor..........404.00 | | | | |
| *Remove* ..........................     Labor..........161.00 | | | | |
| ▶ 40 breaker capacity, 15 breakers installed. | | | | |
| **300 amp exterior breaker panel** | ea | $161.00 | $1,142.00 | $1,303.00 |
| *Replace* Materials....550.00     Labor..........592.00 | | | | |
| *Remove* ..........................     Labor..........161.00 | | | | |
| ▶ 42 breaker capacity, 30 breakers installed. | | | | |
| **300 amp interior breaker panel** | ea | $161.00 | $1,065.00 | $1,226.00 |
| *Replace* Materials.....510.00     Labor..........555.00 | | | | |
| *Remove* ..........................     Labor..........161.00 | | | | |
| ▶ 42 breaker capacity, 30 breakers installed. | | | | |
| **40 amp interior breaker sub-panel** | ea | $161.00 | $264.00 | $425.00 |
| *Replace* Materials....140.00     Labor..........124.00 | | | | |
| *Remove* ..........................     Labor..........161.00 | | | | |
| ▶ 10 breaker capacity, 2 breakers installed. | | | | |

| Item Description | Unit | Remove | Replace | Total | |
|---|---|---|---|---|---|
| **50 amp interior breaker sub-panel** | ea | $161.00 | $316.00 | $477.00 | ◁ sub-panel |
| *Replace* Materials.....185.00    Labor.........131.00 | | | | | |
| *Remove* ................    Labor.........161.00 | | | | | |
| ► 10 breaker capacity, 3 breakers installed. | | | | | |
| **70 amp interior breaker sub-panel** | ea | $161.00 | $359.00 | $520.00 | |
| *Replace* Materials.....215.00    Labor.........144.00 | | | | | |
| *Remove* ................    Labor.........161.00 | | | | | |
| ► 10 breaker capacity, 4 breakers installed. | | | | | |
| **Remove breaker panel for work, then reinstall** | ea | — | $342.00 | $342.00 | ◁ remove & reinstall |
| *Replace* ................    Labor.........342.00 | | | | | |
| **100 amp cable service** | ea | $277.00 | $1,063.00 | $1,340.00 | ◀ **ELECTRIC SERVICE** |
| *Replace* Materials ....570.00    Labor.........493.00 | | | | | |
| *Remove* ................    Labor.........277.00 | | | | | |
| ► Overhead installation. Up to 21 lf service entrance cable type SE, insulator, weather head, meter base, main disconnect breaker, up to 6 lf copper ground wire, grounding rod, clamps, fasteners, and waterproof connectors. (Does not include breaker panel.) Add **13%** for underground supply—includes excavation, trench shaping, sand bed, backfill, up to 38 lf USE cable, and underground materials. | | | | | |
| **150 amp cable service** | ea | $277.00 | $1,352.00 | $1,629.00 | |
| *Replace* Materials ....760.00    Labor.........592.00 | | | | | |
| *Remove* ................    Labor.........277.00 | | | | | |
| ► Overhead installation. Up to 21 lf service entrance cable type SE, insulator, weather head, meter base, main disconnect breaker, up to 6 lf copper ground wire, grounding rod, clamps, fasteners, and waterproof connectors. (Does not include breaker panel.) Add **13%** for underground supply—includes excavation, trench shaping, sand bed, backfill, up to 38 lf USE cable, and underground materials. | | | | | |
| **150 amp conduit service** | ea | $346.00 | $1,443.00 | $1,789.00 | |
| *Replace* Materials ....805.00    Labor.........638.00 | | | | | |
| *Remove* ................    Labor.........346.00 | | | | | |
| ► Overhead installation. Up to 21 lf service entrance cable type SE, insulator, weather head for conduit, EMT conduit with liquid-tight couplings, conduit straps, conduit entrance ell, meter base, main disconnect breaker, up to 6 lf copper ground wire, grounding rod, clamps, fasteners, and waterproof connectors. (Does not include breaker panel.) *Do not use this item if conduit extends through roof.* See rigid steel mast installations. Add **13%** for underground supply—includes excavation, trench shaping, sand bed, backfill, up to 38 lf USE cable, and underground materials. | | | | | cable service △ |
| **150 amp rigid steel mast service** | ea | $407.00 | $1,488.00 | $1,895.00 | |
| *Replace* Materials ....850.00    Labor .........638.00 | | | | | |
| *Remove* ................    Labor.........407.00 | | | | | |
| ► Overhead installation. Rigid steel conduit extends through roof. Up to 21 lf service entrance cable type SE, insulator (clamps to mast), weather head for conduit, 2" galvanized rigid steel conduit with liquid-tight connections, roof flashing, conduit supports, conduit offset fittings, conduit entrance ell, meter base, main disconnect breaker, up to 6 lf copper ground wire, grounding rod, clamps, fasteners, and waterproof connectors. Add **$100** if guy wire is needed to support mast. (Does not include breaker panel.) | | | | | |
| **200 amp cable service** | ea | $277.00 | $1,761.00 | $2,038.00 | |
| *Replace* Materials ....995.00    Labor.........766.00 | | | | | |
| *Remove* ................    Labor.........277.00 | | | | | △ **conduit service** |
| ► Overhead installation. Up to 21 lf service entrance cable type SE, insulator, weatherhead, meter base, main disconnect breaker, up to 6 lf copper ground wire, grounding rod, clamps, fasteners, and waterproof connectors. (Does not include breaker panel.) Add **13%** for underground supply—includes excavation, trench shaping, sand bed, backfill, up to 38 lf USE cable, and underground materials. | | | | | |

| Item Description | Unit | Remove | Replace | Total |
|---|---|---|---|---|
| **ELECTRIC SERVICE ▶** *continued* | | | | |
| **200 amp conduit service** | ea | $346.00 | $1,884.00 | $2,230.00 |
|   *Replace* Materials ..1060.00      Labor.........824.00 | | | | |
|   *Remove* ......................      Labor.........346.00 | | | | |
|   ▶ Overhead installation. Up to 21 lf service entrance cable type SE, insulator, weatherhead for conduit, EMT conduit with liquid-tight couplings, conduit straps, conduit entrance ell, meter base, main disconnect breaker, up to 6 lf copper ground wire, grounding rod, clamps, fasteners, and waterproof connectors. (Does not include breaker panel.) *Do not use this item if conduit extends through roof.* See rigid steel mast installations. Add **13%** for underground supply—includes excavation, trench shaping, sand bed, backfill, up to 38 lf USE cable, and underground materials. | | | | |
| **200 amp rigid steel mast service** | ea | $407.00 | $1,924.00 | $2,331.00 |
|   *Replace* Materials...1100.00      Labor.........824.00 | | | | |
|   *Remove* ......................      Labor.........407.00 | | | | |
|   ▶ Overhead installation. Rigid steel conduit extends through roof. Up to 24 lf service entrance cable type SE, insulator (clamps to mast), weatherhead for conduit, 2" galvanized rigid steel conduit with liquid-tight connections, roof flashing, conduit supports, conduit offset fittings, conduit entrance ell, meter base, main disconnect breaker, up to 6 lf copper ground wire, grounding rod, clamps, fasteners, and waterproof connectors. Add **$100** if guy wire is needed to support mast. (Does not include breaker panel.) | | | | |
| △ *rigid steel mast service* | | | | |
| **CIRCUIT BREAKER ▶** | | | | |
| **Single pole (120 volt) circuit breaker** | ea | $5.24 | $41.30 | $46.54 |
|   *Replace* Materials.......15.00      Labor...........26.30 | | | | |
|   *Remove*...................      Labor ...........5.24 | | | | |
| △ *single pole* | | | | |
| **Double pole (240 volt) circuit breaker** | ea | $5.24 | $60.80 | $66.04 |
|   *Replace* Materials......34.00      Labor...........26.80 | | | | |
|   *Remove*...................      Labor ...........5.24 | | | | |
| **Ground fault circuit interrupter breaker** | ea | $5.24 | $84.50 | $89.74 |
|   *Replace* Materials......56.00      Labor...........28.50 | | | | |
|   *Remove*...................      Labor ...........5.24 | | | | |
| △ *double pole* | | | | |
| main disconnect ▷ **Main disconnect circuit breaker** | ea | $5.24 | $474.00 | $479.24 |
|   *Replace* Materials....330.00      Labor.........144.00 | | | | |
|   *Remove*...................      Labor ...........5.24 | | | | |
| remove & reinstall ▷ **Remove circuit breaker for work, then reinstall** | ea | — | $44.70 | $44.70 |
|   *Replace* ......................      Labor...........44.70 | | | | |
| **DOOR BELL ▶** *See page 140 for wiring.* **Door bell or chime economy grade** | ea | $5.48 | $95.70 | $101.18 |
|   *Replace* Materials ......51.00      Labor...........44.70 | | | | |
|   *Remove* ......................      Labor ...........5.48 | | | | |
|   ▶ Single tone, entry door only. | | | | |
| **Door bell or chime standard grade** | ea | $5.48 | $136.70 | $142.18 |
|   *Replace* Materials ......92.00      Labor...........44.70 | | | | |
|   *Remove* ......................      Labor ...........5.48 | | | | |
|   ▶ Separate tones for entry and secondary doors. | | | | |
| **Door bell or chime high grade** | ea | $5.48 | $169.70 | $175.18 |
|   *Replace* Materials .....125.00      Labor...........44.70 | | | | |
|   *Remove* ......................      Labor ...........5.48 | | | | |
|   ▶ Select from multiple tones. | | | | |
| **Door bell or chime deluxe grade** | ea | $5.48 | $279.70 | $285.18 |
|   *Replace* Materials ....235.00      Labor...........44.70 | | | | |
|   *Remove* ......................      Labor ...........5.48 | | | | |
|   ▶ Programmable, multiple tones. | | | | |

| Item Description | Unit | Remove | Replace | Total | |
|---|---|---|---|---|---|
| **Door bell or chime button** <br> *Replace* Materials........5.70     Labor............4.93 <br> *Remove* .........................     Labor............2.62 <br> ▶ Button only, no wire. | ea | $2.62 | $10.63 | $13.25 | ◁ door bell button |
| **Remove door chime for work, then reinstall** <br> *Replace* .........................     Labor..........68.30 | ea | — | $68.30 | $68.30 | ◁ remove & reinstall |
| **Bathroom exhaust fan, economy grade** <br> *Replace* Materials......32.00     Labor..........24.70 <br> *Remove* .........................     Labor............13.30 <br> ▶ 50 cfm. Includes up to 10 lf of 4" flexible vent duct, and wall outlet. | ea | $13.30 | $56.70 | $70.00 | ◀ **BATH FAN** |
| **Bathroom exhaust fan, standard grade** <br> *Replace* Materials......53.00     Labor..........24.70 <br> *Remove* .........................     Labor............13.30 <br> ▶ 65 cfm, low noise. Includes up to 10 lf of 4" flexible vent duct, and wall outlet. | ea | $13.30 | $77.70 | $91.00 | |
| **Bathroom exhaust fan, high grade** <br> *Replace* Materials ......75.00     Labor..........24.70 <br> *Remove* .........................     Labor............13.30 <br> ▶ 110 cfm, low noise. Includes up to 10 lf of 4" flexible vent duct, and wall outlet. | ea | $13.30 | $99.70 | $113.00 | |
| **Bathroom exhaust fan, deluxe grade** <br> *Replace* Materials.....120.00     Labor..........24.70 <br> *Remove* .........................     Labor............13.30 <br> ▶ 110 cfm, low noise, variable speeds. Includes up to 10 lf of 4" flexible vent duct, and wall outlet. | ea | $13.30 | $144.70 | $158.00 | |
| **Remove bathroom exhaust fan for work, then reinstall** <br> *Replace* .........................     Labor..........40.40 | ea | — | $40.40 | $40.40 | ◁ remove & reinstall |
| **Bathroom exhaust fan with heat lamp, standard grade** <br> *Replace* Materials......65.00     Labor..........31.80 <br> *Remove* .........................     Labor............19.00 <br> ▶ 75 cfm, single heat lamp in center, single switch. Includes up to 10 lf of 4" flexible vent duct, and wall outlet. | ea | $19.00 | $96.80 | $115.80 | ◀ **BATH FAN** <br> **WITH HEAT LAMP** |
| **Bathroom exhaust fan with heat lamp, high grade** <br> *Replace* Materials....100.00     Labor..........31.80 <br> *Remove* .........................     Labor............19.00 <br> ▶ 110 cfm, double heat lamp in center, separate timer switch for heat lamp. Includes up to 10 lf of 4" flexible vent duct, and wall outlet. | ea | $19.00 | $131.80 | $150.80 | |
| **Bathroom exhaust fan with heater, standard grade** <br> *Replace* Materials.....115.00     Labor..........34.20 <br> *Remove* .........................     Labor............19.00 <br> ▶ 110 cfm, 200 watt heater, separate timer switch for heater. Includes up to 10 lf of 4" flexible vent duct, and wall outlet. | ea | $19.00 | $149.20 | $168.20 | ◀ **BATH FAN** <br> **WITH HEATER** |
| **Bathroom exhaust fan with heater, high grade** <br> *Replace* Materials.....165.00     Labor..........34.20 <br> *Remove* .........................     Labor............19.00 <br> ▶ 110 cfm, 450 watt heater, separate timer switch for heater. Includes up to 10 lf of 4" flexible vent duct, and wall outlet. | ea | $19.00 | $199.20 | $218.20 | |
| **Remove bathroom exhaust fan with heater for work, then reinstall** <br> *Replace* .........................     Labor..........51.80 | ea | — | $51.80 | $51.80 | ◁ remove & reinstall |

| | Item Description | Unit | Remove | Replace | Total |
|---|---|---|---|---|---|
| **KITCHEN FAN ▶** *See page 26 for kitchen exhaust fans in range hoods.* | **Kitchen exhaust fan, economy grade** | ea | $14.10 | $105.40 | $119.50 |
| | *Replace* Materials ......65.00        Labor ..........40.40 | | | | |
| | *Remove* ........................        Labor ..........14.10 | | | | |
| | ▶ 110 cfm, no outside vent, charcoal filtration system. | | | | |
| | **Kitchen exhaust fan, standard grade** | ea | $14.10 | $155.40 | $169.50 |
| | *Replace* Materials .....115.00        Labor ..........40.40 | | | | |
| | *Remove* ........................        Labor ..........14.10 | | | | |
| | ▶ 200 cfm.  Includes up to 10 lf of 4" flexible vent duct, and wall outlet. | | | | |
| | **Kitchen exhaust fan, high grade** | ea | $14.10 | $255.40 | $269.50 |
| | *Replace* Materials .....215.00        Labor ..........40.40 | | | | |
| | *Remove* ........................        Labor ..........14.10 | | | | |
| | ▶ 300 cfm.  Includes up to 10 lf of 4" flexible vent duct, and wall outlet. | | | | |
| **remove & reinstall ▷** | **Remove kitchen exhaust fan for work, then reinstall** | ea | — | $58.00 | $58.00 |
| | *Replace* ........................        Labor ..........58.00 | | | | |
| **WHOLE-HOUSE ▶ FAN** | **Whole-house exhaust fan, standard grade** | ea | $39.80 | $656.00 | $695.80 |
| | *Replace* Materials ....545.00        Labor ..........111.00 | | | | |
| | *Remove* ........................        Labor ..........39.80 | | | | |
| | ▶ 4,500 cfm.  Two-speed with automatic shutters. | | | | |
| | **Whole-house exhaust fan, high grade** | ea | $39.80 | $746.00 | $785.80 |
| | *Replace* Materials ....635.00        Labor ..........111.00 | | | | |
| | *Remove* ........................        Labor ..........39.80 | | | | |
| | ▶ 6,500 cfm.  Variable speed with automatic shutters. | | | | |
| **remove & reinstall ▷** | **Remove whole-house exhaust fan for work, then reinstall** | ea | — | $148.00 | $148.00 |
| | *Replace* ........................        Labor ..........148.00 | | | | |
| **INTERCOM ▶ MASTER STATION** | **Intercom system master station, economy grade** | ea | $19.60 | $334.00 | $353.60 |
| | *Replace* Materials .....245.00        Labor ..........89.00 | | | | |
| | *Remove* ........................        Labor ..........19.60 | | | | |
| | ▶ Push to talk, release to listen. | | | | |
| | **Intercom system master station, standard grade** | ea | $19.60 | $589.00 | $608.60 |
| | *Replace* Materials ....500.00        Labor ..........89.00 | | | | |
| | *Remove* ........................        Labor ..........19.60 | | | | |
| | ▶ AM/FM radio, room monitor, hands-free answer, privacy. | | | | |
| | **Intercom system master station, high grade** | ea | $19.60 | $739.00 | $758.60 |
| | *Replace* Materials ....650.00        Labor ..........89.00 | | | | |
| | *Remove* ........................        Labor ..........19.60 | | | | |
| | ▶ AM/FM radio and cassette player, room monitor, hands-free answer, privacy. | | | | |
| | **Intercom system master station, deluxe grade** | ea | $19.60 | $1,109.00 | $1,128.60 |
| | *Replace* Materials ..1020.00        Labor ..........89.00 | | | | |
| | *Remove* ........................        Labor ..........19.60 | | | | |
| | ▶ AM/FM radio with cassette player, built-in telephone, telephone answering machine, room monitor, hands-free answer, privacy, gate or door latch release. | | | | |
| | **Intercom system master station, custom grade** | ea | $19.60 | $1,639.00 | $1,658.60 |
| | *Replace* Materials ...1550.00        Labor ..........89.00 | | | | |
| | *Remove* ........................        Labor ..........19.60 | | | | |
| | ▶ AM/FM radio with cassette player, built-in telephone, telephone answering machine, room monitor, hands-free answer, privacy, gate or door latch release, door video monitor. | | | | |
| **remove & reinstall ▷** | **Remove intercom master station for work, then reinstall** | ea | — | $117.00 | $117.00 |
| | *Replace* ........................        Labor ..........117.00 | | | | |

| Item Description | Unit | Remove | Replace | Total | |
|---|---|---|---|---|---|
| **Intercom system remote station, economy grade** | ea | $7.86 | $84.70 | $92.56 | ◄ INTERCOM REMOTE STATION |
| *Replace* Materials......60.00     Labor..........24.70 | | | | | |
| *Remove* ......................     Labor............7.86 | | | | | |
| ► Push to talk, release to listen. | | | | | |
| **Intercom system remote station, standard grade** | ea | $7.86 | $149.70 | $157.56 | |
| *Replace* Materials.....125.00     Labor..........24.70 | | | | | |
| *Remove* ......................     Labor............7.86 | | | | | |
| ► Hands-free answer, privacy. | | | | | |
| **Intercom system remote station, high grade** | ea | $7.86 | $264.70 | $272.56 | |
| *Replace* Materials ....240.00     Labor..........24.70 | | | | | |
| *Remove* ......................     Labor...........7.86 | | | | | |
| ► Built-in telephone, hands-free answer, and privacy. | | | | | |
| **Remove intercom remote station for work, then reinstall** | ea | — | $37.10 | $37.10 | ◁ remove & reinstall |
| *Replace* ......................     Labor...........37.10 | | | | | |
| **Sound system speaker with grille, economy grade** | ea | $6.16 | $28.76 | $34.92 | ◄ SOUND SYSTEM |
| *Replace* Materials......20.00     Labor............8.76 | | | | | |
| *Remove* ......................     Labor............6.16 | | | | | |
| ► 3" to 5" diameter speaker with plastic grille. | | | | | |
| **Sound system speaker with grille, standard grade** | ea | $6.16 | $33.76 | $39.92 | |
| *Replace* Materials......25.00     Labor............8.76 | | | | | |
| *Remove* ......................     Labor............6.16 | | | | | |
| ► 5" to 8" diameter elliptical speaker with wood-grain plastic grille. | | | | | |
| **Sound system speaker with grille, high grade** | ea | $6.16 | $43.76 | $49.92 | |
| *Replace* Materials......35.00     Labor............8.76 | | | | | |
| *Remove* ......................     Labor............6.16 | | | | | |
| ► 5" to 8" diameter elliptical speaker with 1" to 2" "tweeter" speaker, wood-grain plastic grille. | | | | | |
| **Sound system speaker with grille, deluxe grade** | ea | $6.16 | $63.76 | $69.92 | |
| *Replace* Materials......55.00     Labor............8.76 | | | | | |
| *Remove* ......................     Labor............6.16 | | | | | |
| ► Two 5" to 8" diameter speakers with two or three 1" to 2" "tweeter" speakers, wood-grain plastic grille. | | | | | |
| **Check electrical circuits with megameter in small home** | ea | — | $162.00 | $162.00 | ◄ CHECK CIRCUITS |
| *Replace* ......................     Labor..........162.00 | | | | | |
| **Check electrical circuits with megameter in average size home** | ea | — | $234.00 | $234.00 | |
| *Replace* ......................     Labor .........234.00 | | | | | |
| **Check electrical circuits with megameter in large home** | ea | — | $323.00 | $323.00 | |
| *Replace* ......................     Labor..........323.00 | | | | | |
| **Smoke detector (battery operated)** | ea | $5.24 | $42.80 | $48.04 | ◄ SMOKE DETECTOR |
| *Replace* Materials......30.00     Labor..........12.80 | | | | | |
| *Remove* ......................     Labor ...........5.24 | | | | | |
| **Smoke detector (direct wired)** | ea | $5.24 | $54.40 | $59.64 | |
| *Replace* Materials......40.00     Labor..........14.40 | | | | | |
| *Remove* ......................     Labor ...........5.24 | | | | | |
| **Remove smoke detector for work, then reinstall** | ea | — | $20.00 | $20.00 | ◁ remove & reinstall |
| *Replace* ......................     Labor..........20.00 | | | | | |

| | Item Description | Unit | Remove | Replace | Total |
|---|---|---|---|---|---|
| **CARBON ►** **MONOXIDE** **DETECTOR** | **Carbon monoxide detector (battery operated)** *Replace* Materials ......35.00    Labor ...........12.80 *Remove* .....................    Labor ...........5.24 | ea | $5.24 | $47.80 | $53.04 |
| | **Carbon monoxide detector (direct wired)** *Replace* Materials ......45.00    Labor ...........14.40 *Remove* .....................    Labor ...........5.24 | ea | $5.24 | $59.40 | $64.64 |
| remove & reinstall ▷ | **Remove carbon monoxide detector for work, then reinstall** *Replace* .....................    Labor ...........20.00 | ea | — | $20.00 | $20.00 |
| **RADON DETECTOR ►** | **Radon detector (battery operated)** *Replace* Materials ......40.00    Labor ...........12.80 *Remove* .....................    Labor ...........5.24 | ea | $5.24 | $52.80 | $58.04 |
| | **Radon detector (direct wired)** *Replace* Materials ......50.00    Labor ...........14.40 *Remove* .....................    Labor ...........5.24 | ea | $5.24 | $64.40 | $69.64 |
| remove & reinstall ▷ | **Remove radon detector for work, then reinstall** *Replace* .....................    Labor ...........20.00 | ea | — | $20.00 | $20.00 |
| **THERMOSTAT ►** *Electrical line thermostat. See HVAC on page 278 for additional thermostats.* | **Thermostat for electric-resistance heating system** *Replace* Materials ........7.50    Labor ...........6.57 *Remove* .....................    Labor ...........5.24 | ea | $5.24 | $14.07 | $19.31 |
| | **Thermostat for electric heating system** *Replace* Materials ......16.00    Labor ...........11.70 *Remove* .....................    Labor ...........5.24 | ea | $5.24 | $27.70 | $32.94 |
| **ANTENNA ►** *Includes up to 50 lf coaxial cable. Add $175 for ground wire and grounding rod driven 8' deep into ground. (Required by many local codes.)* | **Television antenna, economy grade** *Replace* Materials ....100.00    Labor ...........44.70 *Remove* .....................    Labor ...........21.90 ► 55" boom. | ea | $21.90 | $144.70 | $166.60 |
| | **Television antenna, standard grade** *Replace* Materials .....170.00    Labor ...........44.70 *Remove* .....................    Labor ...........21.90 ► 100" boom. | ea | $21.90 | $214.70 | $236.60 |
| | **Television antenna, high grade** *Replace* Materials ....255.00    Labor ...........44.70 *Remove* .....................    Labor ...........21.90 ► 150" boom. | ea | $21.90 | $299.70 | $321.60 |
| | **Television antenna, deluxe grade** *Replace* Materials ....365.00    Labor ...........44.70 *Remove* .....................    Labor ...........21.90 ► 200" boom. | ea | $21.90 | $409.70 | $431.60 |
| remove & reinstall ▷ | **Remove television antenna for work, then reinstall** *Replace* .....................    Labor ...........65.40 | ea | — | $65.40 | $65.40 |
| **WALL HEATER ►** | **Electric space heater recessed in wall, economy grade** *Replace* Materials .....195.00    Labor .........89.00 *Remove* .....................    Labor ...........13.30 ► 120 or 240 volt, 1,500 watt. | ea | $13.30 | $284.00 | $297.30 |

| Item Description | Unit | Remove | Replace | Total | |
|---|---|---|---|---|---|
| **Electric space heater recessed in wall, standard grade (240 volt)** | ea | $13.30 | $309.00 | $322.30 | |
| *Replace* Materials ....220.00      Labor .........89.00 | | | | | |
| *Remove* .....................      Labor ..........13.30 | | | | | |
| ▶ 2,250 watt. | | | | | |
| **Electric space heater recessed in wall, high grade (240 volt)** | ea | $13.30 | $354.00 | $367.30 | |
| *Replace* Materials ....265.00      Labor .........89.00 | | | | | |
| *Remove* .....................      Labor ..........13.30 | | | | | |
| ▶ 4,000 watt. | | | | | |
| **Remove electric space heater for work, then reinstall** | ea | — | $148.00 | $148.00 | ◁ remove & reinstall |
| *Replace* .....................      Labor .........148.00 | | | | | |
| **Electric-resistance heating cable, ceiling installation** | sf | — | $3.69 | $3.69 | ◀ **ELECTRIC-RESISTANCE HEATING CABLE** |
| *Replace* Materials ........2.40      Labor ...........1.29 | | | | | *For 120 volt wiring run see page 142. For 240 volt wiring run see page 144.* |
| ▶ Copper inner resistance wire embedded in gypsum. | | | | | |
| **Electric-resistance heating cable, floor installation** | sf | — | $6.55 | $6.55 | |
| *Replace* Materials ........4.40      Labor ...........2.15 | | | | | |
| ▶ Wire contains copper inner resistance core and is sheathed with aluminum and a cross-linked polyethylene outer layer. Per sf of exposed floor space. Do not measure floor space underneath tubs, cabinets, or appliances. | | | | | |
| **Electric-resistance heating floor sensor** | ea | — | $97.70 | $97.70 | |
| *Replace* Materials ......75.00      Labor ..........22.70 | | | | | |
| ▶ For use with floor-installed electric-resistance heating that is not the only heat source. Floor sensors determine when floor is below desired temperature. | | | | | |
| **Electric baseboard heater, economy grade** | lf | $4.32 | $34.40 | $38.72 | ◀ **BASEBOARD HEATER** |
| *Replace* Materials ......16.00      Labor ..........18.40 | | | | | *For 120 volt wiring run see page 142. For 240 volt wiring run see page 144.* |
| *Remove* .....................      Labor ..........4.32 | | | | | |
| ▶ 3 lf minimum. 165 watts per lf. Thermostat on heater. | | | | | |
| **Electric baseboard heater, standard grade** | lf | $4.32 | $35.40 | $39.72 | |
| *Replace* Materials .......17.00      Labor ..........18.40 | | | | | |
| *Remove* .....................      Labor ..........4.32 | | | | | |
| ▶ 3 lf minimum. 188 watts per lf. Includes up to 18 lf #18/2 thermostat wire, box and line thermostat. | | | | | |
| **Remove electric baseboard heater for work, then reinstall** | lf | — | $25.70 | $25.70 | ◁ remove & reinstall |
| *Replace* .....................      Labor ..........25.70 | | | | | |
| **Underground wiring for exterior post light fixture (to 30 lf)** | ea | — | $223.80 | $223.80 | ◀ **POST FIXTURE WIRING** |
| *Replace* Materials ....180.00      Labor ..........43.80 | | | | | |
| ▶ Up to 36 lf #12/2 UF wire, sand bed in trench for wire, and up to 10 lf galvanized conduit. Does not include excavation, see page 178. | | | | | |
| **Underground wiring for exterior post light fixture (to 50 feet)** | ea | — | $326.70 | $326.70 | |
| *Replace* Materials ....280.00      Labor ..........46.70 | | | | | |
| ▶ Up to 56 lf #12/2 UF wire, sand bed in trench for wire, and up to 10 lf galvanized conduit. Does not include excavation, see page 178. | | | | | |
| **Interior incandescent light fixture, economy grade** | ea | $7.86 | $35.70 | $43.56 | ◀ **LIGHT FIXTURE ALLOWANCE** |
| *Replace* Materials .......15.00      Labor ..........20.70 | | | | | *Contractor's allowance per light fixture in complete home.* |
| *Remove* .....................      Labor ...........7.86 | | | | | |
| **Interior incandescent light fixture, standard grade** | ea | $7.86 | $55.70 | $63.56 | |
| *Replace* Materials ......35.00      Labor ..........20.70 | | | | | |
| *Remove* .....................      Labor ...........7.86 | | | | | |

| Item Description | Unit | Remove | Replace | Total |
|---|---|---|---|---|
| **LIGHT FIXTURE** ▶ *continued* — **Interior incandescent light fixture, high grade**<br>*Replace* Materials ......65.00    Labor ..........20.70<br>*Remove* ......................    Labor ...........7.86 | ea | $7.86 | $85.70 | $93.56 |
| **Interior incandescent light fixture, deluxe grade**<br>*Replace* Materials .....110.00    Labor ..........20.70<br>*Remove* ......................    Labor ...........7.86 | ea | $7.86 | $130.70 | $138.56 |
| remove & reinstall ▷ **Remove interior light fixture for work, then reinstall**<br>*Replace* ......................    Labor ..........36.80 | ea | — | $36.80 | $36.80 |
| **LIGHT BAR** ▶ **Bathroom light bar with 2 lights, standard grade**<br>*Replace* Materials ......45.00    Labor ..........22.10<br>*Remove* ......................    Labor ...........8.25 | ea | $8.25 | $67.10 | $75.35 |
| **Bathroom light bar with 2 lights, high grade**<br>*Replace* Materials ......55.00    Labor ..........22.10<br>*Remove* ......................    Labor ...........8.25 | ea | $8.25 | $77.10 | $85.35 |
| **Bathroom bar light with 3 to 4 lights, standard grade**<br>*Replace* Materials ......60.00    Labor ..........22.10<br>*Remove* ......................    Labor ...........8.25 | ea | $8.25 | $82.10 | $90.35 |
| **Bathroom bar light with 3 to 4 lights, high grade**<br>*Replace* Materials ......65.00    Labor ..........22.10<br>*Remove* ......................    Labor ...........8.25 | ea | $8.25 | $87.10 | $95.35 |
| **Bathroom bar light with 5 to 6 lights, standard grade**<br>*Replace* Materials ......80.00    Labor ..........22.10<br>*Remove* ......................    Labor ...........8.25 | ea | $8.25 | $102.10 | $110.35 |
| **Bathroom bar light with 5 to 6 lights, high grade**<br>*Replace* Materials ....100.00    Labor ..........22.10<br>*Remove* ......................    Labor ...........8.25 | ea | $8.25 | $122.10 | $130.35 |
| **Bathroom bar light with 7 to 8 lights, standard grade**<br>*Replace* Materials .....115.00    Labor ..........22.10<br>*Remove* ......................    Labor ...........8.25 | ea | $8.25 | $137.10 | $145.35 |
| **Bathroom bar light with 7 to 8 lights, high grade**<br>*Replace* Materials .....145.00    Labor ..........22.10<br>*Remove* ......................    Labor ...........8.25 | ea | $8.25 | $167.10 | $175.35 |
| **Remove bathroom bar light for work, then reinstall**<br>*Replace* ......................    Labor ..........38.90 | ea | — | $38.90 | $38.90 |
| **CHANDELIER** ▶ **Chandelier, economy grade**<br>*Replace* Materials .....120.00    Labor ..........60.00<br>*Remove* ......................    Labor ..........14.60 | ea | $14.60 | $180.00 | $194.60 |
| **Chandelier, standard grade**<br>*Replace* Materials .....190.00    Labor ..........60.00<br>*Remove* ......................    Labor ..........14.60 | ea | $14.60 | $250.00 | $264.60 |
| **Chandelier, high grade**<br>*Replace* Materials ....265.00    Labor ..........60.00<br>*Remove* ......................    Labor ..........14.60 | ea | $14.60 | $325.00 | $339.60 |
| **Chandelier, deluxe grade**<br>*Replace* Materials ....380.00    Labor ..........60.00<br>*Remove* ......................    Labor ..........14.60 | ea | $14.60 | $440.00 | $454.60 |

*Standard grade light bars have decorative light bulbs. High grade light bars have decorative globe covers.*

**LIGHT FIXTURE QUALITY**

**Economy** Very light-gauge plated metal components, simple, thin glass shades. Chandeliers may contain 4 to 8 arms with turned wood center.

**Standard** Light-gauge plated metal components, simple glass shades. Chandeliers may contain 4 to 8 arms.

**High** Heavy-gauge plated metal components, glass shades with some intricate pattern or design, may have antique finish. Chandeliers may contain 4 to 8 arms.

**Deluxe** Heavy-gauge metal components, solid brass components, intricate glass shades, may have antique finish. Chandeliers may contain 6 to 12 arms.

*To 28" in diameter. Suitable for installations on 8' and taller ceilings.*

**FIXTURE QUALITY** *continued*

**Custom** Heavy-gauge metal components, solid brass components, intricate glass shades, specialty antique finishes, polished brass, antiqued brass, polished nickel (or chrome) over brass. Chandeliers may contain 6 to 14 arms.

| Item Description | Unit | Remove | Replace | Total |
|---|---|---|---|---|
| **Chandelier, custom grade** | ea | $14.60 | $550.00 | $564.60 |
| *Replace* Materials ....490.00     Labor ..........60.00 | | | | |
| *Remove* ......................     Labor ..........14.60 | | | | |
| **Chandelier, custom deluxe grade** | ea | $14.60 | $680.00 | $694.60 |
| *Replace* Materials ....620.00     Labor ..........60.00 | | | | |
| *Remove* ......................     Labor ..........14.60 | | | | |
| **Entrance chandelier, economy grade** | ea | $14.60 | $385.00 | $399.60 |
| *Replace* Materials ....265.00     Labor ..........120.00 | | | | |
| *Remove* ......................     Labor ..........14.60 | | | | |
| **Entrance chandelier, standard grade** | ea | $14.60 | $500.00 | $514.60 |
| *Replace* Materials ....380.00     Labor ..........120.00 | | | | |
| *Remove* ......................     Labor ..........14.60 | | | | |
| **Entrance chandelier, high grade** | ea | $14.60 | $620.00 | $634.60 |
| *Replace* Materials ....500.00     Labor ..........120.00 | | | | |
| *Remove* ......................     Labor ..........14.60 | | | | |
| **Entrance chandelier, deluxe grade** | ea | $14.60 | $755.00 | $769.60 |
| *Replace* Materials ....635.00     Labor ..........120.00 | | | | |
| *Remove* ......................     Labor ..........14.60 | | | | |
| **Entrance chandelier, custom grade** | ea | $14.60 | $935.00 | $949.60 |
| *Replace* Materials .....815.00     Labor ..........120.00 | | | | |
| *Remove* ......................     Labor ..........14.60 | | | | |
| **Entrance chandelier, custom deluxe grade** | ea | $14.60 | $1,130.00 | $1,144.60 |
| *Replace* Materials ...1010.00     Labor ..........120.00 | | | | |
| *Remove* ......................     Labor ..........14.60 | | | | |
| **Grand entrance chandelier, economy grade** | ea | $14.60 | $680.00 | $694.60 |
| *Replace* Materials .....515.00     Labor ..........165.00 | | | | |
| *Remove* ......................     Labor ..........14.60 | | | | |
| **Grand entrance chandelier, standard grade** | ea | $14.60 | $1,010.00 | $1,024.60 |
| *Replace* Materials ....845.00     Labor ..........165.00 | | | | |
| *Remove* ......................     Labor ..........14.60 | | | | |
| **Grand entrance chandelier, high grade** | ea | $14.60 | $1,315.00 | $1,329.60 |
| *Replace* Materials ...1150.00     Labor ..........165.00 | | | | |
| *Remove* ......................     Labor ..........14.60 | | | | |
| **Grand entrance chandelier, deluxe grade** | ea | $14.60 | $1,615.00 | $1,629.60 |
| *Replace* Materials ...1450.00     Labor ..........165.00 | | | | |
| *Remove* ......................     Labor ..........14.60 | | | | |
| **Grand entrance chandelier, custom grade** | ea | $14.60 | $2,015.00 | $2,029.60 |
| *Replace* Materials ..1850.00     Labor ..........165.00 | | | | |
| *Remove* ......................     Labor ..........14.60 | | | | |
| **Grand entrance chandelier, custom deluxe grade** | ea | $14.60 | $3,115.00 | $3,129.60 |
| *Replace* Materials ..2950.00     Labor ..........165.00 | | | | |
| *Remove* ......................     Labor ..........14.60 | | | | |
| **Early American reproduction chandelier, economy grade** | ea | $14.60 | $325.00 | $339.60 |
| *Replace* Materials ....265.00     Labor ..........60.00 | | | | |
| *Remove* ......................     Labor ..........14.60 | | | | |

▶ Usually contains one or more of the following: hand-soldered brass, tin, or pewter, center wood turning, antique finishes, simulated candles (may be wax coated). 3 to 6 arms, curved metal & scalloped candle escutcheons. 12" to 20" diameter.

**RELATED ITEMS**

Cleaning.......................57

◄ **ENTRANCE CHANDELIER**
*To 40" in diameter. Suitable for installations on 12' and taller ceilings.*

**FIXTURE QUALITY** *continued*

**Custom deluxe**
Designed by prominent designer. Heavy-gauge metal components, solid brass components, intricate glass shades, specialty antique finishes, polished brass, antiqued brass, polished nickel (or chrome) over brass. Chandeliers usually contain 6 to 20 arms, often in two tiers.

◄ **GRAND ENTRANCE CHANDELIER**
*To 60" in diameter. Suitable for installations on 18' and taller ceilings.*

**DESIGNER FIXTURES**

The price of a light fixture can vary a great deal, often without any visible explanation.

For example, a light fixture that is designed by a prominent designer may be far more expensive than a light fixture with similar materials and design.

◄ **EARLY AMERICAN CHANDELIER**
*Early American candle chandeliers converted to electrical.*

*continued on next page*

| Item Description | Unit | Remove | Replace | Total |
|---|---|---|---|---|
| **EARLY AMERICAN CHANDELIER** *continued* | | | | |
| These fixtures are antique reproductions and are hand tooled from tin, distressed tin, pewter, brass, or copper. Joints are hand soldered. The electric "candles" may be coated with bees wax. Although many modern fixtures use a candle style, they should not be confused with early American reproduction fixtures. Look for hand tooling inconsistencies and hand-soldered joints. | | | | |

| Item Description | Unit | Remove | Replace | Total |
|---|---|---|---|---|
| **Early American reproduction chandelier, standard grade**<br>*Replace* Materials....360.00  Labor..........60.00<br>*Remove* .....................  Labor..........14.60<br>▶ Same quality as economy grade with 4 to 8 arms. 21" to 30" diameter. | ea | $14.60 | $420.00 | $434.60 |
| **Early American reproduction chandelier, high grade**<br>*Replace* Materials....500.00  Labor..........60.00<br>*Remove* .....................  Labor..........14.60<br>▶ Same quality as economy grade with 10 to 18 arms. 21" to 30" diameter. | ea | $14.60 | $560.00 | $574.60 |
| **Early American reproduction chandelier, deluxe grade**<br>*Replace* Materials.....715.00  Labor..........60.00<br>*Remove* .....................  Labor..........14.60<br>▶ Simulated candle-style light fixture. Same quality as economy grade with 10 to 18 arms. 21" to 30" diameter, two tiers. | ea | $14.60 | $775.00 | $789.60 |
| **Early American reproduction chandelier, custom grade**<br>*Replace* Materials....860.00  Labor..........60.00<br>*Remove* .....................  Labor..........14.60<br>▶ Simulated candle-style light fixture. Same quality as economy grade with intricate metalwork. 10 to 18 arms. 21" to 30" diameter, two tiers. | ea | $14.60 | $920.00 | $934.60 |
| **Early American reproduction chandelier, custom deluxe grade**<br>*Replace* Materials ...1150.00  Labor..........60.00<br>*Remove* .....................  Labor..........14.60<br>▶ Simulated candle-style light fixture. Same quality as economy grade with intricate metalwork. 10 to 18 arms. 31" to 44" diameter, two tiers. | ea | $14.60 | $1,210.00 | $1,224.60 |
| **Early electric reproduction chandelier, economy grade**<br>*Replace* Materials.....310.00  Labor..........60.00<br>*Remove* .....................  Labor..........14.60 | ea | $14.60 | $370.00 | $384.60 |
| **Early electric reproduction chandelier, standard grade**<br>*Replace* Materials ....395.00  Labor..........60.00<br>*Remove* .....................  Labor..........14.60 | ea | $14.60 | $455.00 | $469.60 |
| **Early electric reproduction chandelier, high grade**<br>*Replace* Materials....530.00  Labor..........60.00<br>*Remove* .....................  Labor..........14.60 | ea | $14.60 | $590.00 | $604.60 |
| **Early electric reproduction chandelier, deluxe grade**<br>*Replace* Materials ....755.00  Labor..........60.00<br>*Remove* .....................  Labor..........14.60 | ea | $14.60 | $815.00 | $829.60 |
| **Early electric reproduction chandelier, custom grade**<br>*Replace* Materials ....895.00  Labor..........60.00<br>*Remove* .....................  Labor..........14.60 | ea | $14.60 | $955.00 | $969.60 |
| **Early electric reproduction chandelier, custom deluxe grade**<br>*Replace* Materials ..1200.00  Labor..........60.00<br>*Remove* .....................  Labor..........14.60 | ea | $14.60 | $1,260.00 | $1,274.60 |
| **Early gas reproduction chandelier, economy grade**<br>*Replace* Materials ....325.00  Labor..........60.00<br>*Remove* .....................  Labor..........14.60 | ea | $14.60 | $385.00 | $399.60 |
| **Early gas reproduction chandelier, standard grade**<br>*Replace* Materials ....395.00  Labor..........60.00<br>*Remove* .....................  Labor..........14.60 | ea | $14.60 | $455.00 | $469.60 |

**EARLY ELECTRIC CHANDELIER**
Reproductions of chandeliers that were made when electricity was first introduced. Use these prices for true design reproductions. See quality indicators on pages 154-155.

courtesy of **Rejuvenation Lamp & Fixture Co.**

**EARLY GAS CHANDELIER**
Electrified reproductions of chandeliers that were originally designed to burn coal gas. Can usually be identified by a fake gas valve on the arm.

continued on next page

| Item Description | Unit | Remove | Replace | Total |
|---|---|---|---|---|
| **Early gas reproduction chandelier, high grade** | ea | $14.60 | $615.00 | $629.60 |
| *Replace* Materials ....555.00    Labor ..........60.00 *Remove* ......................    Labor ...........14.60 | | | | |
| **Early gas reproduction chandelier, deluxe grade** | ea | $14.60 | $810.00 | $824.60 |
| *Replace* Materials ....750.00    Labor ..........60.00 *Remove* ......................    Labor ...........14.60 | | | | |
| **Early gas reproduction chandelier, custom grade** | ea | $14.60 | $945.00 | $959.60 |
| *Replace* Materials ....885.00    Labor ..........60.00 *Remove* ......................    Labor ...........14.60 | | | | |
| **Early gas reproduction chandelier, custom deluxe grade** | ea | $14.60 | $1,310.00 | $1,324.60 |
| *Replace* Materials ..1250.00    Labor ..........60.00 *Remove* ......................    Labor ...........14.60 | | | | |
| **Early electric / gas combination reproduction chandelier, economy grade** | ea | $14.60 | $400.00 | $414.60 |
| *Replace* Materials ....340.00    Labor ..........60.00 *Remove* ......................    Labor ...........14.60 | | | | |
| **Early electric / gas combination reproduction chandelier, standard grade** | ea | $14.60 | $470.00 | $484.60 |
| *Replace* Materials .....410.00    Labor ..........60.00 *Remove* ......................    Labor ...........14.60 | | | | |
| **Early electric / gas combination reproduction chandelier, high grade** | ea | $14.60 | $620.00 | $634.60 |
| *Replace* Materials ....560.00    Labor ..........60.00 *Remove* ......................    Labor ...........14.60 | | | | |
| **Early electric / gas combination reproduction chandelier, deluxe grade** | ea | $14.60 | $820.00 | $834.60 |
| *Replace* Materials ....760.00    Labor ..........60.00 *Remove* ......................    Labor ...........14.60 | | | | |
| **Early electric / gas combination reproduction chandelier, custom grade** | ea | $14.60 | $960.00 | $974.60 |
| *Replace* Materials ....900.00    Labor ..........60.00 *Remove* ......................    Labor ...........14.60 | | | | |
| **Early electric / gas combination reproduction chandelier, custom deluxe grade** | ea | $14.60 | $1,260.00 | $1,274.60 |
| *Replace* Materials ..1200.00    Labor ..........60.00 *Remove* ......................    Labor ...........14.60 | | | | |
| **Imitation crystal chandelier, economy grade** | ea | $14.60 | $260.00 | $274.60 |
| *Replace* Materials ....200.00    Labor ..........60.00 *Remove* ......................    Labor ...........14.60 ▶ Cut glass imitation crystal. 4 to 8 arms. | | | | |
| **Imitation crystal chandelier, standard grade** | ea | $14.60 | $330.00 | $344.60 |
| *Replace* Materials ....270.00    Labor ..........60.00 *Remove* ......................    Labor ...........14.60 ▶ Cut glass imitation crystal. 6 to 14 arms. | | | | |
| **Crystal chandelier, standard grade** | ea | $14.60 | $710.00 | $724.60 |
| *Replace* Materials ....650.00    Labor ..........60.00 *Remove* ......................    Labor ...........14.60 ▶ Lower quality crystal components, lightly festooned. | | | | |
| **Crystal chandelier, high grade** | ea | $14.60 | $885.00 | $899.60 |
| *Replace* Materials ....825.00    Labor ..........60.00 *Remove* ......................    Labor ...........14.60 ▶ High quality crystal components, moderately festooned. Crystal fixture width is 65% to 80% of the fixture's height. | | | | |

◀ **EARLY GAS CHANDELIER** continued

Because a flame burns upward, gas reproduction fixture shades always face upward. Also use these prices for electric reproductions of lantern style chandeliers. Modern designs of a gas or lantern style usually fall in the economy and standard grades. See quality indicators on pages 154-155.

◀ **EARLY ELECTRIC / GAS CHANDELIER** When electricity was first introduced, builders were unsure whether it or gas was the wave of the future. Many builders played it safe by installing fixtures that used both. The original gas components can be identified by the fake valve on the arm. Gas components always face up. Electrical components often have a pull switch and usually, but not always, face down. See quality indicators on pages 154-155.

◀ **IMITATION CRYSTAL CHANDELIER** Cut glass components.

◀ **CRYSTAL CHANDELIER** High-quality crystal components. Deduct **15%** for lower quality crystal. To 25" diameter. Suitable for installation on 8' or taller ceilings.

**RELATED ITEMS**
Cleaning......................57

| | Item Description | Unit | Remove | Replace | Total |
|---|---|---|---|---|---|
| **CRYSTAL ▶** **CHANDELIER** *continued* | **Crystal chandelier, deluxe grade** *Replace* Materials....980.00     Labor .........60.00 *Remove* .......................     Labor..........14.60 ▶ High quality crystal components, heavily festooned. Crystal fixture width is 65% to 80% of the fixture's height. | ea | $14.60 | $1,040.00 | $1,054.60 |
| | **Crystal chandelier, custom grade** *Replace* Materials...1100.00     Labor .........60.00 *Remove* .......................     Labor..........14.60 ▶ High quality crystal components. Crystal fixture width is 50% to 60% of the fixture's height. | ea | $14.60 | $1,160.00 | $1,174.60 |
| | **Crystal chandelier, custom deluxe grade** *Replace* Materials ..1200.00     Labor .........60.00 *Remove* .......................     Labor..........14.60 ▶ High quality crystal components, heavily festooned. Crystal fixture width is 50% to 60% of the fixture's height. | ea | $14.60 | $1,260.00 | $1,274.60 |
| **ENTRANCE ▶** **CRYSTAL** **CHANDELIER** *High-quality crystal components. Deduct* **15%** *for lower quality crystal. To 32" diameter. Suitable for installation on 14' or taller ceilings.* | **Entrance crystal chandelier, standard grade** *Replace* Materials....950.00     Labor .........120.00 *Remove* .......................     Labor..........14.60 ▶ Lower quality crystal components, lightly festooned. | ea | $14.60 | $1,070.00 | $1,084.60 |
| | **Entrance crystal chandelier, high grade** *Replace* Materials ...1150.00     Labor .........120.00 *Remove* .......................     Labor..........14.60 ▶ High quality crystal components, moderately festooned. Crystal fixture width is 65% to 80% of the fixture's height. | ea | $14.60 | $1,270.00 | $1,284.60 |
| | **Entrance crystal chandelier, deluxe grade** *Replace* Materials ..1300.00     Labor .........120.00 *Remove* .......................     Labor..........14.60 ▶ High quality crystal components, heavily festooned. Crystal fixture width is 65% to 80% of the fixture's height. | ea | $14.60 | $1,420.00 | $1,434.60 |
| | **Entrance crystal chandelier, custom grade** *Replace* Materials...1700.00     Labor .........120.00 *Remove* .......................     Labor..........14.60 ▶ High quality crystal components. Crystal fixture width is 50% to 60% of the fixture's height. | ea | $14.60 | $1,820.00 | $1,834.60 |
| | **Entrance crystal chandelier, custom deluxe grade** *Replace* Materials ..2400.00     Labor .........120.00 *Remove* .......................     Labor..........14.60 ▶ High quality crystal components, heavily festooned. Crystal fixture width is 50% to 60% of the fixture's height. | ea | $14.60 | $2,520.00 | $2,534.60 |
| **GRAND ▶** **ENTRANCE** **CRYSTAL** **CHANDELIER** *High-quality crystal components. Deduct* **15%** *for lower quality crystal. To 52" diameter. Suitable for installation on 20' or taller ceilings.* | **Grand entrance crystal chandelier, standard grade** *Replace* Materials ..1400.00     Labor .........165.00 *Remove* .......................     Labor..........14.60 ▶ Lower quality crystal components, lightly festooned. | ea | $14.60 | $1,565.00 | $1,579.60 |
| | **Grand entrance crystal chandelier, high grade** *Replace* Materials...3100.00     Labor .........165.00 *Remove* .......................     Labor..........14.60 ▶ High quality crystal components, moderately festooned. Crystal fixture width is 65% to 80% of the fixture's height. | ea | $14.60 | $3,265.00 | $3,279.60 |
| | **Grand entrance crystal chandelier, deluxe grade** *Replace* Materials ..4200.00     Labor .........165.00 *Remove* .......................     Labor..........14.60 ▶ High quality crystal components, heavily festooned. Crystal fixture width is 65% to 80% of the fixture's height. | ea | $14.60 | $4,365.00 | $4,379.60 |

| Item Description | Unit | Remove | Replace | Total |
|---|---|---|---|---|
| **Grand entrance crystal chandelier, custom grade** | ea | $14.60 | $5,865.00 | $5,879.60 |
| *Replace* Materials ..5700.00   Labor .........165.00 | | | | |
| *Remove* ......................   Labor ...........14.60 | | | | |
| ► High quality crystal components. Crystal fixture width is 50% to 60% of the fixture's height. | | | | |
| **Grand entrance crystal chandelier, custom deluxe grade** | ea | $14.60 | $6,815.00 | $6,829.60 |
| *Replace* Materials ..6650.00   Labor .........165.00 | | | | |
| *Remove* ......................   Labor ...........14.60 | | | | |
| ► High quality crystal components, heavily festooned. Crystal fixture width is 50% to 60% of the fixture's height. | | | | |
| **Crystal tier chandelier, standard grade** | ea | $14.60 | $815.00 | $829.60 |
| *Replace* Materials ....755.00   Labor ..........60.00 | | | | |
| *Remove* ......................   Labor ...........14.60 | | | | |
| ► 4 to 5 tiers, 6" to 10" diameter. Minimum 8' to 10' ceilings. | | | | |
| **Crystal tier chandelier, high grade** | ea | $14.60 | $990.00 | $1,004.60 |
| *Replace* Materials ....825.00   Labor .........165.00 | | | | |
| *Remove* ......................   Labor ...........14.60 | | | | |
| ► 4 to 5 tiers, 11" to 14" diameter. Minimum 8' to 10' ceilings. | | | | |
| **Crystal tier chandelier, deluxe grade** | ea | $14.60 | $1,175.00 | $1,189.60 |
| *Replace* Materials ...1010.00   Labor .........165.00 | | | | |
| *Remove* ......................   Labor ...........14.60 | | | | |
| ► 4 to 5 tiers, 15" to 20" diameter. Minimum 12' to 14' ceilings. | | | | |
| **Crystal tier chandelier, custom grade** | ea | $14.60 | $1,265.00 | $1,279.60 |
| *Replace* Materials ...1100.00   Labor .........165.00 | | | | |
| *Remove* ......................   Labor ...........14.60 | | | | |
| ► 4 to 5 tiers, 21" to 25" diameter. Minimum 15' to 18' ceilings. | | | | |
| **Crystal tier chandelier, custom deluxe grade** | ea | $14.60 | $1,665.00 | $1,679.60 |
| *Replace* Materials ..1500.00   Labor .........165.00 | | | | |
| *Remove* ......................   Labor ...........14.60 | | | | |
| ► 4 to 5 tiers, 26" to 34" diameter. Minimum 15' to 18' ceilings. | | | | |
| **Crystal wall fixture, standard grade** | ea | $7.86 | $250.00 | $257.86 |
| *Replace* Materials ....230.00   Labor ..........20.00 | | | | |
| *Remove* ......................   Labor ...........7.86 | | | | |
| ► Lower quality crystal components, lightly festooned. | | | | |
| **Crystal wall fixture, high grade** | ea | $7.86 | $375.00 | $382.86 |
| *Replace* Materials ....355.00   Labor ..........20.00 | | | | |
| *Remove* ......................   Labor ...........7.86 | | | | |
| ► High quality crystal components, moderately festooned. Crystal fixture width is 65% to 80% of the fixture's height. | | | | |
| **Crystal wall fixture, deluxe grade** | ea | $7.86 | $540.00 | $547.86 |
| *Replace* Materials ....520.00   Labor ..........20.00 | | | | |
| *Remove* ......................   Labor ...........7.86 | | | | |
| ► High quality crystal components, heavily festooned. Crystal fixture width is 65% to 80% of the fixture's height. | | | | |
| **Crystal wall fixture, custom grade** | ea | $7.86 | $780.00 | $787.86 |
| *Replace* Materials ....760.00   Labor ..........20.00 | | | | |
| *Remove* ......................   Labor ...........7.86 | | | | |
| ► High quality crystal components. Crystal fixture width is 50% to 60% of the fixture's height. | | | | |
| **Remove crystal wall fixture for work, then reinstall** | ea | — | $36.80 | $36.80 |
| *Replace* ......................   Labor ..........36.80 | | | | |

**RELATED ITEMS**
Cleaning.......................57

◄ **CRYSTAL TIER CHANDELIER**
High-quality crystal components. Deduct **15%** for lower quality crystal. Crystal tier chandeliers resemble an upside down wedding cake. They are usually 1.5 to 2 times taller than they are wide, so normally are installed on taller ceilings.

◄ **CRYSTAL WALL FIXTURE**
High-quality crystal components. Deduct **15%** for lower quality crystal.

◁ remove & reinstall

| Item Description | Unit | Remove | Replace | Total |
|---|---|---|---|---|
| **CRYSTAL ▶ CHANDELIER REPAIR** · **Repair crystal chandelier, minor repairs** | ea | — | $121.20 | $121.20 |
| *Replace* Materials ......55.00    Labor ..........66.20 | | | | |
| ▶ Replace 2 to 4 components. | | | | |
| **Repair crystal chandelier, significant repairs** | ea | — | $247.00 | $247.00 |
| *Replace* Materials .....115.00    Labor..........132.00 | | | | |
| ▶ Replace 5 to 10 components. | | | | |
| **Repair crystal chandelier, major repairs** | ea | — | $460.00 | $460.00 |
| *Replace* Materials.....195.00    Labor..........265.00 | | | | |
| ▶ Replace 11 to 16 components. | | | | |
| **Repair crystal chandelier, rebuild** | ea | — | $926.00 | $926.00 |
| *Replace* Materials ....375.00    Labor..........551.00 | | | | |
| ▶ Dismantle all or most of fixture, replace 25% to 35% of components. | | | | |
| **Remove chandelier for work, then reinstall** | ea | — | $102.00 | $102.00 |
| *Replace* ......................    Labor..........102.00 | | | | |
| **Remove vaulted ceiling chandelier for work, then reinstall** | ea | — | $221.00 | $221.00 |
| *Replace* ......................    Labor..........221.00 | | | | |
| ▶ For ceiling heights to 14'. | | | | |
| **Remove high vaulted-ceiling chandelier for work, then reinstall** | ea | — | $301.00 | $301.00 |
| *Replace* ......................    Labor..........301.00 | | | | |
| ▶ For ceiling heights to 22'. | | | | |
| **TALL CEILING ▶ INSTALLATION** · **Add for hanging chandelier on vaulted ceiling 12' to 14' tall** | ea | — | $33.10 | $33.10 |
| *Replace* ......................    Labor ..........33.10 | | | | |
| **Add for hanging chandelier on vaulted ceiling 14' to 16' tall** | ea | — | $60.00 | $60.00 |
| *Replace* ......................    Labor ..........60.00 | | | | |
| **Add for hanging chandelier on vaulted ceiling 17' to 22' tall** | ea | — | $91.90 | $91.90 |
| *Replace* ......................    Labor..........91.90 | | | | |
| **SINGLE PENDANT ▶ FIXTURE** · **Single pendant light fixture, economy grade** | ea | $7.86 | $75.70 | $83.56 |
| *Replace* Materials ......55.00    Labor ..........20.70 | | | | |
| *Remove* ......................    Labor ..........7.86 | | | | |
| **Single pendant light fixture, standard grade** | ea | $7.86 | $90.70 | $98.56 |
| *Replace* Materials ......70.00    Labor ..........20.70 | | | | |
| *Remove* ......................    Labor ..........7.86 | | | | |
| **Single pendant light fixture, high grade** | ea | $7.86 | $110.70 | $118.56 |
| *Replace* Materials ......90.00    Labor ..........20.70 | | | | |
| *Remove* ......................    Labor ..........7.86 | | | | |
| **Single pendant light fixture, deluxe grade** | ea | $7.86 | $130.70 | $138.56 |
| *Replace* Materials .....110.00    Labor ..........20.70 | | | | |
| *Remove* ......................    Labor ..........7.86 | | | | |
| **Single pendant light fixture, custom grade** | ea | $7.86 | $145.70 | $153.56 |
| *Replace* Materials .....125.00    Labor ..........20.70 | | | | |
| *Remove* ......................    Labor ..........7.86 | | | | |
| **Single pendant light fixture, custom deluxe grade** | ea | $7.86 | $160.70 | $168.56 |
| *Replace* Materials ....140.00    Labor ..........20.70 | | | | |
| *Remove* ......................    Labor ..........7.86 | | | | |

*Pendant fixtures hang from a chain or rod and connect directly to an electrical box in the ceiling. (For hanging fixtures that connect to a switched outlet, see page 168.) See quality indicators on pages 154-155.*

| Item Description | Unit | Remove | Replace | Total |
|---|---|---|---|---|
| **Double pendant light fixture, economy grade**<br>*Replace* Materials....100.00   Labor .........20.70<br>*Remove* .................. Labor ..........7.86 | ea | $7.86 | $120.70 | $128.56 |
| **Double pendant light fixture, standard grade**<br>*Replace* Materials.....120.00   Labor .........20.70<br>*Remove* .................. Labor ..........7.86 | ea | $7.86 | $140.70 | $148.56 |
| **Double pendant light fixture, high grade**<br>*Replace* Materials.....145.00   Labor .........20.70<br>*Remove* .................. Labor ..........7.86 | ea | $7.86 | $165.70 | $173.56 |
| **Double pendant light fixture, deluxe grade**<br>*Replace* Materials.....165.00   Labor .........20.70<br>*Remove* .................. Labor ..........7.86 | ea | $7.86 | $185.70 | $193.56 |
| **Double pendant light fixture, custom grade**<br>*Replace* Materials.....185.00   Labor .........20.70<br>*Remove* .................. Labor ..........7.86 | ea | $7.86 | $205.70 | $213.56 |
| **Double pendant light fixture, custom deluxe grade**<br>*Replace* Materials.....215.00   Labor .........20.70<br>*Remove* .................. Labor ..........7.86 | ea | $7.86 | $235.70 | $243.56 |
| **"Shower" style light fixture, economy grade**<br>*Replace* Materials ....140.00   Labor .........60.00<br>*Remove* .................. Labor ..........14.60 | ea | $14.60 | $200.00 | $214.60 |
| **"Shower" style light fixture, standard grade**<br>*Replace* Materials ....180.00   Labor .........60.00<br>*Remove* .................. Labor ..........14.60 | ea | $14.60 | $240.00 | $254.60 |
| **"Shower" style light fixture, high grade**<br>*Replace* Materials ....240.00   Labor .........60.00<br>*Remove* .................. Labor ..........14.60 | ea | $14.60 | $300.00 | $314.60 |
| **"Shower" style light fixture, deluxe grade**<br>*Replace* Materials ....285.00   Labor .........60.00<br>*Remove* .................. Labor ..........14.60 | ea | $14.60 | $345.00 | $359.60 |
| **"Shower" style light fixture, custom grade**<br>*Replace* Materials ....365.00   Labor .........60.00<br>*Remove* .................. Labor ..........14.60 | ea | $14.60 | $425.00 | $439.60 |
| **"Shower" style light fixture, custom deluxe grade**<br>*Replace* Materials ....395.00   Labor .........60.00<br>*Remove* .................. Labor ..........14.60 | ea | $14.60 | $455.00 | $469.60 |
| **Small bowl-shade or globe light fixture, economy grade**<br>*Replace* Materials......30.00   Labor .........20.70<br>*Remove* .................. Labor ..........7.86 | ea | $7.86 | $50.70 | $58.56 |
| **Small bowl-shade or globe light fixture, standard grade**<br>*Replace* Materials......40.00   Labor .........20.70<br>*Remove* .................. Labor ..........7.86 | ea | $7.86 | $60.70 | $68.56 |
| **Small bowl-shade or globe light fixture, high grade**<br>*Replace* Materials......55.00   Labor .........20.70<br>*Remove* .................. Labor ..........7.86 | ea | $7.86 | $75.70 | $83.56 |

◄ **DOUBLE PENDANT FIXTURE**
Pendant fixtures hang from a chain or rod and connect directly to an electrical box in the ceiling. (For hanging fixtures that connect to a switched outlet, see page 168.) See quality indicators on pages 154-155.

◄ **"SHOWER" FIXTURE**
"Shower" style fixtures have a large base. Two to four (sometimes more) small lights with shades hang from the base on chains or rods. See quality indicators on pages 154-155.

◄ **SMALL BOWL-SHADE FIXTURE**
Fixture with a globe or bowl shade. Small sizes are typically found in halls. See quality indicators on pages 154-155.

**RELATED ITEMS**
Cleaning.......................57

| | Item Description | Unit | Remove | Replace | Total |
|---|---|---|---|---|---|
| **SMALL BOWL-** ▶ **SHADE FIXTURE** *continued* | **Small bowl-shade or globe light fixture, deluxe grade** <br> *Replace* Materials ......75.00    Labor ..........20.70 <br> *Remove* .......................    Labor ...........7.86 | ea | $7.86 | $95.70 | $103.56 |
| | **Small bowl-shade or globe light fixture, custom grade** <br> *Replace* Materials ......85.00    Labor ..........20.70 <br> *Remove* .......................    Labor ...........7.86 | ea | $7.86 | $105.70 | $113.56 |
| | **Small bowl-shade or globe light fixture, custom deluxe grade** <br> *Replace* Materials ....100.00    Labor ..........20.70 <br> *Remove* .......................    Labor ...........7.86 | ea | $7.86 | $120.70 | $128.56 |
| **BOWL-SHADE** ▶ **FIXTURE** <br> *Fixture with a globe or bowl shade. See quality indicators on pages 154-155.* | **Bowl-shade or globe light fixture, economy grade** <br> *Replace* Materials ......45.00    Labor ..........20.70 <br> *Remove* .......................    Labor ...........7.86 | ea | $7.86 | $65.70 | $73.56 |
| | **Bowl-shade or globe light fixture, standard grade** <br> *Replace* Materials ......80.00    Labor ..........20.70 <br> *Remove* .......................    Labor ...........7.86 | ea | $7.86 | $100.70 | $108.56 |
| | **Bowl-shade or globe light fixture, high grade** <br> *Replace* Materials ....100.00    Labor ..........20.70 <br> *Remove* .......................    Labor ...........7.86 | ea | $7.86 | $120.70 | $128.56 |
| | **Bowl-shade or globe light fixture, deluxe grade** <br> *Replace* Materials .....125.00    Labor ..........20.70 <br> *Remove* .......................    Labor ...........7.86 | ea | $7.86 | $145.70 | $153.56 |
| | **Bowl-shade or globe light fixture, custom grade** <br> *Replace* Materials .....155.00    Labor ..........20.70 <br> *Remove* .......................    Labor ...........7.86 | ea | $7.86 | $175.70 | $183.56 |
| | **Bowl-shade or globe light fixture, custom deluxe grade** <br> *Replace* Materials .....175.00    Labor ..........20.70 <br> *Remove* .......................    Labor ...........7.86 | ea | $7.86 | $195.70 | $203.56 |
| **SUSPENDED** ▶ **BOWL-SHADE FIXTURE** <br> *Bowl-shade suspended on three rods or chains. See quality indicators on pages 154-155.* | **Suspended bowl-shade light fixture, economy grade** <br> *Replace* Materials .....165.00    Labor ..........60.00 <br> *Remove* .......................    Labor ...........14.60 | ea | $14.60 | $225.00 | $239.60 |
| | **Suspended bowl-shade light fixture, standard grade** <br> *Replace* Materials ....200.00    Labor ..........60.00 <br> *Remove* .......................    Labor ...........14.60 | ea | $14.60 | $260.00 | $274.60 |
| | **Suspended bowl-shade light fixture, high grade** <br> *Replace* Materials ....280.00    Labor ..........60.00 <br> *Remove* .......................    Labor ...........14.60 | ea | $14.60 | $340.00 | $354.60 |
| | **Suspended bowl-shade light fixture, deluxe grade** <br> *Replace* Materials ....355.00    Labor ..........60.00 <br> *Remove* .......................    Labor ...........14.60 | ea | $14.60 | $415.00 | $429.60 |
| *courtesy of Rejuvenation Lamp & Fixture Co.* | **Suspended bowl-shade light fixture, custom grade** <br> *Replace* Materials ....390.00    Labor ..........60.00 <br> *Remove* .......................    Labor ...........14.60 | ea | $14.60 | $450.00 | $464.60 |
| | **Suspended bowl-shade light fixture, custom deluxe grade** <br> *Replace* Materials ....495.00    Labor ..........60.00 <br> *Remove* .......................    Labor ...........14.60 | ea | $14.60 | $555.00 | $569.60 |

| Item Description | Unit | Remove | Replace | Total |
|---|---|---|---|---|
| **Billiard-table style light fixture, economy grade** | ea | $14.60 | $240.10 | $254.70 |
| *Replace* Materials.....185.00    Labor...........55.10 | | | | |
| *Remove* ........................    Labor...........14.60 | | | | |
| ▶ Single light on rod, with colored glass shade. | | | | |
| **Billiard-table style light fixture, standard grade** | ea | $14.60 | $460.10 | $474.70 |
| *Replace* Materials....405.00    Labor...........55.10 | | | | |
| *Remove* ........................    Labor...........14.60 | | | | |
| ▶ Single light on decorative rod, with ribbed glass shade. | | | | |
| **Billiard-table style light fixture, high grade** | ea | $14.60 | $675.10 | $689.70 |
| *Replace* Materials ....620.00    Labor...........55.10 | | | | |
| *Remove* ........................    Labor...........14.60 | | | | |
| ▶ Double lights on decorative rods, with ribbed glass shades. | | | | |
| **Billiard-table style light fixture, deluxe grade** | ea | $14.60 | $935.10 | $949.70 |
| *Replace* Materials....880.00    Labor...........55.10 | | | | |
| *Remove* ........................    Labor...........14.60 | | | | |
| ▶ Triple lights on decorative rods, with ribbed glass shades. | | | | |
| **Billiard-table style light fixture, custom grade** | ea | $14.60 | $1,205.10 | $1,219.70 |
| *Replace* Materials ...1150.00    Labor...........55.10 | | | | |
| *Remove* ........................    Labor...........14.60 | | | | |
| ▶ Triple lights on decorative rods with brass scroll work above, ribbed glass shades with brass trim. | | | | |
| **Billiard-table style light fixture, custom deluxe grade** | ea | $14.60 | $1,805.10 | $1,819.70 |
| *Replace* Materials...1750.00    Labor...........55.10 | | | | |
| *Remove* ........................    Labor...........14.60 | | | | |
| ▶ Triple lights on decorative rods with elaborate brass scroll work above, ribbed glass shades with brass trim.  May have copper shades. | | | | |
| **Remove billiard-table style light fixture for work, then reinstall** | ea | — | $94.40 | $94.40 |
| *Replace* ........................    Labor...........94.40 | | | | |
| **Wall-mount light fixture, economy grade** | ea | $7.86 | $35.00 | $42.86 |
| *Replace* Materials.......15.00    Labor ..........20.00 | | | | |
| *Remove* ........................    Labor ...........7.86 | | | | |
| **Wall-mount light fixture, standard grade** | ea | $7.86 | $55.00 | $62.86 |
| *Replace* Materials ......35.00    Labor ..........20.00 | | | | |
| *Remove* ........................    Labor ...........7.86 | | | | |
| **Wall-mount light fixture, high grade** | ea | $7.86 | $105.00 | $112.86 |
| *Replace* Materials ......85.00    Labor ..........20.00 | | | | |
| *Remove* ........................    Labor ...........7.86 | | | | |
| **Wall-mount light fixture, deluxe grade** | ea | $7.86 | $170.00 | $177.86 |
| *Replace* Materials ....150.00    Labor ..........20.00 | | | | |
| *Remove* ........................    Labor ...........7.86 | | | | |
| **Wall-mount light fixture, custom grade** | ea | $7.86 | $190.00 | $197.86 |
| *Replace* Materials .....170.00    Labor ..........20.00 | | | | |
| *Remove* ........................    Labor ...........7.86 | | | | |
| **Wall-mount light fixture, custom deluxe grade** | ea | $7.86 | $265.00 | $272.86 |
| *Replace* Materials.....245.00    Labor ..........20.00 | | | | |
| *Remove* ........................    Labor ...........7.86 | | | | |
| **Remove wall-mount light fixture for work, then reinstall** | ea | — | $36.80 | $36.80 |
| *Replace* ........................    Labor ..........36.80 | | | | |

◀ **BILLIARD-TABLE STYLE FIXTURE**
*See quality indicators on pages 154-155.*

◀ **WALL-MOUNT FIXTURE**
*See quality indicators on pages 154-155.*

**RELATED ITEMS**
Cleaning........................57

◁ remove & reinstall

| Item Description | Unit | Remove | Replace | Total |
|---|---|---|---|---|
| **FLUORESCENT FIXTURE** — **1' one-tube surface-mounted fluorescent strip light**<br>*Replace* Materials....15.00  Labor.....37.80<br>*Remove* .............  Labor.....13.10 | ea | $13.10 | $52.80 | $65.90 |
| **1-1/2' one-tube surface-mounted fluorescent strip light**<br>*Replace* Materials....20.00  Labor.....37.80<br>*Remove* .............  Labor.....13.10 | ea | $13.10 | $57.80 | $70.90 |
| **2' one-tube surface-mounted fluorescent strip light**<br>*Replace* Materials....20.00  Labor.....37.80<br>*Remove* .............  Labor.....13.10 | ea | $13.10 | $57.80 | $70.90 |
| **4' one-tube surface-mounted fluorescent strip light**<br>*Replace* Materials....25.00  Labor.....37.80<br>*Remove* .............  Labor.....13.10 | ea | $13.10 | $62.80 | $75.90 |
| **6' one-tube surface-mounted fluorescent strip light**<br>*Replace* Materials....40.00  Labor.....37.80<br>*Remove* .............  Labor.....13.10 | ea | $13.10 | $77.80 | $90.90 |
| **8' one-tube surface-mounted fluorescent strip light**<br>*Replace* Materials....55.00  Labor.....37.80<br>*Remove* .............  Labor.....13.10 | ea | $13.10 | $92.80 | $105.90 |
| **2' one-tube surface-mounted fluorescent strip light with diffuser**<br>*Replace* Materials....30.00  Labor.....37.80<br>*Remove* .............  Labor.....13.10 | ea | $13.10 | $67.80 | $80.90 |
| **4' one-tube surface-mounted fluorescent strip light with diffuser**<br>*Replace* Materials....30.00  Labor.....37.80<br>*Remove* .............  Labor.....13.10 | ea | $13.10 | $67.80 | $80.90 |
| **6' one-tube surface-mounted fluorescent strip light with diffuser**<br>*Replace* Materials....40.00  Labor.....37.80<br>*Remove* .............  Labor.....13.10 | ea | $13.10 | $77.80 | $90.90 |
| **8' one-tube surface-mounted fluorescent strip light with diffuser**<br>*Replace* Materials....65.00  Labor.....37.80<br>*Remove* .............  Labor.....13.10 | ea | $13.10 | $102.80 | $115.90 |
| **two-tube** — **2' two-tube surface-mounted fluorescent strip light**<br>*Replace* Materials....35.00  Labor.....37.80<br>*Remove* .............  Labor.....13.10 | ea | $13.10 | $72.80 | $85.90 |
| **2' two-tube surface-mounted fluorescent strip light with diffuser**<br>*Replace* Materials....50.00  Labor.....37.80<br>*Remove* .............  Labor.....13.10 | ea | $13.10 | $87.80 | $100.90 |
| **2' two-tube surface-mounted fluorescent strip light with vinyl trim & diffuser**<br>*Replace* Materials....55.00  Labor.....37.80<br>*Remove* .............  Labor.....13.10 | ea | $13.10 | $92.80 | $105.90 |
| **2' two-tube surface-mounted fluorescent strip light with solid wood trim & diffuser**<br>*Replace* Materials....65.00  Labor.....37.80<br>*Remove* .............  Labor.....13.10 | ea | $13.10 | $102.80 | $115.90 |
| **4' two-tube surface-mounted fluorescent strip light**<br>*Replace* Materials....45.00  Labor.....37.80<br>*Remove* .............  Labor.....13.10 | ea | $13.10 | $82.80 | $95.90 |

| Item Description | Unit | Remove | Replace | Total |
|---|---|---|---|---|
| **4' two-tube surface-mounted fluorescent strip light with diffuser** | ea | $13.10 | $92.80 | $105.90 |
| *Replace* Materials ......55.00      Labor..........37.80<br>*Remove* .....................      Labor..........13.10 | | | | |
| **4' two-tube surface-mounted fluorescent strip light with vinyl trim & diffuser** | ea | $13.10 | $97.80 | $110.90 |
| *Replace* Materials ......60.00      Labor..........37.80<br>*Remove* .....................      Labor..........13.10 | | | | |
| **4' two-tube surface-mounted fluorescent strip light with solid wood trim & diffuser** | ea | $13.10 | $122.80 | $135.90 |
| *Replace* Materials ......85.00      Labor..........37.80<br>*Remove* .....................      Labor..........13.10 | | | | |
| **6' two-tube surface-mounted fluorescent strip light** | ea | $13.10 | $87.80 | $100.90 |
| *Replace* Materials ......50.00      Labor..........37.80<br>*Remove* .....................      Labor..........13.10 | | | | |
| **6' two-tube surface-mounted fluorescent strip light with diffuser** | ea | $13.10 | $102.80 | $115.90 |
| *Replace* Materials ......65.00      Labor..........37.80<br>*Remove* .....................      Labor..........13.10 | | | | |
| **6' two-tube surface-mounted fluorescent strip light with vinyl trim & diffuser** | ea | $13.10 | $122.80 | $135.90 |
| *Replace* Materials ......85.00      Labor..........37.80<br>*Remove* .....................      Labor..........13.10 | | | | |
| **6' two-tube surface-mounted fluorescent strip light with solid wood trim & diffuser** | ea | $13.10 | $132.80 | $145.90 |
| *Replace* Materials ......95.00      Labor..........37.80<br>*Remove* .....................      Labor..........13.10 | | | | |
| **8' two-tube surface-mounted fluorescent strip light** | ea | $13.10 | $102.80 | $115.90 |
| *Replace* Materials ......65.00      Labor..........37.80<br>*Remove* .....................      Labor..........13.10 | | | | |
| **8' two-tube surface-mounted fluorescent strip light with diffuser** | ea | $13.10 | $117.80 | $130.90 |
| *Replace* Materials ......80.00      Labor..........37.80<br>*Remove* .....................      Labor..........13.10 | | | | |
| **8' two-tube surface-mounted fluorescent strip light with vinyl trim & diffuser** | ea | $13.10 | $137.80 | $150.90 |
| *Replace* Materials ....100.00      Labor..........37.80<br>*Remove* .....................      Labor..........13.10 | | | | |
| **8' two-tube surface-mounted fluorescent strip light with solid wood trim & diffuser** | ea | $13.10 | $157.80 | $170.90 |
| *Replace* Materials ....120.00      Labor..........37.80<br>*Remove* .....................      Labor..........13.10 | | | | |
| **4' four-tube surface-mounted fluorescent strip light** | ea | $13.10 | $107.80 | $120.90 |
| *Replace* Materials ......70.00      Labor..........37.80<br>*Remove* .....................      Labor..........13.10 | | | | |
| **4' four-tube surface-mounted fluorescent strip light with diffuser** | ea | $13.10 | $142.80 | $155.90 |
| *Replace* Materials ....105.00      Labor..........37.80<br>*Remove* .....................      Labor..........13.10 | | | | |
| **4' four-tube surface-mounted fluorescent strip light with vinyl trim & diffuser** | ea | $13.10 | $162.80 | $175.90 |
| *Replace* Materials ....125.00      Labor..........37.80<br>*Remove* .....................      Labor..........13.10 | | | | |
| **4' four-tube surface-mounted fluorescent strip light with solid wood trim & diffuser** | ea | $13.10 | $192.80 | $205.90 |
| *Replace* Materials ....155.00      Labor..........37.80<br>*Remove* .....................      Labor..........13.10 | | | | |

◁ four-tube

| | Item Description | Unit | Remove | Replace | Total |
|---|---|---|---|---|---|
| **FLUORESCENT** ▶ **FIXTURE** *continued* | **2' by 2' drop-in two-tube fluorescent fixture for suspended ceiling** | ea | $13.10 | $146.20 | $159.30 |
| | *Replace* Materials ......70.00  Labor...........76.20 | | | | |
| *for suspended ceilings* ▷ | *Remove* .....................  Labor...........13.10 | | | | |
| *add $14 for boxed-in fixture for fire-rated ceiling.* | **2' by 4' drop-in two-tube fluorescent fixture for suspended ceiling** | ea | $13.10 | $161.20 | $174.30 |
| | *Replace* Materials ......85.00  Labor...........76.20 | | | | |
| | *Remove* .....................  Labor...........13.10 | | | | |
| | **2' by 4' drop-in four-tube fluorescent fixture for suspended ceiling** | ea | $13.10 | $186.20 | $199.30 |
| | *Replace* Materials .....110.00  Labor...........76.20 | | | | |
| | *Remove* .....................  Labor...........13.10 | | | | |
| remove & reinstall ▷ | **Remove fluorescent light fixture for work, then reinstall** | ea | — | $66.20 | $66.20 |
| | *Replace* .....................  Labor...........66.20 | | | | |
| replace ballast ▷ | **Remove and replace fluorescent light fixture ballast** | ea | — | $105.90 | $105.90 |
| | *Replace* Materials ......55.00  Labor...........50.90 | | | | |
| **FLUORESCENT** ▶ **CIRCLINE FIXTURE** | **Fluorescent circline fixture, economy grade** | ea | $9.72 | $64.80 | $74.52 |
| | *Replace* Materials ......30.00  Labor ..........34.80 | | | | |
| | *Remove* .....................  Labor...........9.72 | | | | |
| | ▶ Single, exposed tube. | | | | |
| | **Fluorescent circline fixture, standard grade** | ea | $9.72 | $84.80 | $94.52 |
| | *Replace* Materials ......50.00  Labor ..........34.80 | | | | |
| | *Remove* .....................  Labor ...........9.72 | | | | |
| | ▶ Double, exposed tubes. | | | | |
| | **Fluorescent circline fixture, high grade** | ea | $9.72 | $114.80 | $124.52 |
| | *Replace* Materials ......80.00  Labor ..........34.80 | | | | |
| | *Remove* .....................  Labor ...........9.72 | | | | |
| | ▶ Double tubes with polystyrene diffuser. | | | | |
| | **Fluorescent circline fixture, deluxe grade** | ea | $9.72 | $189.80 | $199.52 |
| | *Replace* Materials .....155.00  Labor ..........34.80 | | | | |
| | *Remove* .....................  Labor ...........9.72 | | | | |
| | ▶ Double tubes with polystyrene diffuser and wood or metal trim. | | | | |
| remove & reinstall ▷ | **Remove fluorescent circline light fixture for work, then reinstall** | ea | — | $60.00 | $60.00 |
| | *Replace* .....................  Labor ..........60.00 | | | | |
| replace ballast ▷ | **Remove and replace fluorescent circline light fixture ballast** | ea | — | $105.90 | $105.90 |
| | *Replace* Materials ......55.00  Labor ..........50.90 | | | | |
| **CEILING FAN** ▶ *Fan only, no light.* | **Ceiling fan, economy grade** | ea | $13.10 | $143.20 | $156.30 |
| | *Replace* Materials ......55.00  Labor ..........88.20 | | | | |
| | *Remove* .....................  Labor ..........13.10 | | | | |
| | ▶ 4 blade fan up to 42" diameter.  Blades may have painted design.  3 speed pull-chain, reversible. | | | | |
| | **Ceiling fan, standard grade** | ea | $13.10 | $183.20 | $196.30 |
| | *Replace* Materials ......95.00  Labor ..........88.20 | | | | |
| | *Remove* .....................  Labor ..........13.10 | | | | |
| | ▶ 4 to 5 blade fan up to 52" diameter.  Plywood blades may have painted design or stained with cane inserts.  3 speed pull-chain, reversible. | | | | |
| | **Ceiling fan, high grade** | ea | $13.10 | $238.20 | $251.30 |
| | *Replace* Materials ....150.00  Labor ..........88.20 | | | | |
| | *Remove* .....................  Labor ..........13.10 | | | | |
| | ▶ 4 to 5 blade fan up to 52" diameter.  Hardwood stained blades may have cane inserts.  Variable speed wall controls, reversible. | | | | |

| Item Description | Unit | Remove | Replace | Total | |
|---|---|---|---|---|---|
| **Ceiling fan, deluxe grade** | ea | $13.10 | $323.20 | $336.30 | |
| *Replace* Materials ....235.00        Labor .........88.20 | | | | | |
| *Remove* ......................        Labor ...........13.10 | | | | | |
| ► 4 to 5 blade fan up to 52" diameter. Hardwood stained blades may have cane inserts. Brass motor housing contains intricate design. Variable speed wall controls, reversible. | | | | | |
| **Remove ceiling fan for work, then reinstall** | ea | — | $98.50 | $98.50 | ◁ remove and reinstall |
| *Replace* ......................        Labor ...........98.50 | | | | | |
| **Ceiling fan with light, economy grade** | ea | $13.10 | $282.00 | $295.10 | ◄ **CEILING FAN WITH LIGHT** |
| *Replace* Materials ....150.00        Labor .........132.00 | | | | | |
| *Remove* ......................        Labor ...........13.10 | | | | | |
| ► 4 blade fan up to 42" diameter. Blades may have painted design. 3 speed pull-chain, reversible. 2 to 3 lights with simple glass or metal shades, plated metal escutcheon. | | | | | |
| **Ceiling fan with light, standard grade** | ea | $13.10 | $342.00 | $355.10 | |
| *Replace* Materials .....210.00        Labor .........132.00 | | | | | |
| *Remove* ......................        Labor ...........13.10 | | | | | |
| ► 4 to 5 blade fan up to 52" diameter. Plywood blades may have painted design or stained with cane inserts. 3 speed pull-chain, reversible. 3 lights with detailed glass shades, plated metal escutcheon. | | | | | |
| **Ceiling fan with light, high grade** | ea | $13.10 | $387.00 | $400.10 | |
| *Replace* Materials ....255.00        Labor .........132.00 | | | | | |
| *Remove* ......................        Labor ...........13.10 | | | | | |
| ► 4 to 5 blade fan up to 52" diameter. Hardwood stained blades may have cane inserts. Variable speed wall controls, reversible. 3 to 4 lights with intricately detailed glass shades, plated metal escutcheon. | | | | | |
| **Ceiling fan with light, deluxe grade** | ea | $13.10 | $492.00 | $505.10 | |
| *Replace* Materials ....360.00        Labor .........132.00 | | | | | |
| *Remove* ......................        Labor ...........13.10 | | | | | |
| ► 4 to 5 blade fan up to 52" diameter. Hardwood blades may have cane inserts. Brass motor housing with intricate design. Variable speed wall control, reversible. 3 to 4 lights with intricate, detailed glass shades, solid brass escutcheon. | | | | | |
| **Ceiling fan with light, custom grade** | ea | $13.10 | $562.00 | $575.10 | |
| *Replace* Materials ....430.00        Labor .........132.00 | | | | | |
| *Remove* ......................        Labor ...........13.10 | | | | | |
| ► 4 to 5 blade fan up to 52" diameter. Hardwood stained blades may have cane inserts. Brass motor housing contains intricate design. Variable speed wall controls, reversible. 3 to 4 lights with intricately detailed glass shades, solid brass escutcheon, detailed, curved arms. | | | | | |
| **Remove ceiling fan with light for work, then reinstall** | ea | — | $102.00 | $102.00 | ◁ remove and reinstall |
| *Replace* ......................        Labor .........102.00 | | | | | |
| **Light for ceiling fan, economy grade** | ea | $7.86 | $48.90 | $56.76 | ◄ **LIGHT FOR CEILING FAN** |
| *Replace* Materials ......30.00        Labor ...........18.90 | | | | | |
| *Remove* ......................        Labor ............7.86 | | | | | |
| ► 2 to 3 lights with simple glass or metal shades, plated metal escutcheon. | | | | | |
| **Light for ceiling fan, standard grade** | ea | $7.86 | $78.90 | $86.76 | |
| *Replace* Materials ......60.00        Labor ...........18.90 | | | | | |
| *Remove* ......................        Labor ............7.86 | | | | | |
| ► 3 lights with detailed glass shades, plated metal escutcheon. | | | | | |
| **Light for ceiling fan, high grade** | ea | $7.86 | $103.90 | $111.76 | |
| *Replace* Materials ......85.00        Labor ...........18.90 | | | | | |
| *Remove* ......................        Labor ............7.86 | | | | | |
| ► 3 to 4 lights with intricately detailed glass shades, plated metal escutcheon. | | | | | |

**RELATED ITEMS**
Cleaning.......................57

| | Item Description | Unit | Remove | Replace | Total |
|---|---|---|---|---|---|
| **LIGHT FOR ▶ CEILING FAN** continued | **Light for ceiling fan, deluxe grade** | ea | $7.86 | $168.90 | $176.76 |
| | *Replace* Materials ....150.00    Labor............18.90 | | | | |
| | *Remove* ........................    Labor............7.86 | | | | |
| | ▶ 3 to 4 lights with intricately detailed glass shades, solid brass escutcheon. | | | | |
| | **Light for ceiling fan, custom grade** | ea | $7.86 | $253.90 | $261.76 |
| | *Replace* Materials ....235.00    Labor............18.90 | | | | |
| | *Remove* ........................    Labor............7.86 | | | | |
| | ▶ 3 to 4 lights with intricately detailed glass shades, solid brass escutcheon, detailed, curved arms. | | | | |
| remove & reinstall ▷ | **Remove light from ceiling fan for work, then reinstall** | ea | — | $33.10 | $33.10 |
| | *Replace* ........................    Labor .........33.10 | | | | |
| **HANGING ▶ FIXTURE** Hanging light fixtures usually hang from ceiling hooks and plug into a switched outlet. For hanging fixtures that connect into a ceiling box, see pendant fixtures on pages 160-161. See quality indicators on pages 154-155. | **Hanging light fixture, economy grade** | ea | $2.62 | $46.00 | $48.62 |
| | *Replace* Materials ......35.00    Labor............11.00 | | | | |
| | *Remove* ........................    Labor ............2.62 | | | | |
| | **Hanging light fixture, standard grade** | ea | $2.62 | $56.00 | $58.62 |
| | *Replace* Materials ......45.00    Labor............11.00 | | | | |
| | *Remove* ........................    Labor ............2.62 | | | | |
| | **Hanging light fixture, high grade** | ea | $2.62 | $66.00 | $68.62 |
| | *Replace* Materials ......55.00    Labor............11.00 | | | | |
| | *Remove* ........................    Labor ............2.62 | | | | |
| | **Hanging light fixture, deluxe grade** | ea | $2.62 | $91.00 | $93.62 |
| | *Replace* Materials......80.00    Labor............11.00 | | | | |
| | *Remove* ........................    Labor ............2.62 | | | | |
| **DOUBLE ▶ HANGING FIXTURE** Hanging light fixtures usually hang from ceiling hooks and plug into a switched outlet. For hanging fixtures that connect into a ceiling box, see pendant fixtures on pages 160-161. See quality indicators on pages 154-155. | **Double hanging light fixture, economy grade** | ea | $2.62 | $61.00 | $63.62 |
| | *Replace* Materials......50.00    Labor............11.00 | | | | |
| | *Remove* ........................    Labor ............2.62 | | | | |
| | **Double hanging light fixture, standard grade** | ea | $2.62 | $86.00 | $88.62 |
| | *Replace* Materials ......75.00    Labor............11.00 | | | | |
| | *Remove* ........................    Labor ............2.62 | | | | |
| | **Double hanging light fixture, high grade** | ea | $2.62 | $111.00 | $113.62 |
| | *Replace* Materials ....100.00    Labor............11.00 | | | | |
| | *Remove* ........................    Labor ............2.62 | | | | |
| | **Double hanging light fixture, deluxe grade** | ea | $2.62 | $146.00 | $148.62 |
| | *Replace* Materials.....135.00    Labor............11.00 | | | | |
| | *Remove* ........................    Labor ............2.62 | | | | |
| **MINIMUM ▶ FIXTURE CHARGE** | **Minimum charge for light fixture work** | ea | — | $86.20 | $86.20 |
| | *Replace* Materials ......20.00    Labor ..........66.20 | | | | |
| **PORCELAIN ▶ FIXTURE** | **Porcelain light fixture** | ea | $2.62 | $12.28 | $14.90 |
| | *Replace* Materials........4.00    Labor ............8.28 | | | | |
| | *Remove* ........................    Labor ............2.62 | | | | |
| | **Porcelain light fixture with pull chain** | ea | $2.62 | $13.28 | $15.90 |
| | *Replace* Materials........5.00    Labor ............8.28 | | | | |
| | *Remove* ........................    Labor ............2.62 | | | | |
| | **Remove porcelain light fixture for work, then reinstall** | ea | — | $13.20 | $13.20 |
| | *Replace* ........................    Labor...........13.20 | | | | |

| Item Description | Unit | Remove | Replace | Total |
|---|---|---|---|---|
| **Recessed spot light fixture, economy grade** | ea | $10.50 | $75.10 | $85.60 |
| *Replace* Materials......45.00  Labor..........30.10 | | | | |
| *Remove* .....................  Labor..........10.50 | | | | |
| ► 5" recessed spot. | | | | |
| **Recessed spot light fixture, standard grade** | ea | $10.50 | $90.10 | $100.60 |
| *Replace* Materials......60.00  Labor..........30.10 | | | | |
| *Remove* .....................  Labor..........10.50 | | | | |
| ► 7" recessed spot. | | | | |
| **Recessed spot light fixture, high grade** | ea | $10.50 | $110.10 | $120.60 |
| *Replace* Materials......80.00  Labor..........30.10 | | | | |
| *Remove* .....................  Labor..........10.50 | | | | |
| ► 7" recessed spot, reflector in can. | | | | |
| **Recessed spot light fixture, deluxe grade** | ea | $10.50 | $135.10 | $145.60 |
| *Replace* Materials ....105.00  Labor..........30.10 | | | | |
| *Remove* .....................  Labor..........10.50 | | | | |
| ► 8" recessed spot. | | | | |
| **Recessed spot light fixture, custom grade** | ea | $10.50 | $170.10 | $180.60 |
| *Replace* Materials ....140.00  Labor..........30.10 | | | | |
| *Remove* .....................  Labor..........10.50 | | | | |
| ► 8" recessed spot, eyeball socket. | | | | |
| **Remove recessed spot light fixture for work, then reinstall** | ea | — | $27.60 | $27.60 |
| *Replace* .....................  Labor..........27.60 | | | | |
| **Remove recessed spot light fixture & can for work, then reinstall** | ea | — | $50.90 | $50.90 |
| *Replace* .....................  Labor..........50.90 | | | | |
| **Electric strip for strip lights (no fixtures) per lf** | lf | $2.88 | $19.44 | $22.32 |
| *Replace* Materials......10.00  Labor..........9.44 | | | | |
| *Remove* .....................  Labor..........2.88 | | | | |
| **Remove electric strip for strip lights for work, then reinstall** | lf | — | $16.50 | $16.50 |
| *Replace* .....................  Labor..........16.50 | | | | |
| **Strip light, economy grade** | ea | $3.93 | $33.20 | $37.13 |
| *Replace* Materials......20.00  Labor..........13.20 | | | | |
| *Remove* .....................  Labor..........3.93 | | | | |
| ► Light gauge metal or plastic. | | | | |
| **Strip light, standard grade** | ea | $3.93 | $43.20 | $47.13 |
| *Replace* Materials......30.00  Labor..........13.20 | | | | |
| *Remove* .....................  Labor..........3.93 | | | | |
| ► Light gauge metal or plastic with brass or chrome trim. | | | | |
| **Strip light, high grade** | ea | $3.93 | $73.20 | $77.13 |
| *Replace* Materials......60.00  Labor..........13.20 | | | | |
| *Remove* .....................  Labor..........3.93 | | | | |
| ► Heavy gauge materials with brass or chrome trim. | | | | |
| **Remove strip light for work, then reinstall** | ea | — | $23.20 | $23.20 |
| *Replace* .....................  Labor..........23.20 | | | | |
| **Exterior flood light fixture, standard grade** | ea | $7.86 | $61.30 | $69.16 |
| *Replace* Materials......40.00  Labor..........21.30 | | | | |
| *Remove* .....................  Labor..........7.86 | | | | |

◄ **RECESSED SPOT FIXTURE**
*See quality indicators on pages 154-155.*

◁ remove and reinstall

◄ **ELECTRIC STRIP**
*Surface-mounted electric strip channel. Does not include strip-mounted spot lights. 3 lf minimum.*

◄ **STRIP SPOT LIGHT**
*Spot light for surface mounted electric strip channel.*

◁ remove and reinstall

◄ **EXTERIOR SPOT LIGHT**

**RELATED ITEMS**
Cleaning.....................57

| Item Description | | Unit | Remove | Replace | Total |
|---|---|---|---|---|---|
| **EXTERIOR ►** **SPOT LIGHT** *continued* | **Exterior flood light fixture, high grade** <br> *Replace* Materials ......55.00    Labor............21.30 <br> *Remove* ........................    Labor ............7.86 | ea | **$7.86** | **$76.30** | **$84.16** |
| | **Exterior double flood light fixture, standard grade** <br> *Replace* Materials......50.00    Labor............21.30 <br> *Remove* ........................    Labor ............7.86 | ea | **$7.86** | **$71.30** | **$79.16** |
| | **Exterior double flood light fixture, high grade** <br> *Replace* Materials ......65.00    Labor............21.30 <br> *Remove* ........................    Labor ............7.86 | ea | **$7.86** | **$86.30** | **$94.16** |
| | **Exterior triple flood light fixture, standard grade** <br> *Replace* Materials ......60.00    Labor............21.30 <br> *Remove* ........................    Labor ............7.86 | ea | **$7.86** | **$81.30** | **$89.16** |
| | **Exterior triple flood light fixture, high grade** <br> *Replace* Materials ......75.00    Labor............21.30 <br> *Remove* ........................    Labor ............7.86 | ea | **$7.86** | **$96.30** | **$104.16** |
| | **Remove exterior flood light fixture for work, then reinstall** <br> *Replace* ........................    Labor ..........38.90 | ea | — | **$38.90** | **$38.90** |
| **EXTERIOR WALL-►** **MOUNT FIXTURE** <br> *See quality indicators on pages 154-155.* <br><br> <br> courtesy of *Rejuvenation Lamp & Fixture Co.* | **Exterior wall-mount light fixture, economy grade** <br> *Replace* Materials......30.00    Labor ......20.70 <br> *Remove* ........................    Labor ............6.55 | ea | **$6.55** | **$50.70** | **$57.25** |
| | **Exterior wall-mount light fixture, standard grade** <br> *Replace* Materials......50.00    Labor ......20.70 <br> *Remove* ........................    Labor ............6.55 | ea | **$6.55** | **$70.70** | **$77.25** |
| | **Exterior wall-mount light fixture, high grade** <br> *Replace* Materials.....125.00    Labor ..........20.70 <br> *Remove* ........................    Labor ............6.55 | ea | **$6.55** | **$145.70** | **$152.25** |
| | **Exterior wall-mount light fixture, deluxe grade** <br> *Replace* Materials ....235.00    Labor ..........20.70 <br> *Remove* ........................    Labor ............6.55 | ea | **$6.55** | **$255.70** | **$262.25** |
| remove & reinstall ▷ | **Remove exterior wall-mount light fixture for work, then reinstall** <br> *Replace* ........................    Labor ..........38.90 | ea | — | **$38.90** | **$38.90** |
| **EXTERIOR ►** **RECESSED FIXTURE** | **Exterior recessed light fixture, economy grade** <br> *Replace* Materials ......55.00    Labor ..........30.10 <br> *Remove* ........................    Labor............13.10 <br> ► 5" recessed spot. | ea | **$13.10** | **$85.10** | **$98.20** |
| | **Exterior recessed light fixture, standard grade** <br> *Replace* Materials ......75.00    Labor ..........30.10 <br> *Remove* ........................    Labor............13.10 <br> ► 7" recessed spot. | ea | **$13.10** | **$105.10** | **$118.20** |
| | **Exterior recessed light fixture, high grade** <br> *Replace* Materials .....135.00    Labor ..........30.10 <br> *Remove* ........................    Labor............13.10 <br> ► 7" recessed spot, reflector in can. | ea | **$13.10** | **$165.10** | **$178.20** |
| | **Exterior recessed light fixture, deluxe grade** <br> *Replace* Materials .....185.00    Labor ..........30.10 <br> *Remove* ........................    Labor............13.10 <br> ► 8" recessed spot. | ea | **$13.10** | **$215.10** | **$228.20** |

| Item Description | Unit | Remove | Replace | Total | |
|---|---|---|---|---|---|
| **Remove exterior recessed light fixture for work, then reinstall** | ea | — | $60.00 | $60.00 | ◁ remove and reinstall |
| *Replace* .......... Labor .......... 60.00 | | | | | |
| **Exterior light fixture, economy grade** | ea | $8.25 | $46.30 | $54.55 | ◀ **EXTERIOR** |
| *Replace* Materials .......25.00  Labor..........21.30 | | | | | **LIGHT FIXTURE** |
| *Remove* .......... Labor ..........8.25 | | | | | **ALLOWANCE** |
| **Exterior light fixture, standard grade** | ea | $8.25 | $66.30 | $74.55 | *Contractor's allowance per light fixture in* |
| *Replace* Materials ......45.00  Labor..........21.30 | | | | | *complete home.* |
| *Remove* .......... Labor ..........8.25 | | | | | |
| **Exterior light fixture, high grade** | ea | $8.25 | $101.30 | $109.55 | |
| *Replace* Materials ......80.00  Labor..........21.30 | | | | | |
| *Remove* .......... Labor ..........8.25 | | | | | |
| **Exterior light fixture, deluxe grade** | ea | $8.25 | $181.30 | $189.55 | |
| *Replace* Materials .....160.00  Labor..........21.30 | | | | | |
| *Remove* .......... Labor ..........8.25 | | | | | |
| **Remove exterior light fixture for work, then reinstall** | ea | — | $38.90 | $38.90 | ◁ remove and reinstall |
| *Replace* .......... Labor ..........38.90 | | | | | |
| **Exterior post with light fixture, economy grade** | ea | $31.40 | $350.00 | $381.40 | ◀ **EXTERIOR POST** |
| *Replace* Materials .....155.00  Labor..........195.00 | | | | | **WITH FIXTURE** |
| *Remove* .......... Labor..........31.40 | | | | | |
| ▶ Redwood post with beveled corners or light turnings or straight metal post, up to 7' tall. Includes post hole, concrete base and hole backfill. Does not include wiring. Plastic or light metal fixture, usually one light with polystyrene lens. | | | | | |
| **Exterior post with light fixture, standard grade** | ea | $31.40 | $420.00 | $451.40 | |
| *Replace* Materials ....225.00  Labor..........195.00 | | | | | |
| *Remove* .......... Labor..........31.40 | | | | | |
| ▶ Turned redwood post to 7' tall. Includes hole, concrete, and hole backfill. Does not include wiring. Black metal fixture, usually one light with polystyrene lens. | | | | | |
| **Exterior post with light fixture, high grade** | ea | $31.40 | $480.00 | $511.40 | |
| *Replace* Materials ....285.00  Labor..........195.00 | | | | | |
| *Remove* .......... Labor..........31.40 | | | | | |
| ▶ Turned redwood post, to 7' tall. Includes hole, concrete, and hole backfill. Does not include wiring. Metal fixture, one to two lights clear plastic or glass lens. | | | | | |
| **Exterior post with light fixture, deluxe grade** | ea | $31.40 | $615.00 | $646.40 | |
| *Replace* Materials ....420.00  Labor..........195.00 | | | | | |
| *Remove* .......... Labor..........31.40 | | | | | |
| ▶ Aluminum post, to 7' tall. Includes hole, concrete, J bolts, and hole backfill. Does not include wiring. Metal fixture, one to two lights clear plastic or glass lens. | | | | | |
| **Exterior post with light fixture, custom grade** | ea | $31.40 | $935.00 | $966.40 | **RELATED ITEMS** |
| *Replace* Materials ....740.00  Labor..........195.00 | | | | | Cleaning..........57 |
| *Remove* .......... Labor..........31.40 | | | | | |
| ▶ Cast-iron post, to 7' tall. Includes post hole, concrete base, J bolts, and hole backfill. Does not include wiring. Cast iron, brass, copper, or pewter fixture, often simulated gas light one to four lights clear plastic or glass lens. | | | | | |
| **Remove exterior post with light fixture for work, then reinstall** | ea | — | $368.00 | $368.00 | ◁ remove and reinstall |
| *Replace* .......... Labor ........368.00 | | | | | |
| **Exterior post light fixture (no post), economy grade** | ea | $13.10 | $96.40 | $109.50 | ◀ **EXTERIOR POST** |
| *Replace* Materials ......55.00  Labor..........41.40 | | | | | **LIGHT FIXTURE** |
| *Remove* .......... Labor..........13.10 | | | | | *Fixture only, no post.* |
| ▶ Plastic or light metal fixture. One interior light with polystyrene lens. | | | | | |

| Item Description | Unit | Remove | Replace | Total |
|---|---|---|---|---|
| **EXTERIOR POST ▶ LIGHT FIXTURE** *continued*    **Exterior post light fixture (no post), standard grade** <br> *Replace* Materials......80.00    Labor...........41.40 <br> *Remove* .....................    Labor...........13.10 <br> ▶ Metal fixture. Two interior lights with clear polystyrene lens. | ea | $13.10 | $121.40 | $134.50 |
| **Exterior post light fixture (no post), high grade** <br> *Replace* Materials.....120.00   Labor...........41.40 <br> *Remove* .....................   Labor...........13.10 <br> ▶ Metal fixture. 2 to 4 interior lights with clear polystyrene lens. | ea | $13.10 | $161.40 | $174.50 |
| **Exterior post light fixture (no post), deluxe grade** <br> *Replace* Materials.....190.00   Labor...........41.40 <br> *Remove* .....................   Labor...........13.10 <br> ▶ Copper, pewter, or antique finish. 2 to 4 interior light with clear glass lens. | ea | $13.10 | $231.40 | $244.50 |
| **Exterior post light fixture (no post), custom grade** <br> *Replace* Materials ....270.00   Labor...........41.40 <br> *Remove* .....................   Labor...........13.10 <br> ▶ Ornate copper, pewter, brass, or antique finish. 2 to 4 interior lights with clear glass lens. | ea | $13.10 | $311.40 | $324.50 |
| **remove & reinstall ▷**   **Remove exterior post light fixture for work (no post), then reinstall** <br> *Replace* .....................   Labor...........69.60 | ea | — | $69.60 | $69.60 |
| **POST FOR ▶ EXTERIOR FIXTURE**   **Redwood post for exterior post light fixture, standard grade** <br> *Replace* Materials ....220.00   Labor.........154.00 <br> *Remove* .....................   Labor...........31.40 <br> ▶ To 7' tall. Beveled edges or light turnings. Diameter to 4". | ea | $31.40 | $374.00 | $405.40 |
| **Redwood post for exterior post light fixture, high grade** <br> *Replace* Materials.....310.00   Labor.........154.00 <br> *Remove* .....................   Labor...........31.40 <br> ▶ Turned post. to 7' tall. Diameter to 4". | ea | $31.40 | $464.00 | $495.40 |
| **Metal post for exterior post light fixture, standard grade** <br> *Replace* Materials ....140.00   Labor .........147.00 <br> *Remove* .....................   Labor...........31.40 <br> ▶ Straight or tapered aluminum or steel post. Diameter to 4". | ea | $31.40 | $287.00 | $318.40 |
| **Metal post for exterior post light fixture, high grade** <br> *Replace* Materials ....220.00   Labor .........147.00 <br> *Remove* .....................   Labor...........31.40 <br> ▶ Straight or tapered aluminum or steel post. with flutes and/or simple turned base and cap. Diameter to 4". | ea | $31.40 | $367.00 | $398.40 |
| **Metal post for exterior post light fixture, deluxe grade** <br> *Replace* Materials.....310.00   Labor .........147.00 <br> *Remove* .....................   Labor...........31.40 <br> ▶ Aluminum post with elaborate turnings, diameter to 6". | ea | $31.40 | $457.00 | $488.40 |
| **Metal post for exterior post light fixture, custom grade** <br> *Replace* Materials ....395.00   Labor .........147.00 <br> *Remove* .....................   Labor...........31.40 <br> ▶ Aluminum post with elaborate turnings with some cast design (e.g. ivy, inlays, etc.) Diameter to 8". | ea | $31.40 | $542.00 | $573.40 |
| **Metal post for exterior post light fixture, custom deluxe grade** <br> *Replace* Materials.....615.00   Labor .........147.00 <br> *Remove* .....................   Labor...........31.40 <br> ▶ Cast iron with turnings and designs. Diameter to 12". | ea | $31.40 | $762.00 | $793.40 |

| Item Description | Unit | Remove | Replace | Total | |
|---|---|---|---|---|---|
| **Add for exterior light motion sensor or infrared detector** <br> *Replace* Materials......60.00 <br> ► Add to the cost of an exterior light fixture or lamp post when fixture is equipped with a motion sensor, infrared detector, or both. | ea | — | $60.00 | $60.00 | ◄ **EXTERIOR LIGHT SENSOR / DETECTOR** |
| **Replace light fixture socket and wiring** <br> *Replace* Materials........5.50    Labor...........17.40 | ea | — | $22.90 | $22.90 | ◄ **FIXTURE REWIRE** |
| **Replace chandelier socket and wiring, per arm** <br> *Replace* Materials........7.50    Labor...........18.40 | ea | — | $25.90 | $25.90 | |
| **Bowl shade or globe for light fixture, economy grade** <br> *Replace* Materials.......11.00    Labor............2.22 <br> ► Glass bowl shade or globe only. Light glass with little or no pattern. | ea | — | $13.22 | $13.22 | ◄ **REPLACEMENT BOWL SHADE** |
| **Bowl shade or globe for light fixture, standard grade** <br> *Replace* Materials.......17.50    Labor............2.22 <br> ► Glass bowl shade or globe only. Light glass with horizontal turnings. | ea | — | $19.72 | $19.72 | |
| **Bowl shade or globe for light fixture, high grade** <br> *Replace* Materials......30.50    Labor............2.22 <br> ► Glass bowl shade or globe only. Thick glass with vertical ridges, etched glass, angles in glass, scalloped edges. | ea | — | $32.72 | $32.72 | |
| **Bowl shade or globe for light fixture, deluxe grade** <br> *Replace* Materials......44.50    Labor............2.22 <br> ► Glass bowl shade or globe only. Thick glass with angles, ornate horizontal turnings, vertical ridges, patterns in glass. | ea | — | $46.72 | $46.72 | |
| **Bowl shade or globe for light fixture, custom grade** <br> *Replace* Materials......54.00    Labor............2.22 <br> ► Glass bowl shade or globe only. Very thick glass with angles, ornate horizontal turnings, vertical ridges, patterns in glass, specialty gradated colors, flower patterns (Entire shade looks like a flower, not just floral patterns on shade. Flower patterns may be made of thin glass.) | ea | — | $56.22 | $56.22 | |

**RELATED ITEMS**

Cleaning.......................57

# TIME & MATERIAL CHARTS (selected items)

## Electrical Materials

See **Electrical** material prices with the line items and other information in the **QuickFinder** column.

## Electrical Labor

| LABORER | BASE WAGE | PAID LEAVE | TRUE WAGE | FICA | FUTA | WORKER'S COMP. | UNEMPLOY. INSUR. | HEALTH INSUR. | RETIRE (401K) | LIABILITY INSUR. | COST PER HOUR |
|---|---|---|---|---|---|---|---|---|---|---|---|
| *Electrician* | $25.10 | 1.96 | $27.06 | 2.07 | .22 | 2.80 | 2.35 | 2.54 | .81 | 3.52 | **$41.40** |
| *Electrician's helper* | $18.00 | 1.40 | $19.40 | 1.48 | .16 | 2.01 | 1.69 | 2.54 | .58 | 2.52 | **$30.40** |
| *Demolition laborer* | $13.40 | 1.05 | $14.45 | 1.11 | .12 | 4.44 | 1.26 | 2.54 | .43 | 1.88 | **$26.20** |

**Paid Leave** is calculated based on two weeks paid vacation, one week sick leave, and seven paid holidays. Employer's matching portion of **FICA** is 7.65 percent. **FUTA** (Federal Unemployment) is .8 percent. **Worker's compensation** for the electrical trade was calculated using a national average of 10.35 percent. **Unemployment insurance** was calculated using a national average of 8.7 percent. **Health insurance** was calculated based on a projected national average for 2001 of $505 per employee (and family when applicable) per month. Employer pays 80 percent for a per month cost of $404 per employee. **Retirement** is based on a 401(k) retirement program with employer matching of 50 percent. Employee contributions to the 401(k) plan are an average of 6 percent of the true wage. **Liability insurance** is based on a national average of 12.9 percent.

## Electrical Labor Productivity

| WORK DESCRIPTION | LABORER | COST PER HOUR | PRODUCTIVITY | UNIT PRICE |
|---|---|---|---|---|
| **Demolition** | | | | |
| remove 240 volt switch or outlet | demolition laborer | $26.20 | .200 | $5.24 ea |
| remove 120 volt switch or outlet | demolition laborer | $26.20 | .150 | $3.93 ea |
| remove bathroom fan | demolition laborer | $26.20 | .506 | $13.30 ea |
| remove bathroom fan / light with heater | demolition laborer | $26.20 | .726 | $19.00 ea |
| remove breaker panel | electrician | $41.40 | 3.88 | $161.00 ea |
| remove cable service drop | electrician | $41.40 | 6.68 | $277.00 ea |
| remove conduit service drop | electrician | $41.40 | 8.35 | $346.00 ea |
| remove rigid steel mast service drop | electrician | $41.40 | 9.82 | $407.00 ea |
| remove circuit breaker | demolition laborer | $26.20 | .200 | $5.24 ea |
| remove door bell or chime | demolition laborer | $26.20 | .100 | $2.62 ea |
| remove kitchen exhaust fan | demolition laborer | $26.20 | .539 | $14.10 ea |
| remove whole-house exhaust fan | demolition laborer | $26.20 | 1.52 | $39.80 ea |
| remove intercom system master station | demolition laborer | $26.20 | .749 | $19.60 ea |
| remove intercom system remote station | demolition laborer | $26.20 | .300 | $7.86 ea |
| remove low-voltage outlet | demolition laborer | $26.20 | .150 | $3.93 ea |
| remove detector | demolition laborer | $26.20 | .200 | $5.24 ea |
| remove thermostat | demolition laborer | $26.20 | .200 | $5.24 ea |
| remove television antenna | demolition laborer | $26.20 | .835 | $21.90 ea |
| remove recessed electric space heater | demolition laborer | $26.20 | .506 | $13.30 ea |
| remove electric baseboard heater | demolition laborer | $26.20 | .165 | $4.32 lf |
| remove light fixture | demolition laborer | $26.20 | .300 | $7.86 ea |
| remove bathroom light bar | demolition laborer | $26.20 | .315 | $8.25 ea |
| remove chandelier | demolition laborer | $26.20 | .557 | $14.60 ea |
| remove fluorescent light fixture | demolition laborer | $26.20 | .500 | $13.10 ea |
| remove fluorescent circline light fixture | demolition laborer | $26.20 | .371 | $9.72 ea |
| remove ceiling fan | demolition laborer | $26.20 | .500 | $13.10 ea |
| remove hanging light fixture | demolition laborer | $26.20 | .100 | $2.62 ea |
| remove porcelain light fixture | demolition laborer | $26.20 | .100 | $2.62 ea |
| remove recessed spot light fixture | demolition laborer | $26.20 | .400 | $10.50 ea |
| remove electric strip for electric strip lights | demolition laborer | $26.20 | .110 | $2.88 lf |
| remove electric strip light | demolition laborer | $26.20 | .150 | $3.93 ea |
| remove exterior flood light | demolition laborer | $26.20 | .300 | $7.86 ea |
| remove exterior post with light fixture | demolition laborer | $26.20 | 1.20 | $31.40 ea |
| remove exterior post light fixture | demolition laborer | $26.20 | .500 | $13.10 ea |
| **Electrical crew** | | | | |
| install wiring, boxes, and fixtures | electrician | $41.40 | | |
| install wiring, boxes, and fixtures | electrician's helper | $30.40 | | |
| install wiring, boxes, and fixtures | electrical crew | $35.90 | | |
| **Install complete house electrical wiring, outlets, switches & light fixtures** | | | | |
| economy grade | electrical crew | $35.90 | .053 | $1.90 ea |
| deluxe grade | electrical crew | $35.90 | .109 | $3.91 ea |
| low-voltage system | electrical crew | $35.90 | .100 | $3.59 ea |
| add for wiring installation in conduit | electrical crew | $35.90 | .055 | $1.97 ea |
| **Install complete house rough electrical (no light fixtures)** | | | | |
| standard | electrical crew | $35.90 | .070 | $2.51 ea |
| in conduit | electrical crew | $35.90 | .154 | $5.53 ea |
| low-voltage system | electrical crew | $35.90 | .075 | $2.69 ea |
| **Install complete house light fixtures** | | | | |
| economy grade | electrical crew | $35.90 | .015 | $.54 ea |
| deluxe grade | electrical crew | $35.90 | .017 | $.61 ea |
| for low-voltage system | electrical crew | $35.90 | .013 | $.47 ea |
| **Install 240 volt** | | | | |
| outlet or switch with wiring run & box | electrical crew | $35.90 | 1.34 | $48.10 ea |
| **Install 120 volt** | | | | |
| switch or outlet with wiring run & box | electrical crew | $35.90 | .977 | $35.10 ea |
| 3-way switch with wiring run & box | electrical crew | $35.90 | 1.95 | $70.00 ea |
| **Install electric wiring run** | | | | |
| for typical 120 volt outlet | electrical crew | $35.90 | .802 | $28.80 ea |
| for 120 volt appliance | electrical crew | $35.90 | 1.02 | $36.60 ea |

*. . . More ➣*

## Electrical Labor Productivity *continued*

| WORK DESCRIPTION | LABORER | COST PER HOUR | PRODUCTIVITY | UNIT PRICE |
|---|---|---|---|---|
| **Install conduit** | | | | |
| electric metallic tubing (EMT), average installation | electrical crew | $35.90 | .077 | $2.76 lf |
| flexible metal, average installation | electrical crew | $35.90 | .041 | $1.47 lf |
| PVC, average installation | electrical crew | $35.90 | .045 | $1.62 lf |
| intermediate (IMC), average installation | electrical crew | $35.90 | .113 | $4.06 lf |
| rigid metal (RMC), average installation | electrical crew | $35.90 | .067 | $2.41 lf |
| **Install wiring** | | | | |
| #10 2 wire with ground Romex | electrical crew | $35.90 | .051 | $1.83 lf |
| #12 2 wire with ground Romex | electrical crew | $35.90 | .047 | $1.69 lf |
| #14 2 wire with ground Romex | electrical crew | $35.90 | .040 | $1.44 lf |
| **Install breaker panel** | | | | |
| 100 amp exterior breaker panel (5 breakers) | electrician | $41.40 | 4.89 | $202.00 ea |
| 100 amp interior breaker panel (5 breakers) | electrician | $41.40 | 4.30 | $178.00 ea |
| 150 amp exterior breaker panel (10 breakers) | electrician | $41.40 | 7.68 | $318.00 ea |
| 150 amp interior breaker panel (10 breakers) | electrician | $41.40 | 7.17 | $297.00 ea |
| 200 amp exterior breaker panel (15 breakers) | electrician | $41.40 | 10.8 | $447.00 ea |
| 200 amp interior breaker panel (15 breakers) | electrician | $41.40 | 9.77 | $404.00 ea |
| 300 amp exterior breaker panel (30 breakers) | electrician | $41.40 | 14.3 | $592.00 ea |
| 300 amp interior breaker panel (30 breakers) | electrician | $41.40 | 13.4 | $555.00 ea |
| 40 amp interior breaker sub-panel (5 breakers) | electrician | $41.40 | 2.99 | $124.00 ea |
| 50 amp interior breaker sub-panel | electrician | $41.40 | 3.16 | $131.00 ea |
| 70 amp interior breaker sub-panel | electrician | $41.40 | 3.47 | $144.00 ea |
| **Install electrical service** | | | | |
| 100 amp cable service | electrician | $41.40 | 11.9 | $493.00 ea |
| 150 amp cable service | electrician | $41.40 | 14.3 | $592.00 ea |
| 150 amp conduit service | electrician | $41.40 | 15.4 | $638.00 ea |
| 150 amp rigid steel mast service | electrician | $41.40 | 15.4 | $638.00 ea |
| 200 amp cable service | electrician | $41.40 | 18.5 | $766.00 ea |
| 200 amp conduit service | electrician | $41.40 | 19.9 | $824.00 ea |
| 200 amp rigid steel mast service | electrician | $41.40 | 19.9 | $824.00 ea |
| **Install breaker** | | | | |
| single-pole (120 volt) circuit breaker | electrician | $41.40 | .636 | $26.30 ea |
| double-pole (240 volt) circuit breaker | electrician | $41.40 | .648 | $26.80 ea |
| ground fault circuit interrupter breaker | electrician | $41.40 | .689 | $28.50 ea |
| main disconnect circuit breaker | electrician | $41.40 | 3.47 | $144.00 ea |
| **Door bell or chime** | | | | |
| door bell or chime button | electrician | $41.40 | .119 | $4.93 ea |
| door bell or chime | electrician | $41.40 | 1.08 | $44.70 ea |
| low-voltage wiring (per button) | electrician | $41.40 | .489 | $20.20 ea |
| **Install exhaust fan** | | | | |
| bathroom exhaust fan | electrician | $41.40 | .597 | $24.70 ea |
| bathroom exhaust fan with heat lamp | electrician | $41.40 | .768 | $31.80 ea |
| bathroom exhaust fan with heater | electrician | $41.40 | .827 | $34.20 ea |
| kitchen exhaust fan | electrician | $41.40 | .977 | $40.40 ea |
| whole-house exhaust fan | electrician | $41.40 | 2.69 | $111.00 ea |
| **Install intercom** | | | | |
| intercom system master station | electrician | $41.40 | 2.15 | $89.00 ea |
| intercom system remote station | electrician | $41.40 | .597 | $24.70 ea |
| 120 volt wiring for intercom master station | electrician | $41.40 | .779 | $32.30 ea |
| intercom wiring (per station) | electrician | $41.40 | .538 | $22.30 ea |
| **Install low-voltage outlet** | | | | |
| Install outlet | electrical crew | $35.90 | .256 | $9.19 ea |
| wiring (per outlet) | electrical crew | $35.90 | .358 | $12.90 ea |
| **Install sound system** | | | | |
| speaker with grille | electrical crew | $35.90 | .244 | $8.76 ea |
| **Install detector** | | | | |
| battery operated | electrician | $41.40 | .308 | $12.80 ea |
| direct-wired | electrician | $41.40 | .347 | $14.40 ea |

. . . More ➤

## Electrical Labor Productivity *continued*

| WORK DESCRIPTION | LABORER | COST PER HOUR | PRODUCTIVITY | UNIT PRICE |
|---|---|---|---|---|
| **Check electrical circuits** | | | | |
| megameter test small home | electrician | $41.40 | 3.91 | $162.00 ea |
| megameter test average size home | electrician | $41.40 | 5.66 | $234.00 ea |
| megameter test large home | electrician | $41.40 | 7.79 | $323.00 ea |
| **Install thermostat** | | | | |
| for electric resistance heating system | electrical crew | $35.90 | .183 | $6.57 ea |
| electric heating system | electrical crew | $35.90 | .326 | $11.70 ea |
| wiring (per thermostat) | electrical crew | $35.90 | .538 | $19.30 ea |
| **Install TV antenna** | | | | |
| television antenna | electrician | $41.40 | 1.08 | $44.70 ea |
| **Install recessed electric space heater** | | | | |
| electric space heater recessed in wall | electrician | $41.40 | 2.15 | $89.00 ea |
| **Install electric-resistance heating** | | | | |
| cable, ceiling installation | electrical crew | $35.90 | .036 | $1.29 ea |
| cable, floor installation | electrical crew | $35.90 | .060 | $2.15 ea |
| electric-resistance heating floor sensor | electrical crew | $35.90 | .632 | $22.70 ea |
| **Install electric baseboard heater** | | | | |
| electric baseboard heater | electrical crew | $35.90 | .512 | $18.40 ea |
| remove for work, then reinstall | electrical crew | $35.90 | .717 | $25.70 ea |
| **Install underground wiring for exterior post light fixture** | | | | |
| up to 30 feet | electrical crew | $35.90 | 1.22 | $43.80 ea |
| up to 50 feet | electrical crew | $35.90 | 1.30 | $46.70 ea |
| **Install interior light fixture** | | | | |
| interior incandescent light fixture | electrician | $41.40 | .499 | $20.70 ea |
| **Install bathroom bar light** | | | | |
| bathroom bar light | electrician | $41.40 | .533 | $22.10 ea |
| **Install chandelier** | | | | |
| chandelier | electrician | $41.40 | 1.45 | $60.00 ea |
| entrance chandelier | electrician | $41.40 | 2.91 | $120.00 ea |
| grand entrance chandelier | electrician | $41.40 | 3.99 | $165.00 ea |
| **Install wall-mount fixture** | | | | |
| wall-mount light fixture | electrician | $41.40 | .484 | $20.00 ea |
| **Install florescent light fixture** | | | | |
| surface-mounted fluorescent light fixture | electrician | $41.40 | .913 | $37.80 ea |
| drop-in fluorescent fixture in suspended ceiling | electrician | $41.40 | 1.84 | $76.20 ea |
| fluorescent circline fixture | electrician | $41.40 | .841 | $34.80 ea |
| **Install ceiling fan** | | | | |
| assemble and install ceiling fan | electrician | $41.40 | 2.13 | $88.20 ea |
| remove ceiling fan for work, then reinstall | electrician | $41.40 | 2.38 | $98.50 ea |
| assemble and install ceiling fan with light | electrician | $41.40 | 3.20 | $132.00 ea |
| light for ceiling fan | electrician | $41.40 | .457 | $18.90 ea |
| **Install hanging light fixture** | | | | |
| hanging light fixture | electrician | $41.40 | .266 | $11.00 ea |
| **Install recessed spot fixture** | | | | |
| recessed spot light fixture | electrician | $41.40 | .726 | $30.10 ea |
| **Install exterior flood light** | | | | |
| exterior flood light fixture | electrician | $41.40 | .515 | $21.30 ea |
| **Install exterior post light fixture** | | | | |
| exterior post with light fixture | electrician | $41.40 | 4.70 | $195.00 ea |
| exterior post light fixture (no post) | electrician | $41.40 | .999 | $41.40 ea |
| wood post for exterior post light fixture | electrician | $41.40 | 3.72 | $154.00 ea |
| metal post for exterior post light fixture | electrician | $41.40 | 3.55 | $147.00 ea |

# 14 ................................................ *Excavation*

| Item Description | Unit | | | Total | |
|---|---|---|---|---|---|
| **Excavation equipment delivery and take-home charge (mobilization)** | ea | — | — | $196.00 | ◀ **MOBILIZATION** |
| *Excavate* ................... Labor ........196.00 | | | | | |
| **Excavate for slab-on-grade structure per sf of floor** | sf | — | — | $.16 | ◀ **SLAB-ON-GRADE** |
| *Excavate* ................... Labor ............ .08 Equipment ............ .08 | | | | | Under-slab excavation up to 1-1/2' deep. Footing |
| **Excavate for slab-on-grade structure in medium rocky or clay soil** | sf | — | — | $.22 | excavation up to 3' deep. Does not include |
| *Excavate* ................... Labor ............ .13 Equipment ............ .09 | | | | | mobilization. See above. |
| **Excavate for slab-on-grade structure in rocky or hardpan soil** | sf | — | — | $.26 | |
| *Excavate* ................... Labor ............ .16 Equipment ............ .10 | | | | | |
| **Backfill for slab-on-grade structure per sf of floor** | sf | — | — | $.13 | |
| *Excavate* ................... Labor ............ .08 Equipment ............ .05 | | | | | |
| **Excavate for structure with crawl space per sf of floor** | sf | — | — | $.28 | ◀ **CRAWL SPACE** |
| *Excavate* ................... Labor ............ .16 Equipment ............ .12 | | | | | Crawl space excavation up to 3' deep. Footing |
| **Excavate for structure with crawl space in medium rocky or clay soil** | sf | — | — | $.35 | excavation up to 4' deep. Does not include |
| *Excavate* ................... Labor ............ .21 Equipment ............ .14 | | | | | mobilization. See above. |
| **Excavate for structure with crawl space in rocky or hardpan soil** | sf | — | — | $.38 | |
| *Excavate* ................... Labor ............ .21 Equipment ............ .17 | | | | | |
| **Backfill for structure with crawl space per sf of floor** | sf | — | — | $.15 | |
| *Excavate* ................... Labor ............ .08 Equipment ............ .07 | | | | | |
| **Excavate for structure with basement per sf of floor** | sf | — | — | $.74 | ◀ **BASEMENT** |
| *Excavate* ................... Labor ............ .43 Equipment ............ .31 | | | | | Basement excavation up to 7' deep. Footing exca- |
| **Excavate for structure with basement in medium rocky or clay soil** | sf | — | — | $.85 | vation up to 8' deep. Does not include |
| *Excavate* ................... Labor ............ .48 Equipment ............ .37 | | | | | mobilization. See above. |
| **Excavate for structure with basement in rocky or hardpan soil** | sf | — | — | $.99 | |
| *Excavate* ................... Labor ............ .56 Equipment ............ .43 | | | | | **RELATED ITEMS** |
| **Backfill for structure with basement per sf of floor** | sf | — | — | $.37 | **Concrete** excavate foundation..............91 drill pier hole......................86 |
| *Excavate* ................... Labor ............ .23 Equipment ............ .14 | | | | | |
| **Excavate 3' to 4' deep footings** | lf | — | — | $.74 | ◀ **3' TO 4' DEEP FOOTINGS** |
| *Excavate* ................... Labor ............ .43 Equipment ............ .31 | | | | | Excavation slopes to 3' width at bottom of |
| **Excavate 3' to 4' deep footings in medium rocky or clay soil** | lf | — | — | $.84 | footing trench. Does not include mobilization. See |
| *Excavate* ................... Labor ............ .48 Equipment ............ .36 | | | | | above. |
| **Excavate 3' to 4' deep footings in rocky or hardpan soil** | lf | — | — | $.98 | |
| *Excavate* ................... Labor ............ .56 Equipment ............ .42 | | | | | |
| **Excavate 5' to 6' deep footings** | lf | — | — | $.91 | ◀ **5' TO 6' DEEP FOOTINGS** |
| *Excavate* ................... Labor ............ .51 Equipment ............ .40 | | | | | Excavation slopes to 3' width at bottom of |
| **Excavate 5' to 6' deep footings in medium rocky or clay soil** | lf | — | — | $1.05 | footing trench. Does not include mobilization. |
| *Excavate* ................... Labor ............ .59 Equipment ............ .46 | | | | | |

| Item Description | Unit | | | Total |
|---|---|---|---|---|
| **5' TO 6' DEEP ▶ FOOTINGS** *continued* | **Excavate 5' to 6' deep footings in rocky or hardpan soil** | lf | — | — | $1.25 |
| | *Excavate* .................... Labor............. .72 Equipment ............. .53 | | | | |
| **7' TO 8' DEEP ▶ FOOTINGS** *Excavation slopes to 3' width at bottom of footing trench. Does not include mobilization. See page 177.* | **Excavate 7' to 8' deep footings** | lf | — | — | $1.14 |
| | *Excavate* .................... Labor............. .64 Equipment ............. .50 | | | | |
| | **Excavate 7' to 8' deep footings in medium rocky or clay soil** | lf | — | — | $1.35 |
| | *Excavate* .................... Labor............. .77 Equipment ............. .58 | | | | |
| | **Excavate 7' to 8' deep footings in rocky or hardpan soil** | lf | — | — | $1.54 |
| | *Excavate* .................... Labor............. .87 Equipment ............. .67 | | | | |
| **9' TO 10' DEEP ▶ FOOTINGS** *Excavation slopes to 3' width at bottom of footing trench. Does not include mobilization. See page 177.* | **Excavate 9' to 10' deep footings** | lf | — | — | $1.39 |
| | *Excavate* .................... Labor............. .79 Equipment ............. .60 | | | | |
| | **Excavate 9' to 10' deep footings in medium rocky or clay soil** | lf | — | — | $1.61 |
| | *Excavate* .................... Labor............. .92 Equipment ............. .69 | | | | |
| | **Excavate 9' to 10' deep footings in rocky or hardpan soil** | lf | — | — | $1.79 |
| | *Excavate* .................... Labor............. 1.00 Equipment ............. .79 | | | | |
| **FOUNDATION ▶ WALL BACKFILL** | **Backfill foundation wall per sf of wall** | lf | — | — | $.48 |
| | *Excavate* .................... Labor............. .28 Equipment ............. .20 | | | | |
| | ▶ Typical backfill on flat lot or mild slope per sf of foundation wall. Does not include mobilization. | | | | |
| **1' TO 2' DEEP ▶ UTILITY TRENCH** *Square trench, 2' wide. Does not include mobilization. See page 177.* | **Excavate utility trench 1' to 2' deep in sandy loam soil** | lf | — | — | $.25 |
| | *Excavate* .................... Labor............. .16 Equipment ............. .09 | | | | |
| | **Excavate utility trench 1' to 2' deep in typical soil** | lf | — | — | $.26 |
| | *Excavate* .................... Labor............. .16 Equipment ............. .10 | | | | |
| | **Excavate utility trench 1' to 2' deep in medium rocky or clay soil** | lf | — | — | $.28 |
| | *Excavate* .................... Labor............. .16 Equipment ............. .12 | | | | |
| | **Excavate utility trench 1' to 2' deep in rocky or hardpan soil** | lf | — | — | $.35 |
| | *Excavate* .................... Labor............. .21 Equipment ............. .14 | | | | |
| | **Backfill 1' to 2' utility trench per lf of trench** | lf | — | — | $.18 |
| | *Excavate* .................... Labor............. .10 Equipment ............. .08 | | | | |
| **3' TO 4' DEEP ▶ UTILITY TRENCH** *Square trench, 2' wide. Does not include mobilization. See page 177.* | **Excavate utility trench 3' to 4' deep in sandy loam soil** | lf | — | — | $.35 |
| | *Excavate* .................... Labor............. .21 Equipment ............. .14 | | | | |
| | **Excavate utility trench 3' to 4' deep in typical soil** | lf | — | — | $.38 |
| | *Excavate* .................... Labor............. .21 Equipment ............. .17 | | | | |
| | **Excavate utility trench 3' to 4' deep in medium rocky or clay soil** | lf | — | — | $.45 |
| | *Excavate* .................... Labor............. .26 Equipment ............. .19 | | | | |
| | **Excavate utility trench 3' to 4' deep in rocky or hardpan soil** | lf | — | — | $.48 |
| | *Excavate* .................... Labor............. .26 Equipment ............. .22 | | | | |
| | **Backfill 3' to 4' utility trench per lf of trench** | lf | — | — | $.32 |
| | *Excavate* .................... Labor............. .15 Equipment ............. .17 | | | | |
| **5' TO 6' DEEP ▶ UTILITY TRENCH** *continued on next page* | **Excavate utility trench 5' to 6' deep in sandy loam soil** | lf | — | — | $.46 |
| | *Excavate* .................... Labor............. .26 Equipment ............. .20 | | | | |

| Item Description | Unit | | | Total |
|---|---|---|---|---|
| **Excavate utility trench 5' to 6' deep in typical soil** | lf | — | — | $.49 |
| *Excavate* .................... Labor ............. Equipment ............ .26 | | | | |
| **Excavate utility trench 5' to 6' deep in medium rocky or clay soil** | lf | — | — | $.58 |
| *Excavate* .................... Labor ............. .31 Equipment ............ .27 | | | | |
| **Excavate utility trench 5' to 6' deep in rocky or hardpan soil** | lf | — | — | $.66 |
| *Excavate* .................... Labor ............. .35 Equipment ............ .31 | | | | |
| **Backfill 5' to 6' utility trench per lf of trench** | lf | — | — | $.50 |
| *Excavate* .................... Labor ............. .25 Equipment ............ .25 | | | | |
| **Excavate water-line trench 2' to 3' deep, sandy loam soil** | lf | — | — | $.54 |
| *Excavate* .................... Labor ............. .34 Equipment ............ .20 | | | | |
| **Excavate water-line trench 2' to 3' deep, typical soil** | lf | — | — | $.57 |
| *Excavate* .................... Labor ............. .34 Equipment ............ .23 | | | | |
| **Excavate water-line trench 2' to 3' deep, medium rocky or clay soil** | lf | — | — | $.66 |
| *Excavate* .................... Labor ............. .39 Equipment ............ .27 | | | | |
| **Excavate water-line trench 2' to 3' deep, rocky or hardpan soil** | lf | — | — | $.74 |
| *Excavate* .................... Labor ............. .43 Equipment ............ .31 | | | | |
| **Backfill 2' to 3' water-line trench per lf of trench** | lf | — | — | $.34 |
| *Excavate* .................... Labor ............. .15 Equipment ............ .19 | | | | |
| **Excavate water-line trench 4' to 5' deep, sandy loam soil** | lf | — | — | $.76 |
| *Excavate* .................... Labor ............. .43 Equipment ............ .33 | | | | |
| **Excavate water-line trench 4' to 5' deep, typical soil** | lf | — | — | $.87 |
| *Excavate* .................... Labor ............. .48 Equipment ............ .39 | | | | |
| **Excavate water-line trench 4' to 5' deep, medium rocky or clay soil** | lf | — | — | $.98 |
| *Excavate* .................... Labor ............. .53 Equipment ............ .45 | | | | |
| **Excavate water-line trench 4' to 5' deep, rocky or hardpan soil** | lf | — | — | $1.10 |
| *Excavate* .................... Labor ............. .58 Equipment ............ .52 | | | | |
| **Backfill 4' to 5' water-line trench per lf of trench** | lf | — | — | $.60 |
| *Excavate* .................... Labor ............. .29 Equipment ............ .31 | | | | |
| **Excavate water-line trench 6' to 7' deep, sandy loam soil** | lf | — | — | $1.05 |
| *Excavate* .................... Labor ............. .58 Equipment ............ .47 | | | | |
| **Excavate water-line trench 6' to 7' deep, typical soil** | lf | — | — | $1.17 |
| *Excavate* .................... Labor ............. .63 Equipment ............ .54 | | | | |
| **Excavate water-line trench 6' to 7' deep, medium rocky or clay soil** | lf | — | — | $1.31 |
| *Excavate* .................... Labor ............. .68 Equipment ............ .63 | | | | |
| **Excavate water-line trench 6' to 7' deep, rocky or hardpan soil** | lf | — | — | $1.50 |
| *Excavate* .................... Labor ............. .78 Equipment ............ .72 | | | | |
| **Backfill 6' to 7' water-line trench per lf of trench** | lf | — | — | $.83 |
| *Excavate* .................... Labor ............. .39 Equipment ............ .44 | | | | |
| **Excavate water-line trench 8' to 9' deep, sandy loam soil** | lf | — | — | $1.39 |
| *Excavate* .................... Labor ............. .79 Equipment ............ .60 | | | | |

◄ **5' TO 6' DEEP UTILITY TRENCH**
*Trench slopes to 2' width at bottom. Does not include mobilization. See page 177.*

◄ **2' TO 3' DEEP WATER-LINE TRENCH**
*Trench slopes to 2' width at bottom. Does not include mobilization. See page 177.*

◄ **4' TO 5' DEEP WATER-LINE TRENCH**
*Trench slopes to 3' width at bottom. Does not include mobilization. See page 177.*

◄ **6' TO 7' DEEP WATER-LINE TRENCH**
*Trench slopes to 3' width at bottom. Does not include mobilization. See page 177.*

**RELATED ITEMS**

**Plumbing**
repair underground line .....364
break-out concrete ..............364

**Concrete**
excavate foundation ..............91
backfill foundation ...............92
drill pier hole ......................86

◄ **8' TO 9' DEEP WATER-LINE TRENCH**

| Item Description | Unit | | | Total |
|---|---|---|---|---|
| **8' TO 9' DEEP WATER-LINE TRENCH** *Trench slopes to 3' width at bottom. Does not include mobilization. .See page 177.* | | | | |
| **Excavate water-line trench 8' to 9' deep, typical soil** | If | — | — | $1.59 |
| *Excavate* .......................... Labor........... .89   Equipment ........... .70 | | | | |
| **Excavate water-line trench 8' to 9' deep, medium rocky or clay soil** | If | — | — | $1.80 |
| *Excavate* .......................... Labor........... .99   Equipment ........... .81 | | | | |
| **Excavate water-line trench 8' to 9' deep, rocky or hardpan soil** | If | — | — | $2.04 |
| *Excavate* .......................... Labor...........1.08   Equipment ........... .96 | | | | |
| **Backfill 8' to 9' water-line trench per If of trench** | If | — | — | $1.05 |
| *Excavate* .......................... Labor........... .49   Equipment ........... .56 | | | | |
| **3' TO 4' DEEP SEWER-LINE TRENCH** *Trench slopes to 3-1/2' width at bottom. Does not include mobilization. See page 177.* | | | | |
| **Excavate sewer-line trench 3' to 4' deep, sandy loam soil** | If | — | — | $.74 |
| *Excavate* .......................... Labor........... .431   Equipment ........... .31 | | | | |
| **Excavate sewer-line trench 3' to 4' deep, typical soil** | If | — | — | $.84 |
| *Excavate* .......................... Labor........... .48   Equipment ........... .36 | | | | |
| **Excavate sewer-line trench 3' to 4' deep, medium rocky or clay soil** | If | — | — | $.95 |
| *Excavate* .......................... Labor........... .53   Equipment ........... .42 | | | | |
| **Excavate sewer-line trench 3' to 4' deep, rocky or hardpan soil** | If | — | — | $1.07 |
| *Excavate* .......................... Labor........... .58   Equipment ........... .49 | | | | |
| **Backfill 3' to 4' sewer-line trench per If of trench** | If | — | — | $.54 |
| *Excavate* .......................... Labor........... .25   Equipment ........... .29 | | | | |
| **5' TO 6' DEEP SEWER-LINE TRENCH** *Trench slopes to 3-1/2' width at bottom. Does not include mobilization. See page 177.* | | | | |
| **Excavate sewer-line trench 5' to 6' deep, sandy loam soil** | If | — | — | $1.05 |
| *Excavate* .......................... Labor........... .58   Equipment ........... .47 | | | | |
| **Excavate sewer-line trench 5' to 6' deep, typical soil** | If | — | — | $1.17 |
| *Excavate* .......................... Labor........... .63   Equipment ........... .54 | | | | |
| **Excavate sewer-line trench 5' to 6' deep, medium rocky or clay soil** | If | — | — | $1.31 |
| *Excavate* .......................... Labor........... .68   Equipment ........... .63 | | | | |
| **Excavate sewer-line trench 5' to 6' deep, rocky or hardpan soil** | If | — | — | $1.51 |
| *Excavate* .......................... Labor........... .78   Equipment ........... .73 | | | | |
| **Backfill 5' to 6' sewer line trench per If of trench** | If | — | — | $.83 |
| *Excavate* .......................... Labor........... .39   Equipment ........... .44 | | | | |
| **7' TO 8' DEEP SEWER-LINE TRENCH** *Trench slopes to 3-1/2' width at bottom. Does not include mobilization. See page 177.* | | | | |
| **Excavate sewer-line trench 7' to 8' deep, sandy loam soil** | If | — | — | $1.30 |
| *Excavate* .......................... Labor........... .68   Equipment ........... .62 | | | | |
| **Excavate sewer-line trench 7' to 8' deep, typical soil** | If | — | — | $1.50 |
| *Excavate* .......................... Labor........... .78   Equipment ........... .72 | | | | |
| **Excavate sewer-line trench 7' to 8' deep, medium rocky or clay soil** | If | — | — | $1.71 |
| *Excavate* .......................... Labor........... .88   Equipment ........... .83 | | | | |
| **Excavate sewer-line trench 7' to 8' deep, rocky or hardpan soil** | If | — | — | $1.93 |
| *Excavate* .......................... Labor........... .97   Equipment ........... .96 | | | | |
| **Backfill 7' to 8' sewer-line trench per If of trench** | If | — | — | $.88 |
| *Excavate* .......................... Labor........... .29   Equipment ........... .59 | | | | |
| **REPAIR HOLE** *Access hole for repairs, per If of hole depth.* | | | | |
| **Excavate hole for repairs to water, sewer, or utility lines** | If | — | — | $3.01 |
| *Excavate* .......................... Labor ...........1.72   Equipment ...........1.29 | | | | |

| Item Description | | | Unit | | | Total | |
|---|---|---|---|---|---|---|---|
| **General foundation, slab, & footing excavation** | | | cy | — | — | **$3.17** | ◄ **GENERAL** |
| *Excavate* .............. | Labor ..........1.80 | Equipment ..........1.37 | | | | | *General excavation per cy.*<br>*No mobilization included.* |
| **Minimum charge for excavation work** | | | ea | — | — | **$476.00** | ◄ **MINIMUM CHARGE** |
| *Excavate* .............. | Labor .........196.00 | Equipment .......280.00 | | | | | |

# TIME & MATERIAL CHARTS *(selected items)*

## Excavation Rental Equipment

| DESCRIPTION | PRICE | COVERAGE | UNIT PRICE |
|---|---|---|---|
| **Backhoe / loader** | | | |
| **excavate slab-on-grade structure** | | | |
| typical soil | $440.00 *per day* | 5,740 *per day* | **$.08** *sf* |
| rocky or hardpan soil | $440.00 *per day* | 4,250 *per day* | **$.10** *sf* |
| backfill | $440.00 *per day* | 9,420 *per day* | **$.05** *sf* |
| **excavate for structure with crawl space** | | | |
| typical soil | $440.00 *per day* | 3,530 *per day* | **$.12** *sf* |
| rocky or hardpan soil | $440.00 *per day* | 2,610 *per day* | **$.17** *sf* |
| backfill | $440.00 *per day* | 6,123 *per day* | **$.07** *sf* |
| **excavate for structure with basement** | | | |
| typical soil | $440.00 *per day* | 1,400 *per day* | **$.31** *sf* |
| rocky or hardpan soil | $440.00 *per day* | 1,030 *per day* | **$.43** *sf* |
| excavation | $440.00 *per day* | 3,140 *per day* | **$.14** *sf* |
| **excavate for 3' to 4' deep footing** | | | |
| typical soil | $440.00 *per day* | 1,420 *per day* | **$.31** *lf* |
| rocky or hardpan soil | $440.00 *per day* | 1,050 *per day* | **$.42** *lf* |
| **excavate for 5' to 6' deep footing** | | | |
| typical soil | $440.00 *per day* | 1,108 *per day* | **$.40** *lf* |
| rocky or hardpan soil | $440.00 *per day* | 830 *per day* | **$.53** *lf* |
| **excavate for 7' to 8' deep footing** | | | |
| typical soil | $440.00 *per day* | 880 *per day* | **$.50** *lf* |
| rocky or hardpan soil | $440.00 *per day* | 660 *per day* | **$.67** *lf* |
| **excavate for 9' to 10' deep footing** | | | |
| typical soil | $440.00 *per day* | 738 *per day* | **$.60** *lf* |
| rocky or hardpan soil | $440.00 *per day* | 560 *per day* | **$.79** *lf* |
| **backfill foundation wall** | | | |
| backfill | $440.00 *per day* | 2,230 *per day* | **$.20** *lf* |
| **excavate for 1' to 2' deep utility trench** | | | |
| sandy loam soil | $440.00 *per day* | 4,930 *per day* | **$.09** *lf* |
| rocky or hardpan soil | $440.00 *per day* | 3,150 *per day* | **$.14** *lf* |
| backfill | $440.00 *per day* | 5,300 *per day* | **$.08** *lf* |
| **excavate for 3' to 4' deep utility trench** | | | |
| sandy loam soil | $440.00 *per day* | 3,057 *per day* | **$.14** *lf* |
| rocky or hardpan soil | $440.00 *per day* | 1,960 *per day* | **$.22** *lf* |
| backfill | $440.00 *per day* | 2,650 *per day* | **$.17** *lf* |
| **excavate for 5' to 6' deep utility trench** | | | |
| sandy loam soil | $440.00 *per day* | 2,219 *per day* | **$.20** *lf* |
| rocky or hardpan soil | $440.00 *per day* | 1,410 *per day* | **$.31** *lf* |
| backfill | $440.00 *per day* | 1,760 *per day* | **$.25** *lf* |
| **excavate for 2' to 3' deep water-line trench** | | | |
| sandy loam soil | $440.00 *per day* | 2,200 *per day* | **$.20** *lf* |
| rocky or hardpan soil | $440.00 *per day* | 1,400 *per day* | **$.31** *lf* |
| backfill | $440.00 *per day* | 2,350 *per day* | **$.19** *lf* |

*. . . More* ➤

## Excavation Rental Equipment *continued*

| DESCRIPTION | APPLICATION | PRICE | COVERAGE | UNIT PRICE |
|---|---|---|---|---|
| **Backhoe / loader** *continued* | | | | |
| **excavate for 4' to 5' deep water-line trench** | | | | |
| sandy loam soil | | $440.00 *per day* | 1,330 *per day* | $.33 *lf* |
| typical soil | | $440.00 *per day* | 1,140 *per day* | $.39 *lf* |
| medium rocky or clay soil | | $440.00 *per day* | 980 *per day* | $.45 *lf* |
| rocky or hardpan soil | | $440.00 *per day* | 850 *per day* | $.52 *lf* |
| backfill | | $440.00 *per day* | 1,410 *per day* | $.31 *lf* |
| **excavate for 6' to 7' deep water-line trench** | | | | |
| sandy loam soil | | $440.00 *per day* | 940 *per day* | $.47 *lf* |
| typical soil | | $440.00 *per day* | 810 *per day* | $.54 *lf* |
| medium rocky or clay soil | | $440.00 *per day* | 700 *per day* | $.63 *lf* |
| rocky or hardpan soil | | $440.00 *per day* | 610 *per day* | $.72 *lf* |
| backfill | | $440.00 *per day* | 1,010 *per day* | $.44 *lf* |
| **excavate for 8' to 9' deep water-line trench** | | | | |
| sandy loam soil | | $440.00 *per day* | 730 *per day* | $.60 *lf* |
| typical soil | | $440.00 *per day* | 630 *per day* | $.70 *lf* |
| medium rocky or clay soil | | $440.00 *per day* | 540 *per day* | $.81 *lf* |
| rocky or hardpan soil | | $440.00 *per day* | 460 *per day* | $.96 *lf* |
| backfill | | $440.00 *per day* | 780 *per day* | $.56 *lf* |
| **excavate for 3' to 4' deep sewer-line trench** | | | | |
| sandy loam soil | | $440.00 *per day* | 1,420 *per day* | $.31 *lf* |
| typical soil | | $440.00 *per day* | 1,220 *per day* | $.36 *lf* |
| medium rocky or clay soil | | $440.00 *per day* | 1,050 *per day* | $.42 *lf* |
| rocky or hardpan soil | | $440.00 *per day* | 900 *per day* | $.49 *lf* |
| backfill | | $440.00 *per day* | 1,520 *per day* | $.29 *lf* |
| **excavate for 5' to 6' deep sewer-line trench** | | | | |
| sandy loam soil | | $440.00 *per day* | 940 *per day* | $.47 *lf* |
| typical soil | | $440.00 *per day* | 810 *per day* | $.54 *lf* |
| medium rocky or clay soil | | $440.00 *per day* | 700 *per day* | $.63 *lf* |
| backfill | | $440.00 *per day* | 1,010 *per day* | $.44 *lf* |
| **excavate for 7' to 8' deep sewer-line trench** | | | | |
| sandy loam soil | | $440.00 *per day* | 710 *per day* | $.62 *lf* |
| typical soil | | $440.00 *per day* | 610 *per day* | $.72 *lf* |
| medium rocky or clay soil | | $440.00 *per day* | 530 *per day* | $.83 *lf* |
| rocky or hardpan soil | | $440.00 *per day* | 460 *per day* | $.96 *lf* |
| backfill | | $440.00 *per day* | 750 *per day* | $.59 *lf* |
| **excavate for repairs** | | | | |
| excavate hole | | $440.00 *per day* | 340 *per day* | $1.29 *lf* |
| **general excavation** | | | | |
| general excavation | | $440.00 *per day* | 322 *per day* | $1.37 *cy* |
| minimum charge | | $280.00 *minimum* | 1 *per day* | $280.00 *ea* |
| **Trenching** | | | | |
| trenching machine | | $320.00 *per day* | 1 *per day* | $320.00 *day* |
| minimum charge for trenching machine | | $200.00 *minimum* | 1 *each* | $200.00 *ea* |
| **Compacting** | | | | |
| "jumping jack" compactor | | $100.00 *per day* | 1 *per day* | $100.00 *day* |
| minimum charge for compactor | | $80.00 *minimum* | 1 *each* | $80.00 *ea* |

## Excavation Labor

| LABORER | BASE WAGE | PAID LEAVE | TRUE WAGE | FICA | FUTA | WORKER'S COMP. | UNEMPLOY. INSUR. | HEALTH INSUR. | RETIRE (401K) | LIABILITY INSUR. | COST PER HOUR |
|---|---|---|---|---|---|---|---|---|---|---|---|
| Equipment operator | $28.70 | 2.24 | $30.94 | 2.37 | .25 | 5.36 | 2.69 | 2.54 | .93 | 4.02 | $49.10 |
| Excavation laborer | $14.50 | 1.13 | $15.63 | 1.20 | .13 | 4.95 | 1.36 | 2.54 | .47 | 2.03 | $28.30 |

**Paid Leave** is calculated based on two weeks paid vacation, one week sick leave, and seven paid holidays. Employer's matching portion of **FICA** is 7.65 percent. **FUTA** (Federal Unemployment) is .8 percent. **Worker's compensation** was calculated using a national average of 17.31 percent for the equipment operator and 31.67 percent for the excavation laborer. **Unemployment insurance** was calculated using a national average of 8.7 percent. **Health insurance** was calculated based on a projected national average for 2001 of $505 per employee (and family when applicable) per month. Employer pays 80 percent for a per month cost of $404 per employee. **Retirement** is based on a 401(k) retirement program with employer matching of 50 percent. Employee contributions to the 401(k) plan are an average of 6 percent of the true wage. **Liability insurance** is based on a national average of 12.9 percent.

## Excavation Labor Productivity

| WORK DESCRIPTION | LABORER | COST PER HOUR | PRODUCTIVITY | UNIT PRICE |
|---|---|---|---|---|
| **Excavation equipment delivery and return labor charges** | | | | |
| backhoe mobilization | machine operator | $49.10 | 4.00 | **$196.00** ea |
| **Excavate slab-on-grade structure (per sf of floor)** | | | | |
| **typical soil** | | | | |
| machine | machine operator | $49.10 | .001 | **$.05** sf |
| hand finish | excavation laborer | $28.30 | .001 | **$.03** sf |
| **rocky or hardpan soil** | | | | |
| machine | machine operator | $49.10 | .002 | **$.10** sf |
| hand finish | excavation laborer | $28.30 | .002 | **$.06** sf |
| **Backfill slab-on-grade structure (per sf of floor)** | | | | |
| **all soil types** | | | | |
| machine | machine operator | $49.10 | .001 | **$.05** sf |
| hand labor | excavation laborer | $28.30 | .001 | **$.03** sf |
| **Excavate for structure with crawl space (per sf of floor)** | | | | |
| **typical soil** | | | | |
| machine | machine operator | $49.10 | .002 | **$.10** sf |
| hand finish | excavation laborer | $28.30 | .002 | **$.06** sf |
| **rocky or hardpan soil** | | | | |
| machine | machine operator | $49.10 | .003 | **$.15** sf |
| hand finish | excavation laborer | $28.30 | .002 | **$.06** sf |
| **Backfill structure with crawl space (per sf of floor)** | | | | |
| **all soil types** | | | | |
| machine | machine operator | $49.10 | .001 | **$.05** sf |
| hand labor | excavation laborer | $28.30 | .001 | **$.03** sf |
| **Excavate for structure with basement (per sf of floor)** | | | | |
| **typical soil** | | | | |
| machine | machine operator | $49.10 | .006 | **$.29** sf |
| hand finish | excavation laborer | $28.30 | .005 | **$.14** sf |
| **rocky or hardpan soil** | | | | |
| machine | machine operator | $49.10 | .008 | **$.39** sf |
| hand finish | excavation laborer | $28.30 | .006 | **$.17** sf |
| **Backfill structure with basement (per sf of floor)** | | | | |
| **all soil types** | | | | |
| machine | machine operator | $49.10 | .003 | **$.15** sf |
| hand labor | excavation laborer | $28.30 | .003 | **$.08** sf |
| **Excavate for 3' to 4' deep footings** | | | | |
| **typical soil** | | | | |
| machine | machine operator | $49.10 | .006 | **$.29** lf |
| hand finish | excavation laborer | $28.30 | .005 | **$.14** lf |
| **rocky or hardpan soil** | | | | |
| machine | machine operator | $49.10 | .008 | **$.39** lf |
| hand finish | excavation laborer | $28.30 | .006 | **$.17** lf |
| **Excavate for 5' to 6' deep footings** | | | | |
| **typical soil** | | | | |
| machine | machine operator | $49.10 | .007 | **$.34** lf |
| hand finish | excavation laborer | $28.30 | .006 | **$.17** lf |
| **rocky or hardpan soil** | | | | |
| machine | machine operator | $49.10 | .010 | **$.49** lf |
| hand finish | excavation laborer | $28.30 | .008 | **$.23** lf |
| **Excavate for 7' to 8' deep footing** | | | | |
| **typical soil** | | | | |
| machine | machine operator | $49.10 | .009 | **$.44** lf |
| hand finish | excavation laborer | $28.30 | .007 | **$.20** lf |
| **hardpan or rocky soil** | | | | |
| machine | machine operator | $49.10 | .012 | **$.59** lf |
| hand finish | excavation laborer | $28.30 | .010 | **$.28** lf |
| **Excavate for 9' to 10' deep footing** | | | | |
| **typical soil** | | | | |
| machine | machine operator | $49.10 | .011 | **$.54** lf |
| hand finish | excavation laborer | $28.30 | .009 | **$.25** lf |

. . . **More** ➤

## Excavation Labor Productivity *continued*

| WORK DESCRIPTION | LABORER | COST PER HOUR | PRODUCTIVITY | UNIT PRICE |
|---|---|---|---|---|
| **Excavate for 9' to 10' deep footing** *continued* | | | | |
| **hardpan or rocky soil** | | | | |
|     machine | machine operator | $49.10 | .014 | **$.69** lf |
|     hand finish | excavation laborer | $28.30 | .011 | **$.31** lf |
| **Machine backfill foundation wall (per sf of wall)** | | | | |
|     machine | machine operator | $49.10 | .004 | **$.20** sf |
|     hand labor | excavation laborer | $28.30 | .003 | **$.08** sf |
| **Machine excavate for 1' to 2' deep utility trench** | | | | |
|     sandy loam soil | machine operator | $49.10 | .002 | **$.10** lf |
|     rocky or hardpan soil | machine operator | $49.10 | .003 | **$.15** lf |
|     backfill | machine operator | $49.10 | .002 | **$.10** lf |
| **Machine excavate for 3' to 4' deep utility trench** | | | | |
|     sandy loam soil | machine operator | $49.10 | .003 | **$.15** lf |
|     rocky or hardpan soil | machine operator | $49.10 | .004 | **$.20** lf |
|     backfill | machine operator | $49.10 | .003 | **$.15** lf |
| **Machine excavate for 5' to 6' deep utility trench** | | | | |
|     sandy loam soil | machine operator | $49.10 | .004 | **$.20** lf |
|     rocky or hardpan soil | machine operator | $49.10 | .006 | **$.29** lf |
|     backfill | machine operator | $49.10 | .005 | **$.25** lf |
| **Hand finish excavation for utility trench** | | | | |
|     all soil types | excavation laborer | $28.30 | .002 | **$.06** lf |
| **Excavate for 2' to 3' deep water-line trench** | | | | |
|     sandy loam soil | machine operator | $49.10 | .004 | **$.20** lf |
|     rocky or hardpan soil | machine operator | $49.10 | .006 | **$.29** lf |
|     backfill | machine operator | $49.10 | .003 | **$.15** lf |
| **Excavate for 4' to 5' deep water-line trench** | | | | |
|     sandy loam soil | machine operator | $49.10 | .006 | **$.29** lf |
|     rocky or hardpan soil | machine operator | $49.10 | .009 | **$.44** lf |
|     backfill | machine operator | $49.10 | .006 | **$.29** lf |
| **Excavate for 6' to 7' deep water-line trench** | | | | |
|     sandy loam soil | machine operator | $49.10 | .009 | **$.44** lf |
|     rocky or hardpan soil | machine operator | $49.10 | .013 | **$.64** lf |
|     backfill | machine operator | $49.10 | .008 | **$.39** lf |
| **Excavate for 8' to 9' deep water-line trench** | | | | |
|     sandy loam soil | machine operator | $49.10 | .011 | **$.54** lf |
|     rocky or hardpan soil | machine operator | $49.10 | .017 | **$.83** lf |
|     backfill | machine operator | $49.10 | .010 | **$.49** lf |
| **Hand finish excavation for water-line trench** | | | | |
|     all soil types | excavation laborer | $28.30 | .005 | **$.14** lf |
| **Excavate for 3' to 4' deep sewer-line trench** | | | | |
|     sandy loam soil | machine operator | $49.10 | .006 | **$.29** lf |
|     rocky or hardpan soil | machine operator | $49.10 | .009 | **$.44** lf |
|     backfill | machine operator | $49.10 | .005 | **$.25** lf |
| **Excavate for 5' to 6' deep sewer-line trench** | | | | |
|     sandy loam soil | machine operator | $49.10 | .009 | **$.44** lf |
|     rocky or hardpan soil | machine operator | $49.10 | .013 | **$.64** lf |
|     backfill | machine operator | $49.10 | .008 | **$.39** lf |
| **Excavate for 7' to 8' deep sewer-line trench** | | | | |
|     sandy loam soil | machine operator | $49.10 | .011 | **$.54** lf |
|     rocky or hardpan soil | machine operator | $49.10 | .017 | **$.83** lf |
|     backfill | machine operator | $49.10 | .006 | **$.29** lf |
| **Hand finish excavation for sewer-line trench** | | | | |
|     all soil types | excavation laborer | $28.30 | .005 | **$.14** lf |
| **Machine excavate hole for repairs to water, sewer, or utility lines** | | | | |
|     machine excavate per lf of depth | machine operator | $49.10 | .024 | **$1.18** lf |
|     hand finish per lf of depth | excavation laborer | $28.30 | .019 | **$.54** lf |
| **General foundation, slab, & footing machine excavation** | | | | |
|     machine excavate per cy | machine operator | $49.10 | .025 | **$1.23** cy |
|     hand-finish per cy | excavation laborer | $28.30 | .020 | **$.57** cy |

# 15 ........................................................... *Fees*

| Item Description | Unit | | | Total |
|---|---|---|---|---|
| **Minimum building permit fee**<br>*Fee*...................85.00 | ea | — | — | $85.00 |
| **Building permit fee for job $2,001 to $5,000**<br>*Fee*..........................90.00 | ea | — | — | $90.00 |
| **Building permit fee for job $5,001 to $10,000**<br>*Fee*........................250.00 | ea | — | — | $250.00 |
| **Building permit fee for job $10,001 to $20,000**<br>*Fee*........................500.00 | ea | — | — | $500.00 |
| **Building permit fee for job $20,001 to $30,000**<br>*Fee*........................650.00 | ea | — | — | $650.00 |
| **Building permit fee for job $30,001 to $40,000**<br>*Fee*........................700.00 | ea | — | — | $700.00 |
| **Building permit fee for job $40,001 to $50,000**<br>*Fee*........................850.00 | ea | — | — | $850.00 |
| **Building permit fee for job $50,001 to $60,000**<br>*Fee*........................1050.00 | ea | — | — | $1,050.00 |
| **Building permit fee for job $60,001 to $70,000**<br>*Fee*........................1200.00 | ea | — | — | $1,200.00 |
| **Building permit fee for job $70,001 to $80,000**<br>*Fee*........................1300.00 | ea | — | — | $1,300.00 |
| **Building permit fee for job $80,001 to $90,000**<br>*Fee*........................1400.00 | ea | — | — | $1,400.00 |
| **Building permit fee for job $90,001 to $100,000**<br>*Fee*........................1500.00 | ea | — | — | $1,500.00 |
| **Building permit fee for job $100,001 to $150,000**<br>*Fee*........................1900.00 | ea | — | — | $1,900.00 |
| **Building permit fee for job $150,001 to $200,000**<br>*Fee*........................2300.00 | ea | — | — | $2,300.00 |
| **Building permit fee for job $200,001 to $250,000**<br>*Fee*........................2700.00 | ea | — | — | $2,700.00 |
| **Building permit fee for job $250,001 to $300,000**<br>*Fee*........................3050.00 | ea | — | — | $3,050.00 |
| **Building permit fee for job $300,001 to $400,000**<br>*Fee*........................3850.00 | ea | — | — | $3,850.00 |
| **Building permit fee for job $400,001 to $500,000**<br>*Fee*........................4650.00 | ea | — | — | $4,650.00 |

◀ **BUILDING PERMIT**
*Permit fees vary widely. These fees are rules of thumb for most areas of the country. Rural areas will be less and high-density areas will be more. Includes plan-check fees.*

| Item Description | Unit | | | Total |
|---|---|---|---|---|
| **SEWER CONNECT ▶** *Rule-of-thumb charge for connecting sewer lines to city service.* | **Sewer connection fee** *Fee*......................2050.00 ▶ Typical charges for labor and materials installed by government entity. Does not include any development upcharges added to the fee. Includes connect to a city sewer line up to 50 lf from the structure, mobilization, excavation, pipe and fittings, backfill, repair to street, curb and gutter, and temporary signs. | ea | — | — | $2,050.00 |
| **WATER CONNECT ▶** *Rule-of-thumb charge for connecting water lines to city service.* | **Water connection fee** *Fee*......................2000.00 ▶ Typical charges for labor and materials installed by government entity. Does not include any development upcharges added to the fee. Includes connect to a city water line up to 50 lf from the structure, mobilization, excavation, pipe and fittings, water meter, backfill, repair to street, curb and gutter, and temporary signs. | ea | — | — | $2,000.00 |
| **ESTIMATING ▶** *Typical rates charged to estimate insurance repair damages.* | **Estimating fees per hour** *Fee*.............................43.50 | hr | — | — | $43.50 |
| | **Estimating fees per day** *Fee*.............................410.00 | dy | — | — | $410.00 |
| | **Estimating fees as percentage of estimate** ▶ Rule of thumb for estimating insurance repair damages on losses under $200,000. Percentage rate drops to as low as **.75%** on large losses or multiple unit losses. This percentage is used across the country. Do not adjust with Area Modification Factor. | % | — | — | 1.5% |
| | **Minimum estimating fee** *Fee*.............................170.00 | ea | — | — | $170.00 |
| **SOILS ENGINEER ▶** | **Soils engineer fee per hour** *Fee*.............................90.00 | hr | — | — | $90.00 |
| **STRUCTURAL ▶ ENGINEER** | **Structural engineer fee per hour** *Fee*.............................100.00 | hr | — | — | $100.00 |
| **PLAN ▶ DRAWING FEES** | **Plan drawing fee, simple structure per sf of floor** *Fee*..............................15 | sf | — | — | $.15 |
| | **Plan drawing fee, typical structure per sf of floor** *Fee*..............................20 | sf | — | — | $.20 |
| | **Plan drawing fee, complex structure per sf of floor** *Fee*..............................30 | sf | — | — | $.30 |
| | **Plan drawing fee, ornate structure per sf of floor** *Fee*..............................45 | sf | — | — | $.45 |
| | **Minimum plan drawing fee** *Fee*.............................185.00 | ea | — | — | $185.00 |

✍ NOTES: _____

_____

_____

_____

_____

_____ end

# 16 ........................................................... *Fences*

| Item Description | Unit | Remove | Replace | Total | |
|---|---|---|---|---|---|
| **Add 11% for redwood wood fences** | | | | | ◀ **OTHER WOODS** |
| **Add 4% for treated-pine wood fences** | | | | | |
| **4' high cedar post embedded in concrete**<br>*Replace* Materials ......18.70    Labor...........31.30<br>*Remove*........................    Labor...........9.62 | ea | $9.62 | $50.00 | $59.62 | ◀ **WOOD FENCE POST**<br>*All wood fence posts include digging of 2' deep hole and setting in concrete. Post height is above ground. For example, a 4' high post is made from a 6' length with 2' underground and 4' above ground.* |
| **6' high cedar post embedded in concrete**<br>*Replace* Materials ......21.50    Labor...........31.30<br>*Remove*........................    Labor...........9.62 | ea | $9.62 | $52.80 | $62.42 | |
| **8' high cedar post embedded in concrete**<br>*Replace* Materials ......24.40    Labor...........31.30<br>*Remove*........................    Labor ...........9.62 | ea | $9.62 | $55.70 | $65.32 | |
| **4' high cedar basketweave fence**<br>*Replace* Materials......11.20    Labor...........10.90<br>*Remove*........................    Labor ...........4.22 | lf | $4.22 | $22.10 | $26.32 | ◀ **BASKETWEAVE FENCE**<br>*Posts are set in concrete and spaced up to 8' on center with an average spacing of 7.2' apart. Fence boards are 1" x 6" to 1" x 10". Gates are 3' wide with a frame made from 2" x 4" lumber, cross braced with turnbuckle and cable. Includes heavy duty hinges, latch, and spring closer.* |
| **6' high cedar basketweave fence**<br>*Replace* Materials......15.20    Labor ...........11.60<br>*Remove*........................    Labor ...........4.32 | lf | $4.32 | $26.80 | $31.12 | |
| **8' high cedar basketweave fence**<br>*Replace* Materials......19.90    Labor ...........12.30<br>*Remove*........................    Labor ...........4.45 | lf | $4.45 | $32.20 | $36.65 | |
| **4' high cedar basketweave fence gate with hardware**<br>*Replace* Materials ......66.20    Labor ...........92.90<br>*Remove*........................    Labor ...........8.49 | ea | $8.49 | $159.10 | $167.59 | |
| **6' high cedar basketweave fence gate with hardware**<br>*Replace* Materials ......81.10    Labor...........98.40<br>*Remove*........................    Labor ...........8.80 | ea | $8.80 | $179.50 | $188.30 | |
| **8' high cedar basketweave fence gate with hardware**<br>*Replace* Materials ......94.70    Labor...........104.00<br>*Remove*........................    Labor ...........9.07 | ea | $9.07 | $198.70 | $207.77 | |
| **4' high cedar board fence**<br>*Replace* Materials.......11.20    Labor ...........9.22<br>*Remove*........................    Labor ...........4.22 | lf | $4.22 | $20.42 | $24.64 | ◀ **BOARD FENCE**<br>*Fence with boards installed vertically or horizontally. Posts are set in concrete and spaced up to 8' on center with an average spacing of 7.2' apart. Fence boards are 1" x 4" to 1" x 8". 8' tall fence contains three supporting rails. All other heights contain two. Gates are 3' wide with horizontal and diagonal rails, heavy duty hinges, latch, and spring closer.* |
| **6' high cedar board fence**<br>*Replace* Materials.......15.20    Labor ...........9.84<br>*Remove*........................    Labor ...........4.32 | lf | $4.32 | $25.04 | $29.36 | |
| **8' high cedar board fence**<br>*Replace* Materials......19.90    Labor...........10.60<br>*Remove*........................    Labor ...........4.45 | lf | $4.45 | $30.50 | $34.95 | |
| **4' high cedar board fence gate with hardware**<br>*Replace* Materials......66.20    Labor...........74.60<br>*Remove*........................    Labor ...........8.49 | ea | $8.49 | $140.80 | $149.29 | |

| Item Description | Unit | Remove | Replace | Total |
|---|---|---|---|---|
| **BOARD FENCE ▶** *continued* **6' high cedar board fence gate with hardware** *Replace* Materials ......81.10    Labor ..........80.20 *Remove*........................    Labor ...........8.80 | ea | $8.80 | $161.30 | $170.10 |
| **8' high cedar board fence gate with hardware** *Replace* Materials ......94.70    Labor ..........83.90 *Remove*........................    Labor ...........9.07 | ea | $9.07 | $178.60 | $187.67 |
| **BOARD FENCE ▶ WITH LATTICE CAP** Board fence with 12" cap. Lattice is trimmed with 2" x 4" lattice rails. Posts are set in concrete and spaced up to 8' on center with an average spacing of 7.2'. Gates are 3' wide with a frame made from 2" x 4" lumber, cross braced with turn buckle and cable. Includes heavy duty hinges, latch, and spring closer. **6' high cedar board fence with lattice cap** *Replace* Materials ......20.50    Labor ..........11.40 *Remove*........................    Labor ...........4.32 | lf | $4.32 | $31.90 | $36.22 |
| **8' high cedar board fence with lattice cap** *Replace* Materials ......25.20    Labor ..........12.30 *Remove*........................    Labor ...........4.45 | lf | $4.45 | $37.50 | $41.95 |
| **6' high cedar board fence gate with lattice cap** *Replace* Materials ......90.40    Labor ..........101.00 *Remove*........................    Labor ...........8.76 | ea | $8.76 | $191.40 | $200.16 |
| **8' high cedar board fence gate with lattice cap** *Replace* Materials ......104.00    Labor ..........119.00 *Remove*........................    Labor ...........9.02 | ea | $9.02 | $223.00 | $232.02 |
| **BOARD-ON- ▶ BOARD FENCE** Fence with overlapping boards installed vertically. Posts are set in concrete and spaced up to 8' on center with an average spacing of 7.2' apart. Fence boards are 1" x 4" to 1" x 8". 8' tall fence contains three supporting rails. All other heights contain two. Gates are 3' wide with horizontal and diagonal rails. Includes heavy duty hinges, latch, and spring closer. **4' high cedar board-on-board fence** *Replace* Materials ......14.90    Labor ..........10.20 *Remove*........................    Labor ...........4.22 | lf | $4.22 | $25.10 | $29.32 |
| **6' high cedar board-on-board fence** *Replace* Materials ......20.70    Labor ..........10.70 *Remove*........................    Labor ...........4.32 | lf | $4.32 | $31.40 | $35.72 |
| **8' high cedar board-on-board fence** *Replace* Materials ......27.30    Labor ..........11.40 *Remove*........................    Labor ...........4.45 | lf | $4.45 | $38.70 | $43.15 |
| **4' high cedar board-on-board fence gate with hardware** *Replace* Materials ......77.20    Labor ..........88.10 *Remove*........................    Labor ...........8.49 | ea | $8.49 | $165.30 | $173.79 |
| **6' high cedar board-on-board fence gate with hardware** *Replace* Materials ......97.70    Labor ..........92.90 *Remove*........................    Labor ...........8.80 | ea | $8.80 | $190.60 | $199.40 |
| **8' high cedar board-on-board fence gate with hardware** *Replace* Materials ......117.00    Labor ..........98.40 *Remove*........................    Labor ...........9.07 | ea | $9.07 | $215.40 | $224.47 |
| **BOARD-AND- ▶ BATTEN FENCE** Vertically installed 1" x 8" to 1" x 12" boards with 1" x 2" to 1" x 4" battens overlapping joints. Posts are set in concrete and spaced up to 8' on center with an average spacing of 7.2' apart. Gates are 3' wide with horizontal and diagonal rails. Includes heavy duty hinges, latch, and spring closer. **4' high cedar board-and-batten fence** *Replace* Materials ......12.80    Labor ..........10.40 *Remove*........................    Labor ...........4.22 | lf | $4.22 | $23.20 | $27.42 |
| **6' high cedar board-and-batten fence** *Replace* Materials ......17.70    Labor ..........10.60 *Remove*........................    Labor ...........4.32 | lf | $4.32 | $28.30 | $32.62 |
| **8' high cedar board-and-batten fence** *Replace* Materials ......23.20    Labor ..........11.10 *Remove*........................    Labor ...........4.45 | lf | $4.45 | $34.30 | $38.75 |

| Item Description | Unit | Remove | Replace | Total |
|---|---|---|---|---|
| **4' high cedar board-and-batten fence gate with hardware** | ea | $8.49 | $161.60 | $170.09 |
| *Replace* Materials ......71.10     Labor ..........90.50 | | | | |
| *Remove* ......................     Labor ...........8.49 | | | | |
| **6' high cedar board-and-batten fence gate with hardware** | ea | $8.80 | $184.10 | $192.90 |
| *Replace* Materials ......88.50     Labor..........95.60 | | | | |
| *Remove* ......................     Labor ...........8.80 | | | | |
| **8' high cedar board-and-batten fence gate with hardware** | ea | $9.07 | $205.50 | $214.57 |
| *Replace* Materials ....104.50     Labor ..........101.00 | | | | |
| *Remove* ......................     Labor ...........9.07 | | | | |
| **3' high cedar picket fence** | lf | $4.22 | $14.29 | $18.51 |
| *Replace* Materials ........6.65     Labor ...........7.64 | | | | |
| *Remove* ......................     Labor ...........4.22 | | | | |
| **5' high cedar picket fence** | lf | $4.32 | $18.38 | $22.70 |
| *Replace* Materials ......10.19     Labor ...........8.19 | | | | |
| *Remove* ......................     Labor ...........4.32 | | | | |
| **3' high cedar picket fence gate with hardware** | ea | $8.49 | $121.00 | $129.49 |
| *Replace* Materials ......52.20     Labor ..........68.80 | | | | |
| *Remove* ......................     Labor ...........8.49 | | | | |
| **5' high cedar picket fence gate with hardware** | ea | $8.80 | $146.90 | $155.70 |
| *Replace* Materials ......65.00     Labor..........81.90 | | | | |
| *Remove* ......................     Labor ...........8.80 | | | | |
| **Minimum charge for board fence work** | ea | — | $88.10 | $88.10 |
| *Replace* Materials ......30.00     Labor ..........58.10 | | | | |
| **Remove & reinstall board fence gate** | ea | — | $27.70 | $27.70 |
| *Replace* ......................     Labor..........27.70 | | | | |
| **Wood gate hardware with self-closing hinges** | ea | $5.16 | $58.10 | $63.26 |
| *Replace* Materials ......32.20     Labor ..........25.90 | | | | |
| *Remove* ......................     Labor ...........5.16 | | | | |
| **Heavy gauge wood gate hardware with self-closing hinges** | ea | $5.16 | $73.50 | $78.66 |
| *Replace* Materials ......47.60     Labor ..........25.90 | | | | |
| *Remove* ......................     Labor ...........5.16 | | | | |
| **Wood gate closing spring** | ea | $2.63 | $31.10 | $33.73 |
| *Replace* Materials ......19.70     Labor ..........11.40 | | | | |
| *Remove* ......................     Labor ...........2.63 | | | | |
| **3' high chain-link fence** | lf | $3.04 | $11.24 | $14.28 |
| *Replace* Materials ........7.32     Labor ...........3.92 | | | | |
| *Remove* ......................     Labor ...........3.04 | | | | |
| ► With 1-5/8" line posts and 2" terminal posts. | | | | |
| **4' high chain-link fence** | lf | $3.17 | $14.70 | $17.87 |
| *Replace* Materials ........9.71     Labor ...........4.99 | | | | |
| *Remove* ......................     Labor ...........3.17 | | | | |
| ► With 1-7/8" line posts and 2" terminal posts. | | | | |
| **5' high chain-link fence** | lf | $3.28 | $18.40 | $21.68 |
| *Replace* Materials ......12.10     Labor ...........6.30 | | | | |
| *Remove* ......................     Labor ...........3.28 | | | | |
| ► With 1-7/8" line posts and 2" terminal posts. | | | | |

**RELATED ITEMS**

Painting .........................337

◄ **PICKET FENCE**
Posts are set in concrete and spaced up to 8' on center with an average spacing of 7.2' apart. Pickets are factory pre-cut. Gates are 3' wide with horizontal and diagonal rails. Includes heavy duty hinges, latch, and spring closer.

◄ **MINIMUM CHARGE FOR BOARD FENCE**

◄ **REMOVE & REINSTALL GATE**

◄ **WOOD GATE HARDWARE**

◄ **CHAIN-LINK FENCE**
11 gauge chain-link. Line posts and terminal posts are set 2' deep in concrete and spaced up to 10' on center with an average spacing of 9.2' apart. Includes all post caps, tie wire, tension bands, nuts, bolts, and tension rods.

| | Item Description | Unit | Remove | Replace | Total |
|---|---|---|---|---|---|
| **CHAIN-LINK ►**<br>**FENCE**<br>*continued* | **6' high chain-link fence**<br>*Replace* Materials ......14.50      Labor ..........8.02<br>*Remove*........................      Labor ..........3.43<br>► With 1-7/8" line posts and 2" terminal posts. | lf | $3.43 | $22.52 | $25.95 |
| | **7' high chain-link fence**<br>*Replace* Materials ......16.90      Labor ..........10.10<br>*Remove*........................      Labor ..........3.56<br>► With 1-7/8" line posts and 2" terminal posts. | lf | $3.56 | $27.00 | $30.56 |
| | **8' high chain-link fence**<br>*Replace* Materials.......19.20      Labor ..........12.90<br>*Remove*........................      Labor ..........3.75<br>► With 2" line posts and 3" terminal posts. | lf | $3.75 | $32.10 | $35.85 |
| | **10' high chain-link fence**<br>*Replace* Materials ......24.00      Labor ..........16.30<br>*Remove*........................      Labor ..........3.98<br>► With 2" line posts and 3" terminal posts. | lf | $3.98 | $40.30 | $44.28 |
| **CHAIN-LINK ►**<br>**FENCE GATE**<br>*3' wide with all*<br>*hardware.* | **3' high chain-link fence gate with hardware**<br>*Replace* Materials ......39.30      Labor ..........88.10<br>*Remove*........................      Labor ..........5.32 | ea | $5.32 | $127.40 | $132.72 |
| | **4' high chain-link fence gate with hardware**<br>*Replace* Materials ......50.70      Labor ..........88.10<br>*Remove*........................      Labor ..........5.32 | ea | $5.32 | $138.80 | $144.12 |
| | **5' high chain-link fence gate with hardware**<br>*Replace* Materials.......61.10      Labor ..........88.10<br>*Remove*........................      Labor ..........5.32 | ea | $5.32 | $149.20 | $154.52 |
| | **6' high chain-link fence gate with hardware**<br>*Replace* Materials ......70.30      Labor ..........90.50<br>*Remove*........................      Labor ..........5.32 | ea | $5.32 | $160.80 | $166.12 |
| | **7' high chain-link fence gate with hardware**<br>*Replace* Materials ......79.30      Labor ..........90.50<br>*Remove*........................      Labor ..........5.32 | ea | $5.32 | $169.80 | $175.12 |
| | **8' high chain-link fence gate with hardware**<br>*Replace* Materials ......87.00      Labor ..........90.50<br>*Remove*........................      Labor ..........5.32 | ea | $5.32 | $177.50 | $182.82 |
| | **10' high chain-link fence gate with hardware**<br>*Replace* Materials ....104.00      Labor ..........90.50<br>*Remove*........................      Labor ..........5.32 | ea | $5.32 | $194.50 | $199.82 |
| **CHAIN-LINK ►**<br>**DRIVEWAY GATE**<br>*Prices per lf. Includes*<br>*all hardware.*<br>*Minimum of 6 lf.* | **3' high chain-link fence driveway gate with hardware**<br>*Replace* Materials.......11.50      Labor ..........22.10<br>*Remove*........................      Labor ..........1.13 | lf | $1.13 | $33.60 | $34.73 |
| | **4' high chain-link fence driveway gate with hardware**<br>*Replace* Materials ......21.30      Labor ..........22.10<br>*Remove*........................      Labor ..........1.13 | lf | $1.13 | $43.40 | $44.53 |
| | **5' high chain-link fence driveway gate with hardware**<br>*Replace* Materials ......34.40      Labor ..........22.10<br>*Remove*........................      Labor ..........1.13 | lf | $1.13 | $56.50 | $57.63 |
| | **6' high chain-link fence driveway gate with hardware**<br>*Replace* Materials ......39.90      Labor ..........22.60<br>*Remove*........................      Labor ..........1.13 | lf | $1.13 | $62.50 | $63.63 |

| Item Description | Unit | Remove | Replace | Total | |
|---|---|---|---|---|---|
| **7' high chain-link fence driveway gate with hardware**<br>*Replace* Materials ......45.00    Labor ..........22.60<br>*Remove*.......................    Labor ............1.13 | lf | $1.13 | $67.60 | $68.73 | |
| **8' high chain-link fence driveway gate with hardware**<br>*Replace* Materials ......49.60    Labor ..........22.60<br>*Remove*.......................    Labor ............1.13 | lf | $1.13 | $72.20 | $73.33 | |
| **Add for additional corner in chain-link fence**<br>*Replace* Materials ......45.50    Labor ..........66.40<br>▶ The chain-link fence prices above allow for an average of 1 corner or terminal posts for every 15 lf of fence. Use this price only when estimating a fence that contains more corner or terminal posts. | ea | — | $111.90 | $111.90 | ◀ **ADDITIONAL CHAIN-LINK COSTS** |
| **Add for vinyl privacy slats (per sf of fence or gate)**<br>*Replace* Materials ........ .58    Labor ............. .21 | sf | — | $.79 | $.79 | |
| **Add for aluminum privacy slats (per sf of fence or gate)**<br>*Replace* Materials ........ .62    Labor ............. .21 | sf | — | $.83 | $.83 | |
| **Add 3% for chain-link fence with top rail** | | | | | |
| **Add 28% for 9 gauge galvanized chain-link** | | | | | |
| **Add 25% for 9 gauge vinyl-coated chain-link and posts** | | | | | |
| **Add 41% for 6 gauge chain-link** | | | | | |
| **Remove chain-link fence gate for work, then reinstall**<br>*Replace* .......................    Labor ..........10.00 | ea | — | $10.00 | $10.00 | ◀ **REMOVE CHAIN-LINK & REINSTALL** |
| **Remove chain-link fence (posts remain) for work, then reinstall**<br>*Replace* .......................    Labor ............. .45 | sf | — | $.45 | $.45 | |
| **Minimum charge for chain-link fence work**<br>*Replace* Materials ......54.50    Labor ..........77.40 | ea | — | $131.90 | $131.90 | ◀ **MINIMUM FOR CHAIN-LINK** |
| **3' high galvanized line post embedded in concrete**<br>*Replace* Materials ......13.30    Labor ..........31.60<br>*Remove*.......................    Labor ..........10.50<br>▶ 1-7/8" diameter post. | ea | $10.50 | $44.90 | $55.40 | ◀ **CHAIN-LINK FENCE POST**<br>*All chain-link fence posts include digging of 2' deep hole and setting in concrete. Post height is above ground. For example, a 4' high post is made from a 6' length with 2' underground and 4' above ground.* |
| **4' high galvanized line post embedded in concrete**<br>*Replace* Materials ......14.40    Labor ..........31.60<br>*Remove*.......................    Labor ..........10.50<br>▶ 1-7/8" diameter post. | ea | $10.50 | $46.00 | $56.50 | |
| **5' high galvanized line post embedded in concrete**<br>*Replace* Materials ......15.50    Labor ..........31.60<br>*Remove*.......................    Labor ..........10.50<br>▶ 1-7/8" diameter post. | ea | $10.50 | $47.10 | $57.60 | |
| **6' high galvanized line post embedded in concrete**<br>*Replace* Materials ......16.50    Labor ..........31.60<br>*Remove*.......................    Labor ..........10.50<br>▶ 1-7/8" diameter post. | ea | $10.50 | $48.10 | $58.60 | |
| **7' high galvanized line post embedded in concrete**<br>*Replace* Materials ......17.60    Labor ..........31.60<br>*Remove*.......................    Labor ..........10.50<br>▶ 1-7/8" diameter post. | ea | $10.50 | $49.20 | $59.70 | |

| | Item Description | Unit | Remove | Replace | Total |
|---|---|---|---|---|---|
| **CHAIN-LINK ►** FENCE POST *continued* | **8' high galvanized line post embedded in concrete** | ea | $10.50 | $50.60 | $61.10 |
| | *Replace* Materials.......19.00    Labor..........31.60 | | | | |
| | *Remove*...........................    Labor..........10.50 | | | | |
| | ► 2" diameter post. | | | | |
| | **10' high galvanized line post embedded in concrete** | ea | $10.50 | $52.90 | $63.40 |
| | *Replace* Materials ......21.30    Labor..........31.60 | | | | |
| | *Remove*...........................    Labor..........10.50 | | | | |
| | ► 2" diameter post. | | | | |
| gate or corner post ▷ | **3' high galvanized gate or corner post embedded in concrete** | ea | $10.50 | $44.20 | $54.70 |
| | *Replace* Materials ......12.60    Labor..........31.60 | | | | |
| | *Remove*...........................    Labor..........10.50 | | | | |
| | ► 2" diameter post. | | | | |
| | **4' high galvanized gate or corner post embedded in concrete** | ea | $10.50 | $45.10 | $55.60 |
| | *Replace* Materials.......13.50    Labor..........31.60 | | | | |
| | *Remove*...........................    Labor..........10.50 | | | | |
| | ► 2" diameter post. | | | | |
| | **5' high galvanized gate or corner post embedded in concrete** | ea | $10.50 | $46.00 | $56.50 |
| | *Replace* Materials ......14.40    Labor..........31.60 | | | | |
| | *Remove*...........................    Labor..........10.50 | | | | |
| | ► 2" diameter post. | | | | |
| | **6' high galvanized gate or corner post embedded in concrete** | ea | $10.50 | $48.40 | $58.90 |
| | *Replace* Materials ......16.80    Labor..........31.60 | | | | |
| | *Remove*...........................    Labor..........10.50 | | | | |
| | ► 2-1/2" diameter post. | | | | |
| | **7' high galvanized gate or corner post embedded in concrete** | ea | $10.50 | $49.50 | $60.00 |
| | *Replace* Materials.......17.90    Labor..........31.60 | | | | |
| | *Remove*...........................    Labor..........10.50 | | | | |
| | ► 2-1/2" diameter post. | | | | |
| | **8' high galvanized gate or corner post embedded in concrete** | ea | $10.50 | $61.60 | $72.10 |
| | *Replace* Materials ......30.00    Labor..........31.60 | | | | |
| | *Remove*...........................    Labor..........10.50 | | | | |
| | ► 3" diameter post. | | | | |
| | **10' high galvanized gate or corner post embedded in concrete** | ea | $10.50 | $66.60 | $77.10 |
| | *Replace* Materials ......35.00    Labor..........31.60 | | | | |
| | *Remove*...........................    Labor..........10.50 | | | | |
| | ► 3" diameter post. | | | | |
| **ADD FOR ►** ALUMINIZED | **Add 22% for aluminized steel fence post** | | | | |
| **VINYL PICKET ►** FENCE | **36" high vinyl picket fence** | lf | $3.64 | $25.40 | $29.04 |
| *36" and 48" fences have* | *Replace* Materials.......13.30    Labor..........12.10 | | | | |
| *2 rails, 60" and 72"* | *Remove*...........................    Labor ...........3.64 | | | | |
| *have three. Pickets are* | **48" high vinyl picket fence** | lf | $3.64 | $28.40 | $32.04 |
| *7/8" x 1-1/2" spaced* | *Replace* Materials ......16.20    Labor..........12.20 | | | | |
| *3-7/8" apart. Top and* | *Remove*...........................    Labor ...........3.64 | | | | |
| *bottom rails are 1-1/2"* | | | | | |
| *x 3-1/2". Bottom rail* | **60" high vinyl picket fence** | lf | $3.64 | $31.70 | $35.34 |
| *includes galvanized steel* | *Replace* Materials ......19.20    Labor..........12.50 | | | | |
| *channel. Posts are 4" x* | *Remove*...........................    Labor ...........3.64 | | | | |
| *4" and spaced up to 8'* | | | | | |
| *on center with an aver-* | **72" high vinyl picket fence** | lf | $3.64 | $34.70 | $38.34 |
| *age spacing of 7.2 feet* | *Replace* Materials ......22.10    Labor..........12.60 | | | | |
| *apart. Includes picket* | *Remove*...........................    Labor ...........3.64 | | | | |
| *and post caps.* | | | | | |

*continued on next page*

| Item Description | Unit | Remove | Replace | Total | |
|---|---|---|---|---|---|
| **36″ high vinyl picket fence gate**<br>*Replace* Materials......39.10    Labor .........22.20<br>*Remove*......................... Labor .........3.98 | If | $3.98 | $61.30 | $65.28 | ◄ **VINYL PICKET FENCE** *continued*<br><br>*Gates are priced per If with a 3 If minimum and a 5 If maximum and include all hardware. For wider gates, measure the gate If, round up to the next even number, multiply by the fence If price, then add $150.* |
| **48″ high vinyl picket fence gate**<br>*Replace* Materials ......41.10    Labor .........22.80<br>*Remove*......................... Labor .........3.98 | If | $3.98 | $63.90 | $67.88 | |
| **60″ high vinyl picket fence gate**<br>*Replace* Materials......43.10    Labor .........23.40<br>*Remove*......................... Labor .........3.98 | If | $3.98 | $66.50 | $70.48 | |
| **72″ high vinyl picket fence gate**<br>*Replace* Materials ......45.10    Labor .........23.90<br>*Remove*......................... Labor .........3.98 | If | $3.98 | $69.00 | $72.98 | |
| **36″ high vinyl picket fence, large pickets**<br>*Replace* Materials.......15.30    Labor..........12.10<br>*Remove*......................... Labor ..........3.64 | If | $3.64 | $27.40 | $31.04 | ◄ **VINYL LARGE PICKET FENCE** *Same as picket fence discussed on previous page with large 7/8″ x 3-1/2″ pickets spaced 3-7/8″ apart.* |
| **48″ high vinyl picket fence, large pickets**<br>*Replace* Materials.......19.00    Labor..........12.20<br>*Remove*......................... Labor ..........3.64 | If | $3.64 | $31.20 | $34.84 | |
| **60″ high vinyl picket fence, large pickets**<br>*Replace* Materials......22.30    Labor..........12.50<br>*Remove*......................... Labor ..........3.64 | If | $3.64 | $34.80 | $38.44 | |
| **36″ high vinyl picket fence gate, large pickets**<br>*Replace* Materials......40.60    Labor .........22.20<br>*Remove*......................... Labor ..........3.98 | If | $3.98 | $62.80 | $66.78 | **VINYL FENCES**<br><br>Also called PVC fences, vinyl fences are made from a molecularly bonded blend of hi-polymer resin with UV inhibitors to prevent damage from sunlight.<br><br>All posts are filled with concrete to about 1/3 of their height and capped with decorative caps |
| **48″ high vinyl picket fence gate, large pickets**<br>*Replace* Materials......43.10    Labor .........22.80<br>*Remove*......................... Labor ..........3.98 | If | $3.98 | $65.90 | $69.88 | |
| **60″ high vinyl picket fence gate, large pickets**<br>*Replace* Materials ......45.60    Labor ..........23.40<br>*Remove*......................... Labor ..........3.98 | If | $3.98 | $69.00 | $72.98 | |
| **36″ high vinyl picket fence, scalloped pickets**<br>*Replace* Materials ......14.30    Labor..........12.10<br>*Remove*......................... Labor ..........3.64 | If | $3.64 | $26.40 | $30.04 | ◄ **VINYL SCALLOPED PICKET FENCE** *Same as picket fence discussed above with decorative scalloped pickets.* |
| **48″ high vinyl picket fence, scalloped pickets**<br>*Replace* Materials.......17.40    Labor..........12.20<br>*Remove*......................... Labor ..........3.64 | If | $3.64 | $29.60 | $33.24 | |
| **60″ high vinyl picket fence, scalloped pickets**<br>*Replace* Materials ......20.50    Labor..........12.50<br>*Remove*......................... Labor ..........3.64 | If | $3.64 | $33.00 | $36.64 | |
| **36″ high vinyl picket fence gate, scalloped pickets**<br>*Replace* Materials ......39.80    Labor .........22.20<br>*Remove*......................... Labor ..........3.98 | If | $3.98 | $62.00 | $65.98 | |
| **48″ high vinyl picket fence gate, scalloped pickets**<br>*Replace* Materials ......41.80    Labor .........22.80<br>*Remove*......................... Labor ..........3.98 | If | $3.98 | $64.60 | $68.58 | |

| Item Description | | Unit | Remove | Replace | Total |
|---|---|---|---|---|---|
| **VINYL SCALLOPED PICKET FENCE** *continued* | **60" high vinyl picket fence gate, scalloped pickets** | lf | $3.98 | $67.50 | $71.48 |
| | *Replace* Materials......44.10   Labor..........23.40 | | | | |
| | *Remove*.........................   Labor..........3.98 | | | | |
| **REMOVE & REINSTALL VINYL FENCE** | **Remove vinyl fence for work, then reinstall (panels only)** | lf | — | $18.50 | $18.50 |
| | *Replace* .........................   Labor..........18.50 | | | | |
| | **Remove vinyl fence gate for work, then reinstall** | lf | — | $23.40 | $23.40 |
| | *Replace* .........................   Labor..........23.40 | | | | |
| **VINYL THREE-RAIL FENCE** *Rails are 1-1/2" x 5-1/2". Posts are 5" x 5" and spaced up to 8' apart with an average spacing of 7.2'. Gates priced per lf: 3 lf minimum, 5 lf maximum.* | **52" high vinyl three-rail fence** | lf | $2.72 | $16.06 | $18.78 |
| | *Replace* Materials........8.80   Labor..........7.26 | | | | |
| | *Remove*.........................   Labor..........2.72 | | | | |
| | **52" high vinyl three-rail fence gate** | lf | $2.72 | $44.40 | $47.12 |
| | *Replace* Materials......34.10   Labor..........10.30 | | | | |
| | *Remove*.........................   Labor..........2.72 | | | | |
| | ▶ For gates longer than 5 lf use lf fence price, round to even number and add **$105**. | | | | |
| **REMOVE & REINSTALL THREE-RAIL FENCE** | **Remove three-rail vinyl fence for work, then reinstall (rails only)** | lf | — | $12.80 | $12.80 |
| | *Replace* .........................   Labor..........12.80 | | | | |
| | **Remove three-rail vinyl fence gate for work, then reinstall** | lf | — | $18.50 | $18.50 |
| | *Replace* .........................   Labor..........18.50 | | | | |
| **VINYL SPACED SLAT FENCE** *Contains two widths of slats. The narrow slat is 7/8" x 1-1/2" and the wide slat is 7/8" x 3-1/2". Slats are spaced 2-1/2" apart. Top and bottom rails are 1-1/2" x 3-1/2". Bottom rail includes galvanized steel channel. Posts are 4" x 4" and spaced up to 8' on center with an average spacing of 7.2 feet apart. Includes post caps. Gates are priced per lf with a 3 lf minimum and a 5 lf maximum and include all hardware. For wider gates, measure the gate lf, round up to the next even number, multiply by the fence lf price, then add $150.* | **48" high vinyl spaced slat fence** | lf | $3.64 | $25.80 | $29.44 |
| | *Replace* Materials.......13.60   Labor..........12.20 | | | | |
| | *Remove*.........................   Labor..........3.64 | | | | |
| | **60" high vinyl spaced slat fence** | lf | $3.64 | $29.10 | $32.74 |
| | *Replace* Materials ......16.60   Labor..........12.50 | | | | |
| | *Remove*.........................   Labor..........3.64 | | | | |
| | **72" high vinyl spaced slat fence** | lf | $3.64 | $32.10 | $35.74 |
| | *Replace* Materials.......19.50   Labor..........12.60 | | | | |
| | *Remove*.........................   Labor..........3.64 | | | | |
| | **48" high vinyl spaced slat fence gate** | lf | $3.98 | $62.10 | $66.08 |
| | *Replace* Materials......39.30   Labor..........22.80 | | | | |
| | *Remove*.........................   Labor..........3.98 | | | | |
| | **60" high vinyl spaced slat fence gate** | lf | $3.98 | $64.70 | $68.68 |
| | *Replace* Materials......41.30   Labor..........23.40 | | | | |
| | *Remove*.........................   Labor..........3.98 | | | | |
| | **72" high vinyl spaced slat fence gate** | lf | $3.98 | $67.30 | $71.28 |
| | *Replace* Materials......43.40   Labor..........23.90 | | | | |
| | *Remove*.........................   Labor..........3.98 | | | | |
| **VINYL SOLID SLAT FENCE** *Slat is 7/8" x 5-1/2" with no space between slats. Top and bottom rails are 1-1/2" x 3-1/2". Bottom rail includes galvanized steel channel. Posts are 5" x 5" and spaced up to 8' on center with an average spacing of 7.2 feet.* | **48" high vinyl solid slat fence** | lf | $3.64 | $26.40 | $30.04 |
| | *Replace* Materials ......14.20   Labor..........12.20 | | | | |
| | *Remove*.........................   Labor..........3.64 | | | | |
| | **60" high vinyl solid slat fence** | lf | $3.64 | $38.10 | $41.74 |
| | *Replace* Materials ......25.60   Labor..........12.50 | | | | |
| | *Remove*.........................   Labor..........3.64 | | | | |
| | **72" high vinyl solid slat fence** | lf | $3.64 | $33.10 | $36.74 |
| | *Replace* Materials......20.50   Labor..........12.60 | | | | |
| | *Remove*.........................   Labor..........3.64 | | | | |

*continued on next page*

| Item Description | Unit | Remove | Replace | Total |
|---|---|---|---|---|
| **48" high vinyl solid slat fence gate**<br>*Replace* Materials....39.70  Labor.........22.80<br>*Remove*....................... Labor.........3.98 | lf | $3.98 | $62.50 | $66.48 |
| **60" high vinyl solid slat fence gate**<br>*Replace* Materials......41.80  Labor.........23.40<br>*Remove*....................... Labor.........3.98 | lf | $3.98 | $65.20 | $69.18 |
| **72" high vinyl solid slat fence gate**<br>*Replace* Materials......44.00  Labor.........23.90<br>*Remove*....................... Labor.........3.98 | lf | $3.98 | $67.90 | $71.88 |
| **60" high vinyl solid slat fence with lattice top**<br>*Replace* Materials......23.60  Labor.........12.80<br>*Remove*....................... Labor.........3.64 | lf | $3.64 | $36.40 | $40.04 |
| **72" high vinyl solid slat fence with lattice top**<br>*Replace* Materials......26.50  Labor.........13.00<br>*Remove*....................... Labor.........3.64 | lf | $3.64 | $39.50 | $43.14 |
| **60" high vinyl solid slat fence with lattice top gate**<br>*Replace* Materials......46.10  Labor.........24.90<br>*Remove*....................... Labor.........3.98 | lf | $3.98 | $71.00 | $74.98 |
| **72" high vinyl solid slat fence with lattice top gate**<br>*Replace* Materials......48.10  Labor.........26.00<br>*Remove*....................... Labor.........3.98 | lf | $3.98 | $74.10 | $78.08 |
| **60" ornamental iron fence, straight pickets**<br>*Replace* Materials......11.80  Labor.........12.80<br>*Remove*....................... Labor.........5.08 | lf | $5.08 | $24.60 | $29.68 |
| **72" ornamental iron fence, straight pickets**<br>*Replace* Materials......13.60  Labor.........13.00<br>*Remove*....................... Labor.........5.08 | lf | $5.08 | $26.60 | $31.68 |
| **60" ornamental iron fence gate, straight pickets**<br>*Replace* Materials......47.30  Labor.........24.90<br>*Remove*....................... Labor.........5.29 | lf | $5.29 | $72.20 | $77.49 |
| **72" ornamental iron fence gate, straight pickets**<br>*Replace* Materials......50.20  Labor.........26.00<br>*Remove*....................... Labor.........5.29 | lf | $5.29 | $76.20 | $81.49 |
| **60" ornamental iron fence, twisted pickets**<br>*Replace* Materials......12.70  Labor.........12.80<br>*Remove*....................... Labor.........5.08 | lf | $5.08 | $25.50 | $30.58 |
| **72" ornamental iron fence, twisted pickets**<br>*Replace* Materials......14.80  Labor.........13.00<br>*Remove*....................... Labor.........5.08 | lf | $5.08 | $27.80 | $32.88 |
| **60" ornamental iron fence gate, twisted pickets**<br>*Replace* Materials......50.60  Labor.........24.90<br>*Remove*....................... Labor.........5.29 | lf | $5.29 | $75.50 | $80.79 |
| **72" ornamental iron fence gate, twisted pickets**<br>*Replace* Materials......53.80  Labor.........26.00<br>*Remove*....................... Labor.........5.29 | lf | $5.29 | $79.80 | $85.09 |

◄ **VINYL SOLID SLAT FENCE** *continued*

*Includes post caps. Gates are priced per lf with a 3 lf minimum and a 5 lf maximum and include all hardware. For wider gates, measure the gate lf, round up to the next even number, multiply by the fence lf price, then add $150.*

◄ **ORNAMENTAL IRON FENCE**
*On all grades except fences with ornamental casting, steel pickets are 5/8" square 3-7/8" apart with 1" x 1" top and bottom rails. Posts are 93-1/2" apart. Pickets with decorative scrolls are straight pickets with the decorative scroll-work riveted or screwed to the pickets. Ornamental iron fences with ornamental casting have pickets that are cast in decorative scroll and plant-like patterns. Gates are priced per lf with a 3 lf minimum and a 5 lf maximum. For wider gates, measure the gate lf, round up to the next even number, multiply by the fence lf price, then add $175.*

**RELATED ITEMS**

| Item Description | Unit | Remove | Replace | Total |
|---|---|---|---|---|
| **ORNAMENTAL ▶ IRON FENCE** *continued* | | | | |
| **60" ornamental iron fence with decorative scrolls** | lf | $5.08 | $30.80 | $35.88 |
| *Replace* Materials ......18.00  Labor...........12.80 | | | | |
| *Remove*...................  Labor ...........5.08 | | | | |
| **72" ornamental iron fence with decorative scrolls** | lf | $5.08 | $33.80 | $38.88 |
| *Replace* Materials ......20.80  Labor...........13.00 | | | | |
| *Remove*...................  Labor ...........5.08 | | | | |
| **60" ornamental iron fence gate with decorative scrolls** | lf | $5.29 | $96.40 | $101.69 |
| *Replace* Materials ......71.50  Labor...........24.90 | | | | |
| *Remove*...................  Labor ...........5.29 | | | | |
| **72" ornamental iron fence gate with decorative scrolls** | lf | $5.29 | $101.90 | $107.19 |
| *Replace* Materials ......75.90  Labor...........26.00 | | | | |
| *Remove*...................  Labor ...........5.29 | | | | |
| **60" ornamental iron fence with ornamental casting** | lf | $5.08 | $44.70 | $49.78 |
| *Replace* Materials ......31.90  Labor...........12.80 | | | | |
| *Remove*...................  Labor ...........5.08 | | | | |
| **72" ornamental iron fence with ornamental casting** | lf | $5.08 | $49.90 | $54.98 |
| *Replace* Materials ......36.90  Labor...........13.00 | | | | |
| *Remove*...................  Labor ...........5.08 | | | | |
| **60" ornamental iron fence gate with ornamental casting** | lf | $5.29 | $151.90 | $157.19 |
| *Replace* Materials .....127.00  Labor...........24.90 | | | | |
| *Remove*...................  Labor ...........5.29 | | | | |
| **72" ornamental iron fence gate with ornamental casting** | lf | $5.29 | $160.00 | $165.29 |
| *Replace* Materials ....134.00  Labor...........26.00 | | | | |
| *Remove*...................  Labor ...........5.29 | | | | |
| **REMOVE & ▶ REINSTALL IRON FENCE** | | | | |
| **Remove ornamental iron fence for work, then reinstall (panels only)** | lf | — | $19.20 | $19.20 |
| *Replace* ...................  Labor...........19.20 | | | | |
| **Remove ornamental iron fence gate for work, then reinstall** | lf | — | $33.50 | $33.50 |
| *Replace* ...................  Labor...........33.50 | | | | |
| **ELECTRIC GATE ▶ OPENER** *For swinging or roll-type gates. Includes two remote transmitters, keypad on post by gate, all hardware and electrical wiring up to 45 lf.* | | | | |
| **1/2 horsepower electric gate opener** | ea | $20.00 | $2,686.00 | $2,706.00 |
| *Replace* Materials ..2550.00  Labor...........136.00 | | | | |
| *Remove*...................  Labor ...........20.00 | | | | |
| **3/4 horsepower electric gate opener** | ea | $20.00 | $3,436.00 | $3,456.00 |
| *Replace* Materials ..3300.00  Labor...........136.00 | | | | |
| *Remove*...................  Labor ...........20.00 | | | | |
| **1 horsepower electric gate opener** | ea | $20.00 | $3,836.00 | $3,856.00 |
| *Replace* Materials ..3700.00  Labor...........136.00 | | | | |
| *Remove*...................  Labor ...........20.00 | | | | |
| **2 horsepower electric gate opener** | ea | $20.00 | $4,486.00 | $4,506.00 |
| *Replace* Materials ..4350.00  Labor...........136.00 | | | | |
| *Remove*...................  Labor ...........20.00 | | | | |
| **5 horsepower electric gate opener** | ea | $20.00 | $5,136.00 | $5,156.00 |
| *Replace* Materials ..5000.00  Labor...........136.00 | | | | |
| *Remove*...................  Labor ...........20.00 | | | | |
| **Remove electric gate opener for work, then reinstall** | ea | — | $219.00 | $219.00 |
| *Replace* ...................  Labor...........219.00 | | | | |

# TIME & MATERIAL CHARTS (selected items)

## Fences Materials (Also see material prices with the line items and other information in the QuickFinder column.)

| DESCRIPTION | MATERIAL PRICE | GROSS COVERAGE | WASTE | NET COVERAGE | UNIT PRICE |
|---|---|---|---|---|---|
| **4" x 4" posts** | | | | | |
| 8' cedar | $11.00 ea | 1 | 4% | .96 | $11.50 ea |
| 10' cedar | $13.80 ea | 1 | 4% | .96 | $14.40 ea |
| 12' cedar | $16.60 ea | 2 | 4% | 1.92 | $8.65 ea |
| **1" x 2" x 8' fence boards** | | | | | |
| #2 cedar | $2.90 ea | 8 | 4% | 7.68 | $.38 lf |
| B grade redwood | $5.40 ea | 8 | 4% | 7.68 | $.70 lf |
| treated-pine | $1.80 ea | 8 | 4% | 7.68 | $.23 lf |
| **1" x 4" x 8' fence boards** | | | | | |
| #2 cedar | $4.30 ea | 8 | 4% | 7.68 | $.56 lf |
| B grade redwood | $8.00 ea | 8 | 4% | 7.68 | $1.04 lf |
| treated-pine | $3.60 ea | 8 | 4% | 7.68 | $.47 lf |
| **1" x 6" x 8' fence boards** | | | | | |
| #2 cedar | $6.40 ea | 8 | 4% | 7.68 | $.83 lf |
| B grade redwood | $11.90 ea | 8 | 4% | 7.68 | $1.55 lf |
| treated-pine | $4.20 ea | 8 | 4% | 7.68 | $.55 lf |
| **1" x 8" x 8' fence boards** | | | | | |
| #2 cedar | $11.40 ea | 8 | 4% | 7.68 | $1.48 lf |
| B grade redwood | $21.20 ea | 8 | 4% | 7.68 | $2.76 lf |
| treated-pine | $7.20 ea | 8 | 4% | 7.68 | $.94 lf |
| **1" x 10" x 8' fence boards** | | | | | |
| #2 cedar | $14.10 ea | 8 | 4% | 7.68 | $1.84 lf |
| B grade redwood | $26.30 ea | 8 | 4% | 7.68 | $3.42 lf |
| treated-pine | $9.00 ea | 8 | 4% | 7.68 | $1.17 lf |
| **2" x 4" x 8' fence boards** | | | | | |
| #2 cedar | $5.20 ea | 8 | 4% | 7.68 | $.68 lf |
| B grade redwood | $8.10 ea | 8 | 4% | 7.68 | $1.05 lf |
| treated-pine | $7.70 ea | 8 | 4% | 7.68 | $1.00 lf |
| **1" x 3" mill-cut fence picket** | | | | | |
| 3' cedar | $1.30 ea | 1 | 4% | .96 | $1.35 ea |
| 5' cedar | $2.80 ea | 1 | 4% | .96 | $2.92 ea |
| **Lattice** | | | | | |
| cedar lattice | $17.40 sh | 32 | 4% | 30.72 | $.57 sf |
| cedar cap mold | $6.70 ea | 8 | 4% | 7.68 | $.87 lf |
| **Chain-link fence materials** | | | | | |
| 11 gauge chain-link | $1.73 sf | 1 | 3% | .97 | $1.78 sf |

## Fences Labor

| LABORER | BASE WAGE | PAID LEAVE | TRUE WAGE | FICA | FUTA | WORKER'S COMP. | UNEMPLOY. INSUR. | HEALTH INSUR. | RETIRE (401K) | LIABILITY INSUR. | COST PER HOUR |
|---|---|---|---|---|---|---|---|---|---|---|---|
| Carpenter | $22.60 | 1.76 | $24.36 | 1.86 | .19 | 4.56 | 2.12 | 2.54 | .73 | 3.17 | $39.50 |
| Carpenter's helper | $16.30 | 1.27 | $17.57 | 1.34 | .14 | 3.29 | 1.53 | 2.54 | .53 | 2.28 | $29.20 |
| Electrician | $25.10 | 1.96 | $27.06 | 2.07 | .22 | 2.80 | 2.35 | 2.54 | .81 | 3.52 | $41.40 |
| Demolition laborer | $13.40 | 1.05 | $14.45 | 1.11 | .12 | 4.44 | 1.26 | 2.54 | .43 | 1.88 | $26.20 |

**Paid Leave** is calculated based on two weeks paid vacation, one week sick leave, and seven paid holidays. Employer's matching portion of **FICA** is 7.65 percent. **FUTA** (Federal Unemployment) is .8 percent. **Worker's compensation** for the fences trade was calculated using a national average of 18.71 percent. **Unemployment insurance** was calculated using a national average of 8.7 percent. **Health insurance** was calculated based on a projected national average for 2001 of $505 per employee (and family when applicable) per month. Employer pays 80 percent for a per month cost of $404 per employee. **Retirement** is based on a 401(k) retirement program with employer matching of 50 percent. Employee contributions to the 401(k) plan are an average of 6 percent of the true wage. **Liability insurance** is based on a national average of 12.9 percent.

## Fences Labor Productivity

| WORK DESCRIPTION | LABORER | COST PER HOUR | PRODUCTIVITY | UNIT PRICE |
|---|---|---|---|---|
| **Demolition** | | | | |
| remove 4' high wood fence | demolition laborer | $26.20 | .161 | $4.22 lf |
| remove 6' high wood fence | demolition laborer | $26.20 | .165 | $4.32 lf |
| remove 8' high wood fence | demolition laborer | $26.20 | .170 | $4.45 lf |
| remove wood fence post | demolition laborer | $26.20 | .367 | $9.62 ea |
| remove 3' high chain-link fence | demolition laborer | $26.20 | .116 | $3.04 lf |
| remove 4' high chain-link fence | demolition laborer | $26.20 | .121 | $3.17 lf |
| remove 5' high chain-link fence | demolition laborer | $26.20 | .125 | $3.28 lf |
| remove 6' high chain-link fence | demolition laborer | $26.20 | .131 | $3.43 lf |
| remove 7' high chain-link fence | demolition laborer | $26.20 | .136 | $3.56 lf |
| remove 8' high chain-link fence | demolition laborer | $26.20 | .143 | $3.75 lf |
| remove 10' high chain-link fence | demolition laborer | $26.20 | .152 | $3.98 lf |
| remove chain-link fence gate | demolition laborer | $26.20 | .203 | $5.32 ea |
| remove chain-link fence driveway gate | demolition laborer | $26.20 | .043 | $1.13 lf |
| remove chain-link fence post | demolition laborer | $26.20 | .402 | $10.50 ea |
| remove vinyl fence | demolition laborer | $26.20 | .139 | $3.64 lf |
| remove vinyl rail fence | demolition laborer | $26.20 | .104 | $2.72 lf |
| remove vinyl fence gate | demolition laborer | $26.20 | .152 | $3.98 lf |
| remove ornamental iron fence | demolition laborer | $26.20 | .194 | $5.08 lf |
| remove ornamental iron fence gate | demolition laborer | $26.20 | .202 | $5.29 ea |
| remove electric gate opener | demolition laborer | $26.20 | .763 | $20.00 ea |
| **Fencing crew** | | | | |
| fencing installation | carpenter | $39.50 | | |
| fencing installation | carpenter's helper | $29.20 | | |
| **fencing installation** | **fencing crew** | **$34.40** | | |
| **Build basketweave fence** | | | | |
| 4' high | fencing crew | $34.40 | .318 | $10.90 lf |
| 8' high | fencing crew | $34.40 | .359 | $12.30 lf |
| 4' high gate | fencing crew | $34.40 | 2.70 | $92.90 ea |
| 8' high gate | fencing crew | $34.40 | 3.03 | $104.00 ea |
| **Build board fence** | | | | |
| 4' high | fencing crew | $34.40 | .268 | $9.22 lf |
| 8' high | fencing crew | $34.40 | .307 | $10.60 lf |
| 4' high gate | fencing crew | $34.40 | 2.17 | $74.60 lf |
| 8' high gate | fencing crew | $34.40 | 2.44 | $83.90 lf |
| **Build board fence with lattice cap** | | | | |
| 6' high | fencing crew | $34.40 | .331 | $11.40 lf |
| 8' high | fencing crew | $34.40 | .359 | $12.30 lf |
| 6' high gate | fencing crew | $34.40 | 2.94 | $101.00 lf |
| 8' high gate | fencing crew | $34.40 | 3.45 | $119.00 lf |
| **Build board-on-board fence** | | | | |
| 4' high | fencing crew | $34.40 | .296 | $10.20 lf |
| 8' high | fencing crew | $34.40 | .331 | $11.40 lf |
| 4' high gate | fencing crew | $34.40 | 2.56 | $88.10 lf |
| 8' high gate | fencing crew | $34.40 | 2.86 | $98.40 lf |
| **Build board-and-batten fence** | | | | |
| 4' high | fencing crew | $34.40 | .301 | $10.40 lf |
| 8' high | fencing crew | $34.40 | .324 | $11.10 lf |
| 4' high gate | fencing crew | $34.40 | 2.63 | $90.50 lf |
| 8' high gate | fencing crew | $34.40 | 2.94 | $101.00 lf |
| **Build picket fence** | | | | |
| 3' high | fencing crew | $34.40 | .222 | $7.64 lf |
| 5' high | fencing crew | $34.40 | .238 | $8.19 lf |
| 3' high gate | fencing crew | $34.40 | 2.00 | $68.80 lf |
| 5' high gate | fencing crew | $34.40 | 2.38 | $81.90 lf |
| **Install chain-link fence** | | | | |
| 3' high | fencing crew | $34.40 | .114 | $3.92 lf |
| 5' high | fencing crew | $34.40 | .183 | $6.30 lf |
| 7' high | fencing crew | $34.40 | .295 | $10.10 lf |
| 10' high | fencing crew | $34.40 | .475 | $16.30 lf |

# 17 ......................................... *Finish Carpentry*

| Item Description | Unit | Remove | Replace | Total | |
|---|---|---|---|---|---|
| **Minimum charge for finish carpentry work**<br>*Replace* Materials......20.00   Labor..........42.70 | ea | — | $62.70 | $62.70 | ◀ **MINIMUM** |
| **Add 70% for walnut** | | | | | ◀ **OTHER WOOD SPECIES**<br>*For moldings made from these species of wood factor the cost of stain-grade pine by the percentage. All grades are kiln-dried select or better.* |
| **Add 563% for teak** | | | | | |
| **Add 73% for cherry** | | | | | |
| **Add 31% for hard maple** | | | | | |
| **Add 24% for cypress** | | | | | |
| **Add 17% for redwood** | | | | | |
| **Add 0% for cedar** | | | | | |
| **1-1/2″ finger-joint pine clamshell base**<br>*Replace* Materials ........ .71   Labor ...........1.50<br>*Remove*........................   Labor............. .68 | lf | $.68 | $2.21 | $2.89 | ◀ **1-1/2″ CLAMSHELL BASE**<br>*Includes 7% waste.* |
| **1-1/2″ stain-grade pine clamshell base**<br>*Replace* Materials ........ .83   Labor ...........1.50<br>*Remove*........................   Labor............. .68 | lf | $.68 | $2.33 | $3.01 | |
| **1-1/2″ poplar clamshell base**<br>*Replace* Materials ........ .89   Labor ...........1.50<br>*Remove*........................   Labor............. .68 | lf | $.68 | $2.39 | $3.07 | |
| **1-1/2″ mahogany clamshell base**<br>*Replace* Materials........1.04   Labor ...........1.50<br>*Remove*........................   Labor............. .68 | lf | $.68 | $2.54 | $3.22 | **WOOD EMBOSSING**<br>Wood moldings are often embossed to appear like they have been carved. Embossing stamps a pattern onto the wood.<br>Embossing is far less expensive than carving and is most successful on softer woods, such as pine. |
| **1-1/2″ red oak clamshell base**<br>*Replace* Materials........1.14   Labor ...........1.50<br>*Remove*........................   Labor............. .68 | lf | $.68 | $2.64 | $3.32 | |
| **2-1/2″ finger-joint pine clamshell base**<br>*Replace* Materials ........ .82   Labor ...........1.50<br>*Remove*........................   Labor............. .68 | lf | $.68 | $2.32 | $3.00 | ◀ **2-1/2″ CLAMSHELL BASE**<br>*Includes 7% waste.* |
| **2-1/2″ stain-grade pine clamshell base**<br>*Replace* Materials ........ .95   Labor ...........1.50<br>*Remove*........................   Labor............. .68 | lf | $.68 | $2.45 | $3.13 | |
| **2-1/2″ poplar clamshell base**<br>*Replace* Materials ...... 1.02   Labor ...........1.50<br>*Remove*........................   Labor............. .68 | lf | $.68 | $2.52 | $3.20 | |
| **2-1/2″ mahogany clamshell base**<br>*Replace* Materials........1.20   Labor ...........1.50<br>*Remove*........................   Labor............. .68 | lf | $.68 | $2.70 | $3.38 | **RELATED ITEMS**<br>Cleaning..........................61<br>Painting.........................337 |

| Item Description | Unit | Remove | Replace | Total |
|---|---|---|---|---|
| **2-1/2" CLAMSHELL BASE** continued      **2-1/2" red oak clamshell base**<br>*Replace* Materials ........1.31    Labor ............1.50<br>*Remove* ........................    Labor ............ .68 | lf | $.68 | $2.81 | $3.49 |
| **3-1/2" CLAMSHELL BASE** Includes 7% waste.      **3-1/2" finger-joint pine clamshell base**<br>*Replace* Materials ........1.15    Labor ............1.50<br>*Remove* ........................    Labor ............ .68 | lf | $.68 | $2.65 | $3.33 |
| **3-1/2" stain-grade pine clamshell base**<br>*Replace* Materials ........1.33    Labor ............1.50<br>*Remove* ........................    Labor ............ .68 | lf | $.68 | $2.83 | $3.51 |
| **3-1/2" poplar clamshell base**<br>*Replace* Materials ........1.44    Labor ............1.50<br>*Remove* ........................    Labor ............ .68 | lf | $2.94 | $3.62 | $1.44 |
| **3-1/2" mahogany clamshell base**<br>*Replace* Materials ........1.70    Labor ............1.50<br>*Remove* ........................    Labor ............ .68 | lf | $.68 | $3.20 | $3.88 |
| **3-1/2" red oak clamshell base**<br>*Replace* Materials ........1.85    Labor ............1.50<br>*Remove* ........................    Labor ............ .68 | lf | $.68 | $3.35 | $4.03 |
| **4-1/2" CLAMSHELL BASE**      **Add 22% for 4-1/2" clamshell base**<br>▶ Add to the cost of 3-1/2" clamshell base. | | | | |
| **1-1/2" PATTERN BASE** Includes 7% waste.      **1-1/2" finger-joint pine pattern base**<br>*Replace* Materials ........ .86    Labor ............1.50<br>*Remove* ........................    Labor ............ .68 | lf | $.68 | $2.36 | $3.04 |
| **1-1/2" stain-grade pine pattern base**<br>*Replace* Materials ...... 1.01    Labor ............1.50<br>*Remove* ........................    Labor ............ .68 | lf | $.68 | $2.51 | $3.19 |
| **1-1/2" poplar pattern base**<br>*Replace* Materials ........1.09    Labor ............1.50<br>*Remove* ........................    Labor ............ .68 | lf | $.68 | $2.59 | $3.27 |
| **1-1/2" mahogany pattern base**<br>*Replace* Materials ........1.27    Labor ............1.50<br>*Remove* ........................    Labor ............ .68 | lf | $.68 | $2.77 | $3.45 |
| **1-1/2" red oak pattern base**<br>*Replace* Materials ........1.39    Labor ............1.50<br>*Remove* ........................    Labor ............ .68 | lf | $.68 | $2.89 | $3.57 |
| **2-1/2" PATTERN BASE** Includes 7% waste.      **2-1/2" finger-joint pine pattern base**<br>*Replace* Materials ........1.39    Labor ............1.50<br>*Remove* ........................    Labor ............ .68 | lf | $.68 | $2.89 | $3.57 |
| **2-1/2" stain-grade pine pattern base**<br>*Replace* Materials ........1.63    Labor ............1.50<br>*Remove* ........................    Labor ............ .68 | lf | $.68 | $3.13 | $3.81 |
| **2-1/2" poplar pattern base**<br>*Replace* Materials ........1.75    Labor ............1.50<br>*Remove* ........................    Labor ............ .68 | lf | $.68 | $3.25 | $3.93 |
| **2-1/2" mahogany pattern base**<br>*Replace* Materials ........2.04    Labor ............1.50<br>*Remove* ........................    Labor ............ .68 | lf | $.68 | $3.54 | $4.22 |

| Item Description | Unit | Remove | Replace | Total | |
|---|---|---|---|---|---|
| **2-1/2″ red oak pattern base**<br>*Replace* Materials........2.24   Labor ............1.50<br>*Remove*.........................   Labor ............. .68 | lf | $.68 | $3.74 | $4.42 | |
| **3-1/2″ finger-joint pine pattern base**<br>*Replace* Materials........1.83   Labor ............1.50<br>*Remove*.........................   Labor ............. .68 | lf | $.68 | $3.33 | $4.01 | ◄ **3-1/2″**<br>**PATTERN BASE**<br>*Includes 7% waste.* |
| **3-1/2″ stain-grade pine pattern base**<br>*Replace* Materials........2.16   Labor ............1.50<br>*Remove*.........................   Labor ............. .68 | lf | $.68 | $3.66 | $4.34 | |
| **3-1/2″ poplar pattern base**<br>*Replace* Materials........2.31   Labor ............1.50<br>*Remove*.........................   Labor ............. .68 | lf | $.68 | $3.81 | $4.49 | |
| **3-1/2″ mahogany pattern base**<br>*Replace* Materials........2.70   Labor ............1.50<br>*Remove*.........................   Labor ............. .68 | lf | $.68 | $4.20 | $4.88 | |
| **3-1/2″ red oak pattern base**<br>*Replace* Materials........2.96   Labor ............1.50<br>*Remove*.........................   Labor ............. .68 | lf | $.68 | $4.46 | $5.14 | |
| **Add 10% for 5″ pattern base**<br>► Add to the cost of 3-1/2″ pattern base. | | | | | ◄ **5″ PATTERN BASE** |
| **Add 31% for 8″ pattern base**<br>► Add to the cost of 3-1/2″ pattern base. | | | | | ◄ **8″ PATTERN BASE** |
| **Remove base for work, then reinstall**<br>*Replace* .........................   Labor ............2.24 | lf | — | $2.24 | $2.24 | ◄ **REMOVE BASE**<br>**& REINSTALL** |
| **3/4″ finger-joint pine base shoe**<br>*Replace* Materials ........ .43   Labor ............1.50<br>*Remove*.........................   Labor ............. .68 | lf | $.68 | $1.93 | $2.61 | ◄ **3/4″ BASE SHOE**<br>*Includes 7% waste.* |
| **3/4″ stain-grade pine base shoe**<br>*Replace* Materials ........ .51   Labor ............1.50<br>*Remove*.........................   Labor ............. .68 | lf | $.68 | $2.01 | $2.69 | |
| **3/4″ poplar base shoe**<br>*Replace* Materials ........ .55   Labor ............1.50<br>*Remove*.........................   Labor ............. .68 | lf | $.68 | $2.05 | $2.73 | |
| **3/4″ mahogany base shoe**<br>*Replace* Materials ........ .63   Labor ............1.50<br>*Remove*.........................   Labor ............. .68 | lf | $.68 | $2.13 | $2.81 | |
| **3/4″ red oak base shoe**<br>*Replace* Materials ........ .70   Labor ............1.50<br>*Remove*.........................   Labor ............. .68 | lf | $.68 | $2.20 | $2.88 | |
| **Remove base shoe for work, then reinstall**<br>*Replace* .........................   Labor ............2.24 | lf | — | $2.24 | $2.24 | |
| **1-1/2″ paint-grade clamshell casing**<br>*Replace* Materials ........ .73   Labor ............1.62<br>*Remove*.........................   Labor ............. .84 | lf | $.84 | $2.35 | $3.19 | ◄ **1-1/2″ CLAM-**<br>**SHELL CASING**<br>*Includes 7% waste.* |

**RELATED ITEMS**

| | |
|---|---|
| Cleaning | 61 |
| Doors | 101 |
| Painting | 337 |

| Item Description | Unit | Remove | Replace | Total |
|---|---|---|---|---|
| **1-1/2" CLAM- ▶ SHELL CASING** *continued* | | | | |
| **1-1/2" stain-grade pine clamshell casing** <br> *Replace* Materials ......... .84    Labor ............1.62 <br> *Remove*........................    Labor............. .84 | If | $.84 | $2.46 | $3.30 |
| **1-1/2" poplar clamshell casing** <br> *Replace* Materials ........ .91    Labor ............1.62 <br> *Remove*........................    Labor............. .84 | If | $.84 | $2.53 | $3.37 |
| **1-1/2" mahogany clamshell casing** <br> *Replace* Materials.......1.06    Labor ............1.62 <br> *Remove*........................    Labor............. .84 | If | $.84 | $2.68 | $3.52 |
| **1-1/2" red oak clamshell casing** <br> *Replace* Materials.......1.16    Labor ............1.62 <br> *Remove*........................    Labor............. .84 | If | $.84 | $2.78 | $3.62 |
| **2-1/2" CLAM- ▶ SHELL CASING** *Includes 7% waste.*   **2-1/2" finger-joint pine clamshell casing** <br> *Replace* Materials ........ .83    Labor ............1.62 <br> *Remove*........................    Labor............. .84 | If | $.84 | $2.45 | $3.29 |
| **2-1/2" stain-grade pine clamshell casing** <br> *Replace* Materials ........ .97    Labor ............1.62 <br> *Remove*........................    Labor............. .84 | If | $.84 | $2.59 | $3.43 |
| **2-1/2" poplar clamshell casing** <br> *Replace* Materials.......1.04    Labor ............1.62 <br> *Remove*........................    Labor............. .84 | If | $.84 | $2.66 | $3.50 |
| **2-1/2" mahogany clamshell casing** <br> *Replace* Materials.......1.22    Labor ............1.62 <br> *Remove*........................    Labor............. .84 | If | $.84 | $2.84 | $3.68 |
| **2-1/2" red oak clamshell casing** <br> *Replace* Materials.......1.34    Labor ............1.62 <br> *Remove*........................    Labor............. .84 | If | $.84 | $2.96 | $3.80 |
| **3-1/2" CLAM- ▶ SHELL CASING** *Includes 7% waste.*   **3-1/2" finger-joint pine clamshell casing** <br> *Replace* Materials.......1.17    Labor ............1.62 <br> *Remove*........................    Labor............. .84 | If | $.84 | $2.79 | $3.63 |
| **3-1/2" stain-grade pine clamshell casing** <br> *Replace* Materials.......1.36    Labor ............1.62 <br> *Remove*........................    Labor............. .84 | If | $.84 | $2.98 | $3.82 |
| **3-1/2" poplar clamshell casing** <br> *Replace* Materials.......1.46    Labor ............1.62 <br> *Remove*........................    Labor............. .84 | If | $.84 | $3.08 | $3.92 |
| **3-1/2" mahogany clamshell casing** <br> *Replace* Materials.......1.73    Labor ............1.62 <br> *Remove*........................    Labor............. .84 | If | $.84 | $3.35 | $4.19 |
| **3-1/2" red oak clamshell casing** <br> *Replace* Materials.......1.88    Labor ............1.62 <br> *Remove*........................    Labor............. .84 | If | $.84 | $3.50 | $4.34 |
| **1-1/2" PATTERN ▶ CASING** *Includes 7% waste.*   **1-1/2" paint-grade pattern casing** <br> *Replace* Materials ........ .87    Labor ............1.62 <br> *Remove*........................    Labor............. .84 | If | $.84 | $2.49 | $3.33 |

| Item Description | Unit | Remove | Replace | Total |
|---|---|---|---|---|
| **1-1/2" stain-grade pine pattern casing** | lf | $.84 | $2.65 | $3.49 |
| *Replace* Materials ...... 1.03   Labor ...........1.62 | | | | |
| *Remove* .......................   Labor .............84 | | | | |
| **1-1/2" poplar pattern casing** | lf | $.84 | $2.73 | $3.57 |
| *Replace* Materials .......1.11   Labor ...........1.62 | | | | |
| *Remove* .......................   Labor .............84 | | | | |
| **1-1/2" mahogany pattern casing** | lf | $.84 | $2.91 | $3.75 |
| *Replace* Materials .......1.29   Labor ...........1.62 | | | | |
| *Remove* .......................   Labor .............84 | | | | |
| **1-1/2" red oak pattern casing** | lf | $.84 | $3.03 | $3.87 |
| *Replace* Materials .......1.41   Labor ...........1.62 | | | | |
| *Remove* .......................   Labor .............84 | | | | |
| **1-1/2" curved pattern casing for half-round top window or door** | lf | $.84 | $11.87 | $12.71 |
| *Replace* Materials .......6.18   Labor ...........5.69 | | | | |
| *Remove* .......................   Labor .............84 | | | | |
| **1-1/2" curved pattern casing for elliptical-top window or door** | lf | $.84 | $12.18 | $13.02 |
| *Replace* Materials .......6.49   Labor ...........5.69 | | | | |
| *Remove* .......................   Labor .............84 | | | | |
| **1-1/2" curved pattern casing for round window per lf of diameter** | lf | $.84 | $26.10 | $26.94 |
| *Replace* Materials ......14.50   Labor ...........11.60 | | | | |
| *Remove* .......................   Labor .............84 | | | | |
| **2-1/2" finger-joint pine pattern casing** | lf | $.84 | $3.03 | $3.87 |
| *Replace* Materials .......1.41   Labor ...........1.62 | | | | |
| *Remove* .......................   Labor .............84 | | | | |
| **2-1/2" stain-grade pine pattern casing** | lf | $.84 | $3.28 | $4.12 |
| *Replace* Materials .......1.66   Labor ...........1.62 | | | | |
| *Remove* .......................   Labor .............84 | | | | |
| **2-1/2" poplar pattern casing** | lf | $.84 | $3.41 | $4.25 |
| *Replace* Materials .......1.79   Labor ...........1.62 | | | | |
| *Remove* .......................   Labor .............84 | | | | |
| **2-1/2" mahogany pattern casing** | lf | $.84 | $3.70 | $4.54 |
| *Replace* Materials .......2.08   Labor ...........1.62 | | | | |
| *Remove* .......................   Labor .............84 | | | | |
| **2-1/2" red oak pattern casing** | lf | $.84 | $3.89 | $4.73 |
| *Replace* Materials .......2.27   Labor ...........1.62 | | | | |
| *Remove* .......................   Labor .............84 | | | | |
| **2-1/2" curved pattern casing for half-round top window or door** | lf | $.84 | $12.32 | $13.16 |
| *Replace* Materials .......6.63   Labor ...........5.69 | | | | |
| *Remove* .......................   Labor .............84 | | | | |
| **2-1/2" curved pattern casing for elliptical-top window or door** | lf | $.84 | $12.66 | $13.50 |
| *Replace* Materials .......6.97   Labor ...........5.69 | | | | |
| *Remove* .......................   Labor .............84 | | | | |
| **2-1/2" curved pattern casing for round window per lf of diameter** | lf | $.84 | $27.20 | $28.04 |
| *Replace* Materials .......15.60   Labor ...........11.60 | | | | |
| *Remove* .......................   Labor .............84 | | | | |

◄ **1-1/2" PATTERN CASING**
Includes 7% waste.

◄ **1-1/2" CURVED PATTERN CASING**
Includes 7% waste. Laminated back, factory fabricated molding. Half-round and elliptical are priced per lf of casing. Round windows are priced per diameter. If curved casing includes wood key see page 204.

◄ **2-1/2" PATTERN CASING**
Includes 7% waste.

**RELATED ITEMS**

Cleaning ............................61
Doors ...............................101
Painting ..........................337

◄ **2-1/2" CURVED PATTERN CASING**
Includes 7% waste. Laminated back, factory fabricated molding. Half-round and elliptical are priced per lf of casing. Round windows are priced per diameter. If casing includes wood key see page 204.

| | Item Description | | Unit | Remove | Replace | Total |
|---|---|---|---|---|---|---|
| **3-1/2" PATTERN ▶ CASING** *Includes 7% waste.* | **3-1/2" finger-joint pine pattern casing** *Replace* Materials........1.86    Labor ............1.62 *Remove*........................    Labor............. .84 | | lf | $.84 | $3.48 | $4.32 |
| | **3-1/2" stain-grade pine pattern casing** *Replace* Materials........2.20    Labor ............1.62 *Remove*........................    Labor............. .84 | | lf | $.84 | $3.82 | $4.66 |
| | **3-1/2" poplar pattern casing** *Replace* Materials........2.36    Labor ............1.62 *Remove*........................    Labor............. .84 | | lf | $.84 | $3.98 | $4.82 |
| | **3-1/2" mahogany pattern casing** *Replace* Materials........2.75    Labor ............1.62 *Remove*........................    Labor............. .84 | | lf | $.84 | $4.37 | $5.21 |
| | **3-1/2" red oak pattern casing** *Replace* Materials........3.01    Labor ............1.62 *Remove*........................    Labor............. .84 | | lf | $.84 | $4.63 | $5.47 |
| **3-1/2" CURVED ▶ PATTERN CASING** *Includes 7% waste. Laminated back, factory fabricated molding. Half-round and elliptical are priced per lf of casing. Round windows are priced per diameter. If casing includes wood key see below.* | **3-1/2" curved pattern casing for half-round top window or door** *Replace* Materials........6.75    Labor ............5.69 *Remove*........................    Labor............. .84 | | lf | $.84 | $12.44 | $13.28 |
| | **3-1/2" curved pattern casing for elliptical-top window or door per lf** *Replace* Materials........7.09    Labor ............5.69 *Remove*........................    Labor............. .84 | | lf | $.84 | $12.78 | $13.62 |
| | **3-1/2" curved pattern casing for round window per lf of diameter** *Replace* Materials.......15.90    Labor ...........11.60 *Remove*........................    Labor............. .84 | | lf | $.84 | $27.50 | $28.34 |
| **5" PATTERN ▶ CASING** | **Add 10% for 5" pattern casing** ▶ Add to the cost of 3-1/2" pattern casing. | | | | | |
| **REMOVE CASING ▶ & REINSTALL** | **Remove casing for work, then reinstall** *Replace* ........................    Labor ...........2.86 | | lf | — | $2.86 | $2.86 |
| **WOOD KEY ▶** △ with rosette | **Wood key for curved molding** *Replace* Materials.......17.00    Labor ............9.91 *Remove*........................    Labor............. .94 | | ea | $.94 | $26.91 | $27.85 |
| | **Wood key with light carvings for curved molding** *Replace* Materials ......26.80    Labor ............9.91 *Remove*........................    Labor............. .94 | | ea | $.94 | $36.71 | $37.65 |
| △ with carvings | **Wood key with medium carvings for curved molding** *Replace* Materials ......33.30    Labor ............9.91 *Remove*........................    Labor............. .94 | | ea | $.94 | $43.21 | $44.15 |
| | **Wood key with heavy carvings for curved molding** *Replace* Materials ......43.50    Labor ............9.91 *Remove*........................    Labor............. .94 | | ea | $.94 | $53.41 | $54.35 |
| **remove & reinstall ▷** | **Remove wood key for work, then reinstall** *Replace* ........................    Labor ...........11.10 | | ea | — | $11.10 | $11.10 |
| **BASE BLOCK ▶** | **Pine base block** *Replace* Materials ......10.60    Labor ...........2.49 *Remove*........................    Labor............. .94 | | ea | $.94 | $13.09 | $14.03 |

| Item Description | Unit | Remove | Replace | Total | |
|---|---|---|---|---|---|
| **Poplar base block** | ea | $.94 | $13.59 | $14.53 | |
| *Replace* Materials.......11.10    Labor ...........2.49 | | | | | |
| *Remove*..........................    Labor.............94 | | | | | |
| **Mahogany base block** | ea | $.94 | $14.69 | $15.63 | |
| *Replace* Materials ......12.20    Labor ...........2.49 | | | | | |
| *Remove*..........................    Labor.............94 | | | | | |
| **Red oak base block** | ea | $.94 | $16.19 | $17.13 | |
| *Replace* Materials.......13.70    Labor ...........2.49 | | | | | |
| *Remove*..........................    Labor.............94 | | | | △ with rosette |
| **Pine corner block with rosette** | ea | $.94 | $10.92 | $11.86 | ◀ CORNER BLOCK |
| *Replace* Materials........8.43    Labor ...........2.49 | | | | | |
| *Remove*..........................    Labor.............94 | | | | | |
| **Poplar corner block with rosette** | ea | $.94 | $12.14 | $13.08 | |
| *Replace* Materials........9.65    Labor ...........2.49 | | | | | |
| *Remove*..........................    Labor.............94 | | | | | |
| **Mahogany corner block with rosette** | ea | $.94 | $13.39 | $14.33 | |
| *Replace* Materials ......10.90    Labor ...........2.49 | | | | | |
| *Remove*..........................    Labor.............94 | | | | | |
| **Red oak corner block with rosette** | ea | $.94 | $14.49 | $15.43 | |
| *Replace* Materials ......12.00    Labor ...........2.49 | | | | | |
| *Remove*..........................    Labor.............94 | | | | | |
| **Add 30% for corner block with carvings** | | | | | ◁ add for carvings |
| **Pine head block with rosette** | ea | $.94 | $13.09 | $14.03 | ◀ HEAD BLOCK |
| *Replace* Materials ......10.60    Labor ...........2.49 | | | | | |
| *Remove*..........................    Labor.............94 | | | | | |
| **Poplar head block with rosette** | ea | $.94 | $14.69 | $15.63 | |
| *Replace* Materials ......12.20    Labor ...........2.49 | | | | | |
| *Remove*..........................    Labor.............94 | | | | | |
| **Mahogany head block with rosette** | ea | $.94 | $16.29 | $17.23 | |
| *Replace* Materials.......13.80    Labor ...........2.49 | | | | | |
| *Remove*..........................    Labor.............94 | | | | | |
| **Red oak head block with rosette** | ea | $.94 | $17.69 | $18.63 | |
| *Replace* Materials.......15.20    Labor ...........2.49 | | | | | |
| *Remove*..........................    Labor.............94 | | | | △ add for carvings |
| **Add 31% for head block with carvings** | | | | | |
| **Remove base, corner, or head block for work, then reinstall** | ea | — | $2.75 | $2.75 | ◀ REMOVE BLOCK & REINSTALL |
| *Replace* .........................    Labor ...........2.75 | | | | | |
| **Pine overdoor molding** | lf | $.73 | $11.62 | $12.35 | ◀ OVERDOOR MOLD |
| *Replace* Materials ......10.00    Labor ...........1.62 | | | | | |
| *Remove*..........................    Labor............. .73 | | | | | |
| **Poplar overdoor molding** | lf | $.73 | $12.92 | $13.65 | |
| *Replace* Materials ......11.30    Labor ...........1.62 | | | | | |
| *Remove*..........................    Labor............. .73 | | | | | |
| **Mahogany overdoor molding** | lf | $.73 | $14.22 | $14.95 | |
| *Replace* Materials ......12.60    Labor ...........1.62 | | | | | |
| *Remove*..........................    Labor............. .73 | | | | | |

RELATED ITEMS

**OVERDOOR MOLD ▶**
*continued*

△ *standard*

△ *with vertical milling*

△ *with hand carvings*

△ *with heavy hand carvings*

| Item Description | Unit | Remove | Replace | Total |
|---|---|---|---|---|
| **Red oak overdoor molding**<br>*Replace* Materials ......14.50     Labor ...........1.62<br>*Remove*.........................     Labor ............ .73 | lf | $.73 | $16.12 | $16.85 |
| *other styles ▷*   **Add 72% for vertical milling in overdoor molding** | | | | |
| **Add 227% for hand carving in overdoor molding** | | | | |
| **Add 411% for heavy hand carving in overdoor molding** | | | | |
| *remove & reinstall ▷*   **Remove overdoor molding for work, then reinstall**<br>*Replace* ........................     Labor ...........1.96 | lf | — | $1.96 | $1.96 |
| **Interior architrave, standard grade**<br>*Replace* Materials ........4.20     Labor ...........2.45<br>*Remove*.........................     Labor ............ .84<br>▶ Standard casing with rosettes in head and base blocks. Paint-grade pine or poplar or stain-grade pine. | lf | $.84 | $6.65 | $7.49 |
| **Interior architrave, high grade**<br>*Replace* Materials ........5.50     Labor ...........2.45<br>*Remove*.........................     Labor ............ .84<br>▶ Rosettes or light embossing in base blocks. Overdoor includes horizontal moldings at top and bottom. Stain-grade pine or red oak with simple overdoor. | lf | $.84 | $7.95 | $8.79 |
| **Interior architrave, deluxe grade**<br>*Replace* Materials ........7.70     Labor ...........2.45<br>*Remove*.........................     Labor ............ .84<br>▶ May have carvings in base blocks. Angled overdoor with horizontal moldings at top and bottom or overdoor with light carvings. Red oak, birch, or similar hardwood or paint grade with more ornate detail. | lf | $.84 | $10.15 | $10.99 |
| **Interior architrave, custom grade**<br>*Replace* Materials ......10.80     Labor ...........2.45<br>*Remove*.........................     Labor ............ .84<br>▶ May have carvings in base blocks. Angled or curved overdoor with horizontal moldings at top and bottom or overdoor with heavy carvings. Red oak birch or similar hardwood or paint-grade with very ornate carvings. | lf | $.84 | $13.25 | $14.09 |
| **Remove interior architrave for work, then reinstall**<br>*Replace* ........................     Labor ...........3.54 | lf | — | $3.54 | $3.54 |
| **Exterior architrave, economy grade**<br>*Replace* Materials ........4.20     Labor ...........3.16<br>*Remove*.........................     Labor ............ .84<br>▶ Standard casing with rosettes in head and base blocks. Paint-grade pine or poplar or stain-grade pine. All materials are back-primed. | lf | $.84 | $7.36 | $8.20 |

**INTERIOR ▶**
**ARCHITRAVE**
*Measure lf all around door: both sides and over door.*

△ *standard*

△ *high*

**EXTERIOR ▶**
**ARCHITRAVE**
*Measure lf all around door: both sides and over door.*

| Item Description | Unit | Remove | Replace | Total |
|---|---|---|---|---|
| **Exterior architrave, standard grade** | lf | $.84 | $9.16 | $10.00 |

*Replace* Materials........6.00      Labor ...........3.16
*Remove*..........................      Labor ............ .84

▶ Wide casing, may be made from two moldings. Rosettes in head and base blocks. Paint-grade pine or poplar or stain-grade pine. All materials are back-primed.

| Item Description | Unit | Remove | Replace | Total |
|---|---|---|---|---|
| **Exterior architrave, high grade** | lf | $.84 | $11.76 | $12.60 |

*Replace* Materials........8.60      Labor ...........3.16
*Remove*..........................      Labor ............ .84

▶ Wide casing, may be made from two moldings. Rosettes or light embossing in base blocks. Overdoor includes horizontal moldings at top and bottom. Stain grade pine or red oak with simple over door. All materials are back-primed.

| Item Description | Unit | Remove | Replace | Total |
|---|---|---|---|---|
| **Exterior architrave, deluxe grade** | lf | $.84 | $15.16 | $16.00 |

*Replace* Materials ......12.00      Labor ...........3.16
*Remove*..........................      Labor ............ .84

▶ Wide casing, may be made from two moldings. May have carvings in base blocks. Angled overdoor with horizontal moldings at top and bottom or overdoor with light carvings. Red oak, birch, or similar hardwood or paint grade with more ornate detail. All materials are back-primed.

| Item Description | Unit | Remove | Replace | Total |
|---|---|---|---|---|
| **Exterior architrave, custom grade** | lf | $.84 | $18.46 | $19.30 |

*Replace* Materials.......15.30      Labor ...........3.16
*Remove*..........................      Labor ............ .84

▶ Wide casing, may be made from two moldings. May have carvings in base blocks. Angled or curved overdoor with horizontal moldings at top and bottom or overdoor and carvings. Red oak, birch, or similar hardwood or paint-grade with very ornate carvings. All materials are back-primed.

| Item Description | Unit | Remove | Replace | Total |
|---|---|---|---|---|
| **Exterior architrave, custom deluxe grade** | lf | $.84 | $24.46 | $25.30 |

*Replace* Materials ......21.30      Labor ...........3.16
*Remove*..........................      Labor ............ .84

▶ Wide casing, may be made from two moldings. May have carvings in base blocks. Curved overdoor with multiple carved moldings. Red oak birch or similar hardwood or paint-grade with very ornate carvings. All materials are back-primed.

| Item Description | Unit | Remove | Replace | Total | |
|---|---|---|---|---|---|
| **Remove exterior architrave for work, then reinstall** | lf | — | $4.37 | $4.37 | ◁ remove & reinstall |

*Replace* ........................      Labor ...........4.37

| Item Description | Unit | Remove | Replace | Total |
|---|---|---|---|---|
| **Exterior door surround, economy grade** | lf | $.89 | $35.44 | $36.33 |

*Replace* Materials ......26.20      Labor ...........9.24
*Remove*..........................      Labor ............ .89

▶ See illustration below for representative example.

◀ **EXTERIOR DOOR SURROUND**
*Measure lf all around door: both sides and over door. All grades are for wood which is carved with intricate detail in the higher grades. Plastic or other synthetic materials should be considered economy or standard grades. Illustrations show typical complexity, actual door styling varies widely.*

△ *economy*

△ *standard*

△ *high*

**EXTERIOR DOOR ▶**
**SURROUND**
*continued*

△ *deluxe*

△ *custom*

△ *custom deluxe*

| Item Description | Unit | Remove | Replace | Total |
|---|---|---|---|---|
| **Exterior door surround, standard grade** | lf | $.89 | $53.60 | $54.49 |
| *Replace* Materials......43.40 Labor..........10.20 | | | | |
| *Remove*........................ Labor.............89 | | | | |
| ▶ See illustration on previous page for representative example. | | | | |
| **Exterior door surround, high grade** | lf | $.89 | $87.50 | $88.39 |
| *Replace* Materials......76.70 Labor..........10.80 | | | | |
| *Remove*........................ Labor.............89 | | | | |
| ▶ See illustration on previous page for representative example. | | | | |
| **Exterior door surround, deluxe grade** | lf | $.89 | $159.50 | $160.39 |
| *Replace* Materials.....147.00 Labor..........12.50 | | | | |
| *Remove*........................ Labor.............89 | | | | |
| ▶ See illustration above for representative example. | | | | |
| **Exterior door surround, custom grade** | lf | $.89 | $242.70 | $243.59 |
| *Replace* Materials....228.00 Labor..........14.70 | | | | |
| *Remove*........................ Labor.............89 | | | | |
| ▶ See illustration above for representative example. | | | | |
| **Exterior door surround, custom deluxe grade** | lf | $.89 | $399.00 | $399.89 |
| *Replace* Materials....382.00 Labor..........17.00 | | | | |
| *Remove*........................ Labor.............89 | | | | |
| ▶ See illustration above for representative example. | | | | |
| **remove & reinstall ▷ Remove exterior door surround for work, then reinstall** | lf | — | $26.60 | $26.60 |
| *Replace* ........................ Labor..........26.60 | | | | |
| **EXTERIOR ▶ Exterior window surround, economy grade** | lf | $.89 | $29.48 | $30.37 |
| **WINDOW** *Replace* Materials......21.30 Labor .........8.18 | | | | |
| **SURROUND** *Remove*........................ Labor.............89 | | | | |
| ▶ See illustration on facing page for representative example. | | | | |
| **Exterior window surround, standard grade** | lf | $.89 | $44.27 | $45.16 |
| *Replace* Materials......35.30 Labor .........8.97 | | | | |
| *Remove*........................ Labor.............89 | | | | |
| ▶ See illustration on facing page for representative example. | | | | |
| **Exterior window surround, high grade** | lf | $.89 | $71.84 | $72.73 |
| *Replace* Materials......62.40 Labor .........9.44 | | | | |
| *Remove*........................ Labor.............89 | | | | |
| ▶ See illustration on facing page for representative example. | | | | |

△ economy          △ standard          △ high

△ deluxe          △ custom          △ custom deluxe

| Item Description | Unit | Remove | Replace | Total |
|---|---|---|---|---|
| **Exterior window surround, deluxe grade** | If | $.89 | $131.10 | $131.99 |
| *Replace* Materials.....120.00    Labor............11.10 | | | | |
| *Remove*........................    Labor.............89 | | | | |
| ▶ See illustration below for representative example. | | | | |
| **Exterior window surround, custom grade** | If | $.89 | $197.90 | $198.79 |
| *Replace* Materials.....185.00    Labor............12.90 | | | | |
| *Remove*........................    Labor.............89 | | | | |
| ▶ See illustration below for representative example. | | | | |
| **Exterior window surround, custom deluxe grade** | If | $.89 | $323.70 | $324.59 |
| *Replace* Materials.....311.00    Labor............12.70 | | | | |
| *Remove*........................    Labor.............89 | | | | |
| ▶ See illustration below for representative example. | | | | |
| **Remove exterior window surround for work, then reinstall** | If | — | $23.70 | $23.70 |
| *Replace* ........................    Labor..........23.70 | | | | |
| **2-1/2" paint-grade window stool** | If | $.68 | $3.86 | $4.54 |
| *Replace* Materials........1.57    Labor............2.29 | | | | |
| *Remove*........................    Labor.............68 | | | | |
| **2-1/2" stain-grade pine window stool** | If | $.68 | $4.11 | $4.79 |
| *Replace* Materials........1.82    Labor............2.29 | | | | |
| *Remove*........................    Labor.............68 | | | | |

**RELATED ITEMS**

Cleaning ............................61
Doors ................................101
**Masonry**
  stone architrave ..............310
Painting ...........................337
**Plaster**
  stucco architrave ..............359

◁ remove & reinstall

◀ **WINDOW STOOL**
*Includes 4% waste.*

| | Item Description | Unit | Remove | Replace | Total |
|---|---|---|---|---|---|
| **WINDOW STOOL** ▶<br>*continued* | 2-1/2" poplar window stool<br>*Replace* Materials........1.96    Labor .........2.29<br>*Remove*....................    Labor.............68 | lf | $.68 | $4.25 | $4.93 |
| | 2-1/2" mahogany window stool<br>*Replace* Materials........2.32    Labor .........2.29<br>*Remove*....................    Labor.............68 | lf | $.68 | $4.61 | $5.29 |
| | 2-1/2" red oak window stool<br>*Replace* Materials........2.51    Labor .........2.29<br>*Remove*....................    Labor.............68 | lf | $.68 | $4.80 | $5.48 |
| | Remove window stool for work, then reinstall<br>*Replace* ....................    Labor .........3.72 | lf | — | $3.72 | $3.72 |
| **WINDOW APRON** ▶<br>*Includes 4% waste.*<br> | 3-1/2" paint-grade window apron<br>*Replace* Materials ....... 1.02    Labor .........1.94<br>*Remove*....................    Labor.............73 | lf | $.73 | $2.96 | $3.69 |
| | 3-1/2" stain-grade pine window apron<br>*Replace* Materials........1.19    Labor .........1.94<br>*Remove*....................    Labor.............73 | lf | $.73 | $3.13 | $3.86 |
| | 3-1/2" poplar window apron<br>*Replace* Materials........1.27    Labor .........1.94<br>*Remove*....................    Labor.............73 | lf | $.73 | $3.21 | $3.94 |
| | 3-1/2" mahogany window apron<br>*Replace* Materials........1.51    Labor .........1.94<br>*Remove*....................    Labor.............73 | lf | $.73 | $3.45 | $4.18 |
| | 3-1/2" red oak window apron<br>*Replace* Materials........1.63    Labor .........1.94<br>*Remove*....................    Labor.............73 | lf | $.73 | $3.57 | $4.30 |
| remove & reinstall ▷ | Remove window apron for work, then reinstall<br>*Replace* ....................    Labor .........2.75 | lf | — | $2.75 | $2.75 |
| **2-1/2" CHAIR**<br>**RAIL** ▶<br>*Includes 4% waste.*<br> | 2-1/2" paint-grade chair rail<br>*Replace* Materials........1.35    Labor .........1.50<br>*Remove*....................    Labor.............68 | lf | $.68 | $2.85 | $3.53 |
| | 2-1/2" stain-grade pine chair rail<br>*Replace* Materials........1.57    Labor .........1.50<br>*Remove*....................    Labor.............68 | lf | $.68 | $3.07 | $3.75 |
| | 2-1/2" poplar chair rail<br>*Replace* Materials........1.71    Labor .........1.50<br>*Remove*....................    Labor.............68 | lf | $.68 | $3.21 | $3.89 |
| | 2-1/2" mahogany chair rail<br>*Replace* Materials ........2.01    Labor .........1.50<br>*Remove*....................    Labor.............68 | lf | $.68 | $3.51 | $4.19 |
| | 2-1/2" red oak chair rail<br>*Replace* Materials........2.17    Labor .........1.50<br>*Remove*....................    Labor.............68 | lf | $.68 | $3.67 | $4.35 |
| **3-1/2" CHAIR**<br>**RAIL** ▶<br>*Includes 4% waste.* | 3-1/2" paint-grade chair rail<br>*Replace* Materials........1.71    Labor .........1.50<br>*Remove*....................    Labor.............68 | lf | $.68 | $3.21 | $3.89 |

| Item Description | Unit | Remove | Replace | Total | |
|---|---|---|---|---|---|
| **3-1/2" stain-grade pine chair rail** | lf | $.68 | $3.48 | $4.16 | |
| *Replace* Materials........1.98    Labor ..........1.50 | | | | | |
| *Remove*......................    Labor ............ .68 | | | | | |
| **3-1/2" poplar chair rail** | lf | $.68 | $3.66 | $4.34 | |
| *Replace* Materials........2.16    Labor ..........1.50 | | | | | |
| *Remove*......................    Labor ............ .68 | | | | | |
| **3-1/2" mahogany chair rail** | lf | $.68 | $4.03 | $4.71 | |
| *Replace* Materials........2.53    Labor ..........1.50 | | | | | |
| *Remove*......................    Labor ............ .68 | | | | | |
| **3-1/2" red oak chair rail** | lf | $.68 | $4.26 | $4.94 | |
| *Replace* Materials........2.76    Labor ..........1.50 | | | | | |
| *Remove*......................    Labor ............ .68 | | | | | |
| **Remove chair rail for work, then reinstall** | lf | — | $2.24 | $2.24 | ◁ remove & reinstall |
| *Replace* ......................    Labor ..........2.24 | | | | | |
| **1-5/8" paint-grade drip cap** | lf | $.84 | $2.75 | $3.59 | ◀ **DRIP CAP** |
| *Replace* Materials........1.25    Labor ..........1.50 | | | | | *Includes 4% waste.* |
| *Remove*......................    Labor ............ .84 | | | | | |
| **1-5/8" redwood drip cap** | lf | $.84 | $2.96 | $3.80 | |
| *Replace* Materials........1.46    Labor ..........1.50 | | | | | |
| *Remove*......................    Labor ............ .84 | | | | | |
| **1-5/8" cedar drip cap** | lf | $.84 | $2.85 | $3.69 | |
| *Replace* Materials........1.35    Labor ..........1.50 | | | | | |
| *Remove*......................    Labor ............ .84 | | | | | |
| **2-1/4" paint-grade drip cap** | lf | $.84 | $2.90 | $3.74 | |
| *Replace* Materials........1.40    Labor ..........1.50 | | | | | |
| *Remove*......................    Labor ............ .84 | | | | | |
| **2-1/4" redwood drip cap** | lf | $.84 | $3.13 | $3.97 | |
| *Replace* Materials........1.63    Labor ..........1.50 | | | | | |
| *Remove*......................    Labor ............ .84 | | | | | |
| **2-1/4" cedar drip cap** | lf | $.84 | $3.01 | $3.85 | |
| *Replace* Materials........1.51    Labor ..........1.50 | | | | | |
| *Remove*......................    Labor ............ .84 | | | | | |
| **Remove drip cap for work, then reinstall** | lf | — | $2.86 | $2.86 | ◁ remove & reinstall |
| *Replace* ......................    Labor ..........2.86 | | | | | |
| **1-3/4" paint-grade astragal** | lf | $.84 | $4.22 | $5.06 | ◀ **ASTRAGAL** |
| *Replace* Materials........2.60    Labor ..........1.62 | | | | | *Includes 4% waste.* |
| *Remove*......................    Labor ............ .84 | | | | | |
| **1-3/4" stain-grade pine astragal** | lf | $.84 | $4.64 | $5.48 | |
| *Replace* Materials........3.02    Labor ..........1.62 | | | | | |
| *Remove*......................    Labor ............ .84 | | | | | |
| **1-3/4" poplar astragal** | lf | $.84 | $4.86 | $5.70 | |
| *Replace* Materials........3.24    Labor ..........1.62 | | | | | |
| *Remove*......................    Labor ............ .84 | | | | | |
| **1-3/4" mahogany astragal** | lf | $.84 | $5.47 | $6.31 | |
| *Replace* Materials........3.85    Labor ..........1.62 | | | | | |
| *Remove*......................    Labor ............ .84 | | | | | |

**RELATED ITEMS**

| | Item Description | Unit | Remove | Replace | Total |
|---|---|---|---|---|---|
| **ASTRAGAL** ▶<br>*continued* | **1-3/4" red oak astragal**<br>*Replace* Materials........4.17    Labor ............1.62<br>*Remove*........................    Labor............ .84 | lf | $.84 | $5.79 | $6.63 |
| | **2-1/4" paint-grade astragal**<br>*Replace* Materials........3.16    Labor ............1.62<br>*Remove*........................    Labor............ .84 | lf | $.84 | $4.78 | $5.62 |
| | **2-1/4" stain-grade pine astragal**<br>*Replace* Materials........3.67    Labor ............1.62<br>*Remove*........................    Labor............ .84 | lf | $.84 | $5.29 | $6.13 |
| | **2-1/4" poplar astragal**<br>*Replace* Materials........3.93    Labor ............1.62<br>*Remove*........................    Labor............ .84 | lf | $.84 | $5.55 | $6.39 |
| | **2-1/4" mahogany astragal**<br>*Replace* Materials........4.67    Labor ............1.62<br>*Remove*........................    Labor............ .84 | lf | $.84 | $6.29 | $7.13 |
| | **2-1/4" red oak astragal**<br>*Replace* Materials........5.05    Labor ............1.62<br>*Remove*........................    Labor............ .84 | lf | $.84 | $6.67 | $7.51 |
| remove & reinstall ▷ | **Remove astragal for work, then reinstall**<br>*Replace* ........................    Labor ............2.86 | lf | — | $2.86 | $2.86 |
| **COVE** ▶<br>*Includes 4% waste.* | **1/2" paint-grade cove**<br>*Replace* Materials ........ .48    Labor ............1.62<br>*Remove*........................    Labor............ .84 | lf | $.84 | $2.10 | $2.94 |
| | **1/2" stain-grade pine cove**<br>*Replace* Materials ........ .56    Labor ............1.62<br>*Remove*........................    Labor............ .84 | lf | $.84 | $2.18 | $3.02 |
| | **1/2" poplar cove**<br>*Replace* Materials ........ .63    Labor ............1.62<br>*Remove*........................    Labor............ .84 | lf | $.84 | $2.25 | $3.09 |
| | **1/2" mahogany cove**<br>*Replace* Materials ........ .72    Labor ............1.62<br>*Remove*........................    Labor............ .84 | lf | $.84 | $2.34 | $3.18 |
| | **1/2" red oak cove**<br>*Replace* Materials ........ .76    Labor ............1.62<br>*Remove*........................    Labor............ .84 | lf | $.84 | $2.38 | $3.22 |
| | **3/4" paint-grade cove**<br>*Replace* Materials ........ .55    Labor ............1.62<br>*Remove*........................    Labor............ .84 | lf | $.84 | $2.17 | $3.01 |
| | **3/4" stain-grade pine cove**<br>*Replace* Materials ........ .65    Labor ............1.62<br>*Remove*........................    Labor............ .84 | lf | $.84 | $2.27 | $3.11 |
| | **3/4" poplar cove**<br>*Replace* Materials ........ .72    Labor ............1.62<br>*Remove*........................    Labor............ .84 | lf | $.84 | $2.34 | $3.18 |
| | **3/4" mahogany cove**<br>*Replace* Materials ........ .82    Labor ............1.62<br>*Remove*........................    Labor............ .84 | lf | $.84 | $2.44 | $3.28 |

| Item Description | | Unit | Remove | Replace | Total | |
|---|---|---|---|---|---|---|
| **3/4" red oak cove**<br>*Replace* Materials ........ .88　　*Labor* ...........1.62<br>*Remove*.......................　　*Labor* ............. .84 | | lf | $.84 | $2.50 | $3.34 | |
| **1" paint-grade cove**<br>*Replace* Materials ........ .69　　*Labor* ...........1.62<br>*Remove*.......................　　*Labor* ............. .84 | | lf | $.84 | $2.31 | $3.15 | |
| **1" stain-grade pine cove**<br>*Replace* Materials ........ .80　　*Labor* ...........1.62<br>*Remove*.......................　　*Labor* ............. .84 | | lf | $.84 | $2.42 | $3.26 | |
| **1" poplar cove**<br>*Replace* Materials ........ .90　　*Labor* ...........1.62<br>*Remove*.......................　　*Labor* ............. .84 | | lf | $.84 | $2.52 | $3.36 | |
| **1" mahogany cove**<br>*Replace* Materials ........1.02　　*Labor* ...........1.62<br>*Remove*.......................　　*Labor* ............. .84 | | lf | $.84 | $2.64 | $3.48 | |
| **1" red oak cove**<br>*Replace* Materials ........1.09　　*Labor* ...........1.62<br>*Remove*.......................　　*Labor* ............. .84 | | lf | $.84 | $2.71 | $3.55 | |
| **Remove cove for work, then reinstall**<br>*Replace* .......................　　*Labor* ...........2.24 | | lf | — | $2.24 | $2.24 | ◁ remove & reinstall |
| **2-1/2" paint-grade ceiling cove**<br>*Replace* Materials ........1.22　　*Labor* ...........1.82<br>*Remove*.......................　　*Labor* ............. .84 | | lf | $.84 | $3.04 | $3.88 | ◀ **CEILING COVE**<br>*"Sprung" cove. Includes 4% waste.* |
| **2-1/2" stain-grade pine ceiling cove**<br>*Replace* Materials ........1.42　　*Labor* ...........1.82<br>*Remove*.......................　　*Labor* ............. .84 | | lf | $.84 | $3.24 | $4.08 | |
| **2-1/2" poplar ceiling cove**<br>*Replace* Materials ........1.52　　*Labor* ...........1.82<br>*Remove*.......................　　*Labor* ............. .84 | | lf | $.84 | $3.34 | $4.18 | |
| **2-1/2" mahogany ceiling cove**<br>*Replace* Materials ........1.83　　*Labor* ...........1.82<br>*Remove*.......................　　*Labor* ............. .84 | | lf | $.84 | $3.65 | $4.49 | |
| **2-1/2" red oak ceiling cove**<br>*Replace* Materials ........2.00　　*Labor* ...........1.82<br>*Remove*.......................　　*Labor* ............. .84 | | lf | $.84 | $3.82 | $4.66 | |
| **3-1/2" paint-grade ceiling cove**<br>*Replace* Materials ........1.58　　*Labor* ...........1.82<br>*Remove*.......................　　*Labor* ............. .84 | | lf | $.84 | $3.40 | $4.24 | |
| **3-1/2" stain-grade pine ceiling cove**<br>*Replace* Materials ........1.84　　*Labor* ...........1.82<br>*Remove*.......................　　*Labor* ............. .84 | | lf | $.84 | $3.66 | $4.50 | |
| **3-1/2" poplar ceiling cove**<br>*Replace* Materials ........1.98　　*Labor* ...........1.82<br>*Remove*.......................　　*Labor* ............. .84 | | lf | $.84 | $3.80 | $4.64 | |
| **3-1/2" mahogany ceiling cove**<br>*Replace* Materials ........2.38　　*Labor* ...........1.82<br>*Remove*.......................　　*Labor* ............. .84 | | lf | $.84 | $4.20 | $5.04 | |

| Item Description | Unit | Remove | Replace | Total |
|---|---|---|---|---|
| **CEILING COVE ▶** *continued* **3-1/2" red oak ceiling cove**<br>*Replace* Materials ........2.59     Labor ............1.82<br>*Remove*........................     Labor............ .84 | lf | $.84 | $4.41 | $5.25 |
| **remove & reinstall ▷** **Remove ceiling cove for work, then reinstall**<br>*Replace* ......................     Labor ............2.24 | lf | — | $2.24 | $2.24 |
| **HALF-ROUND ▶** *Includes 4% waste.* **1" paint-grade half-round**<br>*Replace* Materials ........ .56     Labor ............1.62<br>*Remove*........................     Labor............ .84 | lf | $.84 | $2.18 | $3.02 |
| **1" stain-grade pine half-round**<br>*Replace* Materials ........ .67     Labor ............1.62<br>*Remove*........................     Labor............ .84 | lf | $.84 | $2.29 | $3.13 |
| **1" poplar half-round**<br>*Replace* Materials ........ .72     Labor ............1.62<br>*Remove*........................     Labor............ .84 | lf | $.84 | $2.34 | $3.18 |
| **1" mahogany half-round**<br>*Replace* Materials ........ .83     Labor ............1.62<br>*Remove*........................     Labor............ .84 | lf | $.84 | $2.45 | $3.29 |
| **1" red oak half-round**<br>*Replace* Materials ........ .92     Labor ............1.62<br>*Remove*........................     Labor............ .84 | lf | $.84 | $2.54 | $3.38 |
| **2" paint-grade half-round**<br>*Replace* Materials ........ .79     Labor ............1.62<br>*Remove*........................     Labor............ .84 | lf | $.84 | $2.41 | $3.25 |
| **2" stain-grade pine half-round**<br>*Replace* Materials ........ .95     Labor ............1.62<br>*Remove*........................     Labor............ .84 | lf | $.84 | $2.57 | $3.41 |
| **2" poplar half-round**<br>*Replace* Materials ...... 1.02     Labor ............1.62<br>*Remove*........................     Labor............ .84 | lf | $.84 | $2.64 | $3.48 |
| **2" mahogany half-round**<br>*Replace* Materials ......1.18     Labor ............1.62<br>*Remove*........................     Labor............ .84 | lf | $.84 | $2.80 | $3.64 |
| **2" red oak half-round**<br>*Replace* Materials ........1.30     Labor ............1.62<br>*Remove*........................     Labor............ .84 | lf | $.84 | $2.92 | $3.76 |
| **Add 19% for 3" half-round**<br>▶ Add to the cost of 2" half-round. | | | | |
| **Add 40% for 4" half-round**<br>▶ Add to the cost of 2" half-round. | | | | |
| **remove & reinstall ▷** **Remove half-round for work, then reinstall**<br>*Replace* ......................     Labor ............2.86 | lf | — | $2.86 | $2.86 |
| **QUARTER-ROUND ▶** *Includes 4% waste.* **1/2" paint-grade quarter-round**<br>*Replace* Materials ........ .41     Labor ............1.62<br>*Remove*........................     Labor............ .84 | lf | $.84 | $2.03 | $2.87 |

| Item Description | Unit | Remove | Replace | Total |
|---|---|---|---|---|
| **1/2" stain-grade pine quarter-round**<br>*Replace* Materials ......... .53     Labor ............1.62<br>*Remove*......................     Labor............. .84 | lf | $.84 | $2.15 | $2.99 |
| **1/2" poplar quarter-round**<br>*Replace* Materials ........ .53     Labor ............1.62<br>*Remove*......................     Labor............. .84 | lf | $.84 | $2.15 | $2.99 |
| **1/2" mahogany quarter-round**<br>*Replace* Materials ........ .64     Labor ............1.62<br>*Remove*......................     Labor............. .84 | lf | $.84 | $2.26 | $3.10 |
| **1/2" red oak quarter-round**<br>*Replace* Materials ........ .70     Labor ............1.62<br>*Remove*......................     Labor............. .84 | lf | $.84 | $2.32 | $3.16 |
| **3/4" paint-grade quarter round**<br>*Replace* Materials ........ .48     Labor ............1.62<br>*Remove*......................     Labor............. .84 | lf | $.84 | $2.10 | $2.94 |
| **3/4" stain-grade pine quarter-round**<br>*Replace* Materials ........ .58     Labor ............1.62<br>*Remove*......................     Labor............. .84 | lf | $.84 | $2.20 | $3.04 |
| **3/4" poplar quarter-round**<br>*Replace* Materials ........ .63     Labor ............1.62<br>*Remove*......................     Labor............. .84 | lf | $.84 | $2.25 | $3.09 |
| **3/4" mahogany quarter-round**<br>*Replace* Materials ........ .75     Labor ............1.62<br>*Remove*......................     Labor............. .84 | lf | $.84 | $2.37 | $3.21 |
| **3/4" red oak quarter-round**<br>*Replace* Materials ........ .83     Labor ............1.62<br>*Remove*......................     Labor............. .84 | lf | $.84 | $2.45 | $3.29 |
| **1" paint-grade quarter-round**<br>*Replace* Materials ........ .85     Labor ............1.62<br>*Remove*......................     Labor............. .84 | lf | $.84 | $2.47 | $3.31 |
| **1" stain-grade pine quarter-round**<br>*Replace* Materials ...... 1.04     Labor ............1.62<br>*Remove*......................     Labor............. .84 | lf | $.84 | $2.66 | $3.50 |
| **1" poplar quarter-round**<br>*Replace* Materials.......1.11     Labor ............1.62<br>*Remove*......................     Labor............. .84 | lf | $.84 | $2.73 | $3.57 |
| **1" mahogany quarter-round**<br>*Replace* Materials.......1.33     Labor ............1.62<br>*Remove*......................     Labor............. .84 | lf | $.84 | $2.95 | $3.79 |
| **1" red oak quarter-round**<br>*Replace* Materials.......1.48     Labor ............1.62<br>*Remove*......................     Labor............. .84 | lf | $.84 | $3.10 | $3.94 |
| **Remove quarter-round for work, then reinstall**<br>*Replace* ......................     Labor ............2.86 | lf | — | $2.86 | $2.86 |
| **Paint-grade pine corner bead**<br>*Replace* Materials ........ .96     Labor ............3.04<br>*Remove*......................     Labor ............1.13 | lf | $1.13 | $4.00 | $5.13 |

**RELATED ITEMS**

Cleaning ..............................61
Painting .........................337

◁ remove & reinstall

◀ **CORNER BEAD**
*Standard corner bead
includes 4% waste.*

| | Item Description | Unit | Remove | Replace | Total |
|---|---|---|---|---|---|
| **CORNER BEAD** ▶ continued | **Stain-grade pine corner bead**<br>*Replace* Materials........1.14　　Labor ...........3.04<br>*Remove*..........................　Labor ...........1.13 | lf | $1.13 | $4.18 | $5.31 |
| △ **standard** | **Stain-grade pine corner bead, turned with double finials**<br>*Replace* Materials ......12.50　　Labor ...........3.04<br>*Remove*..........................　Labor ...........1.13 | lf | $1.13 | $15.54 | $16.67 |
| No waste included for turned corner bead with finials. | **Mahogany corner bead**<br>*Replace* Materials........2.13　　Labor ...........3.04<br>*Remove*..........................　Labor ...........1.13 | lf | $1.13 | $5.17 | $6.30 |
| | **Mahogany corner bead, turned with double finials**<br>*Replace* Materials.......15.40　　Labor ...........3.04<br>*Remove*..........................　Labor ...........1.13 | lf | $1.13 | $18.44 | $19.57 |
| | **Red oak corner bead**<br>*Replace* Materials........2.60　　Labor ...........3.04<br>*Remove*..........................　Labor ...........1.13 | lf | $1.13 | $5.64 | $6.77 |
| | **Red oak corner bead, turned with double finials**<br>*Replace* Materials ......16.60　　Labor ...........3.04<br>*Remove*..........................　Labor ...........1.13 | lf | $1.13 | $19.64 | $20.77 |
| △ **turned with double finials** | **Clear plastic corner bead**<br>*Replace* Materials ........ .90　　Labor ...........1.26<br>*Remove*..........................　Labor ...........1.13 | lf | $1.13 | $2.16 | $3.29 |
| remove & reinstall ▷ | **Remove corner bead for work, then reinstall**<br>*Replace* ..........................　Labor ...........3.89 | lf | — | $3.89 | $3.89 |
| **BED MOLD** ▶ Includes 4% waste. | **2-1/2" paint-grade pine bed mold**<br>*Replace* Materials........1.36　　Labor ...........1.50<br>*Remove*..........................　Labor ............. .68 | lf | $.68 | $2.86 | $3.54 |
| | **2-1/2" stain-grade pine bed mold**<br>*Replace* Materials........1.58　　Labor ...........1.50<br>*Remove*..........................　Labor ............. .68 | lf | $.68 | $3.08 | $3.76 |
| | **2-1/2" poplar bed mold**<br>*Replace* Materials........1.73　　Labor ...........1.50<br>*Remove*..........................　Labor ............. .68 | lf | $.68 | $3.23 | $3.91 |
| | **2-1/2" mahogany bed mold**<br>*Replace* Materials........2.05　　Labor ...........1.50<br>*Remove*..........................　Labor ............. .68 | lf | $.68 | $3.55 | $4.23 |
| | **2-1/2" red oak bed mold**<br>*Replace* Materials........2.24　　Labor ...........1.50<br>*Remove*..........................　Labor ............. .68 | lf | $.68 | $3.74 | $4.42 |
| remove & reinstall ▷ | **Remove bed mold for work, then reinstall**<br>*Replace* ..........................　Labor ...........2.24 | lf | — | $2.24 | $2.24 |
| **CROWN** ▶ Includes 4% waste. | **3-1/2" paint-grade crown**<br>*Replace* Materials........1.75　　Labor ...........1.82<br>*Remove*..........................　Labor ............. .68 | lf | $.68 | $3.57 | $4.25 |
| | **3-1/2" stain-grade crown**<br>*Replace* Materials........2.03　　Labor ...........1.82<br>*Remove*..........................　Labor ............. .68 | lf | $.68 | $3.85 | $4.53 |

| Item Description | Unit | Remove | Replace | Total |
|---|---|---|---|---|
| **3-1/2" poplar crown** *Replace* Materials........2.22  Labor............1.82  *Remove*.................  Labor............ .68 | lf | $.68 | $4.04 | $4.72 |
| **3-1/2" mahogany crown** *Replace* Materials........2.64  Labor............1.82  *Remove*.................  Labor............ .68 | lf | $.68 | $4.46 | $5.14 |
| **3-1/2" red oak crown** *Replace* Materials........2.86  Labor............1.82  *Remove*.................  Labor............ .68 | lf | $.68 | $4.68 | $5.36 |
| **4-1/2" paint-grade crown** *Replace* Materials........2.57  Labor............1.82  *Remove*.................  Labor............ .68 | lf | $.68 | $4.39 | $5.07 |
| **4-1/2" stain-grade crown** *Replace* Materials........2.99  Labor............1.82  *Remove*.................  Labor............ .68 | lf | $.68 | $4.81 | $5.49 |
| **4-1/2" poplar crown** *Replace* Materials........3.27  Labor............1.82  *Remove*.................  Labor............ .68 | lf | $.68 | $5.09 | $5.77 |
| **4-1/2" mahogany crown** *Replace* Materials........4.15  Labor............1.82  *Remove*.................  Labor............ .68 | lf | $.68 | $5.97 | $6.65 |
| **4-1/2" red oak crown** *Replace* Materials........4.50  Labor............1.82  *Remove*.................  Labor............ .68 | lf | $.68 | $6.32 | $7.00 |
| **Remove crown for work, then reinstall** *Replace*.................  Labor............2.24 | lf | — | $2.24 | $2.24 |
| **Paint-grade hand rail** *Replace* Materials........2.21  Labor............3.87  *Remove*.................  Labor............ .73 | lf | $.73 | $6.08 | $6.81 |
| **Stain-grade pine hand rail** *Replace* Materials........3.00  Labor............3.87  *Remove*.................  Labor............ .73 | lf | $.73 | $6.87 | $7.60 |
| **Mahogany hand rail** *Replace* Materials........4.27  Labor............3.87  *Remove*.................  Labor............ .73 | lf | $.73 | $8.14 | $8.87 |
| **Red oak hand rail** *Replace* Materials........4.57  Labor............3.87  *Remove*.................  Labor............ .73 | lf | $.73 | $8.44 | $9.17 |
| **Remove hand rail for work, then reinstall** *Replace*.................  Labor............5.30 | lf | — | $5.30 | $5.30 |
| **3/4" paint-grade molding with vertical milling** *Replace* Materials........2.04  Labor............1.62  *Remove*.................  Labor............ .84 | lf | $.84 | $3.66 | $4.50 |
| **3/4" stain-grade pine molding with vertical milling** *Replace* Materials........2.39  Labor............1.62  *Remove*.................  Labor............ .84 | lf | $.84 | $4.01 | $4.85 |

**RELATED ITEMS**
Cleaning ..........................61
Painting ........................337

◁ remove & reinstall

◀ **HAND RAIL**
*Includes 4% waste.*

◁ remove & reinstall

◀ **SPECIALTY MOLDING**
*General moldings for installation as crown, chair rail, panel molds, cabinet trim and so forth. Includes 4% waste.*

| | Item Description | Unit | Remove | Replace | Total |
|---|---|---|---|---|---|
| SPECIALTY ▶ MOLDING continued | 3/4" poplar molding with vertical milling | lf | $.84 | $4.19 | $5.03 |
| | *Replace* Materials........2.57     Labor ............1.62 | | | | |
| | *Remove*.......................     Labor .............. .84 | | | | |
| | 3/4" mahogany molding with vertical milling | lf | $.84 | $4.83 | $5.67 |
| | *Replace* Materials........3.21     Labor ............1.62 | | | | |
| | *Remove*.......................     Labor .............. .84 | | | | |
| △ **dentil** *a vertically milled molding.* | 3/4" red oak molding with vertical milling | lf | $.84 | $5.10 | $5.94 |
| | *Replace* Materials........3.48     Labor ............1.62 | | | | |
| | *Remove*.......................     Labor .............. .84 | | | | |
| | 3/4" polyurethane molding with vertical patterns | lf | $.84 | $4.68 | $5.52 |
| | *Replace* Materials........3.06     Labor ............1.62 | | | | |
| | *Remove*.......................     Labor .............. .84 | | | | |
| △ **bead and reel** *a hand-carved molding.* | 3/4" stain-grade polyurethane molding with vertical patterns | lf | $.84 | $4.91 | $5.75 |
| | *Replace* Materials........3.29     Labor ............1.62 | | | | |
| | *Remove*.......................     Labor .............. .84 | | | | |
| other 3/4" styles ▷ | **Deduct 41% for 3/4" molding with embossed patterns** | | | | |
| | ▶ For pine moldings only. | | | | |
| | **Add 64% for 3/4" molding with hand carvings** | | | | |
| | **Add 198% for 3/4" molding with heavy hand carvings** | | | | |
| 1-1/2" specialty mold ▷ | 1-1/2" paint-grade molding with vertical milling | lf | $.84 | $3.95 | $4.79 |
| | *Replace* Materials........2.33     Labor ............1.62 | | | | |
| | *Remove*.......................     Labor .............. .84 | | | | |
| △ **bead** *a hand-carved molding.* | 1-1/2" stain-grade pine molding with vertical milling | lf | $.84 | $4.34 | $5.18 |
| | *Replace* Materials........2.72     Labor ............1.62 | | | | |
| | *Remove*.......................     Labor .............. .84 | | | | |
| | 1-1/2" poplar molding with vertical milling | lf | $.84 | $4.56 | $5.40 |
| | *Replace* Materials........2.94     Labor ............1.62 | | | | |
| | *Remove*.......................     Labor .............. .84 | | | | |
| | 1-1/2" mahogany molding with vertical milling | lf | $.84 | $5.28 | $6.12 |
| | *Replace* Materials........3.66     Labor ............1.62 | | | | |
| | *Remove*.......................     Labor .............. .84 | | | | |
| △ **rope** *a hand-carved molding.* | 1-1/2" red oak molding with vertical milling | lf | $.84 | $5.59 | $6.43 |
| | *Replace* Materials........3.97     Labor ............1.62 | | | | |
| | *Remove*.......................     Labor .............. .84 | | | | |
| | 1-1/2" polyurethane molding with vertical patterns | lf | $.84 | $6.43 | $7.27 |
| | *Replace* Materials........4.81     Labor ............1.62 | | | | |
| | *Remove*.......................     Labor .............. .84 | | | | |
| | 1-1/2" stain-grade polyurethane molding with vertical patterns | lf | $.84 | $6.79 | $7.63 |
| | *Replace* Materials........5.17     Labor ............1.62 | | | | |
| | *Remove*.......................     Labor .............. .84 | | | | |
| other 1-1/2" styles ▷ | **Deduct 37% for 1-1/2" molding with embossed patterns** | | | | |
| | ▶ For pine moldings only. | | | | |
| △ **reed** *a molding with vertical patterns.* | **Add 66% for 1-1/2" molding with hand carvings** | | | | |
| | **Add 205% for 1-1/2" molding with heavy hand carvings** | | | | |

| Item Description | Unit | Remove | Replace | Total | |
|---|---|---|---|---|---|
| **2-1/2" paint-grade molding with vertical milling**<br>*Replace* Materials........2.61    Labor ............1.62<br>*Remove*........................    Labor............. .84 | lf | $.84 | $4.23 | $5.07 | ◁ 2-1/2" specialty mold |
| **2-1/2" stain-grade pine molding with vertical milling**<br>*Replace* Materials........3.04    Labor ............1.62<br>*Remove*........................    Labor............. .84 | lf | $.84 | $4.66 | $5.50 | △ **acanthus** a heavy hand-carved molding. |
| **2-1/2" poplar molding with vertical milling**<br>*Replace* Materials........3.29    Labor ............1.62<br>*Remove*........................    Labor............. .84 | lf | $.84 | $4.91 | $5.75 | |
| **2-1/2" mahogany molding with vertical milling**<br>*Replace* Materials........4.09    Labor ............1.62<br>*Remove*........................    Labor............. .84 | lf | $.84 | $5.71 | $6.55 | △ **leaf and tongue** a heavy hand-carved molding. |
| **2-1/2" red oak molding with vertical milling**<br>*Replace* Materials........4.45    Labor ............1.62<br>*Remove*........................    Labor............. .84 | lf | $.84 | $6.07 | $6.91 | |
| **2-1/2" polyurethane molding with vertical patterns**<br>*Replace* Materials........5.39    Labor ............1.62<br>*Remove*........................    Labor............. .84 | lf | $.84 | $7.01 | $7.85 | |
| **2-1/2" stain-grade polyurethane molding with vertical patterns**<br>*Replace* Materials........5.79    Labor ............1.62<br>*Remove*........................    Labor............. .84 | lf | $.84 | $7.41 | $8.25 | △ **laurel and ribbon** a heavy hand-carved molding. |

**Deduct 37% for 2-1/2" molding with embossed patterns**
► For pine moldings only.

◁ other 2-1/2" styles

**Add 68% for 2-1/2" molding with hand carvings**

**Add 209% for 2-1/2" molding with heavy hand carvings**

| Item Description | Unit | Remove | Replace | Total | |
|---|---|---|---|---|---|
| **3-1/2" paint-grade molding with vertical milling**<br>*Replace* Materials........2.91    Labor ............1.62<br>*Remove*........................    Labor............. .84 | lf | $.84 | $4.53 | $5.37 | ◁ 3-1/2" specialty mold |
| **3-1/2" stain-grade pine molding with vertical milling**<br>*Replace* Materials........3.39    Labor ............1.62<br>*Remove*........................    Labor............. .84 | lf | $.84 | $5.01 | $5.85 | △ **shell** a heavy hand-carved molding. |
| **3-1/2" poplar molding with vertical milling**<br>*Replace* Materials........3.66    Labor ............1.62<br>*Remove*........................    Labor............. .84 | lf | $.84 | $5.28 | $6.12 | |
| **3-1/2" mahogany molding with vertical milling**<br>*Replace* Materials........4.55    Labor ............1.62<br>*Remove*........................    Labor............. .84 | lf | $.84 | $6.17 | $7.01 | |
| **3-1/2" red oak molding with vertical milling**<br>*Replace* Materials........4.95    Labor ............1.62<br>*Remove*........................    Labor............. .84 | lf | $.84 | $6.57 | $7.41 | △ **oak leaf and ribbon** a heavy hand-carved molding. |
| **3-1/2" polyurethane molding with vertical patterns**<br>*Replace* Materials........5.99    Labor ............1.62<br>*Remove*........................    Labor............. .84 | lf | $.84 | $7.61 | $8.45 | |
| **3-1/2" stain-grade polyurethane molding with vertical patterns**<br>*Replace* Materials........6.44    Labor ............1.62<br>*Remove*........................    Labor............. .84 | lf | $.84 | $8.06 | $8.90 | |

| Item Description | Unit | Remove | Replace | Total |
|---|---|---|---|---|
| **SPECIALTY ▶ MOLDING** *continued* | | | | |
| **Deduct 38% for 3-1/2" molding with embossed patterns**  ▶ For pine moldings only. | | | | |
| *other 3-1/2" styles* | | | | |
| **Add 69% for 3-1/2" molding with hand carvings** | | | | |
| **Add 213% for 3-1/2" molding with heavy hand carvings** | | | | |
| *5" specialty mold ▷* **5" paint-grade molding with vertical milling**  *Replace* Materials........4.19    Labor ...........1.98  *Remove*.......................    Labor.............84 | lf | $.84 | $6.17 | $7.01 |

△ **meander** *a molding with vertical patterns.*

| | | | | |
|---|---|---|---|---|
| **5" stain-grade pine molding with vertical milling**  *Replace* Materials........4.88    Labor ...........1.98  *Remove*.......................    Labor.............84 | lf | $.84 | $6.86 | $7.70 |
| **5" poplar molding with vertical milling**  *Replace* Materials........5.26    Labor ...........1.98  *Remove*.......................    Labor.............84 | lf | $.84 | $7.24 | $8.08 |
| **5" mahogany molding with vertical milling**  *Replace* Materials........6.55    Labor ...........1.98  *Remove*.......................    Labor.............84 | lf | $.84 | $8.53 | $9.37 |

△ **fret** *a molding with vertical patterns.*

| | | | | |
|---|---|---|---|---|
| **5" red oak molding with vertical milling**  *Replace* Materials........7.13    Labor ...........1.98  *Remove*.......................    Labor.............84 | lf | $.84 | $9.11 | $9.95 |
| **5" polyurethane molding with vertical patterns**  *Replace* Materials........8.63    Labor ...........1.98  *Remove*.......................    Labor.............84 | lf | $.84 | $10.61 | $11.45 |

△ **egg and dart** *a hand-carved molding.*

| | | | | |
|---|---|---|---|---|
| **5" stain-grade polyurethane molding with vertical patterns**  *Replace* Materials........9.27    Labor ...........1.98  *Remove*.......................    Labor.............84 | lf | $.84 | $11.25 | $12.09 |
| *other 5" styles ▷* **Deduct 39% for 5" molding with embossed patterns**  ▶ For pine moldings only. | | | | |
| **Add 71% for 5" molding with hand carvings** | | | | |
| **Add 219% for 5" molding with heavy hand carvings** | | | | |
| *8" specialty mold ▷* **8" paint-grade molding with vertical milling**  *Replace* Materials........6.85    Labor ...........2.16  *Remove*.......................    Labor.............84 | lf | $.84 | $9.01 | $9.85 |

△ **bundled reeds** *a hand-carved molding.*

| | | | | |
|---|---|---|---|---|
| **8" stain-grade pine molding with vertical milling**  *Replace* Materials........7.98    Labor ...........2.16  *Remove*.......................    Labor.............84 | lf | $.84 | $10.14 | $10.98 |
| **8" poplar molding with vertical milling**  *Replace* Materials........8.61    Labor ...........2.16  *Remove*.......................    Labor.............84 | lf | $.84 | $10.77 | $11.61 |
| **8" mahogany molding with vertical milling**  *Replace* Materials......10.70    Labor ...........2.16  *Remove*.......................    Labor.............84 | lf | $.84 | $12.86 | $13.70 |

△ **ribbon** *a heavy hand-carved molding.*

| | | | | |
|---|---|---|---|---|
| **8" red oak molding with vertical milling**  *Replace* Materials.......11.70    Labor ...........2.16  *Remove*.......................    Labor.............84 | lf | $.84 | $13.86 | $14.70 |

| Item Description | Unit | Remove | Replace | Total | |
|---|---|---|---|---|---|
| **8" polyurethane molding with vertical patterns**<br>*Replace* Materials ......14.20    Labor ...........2.16<br>*Remove* ........................    Labor ............. .84 | lf | $.84 | $16.36 | $17.20 | △ **grape** a heavy hand-carved molding. |
| **8" stain-grade polyurethane molding with vertical patterns**<br>*Replace* Materials.......15.20    Labor ...........2.16<br>*Remove* ........................    Labor ............. .84 | lf | $.84 | $17.36 | $18.20 | |
| **Deduct 41% for 8" molding with embossed patterns**<br>► For pine moldings only. | | | | | ◁ **other 8" styles** |
| **Add 75% for 8" molding with hand carvings** | | | | | |
| **Add 232% for 8" molding with heavy hand carvings** | | | | | |
| **Remove molding installed on wall for work, then reinstall**<br>*Replace* ........................    Labor ...........2.24 | lf | — | $2.24 | $2.24 | ◁ **remove & reinstall** |
| **Remove window or door casing for work, then reinstall**<br>*Replace* ........................    Labor ...........2.86 | lf | — | $2.86 | $2.86 | |
| **Molder setup charge**<br>*Replace* Materials ....150.00 | ea | — | $150.00 | $150.00 | ◄ **CUSTOM-MILLED MOLDING**<br>*Custom milled to match existing pattern or a specially designed pattern. All milling is horizontal. Includes 4% waste.* |
| **Molder custom knife charges**<br>*Replace* Materials ....335.00 | ea | — | $335.00 | $335.00 | |
| **1" to 2" pine custom-milled molding**<br>*Replace* Materials........1.39    Labor ............1.62<br>*Remove* ........................    Labor ............. .84 | lf | $.84 | $3.01 | $3.85 | |
| **2" to 3" pine custom-milled molding**<br>*Replace* Materials........1.55    Labor ............1.62<br>*Remove* ........................    Labor ............. .84 | lf | $.84 | $3.17 | $4.01 | |
| **3" to 4" pine custom-milled molding**<br>*Replace* Materials........2.21    Labor ............1.98<br>*Remove* ........................    Labor ............. .84 | lf | $.84 | $4.19 | $5.03 | |
| **4" to 5" pine custom-milled molding**<br>*Replace* Materials........3.51    Labor ............1.98<br>*Remove* ........................    Labor ............. .84 | lf | $.84 | $5.49 | $6.33 | |
| **6" to 7" pine custom-milled molding**<br>*Replace* Materials........5.77    Labor ............2.16<br>*Remove* ........................    Labor ............. .84 | lf | $.84 | $7.93 | $8.77 | |
| **7" to 8" pine custom-milled molding**<br>*Replace* Materials........8.15    Labor ............2.16<br>*Remove* ........................    Labor ............. .84 | lf | $.84 | $10.31 | $11.15 | **RELATED ITEMS**<br>Cleaning ..............................61<br>Painting ...........................337<br>*"Wood Embossing"* .......199 |
| **Add 7% for poplar custom-milled molding** | | | | | ◁ **other wood species** |
| **Add 21% for mahogany custom-milled molding** | | | | | |
| **Add 30% for red oak custom-milled molding** | | | | | |
| **Add for corner radius in panel molding**<br>*Replace* Materials........1.56    Labor ............5.89<br>*Remove* ........................    Labor ............. .89 | ea | $.89 | $7.45 | $8.34 | ◄ **PANEL MOLDING CORNER RADIUS**<br>*Includes 4% waste.* |

| Item Description | Unit | Remove | Replace | Total |
|---|---|---|---|---|
| **PANEL MOLDING ▶ CORNER RADIUS** **Add for corner radius in panel molding with vertical milling** Replace Materials........3.68    Labor.........5.89 Remove...............    Labor............89 | ea | $.89 | $9.57 | $10.46 |
| **Add for corner radius in panel molding with embossed pattern** Replace Materials........3.04    Labor.........5.89 Remove...............    Labor............89 | ea | $.89 | $8.93 | $9.82 |
| **Add for corner radius in panel molding with hand carvings** Replace Materials........5.64    Labor.........5.89 Remove...............    Labor............89 | ea | $.89 | $11.53 | $12.42 |
| **Add for corner radius in panel molding with heavy hand carvings** Replace Materials........7.96    Labor.........5.89 Remove...............    Labor............89 | ea | $.89 | $13.85 | $14.74 |
| **CLOSET WORK ▶** **Closet shelf brackets, shelving, & rod** Replace Materials........9.06    Labor.........13.10 Remove...............    Labor............1.65 | lf | $1.65 | $22.16 | $23.81 |
| **Remove closet shelf brackets, shelving, & rod for work, then reinstall** Replace ...............    Labor..........17.20 | lf | — | $17.20 | $17.20 |
| **closet organizer ▷ Closet organizer system, standard grade** Replace Materials........8.43    Labor..........12.00 Remove...............    Labor............1.23 | sf | $1.23 | $20.43 | $21.66 |
| **Closet organizer system, high grade** Replace Materials......10.30    Labor..........16.40 Remove...............    Labor............1.23 | sf | $1.23 | $26.70 | $27.93 |
| **Closet organizer system, deluxe grade** Replace Materials......12.90    Labor..........20.80 Remove...............    Labor............1.23 | sf | $1.23 | $33.70 | $34.93 |
| **Remove closet organizer system for work, then reinstall** Replace ...............    Labor..........23.90 | sf | — | $23.90 | $23.90 |
| **linen closet ▷ Linen closet shelves, standard grade** Replace Materials........6.73    Labor..........26.60 Remove...............    Labor............89 | lf | $.89 | $33.33 | $34.22 |
| **Linen closet shelves, high grade** Replace Materials........7.36    Labor..........26.60 Remove...............    Labor............89 | lf | $.89 | $33.96 | $34.85 |
| **Linen closet pull-out shelves** Replace Materials........8.50    Labor..........27.50 Remove...............    Labor............89 | lf | $.89 | $36.00 | $36.89 |
| **Remove linen closet shelves for work, then reinstall** Replace ...............    Labor..........32.20 | lf | — | $32.20 | $32.20 |
| **closet rod ▷ Closet rod, pine** Replace Materials........2.57    Labor.........3.16 Remove...............    Labor............92 | lf | $.92 | $5.73 | $6.65 |
| **Closet rod, hardwood** Replace Materials........3.23    Labor.........3.16 Remove...............    Labor............92 | lf | $.92 | $6.39 | $7.31 |

| Item Description | Unit | Remove | Replace | Total | |
|---|---|---|---|---|---|
| **Remove closet rod for work, then reinstall**<br>*Replace* .................... Labor ..........4.13 | lf | — | $4.13 | $4.13 | |
| **Aromatic tongue-&-groove cedar board closet lining**<br>*Replace* Materials ........ .16    Labor............2.01<br>*Remove*........................ Labor............ .73 | sf | $.73 | $2.17 | $2.90 | ◁ cedar closet lining |
| **Aromatic 1/4" cedar veneer plywood closet lining**<br>*Replace* Materials....2.38    Labor............1.46<br>*Remove*........................ Labor............ .58 | sf | $.58 | $3.84 | $4.42 | |
| **8" deep built-in paint-grade bookcase**<br>*Replace* Materials.......5.95    Labor...........10.60<br>*Remove*........................ Labor ...........1.34 | sf | $1.34 | $16.55 | $17.89 | ◀ BOOKCASE<br>*Adjustable shelves.*<br>*Shelves approximately*<br>*12" on center. Measure*<br>*sf of bookcase face.* |
| **8" deep built-in stain-grade pine bookcase**<br>*Replace* Materials.......6.90    Labor...........10.60<br>*Remove*........................ Labor ...........1.34 | sf | $1.34 | $17.50 | $18.84 | |
| **8" deep built-in mahogany bookcase**<br>*Replace* Materials.......7.48    Labor...........10.60<br>*Remove*........................ Labor ...........1.34 | sf | $1.34 | $18.08 | $19.42 | |
| **8" deep built-in oak bookcase**<br>*Replace* Materials.......8.80    Labor...........10.60<br>*Remove*........................ Labor ...........1.34 | sf | $1.34 | $19.40 | $20.74 | |
| **8" deep built-in walnut bookcase**<br>*Replace* Materials......12.10    Labor...........10.60<br>*Remove*........................ Labor ...........1.34 | sf | $1.34 | $22.70 | $24.04 | |
| **12" deep built-in paint-grade bookcase**<br>*Replace* Materials.......7.80    Labor...........12.00<br>*Remove*........................ Labor ...........1.34 | sf | $1.34 | $19.80 | $21.14 | ◁ 12" deep |
| **12" deep built-in stain-grade pine bookcase**<br>*Replace* Materials.......9.05    Labor...........12.00<br>*Remove*........................ Labor ...........1.34 | sf | $1.34 | $21.05 | $22.39 | |
| **12" deep built-in mahogany bookcase**<br>*Replace* Materials.......9.81    Labor...........12.00<br>*Remove*........................ Labor ...........1.34 | sf | $1.34 | $21.81 | $23.15 | |
| **12" deep built-in oak bookcase**<br>*Replace* Materials......11.60    Labor...........12.00<br>*Remove*........................ Labor ...........1.34 | sf | $1.34 | $23.60 | $24.94 | |
| **12" deep built-in walnut bookcase**<br>*Replace* Materials......15.80    Labor...........12.00<br>*Remove*........................ Labor ...........1.34 | sf | $1.34 | $27.80 | $29.14 | |
| **18" deep built-in paint-grade bookcase**<br>*Replace* Materials......10.20    Labor...........12.50<br>*Remove*........................ Labor ...........1.34 | sf | $1.34 | $22.70 | $24.04 | ◁ 18" deep |
| **18" deep built-in stain-grade pine bookcase**<br>*Replace* Materials......11.90    Labor...........12.50<br>*Remove*........................ Labor ...........1.34 | sf | $1.34 | $24.40 | $25.74 | |
| **18" deep built-in mahogany bookcase**<br>*Replace* Materials......12.90    Labor...........12.50<br>*Remove*........................ Labor ...........1.34 | sf | $1.34 | $25.40 | $26.74 | |

| | Item Description | Unit | Remove | Replace | Total |
|---|---|---|---|---|---|
| **BOOKCASE ▶**<br>*continued* | **18" deep built-in oak bookcase**<br>*Replace* Materials.......15.20    Labor...........12.50<br>*Remove*.........................    Labor ............1.34 | sf | $1.34 | $27.70 | $29.04 |
| | **18" deep built-in walnut bookcase**<br>*Replace* Materials.......20.70    Labor...........12.50<br>*Remove*.........................    Labor ............1.34 | sf | $1.34 | $33.20 | $34.54 |
| | **24" deep built-in paint-grade bookcase**<br>*Replace* Materials.......13.40    Labor...........13.10<br>*Remove*.........................    Labor ............1.34 | sf | $1.34 | $26.50 | $27.84 |
| △ *economy mantel* | **24" deep built-in stain-grade pine bookcase**<br>*Replace* Materials.......15.60    Labor...........13.10<br>*Remove*.........................    Labor ............1.34 | sf | $1.34 | $28.70 | $30.04 |
| | **24" deep built-in mahogany bookcase**<br>*Replace* Materials.......17.00    Labor...........13.10<br>*Remove*.........................    Labor ............1.34 | sf | $1.34 | $30.10 | $31.44 |
| | **24" deep built-in oak bookcase**<br>*Replace* Materials......20.00    Labor...........13.10<br>*Remove*.........................    Labor ............1.34 | sf | $1.34 | $33.10 | $34.44 |
| △ *standard mantel* | **24" deep built-in walnut bookcase**<br>*Replace* Materials......27.20    Labor...........13.10<br>*Remove*.........................    Labor ............1.34 | sf | $1.34 | $40.30 | $41.64 |
| **MANTEL BEAM ▶** | **Fireplace mantel beam, rough sawn**<br>*Replace* Materials........8.03    Labor...........21.30<br>*Remove*.........................    Labor ............2.10 | lf | $2.10 | $29.33 | $31.43 |
| | **Fireplace mantel beam, glue laminated**<br>*Replace* Materials......22.90    Labor...........21.30<br>*Remove*.........................    Labor ............2.10 | lf | $2.10 | $44.20 | $46.30 |
| | **Remove fireplace mantel beam for work, then reinstall**<br>*Replace* ........................    Labor...........27.50 | lf | — | $27.50 | $27.50 |
| **MANTEL ▶**<br>*Measure the lf of*<br>*mantel width.* | **Fireplace mantel, economy grade**<br>*Replace* Materials......44.30    Labor ..........25.80<br>*Remove*.........................    Labor .........2.46<br>▶ Paint-grade wood with simple pattern and moldings.  See illustration above. | lf | $2.46 | $70.10 | $72.56 |
| | **Fireplace mantel, standard grade**<br>*Replace* Materials......95.40    Labor ..........25.80<br>*Remove*.........................    Labor .........2.46<br>▶ Paint-grade wood or stain-grade pine, may have dentil patterns and fluted pilasters.<br>See illustration above. | lf | $2.46 | $121.20 | $123.66 |
| △ *high* | **Fireplace mantel, high grade**<br>*Replace* Materials....205.00    Labor ..........25.80<br>*Remove*.........................    Labor .........2.46<br>▶ Red oak, birch, stain-grade pine or more ornate paint-grade.  May include a<br>combination of some of the following: carved moldings, carved onlays, embossed<br>patterns, fluted pilasters, face projections. | lf | $2.46 | $230.80 | $233.26 |
| △ *deluxe* | **Fireplace mantel, deluxe grade**<br>*Replace* Materials....460.00    Labor ..........25.80<br>*Remove*.........................    Labor .........2.46<br>▶ Cherry, walnut or more ornate red oak, birch, yellow pine, or paint-grade.  May<br>include a combination of some of the following: carved moldings, carved onlays,<br>fluted pilasters, face projections, carved corbels, circular patterns and moldings. | lf | $2.46 | $485.80 | $488.26 |

| Item Description | Unit | Remove | Replace | Total |
|---|---|---|---|---|
| **Fireplace mantel, custom grade** | lf | $2.46 | $957.80 | $960.26 |
|    *Replace* Materials ....932.00     Labor ..........25.80 | | | | |
|    *Remove*........................     Labor ..........2.46 | | | | |
| ► Cherry, walnut, heart pine or very ornate red oak, birch, or yellow pine. May include a combination of some of the following: carved moldings, carved onlays, fluted pilasters, round columns, capitals (Ionic, Tuscan, contemporary, etc.), face projections, ornately carved corbel (e.g. lion's head), circular openings, paneling above mantel, or mirror. | | | | |
| **Fireplace mantel, custom deluxe grade** | lf | $2.46 | $1,435.80 | $1,438.26 |
|    *Replace* Materials ...1410.00     Labor ..........25.80 | | | | |
|    *Remove*........................     Labor ..........2.46 | | | | |
| ► Cherry, walnut or more ornate red oak, birch, or paint-grade. May include a combination of some of the following: carved moldings, ornate hand-carved patterns, fluted pilasters, round columns, ornate capitals (Scamozzi, Corinthian, etc.), face projections, circular openings, curved pilasters, paneling above mantel, or mirror. | | | | |
| **Remove fireplace mantel for work, then reinstall** | lf | — | $28.50 | $28.50 |
|    *Replace* ........................     Labor ..........28.50 | | | | |
| **Coffered ceiling, economy grade** | sf | $1.23 | $18.45 | $19.68 |
|    *Replace* Materials .......8.65     Labor ..........9.80 | | | | |
|    *Remove*........................     Labor ..........1.23 | | | | |
| ► Coffers are finished drywall with corner bead. Inside corners trimmed with 3-1/2" crown mold or similar. | | | | |
| **Coffered ceiling, standard grade** | sf | $1.23 | $22.90 | $24.13 |
|    *Replace* Materials ......12.00     Labor ..........10.90 | | | | |
|    *Remove*........................     Labor ..........1.23 | | | | |
| ► Coffers and beams are finished drywall. Inside corners trimmed with vertical pattern moldings. May also include wood onlays (see page 230), plaster enrichments (see page 232), or the raised beams may be cased with hardwood plywood. | | | | |
| **Coffered ceiling, high grade** | sf | $1.23 | $26.30 | $27.53 |
|    *Replace* Materials ......14.10     Labor ..........12.20 | | | | |
|    *Remove*........................     Labor ..........1.23 | | | | |
| ► Covered with wood paneling. Inside corners trimmed with vertical-pattern or embossed moldings. Coffers contain panel molding. May also include wood onlays (see page 230). | | | | |
| **Coffered ceiling, deluxe grade** | sf | $1.23 | $34.70 | $35.93 |
|    *Replace* Materials ......21.00     Labor ..........13.70 | | | | |
|    *Remove*........................     Labor ..........1.23 | | | | |
| ► Covered with hardwood plywood. Inside corners trimmed with hand-carved moldings. May also include wood onlays (see page 230). | | | | |
| **Coffered ceiling, custom grade** | sf | $1.23 | $47.00 | $48.23 |
|    *Replace* Materials ......30.00     Labor ..........17.00 | | | | |
|    *Remove*........................     Labor ..........1.23 | | | | |
| ► Covered with wood paneling. Inside corners trimmed with heavy hand-carved moldings. May also include wood onlays at each corner (see page 230), recessed panels on beams or in coffers, and corbels at wall corners. | | | | |
| **Coffered ceiling, custom deluxe grade** | sf | $1.23 | $67.10 | $68.33 |
|    *Replace* Materials ......44.70     Labor ..........22.40 | | | | |
|    *Remove*........................     Labor ..........1.23 | | | | |
| ► Covered with wood paneling. Inside corners trimmed with heavy hand-carved moldings. May also include ornate wood onlays at each corner (see page 230), recessed panels on beams or in coffers, and ornately carved corbels at wall corners (e.g. lion's head). | | | | |

△ *custom*

△ *custom deluxe*

◄ **COFFERED CEILING**
*Coffers 42" to 48" on center. Unless otherwise noted, includes wood underframing, and fire-taped drywall. Does not include painting or staining and varnishing. All inside molding joints are coped.*

△ *economy*

△ *standard*

△ *high*

△ *deluxe*

△ *custom*

△ *custom deluxe*

| Item Description | Unit | Remove | Replace | Total |
|---|---|---|---|---|
| **NICHE ▶** *Niches are high density polyurethane, Opaque bases allow for installation of a light beneath. Add **17%** for niches made from fiber reinforced plaster.* | | | | |
| **Niche with casing and shelf bracket** <br> *Replace* Materials.....152.00  Labor..........51.70 <br> *Remove*........................  Labor ..........8.31 | ea | $8.31 | $203.70 | $212.01 |
| **Niche with clamshell top with casing and shelf bracket** <br> *Replace* Materials ....266.00  Labor..........51.70 <br> *Remove*........................  Labor ..........8.31 | ea | $8.31 | $317.70 | $326.01 |
| **Niche with clamshell top, casing, and clamshell shelf bracket** <br> *Replace* Materials ....347.00  Labor..........51.70 <br> *Remove*........................  Labor ..........8.31 | ea | $8.31 | $398.70 | $407.01 |
| **Remove niche for work, then reinstall** <br> *Replace* ........................  Labor..........73.30 | ea | — | $73.30 | $73.30 |
| **GINGERBREAD ▶ RUNNING TRIM** *Paint-grade poplar. Add **30%** for red oak.* | | | | |
| **Gingerbread fleur-sawn running trim** <br> *Replace* Materials......23.50  Labor ..........6.32 <br> *Remove*........................  Labor ..........1.00 | lf | $1.00 | $29.82 | $30.82 |
| **Gingerbread picket-sawn running trim** <br> *Replace* Materials......30.40  Labor ..........6.32 <br> *Remove*........................  Labor ..........1.00 | lf | $1.00 | $36.72 | $37.72 |
| **ball-and-dowel ▷** **Gingerbread 2" ball-and-dowel running trim (galley rail)** <br> *Replace* Materials........7.24  Labor ..........6.32 <br> *Remove*........................  Labor ..........1.00 | lf | $1.00 | $13.56 | $14.56 |
| △ fleur-sawn **Gingerbread 4" ball-and-dowel running trim** <br> *Replace* Materials ......10.90  Labor ..........6.32 <br> *Remove*........................  Labor ..........1.00 | lf | $1.00 | $17.22 | $18.22 |
| **Gingerbread 6" ball-and-dowel running trim** <br> *Replace* Materials ......12.40  Labor ..........6.32 <br> *Remove*........................  Labor ..........1.00 | lf | $1.00 | $18.72 | $19.72 |
| △ picket-sawn **Gingerbread 8" ball-and-dowel running trim** <br> *Replace* Materials ....14.80  Labor ..........6.32 <br> *Remove*........................  Labor ..........1.00 | lf | $1.00 | $21.12 | $22.12 |
| **Gingerbread 10" ball-and-dowel running trim** <br> *Replace* Materials ......18.70  Labor ..........6.32 <br> *Remove*........................  Labor ..........1.00 | lf | $1.00 | $25.02 | $26.02 |
| △ ball-and-dowel **Gingerbread 12" ball-and-dowel running trim** <br> *Replace* Materials ......22.10  Labor ..........6.32 <br> *Remove*........................  Labor ..........1.00 | lf | $1.00 | $28.42 | $29.42 |
| **Gingerbread 14" ball-and-dowel running trim** <br> *Replace* Materials ......26.60  Labor ..........6.32 <br> *Remove*........................  Labor ..........1.00 | lf | $1.00 | $32.92 | $33.92 |
| **spindle ▷** **Gingerbread 2" spindle running trim (galley rail)** <br> *Replace* Materials......6.84  Labor ..........6.32 <br> *Remove*........................  Labor ..........1.00 | lf | $1.00 | $13.16 | $14.16 |
| △ spindle **Gingerbread 4" spindle running trim** <br> *Replace* Materials.......8.57  Labor ..........6.32 <br> *Remove*........................  Labor ..........1.00 | lf | $1.00 | $14.89 | $15.89 |
| **Gingerbread 6" spindle running trim** <br> *Replace* Materials......10.90  Labor ..........6.32 <br> *Remove*........................  Labor ..........1.00 | lf | $1.00 | $17.22 | $18.22 |

| Item Description | Unit | Remove | Replace | Total |
|---|---|---|---|---|
| **Gingerbread 8" spindle running trim** | lf | $1.00 | $19.52 | $20.52 |
| *Replace* Materials.......13.20      Labor ...........6.32 | | | | |
| *Remove*.........................      Labor ...........1.00 | | | | |
| **Gingerbread 10" spindle running trim** | lf | $1.00 | $24.22 | $25.22 |
| *Replace* Materials.......17.90      Labor ...........6.32 | | | | |
| *Remove*.........................      Labor ...........1.00 | | | | |
| **Gingerbread 12" spindle running trim** | lf | $1.00 | $28.02 | $29.02 |
| *Replace* Materials ......21.70      Labor ...........6.32 | | | | |
| *Remove*.........................      Labor ...........1.00 | | | | |
| **Gingerbread 14" spindle running trim** | lf | $1.00 | $32.62 | $33.62 |
| *Replace* Materials ......26.30      Labor ...........6.32 | | | | |
| *Remove*.........................      Labor ...........1.00 | | | | |
| **Remove gingerbread running trim for work, then reinstall** | lf | — | $7.71 | $7.71 |
| *Replace* ........................      Labor ...........7.71 | | | | |
| **Gingerbread bracket, standard grade** | ea | $4.03 | $38.80 | $42.83 |
| *Replace* Materials ......25.10      Labor ...........13.70 | | | | |
| *Remove*.........................      Labor ...........4.03 | | | | |
| ► Longest leg up to 12" with simple sawn pattern. | | | | |
| **Gingerbread bracket, high grade** | ea | $4.03 | $44.10 | $48.13 |
| *Replace* Materials ......30.40      Labor ...........13.70 | | | | |
| *Remove*.........................      Labor ...........4.03 | | | | |
| ► Longest leg up to 23" with simple sawn pattern. | | | | |
| **Gingerbread bracket, deluxe grade** | ea | $4.03 | $47.20 | $51.23 |
| *Replace* Materials ......33.50      Labor ...........13.70 | | | | |
| *Remove*.........................      Labor ...........4.03 | | | | |
| ► Longest leg up to 30" with ornately sawn pattern. | | | | |
| **Gingerbread bracket, custom grade** | ea | $4.03 | $51.70 | $55.73 |
| *Replace* Materials ......38.00      Labor ...........13.70 | | | | |
| *Remove*.........................      Labor ...........4.03 | | | | |
| ► Longest leg up to 30" with very ornately sawn pattern. | | | | |
| **Gingerbread fan bracket, standard grade** | ea | $4.03 | $43.50 | $47.53 |
| *Replace* Materials ......29.80      Labor ...........13.70 | | | | |
| *Remove*.........................      Labor ...........4.03 | | | | |
| ► Longest leg up to 14" with simple pattern. | | | | |
| **Gingerbread fan bracket, high grade** | ea | $4.03 | $47.10 | $51.13 |
| *Replace* Materials ......33.40      Labor ...........13.70 | | | | |
| *Remove*.........................      Labor ...........4.03 | | | | |
| ► Longest leg up to 25" with simple pattern. | | | | |
| **Gingerbread fan bracket, deluxe grade** | ea | $4.03 | $55.00 | $59.03 |
| *Replace* Materials ......41.30      Labor ...........13.70 | | | | |
| *Remove*.........................      Labor ...........4.03 | | | | |
| ► Longest leg up to 32" with ornate pattern. | | | | |
| **Gingerbread fan bracket, custom grade** | ea | $4.03 | $66.70 | $70.73 |
| *Replace* Materials ......53.00      Labor ...........13.70 | | | | |
| *Remove*.........................      Labor ...........4.03 | | | | |
| ► Longest leg up to 32" with very ornate pattern. | | | | |

*standard bracket △*

◄ **GINGERBREAD BRACKET**
Paint-grade poplar corner brackets. Add **30%** for red oak.

*high △*

*deluxe △*

◄ **GINGERBREAD FAN BRACKET**
Brackets combining sawn elements with radiating spindles or dowel-and-ball elements. Made from paint-grade poplar. Add **30%** for red oak.

| Item Description | Unit | Remove | Replace | Total |
|---|---|---|---|---|
| **GINGERBREAD POST BRACKET** *Made from paint-grade poplar. Add 30% for red oak.* | | | | |
| **Gingerbread post bracket, standard grade** | ea | $4.03 | $52.20 | $56.23 |
| *Replace* Materials......38.50  Labor........13.70 | | | | |
| *Remove*.................. Labor.........4.03 | | | | |
| ► Simple pattern bracket with drop. | | | | |
| **Gingerbread post bracket, high grade** | ea | $4.03 | $61.60 | $65.63 |
| *Replace* Materials......47.90  Labor........13.70 | | | | |
| *Remove*.................. Labor.........4.03 | | | | |
| ► Ornate pattern bracket with drop. | | | | |
| **Gingerbread post bracket, deluxe grade** | ea | $4.03 | $69.90 | $73.93 |
| *Replace* Materials......56.20  Labor........13.70 | | | | |
| *Remove*.................. Labor.........4.03 | | | | |
| ► Very ornate pattern bracket with drop. | | | | |
| ▷ remove & reinstall **Remove gingerbread post bracket for work, then reinstall** | ea | — | $14.80 | $14.80 |
| *Replace*.................. Labor........14.80 | | | | |
| **GINGERBREAD CORBEL** *Made from paint-grade poplar. Add 30% for red oak.* | | | | |
| **Gingerbread corbel, standard grade** | ea | $4.19 | $41.60 | $45.79 |
| *Replace* Materials......27.40  Labor........14.20 | | | | |
| *Remove*.................. Labor.........4.19 | | | | |
| ► Longest leg up to 12" with simple sawn pattern. | | | | |
| **Gingerbread corbel, high grade** | ea | $4.19 | $54.20 | $58.39 |
| *Replace* Materials......40.00  Labor........14.20 | | | | |
| *Remove*.................. Labor.........4.19 | | | | |
| ► Longest leg up to 16" with simple sawn pattern. | | | | |
| **Gingerbread corbel, deluxe grade** | ea | $4.19 | $69.50 | $73.69 |
| *Replace* Materials......55.30  Labor........14.20 | | | | |
| *Remove*.................. Labor.........4.19 | | | | |
| ► Longest leg up to 20" with ornately sawn pattern. | | | | |
| **Gingerbread corbel, custom grade** | ea | $4.19 | $93.40 | $97.59 |
| *Replace* Materials......79.20  Labor........14.20 | | | | |
| *Remove*.................. Labor.........4.19 | | | | |
| ► Longest leg up to 20" with very ornately sawn pattern. | | | | |
| ▷ remove & reinstall **Remove gingerbread corbel for work, then reinstall** | ea | — | $15.00 | $15.00 |
| *Replace*.................. Labor........15.00 | | | | |
| **GINGERBREAD HEADER** *Made from paint-grade poplar. Add 30% for red oak.* | | | | |
| **Gingerbread door or window header, standard grade** | lf | $.97 | $50.16 | $51.13 |
| *Replace* Materials......41.00  Labor........9.16 | | | | |
| *Remove*.................. Labor.........97 | | | | |
| ► Up to 14" long with sawn pattern. | | | | |
| **Gingerbread door or window header, high grade** | lf | $.97 | $66.26 | $67.23 |
| *Replace* Materials......57.10  Labor........9.16 | | | | |
| *Remove*.................. Labor.........97 | | | | |
| ► Up to 25" long with sawn pattern. | | | | |
| **Gingerbread door or window header, deluxe grade** | lf | $..97 | $85.46 | $86.43 |
| *Replace* Materials......76.30  Labor........9.16 | | | | |
| *Remove*.................. Labor.........97 | | | | |
| ► Up to 36" long with sawn pattern. | | | | |
| ▷ remove & reinstall **Remove gingerbread header for work, then reinstall** | lf | — | $11.50 | $11.50 |
| *Replace*.................. Labor........11.50 | | | | |

| Item Description | Unit | Remove | Replace | Total | |
|---|---|---|---|---|---|
| **10" gingerbread post drop**<br>*Replace* Materials........6.09          Labor...........12.70<br>*Remove*..........................          Labor ...........4.03 | ea | $4.03 | $18.79 | $22.82 | ◄ **GINGERBREAD POST DROP**<br>*Made from paint-grade poplar. Add **30%** for red oak.* |
| **12" gingerbread post drop**<br>*Replace* Materials........7.61          Labor...........12.70<br>*Remove*..........................          Labor ...........4.03 | ea | $4.03 | $20.31 | $24.34 | |
| **18" gingerbread post drop**<br>*Replace* Materials........9.13          Labor...........12.70<br>*Remove*..........................          Labor ...........4.03 | ea | $4.03 | $21.83 | $25.86 | |
| **24" gingerbread post drop**<br>*Replace* Materials......10.70          Labor...........12.70<br>*Remove*..........................          Labor ...........4.03 | ea | $4.03 | $23.40 | $27.43 | |
| **Remove gingerbread post drop for work, then reinstall**<br>*Replace* ........................          Labor...........14.10 | ea | — | $14.10 | $14.10 | ◁ **remove & reinstall** |
| **Gingerbread spandrel, standard grade**<br>*Replace* Materials......19.50          Labor ...........9.36<br>*Remove*..........................          Labor ...........1.00<br>▶ Up to 6" deep in center and 14" deep on each side. | lf | $1.00 | $28.86 | $29.86 | ◄ **GINGERBREAD SPANDREL**<br>*Spandrels are horizontal decorative elements for exterior and interior openings. Typically both corners and the center contain sawn elements. The remaining space is filled with either ball-and-dowel or spindle elements. Made from paint-grade poplar. Add **30%** for red oak.* |
| **Gingerbread spandrel, high grade**<br>*Replace* Materials......24.70          Labor ...........9.36<br>*Remove*..........................          Labor ...........1.00<br>▶ Up to 9" deep in center and 17" deep on each side. | lf | $1.00 | $34.06 | $35.06 | |
| **Gingerbread spandrel, custom grade**<br>*Replace* Materials......32.10          Labor ...........9.36<br>*Remove*..........................          Labor ...........1.00<br>▶ Up to 13" deep in center and 21" deep on each side. | lf | $1.00 | $41.46 | $42.46 | |
| **Gingerbread spandrel, deluxe grade**<br>*Replace* Materials......43.80          Labor ...........9.36<br>*Remove*..........................          Labor ...........1.00<br>▶ Up to 16" deep in center and 24" deep on each side. | lf | $1.00 | $53.16 | $54.16 | *high △* |
| **Gingerbread spandrel, custom deluxe grade**<br>*Replace* Materials......54.90          Labor ...........9.36<br>*Remove*..........................          Labor ...........1.00<br>▶ Up to 22" deep in center and 31" deep on each side. | lf | $1.00 | $64.26 | $65.26 | *deluxe △* |
| **Gingerbread arch spandrel, standard grade**<br>*Replace* Materials......37.30          Labor ...........9.36<br>*Remove*..........................          Labor ...........1.00<br>▶ Leg against wall up to 12" long. | lf | $1.00 | $46.66 | $47.66 | ◄ **GINGERBREAD ARCH SPANDREL**<br>*Arched spandrels have arched end sections that typically contain either sawn woodwork or a spindle fan. Made from paint-grade poplar. Add **30%** for red oak.* |
| **Gingerbread arch spandrel, high grade**<br>*Replace* Materials......46.40          Labor ...........9.36<br>*Remove*..........................          Labor ...........1.00<br>▶ Leg against wall up to 20" long, simple pattern. | lf | $1.00 | $55.76 | $56.76 | |
| **Gingerbread arch spandrel, custom grade**<br>*Replace* Materials......53.60          Labor ...........9.36<br>*Remove*..........................          Labor ...........1.00<br>▶ Leg against wall up to 22" long, ornate pattern, often with post drops. | lf | $1.00 | $62.96 | $63.96 | *custom △* |

| Item Description | Unit | Remove | Replace | Total |
|---|---|---|---|---|
| **GINGERBREAD ARCH SPANDREL** continued | | | | |
| **Gingerbread arch spandrel, deluxe grade** | lf | $1.00 | $69.46 | $70.46 |
| *Replace* Materials......60.10   Labor ...........9.36 | | | | |
| *Remove*......................   Labor ...........1.00 | | | | |
| ▶ Leg against wall up to 26" long, simple pattern. | | | | |
| **Gingerbread arch spandrel, custom deluxe grade** | lf | $1.00 | $80.16 | $81.16 |
| *Replace* Materials ......70.80   Labor ...........9.36 | | | | |
| *Remove*......................   Labor ...........1.00 | | | | |
| ▶ Leg against wall up to 28" long, ornate pattern, often with post drops. | | | | |
| **Remove gingerbread spandrel for work, then reinstall** | lf | — | $11.80 | $11.80 |
| *Replace* ......................   Labor ...........11.80 | | | | |
| **Gingerbread window cornice, standard grade** | lf | $1.07 | $27.86 | $28.93 |
| *Replace* Materials ......18.30   Labor ...........9.56 | | | | |
| *Remove*......................   Labor ...........1.07 | | | | |
| ▶ Cornice is 5" deep with a height of 6". Made from finish board with bed mold on top and simple panel mold on bottom. | | | | |
| **Gingerbread window cornice, high grade** | lf | $1.07 | $32.36 | $33.43 |
| *Replace* Materials......22.80   Labor ...........9.56 | | | | |
| *Remove*......................   Labor ...........1.07 | | | | |
| ▶ Cornice is 5-1/2" deep with a height of 8-1/2". Side brackets are sawn with drop. Front of cornice is made from 2" to 4" ball and dowel running trim. | | | | |
| **Gingerbread window cornice, deluxe grade** | lf | $1.07 | $38.46 | $39.53 |
| *Replace* Materials......28.90   Labor ...........9.56 | | | | |
| *Remove*......................   Labor ...........1.07 | | | | |
| ▶ Cornice is 8" deep with a height of 9". Side brackets are sawn with drop and spindles. Front of cornice is made from 6" to 8" spindle running trim with sawn woodwork at center. | | | | |
| **Gingerbread window cornice, custom grade** | lf | $1.07 | $39.46 | $40.53 |
| *Replace* Materials......29.90   Labor ...........9.56 | | | | |
| *Remove*......................   Labor ...........1.07 | | | | |
| ▶ Cornice is 8" deep with a height of 9". Side brackets are sawn with drop and spindles. Front of cornice is made from 6" to 8" spindle running trim with very ornately sawn woodwork at center. | | | | |
| **Gingerbread window cornice, custom deluxe grade** | lf | $1.07 | $44.56 | $45.63 |
| *Replace* Materials ......35.00   Labor ...........9.56 | | | | |
| *Remove*......................   Labor ...........1.07 | | | | |
| ▶ Cornice is 8" deep with a height of 9". Side brackets are sawn with drop and ball and dowels. Front of cornice is made from 6" to 8" ball-and-dowel running trim with very ornately sawn woodwork at center. | | | | |
| **Remove gingerbread window cornice for work, then reinstall** | lf | — | $12.10 | $12.10 |
| *Replace* ......................   Labor ...........12.10 | | | | |
| **Gingerbread gable ornament, standard grade** | ea | $6.65 | $129.00 | $135.65 |
| *Replace* Materials ....106.00   Labor ...........23.00 | | | | |
| *Remove*......................   Labor ...........6.65 | | | | |
| ▶ Fixed or adjustable ornament. Simple sawn pattern with longest leg up to 32". | | | | |
| **Gingerbread gable ornament, high grade** | ea | $6.65 | $202.00 | $208.65 |
| *Replace* Materials.....179.00   Labor ...........23.00 | | | | |
| *Remove*......................   Labor ...........6.65 | | | | |
| ▶ Fixed ornament with legs up to 36". May contain some spindles or ball-and-dowel. Often contains drop in center. | | | | |

Left margin labels:
GINGERBREAD ARCH SPANDREL continued — custom deluxe △
remove & reinstall ▷
GINGERBREAD WINDOW CORNICE — Made from paint-grade poplar. Add **30%** for red oak. — standard △ / high △ / deluxe △ / custom deluxe △
remove & reinstall ▷
GINGERBREAD GABLE ORNAMENT — Gable ornaments can be ordered for roofs of any slope. They are typically found on roofs with a slope of 6 in 12 or more. Ornaments are placed in the gables at the peak of the roof. Made from paint-grade poplar. Add **30%** for red oak.

| Item Description | Unit | Remove | Replace | Total |
|---|---|---|---|---|
| **Gingerbread gable ornament, deluxe grade** | ea | $6.65 | $296.00 | $302.65 |
| *Replace* Materials ....273.00     Labor ..........23.00 | | | | |
| *Remove*........................     Labor ...........6.65 | | | | |
| ► Fixed ornament with legs up to 45". May contain some spindles or ball-and-dowel. Often contains drop in center. | | | | |
| **Gingerbread gable ornament, custom grade** | ea | $6.65 | $507.00 | $513.65 |
| *Replace* Materials ....484.00     Labor ..........23.00 | | | | |
| *Remove*........................     Labor ...........6.65 | | | | |
| ► Fixed ornament with legs up to 48". Ornate combinations of fanned spindles, ball-and-dowel and drops. | | | | |
| **Gingerbread gable ornament, custom deluxe grade** | ea | $6.65 | $613.00 | $619.65 |
| *Replace* Materials ....590.00     Labor ..........23.00 | | | | |
| *Remove*........................     Labor ...........6.65 | | | | |
| ► Fixed ornament with legs up to 60". Very ornate combinations of fanned spindles, ball-and-dowel and drops. | | | | |
| **Remove gingerbread gable ornament for work, then reinstall** | ea | — | $37.20 | $37.20 |
| *Replace* ........................     Labor...........37.20 | | | | |
| **Gingerbread gable finial, standard grade** | ea | $6.26 | $86.80 | $93.06 |
| *Replace* Materials ......64.70     Labor ..........22.10 | | | | |
| *Remove*........................     Labor ...........6.26 | | | | |
| ► Finial with 28" post. | | | | |
| **Gingerbread gable finial, high grade** | ea | $6.26 | $109.60 | $115.86 |
| *Replace* Materials ......87.50     Labor ..........22.10 | | | | |
| *Remove*........................     Labor ...........6.26 | | | | |
| ► Finial with 34" post. | | | | |
| **Remove gingerbread gable finial for work, then reinstall** | ea | — | $35.40 | $35.40 |
| *Replace* ........................     Labor...........35.40 | | | | |
| **4" x 4" porch post, standard grade** | lf | $3.33 | $12.83 | $16.16 |
| *Replace* Materials ........7.50     Labor ............5.33 | | | | |
| *Remove*........................     Labor ............3.33 | | | | |
| ► Turned post. Sometimes called colonist style. | | | | |
| **4" x 4" porch post, high grade** | lf | $3.33 | $20.33 | $23.66 |
| *Replace* Materials .......15.00     Labor ............5.33 | | | | |
| *Remove*........................     Labor ............3.33 | | | | |
| ► Turned post with fluted columns. Or square post with flutes. Square post also trimmed with molding at base, at 1/3 shaft, and at about 12" to 16" from top. | | | | |
| **4" x 4" porch post, deluxe grade** | lf | $3.33 | $37.23 | $40.56 |
| *Replace* Materials ......31.90     Labor ............5.33 | | | | |
| *Remove*........................     Labor ............3.33 | | | | |
| ► Turned post with spiral pattern. Or square post with flutes. Square post also trimmed with panels to 1/3 shaft, capped at base and top of panel with moldings, and with molding trim about 12" to 16" from top. | | | | |
| **6" x 6" porch post, standard grade** | lf | $3.33 | $16.33 | $19.66 |
| *Replace* Materials .......11.00     Labor ............5.33 | | | | |
| *Remove*........................     Labor ............3.33 | | | | |
| ► Turned post. Sometimes called colonist style. | | | | |
| **6" x 6" porch post, high grade** | lf | $3.33 | $27.73 | $31.06 |
| *Replace* Materials ......22.40     Labor ............5.33 | | | | |
| *Remove*........................     Labor ............3.33 | | | | |
| ► Turned post with fluted columns. Or square post with flutes. Square post also trimmed with molding at base, at 1/3 shaft, and at about 12" to 16" from top. | | | | |

standard △

custom deluxe △

◁ remove & reinstall

◄ **GINGERBREAD GABLE FINIAL**
Finials are placed at the peak of the roof on each end. Made from cedar.

◄ **PORCH POST**
For stain-grade add **16%**. Non-laminated posts made from clear, select Douglas fir or clear all-heart redwood. Standard grade posts may be made from cedar. Square posts are hollow and include a structural post inside.

▽ standard

high △

| | Item Description | Unit | Remove | Replace | Total |
|---|---|---|---|---|---|
| **PORCH POST ▶**<br>*continued* | **6" x 6" porch post, deluxe grade**<br>*Replace* Materials ......28.30     Labor ............5.33<br>*Remove* ..........................     Labor ............3.33<br>▶ Turned post with spiral pattern. Or square post with flutes. Square post also trimmed with panels to 1/3 shaft, capped at base and top of panel with moldings, and with molding trim about 12" to 16" from top. | lf | $3.33 | $33.63 | $36.96 |
| ▽ *high* | **8" x 8" porch post, standard grade**<br>*Replace* Materials ......12.60     Labor ............5.33<br>*Remove* ..........................     Labor ............3.33<br>▶ Turned post. Sometimes called colonist style. | lf | $3.33 | $17.93 | $21.26 |
| | **8" x 8" porch post, high grade**<br>*Replace* Materials ......25.60     Labor ............5.33<br>*Remove* ..........................     Labor ............3.33<br>▶ Turned post with fluted columns. Or square post with flutes. Square post also trimmed with molding at base, at 1/3 shaft, and about at 12" to 16" from top. | lf | $3.33 | $30.93 | $34.26 |
| *deluxe* △ | **8" x 8" porch post, deluxe grade**<br>*Replace* Materials ......32.30     Labor ............5.33<br>*Remove* ..........................     Labor ............3.33<br>▶ Turned post with spiral pattern. Or square post with flutes. Square post also trimmed with panels to 1/3 shaft, capped at base and top of panel with moldings, and with molding trim about 12" to 16" from top. | lf | $3.33 | $37.63 | $40.96 |
| **remove & reinstall** ▷ | **Remove porch post for work, then reinstall**<br>*Replace* ........................     Labor ............7.43 | lf | — | $7.43 | $7.43 |
| **CARVED ONLAY ▶**<br>*Onlays are available in a wide variety of styles and prices. Use these listings as indicators of complexity and price range. Made from maple. Add **25%** for red oak.* | **Small carved wood onlay, acanthus**<br>*Replace* Materials ......29.20     Labor ..........20.50<br>*Remove* ..........................     Labor ............1.62 | ea | $1.62 | $49.70 | $51.32 |
| | **Small carved wood onlay, ribbon**<br>*Replace* Materials ......30.60     Labor ..........20.50<br>*Remove* ..........................     Labor ............1.62 | ea | $1.62 | $51.10 | $52.72 |
| | **Small carved wood onlay, grape**<br>*Replace* Materials ......48.90     Labor ..........20.50<br>*Remove* ..........................     Labor ............1.62 | ea | $1.62 | $69.40 | $71.02 |
| *acanthus* △ | **Small carved wood onlay, shell**<br>*Replace* Materials ......42.80     Labor ..........20.50<br>*Remove* ..........................     Labor ............1.62 | ea | $1.62 | $63.30 | $64.92 |
| | **Small carved wood onlay, floral**<br>*Replace* Materials ......44.90     Labor ..........20.50<br>*Remove* ..........................     Labor ............1.62 | ea | $1.62 | $65.40 | $67.02 |
| *ribbon* △ | **Medium carved wood onlay, acanthus**<br>*Replace* Materials ......45.50     Labor ..........20.50<br>*Remove* ..........................     Labor ............1.62 | ea | $1.62 | $66.00 | $67.62 |
| | **Medium carved wood onlay, ribbon**<br>*Replace* Materials ......47.60     Labor ..........20.50<br>*Remove* ..........................     Labor ............1.62 | ea | $1.62 | $68.10 | $69.72 |
| *grape* △ | **Medium carved wood onlay, grape**<br>*Replace* Materials ......76.10     Labor ..........20.50<br>*Remove* ..........................     Labor ............1.62 | ea | $1.62 | $96.60 | $98.22 |

| Item Description | Unit | Remove | Replace | Total | |
|---|---|---|---|---|---|
| **Medium carved wood onlay, shell** | ea | $1.62 | $87.10 | $88.72 | |
| *Replace* Materials ......66.60     Labor ..........20.50 | | | | | |
| *Remove* ........................     Labor ............1.62 | | | | | *shell △* |
| **Medium carved wood onlay, floral** | ea | $1.62 | $89.80 | $91.42 | |
| *Replace* Materials ......69.30     Labor ..........20.50 | | | | | |
| *Remove* ........................     Labor ............1.62 | | | | | |
| **Large carved wood onlay, acanthus** | ea | $1.62 | $78.30 | $79.92 | |
| *Replace* Materials ......57.80     Labor ..........20.50 | | | | | |
| *Remove* ........................     Labor ............1.62 | | | | | |
| **Large carved wood onlay, ribbon** | ea | $1.62 | $81.70 | $83.32 | *floral △* |
| *Replace* Materials .......61.20     Labor ..........20.50 | | | | | |
| *Remove* ........................     Labor ............1.62 | | | | | |
| **Large carved wood onlay, grape** | ea | $1.62 | $115.60 | $117.22 | |
| *Replace* Materials ......95.10     Labor ..........20.50 | | | | | |
| *Remove* ........................     Labor ............1.62 | | | | | |
| **Large carved wood onlay, shell** | ea | $1.62 | $106.10 | $107.72 | |
| *Replace* Materials ......85.60     Labor ..........20.50 | | | | | |
| *Remove* ........................     Labor ............1.62 | | | | | |
| **Large carved wood onlay, floral** | ea | $1.62 | $108.80 | $110.42 | |
| *Replace* Materials ......88.30     Labor ..........20.50 | | | | | |
| *Remove* ........................     Labor ............1.62 | | | | | |
| **Remove onlay for work, then reinstall** | ea | — | $25.60 | $25.60 | ◁ **remove & reinstall** |
| *Replace* ........................     Labor ..........25.60 | | | | | |
| **1″ x 2″ S4S select pine** | lf | $.68 | $2.45 | $3.13 | ◀ **FINISH BOARD** |
| *Replace* Materials ......... .51     Labor ............1.94 | | | | | *Smooth four sides.* |
| *Remove* ........................     Labor ............. .68 | | | | | *Includes 4% waste.* |
| **1″ x 4″ S4S select pine** | lf | $.68 | $2.96 | $3.64 | |
| *Replace* Materials ...... 1.02     Labor ............1.94 | | | | | |
| *Remove* ........................     Labor ............. .68 | | | | | |
| **1″ x 6″ S4S select pine** | lf | $.68 | $3.47 | $4.15 | |
| *Replace* Materials ........1.53     Labor ............1.94 | | | | | |
| *Remove* ........................     Labor ............. .68 | | | | | |
| **1″ x 8″ S4S select pine** | lf | $.68 | $3.98 | $4.66 | |
| *Replace* Materials ........2.04     Labor ............1.94 | | | | | |
| *Remove* ........................     Labor ............. .68 | | | | | |
| **1″ x 10″ S4S select pine** | lf | $.68 | $4.49 | $5.17 | |
| *Replace* Materials ........2.55     Labor ............1.94 | | | | | |
| *Remove* ........................     Labor ............. .68 | | | | | |
| **1″ x 12″ S4S select pine** | lf | $.68 | $5.00 | $5.68 | |
| *Replace* Materials ........3.06     Labor ............1.94 | | | | | |
| *Remove* ........................     Labor ............. .68 | | | | | |
| **Add 3% for S4S poplar** | | | | | ◁ **other wood species** |
| **Add 13% for S4S mahogany** | | | | | |
| **Add 17% for S4S red oak** | | | | | |

**RELATED ITEMS**

| Item Description | Unit | Remove | Replace | Total |
|---|---|---|---|---|
| **FINISH BOARD ▶** *continued* **Add for bull nose on 1 x boards** *Replace* Materials ........ .47 | lf | — | $.47 | $.47 |
| **remove & reinstall ▷ Remove finish board trim for work, then reinstall** *Replace* Labor ...........2.75 | lf | — | $2.75 | $2.75 |
| **FINISH PLYWOOD ▶** *Includes 4% waste.* **1/4" aromatic cedar veneer plywood** *Replace* Materials ......2.39 Labor ...........1.11 *Remove* Labor ............. .58 | sf | $.58 | $3.50 | $4.08 |
| **1/4" birch veneer plywood** *Replace* Materials ......2.31 Labor ...........1.11 *Remove* Labor ............. .58 | sf | $.58 | $3.42 | $4.00 |
| **1/4" cherry veneer plywood** *Replace* Materials ......2.57 Labor ...........1.11 *Remove* Labor ............. .58 | sf | $.58 | $3.68 | $4.26 |
| **1/4" chestnut veneer plywood** *Replace* Materials ......4.07 Labor ...........1.11 *Remove* Labor ............. .58 | sf | $.58 | $5.18 | $5.76 |
| **1/4" knotty pine veneer plywood** *Replace* Materials ......1.79 Labor ...........1.11 *Remove* Labor ............. .58 | sf | $.58 | $2.90 | $3.48 |
| **1/4" lauan mahogany veneer plywood** *Replace* Materials ........ .91 Labor ...........1.11 *Remove* Labor ............. .58 | sf | $.58 | $2.02 | $2.60 |
| **1/4" mahogany veneer plywood** *Replace* Materials ......2.60 Labor ...........1.11 *Remove* Labor ............. .58 | sf | $.58 | $3.71 | $4.29 |
| **1/4" pecan veneer plywood** *Replace* Materials ......2.67 Labor ...........1.11 *Remove* Labor ............. .58 | sf | $.58 | $3.78 | $4.36 |
| **1/4" red oak veneer plywood** *Replace* Materials ......2.34 Labor ...........1.11 *Remove* Labor ............. .58 | sf | $.58 | $3.45 | $4.03 |
| **1/4" rosewood veneer plywood** *Replace* Materials ......3.61 Labor ...........1.11 *Remove* Labor ............. .58 | sf | $.58 | $4.72 | $5.30 |
| **1/4" teak veneer plywood** *Replace* Materials ......4.79 Labor ...........1.11 *Remove* Labor ............. .58 | sf | $.58 | $5.90 | $6.48 |
| **1/4" walnut veneer plywood** *Replace* Materials ......3.45 Labor ...........1.11 *Remove* Labor ............. .58 | sf | $.58 | $4.56 | $5.14 |
| **remove & reinstall ▷ Remove 1/4" finish plywood for work, then reinstall** *Replace* Labor ...........1.44 | sf | — | $1.44 | $1.44 |

NOTES: _____

_____ end

# TIME & MATERIAL CHARTS (selected items)

## Finish Carpentry Materials

| DESCRIPTION | MATERIAL PRICE | GROSS COVERAGE | WASTE | NET COVERAGE | UNIT PRICE |
|---|---|---|---|---|---|
| **Clamshell base** | | | | | |
| 1-1/2" stain-grade pine | $.77 lf | 1 | 7% | .93 | $.83 lf |
| 3-1/2" stain-grade pine | $1.24 lf | 1 | 7% | .93 | $1.33 lf |
| **Pattern base** | | | | | |
| 1-1/2" stain-grade pine | $.94 lf | 1 | 7% | .93 | $1.01 lf |
| 2-1/2" stain-grade pine | $1.52 lf | 1 | 7% | .93 | $1.63 lf |
| 3-1/2" stain-grade pine | $2.01 lf | 1 | 7% | .93 | $2.16 lf |
| **Base shoe** | | | | | |
| 3/4" stain-grade pine | $.47 lf | 1 | 7% | .93 | $.51 lf |
| **Clamshell casing** | | | | | |
| 1-1/2" stain-grade pine | $.80 lf | 1 | 5% | .95 | $.84 lf |
| 2-1/2" stain-grade pine | $.92 lf | 1 | 5% | .95 | $.97 lf |
| 3-1/2" stain-grade pine | $1.29 lf | 1 | 5% | .95 | $1.36 lf |
| **Pattern casing** | | | | | |
| 1-1/2" stain-grade pine | $.98 lf | 1 | 5% | .95 | $1.03 lf |
| 2-1/2" stain-grade pine | $1.58 lf | 1 | 5% | .95 | $1.66 lf |
| 3-1/2" stain-grade pine | $2.09 lf | 1 | 5% | .95 | $2.20 lf |
| **Window moldings** | | | | | |
| 2-1/2" stain-grade pine stool | $1.75 lf | 1 | 4% | .96 | $1.82 lf |
| 3-1/2" stain-grade pine apron | $1.14 lf | 1 | 4% | .96 | $1.19 lf |
| **Chair rail** | | | | | |
| 2-1/2" stain-grade pine | $1.51 lf | 1 | 4% | .96 | $1.57 lf |
| 3-1/2" stain-grade pine | $1.90 lf | 1 | 4% | .96 | $1.98 lf |
| **Drip cap** | | | | | |
| 1-5/8" redwood | $1.40 lf | 1 | 4% | .96 | $1.46 lf |
| 2-1/4" redwood | $1.56 lf | 1 | 4% | .96 | $1.63 lf |
| **Astragal** | | | | | |
| 1-3/4" stain-grade pine | $2.90 lf | 1 | 4% | .96 | $3.02 lf |
| 2-1/4" stain-grade pine | $3.52 lf | 1 | 4% | .96 | $3.67 lf |
| **Cove** | | | | | |
| 1/2" stain-grade pine | $.54 lf | 1 | 4% | .96 | $.56 lf |
| 3/4" stain-grade pine | $.62 lf | 1 | 4% | .96 | $.65 lf |
| 1" stain-grade pine | $.77 lf | 1 | 4% | .96 | $.80 lf |
| 2-1/2" stain-grade pine | $1.36 lf | 1 | 4% | .96 | $1.42 lf |
| 3-1/2" stain-grade pine | $1.77 lf | 1 | 4% | .96 | $1.84 lf |
| **Half-round** | | | | | |
| 1" stain-grade pine | $.64 lf | 1 | 4% | .96 | $.67 lf |
| 2" stain-grade pine | $.91 lf | 1 | 4% | .96 | $.95 lf |
| **Quarter-round** | | | | | |
| 1/2" stain-grade pine | $.47 lf | 1 | 4% | .96 | $.49 lf |
| 3/4" stain-grade pine | $.56 lf | 1 | 4% | .96 | $.58 lf |
| 1" stain-grade pine | $1.00 lf | 1 | 4% | .96 | $1.04 lf |
| **Corner bead** | | | | | |
| stain-grade pine | $1.09 lf | 1 | 4% | .96 | $1.14 lf |
| turned stain-grade pine with finials | $12.00 lf | 1 | 4% | .96 | $12.50 lf |
| clear plastic | $.86 lf | 1 | 4% | .96 | $.90 lf |
| **Bed mold** | | | | | |
| 2-1/2" stain-grade pine | $1.52 lf | 1 | 4% | .96 | $1.58 lf |

. . . More ➤

## Finish Carpentry Materials *continued*

| DESCRIPTION | MATERIAL PRICE | GROSS COVERAGE | WASTE | NET COVERAGE | UNIT PRICE |
|---|---|---|---|---|---|
| **Crown** | | | | | |
| 3-1/2" stain-grade pine | $1.95 lf | 1 | 4% | .96 | $2.03 lf |
| 4-1/2" stain-grade pine | $2.87 lf | 1 | 4% | .96 | $2.99 lf |
| **Hand rail** | | | | | |
| stain-grade pine | $2.88 lf | 1 | 4% | .96 | $3.00 lf |
| **Specialty moldings, 3/4"** | | | | | |
| stain-grade pine with vertical milling | $2.29 lf | 1 | 4% | .96 | $2.39 lf |
| stain-grade pine embossed | $1.36 lf | 1 | 4% | .96 | $1.42 lf |
| stain-grade pine with hand carving | $4.23 lf | 1 | 4% | .96 | $4.41 lf |
| stain-grade pine with heavy hand carving | $8.29 lf | 1 | 4% | .96 | $8.64 lf |
| **Specialty moldings, 1-1/2"** | | | | | |
| stain-grade pine with vertical milling | $2.61 lf | 1 | 4% | .96 | $2.72 lf |
| stain-grade pine embossed | $1.55 lf | 1 | 4% | .96 | $1.61 lf |
| stain-grade pine with hand carving | $4.83 lf | 1 | 4% | .96 | $5.03 lf |
| stain-grade pine with heavy hand carving | $9.46 lf | 1 | 4% | .96 | $9.85 lf |
| **Specialty moldings, 2-1/2"** | | | | | |
| stain-grade pine with vertical milling | $2.92 lf | 1 | 4% | .96 | $3.04 lf |
| stain-grade pine embossed | $1.74 lf | 1 | 4% | .96 | $1.81 lf |
| stain-grade pine with hand carving | $5.41 lf | 1 | 4% | .96 | $5.64 lf |
| stain-grade pine with heavy hand carving | $10.60 lf | 1 | 4% | .96 | $11.00 lf |
| **Specialty moldings, 3-1/2"** | | | | | |
| stain-grade pine with vertical milling | $3.25 lf | 1 | 4% | .96 | $3.39 lf |
| stain-grade pine embossed | $1.94 lf | 1 | 4% | .96 | $2.02 lf |
| stain-grade pine with hand carving | $6.02 lf | 1 | 4% | .96 | $6.27 lf |
| stain-grade pine with heavy hand carving | $11.80 lf | 1 | 4% | .96 | $12.30 lf |
| **Specialty moldings, 5"** | | | | | |
| stain-grade pine with vertical milling | $4.68 lf | 1 | 4% | .96 | $4.88 lf |
| stain-grade pine embossed | $2.79 lf | 1 | 4% | .96 | $2.91 lf |
| stain-grade pine with hand carving | $8.67 lf | 1 | 4% | .96 | $9.03 lf |
| stain-grade pine with heavy hand carving | $17.00 lf | 1 | 4% | .96 | $17.70 lf |
| **Specialty moldings, 8"** | | | | | |
| stain-grade pine with vertical milling | $7.66 lf | 1 | 4% | .96 | $7.98 lf |
| stain-grade pine embossed | $4.57 lf | 1 | 4% | .96 | $4.76 lf |
| stain-grade pine with hand carving | $14.20 lf | 1 | 4% | .96 | $14.80 lf |
| stain-grade pine with heavy hand carving | $27.80 lf | 1 | 4% | .96 | $29.00 lf |
| **Custom-milled moldings** | | | | | |
| molder setup charge | $150.00 ea | | | | $150.00 ea |
| molder custom knife charges | $335.00 ea | | | | $335.00 ea |
| 2" to 3" pine | $1.49 lf | 1 | 4% | .96 | $1.55 lf |
| 2" to 3" poplar | $1.65 lf | 1 | 4% | .96 | $1.72 lf |
| 2" to 3" mahogany | $1.97 lf | 1 | 4% | .96 | $2.05 lf |
| 2" to 3" red oak | $2.15 lf | 1 | 4% | .96 | $2.24 lf |
| **Inside corner radius for panel molding** | | | | | |
| typical | $1.50 ea | 1 | 4% | .96 | $1.56 ea |
| with heavy carving | $7.64 ea | 1 | 4% | .96 | $7.96 ea |
| **Closet work** | | | | | |
| shelf brackets, shelving, & rod | $8.70 lf | 1 | 4% | .96 | $9.06 lf |
| organizer system, standard grade | $8.09 sf | 1 | 4% | .96 | $8.43 sf |
| organizer system, deluxe grade | $12.40 sf | 1 | 4% | .96 | $12.90 sf |
| linen closet shelves, standard grade | $6.46 lf | 1 | 4% | .96 | $6.73 lf |
| linen closet pull-out shelves | $8.16 ea | 1 | 4% | .96 | $8.50 ea |
| closet rod, pine | $2.47 lf | 1 | 4% | .96 | $2.57 lf |
| **Built-in bookcase** | | | | | |
| 8" deep stain-grade pine | $6.62 sf | 1 | 4% | .96 | $6.90 sf |
| 12" deep stain-grade pine | $8.69 sf | 1 | 4% | .96 | $9.05 sf |
| 18" deep stain-grade pine | $11.40 sf | 1 | 4% | .96 | $11.90 sf |
| 24" deep stain-grade pine | $15.00 sf | 1 | 4% | .96 | $15.60 sf |

*. . . More >*

## Finish Carpentry Materials *continued*

| DESCRIPTION | MATERIAL PRICE | GROSS COVERAGE | WASTE | NET COVERAGE | UNIT PRICE |
|---|---|---|---|---|---|
| **Fireplace mantel beam** | | | | | |
| rough sawn | $7.71 *lf* | 1 | 4% | .96 | $8.03 *lf* |
| glue laminated | $22.00 *lf* | 1 | 4% | .96 | $22.90 *lf* |
| **Fireplace mantel** | | | | | |
| economy grade | $44.30 *lf* | | | | $44.30 *lf* |
| custom deluxe grade | $1,410.00 *lf* | | | | $1,410.00 *lf* |
| **Coffered ceiling** | | | | | |
| economy grade | $7.61 *sf* | 1 | 12% | .88 | $8.65 *sf* |
| custom deluxe grade | $39.30 *sf* | 1 | 12% | .88 | $44.70 *sf* |
| **Niche with casing and shelf bracket** | | | | | |
| typical | $152.00 *ea* | | | | $152.00 *ea* |
| with clamshell top | $266.00 *ea* | | | | $266.00 *ea* |
| clamshell top and clamshell shelf | $347.00 *ea* | | | | $347.00 *ea* |
| **Gingerbread running trim** | | | | | |
| fleur-sawn | $23.00 *lf* | 1 | 2% | .98 | $23.50 *lf* |
| picket-sawn | $29.80 *lf* | 1 | 2% | .98 | $30.40 *lf* |
| 2" ball-and-dowel | $7.10 *lf* | 1 | 2% | .98 | $7.24 *lf* |
| 14" ball-and-dowel | $26.10 *lf* | 1 | 2% | .98 | $26.60 *lf* |
| 2" spindle | $6.70 *lf* | 1 | 2% | .98 | $6.84 *lf* |
| 14" spindle | $25.80 *lf* | 1 | 2% | .98 | $26.30 *lf* |
| **Gingerbread bracket** | | | | | |
| standard grade | $25.10 *ea* | | | | $25.10 *ea* |
| custom grade | $38.00 *ea* | | | | $38.00 *ea* |
| **Gingerbread fan bracket** | | | | | |
| standard grade | $29.80 *ea* | | | | $29.80 *ea* |
| custom grade | $53.00 *ea* | | | | $53.00 *ea* |
| **Gingerbread post bracket** | | | | | |
| standard grade | $38.50 *ea* | | | | $38.50 *ea* |
| deluxe grade | $56.20 *ea* | | | | $56.20 *ea* |
| **Gingerbread corbel** | | | | | |
| standard grade | $27.40 *ea* | | | | $27.40 *ea* |
| custom grade | $79.20 *ea* | | | | $79.20 *ea* |
| **Gingerbread door or window header** | | | | | |
| standard grade | $41.00 *ea* | | | | $41.00 *ea* |
| deluxe grade | $76.30 *ea* | | | | $76.30 *ea* |
| **Gingerbread post drop** | | | | | |
| 10" | $6.09 *ea* | | | | $6.09 *ea* |
| 24" | $10.70 *ea* | | | | $10.70 *ea* |
| **Gingerbread spandrel** | | | | | |
| standard grade | $19.50 *lf* | | | | $19.50 *lf* |
| custom deluxe grade | $54.90 *lf* | | | | $54.90 *lf* |
| **Gingerbread arch spandrel** | | | | | |
| standard grade | $37.30 *lf* | | | | $37.30 *lf* |
| custom deluxe grade | $70.80 *lf* | | | | $70.80 *lf* |
| **Gingerbread window cornice** | | | | | |
| standard grade | $18.30 *lf* | | | | $18.30 *lf* |
| custom deluxe grade | $35.00 *lf* | | | | $35.00 *lf* |
| **Gingerbread gable ornament** | | | | | |
| standard grade | $106.00 *lf* | | | | $106.00 *lf* |
| custom deluxe grade | $590.00 *lf* | | | | $590.00 *lf* |
| **Gingerbread gable finial** | | | | | |
| standard grade | $64.70 *ea* | | | | $64.70 *ea* |
| high grade | $87.50 *ea* | | | | $87.50 *ea* |

... *More* >

## Finish Carpentry Materials *continued*

| DESCRIPTION | MATERIAL PRICE | GROSS COVERAGE | WASTE | NET COVERAGE | UNIT PRICE |
|---|---|---|---|---|---|
| **Porch post** | | | | | |
| 4" x 4", standard grade | $60.00 8' post | 8 | 0% | 8 | $7.50 lf |
| 4" x 4", deluxe grade | $255.00 8' post | 8 | 0% | 8 | $31.90 lf |
| 6" x 6", standard grade | $88.00 8' post | 8 | 0% | 8 | $11.00 lf |
| 6" x 6", deluxe grade | $226.00 8' post | 8 | 0% | 8 | $28.30 lf |
| 8" x 8", standard grade | $101.00 8' post | 8 | 0% | 8 | $12.60 lf |
| 8" x 8", deluxe grade | $258.00 8' post | 8 | 0% | 8 | $32.30 lf |
| **Carved wood onlay** | | | | | |
| medium, acanthus | $45.50 ea | | | | $45.50 ea |
| medium, ribbon | $47.60 ea | | | | $47.60 ea |
| medium, grape | $76.10 ea | | | | $76.10 ea |
| medium, shell | $66.60 ea | | | | $66.60 ea |
| medium, floral | $69.30 ea | | | | $69.30 ea |
| **Finish boards** | | | | | |
| 1" x 12" S4S select pine | $2.94 lf | 1 | 4% | .96 | $3.06 lf |
| **Hardwood plywood** | | | | | |
| 1/4" aromatic cedar veneer | $73.40 sheet | 32 | 4% | 30.72 | $2.39 sf |
| 1/4" birch veneer | $71.00 sheet | 32 | 4% | 30.72 | $2.31 sf |
| 1/4" cherry veneer | $79.00 sheet | 32 | 4% | 30.72 | $2.57 sf |
| 1/4" chestnut veneer | $125.00 sheet | 32 | 4% | 30.72 | $4.07 sf |
| 1/4" knotty pine veneer | $55.00 sheet | 32 | 4% | 30.72 | $1.79 sf |
| 1/4" lauan mahogany veneer | $28.00 sheet | 32 | 4% | 30.72 | $.91 sf |
| 1/4" mahogany veneer | $80.00 sheet | 32 | 4% | 30.72 | $2.60 sf |
| 1/4" pecan veneer | $82.00 sheet | 32 | 4% | 30.72 | $2.67 sf |
| 1/4" red oak veneer | $72.00 sheet | 32 | 4% | 30.72 | $2.34 sf |
| 1/4" rosewood veneer | $111.00 sheet | 32 | 4% | 30.72 | $3.61 sf |
| 1/4" teak veneer | $147.00 sheet | 32 | 4% | 30.72 | $4.79 sf |
| 1/4" walnut veneer | $106.00 sheet | 32 | 4% | 30.72 | $3.45 sf |

## Finish Carpentry Labor

| LABORER | BASE WAGE | PAID LEAVE | TRUE WAGE | FICA | FUTA | WORKER'S COMP. | UNEMPLOY. INSUR. | HEALTH INSUR. | RETIRE (401k) | LIABILITY INSUR. | COST PER HOUR |
|---|---|---|---|---|---|---|---|---|---|---|---|
| Carpenter | $22.60 | 1.76 | $24.36 | 1.86 | .19 | 4.56 | 2.12 | 2.54 | .73 | 3.17 | $39.50 |
| Carpenter's helper | $16.30 | 1.27 | $17.57 | 1.34 | .14 | 3.29 | 1.53 | 2.54 | .53 | 2.28 | $29.20 |
| Demolition laborer | $13.40 | 1.05 | $14.45 | 1.11 | .12 | 4.44 | 1.26 | 2.54 | .43 | 1.88 | $26.20 |

**Paid Leave** is calculated based on two weeks paid vacation, one week sick leave, and seven paid holidays. Employer's matching portion of **FICA** is 7.65 percent. **FUTA** (Federal Unemployment) is .8 percent. **Worker's compensation** for the finish carpentry trade was calculated using a national average of 18.71 percent. **Unemployment insurance** was calculated using a national average of 8.7 percent. **Health insurance** was calculated based on a projected national average for 2001 of $505 per employee (and family when applicable) per month. Employer pays 80 percent for a per month cost of $404 per employee. **Retirement** is based on a 401(k) retirement program with employer matching of 50 percent. Employee contributions to the 401(k) plan are an average of 6 percent of the true wage. **Liability insurance** is based on a national average of 12.9 percent.

# Finish Carpentry Labor Productivity

| WORK DESCRIPTION | LABORER | COST PER HOUR | PRODUCTIVITY | UNIT PRICE |
|---|---|---|---|---|
| **Demolition** | | | | |
| remove wall molding (base, chair rail, crown) | demolition laborer | $26.20 | .026 | $.68 lf |
| remove door and window molding | demolition laborer | $26.20 | .032 | $.84 lf |
| remove base or corner block | demolition laborer | $26.20 | .036 | $.94 ea |
| remove head block | demolition laborer | $26.20 | .037 | $.97 ea |
| remove overdoor molding | demolition laborer | $26.20 | .028 | $.73 lf |
| remove window stool | demolition laborer | $26.20 | .026 | $.68 lf |
| remove window apron | demolition laborer | $26.20 | .028 | $.73 lf |
| remove corner bead | demolition laborer | $26.20 | .043 | $1.13 lf |
| remove hand rail | demolition laborer | $26.20 | .028 | $.73 lf |
| remove shelf brackets, shelving, and rod | demolition laborer | $26.20 | .063 | $1.65 lf |
| remove closet organizer system | demolition laborer | $26.20 | .047 | $1.23 sf |
| remove linen closet shelves | demolition laborer | $26.20 | .034 | $.89 lf |
| remove closet rod | demolition laborer | $26.20 | .035 | $.92 lf |
| remove tongue-&-groove cedar closet lining | demolition laborer | $26.20 | .028 | $.73 sf |
| remove cedar veneer plywood closet lining | demolition laborer | $26.20 | .022 | $.58 sf |
| remove built-in bookcase | demolition laborer | $26.20 | .051 | $1.34 sf |
| remove fireplace mantel beam | demolition laborer | $26.20 | .080 | $2.10 lf |
| remove fireplace mantel | demolition laborer | $26.20 | .094 | $2.46 lf |
| remove coffered ceiling | demolition laborer | $26.20 | .047 | $1.23 sf |
| remove niche | demolition laborer | $26.20 | .317 | $8.31 ea |
| remove gingerbread running trim | demolition laborer | $26.20 | .038 | $1.00 lf |
| remove gingerbread bracket | demolition laborer | $26.20 | .154 | $4.03 ea |
| remove gingerbread corbel | demolition laborer | $26.20 | .160 | $4.19 ea |
| remove gingerbread door or window header | demolition laborer | $26.20 | .037 | $.97 lf |
| remove gingerbread post drop | demolition laborer | $26.20 | .154 | $4.03 ea |
| remove gingerbread spandrel | demolition laborer | $26.20 | .038 | $1.00 lf |
| remove gingerbread window cornice | demolition laborer | $26.20 | .041 | $1.07 lf |
| remove gingerbread gable ornament | demolition laborer | $26.20 | .254 | $6.65 lf |
| remove gingerbread gable finial | demolition laborer | $26.20 | .239 | $6.26 ea |
| remove porch post | demolition laborer | $26.20 | .127 | $3.33 lf |
| remove onlay | demolition laborer | $26.20 | .062 | $1.62 ea |
| remove finish trim board | demolition laborer | $26.20 | .026 | $.68 lf |
| remove finish plywood | demolition laborer | $26.20 | .022 | $.58 sf |
| **Finish carpentry crew** | | | | |
| finish carpentry | finish carpenter | $39.50 | | |
| finish carpentry | finish carpenter's helper | $29.20 | | |
| **finish carpentry** | **finish crew** | **$34.40** | | |
| **Install molding** | | | | |
| base, chair rail | finish carpenter | $39.50 | .038 | $1.50 lf |
| window or door casing or panel moldings | finish carpenter | $39.50 | .041 | $1.62 lf |
| crown | finish carpenter | $39.50 | .046 | $1.82 lf |
| **Install casing on curved window or door** | | | | |
| half-round top window or door per lf | finish carpenter | $39.50 | .144 | $5.69 lf |
| elliptical top window or door per lf | finish carpenter | $39.50 | .144 | $5.69 lf |
| round window per lf of diameter | finish carpenter | $39.50 | .294 | $11.60 lf |
| **Install wood key in curved molding** | | | | |
| install | finish carpenter | $39.50 | .251 | $9.91 ea |
| **Install base, corner, or head block** | | | | |
| install | finish carpenter | $39.50 | .063 | $2.49 ea |
| **Install overdoor molding** | | | | |
| install | finish carpenter | $39.50 | .041 | $1.62 lf |
| **Install door architrave** | | | | |
| interior | finish carpenter | $39.50 | .062 | $2.45 lf |
| exterior | finish carpenter | $39.50 | .080 | $3.16 lf |
| **Install exterior door surround** | | | | |
| economy grade | finish carpenter | $39.50 | .234 | $9.24 lf |
| custom deluxe grade | finish carpenter | $39.50 | .431 | $17.00 lf |

. . . More ➢

## Finish Carpentry Labor Productivity *continued*

| WORK DESCRIPTION | LABORER | COST PER HOUR | PRODUCTIVITY | UNIT PRICE |
|---|---|---|---|---|
| **Install exterior window surround** | | | | |
| economy grade | finish carpenter | $39.50 | .207 | $8.18 lf |
| custom deluxe grade | finish carpenter | $39.50 | .322 | $12.70 lf |
| **Install window trim** | | | | |
| stool | finish carpenter | $39.50 | .058 | $2.29 lf |
| apron | finish carpenter | $39.50 | .049 | $1.94 lf |
| **Install corner bead** | | | | |
| wood | finish carpenter | $39.50 | .077 | $3.04 lf |
| plastic | finish carpenter | $39.50 | .032 | $1.26 lf |
| **Install hand rail** | | | | |
| install | finish carpenter | $39.50 | .098 | $3.87 lf |
| **Install panel molding inside corner radius** | | | | |
| install | finish carpenter | $39.50 | .149 | $5.89 ea |
| **Install closet shelf brackets, shelving, & rod** | | | | |
| install | finish carpenter | $39.50 | .332 | $13.10 lf |
| **Install closet organizer system** | | | | |
| standard grade | finish carpenter | $39.50 | .304 | $12.00 sf |
| deluxe grade | finish carpenter | $39.50 | .526 | $20.80 sf |
| **Install linen closet shelves** | | | | |
| typical | finish carpenter | $39.50 | .673 | $26.60 lf |
| with pull-out shelves | finish carpenter | $39.50 | .695 | $27.50 lf |
| **Install closet rod** | | | | |
| install | finish carpenter | $39.50 | .080 | $3.16 lf |
| **Install closet lining** | | | | |
| tongue-&-groove cedar board | finish carpenter | $39.50 | .051 | $2.01 sf |
| 1/4" cedar veneer plywood | finish carpenter | $39.50 | .037 | $1.46 sf |
| **Install built-in bookcase** | | | | |
| 8" deep | finish carpenter | $39.50 | .269 | $10.60 sf |
| 12" deep | finish carpenter | $39.50 | .304 | $12.00 sf |
| 18" deep | finish carpenter | $39.50 | .317 | $12.50 sf |
| 24" deep | finish carpenter | $39.50 | .332 | $13.10 sf |
| **Install fireplace mantel beam** | | | | |
| install | finish carpenter | $39.50 | .539 | $21.30 lf |
| **Install fireplace mantel** | | | | |
| install | finish carpenter | $39.50 | .653 | $25.80 lf |
| **Install coffered ceiling** | | | | |
| economy grade | finish carpenter | $39.50 | .248 | $9.80 sf |
| custom deluxe grade | finish carpenter | $39.50 | .567 | $22.40 sf |
| **Install niche** | | | | |
| with casing and shelf bracket | finish carpenter | $39.50 | 1.31 | $51.70 ea |
| **Install gingerbread** | | | | |
| running trim | finish carpenter | $39.50 | .160 | $6.32 lf |
| post bracket | finish carpenter | $39.50 | .348 | $13.70 ea |
| corbel | finish carpenter | $39.50 | .359 | $14.20 ea |
| door or window header | finish carpenter | $39.50 | .232 | $9.16 lf |
| post drop | finish carpenter | $39.50 | .322 | $12.70 ea |
| spandrel | finish carpenter | $39.50 | .237 | $9.36 lf |
| window cornice | finish carpenter | $39.50 | .242 | $9.56 lf |
| gable ornament | finish carpenter | $39.50 | .582 | $23.00 ea |
| gable finial | finish carpenter | $39.50 | .560 | $22.10 ea |
| **Install porch post** | | | | |
| install | finish carpenter | $39.50 | .135 | $5.33 lf |
| **Install carved wood onlay** | | | | |
| install | finish carpenter | $39.50 | .519 | $20.50 ea |
| **Install finish board trim** | | | | |
| install | finish carpenter | $39.50 | .049 | $1.94 lf |
| **Install 1/4" hardwood plywood** | | | | |
| install | finish carpenter | $39.50 | .028 | $1.11 sf |

# 18 .................................................................... *Fireplaces*

| Item Description | Unit | Remove | Replace | Total |
|---|---|---|---|---|
| **Fireplace, 30″ wide by 16″ deep by 29″ high, open front** | ea | $101.00 | $1,075.00 | $1,176.00 |
| *Replace* Materials ....373.00        Labor.........702.00 | | | | |
| *Remove* ......................        Labor .........101.00 | | | | |
| **Fireplace, 36″ wide by 16″ deep by 29″ high, open front** | ea | $101.00 | $1,185.00 | $1,286.00 |
| *Replace* Materials ....448.00        Labor.........737.00 | | | | |
| *Remove* ......................        Labor .........101.00 | | | | |
| **Fireplace, 40″ wide by 16″ deep by 29″ high, open front** | ea | $101.00 | $1,261.00 | $1,362.00 |
| *Replace* Materials ....498.00        Labor.........763.00 | | | | |
| *Remove* ......................        Labor .........101.00 | | | | |
| **Fireplace, 48″ wide by 18″ deep by 32″ high, open front** | ea | $101.00 | $1,405.00 | $1,506.00 |
| *Replace* Materials ....598.00        Labor.........807.00 | | | | |
| *Remove* ......................        Labor .........101.00 | | | | |
| **Fireplace, 32″ wide by 16″ deep by 26″ high, open front & one side** | ea | $101.00 | $1,078.00 | $1,179.00 |
| *Replace* Materials ....350.00        Labor.........728.00 | | | | |
| *Remove* ......................        Labor .........101.00 | | | | |
| **Fireplace, 40″ wide by 16″ deep by 29″ high, open front & one side** | ea | $101.00 | $1,251.00 | $1,352.00 |
| *Replace* Materials ....488.00        Labor.........763.00 | | | | |
| *Remove* ......................        Labor .........101.00 | | | | |
| **Fireplace, 48″ wide by 20″ deep by 29″ high, open front & one side** | ea | $101.00 | $1,408.00 | $1,509.00 |
| *Replace* Materials ....584.00        Labor.........824.00 | | | | |
| *Remove* ......................        Labor .........101.00 | | | | |
| **Fireplace, 32″ wide by 28″ deep by 29″ high, open two faces** | ea | $101.00 | $1,149.00 | $1,250.00 |
| *Replace* Materials ....342.00        Labor.........807.00 | | | | |
| *Remove* ......................        Labor .........101.00 | | | | |
| **Fireplace, 36″ wide by 28″ deep by 29″ high, open two faces** | ea | $101.00 | $1,209.00 | $1,310.00 |
| *Replace* Materials ....385.00        Labor.........824.00 | | | | |
| *Remove* ......................        Labor .........101.00 | | | | |
| **Fireplace, 40″ wide by 28″ deep by 29″ high, open two faces** | ea | $101.00 | $1,265.00 | $1,366.00 |
| *Replace* Materials ....428.00        Labor.........837.00 | | | | |
| *Remove* ......................        Labor .........101.00 | | | | |
| **Fireplace, 36″ wide by 32″ deep by 27″ high, open three sides** | ea | $101.00 | $1,256.00 | $1,357.00 |
| *Replace* Materials ....419.00        Labor.........837.00 | | | | |
| *Remove* ......................        Labor .........101.00 | | | | |
| **Fireplace, 36″ wide by 36″ deep by 27″ high, open three sides** | ea | $101.00 | $1,343.00 | $1,444.00 |
| *Replace* Materials ....471.00        Labor.........872.00 | | | | |
| *Remove* ......................        Labor .........101.00 | | | | |
| **Fireplace, 44″ wide by 40″ deep by 27″ high, open three sides** | ea | $101.00 | $1,515.00 | $1,616.00 |
| *Replace* Materials ....626.00        Labor .......889.00 | | | | |
| *Remove* ......................        Labor .........101.00 | | | | |
| **Prefab. fireplace, 30″ wide by 16″ deep by 29″ high, open front** | ea | $63.90 | $620.00 | $683.90 |
| *Replace* Materials ....422.00        Labor.........198.00 | | | | |
| *Remove* ......................        Labor ..........63.90 | | | | |

◀ **FIREPLACE**
*Includes concrete reinforced hearth, ash drop, fire brick, damper, throat, smoke shelf and smoke chamber. Does not include foundation, flue or chimney, face, or finish hearth.*

◁ **open front**

◁ **open front and side**

---

**RELATED ITEMS**

**Cleaning**
fireplaces.............................62
masonry...............................63
**Finish Carpentry**
mantel beam, mantel.......224
**Masonry**..............................287
**Painting**..............................339
**Rough Carpentry**
chimney cricket ..............444

---

◁ **open both faces "see through"**

◁ **open two faces and side**

◀ **PREFABRICATED FIREPLACE**
◁ **open front**
*continued on next page*

| Item Description | Unit | Remove | Replace | Total |
|---|---|---|---|---|
| **PREFABRICATED ▶ FIREPLACE** *continued* | | | | |
| **Prefab. convection fireplace, 30" wide by 16" deep by 29" high, open front** *Replace* Materials....486.00   Labor ........208.00 *Remove* ........................   Labor ..........63.90 | ea | $63.90 | $694.00 | $757.90 |
| *Zero clearance box. Does not include flue. Actual sizes and style available vary from manufacturer to manufacturer. Choose the size and style that most closely matches.*  **Prefab. forced-air fireplace, 30" wide by 16" deep by 29" high, open front** *Replace* Materials....528.00   Labor ........229.00 *Remove* ........................   Labor ..........63.90 | ea | $63.90 | $757.00 | $820.90 |
| **Prefab. fireplace, 36" wide by 16" deep by 29" high, open front** *Replace* Materials.....511.00   Labor ........198.00 *Remove* ........................   Labor ..........63.90 | ea | $63.90 | $709.00 | $772.90 |
| **Prefab. convection fireplace, 36" wide by 16" deep by 29" high, open front** *Replace* Materials....589.00   Labor ........208.00 *Remove* ........................   Labor ..........63.90 | ea | $63.90 | $797.00 | $860.90 |
| **Prefab. forced-air fireplace, 36" wide by 16" deep by 29" high, open front** *Replace* Materials....639.00   Labor ........229.00 *Remove* ........................   Labor ..........63.90 | ea | $63.90 | $868.00 | $931.90 |
| **Prefab. fireplace, 40" wide by 16" deep by 29" high, open front** *Replace* Materials....744.00   Labor ........198.00 *Remove* ........................   Labor ..........63.90 | ea | $63.90 | $942.00 | $1,005.90 |
| **Prefab. convection fireplace, 40" wide by 16" deep by 29" high, open front** *Replace* Materials....654.00   Labor ........208.00 *Remove* ........................   Labor ..........63.90 | ea | $63.90 | $862.00 | $925.90 |
| **Prefab. forced-air fireplace, 40" wide by 16" deep by 29" high, open front** *Replace* Materials ....710.00   Labor ........229.00 *Remove* ........................   Labor ..........63.90 | ea | $63.90 | $939.00 | $1,002.90 |
| **Prefab. fireplace, 48" wide by 18" deep by 32" high, open front** *Replace* Materials....893.00   Labor .........198.00 *Remove* ........................   Labor ..........63.90 | ea | $63.90 | $1,091.00 | $1,154.90 |
| **Prefab. convection fireplace, 48" wide by 18" deep by 32" high, open front** *Replace* Materials ....785.00   Labor ........208.00 *Remove* ........................   Labor ..........63.90 | ea | $63.90 | $993.00 | $1,056.90 |
| **Prefab. forced-air fireplace, 48" wide by 18" deep by 32" high, open front** *Replace* Materials ....852.00   Labor ........229.00 *Remove* ........................   Labor ..........63.90 | ea | $63.90 | $1,081.00 | $1,144.90 |
| **open front and side ▷** **Prefab. fireplace, 32" wide by 16" deep by 26" high, open front & side** *Replace* Materials ....708.00   Labor .........198.00 *Remove* ........................   Labor ..........63.90 | ea | $63.90 | $906.00 | $969.90 |
| **Prefab. fireplace, 40" wide by 16" deep by 29" high, open front & side** *Replace* Materials ....849.00   Labor ........208.00 *Remove* ........................   Labor ..........63.90 | ea | $63.90 | $1,057.00 | $1,120.90 |
| **Prefab. fireplace, 48" wide by 20" deep by 29" high, open front & side** *Replace* Materials ..1020.00   Labor ........229.00 *Remove* ........................   Labor ..........63.90 | ea | $63.90 | $1,249.00 | $1,312.90 |
| **open both faces ▷** *"see through"* **Prefab. fireplace, 32" wide by 28" deep by 29" high, open two faces** *Replace* Materials....865.00   Labor .........198.00 *Remove* ........................   Labor ..........63.90 | ea | $63.90 | $1,063.00 | $1,126.90 |

| Item Description | Unit | Remove | Replace | Total | |
|---|---|---|---|---|---|
| **Prefab. fireplace, 36" wide by 28" deep by 29" high, open two faces** *Replace* Materials ..1040.00 Labor .........208.00 *Remove* ...................... Labor ...........63.90 | ea | $63.90 | $1,248.00 | $1,311.90 |  |
| **Prefab. fireplace, 40" wide by 28" deep by 29" high, open two faces** *Replace* Materials ..1250.00 Labor .........229.00 *Remove* ...................... Labor ...........63.90 | ea | $63.90 | $1,479.00 | $1,542.90 | |
| **Prefab. fireplace, 36" wide by 32" deep by 27" high, open three sides** *Replace* Materials ..1020.00 Labor ..........198.00 *Remove* ...................... Labor ...........63.90 | ea | $63.90 | $1,218.00 | $1,281.90 | ◁ **open two faces and side**  |
| **Prefab. fireplace, 36" wide by 36" deep by 27" high, open three sides** *Replace* Materials...1220.00 Labor .........208.00 *Remove* ...................... Labor ...........63.90 | ea | $63.90 | $1,428.00 | $1,491.90 | |
| **Prefab. fireplace, 44" wide by 40" deep by 27" high, open three sides** *Replace* Materials ...1470.00 Labor .........229.00 *Remove* ...................... Labor ...........63.90 | ea | $63.90 | $1,699.00 | $1,762.90 | |
| **Fireplace form, 30" wide by 16" deep by 29" high, open front** *Replace* Materials....486.00 Labor..........132.00 *Remove* ...................... Labor...........72.80 | ea | $72.80 | $618.00 | $690.80 | ◀ **FIREPLACE FORM** *Does not include face, hearth, flue or chimney. Actual sizes and style available vary from manufacturer to manufacturer. Choose the size and style that most closely matches.* |
| **Fireplace form, 36" wide by 16" deep by 29" high, open front** *Replace* Materials....583.00 Labor..........132.00 *Remove* ...................... Labor...........72.80 | ea | $72.80 | $715.00 | $787.80 | |
| **Fireplace form, 40" wide by 16" deep by 29" high, open front** *Replace* Materials....648.00 Labor..........132.00 *Remove* ...................... Labor...........72.80 | ea | $72.80 | $780.00 | $852.80 | ◁ **open front**  |
| **Fireplace form, 48" wide by 18" deep by 32" high, open front** *Replace* Materials....799.00 Labor..........132.00 *Remove* ...................... Labor...........72.80 | ea | $72.80 | $931.00 | $1,003.80 | |
| **Fireplace form, 32" wide by 16" deep by 26" high, open front & side** *Replace* Materials....902.00 Labor..........132.00 *Remove* ...................... Labor...........72.80 | ea | $72.80 | $1,034.00 | $1,106.80 | ◁ **open front and side**  |
| **Fireplace form, 40" wide by 16" deep by 29" high, open front & side** *Replace* Materials ..1080.00 Labor..........132.00 *Remove* ...................... Labor...........72.80 | ea | $72.80 | $1,212.00 | $1,284.80 | |
| **Fireplace form, 48" wide by 20" deep by 29" high, open front & side** *Replace* Materials...1730.00 Labor..........132.00 *Remove* ...................... Labor...........72.80 | ea | $72.80 | $1,862.00 | $1,934.80 | |
| **Fireplace form, 32" wide by 28" deep by 29" high, open two faces** *Replace* Materials ..1090.00 Labor..........132.00 *Remove* ...................... Labor...........72.80 | ea | $72.80 | $1,222.00 | $1,294.80 | ◁ **open both faces** *"see through"*  |
| **Fireplace form, 36" wide by 28" deep by 29" high, open two faces** *Replace* Materials...1230.00 Labor..........132.00 *Remove* ...................... Labor...........72.80 | ea | $72.80 | $1,362.00 | $1,434.80 | |
| **Fireplace form, 40" wide by 28" deep by 29" high, open two faces** *Replace* Materials ...1370.00 Labor..........132.00 *Remove* ...................... Labor...........72.80 | ea | $72.80 | $1,502.00 | $1,574.80 | |

**RELATED ITEMS**

**Cleaning**
fireplaces.....................62
masonry......................63
**Finish Carpentry**
mantel beam, mantel.......224

**RELATED ITEMS**

**Masonry**.........................287
**Painting**..........................339
**Rough Carpentry**
chimney cricket.............444

| | Item Description | Unit | Remove | Replace | Total |
|---|---|---|---|---|---|
| **FIREPLACE** ▶ FORM *continued* open two faces and side ▷ | **Fireplace form, 36" wide by 32" deep by 27" high, open three sides** *Replace* Materials ..1340.00  Labor..........132.00 *Remove* .......................  Labor............72.80 | ea | $72.80 | $1,472.00 | $1,544.80 |
| | **Fireplace form, 36" wide by 36" deep by 27" high, open three sides** *Replace* Materials...1520.00  Labor..........132.00 *Remove* .......................  Labor............72.80 | ea | $72.80 | $1,652.00 | $1,724.80 |
| | **Fireplace form, 44" wide by 40" deep by 27" high, open three sides** *Replace* Materials...1690.00  Labor..........132.00 *Remove* .......................  Labor............72.80 | ea | $72.80 | $1,822.00 | $1,894.80 |
| **FIREPLACE** ▶ **FURNACE** *Also called masonry heaters.* | **Fireplace furnace** *Replace* Materials ..4470.00  Labor........1500.00 *Remove* .......................  Labor.........101.00 ▶ Complete fireplace furnace including two air ducts with automatic dampers, outside air supply, heat exchanger, supply and outlet ducts connected to furnace ducts. | ea | $101.00 | $5,970.00 | $6,071.00 |
| **FIRE BRICK** ▶ *Installation of fire brick with fire clay only, no surrounding masonry.* | **Fire brick (complete fireplace)** *Replace* Materials .....119.00  Labor..........132.00 *Remove* .......................  Labor............24.90 | ea | $24.90 | $251.00 | $275.90 |
| | **Concrete simulated fire brick (complete fireplace)** *Replace* Materials ......89.40  Labor ..........80.70 *Remove* .......................  Labor............13.90 ▶ Three-piece unit stamped and colored to look like fire brick. | ea | $13.90 | $170.10 | $184.00 |
| **FIREPLACE** ▶ **CHIMNEY** *All brick types. Add* **14%** *for rubble or ashlar stone. Does not include foundation.* | **16" by 16" fireplace chimney with one 8" x 8" flue** *Replace* Materials ......31.60  Labor ..........92.40 *Remove* .......................  Labor .............9.07 | lf | $9.07 | $124.00 | $133.07 |
| | **16" by 24" fireplace chimney with two 8" x 8" flues** *Replace* Materials ......41.70  Labor..........129.00 *Remove* .......................  Labor............12.40 | lf | $12.40 | $170.70 | $183.10 |
| | **16" by 20" fireplace chimney with one 8" x 12" flue** *Replace* Materials ......37.60  Labor ...........93.60 *Remove* .......................  Labor .............9.07 | lf | $9.07 | $131.20 | $140.27 |
| | **20" by 24" fireplace chimney with two 8" x 12" flues** *Replace* Materials ......48.10  Labor..........132.00 *Remove* .......................  Labor............12.40 | lf | $12.40 | $180.10 | $192.50 |
| | **20" by 20" fireplace chimney with one 12" x 12" flue** *Replace* Materials ......39.80  Labor...........94.90 *Remove* .......................  Labor .............9.07 | lf | $9.07 | $134.70 | $143.77 |
| | **20" by 32" fireplace chimney with two 12" x 12" flues** *Replace* Materials ......55.00  Labor..........135.00 *Remove* .......................  Labor............12.40 | lf | $12.40 | $190.00 | $202.40 |
| | **20" by 24" fireplace chimney with one 12" x 16" flue** *Replace* Materials ......42.10  Labor...........96.60 *Remove* .......................  Labor .............9.07 | lf | $9.07 | $138.70 | $147.77 |
| | **20" by 40" fireplace chimney with two 12" x 16" flues** *Replace* Materials ......70.00  Labor..........138.00 *Remove* .......................  Labor............12.40 | lf | $12.40 | $208.00 | $220.40 |
| | **24" by 24" fireplace chimney with one 16" x 16" flue** *Replace* Materials......44.30  Labor...........98.20 *Remove* .......................  Labor .............9.07 | lf | $9.07 | $142.50 | $151.57 |

| Item Description | Unit | Remove | Replace | Total | |
|---|---|---|---|---|---|
| **24" by 40" fireplace chimney with two 16" x 16" flues**<br>*Replace* Materials......79.10          Labor.........140.00<br>*Remove* .....................          Labor.........12.40 | lf | $12.40 | $219.10 | $231.50 | |
| **Add for bend in fireplace chimney with one flue**<br>*Replace* Materials......20.80          Labor.........139.00 | ea | — | $159.80 | $159.80 | ◁ add for chimney bend |
| **Add for bend in fireplace chimney with two flues**<br>*Replace* Materials......23.40          Labor.........169.00 | ea | — | $192.40 | $192.40 | |
| **Add 14% for stone facing on chimney** | | | | | ◁ add for stone face |
| **Reline chimney using grout and inflatable tube method**<br>*Replace* Materials........5.50          Labor.........25.00 | lf | — | $30.50 | $30.50 | ◀ **RELINE CHIMNEY**<br>With a technique designed and licensed by Ahrens Chimney Technique. |
| **Add per bend in chimney when relining**<br>*Replace* Materials......16.30          Labor.........130.00 | ea | — | $146.30 | $146.30 | |
| **Minimum charge to reline chimney**<br>*Replace* Materials.....33.00          Labor.........198.00 | ea | — | $231.00 | $231.00 | |
| **2" concrete single-flue chimney cap**<br>*Replace* Materials......14.40          Labor.........43.60<br>*Remove* ....................          Labor.........7.94 | ea | $7.94 | $58.00 | $65.94 | ◀ **CONCRETE CHIMNEY CAP** |
| **2" concrete double-flue chimney cap**<br>*Replace* Materials.....22.90          Labor.........65.00<br>*Remove* ....................          Labor.........9.48 | ea | $9.48 | $87.90 | $97.38 | |
| **Cast stone molded chimney cap, standard grade**<br>*Replace* Materials.....138.00          Labor.........55.80<br>*Remove* ....................          Labor.........9.48<br>▶ With simple pattern moldings on edge. | ea | $9.48 | $193.80 | $203.28 | ◀ **CAST STONE CHIMNEY CAP**<br>Manufactured cast stone cap with decorative patterns. |
| **Cast stone molded chimney cap, high grade**<br>*Replace* Materials ....164.00          Labor.........55.80<br>*Remove* ....................          Labor.........9.48<br>▶ With complex pattern moldings on edge. | ea | $9.48 | $219.80 | $229.28 | |
| **Cast stone molded chimney cap, deluxe grade**<br>*Replace* Materials.....216.00          Labor.........55.80<br>*Remove* ....................          Labor.........9.48<br>▶ With very complex moldings on edge or with curved elements. | ea | $9.48 | $271.80 | $281.28 | |
| **Galvanized steel chimney cap**<br>*Replace* Materials.....110.00          Labor.........11.90<br>*Remove* ....................          Labor.........4.64<br>▶ For use on metal or masonry flues, with spark arrestor. | ea | $4.64 | $121.90 | $126.54 | ◀ **STEEL CHIMNEY CAP** |
| **Remove steel chimney cap for work, then reinstall**<br>*Replace* ....................          Labor.........19.90 | ea | — | $19.90 | $19.90 | |
| **Chimney pot, standard grade**<br>*Replace* Materials.....177.00          Labor.........51.40<br>*Remove* ....................          Labor.........12.30<br>▶ No designs on pot or arched design over flue. | ea | $12.30 | $228.40 | $240.70 | ◀ **CHIMNEY POT** |
| **Chimney pot, high grade**<br>*Replace* Materials ....260.00          Labor.........51.40<br>*Remove* ....................          Labor.........12.30<br>▶ Simple designs on pot. | ea | $12.30 | $311.40 | $323.70 | △ standard |

| | Item Description | Unit | Remove | Replace | Total |
|---|---|---|---|---|---|
| **CHIMNEY POT** ▶ *continued* | **Chimney pot, deluxe grade** *Replace* Materials....324.00   Labor..........51.40 *Remove* ...................   Labor..........12.30  ▶ Ornate designs on pot and ornate pattern around top edge. | ea | $12.30 | $375.40 | $387.70 |
| △ *high* | **Chimney pot, custom grade** *Replace* Materials....400.00   Labor..........51.40 *Remove* ...................   Labor..........12.30  ▶ Ornate designs on pot and ornate pattern around top edge with molded bands around pot. | ea | $12.30 | $451.40 | $463.70 |
| *custom deluxe* ▽ | **Chimney pot, custom deluxe grade** *Replace* Materials....509.00   Labor..........51.40 *Remove* ...................   Labor..........12.30  ▶ Ornate designs on pot and ornate pattern around top edge with molded bands around pot. Octagonal or other specialty shape. | ea | $12.30 | $560.40 | $572.70 |
| | **Remove chimney pot for work, then reinstall** *Replace* ...................   Labor ..........88.90 | ea | — | $88.90 | $88.90 |
| **CHIMNEY SCREEN** ▶ | **Chimney bird screen for single flue chimney** *Replace* Materials......43.00   Labor..........17.40 | ea | — | $60.40 | $60.40 |
| | **Chimney bird screen for double flue chimney** *Replace* Materials ......52.00   Labor..........19.00 | ea | — | $71.00 | $71.00 |
| **FIREPLACE GRATE** ▶ | **Fireplace grate, 22" x 16"** *Replace* Materials......43.00   Labor ...........4.75 *Remove* ...................   Labor.............79 | ea | $.79 | $47.75 | $48.54 |
| | **Fireplace grate, 28" x 16"** *Replace* Materials......56.00   Labor ...........4.75 *Remove* ...................   Labor.............79 | ea | $.79 | $60.75 | $61.54 |
| | **Fireplace grate, 32" x 16"** *Replace* Materials......63.00   Labor ...........4.75 *Remove* ...................   Labor.............79 | ea | $.79 | $67.75 | $68.54 |
| | **Fireplace grate, 38" x 16"** *Replace* Materials......72.00   Labor ...........4.75 *Remove* ...................   Labor.............79 | ea | $.79 | $76.75 | $77.54 |
| | **Fireplace grate, 38" x 20"** *Replace* Materials......76.00   Labor ...........4.75 *Remove* ...................   Labor.............79 | ea | $.79 | $80.75 | $81.54 |
| | **Fireplace grate, 32" x 28"** *Replace* Materials......83.00   Labor ...........4.75 *Remove* ...................   Labor.............79 | ea | $.79 | $87.75 | $88.54 |
| | **Fireplace grate, 36" x 28"** *Replace* Materials......88.00   Labor ...........4.75 *Remove* ...................   Labor.............79 | ea | $.79 | $92.75 | $93.54 |
| | **Fireplace grate, 40" x 28"** *Replace* Materials......92.00   Labor ...........4.75 *Remove* ...................   Labor.............79 | ea | $.79 | $96.75 | $97.54 |
| | **Fireplace grate, 36" x 32"** *Replace* Materials ......96.00   Labor ...........4.75 *Remove* ...................   Labor........... .79 | ea | $.79 | $100.75 | $101.54 |

| Item Description | Unit | Remove | Replace | Total |
|---|---|---|---|---|
| **Fireplace grate, 36" x 36"** | ea | $.79 | $112.75 | $113.54 |
| *Replace* Materials ....108.00    Labor .........4.75 | | | | |
| *Remove* .................    Labor ........... .79 | | | | |
| **Fireplace grate, 44" x 40"** | ea | $.79 | $150.75 | $151.54 |
| *Replace* Materials ....146.00    Labor .........4.75 | | | | |
| *Remove* .................    Labor ........... .79 | | | | |
| **Remove fireplace grate for work, then reinstall** | ea | — | $5.87 | $5.87 |
| *Replace* .................    Labor .........5.87 | | | | |
| **Fireplace screen, standard grade** | ea | $4.85 | $127.70 | $132.55 |
| *Replace* Materials ......96.00    Labor.........31.70 | | | | |
| *Remove* .................    Labor .........4.85 | | | | |
| ► Plain black with no trim. | | | | |
| **Fireplace screen, high grade** | ea | $4.85 | $178.70 | $183.55 |
| *Replace* Materials .....147.00    Labor.........31.70 | | | | |
| *Remove* .................    Labor .........4.85 | | | | |
| ► Plain black with brass or similar trim at top. | | | | |
| **Fireplace screen, deluxe grade** | ea | $4.85 | $232.70 | $237.55 |
| *Replace* Materials ....201.00    Labor.........31.70 | | | | |
| *Remove* .................    Labor .........4.85 | | | | |
| ► Brass screen with brass or similar trim at top. | | | | |
| **Remove fireplace screen for work, then reinstall** | ea | — | $47.50 | $47.50 |
| *Replace* .................    Labor.........47.50 | | | | |
| **Fireplace door, standard grade** | ea | $6.63 | $203.90 | $210.53 |
| *Replace* Materials ....164.00    Labor .........39.90 | | | | |
| *Remove* .................    Labor .........6.63 | | | | |
| ► Plain black. | | | | |
| **Fireplace door, high grade** | ea | $6.63 | $289.90 | $296.53 |
| *Replace* Materials ....250.00    Labor .........39.90 | | | | |
| *Remove* .................    Labor .........6.63 | | | | |
| ► Brass face. | | | | |
| **Fireplace door, deluxe grade** | ea | $6.63 | $363.90 | $370.53 |
| *Replace* Materials .....324.00    Labor .........39.90 | | | | |
| *Remove* .................    Labor ...........6.63 | | | | |
| ► Brass face with designs. | | | | |
| **Fireplace door, custom grade** | ea | $6.63 | $469.90 | $476.53 |
| *Replace* Materials ....430.00    Labor .........39.90 | | | | |
| *Remove* .................    Labor ...........6.63 | | | | |
| ► Brass face with designs and specialty "clear view" glass. | | | | |
| **Remove fireplace door for work, then reinstall** | ea | — | $62.20 | $62.20 |
| *Replace* .................    Labor.........62.20 | | | | |
| **8" x 8" fireplace clean-out door** | ea | $1.81 | $45.30 | $47.11 |
| *Replace* Materials ......18.00    Labor.........27.30 | | | | |
| *Remove* .................    Labor ...........1.81 | | | | |
| **12" x 12" fireplace clean-out door** | ea | $1.81 | $65.30 | $67.11 |
| *Replace* Materials ......38.00    Labor.........27.30 | | | | |
| *Remove* .................    Labor ...........1.81 | | | | |

**RELATED ITEMS**

**Cleaning**
fireplaces ..........................62
masonry ...........................63
**Finish Carpentry**
mantel beam, mantel.......224
**Masonry** ..........................287
**Painting** .............................339
**Rough Carpentry**
chimney cricket .............444

◄ **FIREPLACE SCREEN**

◄ **FIREPLACE DOOR**

◄ **FIREPLACE CLEAN-OUT DOOR**
*Cast iron door and jamb.*

| Item Description | Unit | Remove | Replace | Total |
|---|---|---|---|---|
| **FIREPLACE ▶ CLEAN-OUT DOOR** continued **18" x 24" fireplace clean-out door** Replace Materials.....113.00 Labor..........27.30 Remove Labor..........1.81 | ea | $1.81 | $140.30 | $142.11 |
| **Salvage fireplace clean-out door, then reinstall** Replace Labor..........42.30 | ea | — | $42.30 | $42.30 |
| **DAMPER ▶ Rotary control damper for 30" wide fireplace** Replace Materials.......77.00 Labor..........48.40 | ea | — | $125.40 | $125.40 |
| **Rotary control damper for 36" wide fireplace** Replace Materials......83.00 Labor..........48.40 | ea | — | $131.40 | $131.40 |
| **Rotary control for 40" wide fireplace** Replace Materials.....101.00 Labor..........48.40 | ea | — | $149.40 | $149.40 |
| **Rotary control damper for 48" wide fireplace** Replace Materials.....119.00 Labor..........48.40 | ea | — | $167.40 | $167.40 |
| **Poker control damper for 30" wide fireplace** Replace Materials......60.00 Labor..........39.30 | ea | — | $99.30 | $99.30 |
| **Poker control damper for 36" wide fireplace** Replace Materials......65.00 Labor..........39.30 | ea | — | $104.30 | $104.30 |
| **Poker control damper for 40" wide fireplace** Replace Materials......79.00 Labor..........39.30 | ea | — | $118.30 | $118.30 |
| **Poker control damper for 48" wide fireplace** Replace Materials......93.00 Labor..........39.30 | ea | — | $132.30 | $132.30 |
| **DOUBLE WALL ▶ CHIMNEY PIPE** stainless steel **8" diameter double wall chimney pipe** Replace Materials......26.00 Labor..........23.10 Remove Labor..........55 | lf | $.55 | $49.10 | $49.65 |
| **10" diameter double wall chimney pipe** Replace Materials......37.00 Labor..........23.10 Remove Labor..........55 | lf | $.55 | $60.10 | $60.65 |
| **12" diameter double wall chimney pipe** Replace Materials......49.00 Labor..........23.10 Remove Labor..........55 | lf | $.55 | $72.10 | $72.65 |
| **14" diameter double wall chimney pipe** Replace Materials.......61.00 Labor..........23.10 Remove Labor..........55 | lf | $.55 | $84.10 | $84.65 |
| **TRIPLE WALL ▶ CHIMNEY PIPE** stainless steel **8" diameter triple wall chimney pipe** Replace Materials......33.00 Labor..........23.10 Remove Labor..........55 | lf | $.55 | $56.10 | $56.65 |
| **10" diameter triple wall chimney pipe** Replace Materials......48.00 Labor..........23.10 Remove Labor..........55 | lf | $.55 | $71.10 | $71.65 |
| **12" diameter triple wall chimney pipe** Replace Materials......63.00 Labor..........23.10 Remove Labor..........55 | lf | $.55 | $86.10 | $86.65 |

| Item Description | Unit | Remove | Replace | Total | |
|---|---|---|---|---|---|
| **14" diameter triple wall chimney pipe** | lf | $.55 | $101.10 | $101.65 | |
| *Replace* Materials ......78.00    Labor ..........23.10 | | | | | |
| *Remove* .....................    Labor ............. .55 | | | | | |
| **Add for chimney pipe through interior ceiling** | ea | — | $89.30 | $89.30 | ◄ **ADDITIONAL CHIMNEY PIPE COSTS** |
| *Replace* Materials ......45.00    Labor ..........44.30 | | | | | |
| ► Kit to run chimney pipe through interior drywall or plaster ceiling. Includes bracket that allows for 2" clearance. | | | | | |
| **Add for chimney pipe through roof** | ea | — | $242.00 | $242.00 | |
| *Replace* Materials .....125.00    Labor ..........117.00 | | | | | |
| ► Kit to run chimney pipe through roof. Includes bracket, boots, and so forth. | | | | | |
| **Remove chimney pipe for work, then reinstall** | lf | — | $35.30 | $35.30 | |
| *Replace* .....................    Labor ..........35.30 | | | | | |
| **Gas log lighter** | ea | $5.95 | $132.10 | $138.05 | ◄ **GAS LOG LIGHTER** |
| *Replace* Materials ......85.00    Labor ..........47.10 | | | | | |
| *Remove* .....................    Labor ..........5.95 | | | | | |
| ► Log lighter, valve, key and up to 24 lf copper gas piping. | | | | | |
| **Remove gas log lighter for work, then reinstall** | ea | — | $78.20 | $78.20 | |
| *Replace* .....................    Labor ..........78.20 | | | | | |
| **Gas fireplace kit** | ea | $6.58 | $567.90 | $574.48 | ◄ **GAS FIREPLACE** |
| *Replace* Materials .....518.00    Labor ..........49.90 | | | | | |
| *Remove* .....................    Labor ..........6.58 | | | | | |
| ► Burners, fake logs, valve, key and up to 24 lf copper gas piping. | | | | | |
| **Remove gas fireplace kit for work, then reinstall** | ea | — | $85.00 | $85.00 | |
| *Replace* .....................    Labor ..........85.00 | | | | | |
| **Marble fireplace face, economy grade** | ea | $43.50 | $241.00 | $284.50 | ◄ **MARBLE FIREPLACE FACE** |
| *Replace* Materials ......85.00    Labor ..........156.00 | | | | | |
| *Remove* .....................    Labor ..........43.50 | | | | | |
| ► Marble tiles laid around inside of mantel. | | | | | |
| **Marble fireplace face, standard grade** | ea | $79.40 | $593.00 | $672.40 | |
| *Replace* Materials ....260.00    Labor ........333.00 | | | | | |
| *Remove* .....................    Labor ..........79.40 | | | | | |
| ► From single or large pieces up to 5' tall and 4' wide, polished or natural finish. | | | | | |
| **Marble fireplace face, high grade** | ea | $79.40 | $763.00 | $842.40 | |
| *Replace* Materials ....422.00    Labor ........341.00 | | | | | |
| *Remove* .....................    Labor ..........79.40 | | | | | |
| ► From single pieces or large pieces up to 5' tall and 4' wide, polished or natural finish with simple designs around opening and at corner (cove or similar). Or same as standard grade up to 8' tall and 6' wide. | | | | | |
| **Marble fireplace face, deluxe grade** | ea | $79.40 | $978.00 | $1,057.40 | |
| *Replace* Materials ....629.00    Labor ........349.00 | | | | | |
| *Remove* .....................    Labor ..........79.40 | | | | | |
| ► From single pieces or large pieces up to 5' tall and 4' wide, polished or natural finish with ornate designs around opening and at corner (crown or similar). Or same as high grade up to 8' tall and 6' wide. | | | | | |
| **Brick fireplace face, economy grade** | ea | $84.60 | $941.00 | $1,025.60 | ◄ **BRICK FIREPLACE FACE** |
| *Replace* Materials ....239.00    Labor ........702.00 | | | | | |
| *Remove* .....................    Labor ..........84.60 | | | | | |
| ► Brick face in stacked or running bond, up to 5' tall and 5' wide. | | | | | |

| | Item Description | Unit | Remove | Replace | Total |
|---|---|---|---|---|---|
| **BRICK ►** FIREPLACE FACE *continued* | **Brick fireplace face, standard grade** | ea | $84.60 | $1,155.00 | $1,239.60 |
| | *Replace* Materials ....266.00    Labor ........889.00 | | | | |
| | *Remove* .......................    Labor ..........84.60 | | | | |
| | ► Brick face in specialty bond (see *Masonry*, page 297), up to 5' tall and 5' wide. May include built-in shelf brackets, or small patterns in face. Or same as economy up to 8' tall and 6' wide. | | | | |
| | **Brick fireplace face, high grade** | ea | $84.60 | $1,412.00 | $1,496.60 |
| | *Replace* Materials ....322.00    Labor .......1090.00 | | | | |
| | *Remove* .......................    Labor ..........84.60 | | | | |
| | ► Brick face in specialty bond (see *Masonry*, page 297), up to 5' tall and 5' wide. With arch over opening. May include built-in shelf brackets, or small patterns in face. Or same as standard up to 8' tall and 6' wide. Or same as economy up to 11' tall and 7' wide. | | | | |
| | **Brick fireplace face, deluxe grade** | ea | $84.60 | $1,800.00 | $1,884.60 |
| | *Replace* Materials ....390.00    Labor .......1410.00 | | | | |
| | *Remove* .......................    Labor ..........84.60 | | | | |
| | ► Brick face in specialty bond like herringbone or basket weave mixed with other patterns (see *Masonry*, page 297), up to 5' tall and 5' wide. May have arched openings or curving sides. Or same as high up to 8' tall and 6' wide. Or same as standard up to 11' tall and 7' wide. Or same as economy up to 15' tall and 10' wide. | | | | |
| **RUBBLE STONE ►** FIREPLACE FACE | **Rubble stone fireplace face, economy grade** | ea | $90.40 | $1,170.00 | $1,260.40 |
| | *Replace* Materials ....407.00    Labor .........763.00 | | | | |
| | *Remove* .......................    Labor ..........90.40 | | | | |
| | ► Up to 5' tall and 5' wide, with flagstone or equivalent stone. | | | | |
| | **Rubble stone fireplace face, standard grade** | ea | $90.40 | $1,421.00 | $1,511.40 |
| | *Replace* Materials ....453.00    Labor .......968.00 | | | | |
| | *Remove* .......................    Labor ..........90.40 | | | | |
| | ► Up to 5' tall and 5' wide, with sandstone, limestone, or similar stone. Or same as economy up to 8' tall and 6' wide. | | | | |
| | **Rubble stone fireplace face, high grade** | ea | $90.40 | $1,729.00 | $1,819.40 |
| | *Replace* Materials ....549.00    Labor .......1180.00 | | | | |
| | *Remove* .......................    Labor ..........90.40 | | | | |
| | ► Up to 5' tall and 5' wide, with specialty high priced stones or stones with high priced finishes. Or same as standard up to 8' tall and 6' wide. Or same as economy up to 10' tall and 7' wide. | | | | |
| | **Rubble stone fireplace face, deluxe grade** | ea | $90.40 | $2,165.00 | $2,255.40 |
| | *Replace* Materials ....665.00    Labor .......1500.00 | | | | |
| | *Remove* .......................    Labor ..........90.40 | | | | |
| | ► Up to 5' tall and 5' wide, with specialty high priced stones or stones with high priced finishes. With arch over opening or other specialty compartments or designs. Or same as high up to 8' tall and 6' wide. Or same as standard up to 11' tall and 7' wide. Or same as economy up to 14' tall and 8' wide. | | | | |
| **ASHLAR STONE ►** FIREPLACE FACE | **Ashlar stone fireplace face, economy grade** | ea | $90.40 | $1,224.00 | $1,314.40 |
| | *Replace* Materials .....474.00    Labor.........750.00 | | | | |
| | *Remove* .......................    Labor ..........90.40 | | | | |
| | ► Up to 5' tall and 5' wide, with lowest priced stone for your area. | | | | |
| | **Ashlar stone fireplace face, standard grade** | ea | $90.40 | $1,473.00 | $1,563.40 |
| | *Replace* Materials ....527.00    Labor.........946.00 | | | | |
| | *Remove* .......................    Labor ..........90.40 | | | | |
| | ► Up to 5' tall and 5' wide, with sandstone, limestone, or similar stone. Or same as economy up to 8' tall and 6' wide | | | | |

| Item Description | Unit | Remove | Replace | Total |
|---|---|---|---|---|
| **Ashlar stone fireplace face, high grade** | ea | $90.40 | $1,789.00 | $1,879.40 |
| *Replace* Materials ....639.00    Labor........1150.00 | | | | |
| *Remove* ......................    Labor ..........90.40 | | | | |
| ▶ Up to 5' tall and 5' wide, with specialty high priced stones or stones with high priced finishes. Or same as standard up to 8' tall and 6' wide. Or same as economy up to 10' tall and 7' wide. | | | | |
| **Ashlar stone fireplace face, deluxe grade** | ea | $90.40 | $2,224.00 | $2,314.40 |
| *Replace* Materials ....774.00    Labor ........1450.00 | | | | |
| *Remove* ......................    Labor ..........90.40 | | | | |
| ▶ Up to 5' tall and 5' wide, with specialty high priced stones or stones with high priced finishes. With arch over opening or other specialty compartments or designs. Or same as high up to 8' tall and 6' wide. Or same as standard up to 11' tall and 7' wide. Or same as economy up to 14' tall and 8' wide. | | | | |
| **Tile fireplace face, economy grade** | ea | $47.70 | $227.00 | $274.70 |
| *Replace* Materials ......66.00    Labor ..........161.00 | | | | |
| *Remove* ......................    Labor ..........47.70 | | | | |
| ▶ Standard priced tiles laid around inside of mantel. | | | | |
| **Tile fireplace face, standard grade** | ea | $77.00 | $483.00 | $560.00 |
| *Replace* Materials .....137.00    Labor ........346.00 | | | | |
| *Remove* ......................    Labor ..........77.00 | | | | |
| ▶ High priced tiles laid around inside of mantel. | | | | |
| **Tile fireplace face, high grade** | ea | $77.00 | $529.00 | $606.00 |
| *Replace* Materials .....178.00    Labor ..........351.00 | | | | |
| *Remove* ......................    Labor ..........77.00 | | | | |
| ▶ Specialty antique tiles laid around inside of mantel. Including designer hand-painted designs and raised pattern designs. May include tiles in fireback. | | | | |
| **Tile fireplace face, deluxe grade** | ea | $77.00 | $740.00 | $817.00 |
| *Replace* Materials ....380.00    Labor ........360.00 | | | | |
| *Remove* ......................    Labor ..........77.00 | | | | |
| ▶ Same as high with specialty trim pieces and patterns that match antique Victorian styles. | | | | |
| **Marble fireplace hearth, economy grade** | ea | $20.30 | $223.20 | $243.50 |
| *Replace* Materials ....129.00    Labor..........94.20 | | | | |
| *Remove* ......................    Labor ..........20.30 | | | | |
| **Marble fireplace hearth, standard grade** | ea | $38.00 | $381.00 | $419.00 |
| *Replace* Materials ....180.00    Labor..........201.00 | | | | |
| *Remove* ......................    Labor ..........38.00 | | | | |
| **Marble fireplace hearth, high grade** | ea | $38.00 | $499.00 | $537.00 |
| *Replace* Materials ....293.00    Labor ........206.00 | | | | |
| *Remove* ......................    Labor ..........38.00 | | | | |
| **Marble fireplace hearth, deluxe grade** | ea | $38.00 | $647.00 | $685.00 |
| *Replace* Materials ....436.00    Labor ........211.00 | | | | |
| *Remove* ......................    Labor ..........38.00 | | | | |
| **Brick fireplace hearth, economy grade** | ea | $39.80 | $466.00 | $505.80 |
| *Replace* Materials .....159.00    Labor........307.00 | | | | |
| *Remove* ......................    Labor ..........39.80 | | | | |
| **Brick fireplace hearth, standard grade** | ea | $39.80 | $563.00 | $602.80 |
| *Replace* Materials .....177.00    Labor ........386.00 | | | | |
| *Remove* ......................    Labor ..........39.80 | | | | |

**RELATED ITEMS**

**Cleaning**
fireplaces ......................62
masonry ......................63
**Finish Carpentry**
mantel beam, mantel ......224
**Masonry** ......................287
**Painting** ......................339
**Rough Carpentry**
chimney cricket ..........444

◀ **TILE FIREPLACE FACE**

◀ **MARBLE HEARTH**
Economy grade is flat hearth. All other grades are raised hearths. See marble fireplace face items for more information about quality.

◀ **BRICK HEARTH**
Economy grade is flat hearth. All other grades are raised hearths. See brick fireplace face items for more information about quality.

| Item Description | Unit | Remove | Replace | Total |
|---|---|---|---|---|
| **BRICK HEARTH ▶** continued | | | | |
| **Brick fireplace hearth, high grade** | ea | $39.80 | $626.00 | $665.80 |
| Replace Materials.....215.00    Labor.........411.00<br>Remove ....................    Labor .........39.80 | | | | |
| **Brick fireplace hearth, deluxe grade** | ea | $39.80 | $745.00 | $784.80 |
| Replace Materials.....261.00    Labor.........484.00<br>Remove ....................    Labor .........39.80 | | | | |
| **RUBBLE STONE ▶ HEARTH**<br>Economy grade is flat hearth. All other grades are raised hearths. See rubble stone fireplace face items for more information about quality. | | | | |
| **Rubble stone fireplace hearth, economy grade** | ea | $40.90 | $605.00 | $645.90 |
| Replace Materials ....272.00    Labor .......333.00<br>Remove ....................    Labor .........40.90 | | | | |
| **Rubble stone fireplace hearth, standard grade** | ea | $40.90 | $721.00 | $761.90 |
| Replace Materials....302.00    Labor.......419.00<br>Remove ....................    Labor .........40.90 | | | | |
| **Rubble stone fireplace hearth, high grade** | ea | $40.90 | $811.00 | $851.90 |
| Replace Materials....366.00    Labor.......445.00<br>Remove ....................    Labor .........40.90 | | | | |
| **Rubble stone fireplace hearth, deluxe grade** | ea | $40.90 | $967.00 | $1,007.90 |
| Replace Materials....444.00    Labor.......523.00<br>Remove ....................    Labor .........40.90 | | | | |
| **ASHLAR STONE ▶ HEARTH**<br>Economy grade is flat hearth. All other grades are raised hearths. See ashlar stone fireplace face items for more information about quality. | | | | |
| **Ashlar stone fireplace hearth, economy grade** | ea | $40.90 | $641.00 | $681.90 |
| Replace Materials.....316.00    Labor.........325.00<br>Remove ....................    Labor .........40.90 | | | | |
| **Ashlar stone fireplace hearth, standard grade** | ea | $40.90 | $762.00 | $802.90 |
| Replace Materials .....351.00    Labor.........411.00<br>Remove ....................    Labor .........40.90 | | | | |
| **Ashlar stone fireplace hearth, high grade** | ea | $40.90 | $861.00 | $901.90 |
| Replace Materials ....425.00    Labor .........436.00<br>Remove ....................    Labor .........40.90 | | | | |
| **Ashlar stone fireplace hearth, deluxe grade** | ea | $40.90 | $1,029.00 | $1,069.90 |
| Replace Materials.....515.00    Labor .........514.00<br>Remove ....................    Labor .........40.90 | | | | |
| **TILE HEARTH ▶**<br>Economy grade is flat hearth. All other grades are raised hearths. See tile fireplace face items for more information about quality. | | | | |
| **Tile fireplace hearth economy grade** | ea | $23.00 | $197.70 | $220.70 |
| Replace Materials ....100.00    Labor.........97.70<br>Remove ....................    Labor .........23.00 | | | | |
| **Tile fireplace hearth standard grade** | ea | $37.50 | $345.00 | $382.50 |
| Replace Materials.....137.00    Labor .......208.00<br>Remove ....................    Labor.........37.50 | | | | |
| **Tile fireplace hearth high grade** | ea | $37.50 | $391.00 | $428.50 |
| Replace Materials.....178.00    Labor.......213.00<br>Remove ....................    Labor.........37.50 | | | | |
| **Tile fireplace hearth deluxe grade** | ea | $37.50 | $598.00 | $635.50 |
| Replace Materials....380.00    Labor.......218.00<br>Remove ....................    Labor.........37.50 | | | | |

NOTES: _____

# TIME & MATERIAL CHARTS (selected items)

## Fireplaces Materials (Also see material prices with the line items and other information in the **QuickFinder** column.)

| DESCRIPTION | UNIT PRICE |
|---|---|
| **Fireplace** | |
| 30" wide by 16" deep by 29" high, open front | $373.00 ea |
| 32" wide by 16" deep by 26" high, open front and one side | $350.00 ea |
| 32" wide by 28" deep by 29" high, open two sides | $342.00 ea |
| 36" wide by 32" deep by 27" high, open two faces and one side | $419.00 ea |
| **Prefabricated fireplace** | |
| 30" wide by 16" deep by 29" high, open front | $422.00 ea |
| 32" wide by 16" deep by 26" high, open front and one side | $708.00 ea |
| 32" wide by 28" deep by 29" high, open two faces ("see through") | $865.00 ea |
| 36" wide by 32" deep by 27" high, open two faces and one side | $1,020.00 ea |
| **Fireplace form** | |
| 30" wide by 16" deep by 29" high, open front | $486.00 ea |
| 32" wide by 16" deep by 26" high, open front and one side | $902.00 ea |
| 32" wide by 28" deep by 29" high, open two faces ("see through") | $1,090.00 ea |
| 36" wide by 32" deep by 27" high, open two faces and one side | $1,340.00 ea |
| **Fireplace chimney** | |
| 16" by 16" with one 8" x 8" flue | $31.60 lf |
| 16" by 24" with two 8" x 8" flues | $41.70 lf |
| 20" by 32" with two 12" x 12" flues | $55.00 lf |
| 20" by 40" with two 12" x 16" flues | $70.00 lf |
| 24" by 40" with two 16" x 16" flues | $79.10 lf |
| **Fireplace face** | |
| **marble** | |
| economy grade | $85.00 ea |
| deluxe grade | $629.00 ea |
| **brick** | |
| economy grade | $239.00 ea |
| deluxe grade | $390.00 ea |
| **rubble stone** | |
| economy grade | $407.00 ea |
| deluxe grade | $665.00 ea |
| **ashlar stone** | |
| economy grade | $474.00 ea |
| deluxe grade | $774.00 ea |
| **tile** | |
| economy grade | $66.00 ea |
| deluxe grade | $380.00 ea |
| **Fireplace hearth** | |
| **marble** | |
| economy grade | $129.00 ea |
| deluxe grade | $436.00 ea |
| **brick** | |
| economy grade | $159.00 ea |
| deluxe grade | $261.00 ea |
| **rubble stone** | |
| economy grade | $272.00 ea |
| deluxe grade | $444.00 ea |
| **ashlar stone** | |
| economy grade | $316.00 ea |
| deluxe grade | $515.00 ea |
| **tile** | |
| economy grade | $100.00 ea |
| deluxe grade | $380.00 ea |

## Fireplaces Labor

| LABORER | BASE WAGE | PAID LEAVE | TRUE WAGE | FICA | FUTA | WORKER'S COMP. | UNEMPLOY. INSUR. | HEALTH INSUR. | RETIRE (401k) | LIABILITY INSUR. | COST PER HOUR |
|---|---|---|---|---|---|---|---|---|---|---|---|
| Mason | $23.40 | 1.83 | $25.23 | 1.93 | .20 | 7.50 | 2.20 | 2.54 | .76 | 3.28 | $43.60 |
| Mason's helper | $21.30 | 1.66 | $22.96 | 1.76 | .18 | 6.83 | 2.00 | 2.54 | .69 | 2.98 | $39.90 |
| Demolition laborer | $13.40 | 1.05 | $14.45 | 1.11 | .12 | 4.44 | 1.26 | 2.54 | .43 | 1.88 | $26.20 |

**Paid Leave** is calculated based on two weeks paid vacation, one week sick leave, and seven paid holidays. Employer's matching portion of **FICA** is 7.65 percent. **FUTA** (Federal Unemployment) is .8 percent. **Worker's compensation** for the masonry (fireplaces) trade was calculated using a national average of 29.74 percent. **Unemployment insurance** was calculated using a national average of 8.7 percent. **Health insurance** was calculated based on a projected national average for 2001 of $505 per employee (and family when applicable) per month. Employer pays 80 percent for a per month cost of $404 per employee. **Retirement** is based on a 401(k) retirement program with employer matching of 50 percent. Employee contributions to the 401(k) plan are an average of 6 percent of the true wage. **Liability insurance** is based on a national average of 12.9 percent.

## Fireplaces Labor Productivity

| WORK DESCRIPTION | LABORER | COST PER HOUR | PRODUCTIVITY | UNIT PRICE |
|---|---|---|---|---|
| **Demolition** | | | | |
| remove fireplace | demolition laborer | $26.20 | 3.85 | $101.00 ea |
| remove prefabricated fireplace | demolition laborer | $26.20 | 2.44 | $63.90 ea |
| remove fire brick | demolition laborer | $26.20 | .952 | $24.90 ea |
| remove concrete simulated firebrick | demolition laborer | $26.20 | .529 | $13.90 ea |
| remove fireplace chimney with single flue | demolition laborer | $26.20 | .346 | $9.07 lf |
| remove fireplace chimney with double flue | demolition laborer | $26.20 | .472 | $12.40 lf |
| remove 2" concrete single flue chimney cap | demolition laborer | $26.20 | .303 | $7.94 ea |
| remove 2" concrete double flue chimney cap | demolition laborer | $26.20 | .362 | $9.48 ea |
| remove galvanized steel chimney cap | demolition laborer | $26.20 | .177 | $4.64 ea |
| remove chimney pot | demolition laborer | $26.20 | .469 | $12.30 ea |
| remove fireplace grate | demolition laborer | $26.20 | .030 | $.79 ea |
| remove fireplace screen | demolition laborer | $26.20 | .185 | $4.85 ea |
| remove fireplace door | demolition laborer | $26.20 | .253 | $6.63 ea |
| remove fireplace clean-out | demolition laborer | $26.20 | .069 | $1.81 ea |
| remove chimney pipe | demolition laborer | $26.20 | .021 | $.55 lf |
| remove gas log lighter | demolition laborer | $26.20 | .227 | $5.95 ea |
| remove gas fireplace kit | demolition laborer | $26.20 | .251 | $6.58 ea |
| remove marble fireplace face | demolition laborer | $26.20 | 3.03 | $79.40 ea |
| remove brick fireplace face | demolition laborer | $26.20 | 3.23 | $84.60 ea |
| remove stone fireplace face | demolition laborer | $26.20 | 3.45 | $90.40 ea |
| remove tile fireplace face | demolition laborer | $26.20 | 2.94 | $77.00 ea |
| remove marble fireplace hearth | demolition laborer | $26.20 | 1.45 | $38.00 ea |
| remove brick fireplace hearth | demolition laborer | $26.20 | 1.52 | $39.80 ea |
| remove stone fireplace hearth | demolition laborer | $26.20 | 1.56 | $40.90 ea |
| remove tile fireplace hearth | demolition laborer | $26.20 | 1.43 | $37.50 ea |
| **Fireplace crew** | | | | |
| build fireplace | mason | $43.60 | | |
| build fireplace | mason's helper | $39.90 | | |
| build fireplace | **mason & helper** | $41.80 | | |
| **Build fireplace** | | | | |
| **open front** | | | | |
| 30" wide by 16" deep by 29" high | mason | $43.60 | 16.1 | $702.00 ea |
| 36" wide by 16" deep by 29" high | mason | $43.60 | 16.9 | $737.00 ea |
| 40" wide by 16" deep by 29" high | mason | $43.60 | 17.5 | $763.00 ea |
| 48" wide by 18" deep by 32" high | mason | $43.60 | 18.5 | $807.00 ea |
| **open front and one side** | | | | |
| 32" wide by 16" deep by 26" high | mason | $43.60 | 16.7 | $728.00 ea |
| 40" wide by 16" deep by 29" high | mason | $43.60 | 17.5 | $763.00 ea |
| 48" wide by 20" deep by 29" high | mason | $43.60 | 18.9 | $824.00 ea |

*. . . More ➤*

## Fireplaces Labor Productivity *continued*

| WORK DESCRIPTION | LABORER | COST PER HOUR | PRODUCTIVITY | UNIT PRICE |
|---|---|---|---|---|
| **Build fireplace** *continued* | | | | |
| **open two faces (see through)** | | | | |
| *32" wide by 28" deep by 29" high* | mason | $43.60 | 18.5 | $807.00 *ea* |
| *36" wide by 28" deep by 29" high* | mason | $43.60 | 18.9 | $824.00 *ea* |
| *40" wide by 28" deep by 29" high* | mason | $43.60 | 19.2 | $837.00 *ea* |
| **open two faces and one side** | | | | |
| *36" wide by 32" deep by 27" high* | mason | $43.60 | 19.2 | $837.00 *ea* |
| *36" wide by 36" deep by 27" high* | mason | $43.60 | 20.0 | $872.00 *ea* |
| *44" wide by 40" deep by 27" high* | mason | $43.60 | 20.4 | $889.00 *ea* |
| **Install prefabricated fireplace** | | | | |
| *radiant* | mason | $43.60 | 4.55 | $198.00 *ea* |
| *convection* | mason | $43.60 | 4.76 | $208.00 *ea* |
| *forced-air* | mason | $43.60 | 5.26 | $229.00 *ea* |
| **Install fireplace form** | | | | |
| *form* | mason | $43.60 | 3.03 | $132.00 *ea* |
| **Install fireplace furnace** | | | | |
| *typical* | mason | $43.60 | 34.5 | $1,500.00 *ea* |
| **Install fire brick** | | | | |
| *complete fireplace* | mason | $43.60 | 3.03 | $132.00 *ea* |
| *concrete simulated firebrick (complete fireplace)* | mason | $43.60 | 1.85 | $80.70 *ea* |
| **Build brick chimney** | | | | |
| *16" by 16" with one 8" x 8" flue* | mason & helper | $41.80 | 2.21 | $92.40 *lf* |
| *16" by 24" with two 8" x 8" flues* | mason & helper | $41.80 | 3.09 | $129.00 *lf* |
| *16" by 20" with one 8" x 12" flue* | mason & helper | $41.80 | 2.24 | $93.60 *lf* |
| *20" by 24" with two 8" x 12" flues* | mason & helper | $41.80 | 3.15 | $132.00 *lf* |
| *20" by 20" with one 12" x 12" flue* | mason & helper | $41.80 | 2.27 | $94.90 *lf* |
| *20" by 32" with two 12" x 12" flues* | mason & helper | $41.80 | 3.24 | $135.00 *lf* |
| *20" by 24" with one 12" x 16" flue* | mason & helper | $41.80 | 2.31 | $96.60 *lf* |
| *20" by 40" with two 12" x 16" flues* | mason & helper | $41.80 | 3.30 | $138.00 *lf* |
| *24" by 24" with one 16" x 16" flue* | mason & helper | $41.80 | 2.35 | $98.20 *lf* |
| *24" by 40" with two 16" x 16" flues* | mason & helper | $41.80 | 3.36 | $140.00 *lf* |
| *add for bend in one flue* | mason & helper | $41.80 | 3.33 | $139.00 *ea* |
| *add for bend in two flues* | mason & helper | $41.80 | 4.05 | $169.00 *ea* |
| **Pour 2" thick concrete chimney cap** | | | | |
| *single-flue* | mason | $43.60 | 1.00 | $43.60 *ea* |
| *double-flue* | mason | $43.60 | 1.49 | $65.00 *ea* |
| **Install cast stone chimney cap** | | | | |
| *typical* | mason | $43.60 | 1.28 | $55.80 *ea* |
| **Install galvanized steel chimney cap** | | | | |
| *with spark arrestor* | mason's helper | $39.90 | .298 | $11.90 *ea* |
| **Install chimney pot** | | | | |
| *typical* | mason | $43.60 | 1.18 | $51.40 *ea* |
| **Install chimney bird screen** | | | | |
| *for single flue* | mason's helper | $39.90 | .437 | $17.40 *ea* |
| *for double flue* | mason's helper | $39.90 | .476 | $19.00 *ea* |
| **Install fireplace grate** | | | | |
| *typical* | mason's helper | $39.90 | .119 | $4.75 *ea* |
| **Install fireplace screen** | | | | |
| *typical* | mason's helper | $39.90 | .794 | $31.70 *ea* |
| **Install fireplace door** | | | | |
| *typical* | mason's helper | $39.90 | 1.00 | $39.90 *ea* |
| **Install fireplace clean-out** | | | | |
| *typical* | mason | $43.60 | .625 | $27.30 *ea* |
| **Install fireplace damper** | | | | |
| *rotary control* | mason | $43.60 | 1.11 | $48.40 *ea* |
| *poker control* | mason | $43.60 | .901 | $39.30 *ea* |

. . . More ➤

## Fireplaces Labor Productivity *continued*

| WORK DESCRIPTION | LABORER | COST PER HOUR | PRODUCTIVITY | UNIT PRICE |
|---|---|---|---|---|
| **Install chimney pipe** | | | | |
| typical | mason's helper | $39.90 | .578 | $23.10 *lf* |
| add through interior ceiling | mason's helper | $39.90 | 1.11 | $44.30 *ea* |
| add through roof | mason's helper | $39.90 | 2.94 | $117.00 *ea* |
| **Install gas log lighter** | | | | |
| typical | mason's helper | $39.90 | 1.18 | $47.10 *ea* |
| **Install gas fireplace kit** | | | | |
| typical | mason's helper | $39.90 | 1.25 | $49.90 *ea* |
| **Install fireplace face** | | | | |
| **marble** | | | | |
| economy grade | mason | $43.60 | 3.57 | $156.00 *ea* |
| deluxe grade | mason | $43.60 | 8.00 | $349.00 *ea* |
| **brick** | | | | |
| economy grade | mason | $43.60 | 16.1 | $702.00 *ea* |
| deluxe grade | mason | $43.60 | 32.3 | $1,410.00 *ea* |
| **rubble stone** | | | | |
| economy grade | mason | $43.60 | 17.5 | $763.00 *ea* |
| deluxe grade | mason | $43.60 | 34.5 | $1,500.00 *ea* |
| **ashlar stone** | | | | |
| economy grade | mason | $43.60 | 17.2 | $750.00 *ea* |
| deluxe grade | mason | $43.60 | 33.3 | $1,450.00 *ea* |
| **tile** | | | | |
| economy grade | mason | $43.60 | 3.70 | $161.00 *ea* |
| deluxe grade | mason | $43.60 | 8.26 | $360.00 *ea* |
| **Install fireplace hearth** | | | | |
| **marble** | | | | |
| economy grade | mason | $43.60 | 2.16 | $94.20 *ea* |
| deluxe grade | mason | $43.60 | 4.83 | $211.00 *ea* |
| **brick** | | | | |
| economy grade | mason | $43.60 | 7.04 | $307.00 *ea* |
| deluxe grade | mason | $43.60 | 11.1 | $484.00 *ea* |
| **rubble stone** | | | | |
| economy grade | mason | $43.60 | 7.63 | $333.00 *ea* |
| deluxe grade | mason | $43.60 | 12.0 | $523.00 *ea* |
| **ashlar stone** | | | | |
| economy grade | mason | $43.60 | 7.46 | $325.00 *ea* |
| deluxe grade | mason | $43.60 | 11.8 | $514.00 *ea* |
| **tile** | | | | |
| economy grade | mason | $43.60 | 2.24 | $97.70 *ea* |
| deluxe grade | mason | $43.60 | 5.00 | $218.00 *ea* |

✏ NOTES: _____

_____

_____

_____

_____

_____

_____

_____

_____

_____

_____ *end*

# 19 ........................................................................ *Flooring*

| Item Description | Unit | Remove | Replace | Total | |
|---|---|---|---|---|---|
| **Carpet, economy grade**<br>*Replace* Materials.......15.60    Labor ...........4.73<br>*Remove* .....................    Labor ...........1.62 | sy | $1.62 | $20.33 | $21.95 | ◄ **CARPET**<br>*Includes 12% waste. Carpet is available in virtually every price imaginable. These prices should be considered allowances for typical grades found in residential and light commercial structures. Top grades include wool carpets, pattern carpets, and 52 ounce cut pile carpets.* |
| **Carpet, standard grade**<br>*Replace* Materials.......19.10    Labor ...........4.73<br>*Remove* .....................    Labor ...........1.62 | sy | $1.62 | $23.83 | $25.45 | |
| **Carpet, high grade**<br>*Replace* Materials.......25.30    Labor ...........4.73<br>*Remove* .....................    Labor ...........1.62 | sy | $1.62 | $30.03 | $31.65 | |
| **Carpet, deluxe grade**<br>*Replace* Materials.......30.50    Labor ...........4.73<br>*Remove* .....................    Labor ...........1.62 | sy | $1.62 | $35.23 | $36.85 | |
| **Carpet, custom grade**<br>*Replace* Materials.......36.30    Labor ...........4.73<br>*Remove* .....................    Labor ...........1.62 | sy | $1.62 | $41.03 | $42.65 | |
| **Remove carpet for work, then re-lay**<br>*Replace* .....................    Labor ...........7.24 | sy | — | $7.24 | $7.24 | ◄ **REMOVE CARPET AND RE-LAY** |
| **Glue-down carpet, economy grade**<br>*Replace* Materials.......11.70    Labor ...........5.73<br>*Remove* .....................    Labor ...........4.06 | sy | $4.06 | $17.43 | $21.49 | ◄ **GLUE-DOWN CARPET**<br>*Includes 12% waste. These prices should be considered allowances for typical grades found in residential and light commercial structures.* |
| **Glue-down carpet, standard grade**<br>*Replace* Materials ......14.00    Labor ...........5.73<br>*Remove* .....................    Labor ...........4.06 | sy | $4.06 | $19.73 | $23.79 | |
| **Glue-down carpet, high grade**<br>*Replace* Materials ......18.30    Labor ...........5.73<br>*Remove* .....................    Labor ...........4.06 | sy | $4.06 | $24.03 | $28.09 | |
| **Glue-down carpet, deluxe grade**<br>*Replace* Materials ......21.90    Labor ...........5.73<br>*Remove* .....................    Labor ...........4.06 | sy | $4.06 | $27.63 | $31.69 | |
| **Indoor-outdoor carpet, economy grade**<br>*Replace* Materials.........8.64    Labor ...........5.73<br>*Remove* .....................    Labor ...........4.01 | sy | $4.01 | $14.37 | $18.38 | ◄ **INDOOR-OUTDOOR CARPET**<br>*Includes 12% waste. These prices should be considered allowances for typical grades found in residential and light commercial structures. Economy grade is plastic grass.* |
| **Indoor-outdoor carpet, standard grade**<br>*Replace* Materials ......12.40    Labor ...........5.73<br>*Remove* .....................    Labor ...........4.01 | sy | $4.01 | $18.13 | $22.14 | |
| **Indoor-outdoor carpet, high grade**<br>*Replace* Materials ......18.40    Labor ...........5.73<br>*Remove* .....................    Labor ...........4.01 | sy | $4.01 | $24.13 | $28.14 | |
| **Indoor-outdoor carpet, deluxe grade**<br>*Replace* Materials ......27.60    Labor ...........5.73<br>*Remove* .....................    Labor ...........4.01 | sy | $4.01 | $33.33 | $37.34 | |

| Item Description | Unit | Remove | Replace | Total |
|---|---|---|---|---|
| **WOOL CARPET** ▶ *Includes 12% waste. These prices should be considered allowances for typical grades found in residential and light commercial structures. Standard and high grade may be used for simulated wool Berber style carpets.* | | | | |
| **Wool carpet, standard grade** | sy | $1.62 | $27.97 | $29.59 |
| *Replace* Materials......23.20    Labor..........4.77 | | | | |
| *Remove* .....................    Labor..........1.62 | | | | |
| **Wool carpet, high grade** | sy | $1.62 | $33.97 | $35.59 |
| *Replace* Materials......29.20    Labor..........4.77 | | | | |
| *Remove* .....................    Labor..........1.62 | | | | |
| **Wool carpet, deluxe grade** | sy | $1.62 | $43.17 | $44.79 |
| *Replace* Materials......38.40    Labor..........4.77 | | | | |
| *Remove* .....................    Labor..........1.62 | | | | |
| **Wool carpet, custom grade** | sy | $1.62 | $53.17 | $54.79 |
| *Replace* Materials......48.40    Labor..........4.77 | | | | |
| *Remove* .....................    Labor..........1.62 | | | | |
| **ADD FOR STAIRS** ▶ **Add per step for carpet installation on stairs** | ea | — | $7.67 | $7.67 |
| *Replace* Materials........1.50    Labor..........6.17 | | | | |
| **CARPET PAD** ▶ **Carpet pad, urethane rebound** | sy | $.79 | $4.75 | $5.54 |
| *Replace* Materials........4.20    Labor............ .55 | | | | |
| *Remove* .....................    Labor............ .79 | | | | |
| **Carpet pad, urethane** | sy | $.79 | $3.39 | $4.18 |
| *Replace* Materials........2.84    Labor............ .55 | | | | |
| *Remove* .....................    Labor............ .79 | | | | |
| **Carpet pad, rubber waffle** | sy | $.79 | $3.85 | $4.64 |
| *Replace* Materials........3.30    Labor............ .55 | | | | |
| *Remove* .....................    Labor............ .79 | | | | |
| **Carpet pad, jute** | sy | $.79 | $3.50 | $4.29 |
| *Replace* Materials........2.95    Labor............ .55 | | | | |
| *Remove* .....................    Labor............ .79 | | | | |
| **CARPET COVE** ▶ *Carpet wrapped up the wall up to 8" high with metal cap. Grades refer to allowances for quality of carpet.* **Add for carpet cove, economy grade** | lf | $.58 | $6.45 | $7.03 |
| *Replace* Materials........1.82    Labor..........4.63 | | | | |
| *Remove* .....................    Labor............ .58 | | | | |
| **Add for carpet cove, standard grade** | lf | $.58 | $6.79 | $7.37 |
| *Replace* Materials........2.16    Labor..........4.63 | | | | |
| *Remove* .....................    Labor............ .58 | | | | |
| **Add for carpet cove, high grade** | lf | $.58 | $7.47 | $8.05 |
| *Replace* Materials........2.84    Labor..........4.63 | | | | |
| *Remove* .....................    Labor............ .58 | | | | |
| **Add for carpet cove, deluxe grade** | lf | $.58 | $8.04 | $8.62 |
| *Replace* Materials........3.41    Labor..........4.63 | | | | |
| *Remove* .....................    Labor............ .58 | | | | |
| **Add for carpet cove, custom grade** | lf | $.58 | $8.72 | $9.30 |
| *Replace* Materials........4.09    Labor..........4.63 | | | | |
| *Remove* .....................    Labor............ .58 | | | | |
| **Remove carpet cove for work, then re-lay** | lf | — | $6.93 | $6.93 |
| *Replace* .....................    Labor..........6.93 | | | | |
| **CARPET TILE** ▶ *Includes 12% waste. Commercial grades.* **Carpet tile, economy grade** | sy | $4.06 | $29.17 | $33.23 |
| *Replace* Materials......25.50    Labor..........3.67 | | | | |
| *Remove* .....................    Labor..........4.06 | | | | |

| Item Description | Unit | Remove | Replace | Total | RELATED ITEMS |
|---|---|---|---|---|---|
| **Carpet tile, standard grade**<br>*Replace* Materials......30.80    Labor............3.67<br>*Remove* .....................    Labor............4.06 | sy | $4.06 | $34.47 | $38.53 | Cleaning.......................62<br>*"Stone Quality"*.........306 |
| **Carpet tile, high grade**<br>*Replace* Materials......39.00    Labor............3.67<br>*Remove* .....................    Labor............4.06 | sy | $4.06 | $42.67 | $46.73 | |
| **Minimum charge for carpeting work**<br>*Replace* Materials......55.00    Labor..........34.30 | ea | — | $89.30 | $89.30 | ◁ minimum carpeting |
| **Stone floor, standard grade**<br>*Replace* Materials........5.73    Labor............6.55<br>*Remove* .....................    Labor............2.15 | sf | $2.15 | $12.28 | $14.43 | ◀ **STONE FLOOR**<br>*Grades vary by region. Standard grade includes flagstone, Chattahoochee, and some sandstone. High grade includes better sandstone and lower to medium grade limestone. Deluxe grade includes higher grade limestone, sandstone and granite.* |
| **Stone floor, high grade**<br>*Replace* Materials........7.60    Labor............6.55<br>*Remove* .....................    Labor............2.15 | sf | $2.15 | $14.15 | $16.30 | |
| **Stone floor, deluxe grade**<br>*Replace* Materials........9.06    Labor............6.55<br>*Remove* .....................    Labor............2.15 | sf | $2.15 | $15.61 | $17.76 | |
| **Salvage stone floor, then reinstall**<br>*Replace* Materials........1.15    Labor..........17.20<br>*Remove* .....................    Labor............2.15<br>▶ Usually only stone floors in grout bed built over wood framing are salvageable. Includes cost to selectively remove and re-lay. | sf | $2.15 | $18.35 | $20.50 | |
| **Regrout stone floor**<br>*Replace* Materials ........ .42    Labor............1.30<br>▶ Regrouting only, for repointing see *Masonry* page 318. | sf | — | $1.72 | $1.72 | |
| **Minimum charge for stone floor work**<br>*Replace* .....................    Labor..........46.30 | ea | — | $46.30 | $46.30 | ◁ minimum stone floor |
| **Marble floor, standard grade**<br>*Replace* Materials........9.48    Labor............6.48<br>*Remove* .....................    Labor............2.10 | sf | $2.10 | $15.96 | $18.06 | ◀ **MARBLE FLOOR**<br>*Allowances for typical grades of marble used in residential and light commercial structures. See Masonry, pages 306-307 for more information about marble quality.* |
| **Marble floor, high grade**<br>*Replace* Materials......20.10    Labor............6.48<br>*Remove* .....................    Labor............2.10 | sf | $2.10 | $26.58 | $28.68 | |
| **Marble floor, deluxe grade**<br>*Replace* Materials......31.10    Labor............6.48<br>*Remove* .....................    Labor............2.10 | sf | $2.10 | $37.58 | $39.68 | |
| **Regrout marble floor**<br>*Replace* Materials ........ .31    Labor............1.17<br>▶ Regrouting only, for repointing see *Masonry* page 318. | sf | — | $1.48 | $1.48 | |
| **Minimum charge for marble floor work**<br>*Replace* Materials......70.00    Labor..........46.30 | ea | — | $116.30 | $116.30 | ◁ minimum marble floor |
| **Slate floor, standard grade**<br>*Replace* Materials........7.50    Labor............6.48<br>*Remove* .....................    Labor............2.10 | sf | $2.10 | $13.98 | $16.08 | ◀ **SLATE FLOOR**<br>*Allowances for typical grades of marble used in residential and light commercial structures.* |

| Item Description | Unit | Remove | Replace | Total |
|---|---|---|---|---|
| **SLATE FLOOR ▶** *continued* | | | | |
| **Slate floor, high grade**<br>*Replace* Materials........9.17 Labor ............6.48<br>*Remove* .................... Labor ............2.10 | sf | $2.10 | $15.65 | $17.75 |
| **Slate floor, deluxe grade**<br>*Replace* Materials.......11.00 Labor ............6.48<br>*Remove* .................... Labor ............2.10 | sf | $2.10 | $17.48 | $19.58 |
| **Regrout slate floor**<br>*Replace* Materials ........ .36 Labor ............1.17<br>▶ Regrouting only, for repointing see *Masonry* page 318. | sf | — | $1.53 | $1.53 |
| **Salvage slate floor, then reinstall**<br>*Replace* Materials ........ .68 Labor ...........16.80<br>▶ Usually only slate floors built in grout bed over wood framing are salvageable. Includes cost to selectively remove and re-lay. | sf | — | $17.48 | $17.48 |
| minimum slate floor ▷ **Minimum charge for slate floor work**<br>*Replace* Materials ......69.00 Labor ..........46.30 | ea | — | $115.30 | $115.30 |
| **TILE FLOOR ▶** *Allowances for typical grades of tile used in residential and light commercial structures.* **Tile floor, standard grade**<br>*Replace* Materials........4.79 Labor ............6.17<br>*Remove* .................... Labor ............2.10 | sf | $2.10 | $10.96 | $13.06 |
| **Tile floor, high grade**<br>*Replace* Materials........6.46 Labor ............6.17<br>*Remove* .................... Labor ............2.10 | sf | $2.10 | $12.63 | $14.73 |
| **Tile floor, deluxe grade**<br>*Replace* Materials........8.02 Labor ............6.17<br>*Remove* .................... Labor ............2.10 | sf | $2.10 | $14.19 | $16.29 |
| **Regrout tile floor**<br>*Replace* Materials ........ .53 Labor ............1.20<br>▶ Regrouting only, for repointing see *Masonry* page 318. | sf | — | $1.73 | $1.73 |
| minimum tile floor ▷ **Minimum charge for tile floor work**<br>*Replace* Materials ......55.00 Labor ..........46.30 | ea | — | $101.30 | $101.30 |
| **QUARRY ▶ TILE FLOOR** *Allowances for typical grades of tile used in residential and light commercial structures.* **Quarry tile floor, standard grade**<br>*Replace* Materials........6.46 Labor ............4.90<br>*Remove* .................... Labor ............2.04 | sf | $2.04 | $11.36 | $13.40 |
| **Quarry tile floor, high grade**<br>*Replace* Materials........9.38 Labor ............4.90<br>*Remove* .................... Labor ............2.04 | sf | $2.04 | $14.28 | $16.32 |
| **Quarry tile floor, deluxe grade**<br>*Replace* Materials .......12.60 Labor ............4.90<br>*Remove* .................... Labor ............2.04 | sf | $2.04 | $17.50 | $19.54 |
| **TILE BASE ▶** *Allowances for typical grades of tile used in residential and light commercial structures.* **Tile base, standard grade**<br>*Replace* Materials........4.06 Labor ............4.39<br>*Remove* .................... Labor ............1.60 | lf | $1.60 | $8.45 | $10.05 |
| **Tile base, high grade**<br>*Replace* Materials........5.52 Labor ............4.39<br>*Remove* .................... Labor ............1.60 | lf | $1.60 | $9.91 | $11.51 |

| Item Description | Unit | Remove | Replace | Total |
|---|---|---|---|---|
| **Tile base, deluxe grade** | lf | $1.60 | $11.27 | $12.87 |
| *Replace* Materials........6.88    Labor ............4.39 | | | | |
| *Remove* ...................... Labor ............1.60 | | | | |
| **Precast terrazzo floor tiles, standard grade** | sf | $2.12 | $15.98 | $18.10 |
| *Replace* Materials ......12.00    Labor ............3.98 | | | | |
| *Remove* ...................... Labor ............2.12 | | | | |
| **Precast terrazzo floor tiles, high grade** | sf | $2.12 | $17.58 | $19.70 |
| *Replace* Materials.......13.60    Labor ............3.98 | | | | |
| *Remove* ...................... Labor ............2.12 | | | | |
| **Minimum charge for precast terrazzo floor work** | ea | — | $107.80 | $107.80 |
| *Replace* Materials ......55.00    Labor............52.80 | | | | |
| **6" high precast terrazzo base** | sf | $1.60 | $16.91 | $18.51 |
| *Replace* Materials........8.13    Labor ............8.78 | | | | |
| *Remove* ...................... Labor ............1.60 | | | | |
| **8" high precast terrazzo base** | sf | $1.60 | $17.53 | $19.13 |
| *Replace* Materials........8.75    Labor ............8.78 | | | | |
| *Remove* ...................... Labor ............1.60 | | | | |
| **Cast-in-place thinset terrazzo floor, standard grade** | sf | $2.15 | $7.00 | $9.15 |
| *Replace* Materials........2.61    Labor ............4.39 | | | | |
| *Remove* ...................... Labor ............2.15 | | | | |
| **Cast-in-place thinset terrazzo floor, high grade** | sf | $2.15 | $8.25 | $10.40 |
| *Replace* Materials........3.86    Labor ............4.39 | | | | |
| *Remove* ...................... Labor ............2.15 | | | | |
| **Minimum charge for cast-in-place terrazzo floor work** | ea | — | $217.00 | $217.00 |
| *Replace* Materials......80.00    Labor .........137.00 | | | | |
| **Vinyl floor, economy grade** | sy | $4.59 | $20.38 | $24.97 |
| *Replace* Materials ......14.10    Labor ............6.28 | | | | |
| *Remove* ...................... Labor ............4.59 | | | | |
| **Vinyl floor, standard grade** | sy | $4.59 | $24.88 | $29.47 |
| *Replace* Materials ......18.60    Labor ............6.28 | | | | |
| *Remove* ...................... Labor ............4.59 | | | | |
| **Vinyl floor, high grade** | sy | $4.59 | $29.58 | $34.17 |
| *Replace* Materials ......23.30    Labor ............6.28 | | | | |
| *Remove* ...................... Labor ............4.59 | | | | |
| **Vinyl floor, deluxe grade** | sy | $4.59 | $38.78 | $43.37 |
| *Replace* Materials ......32.50    Labor ............6.28 | | | | |
| *Remove* ...................... Labor ............4.59 | | | | |
| **Minimum charge for vinyl floor work** | ea | — | $84.30 | $84.30 |
| *Replace* Materials......50.00    Labor .........34.30 | | | | |
| **Vinyl tile floor, economy grade** | sf | $.63 | $2.01 | $2.64 |
| *Replace* Materials ...... 1.02    Labor ............ .99 | | | | |
| *Remove* ...................... Labor ............ .63 | | | | |
| **Vinyl tile floor, standard grade** | sf | $.63 | $2.58 | $3.21 |
| *Replace* Materials........1.59    Labor ............ .99 | | | | |
| *Remove* ...................... Labor ............ .63 | | | | |

**RELATED ITEMS**

Cleaning........................62
"Stone Quality"........306

◄ **PRECAST TERRAZZO TILE**
Cast in gray cement. Add **2%** for white cement. Tiles are 12" x 12". Standard grade is 1" thick, high grade is 1-1/4" thick

◁ minimum terrazzo floor

◄ **PRECAST TERRAZZO BASE**
Cast in gray cement.

◄ **CAST-IN-PLACE TERRAZZO FLOOR**
Cast in gray cement with zinc divider strips. Add **3%** for brass divider strips. Standard grade is 1-1/2" deep, high grade is up to 3" thick. Add **2%** for white cement.

◄ **VINYL FLOOR**
Includes 12% waste. These prices should be considered allowances for typical grades found in residential and light commercial structures. Lower grades have smoother faces and are thinner. Higher grades are embossed, marbleized, and thicker vinyl.

◁ minimum vinyl floor

◄ **VINYL TILE FLOOR**
Includes 12% waste. These prices should be considered allowances for typical grades found in residential and light commercial structures. See vinyl floor above for general grade guidelines.

| | Item Description | | Unit | Remove | Replace | Total |
|---|---|---|---|---|---|---|
| **VINYL TILE FLOOR ▶** *continued* | **Vinyl tile floor, high grade** | | sf | $.63 | $2.81 | $3.44 |
| | *Replace* Materials........1.82 | Labor............99 | | | | |
| | *Remove* ..................... | Labor............63 | | | | |
| | **Vinyl tile floor, deluxe grade** | | sf | $.63 | $3.83 | $4.46 |
| | *Replace* Materials........2.84 | Labor............99 | | | | |
| | *Remove* ..................... | Labor............63 | | | | |
| minimum vinyl tile floor ▷ | **Minimum charge for vinyl tile floor work** | | ea | — | $64.30 | $64.30 |
| | *Replace* Materials......30.00 | Labor .........34.30 | | | | |
| **RESILIENT ▶ TILE FLOOR** *Allowances for typical grades of resilient tile used in residential and light commercial structures.* | **Resilient tile floor, economy grade** | | sf | $.63 | $2.01 | $2.64 |
| | *Replace* Materials........1.02 | Labor............99 | | | | |
| | *Remove* ..................... | Labor............63 | | | | |
| | **Resilient tile floor, standard grade** | | sf | $.63 | $2.35 | $2.98 |
| | *Replace* Materials........1.36 | Labor............99 | | | | |
| | *Remove* ..................... | Labor............63 | | | | |
| | **Resilient tile floor, high grade** | | sf | $.63 | $2.58 | $3.21 |
| | *Replace* Materials........1.59 | Labor............99 | | | | |
| | *Remove* ..................... | Labor............63 | | | | |
| | **Resilient tile floor, deluxe grade** | | sf | $.63 | $3.26 | $3.89 |
| | *Replace* Materials........2.27 | Labor............99 | | | | |
| | *Remove* ..................... | Labor............63 | | | | |
| minimum resilient tile ▷ | **Minimum charge for resilient tile floor work** | | ea | — | $64.30 | $64.30 |
| | *Replace* Materials......30.00 | Labor .........34.30 | | | | |
| **ANTIQUE STYLE ▶ LINOLEUM** *Antique style linoleum is no longer made in the USA and must be imported from Europe. In recent years linoleum has become much more common in commercial and residential applications. Tiles are normally available in limited styles and colors.* | **Antique style linoleum, plain and marbleized** | | sy | $4.59 | $38.98 | $43.57 |
| | *Replace* Materials......32.50 | Labor ..........6.48 | | | | |
| | *Remove* ..................... | Labor ..........4.59 | | | | |
| | **Antique style linoleum, inlaid & molded** | | sy | $4.59 | $48.88 | $53.47 |
| | *Replace* Materials......42.40 | Labor ..........6.48 | | | | |
| | *Remove* ..................... | Labor ..........4.59 | | | | |
| | **Antique style linoleum, battleship** | | sy | $4.59 | $36.18 | $40.77 |
| | *Replace* Materials......29.70 | Labor ..........6.48 | | | | |
| | *Remove* ..................... | Labor ..........4.59 | | | | |
| | **Antique style linoleum tile** | | sf | $4.59 | $5.53 | $10.12 |
| | *Replace* Materials........4.43 | Labor ..........1.10 | | | | |
| | *Remove* ..................... | Labor ..........4.59 | | | | |
| minimum linoleum floor ▷ | **Minimum charge for antique style linoleum floor work** | | ea | — | $147.80 | $147.80 |
| | *Replace* Materials ......95.00 | Labor.........52.80 | | | | |
| **VINYL COVE ▶** *Vinyl wrapped up wall with metal cap. Grades refer to allowances for quality of vinyl.* | **4" high vinyl cove** | | lf | $.94 | $5.05 | $5.99 |
| | *Replace* Materials........1.93 | Labor ..........3.12 | | | | |
| | *Remove* ..................... | Labor ............94 | | | | |
| | **6" high vinyl cove** | | lf | $.94 | $5.28 | $6.22 |
| | *Replace* Materials........2.16 | Labor ..........3.12 | | | | |
| | *Remove* ..................... | Labor ............94 | | | | |
| | **8" high vinyl cove** | | lf | $.94 | $5.39 | $6.33 |
| | *Replace* Materials........2.27 | Labor ..........3.12 | | | | |
| | *Remove* ..................... | Labor ............94 | | | | |

| Item Description | Unit | Remove | Replace | Total | |
|---|---|---|---|---|---|
| **Minimum charge for vinyl cove work** | ea | — | $48.70 | $48.70 | ◁ minimum vinyl cove |
| *Replace* Materials......25.00   Labor.........23.70 | | | | | |
| **Rubber base, economy grade** | lf | $.29 | $2.05 | $2.34 | ◀ **RUBBER BASE** |
| *Replace* Materials........1.36   Labor............ .69 | | | | | *Economy grade is black or* |
| *Remove* ......................   Labor............ .29 | | | | | *brown 2-1/2" high.* |
| **Rubber base, standard grade** | lf | $.29 | $2.51 | $2.80 | *Standard grade is 4" high standard colors. High* |
| *Replace* Materials........1.82   Labor............ .69 | | | | | *grade is 6" high. Deluxe* |
| *Remove* ......................   Labor............ .29 | | | | | *grade is 6" high,* |
| **Rubber base, high grade** | lf | $.29 | $3.08 | $3.37 | *specialty colors.* |
| *Replace* Materials........2.39   Labor............ .69 | | | | | |
| *Remove* ......................   Labor............ .29 | | | | | |
| **Rubber base, deluxe grade** | lf | $.29 | $3.53 | $3.82 | |
| *Replace* Materials........2.84   Labor............ .69 | | | | | |
| *Remove* ......................   Labor............ .29 | | | | | |
| **Minimum charge for rubber base work** | ea | — | $29.90 | $29.90 | ◁ minimum rubber base |
| *Replace* Materials.......15.00   Labor...........14.90 | | | | | |
| **Maple strip flooring, first grade** | sf | $.52 | $10.15 | $10.67 | ◀ **MAPLE STRIP FLOORING** |
| *Replace* Materials........7.13   Labor............3.02 | | | | | *Strip flooring is up to* |
| *Remove* ......................   Labor............ .52 | | | | | *3/4" thick and up to* |
| ▶ Face almost free of defects. (Variation in color is not a defect.) | | | | | *3-1/4" wide. Grading information based on* |
| **Maple strip flooring, second grade** | sf | $.52 | $8.55 | $9.07 | *rules established by the* |
| *Replace* Materials........5.53   Labor............3.02 | | | | | *Maple Flooring* |
| *Remove* ......................   Labor............ .52 | | | | | *Manufacturers Association* |
| ▶ Small tight knots, slight dressing imperfections. | | | | | *(MFMA). All wood is kiln-dried, tongue-and-groove,* |
| **Maple strip flooring, third grade** | sf | $.52 | $7.28 | $7.80 | *end-matched and hollow* |
| *Replace* Materials........4.26   Labor............3.02 | | | | | *or scratch backed.* |
| *Remove* ......................   Labor............ .52 | | | | | |
| ▶ Larger knots and imperfections that may cause waste. | | | | | |
| **Red oak strip flooring, select & better grade** | sf | $.52 | $8.55 | $9.07 | ◀ **RED OAK STRIP FLOORING** |
| *Replace* Materials.....5.53   Labor............3.02 | | | | | *Strip flooring is up to* |
| *Remove* ......................   Labor............ .52 | | | | | *3/4" thick and up to* |
| ▶ At least 50% is clear grade. Clear grade face is practically clear, may have very small areas of bright sap. Select grade face may contain very small areas of burl, one small tight knot every 3 lf, pinworm holes and working imperfections. | | | | | *3-1/4" wide. Grading information based on rules established by the National Oak Flooring Manufacturers Association* |
| **Red oak strip flooring, #1 common grade** | sf | $.52 | $7.70 | $8.22 | *(NOFMA). All wood is* |
| *Replace* Materials........4.68   Labor............3.02 | | | | | *kiln-dried, tongue-and-groove, end-matched and* |
| *Remove* ......................   Labor............ .52 | | | | | *hollow or scratch backed.* |
| ▶ Same as select with larger and more common imperfections with some flags, heavy streaks, and checks. | | | | | |
| **Red oak strip flooring, #2 common grade** | sf | $.52 | $6.32 | $6.84 | |
| *Replace* Materials........3.30   Labor............3.02 | | | | | |
| *Remove* ......................   Labor............ .52 | | | | | |
| ▶ Many natural wood imperfections and milling flaws. Used in rustic or general utility applications. | | | | | |
| **Red oak strip flooring, quartersawn, clear grade** | sf | $.52 | $12.38 | $12.90 | ◀ **QUARTERSAWN RED OAK STRIP FLOORING** |
| *Replace* Materials........9.36   Labor............3.02 | | | | | *See grading information* |
| *Remove* ......................   Labor............ .52 | | | | | *above for red oak strip* |
| ▶ Face is practically clear, may have very small areas of bright sap. | | | | | *flooring.* |

**RELATED ITEMS**

| | |
|---|---|
| Cleaning..........................62 | |
| Painting.....................340 | |

| Item Description | Unit | Remove | Replace | Total |
|---|---|---|---|---|

**QUARTERSAWN ▶ RED OAK STRIP FLOORING** *continued*

**Red oak strip flooring, quartersawn, select grade** — sf | $.52 | $11.00 | $11.52
*Replace* Materials........7.98    Labor............3.02
*Remove* .......................    Labor.............52
▶ Face may contain very small areas of burl, one small tight knot every 3 lf, pin-worm holes and working imperfections.

**PREFINISHED ▶ RED OAK STRIP FLOORING**
*Strip flooring is up to 3/4" thick and up to 3-1/4" wide. Grading information based on rules established by the National Oak Flooring Manufacturers Association (NOFMA). All wood is kiln-dried, tongue-and-groove, end-matched and hollow or scratch backed.*

**Prefinished red oak strip flooring, prime grade** — sf | $.52 | $9.40 | $9.92
*Replace* Materials........6.28    Labor............3.12
*Remove* .......................    Labor.............52
▶ Almost flawless appearance with very small character marks. Sap and color variations are not flaws.

**Prefinished red oak strip flooring, standard & better grade** — sf | $.52 | $8.55 | $9.07
*Replace* Materials........5.43    Labor............3.12
*Remove* .......................    Labor.............52
▶ Combination of standard and prime grade. See above for prime grade characteristics. Standard grade may contain filled flaws.

**Prefinished red oak strip flooring, standard grade** — sf | $.52 | $9.50 | $10.02
*Replace* Materials........6.38    Labor............3.12
*Remove* .......................    Labor.............52
▶ May contain filled flaws.

**Prefinished red oak strip flooring, tavern & better grade** — sf | $.52 | $10.67 | $11.19
*Replace* Materials........7.55    Labor............3.12
*Remove* .......................    Labor.............52
▶ Combination of standard and tavern grade. See above for standard grade characteristics. Tavern grade contains filled flaws and imperfections which produce rustic appearance.

**Prefinished red oak strip flooring, tavern grade** — sf | $.52 | $12.06 | $12.58
*Replace* Materials........8.94    Labor............3.12
*Remove* .......................    Labor.............52
▶ Contains filled flaws and imperfections which produce rustic appearance.

**RED OAK PLANK ▶ FLOORING**
*Plank flooring is up to 3/4" thick and over 3-1/4" wide. Floors that contain a mix of plank and strip floor widths are usually considered plank floors. Grading information based on rules established by the National Oak Flooring Manufacturers Association (NOFMA). All wood is kiln-dried, tongue-and-groove, end-matched and hollow or scratch backed.*

**Red oak plank flooring, select & better grade** — sf | $.50 | $11.33 | $11.83
*Replace* Materials........8.62    Labor............2.71
*Remove* .......................    Labor.............50
▶ At least 50% is clear grade. Clear grade face is practically clear, may have very small areas of bright sap. Select grade face may contain very small areas of burl, one small tight knot every 3 lf, pinworm holes and working imperfections.

**Red oak plank flooring, #1 common grade** — sf | $.50 | $9.94 | $10.44
*Replace* Materials........7.23    Labor............2.71
*Remove* .......................    Labor.............50
▶ Same as select with larger and more common imperfections with some flags, heavy streaks, and checks.

**Red oak plank flooring, #2 common grade** — sf | $.50 | $7.82 | $8.32
*Replace* Materials........5.11    Labor............2.71
*Remove* .......................    Labor.............50
▶ Same as select with larger and more common imperfections with some flags, heavy streaks, and checks.

**MAPLE PARQUET ▶**
*Face pieces are practically clear, may have some small areas of bright sap. For select grade deduct **8%.** For #1 common grade deduct **15%**.*

**Maple parquet unit block flooring, clear grade** — sf | $.47 | $8.47 | $8.94
*Replace* Materials........5.31    Labor............3.16
*Remove* .......................    Labor.............47
▶ Made from solid wood pieces glued side by side.

**Maple laminated block flooring, clear grade** — sf | $.47 | $9.51 | $9.98
*Replace* Materials........6.35    Labor............3.16
*Remove* .......................    Labor.............47
▶ Made from at least three laminated layers (like plywood).

| Item Description | Unit | Remove | Replace | Total |
|---|---|---|---|---|
| **Maple parquet slat block flooring, clear grade** | sf | $.47 | $9.93 | $10.40 |
| *Replace* Materials........6.77　　Labor ...........3.16 | | | | |
| *Remove* ......................　　Labor............ .47 | | | | |
| ▶ Made from many wood slats glued side by side with parquet pattern in block. | | | | |
| **Prefinished maple parquet unit block flooring, prime grade** | sf | $.47 | $9.26 | $9.73 |
| *Replace* Materials........6.04　　Labor ...........3.22 | | | | |
| *Remove* ......................　　Labor............ .47 | | | | |
| ▶ Made from solid wood pieces glued side by side. | | | | |
| **Prefinished maple laminated block flooring, prime grade** | sf | $.47 | $10.20 | $10.67 |
| *Replace* Materials........6.98　　Labor ...........3.22 | | | | |
| *Remove* ......................　　Labor............ .47 | | | | |
| ▶ Made from at least three laminated layers (like plywood). | | | | |
| **Prefinished maple parquet slat block flooring, prime grade** | sf | $.47 | $10.72 | $11.19 |
| *Replace* Materials........7.50　　Labor ...........3.22 | | | | |
| *Remove* ......................　　Labor............ .47 | | | | |
| ▶ Made from many wood slats glued side by side with parquet pattern in block. | | | | |
| **Red oak parquet unit block flooring, clear grade** | sf | $.47 | $8.47 | $8.94 |
| *Replace* Materials........5.31　　Labor ...........3.16 | | | | |
| *Remove* ......................　　Labor............ .47 | | | | |
| ▶ Made from solid wood pieces glued side by side. | | | | |
| **Red oak laminated block flooring, clear grade** | sf | $.47 | $9.31 | $9.78 |
| *Replace* Materials........6.15　　Labor ...........3.16 | | | | |
| *Remove* ......................　　Labor............ .47 | | | | |
| ▶ Made from at least three laminated layers (like plywood). | | | | |
| **Red oak parquet slat block flooring, clear grade** | sf | $.47 | $9.83 | $10.30 |
| *Replace* Materials........6.67　　Labor ...........3.16 | | | | |
| *Remove* ......................　　Labor............ .47 | | | | |
| ▶ Made from many wood slats glued side by side with parquet pattern in block. | | | | |
| **Prefinished red oak parquet unit block flooring, prime grade** | sf | $.47 | $9.26 | $9.73 |
| *Replace* Materials........6.04　　Labor ...........3.22 | | | | |
| *Remove* ......................　　Labor............ .47 | | | | |
| ▶ Made from solid wood pieces glued side by side. | | | | |
| **Prefinished red oak laminated block flooring, prime grade** | sf | $.47 | $10.10 | $10.57 |
| *Replace* Materials........6.88　　Labor ...........3.22 | | | | |
| *Remove* ......................　　Labor............ .47 | | | | |
| ▶ Made from at least three laminated layers (like plywood). | | | | |
| **Prefinished red oak parquet slat block flooring, prime grade** | sf | $.47 | $10.62 | $11.09 |
| *Replace* Materials........7.40　　Labor ...........3.22 | | | | |
| *Remove* ......................　　Labor............ .47 | | | | |
| ▶ Made from many wood slats glued side by side with parquet pattern in block. | | | | |

**Add 8% for pickets around unit block**
▶ Add for mitered wood trim around edges of block, called "pickets."

**Deduct 7% for beech flooring**

**Deduct 7% for birch flooring**

**Deduct 6% for ash flooring**

**Add 46% for cherry flooring**

---

**RELATED ITEMS**

Cleaning.....................62
Finish Carpentry...........199
Painting.....................340

◀ **PREFINISHED MAPLE PARQUET**
*Face pieces are almost flawless with very small character marks. (Sap and color variations are not flaws.) For standard grade deduct **10%.** For tavern grade deduct **14%.***

◀ **RED OAK PARQUET**
*Face pieces are practically clear, may have some small areas of bright sap. For select grade deduct **8%.** For #1 common grade deduct **15%.***

◀ **PREFINISHED RED OAK PARQUET**
*Face pieces are almost flawless with very small character marks. (Sap and color variations are not flaws.) For standard grade deduct **10%.** For tavern grade deduct **14%.***

◀ **ADDITIONAL WOOD SPECIES**
*Deduct or add these percentages to the costs listed for red oak.*

| Item Description | Unit | Remove | Replace | Total |
|---|---|---|---|---|

**ADDITIONAL WOOD SPECIES** *continued*

**Deduct 5% for hickory flooring**

**Add 182% for teak flooring**

**Add for 70% walnut flooring**

**Deduct 7% for white oak flooring**

**SOUTHERN PINE STRIP FLOORING**
*Strip flooring is up to 3/4" thick and up to 3-1/4" wide. Grading information based on rules established by the Southern Pine Inspection Bureau (SPIB). All wood is kiln-dried, tongue-and-groove, end-matched and hollow or scratch backed.*

| Item Description | Unit | Remove | Replace | Total |
|---|---|---|---|---|
| **Southern pine strip flooring, B&B grade** | sf | $.52 | $5.36 | $5.88 |

*Replace* Materials........2.34    Labor............3.02
*Remove* ........................    Labor.............52
► Best quality, allows very small surface checks, pin knots, small closed pitch pockets, light stain and very light warp. Usually no more than one character flaw per 4 lf.

| **Southern pine strip flooring, C & better grade** | sf | $.52 | $5.25 | $5.77 |

*Replace* Materials........2.23    Labor............3.02
*Remove* ........................    Labor.............52
► Combination of B&B and C grades. See B&B grade above. C grade is same as B&B with slightly larger and more frequent imperfections with some shakes, wane, splits, and skips.

| **Southern pine strip flooring, C grade** | sf | $.52 | $5.04 | $5.56 |

*Replace* Materials........2.02    Labor............3.02
*Remove* ........................    Labor............. .52
► C grade is same as B&B (see item above) with slightly larger and more frequent imperfections with some shakes, wane, splits, and skips.

**SOUTHERN PINE PLANK FLOORING**
*Plank flooring is up to 3/4" thick and over 3-1/4" wide. Floors that contain a mix of plank and strip floor widths are usually considered plank floors. See southern pine strip flooring above for grading information.*

| **Southern pine plank flooring, B&B grade** | sf | $.50 | $5.58 | $6.08 |

*Replace* Materials........2.87    Labor............2.71
*Remove* ........................    Labor............. .50
► See information under same grade of southern pine strip flooring.

| **Southern pine plank flooring, C & better grade** | sf | $.50 | $5.37 | $5.87 |

*Replace* Materials........2.66    Labor............2.71
*Remove* ........................    Labor............2.71
► See information under same grade of southern pine strip flooring.

| **Southern pine plank flooring, C grade** | sf | $.50 | $5.05 | $5.55 |

*Replace* Materials........2.34    Labor............2.71
*Remove* ........................    Labor............. .50
► See information under same grade of southern pine strip flooring.

**DOUGLAS FIR STRIP FLOORING**
*Douglas fir or western hemlock, or white fir, or Sitka spruce. Strip flooring is up to 3/4" thick and up to 3-1/4" wide. Grading information based on rules established by the West Coast Lumbermen's Inspection Bureau (WCLIB). All wood is kiln-dried, tongue-and-groove, end-matched and hollow or scratch backed.*

| **Douglas fir strip flooring, C & better grade** | sf | $.52 | $5.57 | $6.09 |

*Replace* Materials........2.55    Labor............3.02
*Remove* ........................    Labor............. .52
► Highest quality with some pieces perfectly clear. Other pieces may contain infrequent medium stained sapwood, very small seasoning checks, small light skips, light warp, tight knots, and raised grain.

| **Douglas fir strip flooring, D grade** | sf | $.52 | $5.47 | $5.99 |

*Replace* Materials........2.45    Labor............3.02
*Remove* ........................    Labor............. .52
► Contains some stained wood, medium splits, seasoning checks, small and infrequent holes, torn or raised grain, large pitch streaks, larger and more frequent knots than are found in C grade, and some pieces with medium warp.

| Item Description | Unit | Remove | Replace | Total |
|---|---|---|---|---|
| **Douglas fir strip flooring, E grade** | sf | $.52 | $5.25 | $5.77 |
| *Replace* Materials........2.23   Labor............3.02 | | | | |
| *Remove* ....................   Labor............. .52 | | | | |
| ▶ A subfloor grade that is normally not used in exposed applications. Includes larger and more frequent defects than are found in D grade, with loose knots and knot holes. | | | | |
| **Douglas fir plank flooring, C & better grade** | sf | $.50 | $5.80 | $6.30 |
| *Replace* Materials........3.09   Labor............2.71 | | | | |
| *Remove* ....................   Labor............. .50 | | | | |
| ▶ See information under same grade of Douglas fir strip flooring. | | | | |
| **Douglas fir plank flooring, D grade** | sf | $.50 | $5.58 | $6.08 |
| *Replace* Materials........2.87   Labor............2.71 | | | | |
| *Remove* ....................   Labor............. .50 | | | | |
| ▶ See information under same grade of Douglas fir strip flooring. | | | | |
| **Douglas fir plank flooring, E grade** | sf | $.50 | $5.26 | $5.76 |
| *Replace* Materials........2.55   Labor............2.71 | | | | |
| *Remove* ....................   Labor............. .50 | | | | |
| ▶ See information under same grade of Douglas fir strip flooring. | | | | |
| **Reclaimed antique longleaf pine flooring, crown grade** | sf | $.52 | $13.62 | $14.14 |
| *Replace* Materials......10.60   Labor............3.02 | | | | |
| *Remove* ....................   Labor............. .52 | | | | |
| ▶ Best grade. 90% is free of knots with 100% dense grade heartwood face and very infrequent nail holes. Knots are tight and less than 1-1/4" in diameter. | | | | |
| **Reclaimed antique longleaf pine flooring, select prime grade** | sf | $.52 | $11.42 | $11.94 |
| *Replace* Materials.......8.40   Labor............3.02 | | | | |
| *Remove* ....................   Labor............. .52 | | | | |
| ▶ 75% is free of knots with at least 97% dense grade heartwood and infrequent nail holes. Knots are tight and less than 1-1/2" in diameter. | | | | |
| **Reclaimed antique longleaf pine flooring, prime grade** | sf | $.52 | $11.21 | $11.73 |
| *Replace* Materials.......8.19   Labor............3.02 | | | | |
| *Remove* ....................   Labor............. .52 | | | | |
| ▶ Varying degree of knots and nail holes with at least 85% dense grade heartwood. Knots are tight and less than 2" in diameter. | | | | |
| **Reclaimed antique longleaf pine flooring, naily grade** | sf | $.52 | $10.15 | $10.67 |
| *Replace* Materials.......7.13   Labor............3.02 | | | | |
| *Remove* ....................   Labor............. .52 | | | | |
| ▶ Same as select prime grade above with many nail holes. | | | | |
| **Reclaimed antique longleaf pine flooring, cabin grade** | sf | $.52 | $10.25 | $10.77 |
| *Replace* Materials.......7.23   Labor............3.02 | | | | |
| *Remove* ....................   Labor............. .52 | | | | |
| ▶ Similar to prime grade with more sapwood, larger knots, and some boards with many nail holes. | | | | |
| **Reclaimed antique longleaf pine flooring, distressed grade** | sf | $.52 | $16.02 | $16.54 |
| *Replace* Materials.......13.00   Labor............3.02 | | | | |
| *Remove* ....................   Labor............. .52 | | | | |
| ▶ Crown grade with as-is finish, including gouges, tight cracks, worm holes, worn spots, and raised grain. Boards are also machined to enhance the time-worn look. Edges and back are remilled. | | | | |

**RELATED ITEMS**

Cleaning........................62
Finish Carpentry..........199
Painting.....................340

◀ **DOUGLAS FIR PLANK FLOORING**
*Plank flooring is up to 3/4" thick and over 3-1/4" wide. Floors that contain a mix of plank and strip floor widths are usually considered plank floors. See Douglas fir strip flooring on facing page for grading information.*

◀ **RECLAIMED ANTIQUE LONGLEAF PINE**
*Strip or plank flooring. Although longleaf pine was once common in Southeastern America, new lumber is no longer available. Longleaf pine must be salvaged from existing structures. (Although Goodwin Heart Pine Company of Micanopy, Florida does salvage logs that sank to the bottom of rivers.) Grading is based on grades marketed by Mountain Lumber Company, Inc. of Ruckersville, Virginia.*

| Item Description | Unit | Remove | Replace | Total |
|---|---|---|---|---|
| **SAND, EDGE, & FILL WOOD FLOOR** | | | | |
| **Sand, edge, and fill new wood floor** | sf | — | $1.15 | $1.15 |
| *Replace* Materials ........ .26    Labor............ .89 | | | | |
| **Light sand, edge, and fill existing wood floor** | sf | — | $1.25 | $1.25 |
| *Replace* Materials ........ .22    Labor............ 1.03 | | | | |
| **Medium sand, edge, and fill old wood floor** | sf | — | $1.43 | $1.43 |
| *Replace* Materials ........ .30    Labor............ 1.13 | | | | |
| **Heavy sand, edge, and fill old wood floor** | sf | — | $1.76 | $1.76 |
| *Replace* Materials ........ .35    Labor............ 1.41 | | | | |
| **WOOD FLOOR SLEEPERS** *Glued and nailed with case-hardened nails to concrete floor.* | | | | |
| **1" x 2" sleepers on concrete floor, 24" oc** | sf | $.18 | $.46 | $.64 |
| *Replace* Materials ........ .19    Labor............ .27 / *Remove* Labor............ .18 | | | | |
| **1" x 3" sleepers on concrete floor, 24" oc** | sf | $.18 | $.61 | $.79 |
| *Replace* Materials ........ .30    Labor............ .31 / *Remove* Labor............ .18 | | | | |
| **2" x 4" sleepers on concrete floor, 24" oc** | sf | $.18 | $1.11 | $1.29 |
| *Replace* Materials ........ .70    Labor............ .41 / *Remove* Labor............ .18 | | | | |
| **2" x 6" sleepers on concrete floor, 24" oc** | sf | $.18 | $1.55 | $1.73 |
| *Replace* Materials ........ 1.10    Labor............ .45 / *Remove* Labor............ .18 | | | | |
| **UNDERLAYMENT** *Includes 5% waste. When removing underlayment that has been heavily glued and stapled, double the removal cost.* | | | | |
| **3/8" particleboard floor underlayment** | sy | $1.83 | $9.31 | $11.14 |
| *Replace* Materials ........ 3.58    Labor............ 5.73 / *Remove* Labor............ 1.83 | | | | |
| **1/2" particleboard floor underlayment** | sy | $1.83 | $9.46 | $11.29 |
| *Replace* Materials ........ 3.70    Labor............ 5.76 / *Remove* Labor............ 1.83 | | | | |
| **5/8" particleboard floor underlayment** | sy | $1.83 | $9.84 | $11.67 |
| *Replace* Materials ........ 4.08    Labor............ 5.76 / *Remove* Labor............ 1.83 | | | | |
| **3/4" particleboard floor underlayment** | sy | $1.83 | $10.56 | $12.39 |
| *Replace* Materials ........ 4.76    Labor............ 5.80 / *Remove* Labor............ 1.83 | | | | |
| **1/4" hardboard floor underlayment** | sy | $1.83 | $10.70 | $12.53 |
| *Replace* Materials ........ 4.73    Labor............ 5.97 / *Remove* Labor............ 1.83 | | | | |
| **1/2" plywood floor underlayment** | sy | $1.83 | $11.83 | $13.66 |
| *Replace* Materials ........ 6.07    Labor............ 5.76 / *Remove* Labor............ 1.83 | | | | |
| **Minimum charge for floor underlayment work** | ea | — | $54.50 | $54.50 |
| *Replace* Materials ...... 30.00    Labor............ 24.50 | | | | |

NOTES: _____

_____

_____ end

# TIME & MATERIAL CHARTS *(selected items)*

## Flooring Materials

| DESCRIPTION | MATERIAL PRICE | GROSS COVERAGE | WASTE | NET COVERAGE | UNIT PRICE |
|---|---|---|---|---|---|
| **Carpet** | | | | | |
| economy grade | $13.10 sy | 1 | 12% | .88 | $15.60 sy |
| custom grade | $31.90 sy | 1 | 12% | .88 | $36.30 sy |
| **Glue-down carpet** | | | | | |
| economy grade | $10.30 sy | 1 | 12% | .88 | $11.70 sy |
| deluxe grade | $19.30 sy | 1 | 12% | .88 | $21.90 sy |
| **Indoor-outdoor carpet** | | | | | |
| economy grade | $7.60 sy | 1 | 12% | .88 | $8.64 sy |
| deluxe grade | $24.30 sy | 1 | 12% | .88 | $27.60 sy |
| **Wool carpet** | | | | | |
| standard grade | $20.40 sy | 1 | 12% | .88 | $23.20 sy |
| custom grade | $42.60 sy | 1 | 12% | .88 | $48.40 sy |
| **Simulated wool berber carpet** | | | | | |
| standard grade | $18.80 sy | 1 | 12% | .88 | $21.40 sy |
| custom grade | $30.20 sy | 1 | 12% | .88 | $34.30 sy |
| **Carpet pad** | | | | | |
| urethane rebound | $3.70 sy | 1 | 12% | .88 | $4.20 sy |
| jute | $2.60 sy | 1 | 12% | .88 | $2.95 sy |
| **Carpet tile** | | | | | |
| standard grade | $22.40 sy | 1 | 12% | .88 | $25.50 sy |
| custom grade | $34.30 sy | 1 | 12% | .88 | $39.00 sy |
| **Stone floor** | | | | | |
| standard grade | $5.50 sf | 1 | 4% | .96 | $5.73 sf |
| deluxe grade | $8.70 sf | 1 | 4% | .96 | $9.06 sf |
| **Marble floor** | | | | | |
| standard grade | $9.10 sf | 1 | 4% | .96 | $9.48 sf |
| deluxe grade | $29.90 sf | 1 | 4% | .96 | $31.10 sf |
| **Slate floor** | | | | | |
| standard grade | $7.20 sf | 1 | 4% | .96 | $7.50 sf |
| deluxe grade | $10.60 sf | 1 | 4% | .96 | $11.00 sf |
| **Tile floor** | | | | | |
| standard grade | $4.60 sf | 1 | 4% | .96 | $4.79 sf |
| deluxe grade | $7.70 sf | 1 | 4% | .96 | $8.02 sf |
| **Quarry tile floor** | | | | | |
| standard grade | $6.20 sf | 1 | 4% | .96 | $6.46 sf |
| deluxe grade | $12.10 sf | 1 | 4% | .96 | $12.60 sf |
| **Precast terrazzo floor tiles** | | | | | |
| standard grade | $11.50 sf | 1 | 4% | .96 | $12.00 sf |
| high grade | $13.10 sf | 1 | 4% | .96 | $13.60 sf |
| **Cast-in-place thinset terrazzo floor** | | | | | |
| standard grade | $2.30 sf | 1 | 12% | .88 | $2.61 sf |
| high grade | $3.40 sf | 1 | 12% | .88 | $3.86 sf |
| **Vinyl floor** | | | | | |
| economy grade | $12.40 sy | 1 | 12% | .88 | $14.10 sy |
| deluxe grade | $28.60 sy | 1 | 12% | .88 | $32.50 sy |
| **Vinyl tile floor** | | | | | |
| economy grade | $.90 sf | 1 | 12% | .88 | $1.02 sf |
| deluxe grade | $2.50 sf | 1 | 12% | .88 | $2.84 sf |

. . . *More* ➤

## Flooring Materials *continued*

| DESCRIPTION | MATERIAL PRICE | GROSS COVERAGE | WASTE | NET COVERAGE | UNIT PRICE |
|---|---|---|---|---|---|
| **Resilient tile floor** | | | | | |
| economy grade | $.90 sf | 1 | 12% | .88 | $1.02 sf |
| deluxe grade | $2.00 sf | 1 | 12% | .88 | $2.27 sf |
| **Antique style linoleum** | | | | | |
| battleship | $26.10 sy | 1 | 12% | .88 | $29.70 sy |
| **Rubber base** | | | | | |
| economy grade | $1.20 lf | 1 | 12% | .88 | $1.36 lf |
| deluxe grade | $2.50 lf | 1 | 12% | .88 | $2.84 lf |
| **Strip flooring** | | | | | |
| maple, first grade | $6.70 sf | 1 | 6% | .94 | $7.13 sf |
| red oak, select & better grade | $5.20 sf | 1 | 6% | .94 | $5.53 sf |
| red oak, quartersawn, clear grade | $8.80 sf | 1 | 6% | .94 | $9.36 sf |
| prefinished red oak, prime grade | $5.90 sf | 1 | 6% | .94 | $6.28 sf |
| **Plank flooring** | | | | | |
| red oak, select & better grade | $8.10 sf | 1 | 6% | .94 | $8.62 sf |
| **Parquet or block flooring** | | | | | |
| maple, slat block, clear grade | $6.50 sf | 1 | 4% | .96 | $6.77 sf |
| prefinished maple, slat block, prime grade | $5.80 sf | 1 | 4% | .96 | $6.04 sf |
| red oak, slat block, clear grade | $5.10 sf | 1 | 4% | .96 | $5.31 sf |
| prefinished red oak, slat block, prime grade | $5.80 sf | 1 | 4% | .96 | $6.04 sf |
| **Softwood flooring** | | | | | |
| Southern pine strip, B&B grade | $2.20 sf | 1 | 6% | .94 | $2.34 sf |
| Southern pine plank, B&B grade | $2.70 sf | 1 | 6% | .94 | $2.87 sf |
| Douglas fir strip, C & better grade | $2.40 sf | 1 | 6% | .94 | $2.55 sf |
| Douglas fir plank, C & better grade | $2.90 sf | 1 | 6% | .94 | $3.09 sf |
| reclaimed antique longleaf pine, crown grade | $10.00 sf | 1 | 6% | .94 | $10.60 sf |
| **Sleepers on concrete floor, 24" on center** | | | | | |
| 1" x 2" | | | | | $.19 sf |
| 2" x 4" | | | | | $.70 sf |
| **Floor underlayment** | | | | | |
| 3/8" particleboard | $12.10 sheet | 3.56 | 5% | 3.38 | $3.58 sy |
| 1/2" particleboard | $12.50 sheet | 3.56 | 5% | 3.38 | $3.70 sy |
| 5/8" particleboard | $13.80 sheet | 3.56 | 5% | 3.38 | $4.08 sy |
| 3/4" particleboard | $16.10 sheet | 3.56 | 5% | 3.38 | $4.76 sy |
| 1/4" hardboard | $8.00 sheet | 1.78 | 5% | 1.69 | $4.73 sy |
| 1/2" plywood | $20.50 sheet | 3.56 | 5% | 3.38 | $6.07 sy |

## Flooring Labor

| LABORER | BASE WAGE | PAID LEAVE | TRUE WAGE | FICA | FUTA | WORKER'S COMP. | UNEMPLOY. INSUR. | HEALTH INSUR. | RETIRE (401k) | LIABILITY INSUR. | COST PER HOUR |
|---|---|---|---|---|---|---|---|---|---|---|---|
| Flooring installer | $22.30 | 1.74 | $24.04 | 1.84 | .19 | 4.80 | 2.09 | 2.54 | .72 | 3.13 | $39.40 |
| Flooring installer's helper | $16.10 | 1.26 | $17.36 | 1.33 | .14 | 3.46 | 1.51 | 2.54 | .52 | 2.26 | $29.10 |
| Demolition laborer | $13.40 | 1.05 | $14.45 | 1.11 | .12 | 4.44 | 1.26 | 2.54 | .43 | 1.88 | $26.20 |

**Paid Leave** is calculated based on two weeks paid vacation, one week sick leave, and seven paid holidays. Employer's matching portion of **FICA** is 7.65 percent. **FUTA** (Federal Unemployment) is .8 percent. **Worker's compensation** for the flooring trade was calculated using a national average of 19.95 percent. **Unemployment insurance** was calculated using a national average of 8.7 percent. **Health insurance** was calculated based on a projected national average for 2001 of $505 per employee (and family when applicable) per month. Employer pays 80 percent for a per month cost of $404 per employee. **Retirement** is based on a 401(k) retirement program with employer matching of 50 percent. Employee contributions to the 401(k) plan are an average of 6 percent of the true wage. **Liability insurance** is based on a national average of 12.9 percent.

## Flooring Labor Productivity

| WORK DESCRIPTION | LABORER | COST PER HOUR | PRODUCTIVITY | UNIT PRICE |
|---|---|---|---|---|
| **Demolition** | | | | |
| remove carpet | demolition laborer | $26.20 | .062 | $1.62 sy |
| remove glue-down carpet | demolition laborer | $26.20 | .155 | $4.06 sy |
| remove indoor-outdoor carpet | demolition laborer | $26.20 | .153 | $4.01 sy |
| remove carpet pad | demolition laborer | $26.20 | .030 | $.79 sy |
| remove carpet cove | demolition laborer | $26.20 | .022 | $.58 lf |
| remove carpet tile | demolition laborer | $26.20 | .155 | $4.06 sy |
| remove stone floor | demolition laborer | $26.20 | .082 | $2.15 sf |
| remove marble floor | demolition laborer | $26.20 | .080 | $2.10 sf |
| remove slate floor | demolition laborer | $26.20 | .080 | $2.10 sf |
| remove tile floor | demolition laborer | $26.20 | .080 | $2.10 sf |
| remove quarry tile floor | demolition laborer | $26.20 | .078 | $2.04 sf |
| remove tile base | demolition laborer | $26.20 | .061 | $1.60 lf |
| remove precast terrazzo floor tiles | demolition laborer | $26.20 | .081 | $2.12 sf |
| remove cast-in-place terrazzo floor | demolition laborer | $26.20 | .082 | $2.15 sf |
| remove vinyl floor | demolition laborer | $26.20 | .175 | $4.59 sy |
| remove vinyl tile floor | demolition laborer | $26.20 | .024 | $.63 sf |
| remove resilient tile floor | demolition laborer | $26.20 | .024 | $.63 sf |
| remove antique style linoleum floor | demolition laborer | $26.20 | .175 | $4.59 sy |
| remove vinyl cove | demolition laborer | $26.20 | .036 | $.94 lf |
| remove rubber base | demolition laborer | $26.20 | .011 | $.29 lf |
| remove wood strip flooring | demolition laborer | $26.20 | .020 | $.52 sf |
| remove wood plank flooring | demolition laborer | $26.20 | .019 | $.50 sf |
| remove wood unit block flooring | demolition laborer | $26.20 | .018 | $.47 sf |
| remove floor sleepers | demolition laborer | $26.20 | .007 | $.18 sf |
| remove floor underlayment | demolition laborer | $26.20 | .070 | $1.83 sy |
| **Flooring crew** | | | | |
| install flooring | flooring installer | $39.40 | | |
| install flooring | flooring installer's helper | $29.10 | | |
| install flooring | **flooring crew** | $34.30 | | |
| **Install carpet** | | | | |
| typical on tackless | flooring crew | $34.30 | .138 | $4.73 sy |
| cove | flooring crew | $34.30 | .135 | $4.63 lf |
| remove for work, then re-lay | flooring crew | $34.30 | .211 | $7.24 sy |
| glue-down | flooring crew | $34.30 | .167 | $5.73 sy |
| wool or simulated wool | flooring crew | $34.30 | .139 | $4.77 sy |
| add per step for installation on stairs | flooring crew | $34.30 | .180 | $6.17 ea |
| pad | flooring crew | $34.30 | .0166 | $.55 sy |
| tile | flooring crew | $34.30 | .107 | $3.67 sy |
| **Install stone floor** | | | | |
| typical | flooring crew | $34.30 | .191 | $6.55 sf |
| salvage, then reinstall | flooring crew | $34.30 | .500 | $17.20 sf |
| regrout | flooring crew | $34.30 | .038 | $1.30 sf |
| **Install marble floor** | | | | |
| typical | flooring crew | $34.30 | .189 | $6.48 sf |
| regrout | flooring crew | $34.30 | .034 | $1.17 sf |
| **Install slate floor** | | | | |
| typical | flooring crew | $34.30 | .189 | $6.48 sf |
| regrout | flooring crew | $34.30 | .034 | $1.17 sf |
| salvage, then reinstall | flooring crew | $34.30 | .490 | $16.80 sf |
| **Install tile floor** | | | | |
| typical | flooring crew | $34.30 | .180 | $6.17 sf |
| regrout | flooring crew | $34.30 | .035 | $1.20 sf |
| base | flooring crew | $34.30 | .128 | $4.39 lf |
| **Install quarry tile floor** | | | | |
| typical | flooring crew | $34.30 | .143 | $4.90 sf |
| **Install terrazzo floor** | | | | |
| precast tiles | flooring crew | $34.30 | .116 | $3.98 sf |
| precast base | flooring crew | $34.30 | .256 | $8.78 sf |
| cast-in-place thinset | flooring crew | $34.30 | .128 | $4.39 sf |

. . . More ➤

## Flooring Labor Productivity *continued*

| WORK DESCRIPTION | LABORER | COST PER HOUR | PRODUCTIVITY | UNIT PRICE |
|---|---|---|---|---|
| **Install vinyl floor** | | | | |
| sheet goods | flooring crew | $34.30 | .183 | $6.28 sy |
| cove | flooring crew | $34.30 | .091 | $3.12 lf |
| tile | flooring crew | $34.30 | .029 | $.99 sf |
| resilient tile | flooring crew | $34.30 | .029 | $.99 sf |
| **Install antique style linoleum** | | | | |
| typical | flooring crew | $34.30 | .189 | $6.48 sy |
| tile | flooring crew | $34.30 | .032 | $1.10 sf |
| **Install rubber base** | | | | |
| typical | flooring crew | $34.30 | .020 | $.69 lf |
| **Install wood floor** | | | | |
| hardwood strip | flooring crew | $34.30 | .088 | $3.02 sf |
| prefinished hardwood strip | flooring crew | $34.30 | .091 | $3.12 sf |
| hardwood plank | flooring crew | $34.30 | .079 | $2.71 sf |
| parquet or block | flooring crew | $34.30 | .092 | $3.16 sf |
| prefinished hardwood block or parquet | flooring crew | $34.30 | .094 | $3.22 sf |
| softwood strip | flooring crew | $34.30 | .088 | $3.02 sf |
| softwood plank | flooring crew | $34.30 | .079 | $2.71 sf |
| **Sand, edge, and fill wood floor** | | | | |
| new | flooring crew | $34.30 | .026 | $.89 sf |
| light sand | flooring crew | $34.30 | .030 | $1.03 sf |
| medium | flooring crew | $34.30 | .033 | $1.13 sf |
| heavy sand | flooring crew | $34.30 | .041 | $1.41 sf |
| **Install sleepers on concrete floor, 24" on center** | | | | |
| 1" x 2" | flooring crew | $34.30 | .008 | $.27 sf |
| 1" x 3" | flooring crew | $34.30 | .009 | $.31 sf |
| 2" x 4" | flooring crew | $34.30 | .012 | $.41 sf |
| 2" x 6" | flooring crew | $34.30 | .013 | $.45 sf |
| **Install floor underlayment** | | | | |
| 3/8" particleboard | flooring crew | $34.30 | .167 | $5.73 sy |
| 1/2" particleboard | flooring crew | $34.30 | .168 | $5.76 sy |
| 5/8" particleboard | flooring crew | $34.30 | .168 | $5.76 sy |
| 3/4" particleboard | flooring crew | $34.30 | .169 | $5.80 sy |
| 1/4" hardboard | flooring crew | $34.30 | .174 | $5.97 sy |
| 1/2" plywood | flooring crew | $34.30 | .168 | $5.76 sy |

NOTES:

# 20 ................................ *Hazardous Materials*

| Item Description | Unit | Remove | Replace | Total | |
|---|---|---|---|---|---|
| **Minimum asbestos removal charge** | ea | $935.00 | — | $935.00 | ◄ **MINIMUM** |
| *Remove* Materials....129.00    Labor ........648.00    Equipment ......158.00 | | | | | |
| **Asbestos analysis** | ea | $676.00 | — | $676.00 | ◄ **ASBESTOS ANALYSIS** |
| *Remove* ...................    Labor ........676.00 | | | | | |
| ► Includes up to four hours, up to 12 analyzed samples, and a written report indicating severity of asbestos risk for a typical home or small commercial structure. | | | | | |
| **Plastic cover attached to ceiling** | sf | $3.05 | — | $3.05 | ◄ **SEAL AREA** |
| *Remove* Materials........1.27    Labor ..........1.78 | | | | | *Seal area where asbestos exists. Includes tape* |
| **Plastic cover attached to walls** | sf | $2.98 | — | $2.98 | *along all seams, caulk or foam insulation in any* |
| *Remove* Materials........1.28    Labor ..........1.70 | | | | | *cracks, and negative air vent system.* |
| **Plastic cover and plywood over floor (2 layers)** | sf | $6.17 | — | $6.17 | |
| *Remove* Materials........2.04    Labor ..........4.13 | | | | | |
| **Temporary containment walls with plastic cover** | sf | $9.71 | — | $9.71 | |
| *Remove* Materials........2.46    Labor ..........7.25 | | | | | |
| ► 2" x 4" walls covered with 1/2" cdx plywood and plastic. | | | | | |
| **Prefabricated decontamination unit** | dy | $70.00 | — | $70.00 | ◄ **DECONTAMINATION UNIT** |
| *Remove* ...................    ...............    Equipment ..........70.00 | | | | | |
| ► Four day minimum. Includes decontamination equipment, shower, and clean room. | | | | | |
| **Encapsulate asbestos-based acoustical ceiling with sealant** | sf | $.98 | — | $.98 | ◄ **ENCAPSULATE ASBESTOS** |
| *Remove* Materials........ .31    Labor ........... .57    Equipment ............ .10 | | | | | |
| ► Penetrating sealant sprayed on ceiling with airless sprayer. | | | | | |
| **Scrape asbestos-based acoustical ceiling** | sf | $1.62 | — | $1.62 | ◄ **REMOVE ASBESTOS** |
| *Remove* Materials........ .08    Labor ..........1.38    Equipment ............ .16 | | | | | *Includes full Tyvek suits for workers changed four* |
| ► Includes disposal in glove bags and fiber drums. | | | | | *times per eight hour shift, respirators, (add* |
| **Remove asbestos-based insulation over 1/2" to 3/4" pipe** | lf | $1.29 | — | $1.29 | **20%** *for respirators with air supply) air* |
| *Remove* Materials........ .16    Labor .......... 1.05    Equipment ............ .08 | | | | | *monitoring, supervision by qualified hygiene* |
| ► Includes disposal in glove bags and fiber drums. | | | | | *professionals, final seal of scraped or demo'ed* |
| **Remove asbestos-based insulation over 1" to 3" pipe** | lf | $3.70 | — | $3.70 | *walls, final seal and disposal of plastic cover* |
| *Remove* Materials........ .29    Labor ..........3.24    Equipment ............ .17 | | | | | *materials, disposal in fiber drums and hauling* |
| ► Includes disposal in glove bags and fiber drums. | | | | | *to dump. Does not include dump fees* |
| **Remove asbestos-based siding** | sf | $8.28 | — | $8.28 | *(typically about* **$12** *per drum).* |
| *Remove* Materials........ .85    Labor ..........7.25    Equipment ............ .18 | | | | | |
| ► Includes disposal in fiber drums. | | | | | |
| **Remove asbestos-based plaster** | sf | $6.28 | — | $6.28 | |
| *Remove* Materials........ .55    Labor ..........5.55    Equipment ............ .18 | | | | | |
| ► Includes disposal in fiber drums. | | | | | |

✍ NOTES: _____

_____ end

# TIME & MATERIAL CHARTS *(selected items)*

## Materials for Hazardous Materials Removal

| DESCRIPTION | MATERIAL PRICE | UNIT PRICE |
|---|---|---|
| polyethylene (plastic) | $.18 *sf* | **$.18** *sf* |
| Tyvek whole body suit | $15.00 *ea* | **$15.00** *ea* |
| respirator cartridge | $4.30 *ea* | **$4.30** *ea* |
| glove bag, 7 mil., 50" x 64" | $8.20 *ea* | **$8.20** *ea* |
| glove bag, 10 mil., 44" x 60" | $8.80 *ea* | **$8.80** *ea* |
| 3 cf disposable polyethylene bags, 6 mil | $1.10 *ea* | **$1.10** *ea* |
| 3 cf disposable fiber drums | $9.00 *ea* | **$9.00** *ea* |
| caution labels | $.21 *ea* | **$.21** *ea* |
| encapsulation quality sealant | $77.00 *gallon* | **$77.00** *gal* |
| vent fan filters | $7.40 *ea* | **$7.40** *ea* |
| respirator | $22.00 *ea* | **$22.00** *ea* |

## Hazardous Materials Rental Equipment

| DESCRIPTION | PRICE | COVERAGE | UNIT PRICE |
|---|---|---|---|
| negative air vent system, two fans | $50.00 *per day* | 1 *per day* | **$50.00** *day* |
| HEPA vacuum cleaner, 16 gallon wet/dry | $60.00 *per day* | 1 *per day* | **$60.00** *day* |
| airless sprayer unit | $45.00 *per day* | 1 *per day* | **$45.00** *day* |
| light stand | $15.00 *per day* | 1 *per day* | **$15.00** *day* |
| prefabricated decontamination unit | $70.00 *per day* | 1 *per day* | **$70.00** *day* |

## Hazardous Materials Labor

| LABORER | BASE WAGE | PAID LEAVE | TRUE WAGE | FICA | FUTA | WORKER'S COMP. | UNEMPLOY. INSUR. | HEALTH INSUR. | RETIRE (401k) | LIABILITY INSUR. | COST PER HOUR |
|---|---|---|---|---|---|---|---|---|---|---|---|
| Haz. mat. laborer | $17.60 | 1.37 | $18.97 | 1.45 | .15 | 12.70 | 1.65 | 2.54 | .57 | 2.47 | **$40.50** |

**Paid Leave** is calculated based on two weeks paid vacation, one week sick leave, and seven paid holidays. Employer's matching portion of **FICA** is 7.65 percent. **FUTA** (Federal Unemployment) is .8 percent. **Worker's compensation** for the hazardous materials trade was calculated using a national average of 66.96 percent. **Unemployment insurance** was calculated using a national average of 8.7 percent. **Health insurance** was calculated based on a projected national average for 2001 of $505 per employee (and family when applicable) per month. Employer pays 80 percent for a per month cost of $404 per employee. **Retirement** is based on a 401(k) retirement program with employer matching of 50 percent. Employee contributions to the 401(k) plan are an average of 6 percent of the true wage. **Liability insurance** is based on a national average of 12.9 percent.

## Hazardous Materials Labor Productivity

| WORK DESCRIPTION | LABORER | COST PER HOUR | PRODUCTIVITY | UNIT PRICE |
|---|---|---|---|---|
| **Minimum** | | | | |
| for asbestos removal | haz. mat. laborer | $40.50 | 16.0 | **$648.00** *ea* |
| **Asbestos analysis** | | | | |
| typical home | haz. mat. laborer | $40.50 | 16.7 | **$676.00** *ea* |
| **Seal area for work** | | | | |
| attach plastic cover to ceiling | haz. mat. laborer | $40.50 | .044 | **$1.78** *sf* |
| attach plastic cover to walls | haz. mat. laborer | $40.50 | .042 | **$1.70** *sf* |
| attach plastic cover & plywood to floor | haz. mat. laborer | $40.50 | .102 | **$4.13** *sf* |
| build walls and attach plastic cover | haz. mat. laborer | $40.50 | .179 | **$7.25** *sf* |
| **Remove asbestos-based materials** | | | | |
| scrape acoustical ceiling | haz. mat. laborer | $40.50 | .034 | **$1.38** *sf* |
| encapsulate acoustical ceiling with sealant | haz. mat. laborer | $40.50 | .014 | **$.57** *sf* |
| insulation over 1/2" to 3/4" pipe | haz. mat. laborer | $40.50 | .026 | **$1.05** *lf* |
| insulation over 1" to 3" pipe | haz. mat. laborer | $40.50 | .080 | **$3.24** *lf* |
| siding | haz. mat. laborer | $40.50 | .179 | **$7.25** *sf* |
| plaster | haz. mat. laborer | $40.50 | .137 | **$5.55** *sf* |

# 21 ............................................................ *HVAC*

| Item Description | Unit | Remove | Replace | Total | |
|---|---|---|---|---|---|
| **Duct work per duct** <br> *Replace* Materials ....140.00   Labor.........221.00 | ea | — | $361.00 | $361.00 | ◀ **Ducts** |
| **Duct work per sf of floor** <br> *Replace* Materials ........ .40   Labor ...........1.41 | sf | — | $1.81 | $1.81 | |
| **Forced-air ducting for home to 1,200 sf** <br> *Replace* Materials ....521.00   Labor.......1580.00 | ea | — | $2,101.00 | $2,101.00 | ◀ **Ducts per home** |
| **Forced-air ducting for home 1,200 to 1,900 sf** <br> *Replace* Materials ....710.00   Labor .......1940.00 | ea | — | $2,650.00 | $2,650.00 | |
| **Forced-air ducting for home 1,900 to 2,400 sf** <br> *Replace* Materials ..1080.00   Labor ......2380.00 | ea | — | $3,460.00 | $3,460.00 | |
| **Forced-air ducting for home 2,400 to 2,900 sf** <br> *Replace* Materials ..1530.00   Labor ......3090.00 | ea | — | $4,620.00 | $4,620.00 | |
| **Forced-air ducting for home 2,900 to 3,400 sf** <br> *Replace* Materials ..2200.00   Labor.......4420.00 | ea | — | $6,620.00 | $6,620.00 | |
| **Forced-air ducting for home 3,400 to 3,900 sf** <br> *Replace* Materials ..3260.00   Labor.......5750.00 | ea | — | $9,010.00 | $9,010.00 | |
| **Forced-air ducting for home 3,900 to 4,500 sf** <br> *Replace* Materials ..4920.00   Labor ......7200.00 | ea | — | $12,120.00 | $12,120.00 | |
| **Electric forced-air furnace 10,200 btu** <br> *Replace* Materials ....375.00   Labor.........477.00 <br> *Remove* ......................   Labor.........49.50 | ea | $49.50 | $852.00 | $901.50 | ◀ **Electric furnace** <br> *Includes connection only. Does not include wiring run, plenums, ducts, or flues.* |
| **Electric forced-air furnace 17,100 btu** <br> *Replace* Materials....400.00   Labor ...504.00 <br> *Remove* ......................   Labor.........49.50 | ea | $49.50 | $904.00 | $953.50 | |
| **Electric forced-air furnace 27,300 btu** <br> *Replace* Materials ....450.00   Labor.........557.00 <br> *Remove* ......................   Labor.........49.50 | ea | $49.50 | $1,007.00 | $1,056.50 | |
| **Electric forced-air furnace 34,100 btu** <br> *Replace* Materials....500.00   Labor .........610.00 <br> *Remove* ......................   Labor.........49.50 | ea | $49.50 | $1,110.00 | $1,159.50 | |
| **Remove electric forced-air furnace for work, then reinstall** <br> *Replace* ......................   Labor .......230.00 | ea | — | $230.00 | $230.00 | |
| **Gas forced-air furnace 45,000 btu** <br> *Replace* Materials....400.00   Labor.........499.00 <br> *Remove* ......................   Labor...........47.70 | ea | $47.70 | $899.00 | $946.70 | ◀ **Gas furnace** <br> *Includes connection only. Does not include wiring run, plenums, ducts, or flues.* |
| **Gas forced-air furnace 60,000 btu** <br> *Replace* Materials ....450.00   Labor........544.00 <br> *Remove* ......................   Labor...........47.70 | ea | $47.70 | $994.00 | $1,041.70 | |

**RELATED ITEMS**

| Item Description | Unit | Remove | Replace | Total |
|---|---|---|---|---|
| **GAS FURNACE** ▶ *continued* — **Gas forced-air furnace 75,000 btu** | ea | $47.70 | $1,067.00 | $1,114.70 |
| *Replace* Materials.....475.00    Labor..........592.00 | | | | |
| *Remove* .....................  Labor...........47.70 | | | | |
| **Gas forced-air furnace 100,000 btu** | ea | $47.70 | $1,188.00 | $1,235.70 |
| *Replace* Materials ....525.00    Labor ........663.00 | | | | |
| *Remove* .....................  Labor...........47.70 | | | | |
| **Gas forced-air furnace, 125,000 btu** | ea | $47.70 | $1,340.00 | $1,387.70 |
| *Replace* Materials .....615.00    Labor..........725.00 | | | | |
| *Remove* .....................  Labor...........47.70 | | | | |
| **Gas forced-air furnace, 150,000 btu** | ea | $47.70 | $1,525.00 | $1,572.70 |
| *Replace* Materials ....760.00    Labor..........765.00 | | | | |
| *Remove* .....................  Labor...........47.70 | | | | |
| **Remove gas forced-air furnace for work, then reinstall** | ea | — | $225.00 | $225.00 |
| *Replace* .....................  Labor .........225.00 | | | | |
| **OIL FURNACE** ▶ *Includes connection only. Does not include wiring run, plenums, ducts, or flues.* — **Oil forced-air furnace 56,000 btu** | ea | $53.40 | $1,498.00 | $1,551.40 |
| *Replace* Materials ....950.00    Labor ........548.00 | | | | |
| *Remove* .....................  Labor ...........53.40 | | | | |
| **Oil forced-air furnace 84,000 btu** | ea | $53.40 | $1,541.00 | $1,594.40 |
| *Replace* Materials ....975.00    Labor ........566.00 | | | | |
| *Remove* .....................  Labor ...........53.40 | | | | |
| **Oil forced-air furnace 95,000 btu** | ea | $53.40 | $1,590.00 | $1,643.40 |
| *Replace* Materials ..1000.00    Labor..........590.00 | | | | |
| *Remove* .....................  Labor ...........53.40 | | | | |
| **Oil forced-air furnace 134,000 btu** | ea | $53.40 | $2,287.00 | $2,340.40 |
| *Replace* Materials ..1500.00    Labor..........787.00 | | | | |
| *Remove* .....................  Labor ...........53.40 | | | | |
| **Remove oil forced-air furnace for work, then reinstall** | ea | — | $241.00 | $241.00 |
| *Replace* .....................  Labor .........241.00 | | | | |
| **SERVICE FURNACE** ▶ **Service furnace** | ea | — | $84.60 | $84.60 |
| *Replace* Materials........8.60    Labor...........76.00 | | | | |
| ▶ Check, replace filters, and clean. | | | | |
| **HEAT PUMP** ▶ **Heat pump, 2 ton with supplementary heat coil** | ea | $61.00 | $3,112.00 | $3,173.00 |
| *Replace* Materials ..2250.00    Labor..........862.00 | | | | |
| *Remove* .....................  Labor ...........61.00 | | | | |
| **Heat pump, 4 ton with supplementary heat coil** | ea | $61.00 | $5,290.00 | $5,351.00 |
| *Replace* Materials ..4000.00    Labor.......1290.00 | | | | |
| *Remove* .....................  Labor ...........61.00 | | | | |
| **Heat pump, 5 ton with supplementary heat coil** | ea | $61.00 | $6,050.00 | $6,111.00 |
| *Replace* Materials ..4500.00    Labor.......1550.00 | | | | |
| *Remove* .....................  Labor ...........61.00 | | | | |
| **Remove heat pump for work, then reinstall** | ea | — | $964.00 | $964.00 |
| *Replace* .....................  Labor.........964.00 | | | | |
| **HUMIDIFIER** ▶ *Centrifugal atomizing.* — **Humidifier, 5 pounds per hour** | ea | $44.30 | $1,419.00 | $1,463.30 |
| *Replace* Materials ..1250.00    Labor .........169.00 | | | | |
| *Remove* .....................  Labor ...........44.30 | | | | |

| Item Description | Unit | Remove | Replace | Total | |
|---|---|---|---|---|---|
| **Humidifier, 10 pounds per hour** | ea | $44.30 | $1,696.00 | $1,740.30 | |
| *Replace* Materials ..1500.00   Labor .........196.00 | | | | | |
| *Remove* ....................   Labor .........44.30 | | | | | |
| **Remove humidifier for work, then reinstall** | ea | — | $131.00 | $131.00 | |
| *Replace* ....................   Labor .........131.00 | | | | | |
| **3" diameter double wall furnace vent pipe (all fuels)** | lf | $1.05 | $16.00 | $17.05 | ◄ **FURNACE VENT PIPE** |
| *Replace* Materials ........3.50   Labor ...........12.50 | | | | | |
| *Remove* ....................   Labor ...........1.05 | | | | | |
| **4" diameter double wall furnace vent pipe (all fuels)** | lf | $1.05 | $18.40 | $19.45 | |
| *Replace* Materials ........4.30   Labor ...........14.10 | | | | | |
| *Remove* ....................   Labor ...........1.05 | | | | | |
| **5" diameter double wall furnace vent pipe (all fuels)** | lf | $1.05 | $20.60 | $21.65 | |
| *Replace* Materials ........5.10   Labor ...........15.50 | | | | | |
| *Remove* ....................   Labor ...........1.05 | | | | | |
| **6" diameter double wall furnace vent pipe (all fuels)** | lf | $1.05 | $23.20 | $24.25 | |
| *Replace* Materials ........6.00   Labor ...........17.20 | | | | | |
| *Remove* ....................   Labor ...........1.05 | | | | | |
| **7" diameter double wall furnace vent pipe (all fuels)** | lf | $1.05 | $30.20 | $31.25 | |
| *Replace* Materials ........8.80   Labor ...........21.40 | | | | | |
| *Remove* ....................   Labor ...........1.05 | | | | | |
| **8" diameter double wall furnace vent pipe (all fuels)** | lf | $1.05 | $33.50 | $34.55 | |
| *Replace* Materials ........9.90   Labor ...........23.60 | | | | | |
| *Remove* ....................   Labor ...........1.05 | | | | | |
| **Remove furnace vent pipe for work, then reinstall** | lf | — | $12.50 | $12.50 | |
| *Replace* ....................   Labor ...........12.50 | | | | | |
| **Central air conditioning system, complete, 1 ton** | ea | — | $965.50 | $965.50 | ◄ **CENTRAL AC** *Includes condensing unit, coil, copper lines, and installation.* |
| *Replace* Materials .....695.00   Labor .........270.50 | | | | | |
| **Central air conditioning system, complete, 1-1/2 ton** | ea | — | $1,097.90 | $1,097.90 | |
| *Replace* Materials ....785.00   Labor .........312.90 | | | | | |
| **Central air conditioning system, complete, 2 ton** | ea | — | $1,246.60 | $1,246.60 | |
| *Replace* Materials ....870.00   Labor .........376.60 | | | | | |
| **Central air conditioning system, complete, 3 ton** | ea | — | $1,712.30 | $1,712.30 | |
| *Replace* Materials ...1390.00   Labor .........322.30 | | | | | |
| **Central air conditioning system, complete, 4 ton** | ea | — | $2,466.00 | $2,466.00 | |
| *Replace* Materials ...1750.00   Labor .........716.00 | | | | | |
| **Central air conditioning system, complete, 5 ton** | ea | — | $3,185.00 | $3,185.00 | |
| *Replace* Materials ...2155.00   Labor .......1030.00 | | | | | |
| **Air conditioning unit service** | ea | — | $117.40 | $117.40 | ◄ **AC SERVICE** |
| *Replace* Materials ......40.00   Labor ..........77.40 | | | | | |
| **Recharge AC system, 5 lbs of refrigerant** | ea | — | $166.30 | $166.30 | ◄ **RECHARGE AC UNIT** |
| *Replace* Materials ....100.00   Labor ..........66.30 | | | | | |
| **Recharge AC system, 10 lbs of refrigerant** | ea | — | $277.90 | $277.90 | |
| *Replace* Materials ....205.00   Labor ...........72.90 | | | | | |

**RELATED ITEMS**

Cleaning .......................63
Electrical
*baseboard heater* ..............153
*baseboard
heater wiring* ...........142, 144
*furnace wiring* .......................142
*humidifier wiring* ...............143
*resistance wiring run* .........142
*resistance cable* ...............153
*thermostat* ...............152, 278
*thermostat wiring* .............145
*wall heater* .......................152

| Item Description | | Unit | Remove | Replace | Total |
|---|---|---|---|---|---|
| **RECHARGE ▶ AC UNIT** *continued* | **Recharge AC system, 14 lbs of refrigerant**<br>*Replace* Materials ....285.00    Labor...........79.60 | ea | — | $364.60 | $364.60 |
| **THROUGH-WALL ▶ AC UNIT** | **Through-wall AC unit, 5,000 btu**<br>*Replace* Materials ....725.00    Labor .........390.00<br>*Remove* ......................    Labor ..........39.00 | ea | $39.00 | $1,115.00 | $1,154.00 |
| | **Through-wall AC unit, 8,000 btu**<br>*Replace* Materials ....750.00    Labor .........403.00<br>*Remove* ......................    Labor ..........39.00 | ea | $39.00 | $1,153.00 | $1,192.00 |
| | **Through-wall AC unit, 12,000 btu**<br>*Replace* Materials ....900.00    Labor..........469.00<br>*Remove* ......................    Labor ..........39.00 | ea | $39.00 | $1,369.00 | $1,408.00 |
| | **Through-wall AC unit, 18,000 btu**<br>*Replace* Materials ..1000.00    Labor..........522.00<br>*Remove* ......................    Labor ..........39.00 | ea | $39.00 | $1,522.00 | $1,561.00 |
| | **Remove through-wall AC unit for work, then reinstall**<br>*Replace* ......................    Labor .........220.00 | ea | — | $220.00 | $220.00 |
| **THROUGH-WALL ▶ AC & HEAT UNIT** | **Through-wall combination 6,000 btu AC and 4,040 btu heat unit**<br>*Replace* Materials ..1250.00    Labor..........451.00<br>*Remove* ......................    Labor ..........40.90 | ea | $40.90 | $1,701.00 | $1,741.90 |
| | **Through-wall combination 9,500 btu AC and 4,040 btu heat unit**<br>*Replace* Materials ..1250.00    Labor .........464.00<br>*Remove* ......................    Labor ..........40.90 | ea | $40.90 | $1,714.00 | $1,754.90 |
| | **Through-wall combination 11,300 btu AC and 9,200 btu heat unit**<br>*Replace* Materials ..1500.00    Labor .........539.00<br>*Remove* ......................    Labor ..........40.90 | ea | $40.90 | $2,039.00 | $2,079.90 |
| | **Remove combination AC & heat unit for work, then reinstall**<br>*Replace* ......................    Labor.........237.00 | ea | — | $237.00 | $237.00 |
| **EVAPORATIVE ▶ COOLER** *Roof mount. Includes up to 36 lf of copper water supply tubing and electrical hookup.* | **Evaporative cooler, 2,000 cfm**<br>*Replace* Materials .....675.00    Labor.........331.00<br>*Remove* ......................    Labor ..........43.00 | ea | $43.00 | $1,006.00 | $1,049.00 |
| | **Evaporative cooler, 4,300 cfm**<br>*Replace* Materials ....925.00    Labor.........422.00<br>*Remove* ......................    Labor ..........43.00 | ea | $43.00 | $1,347.00 | $1,390.00 |
| | **Evaporative cooler, 4,700 cfm**<br>*Replace* Materials ....975.00    Labor.........446.00<br>*Remove* ......................    Labor ..........43.00 | ea | $43.00 | $1,421.00 | $1,464.00 |
| | **Evaporative cooler, 5,600 cfm**<br>*Replace* Materials ..1000.00    Labor.........482.00<br>*Remove* ......................    Labor ..........43.00 | ea | $43.00 | $1,482.00 | $1,525.00 |
| grille ▷ | **Evaporative cooler grille**<br>*Replace* Materials ......60.00    Labor ..........30.10<br>*Remove* ......................    Labor ...........4.38 | ea | $4.38 | $90.10 | $94.48 |
| | **Remove evaporative cooler for work, then reinstall**<br>*Replace* ......................    Labor .........416.00 | ea | — | $416.00 | $416.00 |

| Item Description | Unit | Remove | Replace | Total | |
|---|---|---|---|---|---|
| **Cold-air return grille**<br>*Replace* Materials......30.00  Labor..........42.10<br>*Remove* ......................  Labor ...........4.38 | ea | $4.38 | $72.10 | $76.48 | ◄ COLD-AIR GRILLE |
| **Remove cold-air return grille for work, then reinstall**<br>*Replace* Materials..........  Labor...........11.00 | ea | — | $11.00 | $11.00 | |
| **Heat register**<br>*Replace* Materials......20.00  Labor..........27.80<br>*Remove* ......................  Labor ...........3.54 | ea | $3.54 | $47.80 | $51.34 | ◄ HEAT REGISTER |
| **Remove heat register for work, then reinstall**<br>*Replace* ......................  Labor...........7.07 | ea | — | $7.07 | $7.07 | |
| **Thermostat, heat only**<br>*Replace* Materials......40.00  Labor..........67.60<br>*Remove* ......................  Labor ...........6.10 | ea | $6.10 | $107.60 | $113.70 | ◄ THERMOSTAT<br>*See Electrical on page 152 for electrical system and baseboard heater thermostats.* |
| **Thermostat, heat and air conditioning**<br>*Replace* Materials ......70.00  Labor......105.00<br>*Remove* ......................  Labor ...........6.10 | ea | $6.10 | $175.00 | $181.10 | |
| **Thermostat, programmable**<br>*Replace* Materials......80.00  Labor........154.00<br>*Remove* ......................  Labor ...........6.10 | ea | $6.10 | $234.00 | $240.10 | |
| **Thermostat, programmable, with zone control**<br>*Replace* Materials......95.00  Labor........190.00<br>*Remove* ......................  Labor ...........6.10 | ea | $6.10 | $285.00 | $291.10 | |
| **Remove thermostat for work, then reinstall**<br>*Replace* ......................  Labor..........27.50 | ea | — | $27.50 | $27.50 | |

✍ NOTES: _____

_____

_____ end

# TIME & MATERIAL CHARTS *(selected items)*

## HVAC Materials

| DESCRIPTION | UNIT PRICE |
|---|---|
| **Ductwork**<br>per sf of floor.................................................................... | $.40 *sf* |
| **Electric forced-air furnace**<br>10,200 btu............................................................... | $375.00 *ea* |
| 34,100 btu............................................................... | $500.00 *ea* |
| **Gas forced-air furnace**<br>45,000 btu............................................................... | $400.00 *ea* |
| 150,000 btu............................................................. | $760.00 *ea* |
| **Oil forced-air furnace**<br>56,000 btu............................................................... | $950.00 *ea* |
| 134,000 btu............................................................. | $1500.00 *ea* |

## HVAC Labor

| LABORER | BASE WAGE | PAID LEAVE | TRUE WAGE | FICA | FUTA | WORKER'S COMP. | UNEMPLOY. INSUR. | HEALTH INSUR. | RETIRE (401K) | LIABILITY INSUR. | COST PER HOUR |
|---------|-----------|------------|-----------|------|------|----------------|------------------|---------------|---------------|------------------|---------------|
| HVAC installer | $26.30 | 2.05 | $28.35 | 2.17 | .23 | 3.91 | 2.47 | 2.54 | .85 | 3.69 | **$44.20** |
| Demolition laborer | $13.40 | 1.05 | $14.45 | 1.11 | .12 | 4.44 | 1.26 | .43 | 1.88 | 26.20 | **$26.20** |

**Paid Leave** is calculated based on two weeks paid vacation, one week sick leave, and seven paid holidays. Employer's matching portion of **FICA** is 7.65 percent. **FUTA** (Federal Unemployment) is .8 percent. **Worker's compensation** for the HVAC trade was calculated using a national average of 13.79 percent. **Unemployment insurance** was calculated using a national average of 8.7 percent. **Health insurance** was calculated based on a projected national average for 2001 of $505 per employee (and family when applicable) per month. Employer pays 80 percent for a per month cost of $404 per employee. **Retirement** is based on a 401(k) retirement program with employer matching of 50 percent. Employee contributions to the 401(k) plan are an average of 6 percent of the true wage. **Liability insurance** is based on a national average of 12.9 percent.

## HVAC Labor Productivity

| WORK DESCRIPTION | LABORER | COST PER HOUR | PRODUCTIVITY | UNIT PRICE |
|------------------|---------|---------------|--------------|------------|
| **Demolition** | | | | |
| remove electric forced-air furnace | demolition laborer | $26.20 | 1.89 | **$49.50** ea |
| remove gas forced-air furnace | demolition laborer | $26.20 | 1.82 | **$47.70** ea |
| remove oil forced-air furnace | demolition laborer | $26.20 | 2.04 | **$53.40** ea |
| remove heat pump | demolition laborer | $26.20 | 2.33 | **$61.00** ea |
| remove humidifier | demolition laborer | $26.20 | 1.69 | **$44.30** ea |
| remove through-wall AC unit | demolition laborer | $26.20 | 1.49 | **$39.00** ea |
| remove combination AC and heat unit | demolition laborer | $26.20 | 1.56 | **$40.90** ea |
| remove evaporative cooler | demolition laborer | $26.20 | 1.64 | **$43.00** ea |
| remove heat register | demolition laborer | $26.20 | .135 | **$3.54** ea |
| remove thermostat | demolition laborer | $26.20 | .233 | **$6.10** ea |
| **Install electric forced air furnace** | | | | |
| 10,200 btu | HVAC installer | $44.20 | 10.8 | **$477.00** ea |
| 34,100 btu | HVAC installer | $44.20 | 13.8 | **$610.00** ea |
| **Install gas forced-air furnace** | | | | |
| 45,000 btu | HVAC installer | $44.20 | 11.3 | **$499.00** ea |
| 150,000 btu | HVAC installer | $44.20 | 17.3 | **$765.00** ea |
| **Install oil forced-air furnace** | | | | |
| 56,000 btu | HVAC installer | $44.20 | 12.4 | **$548.00** ea |
| 134,000 btu | HVAC installer | $44.20 | 17.8 | **$787.00** ea |
| **Install heat pump with supplementary heat coil** | | | | |
| 2 ton | HVAC installer | $44.20 | 19.5 | **$862.00** ea |
| **Install humidifier** | | | | |
| 5 pounds | HVAC installer | $44.20 | 3.83 | **$169.00** ea |
| **Double wall furnace flue (all fuels)** | | | | |
| 4" diameter | HVAC installer | $44.20 | .318 | **$14.10** lf |
| 8" diameter | HVAC installer | $44.20 | .533 | **$23.60** lf |
| **Through-wall AC unit** | | | | |
| 5,000 btu | HVAC installer | $44.20 | 8.83 | **$390.00** ea |
| 18,000 btu | HVAC installer | $44.20 | 11.8 | **$522.00** ea |
| **Through-wall combination AC and heat unit** | | | | |
| 6,000 btu AC and 4,040 btu heat unit | HVAC installer | $44.20 | 10.2 | **$451.00** ea |
| 11,300 btu AC and 9,200 btu heat unit | HVAC installer | $44.20 | 12.2 | **$539.00** ea |
| **Evaporative cooler** | | | | |
| 2,000 cfm | HVAC installer | $44.20 | 7.49 | **$331.00** ea |
| 5,600 cfm | HVAC installer | $44.20 | 10.9 | **$482.00** ea |
| **Thermostat** | | | | |
| heat only | HVAC installer | $44.20 | 1.53 | **$67.60** ea |
| heat and air conditioning | HVAC installer | $44.20 | 2.38 | **$105.00** ea |
| programmable | HVAC installer | $44.20 | 3.49 | **$154.00** ea |
| programmable, with zone control | HVAC installer | $44.20 | 4.29 | **$190.00** ea |

# 22 ........................................................ *Insulation*

| Item Description | Unit | Remove | Replace | Total | |
|---|---|---|---|---|---|
| **Minimum charge for insulation work** <br> *Replace* Material ......35.00      Labor............62.50 | ea | — | $97.50 | $97.50 | ◀ **MINIMUM** |
| **3″ deep vermiculite attic insulation** <br> *Replace* Material....... 1.01      Labor.............. .23 <br> *Remove* .......................... Labor.............. .37 | sf | $.37 | $1.24 | $1.61 | ◀ **VERMICULITE** <br> *Poured by hand from 3 cf bags.* |
| **4″ deep vermiculite attic insulation** <br> *Replace* Material ......1.34      Labor.............. .26 <br> *Remove* .......................... Labor.............. .45 | sf | $.45 | $1.60 | $2.05 | |
| **5″ deep vermiculite attic insulation** <br> *Replace* Material ......1.69      Labor.............. .26 <br> *Remove* .......................... Labor.............. .52 | sf | $.52 | $1.95 | $2.47 | |
| **6″ deep vermiculite attic insulation** <br> *Replace* Material ......2.02      Labor.............. .29 <br> *Remove* .......................... Labor.............. .66 | sf | $.66 | $2.31 | $2.97 | |
| **R11 blown mineral wool attic insulation (3-1/2″ deep)** <br> *Replace* Material........... .52      Labor.............. .29 <br> *Remove* .......................... Labor.............. .31 | sf | $.31 | $.81 | $1.12 | ◀ **MINERAL WOOL** <br> *See the next page for additional costs to blow into existing walls.* |
| **R19 blown mineral wool attic insulation (6″ deep)** <br> *Replace* Material........... .79      Labor.............. .32 <br> *Remove* .......................... Labor.............. .34 | sf | $.34 | $1.11 | $1.45 | |
| **R30 blown mineral wool attic insulation (10″ deep)** <br> *Replace* Material .........1.30      Labor.............. .37 <br> *Remove* .......................... Labor.............. .50 | sf | $.50 | $1.67 | $2.17 | |
| **R38 blown mineral wool attic insulation (12″ deep)** <br> *Replace* Material .......1.74      Labor.............. .46 <br> *Remove* .......................... Labor.............. .58 | sf | $.58 | $2.20 | $2.78 | |
| **R12 blown cellulose attic insulation (3-1/2″ deep)** <br> *Replace* Material........... .51      Labor.............. .29 <br> *Remove* .......................... Labor.............. .37 | sf | $.37 | $.80 | $1.17 | ◀ **CELLULOSE** <br> *See the next page for additional costs to blow into existing walls.* |
| **R21 blown cellulose attic insulation (6″ deep)** <br> *Replace* Material........... .76      Labor.............. .35 <br> *Remove* .......................... Labor.............. .39 | sf | $.39 | $1.11 | $1.50 | |
| **R33 blown cellulose attic insulation (10″ deep)** <br> *Replace* Material .........1.25      Labor.............. .37 <br> *Remove* .......................... Labor.............. .60 | sf | $.60 | $1.62 | $2.22 | |
| **R42 blown cellulose attic insulation (12″ deep)** <br> *Replace* Material .........1.68      Labor.............. .46 <br> *Remove* .......................... Labor.............. .68 | sf | $.68 | $2.14 | $2.82 | |
| **R11 blown fiberglass attic insulation (5″ deep)** <br> *Replace* Material........... .45      Labor.............. .29 <br> *Remove* .......................... Labor.............. .31 | sf | $.31 | $.74 | $1.05 | ◀ **BLOWN FIBERGLASS** <br> *See the next page for additional costs to blow into existing walls.* |

**RELATED ITEMS**

**Masonry**
*Polystyrene block inserts...301*
*loose block insulation.......302*
*2″ polystyrene*
*cavity wall insulation.....295*

**Rough Carpentry**
*factory built panels.........443*
*insulating sheathing..........441*

| Item Description | Unit | Remove | Replace | Total |
|---|---|---|---|---|
| **R19 blown fiberglass attic insulation (8" deep)**<br>*Replace* Material.........67    Labor.............32<br>*Remove* .....................    Labor.............34 | sf | $.34 | $.99 | $1.33 |
| **R30 blown fiberglass attic insulation (13" deep)**<br>*Replace* Material ........1.10    Labor.............37<br>*Remove* .....................    Labor.............50 | sf | $.50 | $1.47 | $1.97 |
| **R38 blown fiberglass attic insulation (16" deep)**<br>*Replace* Material ........1.47    Labor.............46<br>*Remove* .....................    Labor.............58 | sf | $.58 | $1.93 | $2.51 |
| **Add 285% to blow insulation into existing wall with stucco** | | | | |
| **Add 233% to blow insulation into existing wall with siding** | | | | |
| **Add 318% to blow insulation into existing wall with masonry veneer** | | | | |
| **Add 216% to blow insulation into existing wall through drywall** | | | | |
| **R11 batt insulation (3-1/2" deep) attic, ceiling or floor installation**<br>*Replace* Material...........38    Labor.............26<br>*Remove* .....................    Labor.............24 | sf | $.24 | $.64 | $.88 |
| **R19 batt insulation (6" deep) attic, ceiling or floor installation**<br>*Replace* Material...........56    Labor.............32<br>*Remove* .....................    Labor.............34 | sf | $.34 | $.88 | $1.22 |
| **R30 batt insulation (9-1/2" deep) attic, ceiling or floor installation**<br>*Replace* Material...........93    Labor.............35<br>*Remove* .....................    Labor.............39 | sf | $.39 | $1.28 | $1.67 |
| **R38 batt insulation (12" deep) attic, ceiling or floor installation**<br>*Replace* Material ........1.24    Labor.............43<br>*Remove* .....................    Labor.............47 | sf | $.47 | $1.67 | $2.14 |
| **R6 batt insulation (1-3/4" deep) wall installation (between furring strips)**<br>*Replace* Material...........22    Labor.............29<br>*Remove* .....................    Labor.............18 | sf | $.18 | $.51 | $.69 |
| **R11 batt insulation (3-1/2" deep) wall installation**<br>*Replace* Material...........38    Labor.............32<br>*Remove* .....................    Labor.............24 | sf | $.24 | $.70 | $.94 |
| **R19 batt insulation (6" deep) wall installation**<br>*Replace* Material...........56    Labor.............37<br>*Remove* .....................    Labor.............34 | sf | $.34 | $.93 | $1.27 |
| **R19 batt insulation (8" deep) wall installation**<br>*Replace* Material...........74    Labor.............43<br>*Remove* .....................    Labor.............39 | sf | $.39 | $1.17 | $1.56 |
| **Add 8% for Kraft face** | | | | |
| **Add 10% for foil face** | | | | |
| **Add 14% for plastic vapor barrier** | | | | |
| **1/2" rigid foam insulation board**<br>*Replace* Material...........46    Labor.............40<br>*Remove* .....................    Labor.............18 | sf | $.18 | $.86 | $1.04 |

**BLOWN ▶ FIBERGLASS** *continued*

**ADD TO INSULATE ▶ EXISTING WALLS**
*Add to blown in costs. Includes holes drilled 16" on center every 4' of height, patching, and painting if necessary.*

**FIBERGLASS ▶ BATT IN CEILING OR FLOOR**
*Based on installation in framing 16" on center. Add 5% for 12" oc and deduct 7% for 24" oc.*

**FIBERGLASS ▶ BATT IN WALL**
*Based on installation in framing 16" on center. Add 5% for 12" oc and deduct 7% for 24" oc.*

**ADD FOR ▶ BATT FACE**

**RIGID FOAM ▶**
*Glued and/or nailed in place on walls or roof.*

| Item Description | Unit | Remove | Replace | Total |
|---|---|---|---|---|
| **3/4" rigid foam insulation board**<br>*Replace* Material.......... .56  Labor............. .40<br>*Remove* ..................  Labor............. .18 | sf | $.18 | $.96 | $1.14 |
| **1" rigid foam insulation board**<br>*Replace* Material.......... .75  Labor............. .40<br>*Remove* ..................  Labor............. .18 | sf | $.18 | $1.15 | $1.33 |
| **2" rigid foam insulation board**<br>*Replace* Material.......... .99  Labor............. .40<br>*Remove* ..................  Labor............. .18 | sf | $.18 | $1.39 | $1.57 |

| RELATED ITEMS |
|---|
| **Masonry**<br>Polystyrene block inserts...301<br>loose block insulation.......302<br>2" polystyrene<br>cavity wall insulation.....295<br>**Rough Carpentry**<br>factory built panels..........443<br>insulating sheathing..........441 |

✍ NOTES: _____

_____ end

# TIME & MATERIAL CHARTS *(selected items)*

## Insulation Materials

| DESCRIPTION | MATERIAL PRICE | GROSS COVERAGE | WASTE | NET COVERAGE | UNIT PRICE |
|---|---|---|---|---|---|
| **Vermiculite attic insulation** | | | | | |
| 3" deep | $.97 sf | 1 | 4% | .96 | $1.01 sf |
| 4" deep | $1.29 sf | 1 | 4% | .96 | $1.34 sf |
| 5" deep | $1.62 sf | 1 | 4% | .96 | $1.69 sf |
| 6" deep | $1.94 sf | 1 | 4% | .96 | $2.02 sf |
| **Blown mineral wool insulation** | | | | | |
| R 11 (3-1/2" deep) | $.50 sf | 1 | 4% | .96 | $.52 sf |
| R 19 (6" deep) | $.76 sf | 1 | 4% | .96 | $.79 sf |
| R 30 (10" deep) | $1.25 sf | 1 | 4% | .96 | $1.30 sf |
| R 38 (12" deep) | $1.67 sf | 1 | 4% | .96 | $1.74 sf |
| **Blown cellulose insulation** | | | | | |
| R 12 blown (3-1/2" deep) | $.49 sf | 1 | 4% | .96 | $.51 sf |
| R 21 blown (6" deep) | $.73 sf | 1 | 4% | .96 | $.76 sf |
| R 33 blown (10" deep) | $1.20 sf | 1 | 4% | .96 | $1.25 sf |
| R 42 blown (12" deep) | $1.61 sf | 1 | 4% | .96 | $1.68 sf |
| **Blown fiberglass insulation** | | | | | |
| R 11 (5" deep) | $.43 sf | 1 | 4% | .96 | $.45 sf |
| R 19 (8" deep) | $.64 sf | 1 | 4% | .96 | $.67 sf |
| R 30 (13" deep) | $1.06 sf | 1 | 4% | .96 | $1.10 sf |
| R 38 (16" deep) | $1.41 sf | 1 | 4% | .96 | $1.47 sf |
| **Fiberglass batt insulation in ceiling or floor** | | | | | |
| R 11 (3-1/2" deep) | $.36 sf | 1 | 4% | .96 | $.38 sf |
| R 19 (6" deep) | $.54 sf | 1 | 4% | .96 | $.56 sf |
| R 30 (9-1/2" deep) | $.89 sf | 1 | 4% | .96 | $.93 sf |
| R 38 (12" deep) | $1.19 sf | 1 | 4% | .96 | $1.24 sf |
| **Fiberglass batt insulation in wall** | | | | | |
| R 6 (1-3/4" deep) (between furring strips) | $.21 sf | 1 | 4% | .96 | $.22 sf |
| R 11 (3-1/2" deep) | $.36 sf | 1 | 4% | .96 | $.38 sf |
| R 19 (6" deep) | $.54 sf | 1 | 4% | .96 | $.56 sf |
| R 25 (8" deep) | $.71 sf | 1 | 4% | .96 | $.74 sf |
| **Rigid foam insulation board** | | | | | |
| 1/2" | $.44 sf | 1 | 4% | .96 | $.46 sf |
| 3/4" | $.54 sf | 1 | 4% | .96 | $.56 sf |
| 1" | $.72 sf | 1 | 4% | .96 | $.75 sf |
| 2" | $.95 sf | 1 | 4% | .96 | $.99 sf |

## Insulation Labor

| LABORER | BASE WAGE | PAID LEAVE | TRUE WAGE | FICA | FUTA | WORKER'S COMP. | UNEMPLOY. INSUR. | HEALTH INSUR. | RETIRE (401k) | LIABILITY INSUR. | COST PER HOUR |
|---|---|---|---|---|---|---|---|---|---|---|---|
| Insulation installer | $15.40 | 1.20 | $16.60 | 1.27 | .13 | 4.15 | 1.44 | 2.54 | .50 | 2.16 | $28.80 |
| Demolition laborer | $13.40 | 1.05 | $14.45 | 1.11 | .12 | 4.44 | 1.26 | 2.54 | .43 | 1.88 | $26.20 |

**Paid Leave** is calculated based on two weeks paid vacation, one week sick leave, and seven paid holidays. Employer's matching portion of **FICA** is 7.65 percent. **FUTA** (Federal Unemployment) is .8 percent. **Worker's compensation** for the insulation trade was calculated using a national average of 24.98 percent. **Unemployment insurance** was calculated using a national average of 8.7 percent. **Health insurance** was calculated based on a projected national average for 2001 of $505 per employee (and family when applicable) per month. Employer pays 80 percent for a per month cost of $404 per employee. **Retirement** is based on a 401(k) retirement program with employer matching of 50 percent. Employee contributions to the 401(k) plan are an average of 6 percent of the true wage. **Liability insurance** is based on a national average of 12.9 percent.

## Insulation Labor Productivity

| WORK DESCRIPTION | LABORER | COST PER HOUR | PRODUCTIVITY | UNIT PRICE |
|---|---|---|---|---|
| **Pour vermiculite attic insulation** | | | | |
| 3" deep | insulation installer | $28.80 | .008 | $.23 sf |
| 4" deep | insulation installer | $28.80 | .009 | $.26 sf |
| 5" deep | insulation installer | $28.80 | .009 | $.26 sf |
| 6" deep | insulation installer | $28.80 | .010 | $.29 sf |
| **Blow in mineral wool insulation** | | | | |
| R11 (3-1/2" deep) | insulation installer | $28.80 | .010 | $.29 sf |
| R19 (6" deep) | insulation installer | $28.80 | .011 | $.32 sf |
| R30 (10" deep) | insulation installer | $28.80 | .013 | $.37 sf |
| R38 (12" deep) | insulation installer | $28.80 | .016 | $.46 sf |
| **Blow in cellulose insulation** | | | | |
| R12 (3-1/2" deep) | insulation installer | $28.80 | .29 | $.29 sf |
| R21 (6" deep) | insulation installer | $28.80 | .012 | $.35 sf |
| R33 (10" deep) | insulation installer | $28.80 | .013 | $.37 sf |
| R42 (12" deep) | insulation installer | $28.80 | .016 | $.46 sf |
| **Blow in fiberglass insulation** | | | | |
| R11 (5" deep) | insulation installer | $28.80 | .010 | $.29 sf |
| R19 (8" deep) | insulation installer | $28.80 | .011 | $.32 sf |
| R30 (13" deep) | insulation installer | $28.80 | .013 | $.37 sf |
| R38 (16" deep) | insulation installer | $28.80 | .016 | $.46 sf |
| **Install fiberglass batt insulation in ceiling or floor** | | | | |
| R11 (3-1/2" deep) | insulation installer | $28.80 | .26 | $.26 sf |
| R19 (6" deep) | insulation installer | $28.80 | .011 | $.32 sf |
| R30 (9-1/2" deep) | insulation installer | $28.80 | .012 | $.35 sf |
| R38 (12" deep) | insulation installer | $28.80 | .015 | $.43 sf |
| **Install fiberglass batt insulation in wall** | | | | |
| R6 (1-3/4" deep) (between furring strips) | insulation installer | $28.80 | .010 | $.29 sf |
| R11 (3-1/2" deep) | insulation installer | $28.80 | .011 | $.32 sf |
| R19 (6" deep) | insulation installer | $28.80 | .013 | $.37 sf |
| R25 (8" deep) | insulation installer | $28.80 | .015 | $.43 sf |
| **Install rigid foam insulation board** | | | | |
| all thicknesses | insulation installer | $28.80 | .014 | $.40 sf |

✍ NOTES: _____

_____

_____

_____

_____ end

# 23 Masking & Moving

| Item Description | Unit | | | Total | |
|---|---|---|---|---|---|
| **Minimum charge for masking or moving work**<br>*Mask* Material...........16.00    Labor ..........54.00 | ea | — | — | $70.00 | ◄ MINIMUM |
| **Mask small room**<br>*Mask* Material ...........2.93    Labor..........27.80 | ea | — | — | $30.73 | ◄ MASK ROOM |
| **Mask average size room**<br>*Mask* Material ...........3.34    Labor..........31.90 | ea | — | — | $35.24 | |
| **Mask large room**<br>*Mask* Material ...........3.89    Labor..........37.80 | ea | — | — | $41.69 | |
| **Mask very large room**<br>*Mask* Material ...........4.12    Labor .......46.10 | ea | — | — | $50.22 | |
| **Mask room per lf of wall**<br>*Mask* Material ............. .10    Labor............. .80 | lf | — | — | $.90 | ◄ MASK ROOM PER LF |
| **Mask small window**<br>*Mask* Material ...........1.48    Labor ..........6.55 | ea | — | — | $8.03 | ◄ MASK WINDOW |
| **Mask average size window**<br>*Mask* Material ...........1.55    Labor ..........7.67 | ea | — | — | $9.22 | |
| **Mask large window**<br>*Mask* Material ...........1.65    Labor ..........9.21 | ea | — | — | $10.86 | |
| **Mask very large window**<br>*Mask* Material ...........1.73    Labor ..........11.30 | ea | — | — | $13.03 | |
| **Mask door or opening per lf of opening**<br>*Mask* Material ............. .06    Labor............. .75 | lf | — | — | $.81 | ◄ MASK DOOR OR OPENING PER LF |
| **Mask small door or opening**<br>*Mask* Material ...........1.63    Labor ..........6.47 | ea | — | — | $8.10 | ◄ MASK DOOR OR OPENING |
| **Mask average size door or opening**<br>*Mask* Material ...........1.70    Labor ..........7.54 | ea | — | — | $9.24 | |
| **Mask large door or opening**<br>*Mask* Material ...........1.80    Labor ..........9.06 | ea | — | — | $10.86 | |
| **Mask very large door or opening**<br>*Mask* Material ...........1.87    Labor ..........11.10 | ea | — | — | $12.97 | |
| **Mask woodwork per lf of woodwork**<br>*Mask* Material ............. .06    Labor............. .72 | lf | — | — | $.78 | ◄ MASK WOODWORK |
| **Mask baseboard heater**<br>*Mask* Material ...........1.24    Labor ..........5.53 | ea | — | — | $6.77 | ◄ MASK HEATER |
| **Mask light fixture**<br>*Mask* Material ............. .95    Labor ..........4.53 | ea | — | — | $5.48 | ◄ MASK LIGHT FIXTURE |

| Item Description | Unit | | | Total |
|---|---|---|---|---|
| **MASK OUTLET** ▶ **OR SWITCH** | **Mask outlet or switch (remove cover)**<br>**Mask** Material............ .22　　Labor ............2.84 | ea | — | — | $3.06 |
| **MASK BATHROOM** ▶ | **Mask small bathroom**<br>**Mask** Material ............2.96　　Labor ..........28.90 | ea | — | — | $31.86 |
| | **Mask average size bathroom**<br>**Mask** Material ............3.38　　Labor ..........33.60 | ea | — | — | $36.98 |
| | **Mask large bathroom**<br>**Mask** Material ............3.96　　Labor ..........40.10 | ea | — | — | $44.06 |
| | **Mask very large bathroom**<br>**Mask** Material ............4.22　　Labor..........49.80 | ea | — | — | $54.02 |
| **MASK KITCHEN** ▶ | **Mask small kitchen**<br>**Mask** Material ............3.51　　Labor ..........29.90 | ea | — | — | $33.41 |
| | **Mask average size kitchen**<br>**Mask** Material ............3.82　　Labor ..........35.10 | ea | — | — | $38.92 |
| | **Mask large kitchen**<br>**Mask** Material ............4.18　　Labor..........42.10 | ea | — | — | $46.28 |
| | **Mask very large kitchen**<br>**Mask** Material ............4.35　　Labor ..........53.00 | ea | — | — | $57.35 |
| **MASK TILE,** ▶ **MARBLE, OR STONE** | **Mask tile, marble, or stone per lf of edge**<br>**Mask** Material............. .07　　Labor............. .77 | lf | — | — | $.84 |
| **MOVE & COVER** ▶ **ROOM CONTENTS** | **Move and cover small room contents**<br>**Move** Material............8.30　　Labor..........31.10 | ea | — | — | $39.40 |
| | **Move and cover average room contents**<br>**Move** Material............9.36　　Labor..........37.80 | ea | — | — | $47.16 |
| | **Move and cover heavy or above average room contents**<br>**Move** Material ..........10.50　　Labor..........47.80 | ea | — | — | $58.30 |
| | **Move and cover very heavy or above average room contents**<br>**Move** Material............11.70　　Labor..........67.20 | ea | — | — | $78.90 |

# TIME & MATERIAL CHARTS (selected items)

## Masking & Moving Labor

| LABORER | BASE WAGE | PAID LEAVE | TRUE WAGE | FICA | FUTA | WORKER'S COMP. | UNEMPLOY. INSUR. | HEALTH INSUR. | RETIRE (401K) | LIABILITY INSUR. | COST PER HOUR |
|---|---|---|---|---|---|---|---|---|---|---|---|
| Laborer.............. | $13.50 | 1.05 | $14.55 | 1.11 | .12 | 3.08 | 1.27 | 2.54 | .44 | 1.89 | $25.00 |

**Paid Leave** is calculated based on two weeks paid vacation, one week sick leave, and seven paid holidays. Employer's matching portion of **FICA** is 7.65 percent. **FUTA** (Federal Unemployment) is .8 percent. **Worker's compensation** for the masking & movingtrade was calculated using a national average of 21.20 percent. **Unemployment insurance** was calculated using a national average of 8.7 percent. **Health insurance** was calculated based on a projected national average for 2001 of $505 per employee (and family when applicable) per month. Employer pays 80 percent for a per month cost of $404 per employee. **Retirement** is based on a 401(k) retirement program with employer matching of 50 percent. Employee contributions to the 401(k) plan are an average of 6 percent of the true wage. **Liability insurance** is based on a national average of 12.9 percent.

# 24 ............................................ *Masonry*

| Item Description | Unit | Remove | Replace | Total | |
|---|---|---|---|---|---|
| **Minimum charge for masonry work** | ea | — | $378.00 | $378.00 | ◄ MINIMUM |
| *Replace* Materials.....125.00    Labor ........253.00 | | | | | |
| | | | | | ◄ COMMON BRICK |
| **Deduct 16% for common brick** | | | | | |
| **4" wide standard non-modular brick wall** | sf | $2.28 | $11.31 | $13.59 | ◄ 4" WIDE |
| *Replace* Materials.......4.85   Labor ...........6.46 | | | | | BRICK WALL |
| *Remove* .................. Labor ...........2.28 | | | | | With 3/8" wide mortar |
| ► Non-modular bricks. Actual dimensions: 3-3/4" thick by 2-1/4" high by 8" long. | | | | | joints. Includes 4% waste for brick and 25% waste |
| **4" wide oversize non-modular brick wall** | sf | $2.28 | $10.47 | $12.75 | for mortar. |
| *Replace* Materials.......4.09   Labor ...........6.38 | | | | | |
| *Remove* .................. Labor ...........2.28 | | | | | |
| ► Non-modular bricks. Actual dimensions: 3-3/4" thick by 2-3/4" high by 8" long. | | | | | |
| **4" wide three-inch non-modular brick wall** | sf | $2.28 | $10.39 | $12.67 | |
| *Replace* Materials.......4.04   Labor ...........6.35 | | | | | |
| *Remove* .................. Labor ...........2.28 | | | | | |
| ► Non-modular bricks. Actual dimensions: 3" thick by 2-3/4" high by 9-3/4" long. Three-inch bricks also come in lengths of 9-5/8" and 8-3/4" and widths vary from 2-5/8" to 3". Normally used as a veneer unit. | | | | | |
| **4" wide standard brick wall** | sf | $2.28 | $9.90 | $12.18 | |
| *Replace* Materials.......3.48   Labor ...........6.42 | | | | | |
| *Remove* .................. Labor ...........2.28 | | | | | |
| ► Modular bricks. Nominal dimensions: 4" thick by 2-2/3" high by 8" long. | | | | | |
| **4" wide engineer brick wall** | sf | $2.28 | $8.97 | $11.25 | |
| *Replace* Materials.......3.61   Labor ...........5.36 | | | | | |
| *Remove* .................. Labor ...........2.28 | | | | | |
| ► Modular bricks. Nominal dimensions: 4" thick by 3-1/5" high by 8" long. | | | | | |
| **4" wide jumbo closure brick wall** | sf | $2.28 | $8.16 | $10.44 | |
| *Replace* Materials.......3.60   Labor ...........4.56 | | | | | |
| *Remove* .................. Labor ...........2.28 | | | | | |
| ► Also called economy 8. Modular bricks. Nominal dimensions: 4" thick by 4" high by 8" long. | | | | | |
| **4" wide double brick wall** | sf | $2.28 | $6.80 | $9.08 | |
| *Replace* Materials.......2.96   Labor ...........3.84 | | | | | |
| *Remove* .................. Labor ...........2.28 | | | | | |
| ► Modular bricks. Nominal dimensions: 4" thick by 5-1/3" high by 8" long. | | | | | |
| **4" wide Roman brick wall** | sf | $2.28 | $10.89 | $13.17 | |
| *Replace* Materials.......4.81   Labor ...........6.08 | | | | | |
| *Remove* .................. Labor ...........2.28 | | | | | |
| ► Modular bricks. Nominal dimensions: 4" thick by 2" high by 12" long. | | | | | |
| **4" wide Norman brick wall** | sf | $2.28 | $8.88 | $11.16 | |
| *Replace* Materials.......3.94   Labor ...........4.94 | | | | | |
| *Remove* .................. Labor ...........2.28 | | | | | |
| ► Modular bricks. Nominal dimensions: 4" thick by 2-2/3" high by 12" long. | | | | | |
| **4" wide Norwegian brick wall** | sf | $2.28 | $7.26 | $9.54 | |
| *Replace* Materials.......3.04   Labor ...........4.22 | | | | | |
| *Remove* .................. Labor ...........2.28 | | | | | |
| ► Modular bricks. Nominal dimensions: 4" thick by 3-1/5" high by 12" long. | | | | | |

**BRICK WALLS**

All brick walls are made from average to high quality face brick. Standard quality bricks will be up to **15%** less and higher quality bricks will vary by as much as **45%**.

Brick sizes come in two general categories: non-modular and modular. Actual dimensions are listed for non-modular bricks.

Modular bricks are designed to fit together with a minimum of cutting which saves labor and reduces waste.

Nominal dimensions for modular bricks include the manufactured dimensions *plus* the thickness of the mortar joint for which the unit was designed (usually 1/2").

Actual brick sizes vary from manufacturer to manufacturer. The sizes in this section are typical.

**RELATED ITEMS**

| Item Description | Unit | Remove | Replace | Total |
|---|---|---|---|---|

**4" WIDE BRICK WALL** continued

**4" wide jumbo utility brick wall** — sf, $2.28, $7.73, $10.01
Replace Materials........3.85   Labor ............3.88
Remove ......................   Labor ............2.28
▶ Also called economy 12. Modular bricks. Nominal dimensions: 4" thick by 4" high by 12" long.

**4" wide triple brick wall** — sf, $2.28, $6.81, $9.09
Replace Materials........3.16   Labor ............3.65
Remove ......................   Labor ............2.28
▶ Modular bricks. Nominal dimensions: 4" thick by 5-1/3" high by 12" long.

**6" WIDE BRICK WALL**
With 3/8" wide mortar joints. Includes 4% waste for brick and 25% waste for mortar.

**6" wide Norwegian brick wall** — sf, $2.72, $8.89, $11.61
Replace Materials........4.18   Labor ............4.71
Remove ......................   Labor ............2.72
▶ Modular bricks. Nominal dimensions: 6" thick by 3-1/5" high by 12" long.

**6" wide Norman brick wall** — sf, $2.72, $10.79, $13.51
Replace Materials........5.17   Labor ............5.62
Remove ......................   Labor ............2.72
▶ Modular bricks. Nominal dimensions: 6" thick by 2-2/3" high by 12" long.

**6" wide jumbo brick wall** — sf, $2.72, $8.99, $11.71
Replace Materials........4.70   Labor ............4.29
Remove ......................   Labor ............2.72
▶ Modular bricks. Nominal dimensions: 6" thick by 4" high by 12" long.

**8" WIDE BRICK WALL**

**8" wide jumbo brick wall** — sf, $3.46, $10.30, $13.76
Replace Materials........5.47   Labor ............4.83
Remove ......................   Labor ............3.46
▶ Modular bricks. Nominal dimensions: 8" thick by 4" high by 12" long. With 3/8" wide mortar joints, Includes 4% waste for brick and 25% waste for mortar.

**8" WIDE DOUBLE WYTHE BRICK WALL**
With 3/8" wide mortar joints. Includes 4% waste for brick and 25% waste for mortar.

**8" wide double wythe standard non-modular brick wall** — sf, $3.46, $21.71, $25.17
Replace Materials......10.01   Labor ............11.70
Remove ......................   Labor ............3.46
▶ Non-modular bricks. Actual dimensions: 3-3/4" thick by 2-1/4" high by 8" long.

**8" wide double wythe oversize non-modular brick wall** — sf, $3.46, $19.99, $23.45
Replace Materials........8.49   Labor ............11.50
Remove ......................   Labor ............3.46
▶ Non-modular bricks. Actual dimensions: 3-3/4" thick by 2-3/4" high by 8" long.

**8" wide double wythe three-inch non-modular brick wall** — sf, $3.46, $19.79, $23.25
Replace Materials........8.39   Labor ............11.40
Remove ......................   Labor ............3.46
▶ Non-modular bricks. Actual dimensions: 3" thick by 2-3/4" high by 9-3/4" long. Three-inch bricks also come in lengths of 9-5/8" and 8-3/4" and widths vary from 2-5/8" to 3". Normally used as a veneer unit.

**8" wide double wythe standard brick wall** — sf, $3.46, $18.87, $22.33
Replace Materials........7.27   Labor ............11.60
Remove ......................   Labor ............3.46
▶ Modular bricks. Nominal dimensions: 4" thick by 2-2/3" high by 8" long.

**8" wide double wythe engineer brick wall** — sf, $3.46, $17.14, $20.60
Replace Materials........7.53   Labor ............9.61
Remove ......................   Labor ............3.46
▶ Modular bricks. Nominal dimensions: 4" thick by 3-1/5" high by 8" long.

**8" wide double wythe jumbo closure brick wall** — sf, $3.46, $15.72, $19.18
Replace Materials........7.51   Labor ............8.21
Remove ......................   Labor ............3.46
▶ Also called economy 8. Modular bricks. Nominal dimensions: 4" thick by 4" high by 8" long.

Insurance Repair Estimator

| Item Description | Unit | Remove | Replace | Total |
|---|---|---|---|---|
| **8" wide double wythe double brick wall**<br>*Replace* Materials........6.23    Labor ............6.88<br>*Remove* ......................    Labor ............3.46<br>▶ Modular bricks. Nominal dimensions: 4" thick by 5-1/3" high by 8" long. | sf | $3.46 | $13.11 | $16.57 |
| **8" wide double wythe Roman brick wall**<br>*Replace* Materials........9.93    Labor............10.90<br>*Remove* ......................    Labor ............3.46<br>▶ Modular bricks. Nominal dimensions: 4" thick by 2" high by 12" long. | sf | $3.46 | $20.83 | $24.29 |
| **8" wide double wythe Norman brick wall**<br>*Replace* Materials........8.19    Labor ............8.89<br>*Remove* ......................    Labor ............3.46<br>▶ Modular bricks. Nominal dimensions: 4" thick by 2-2/3" high by 12" long. | sf | $3.46 | $17.08 | $20.54 |
| **8" wide double wythe Norwegian brick wall**<br>*Replace* Materials........6.39    Labor ............7.56<br>*Remove* ......................    Labor ............3.46<br>▶ Modular bricks. Nominal dimensions: 4" thick by 3-1/5" high by 12" long. | sf | $3.46 | $13.95 | $17.41 |
| **8" wide double wythe jumbo utility brick wall**<br>*Replace* Materials........8.01    Labor ............6.99<br>*Remove* ......................    Labor ............3.46<br>▶ Also called economy 12. Modular bricks. Nominal dimensions: 4" thick by 4" high by 12" long. | sf | $3.46 | $15.00 | $18.46 |
| **8" wide double wythe triple brick wall**<br>*Replace* Materials........6.63    Labor ............6.57<br>*Remove* ......................    Labor ............3.46<br>▶ Modular bricks. Nominal dimensions: 4" thick by 5-1/3" high by 12" long. | sf | $3.46 | $13.20 | $16.66 |
| **8" wide wall from 4" standard non-mod. brick and 4" block**<br>*Replace* Materials........7.00    Labor ............8.85<br>*Remove* ......................    Labor ............3.46<br>▶ Modular bricks. Actual dimensions: 3-3/4" thick by 2-1/4" high by 8" long. Concrete block: 4" thick by 8" high by 16" long. | sf | $3.46 | $15.85 | $19.31 |
| **8" wide wall from 4" oversize non-mod. brick and 4" block**<br>*Replace* Materials........6.24    Labor ............8.78<br>*Remove* ......................    Labor ............3.46<br>▶ Modular bricks. Actual dimensions: 3-3/4" thick by 2-3/4" high by 8" long. Concrete block: 4" thick by 8" high by 16" long. | sf | $3.46 | $15.02 | $18.48 |
| **8" wide wall from three-inch non-mod. brick and 4" block**<br>*Replace* Materials........6.19    Labor ............8.74<br>*Remove* ......................    Labor ............3.46<br>▶ Modular bricks. Actual dimensions: 3" thick by 2-3/4" high by 9-3/4" long. Three-inch bricks also come in lengths of 9-5/8" and 8-3/4" and widths vary from 2-5/8" to 3". Concrete block: 4" thick by 8" high by 16" long. | sf | $3.46 | $14.93 | $18.39 |
| **8" wide ick wall from 4" standard brick and 4" concrete block**<br>*Replace* Materials........5.63    Labor ............8.85<br>*Remove* ......................    Labor ............3.46<br>▶ Modular bricks. Nominal dimensions: 4" thick by 2-2/3" high by 8" long. Concrete block: 4" thick by 8" high by 16" long. | sf | $3.46 | $14.48 | $17.94 |
| **8" wide wall from 4" engineer brick and 4" concrete block**<br>*Replace* Materials........5.76    Labor ............7.83<br>*Remove* ......................    Labor ............3.46<br>▶ Modular bricks. Nominal dimensions: 4" thick by 3-1/5" high by 8" long. Concrete block: 4" thick by 8" high by 16" long. | sf | $3.46 | $13.59 | $17.05 |

◀ **8" WIDE BRICK & BLOCK WALL**
With 3/8" wide mortar joints. Includes 4% waste for brick and block and 25% waste for mortar.

| Item Description | Unit | Remove | Replace | Total |
|---|---|---|---|---|

**8" WIDE BRICK & BLOCK WALL** *continued*

### 8" wide wall from 4" jumbo closure brick and 4" concrete block

| | sf | $3.46 | $12.89 | $16.35 |

*Replace* Materials........5.75   Labor ............7.14
*Remove* ........................   Labor ............3.46
► Modular bricks. Nominal dimensions: 4" thick by 4" high by 8" long. Concrete block: 4" thick by 8" high by 16" long.

### 8" wide wall from 4" double brick and 4" concrete block

| | sf | $3.46 | $11.57 | $15.03 |

*Replace* Materials........5.11   Labor ............6.46
*Remove* ........................   Labor ............3.46
► Modular bricks. Nominal dimensions: 4" thick by 5-1/3" high by 8" long. Concrete block: 4" thick by 8" high by 16" long.

### 8" wide wall from 4" Roman brick and 4" concrete block

| | sf | $3.46 | $15.47 | $18.93 |

*Replace* Materials........6.96   Labor ............8.51
*Remove* ........................   Labor ............3.46
► Modular bricks. Nominal dimensions: 4" thick by 2" high by 12" long. Concrete block: 4" thick by 8" high by 16" long.

### 8" wide wall from 4" Norman and 4" concrete block

| | sf | $3.46 | $13.58 | $17.04 |

*Replace* Materials........6.09   Labor ............7.49
*Remove* ........................   Labor ............3.46
► Modular bricks. Nominal dimensions: 4" thick by 2-2/3" high by 12" long. Concrete block: 4" thick by 8" high by 16" long.

### 8" wide wall from 4" Norwegian and 4" concrete block

| | sf | $3.46 | $12.03 | $15.49 |

*Replace* Materials........5.19   Labor ............6.84
*Remove* ........................   Labor ............3.46
► Modular bricks. Nominal dimensions: 4" thick by 3-1/5" high by 12" long. Concrete block: 4" thick by 8" high by 16" long.

### 8" wide wall from 4" jumbo utility and 4" concrete block

| | sf | $3.46 | $12.54 | $16.00 |

*Replace* Materials........6.00   Labor ............6.54
*Remove* ........................   Labor ............3.46
► Modular bricks. Nominal dimensions: 4" thick by 4" high by 12" long. Concrete block: 4" thick by 8" high by 16" long.

### 8" wide wall from 4" triple and 4" concrete block

| | sf | $3.46 | $11.62 | $15.08 |

*Replace* Materials........5.31   Labor ............6.31
*Remove* ........................   Labor ............3.46
► Modular bricks. Nominal dimensions: 4" thick by 5-1/3" high by 12" long. Concrete block: 4" thick by 8" high by 16" long.

**10" WIDE BRICK & BLOCK WALL**
*With 3/8" wide mortar joints. Includes 4% waste for brick and block and 25% waste for mortar.*

### 10" wide wall from 4" standard non-mod. brick and 6" block

| | sf | $3.90 | $16.28 | $20.18 |

*Replace* Materials........7.31   Labor ............8.97
*Remove* ........................   Labor ............3.90
► Modular bricks. Actual dimensions: 3-3/4" thick by 2-1/4" high by 8" long. Concrete block: 6" thick by 8" high by 16" long.

### 10" wide wall from 4" oversize non-mod. brick and 6" block

| | sf | $3.90 | $15.44 | $19.34 |

*Replace* Materials........6.55   Labor ............8.89
*Remove* ........................   Labor ............3.90
► Modular bricks. Actual dimensions: 3-3/4" thick by 2-3/4" high by 8" long. Concrete block: 6" thick by 8" high by 16" long.

### 10" wide wall from three-inch non-mod. brick and 6" block

| | sf | $3.90 | $15.35 | $19.25 |

*Replace* Materials........6.50   Labor ............8.85
*Remove* ........................   Labor ............3.90
► Modular bricks. Actual dimensions: 3" thick by 2-3/4" high by 9-3/4" long. Three-inch bricks also come in lengths of 9-5/8" and 8-3/4" and widths vary from 2-5/8" to 3". Concrete block: 6" thick by 8" high by 16" long.

### 10" wide wall from 4" standard brick and 6" concrete block

| | sf | $3.90 | $14.87 | $18.77 |

*Replace* Materials........5.94   Labor ............8.93
*Remove* ........................   Labor ............3.90
► Modular bricks. Nominal dimensions: 4" thick by 2-2/3" high by 8" long. Concrete block: 6" thick by 8" high by 16" long.

| Item Description | Unit | Remove | Replace | Total |
|---|---|---|---|---|
| **10" wide wall from 4" engineer brick and 6" concrete block** | sf | $3.90 | $14.01 | $17.91 |
| *Replace* Materials......6.07    Labor ..........7.94 | | | | |
| *Remove* .................    Labor ..........3.90 | | | | |
| ► Modular bricks. Nominal dimensions: 4" thick by 3-1/5" high by 8" long. Concrete block: 6" thick by 8" high by 16" long. | | | | |
| **10" wide wall from 4" jumbo closure and 6" concrete block** | sf | $3.90 | $13.28 | $17.18 |
| *Replace* Materials......6.06    Labor ..........7.22 | | | | |
| *Remove* .................    Labor ..........3.90 | | | | |
| ► Modular bricks. Nominal dimensions: 4" thick by 4" high by 8" long. Concrete block: 6" thick by 8" high by 16" long. | | | | |
| **10" wide wall from 4" double brick and 6" concrete block** | sf | $3.90 | $11.99 | $15.89 |
| *Replace* Materials......5.42    Labor ..........6.57 | | | | |
| *Remove* .................    Labor ..........3.90 | | | | |
| ► Modular bricks. Nominal dimensions: 4" thick by 5-1/3" high by 8" long. Concrete block: 6" thick by 8" high by 16" long. | | | | |
| **10" wide wall from 4" Roman brick and 6" concrete block** | sf | $3.90 | $15.86 | $19.76 |
| *Replace* Materials......7.27    Labor ..........8.59 | | | | |
| *Remove* .................    Labor ..........3.90 | | | | |
| ► Modular bricks. Nominal dimensions: 4" thick by 2" high by 12" long. Concrete block: 6" thick by 8" high by 16" long. | | | | |
| **10" wide wall from 4" Norman and 6" concrete block** | sf | $3.90 | $14.00 | $17.90 |
| *Replace* Materials......6.40    Labor ..........7.60 | | | | |
| *Remove* .................    Labor ..........3.90 | | | | |
| ► Modular bricks. Nominal dimensions: 4" thick by 2-2/3" high by 12" long. Concrete block: 6" thick by 8" high by 16" long. | | | | |
| **10" wide wall from 4" Norwegian and 6" concrete block** | sf | $3.90 | $12.42 | $16.32 |
| *Replace* Materials......5.50    Labor ..........6.92 | | | | |
| *Remove* .................    Labor ..........3.90 | | | | |
| ► Modular bricks. Nominal dimensions: 4" thick by 3-1/5" high by 12" long. Concrete block: 6" thick by 8" high by 16" long. | | | | |
| **10" wide wall from 4" jumbo utility and 6" concrete block** | sf | $3.90 | $12.96 | $16.86 |
| *Replace* Materials......6.31    Labor ..........6.65 | | | | |
| *Remove* .................    Labor ..........3.90 | | | | |
| ► Modular bricks. Nominal dimensions: 4" thick by 4" high by 12" long. Concrete block: 6" thick by 8" high by 16" long. | | | | |
| **10" wide brick wall from 4" triple and 6" concrete block** | sf | $3.90 | $12.08 | $15.98 |
| *Replace* Materials......5.62    Labor ..........6.46 | | | | |
| *Remove* .................    Labor ..........3.90 | | | | |
| ► Modular bricks. Nominal dimensions: 4" thick by 5-1/3" high by 12" long. Concrete block: 6" thick by 8" high by 16" long. | | | | |
| **12" wide wall from 4" standard non-mod. brick and 8" concrete block** | sf | $4.64 | $16.98 | $21.62 |
| *Replace* Materials......7.86    Labor ..........9.12 | | | | |
| *Remove* .................    Labor ..........4.64 | | | | |
| ► Modular bricks. Actual dimensions: 3-3/4" thick by 2-1/4" high by 8" long. Concrete block: 8" thick by 8" high by 16" long. | | | | |
| **12" wide wall from 4" oversize non-mod. brick and 8" concrete block** | sf | $4.64 | $16.18 | $20.82 |
| *Replace* Materials......7.10    Labor ..........9.08 | | | | |
| *Remove* .................    Labor ..........4.64 | | | | |
| ► Modular bricks. Actual dimensions: 3-3/4" thick by 2-3/4" high by 8" long. Concrete block: 8" thick by 8" high by 16" long. | | | | |
| **12" wide wall from three-inch non-mod. brick and 8" concrete block** | sf | $4.64 | $16.06 | $20.70 |
| *Replace* Materials......7.05    Labor ..........9.01 | | | | |
| *Remove* .................    Labor ..........4.64 | | | | |
| ► Modular bricks. Actual dimensions: 3" thick by 2-3/4" high by 9-3/4" long. Three-inch bricks also come in lengths of 9-5/8" and 8-3/4" and widths vary from 2-5/8" to 3". Concrete block: 8" thick by 8" high by 16" long. | | | | |

**RELATED ITEMS**
Cleaning ..........63
Fireplaces..........241
Painting ..........340

◄ **12" WIDE BRICK & BLOCK WALL** With 3/8" wide mortar joints. Includes 4% waste for brick and block and 25% waste for mortar.

| Item Description | Unit | Remove | Replace | Total |
|---|---|---|---|---|

**12" WIDE BRICK ▶ & BLOCK WALL**
*continued*

| Item Description | Unit | Remove | Replace | Total |
|---|---|---|---|---|
| **12" wide wall from 4" standard brick and 8" concrete block**<br>*Replace* Materials........6.49    Labor ...........9.12<br>*Remove* ......................    Labor ...........4.64<br>▶ Modular bricks. Nominal dimensions: 4" thick by 2-2/3" high by 8" long. Concrete block: 8" thick by 8" high by 16" long. | sf | $4.64 | $15.61 | $20.25 |
| **12" wide wall from 4" engineer brick and 8" concrete block**<br>*Replace* Materials........6.62    Labor ...........8.13<br>*Remove* ......................    Labor ...........4.64<br>▶ Modular bricks. Nominal dimensions: 4" thick by 3-1/5" high by 8" long. Concrete block: 8" thick by 8" high by 16" long. | sf | $4.64 | $14.75 | $19.39 |
| **12" wide wall from 4" jumbo closure brick and 8" concrete block**<br>*Replace* Materials........6.61    Labor ...........7.41<br>*Remove* ......................    Labor ...........4.64<br>▶ Modular bricks. Nominal dimensions: 4" thick by 4" high by 8" long. Concrete block: 8" thick by 8" high by 16" long. | sf | $4.64 | $14.02 | $18.66 |
| **12" wide wall from 4" double brick and 8" concrete block**<br>*Replace* Materials........5.97    Labor ...........6.76<br>*Remove* ......................    Labor ...........4.64<br>▶ Modular bricks. Nominal dimensions: 4" thick by 5-1/3" high by 8" long. Concrete block: 8" thick by 8" high by 16" long. | sf | $4.64 | $12.73 | $17.37 |
| **12" wide wall from 4" Roman brick and 8" concrete block**<br>*Replace* Materials........7.82    Labor ...........8.78<br>*Remove* ......................    Labor ...........4.64<br>▶ Modular bricks. Nominal dimensions: 4" thick by 2" high by 12" long. Concrete block: 8" thick by 8" high by 16" long. | sf | $4.64 | $16.60 | $21.24 |
| **12" wide wall from 4" Norman brick and 8" concrete block**<br>*Replace* Materials........6.95    Labor ...........7.75<br>*Remove* ......................    Labor ...........4.64<br>▶ Modular bricks. Nominal dimensions: 4" thick by 2-2/3" high by 12" long. Concrete block: 8" thick by 8" high by 16" long. | sf | $4.64 | $14.70 | $19.34 |
| **12" wide wall from 4" Norwegian brick and 8" concrete block**<br>*Replace* Materials........6.05    Labor ...........7.11<br>*Remove* ......................    Labor ...........4.64<br>▶ Modular bricks. Nominal dimensions: 4" thick by 3-1/5" high by 12" long. Concrete block: 8" thick by 8" high by 16" long. | sf | $4.64 | $13.16 | $17.80 |
| **12" wide wall from 4" jumbo utility brick and 8" concrete block**<br>*Replace* Materials........6.86    Labor ...........6.84<br>*Remove* ......................    Labor ...........4.64<br>▶ Modular bricks. Nominal dimensions: 4" thick by 4" high by 12" long. Concrete block: 8" thick by 8" high by 16" long. | sf | $4.64 | $13.70 | $18.34 |
| **12" wide wall from 4" triple brick and 8" concrete block**<br>*Replace* Materials........6.17    Labor ...........6.61<br>*Remove* ......................    Labor ...........4.64<br>▶ Modular bricks. Nominal dimensions: 4" thick by 5-1/3" high by 12" long. Concrete block: 8" thick by 8" high by 16" long. | sf | $4.64 | $12.78 | $17.42 |

**12" WIDE ▶ TRIPLE WYTHE BRICK WALL**
*With 3/8" wide mortar joints. Includes 4% waste for brick and 25% waste for mortar.*

| Item Description | Unit | Remove | Replace | Total |
|---|---|---|---|---|
| **12" wide triple wythe standard non-modular brick wall**<br>*Replace* Materials ......14.90    Labor ...........16.50<br>*Remove* ......................    Labor ...........4.64<br>▶ Non-modular bricks. Actual dimensions: 3-3/4" thick by 2-1/4" high by 8" long. | sf | $4.64 | $31.40 | $36.04 |
| **12" wide triple wythe oversize non-modular brick wall**<br>*Replace* Materials ......12.60    Labor ...........16.20<br>*Remove* ......................    Labor ...........4.64<br>▶ Non-modular bricks. Actual dimensions: 3-3/4" thick by 2-3/4" high by 8" long. | sf | $4.64 | $28.80 | $33.44 |

| Item Description | Unit | Remove | Replace | Total |
|---|---|---|---|---|
| **12" wide triple wythe three-inch non-modular brick wall** | sf | $4.64 | $28.60 | $33.24 |
| *Replace* Materials ......12.50    Labor ...........16.10 | | | | |
| *Remove* ...................    Labor ...........4.64 | | | | |
| ► Non-modular bricks. Actual dimensions: 3" thick by 2-3/4" high by 9-3/4" long. Three-inch bricks also come in lengths of 9-5/8" and 8-3/4" and widths vary from 2-5/8" to 3". | | | | |
| **12" wide triple wythe standard brick wall** | sf | $4.64 | $27.10 | $31.74 |
| *Replace* Materials ......10.80    Labor ...........16.30 | | | | |
| *Remove* ...................    Labor ...........4.64 | | | | |
| ► Modular bricks. Nominal dimensions: 4" thick by 2-2/3" high by 8" long. | | | | |
| **12" wide triple wythe engineer brick wall** | sf | $4.64 | $24.80 | $29.44 |
| *Replace* Materials......11.20    Labor ...........13.60 | | | | |
| *Remove* ...................    Labor ...........4.64 | | | | |
| ► Modular bricks. Nominal dimensions: 4" thick by 3-1/5" high by 8" long. | | | | |
| **12" wide triple wythe jumbo closure brick wall** | sf | $4.64 | $22.70 | $27.34 |
| *Replace* Materials......11.10    Labor ...........11.60 | | | | |
| *Remove* ...................    Labor ...........4.64 | | | | |
| ► Also called Economy 8. Modular bricks. Nominal dimensions: 4" thick by 4" high by 8" long. | | | | |
| **12" wide triple wythe double brick wall** | sf | $4.64 | $18.91 | $23.55 |
| *Replace* Materials........9.22    Labor ...........9.69 | | | | |
| *Remove* ...................    Labor ...........4.64 | | | | |
| ► Modular bricks. Nominal dimensions: 4" thick by 5-1/3" high by 8" long. | | | | |
| **12" wide triple wythe Roman brick wall** | sf | $4.64 | $30.30 | $34.94 |
| *Replace* Materials ......14.80    Labor ...........15.50 | | | | |
| *Remove* ...................    Labor ...........4.64 | | | | |
| ► Modular bricks. Nominal dimensions: 4" thick by 2" high by 12" long. | | | | |
| **12" wide triple wythe Norman brick wall** | sf | $4.64 | $24.70 | $29.34 |
| *Replace* Materials .......12.20    Labor ...........12.50 | | | | |
| *Remove* ...................    Labor ...........4.64 | | | | |
| ► Modular bricks. Nominal dimensions: 4" thick by 2-2/3" high by 12" long. | | | | |
| **12" wide triple wythe Norwegian brick wall** | sf | $4.64 | $20.16 | $24.80 |
| *Replace* Materials........9.46    Labor ...........10.70 | | | | |
| *Remove* ...................    Labor ...........4.64 | | | | |
| ► Modular bricks. Nominal dimensions: 4" thick by 3-1/5" high by 12" long. | | | | |
| **12" wide triple wythe jumbo utility brick wall** | sf | $4.64 | $21.78 | $26.42 |
| *Replace* Materials.......11.90    Labor ...........9.88 | | | | |
| *Remove* ...................    Labor ...........4.64 | | | | |
| ► Also called Economy 12. Modular bricks. Nominal dimensions: 4" thick by 4" high by 12" long. | | | | |
| **12" wide triple wythe triple brick wall** | sf | $4.64 | $19.09 | $23.73 |
| *Replace* Materials........9.82    Labor ...........9.27 | | | | |
| *Remove* ...................    Labor ...........4.64 | | | | |
| ► Modular bricks. Nominal dimensions: 4" thick by 5-1/3" high by 12" long. | | | | |
| **10" wide cavity wall from 4" standard non-mod. brick and 4" block** | sf | $3.46 | $16.37 | $19.83 |
| *Replace* Materials........7.10    Labor ...........9.27 | | | | |
| *Remove* ...................    Labor ...........3.46 | | | | |
| ► Modular bricks. Actual dimensions: 3-3/4" thick by 2-1/4" high by 8" long. Concrete block: 4" thick by 8" high by 16" long. | | | | |
| **10" wide cavity wall from 4" oversize non-mod. brick and 4" block** | sf | $3.46 | $15.54 | $19.00 |
| *Replace* Materials........6.34    Labor ...........9.20 | | | | |
| *Remove* ...................    Labor ...........3.46 | | | | |
| ► Modular bricks. Actual dimensions: 3-3/4" thick by 2-3/4" high by 8" long. Concrete block: 4" thick by 8" high by 16" long. | | | | |

---

**RELATED ITEMS**

Cleaning ......................63
Fireplaces....................241
Painting .....................340

---

◄ **10" WIDE BRICK & BLOCK CAVITY WALL**
With 2" dead air space. (see page 295 for foam insulation in air space) and 3/8" wide mortar joints. Includes 4% waste for brick and block and 25% waste for mortar.

| | Item Description | Unit | Remove | Replace | Total |
|---|---|---|---|---|---|
| **10" WIDE BRICK ▶ & BLOCK CAVITY WALL** *continued* | **10" wide cavity wall from three-inch non-mod. brick and 4" block**<br>*Replace* Materials.........6.29    Labor ...........9.16<br>*Remove* .....................    Labor ...........3.46<br>▶ Modular bricks. Actual dimensions: 3" thick by 2-3/4" high by 9-3/4" long. Three-inch bricks also come in lengths of 9-5/8" and 8-3/4" and widths vary from 2-5/8" to 3". Concrete block: 4" thick by 8" high by 16" long. | sf | $3.46 | $15.45 | $18.91 |
| | **10" wide cavity wall from 4" standard brick and 4" concrete block**<br>*Replace* Materials.........5.73    Labor ...........9.23<br>*Remove* .....................    Labor ...........3.46<br>▶ Modular bricks. Nominal dimensions: 4" thick by 2-2/3" high by 8" long. Concrete block: 4" thick by 8" high by 16" long. | sf | $3.46 | $14.96 | $18.42 |
| | **10" wide cavity wall from 4" engineer brick and 4" concrete block**<br>*Replace* Materials.........5.86    Labor ...........8.21<br>*Remove* .....................    Labor ...........3.46<br>▶ Modular bricks. Nominal dimensions: 4" thick by 3-1/5" high by 8" long. Concrete block: 4" thick by 8" high by 16" long. | sf | $3.46 | $14.07 | $17.53 |
| | **10" wide cavity wall from 4" jumbo closure brick and 4" concrete block**<br>*Replace* Materials.........5.85    Labor ...........7.45<br>*Remove* .....................    Labor ...........3.46<br>▶ Modular bricks. Nominal dimensions: 4" thick by 4" high by 8" long. Concrete block: 4" thick by 8" high by 16" long. | sf | $3.46 | $13.30 | $16.76 |
| | **10" wide cavity wall from 4" double brick and 4" concrete block**<br>*Replace* Materials.........5.21    Labor ...........6.76<br>*Remove* .....................    Labor ...........3.46<br>▶ Modular bricks. Nominal dimensions: 4" thick by 5-1/3" high by 8" long. Concrete block: 4" thick by 8" high by 16" long. | sf | $3.46 | $11.97 | $15.43 |
| | **10" wide cavity wall from 4" Roman brick and 4" concrete block**<br>*Replace* Materials.........7.06    Labor ...........8.89<br>*Remove* .....................    Labor ...........3.46<br>▶ Modular bricks. Nominal dimensions: 4" thick by 2" high by 12" long. Concrete block: 4" thick by 8" high by 16" long. | sf | $3.46 | $15.95 | $19.41 |
| | **10" wide cavity wall from 4" Norman and 4" concrete block**<br>*Replace* Materials.........6.19    Labor ...........7.83<br>*Remove* .....................    Labor ...........3.46<br>▶ Modular bricks. Nominal dimensions: 4" thick by 2-2/3" high by 12" long. Concrete block: 4" thick by 8" high by 16" long. | sf | $3.46 | $14.02 | $17.48 |
| | **10" wide cavity wall from 4" Norwegian brick and 4" concrete block**<br>*Replace* Materials.........5.29    Labor ...........7.14<br>*Remove* .....................    Labor ...........3.46<br>▶ Modular bricks. Nominal dimensions: 4" thick by 3-1/5" high by 12" long. Concrete block: 4" thick by 8" high by 16" long. | sf | $3.46 | $12.43 | $15.89 |
| | **10" wide cavity wall from 4" jumbo utility brick and 4" concrete block**<br>*Replace* Materials.........6.10    Labor ...........6.84<br>*Remove* .....................    Labor ...........3.46<br>▶ Modular bricks. Nominal dimensions: 4" thick by 4" high by 12" long. Concrete block: 4" thick by 8" high by 16" long. | sf | $3.46 | $12.94 | $16.40 |
| | **10" wide cavity wall from 4" triple brick and 4" concrete block**<br>*Replace* Materials.........5.41    Labor ...........6.61<br>*Remove* .....................    Labor ...........3.46<br>▶ Modular bricks. Nominal dimensions: 4" thick by 5-1/3" high by 12" long. Concrete block: 4" thick by 8" high by 16" long. | sf | $3.46 | $12.02 | $15.48 |
| **10" WIDE BRICK ▶ CAVITY WALL** *continued on next page* | **10" wide cavity wall from 4" standard non-modular brick, both sides**<br>*Replace* Materials......10.11    Labor ..........12.20<br>*Remove* .....................    Labor ...........3.46<br>▶ Non-modular bricks. Actual dimensions: 3-3/4" thick by 2-1/4" high by 8" long. | sf | $3.46 | $22.31 | $25.77 |

| Item Description | Unit | Remove | Replace | Total |
|---|---|---|---|---|
| **10" wide cavity wall from 4" oversize non-modular brick, both sides** | sf | $3.46 | $20.59 | $24.05 |
| *Replace* Materials........8.59    Labor...........12.00 | | | | |
| *Remove* ......................    Labor ...........3.46 | | | | |
| ► Non-modular bricks. Actual dimensions: 3-3/4" thick by 2-3/4" high by 8" long. | | | | |
| **10" wide cavity wall from three-inch non-modular brick, both sides** | sf | $3.46 | $20.39 | $23.85 |
| *Replace* Materials........8.49    Labor ...........11.90 | | | | |
| *Remove* ......................    Labor ...........3.46 | | | | |
| ► Non-modular bricks. Actual dimensions: 3" thick by 2-3/4" high by 9-3/4" long. Three-inch bricks also come in lengths of 9-5/8" and 8-3/4" and widths vary from 2-5/8" to 3". | | | | |
| **10" wide cavity wall from 4" standard brick, both sides** | sf | $3.46 | $19.47 | $22.93 |
| *Replace* Materials........7.37    Labor ...........12.10 | | | | |
| *Remove* ......................    Labor ...........3.46 | | | | |
| ► Modular bricks. Nominal dimensions: 4" thick by 2-2/3" high by 8" long. | | | | |
| **10" wide cavity wall from 4" engineer brick, both sides** | sf | $3.46 | $17.73 | $21.19 |
| *Replace* Materials........7.63    Labor...........10.10 | | | | |
| *Remove* ......................    Labor ...........3.46 | | | | |
| ► Modular bricks. Nominal dimensions: 4" thick by 3-1/5" high by 8" long. | | | | |
| **10" wide cavity wall from 4" jumbo closure brick, both sides** | sf | $3.46 | $16.20 | $19.66 |
| *Replace* Materials........7.61    Labor ...........8.59 | | | | |
| *Remove* ......................    Labor ...........3.46 | | | | |
| ► Also called Economy 8. Modular bricks. Nominal dimensions: 4" thick by 4" high by 8" long. | | | | |
| **10" wide cavity wall from 4" double brick, both sides** | sf | $3.46 | $13.51 | $16.97 |
| *Replace* Materials........6.33    Labor ...........7.18 | | | | |
| *Remove* ......................    Labor ...........3.46 | | | | |
| ► Modular bricks. Nominal dimensions: 4" thick by 5-1/3" high by 8" long. | | | | |
| **10" wide cavity wall from 4" Roman brick, both sides** | sf | $3.46 | $21.43 | $24.89 |
| *Replace* Materials......10.03    Labor ...........11.40 | | | | |
| *Remove* ......................    Labor ...........3.46 | | | | |
| ► Modular bricks. Nominal dimensions: 4" thick by 2" high by 12" long. | | | | |
| **10" wide cavity wall from 4" Norman brick, both sides** | sf | $3.46 | $17.60 | $21.06 |
| *Replace* Materials........8.29    Labor ...........9.31 | | | | |
| *Remove* ......................    Labor ...........3.46 | | | | |
| ► Modular bricks. Nominal dimensions: 4" thick by 2-2/3" high by 12" long. | | | | |
| **10" wide cavity wall from 4" Norwegian both sides** | sf | $3.46 | $14.43 | $17.89 |
| *Replace* Materials........6.49    Labor ...........7.94 | | | | |
| *Remove* ......................    Labor ...........3.46 | | | | |
| ► Modular bricks. Nominal dimensions: 4" thick by 3-1/5" high by 12" long. | | | | |
| **10" wide cavity wall from 4" jumbo utility brick, both sides** | sf | $3.46 | $15.44 | $18.90 |
| *Replace* Materials........8.11    Labor ...........7.33 | | | | |
| *Remove* ......................    Labor ...........3.46 | | | | |
| ► Also called Economy 12. Modular bricks. Nominal dimensions: 4" thick by 4" high by 12" long. | | | | |
| **10" wide cavity wall from 4" triple brick, both sides** | sf | $3.46 | $13.61 | $17.07 |
| *Replace* Materials........6.73    Labor ...........6.88 | | | | |
| *Remove* ......................    Labor ...........3.46 | | | | |
| ► Modular bricks. Nominal dimensions: 4" thick by 5-1/3" high by 12" long. | | | | |
| **Add for 2" polystyrene insulation in cavity wall** | sf | — | $.78 | $.78 |
| *Replace* Materials ........ .73    Labor ............ .05 | | | | |

◄ **10" WIDE BRICK CAVITY WALL** *continued*

With 2" dead air space. (See below for foam insulation in air space.) and 3/8" wide mortar joints. Includes 4% waste for brick and 25% waste for mortar.

---

**RELATED ITEMS**

---

◄ **ADD FOR CAVITY WALL INSULATION**

| Item Description | Unit | Remove | Replace | Total |
|---|---|---|---|---|

**BRICK VENEER** ▶
*With 3/8" wide mortar joints and galvanized wall ties. Includes 4% waste for brick and block and 25% waste for mortar.*

*common bond △*

*Flemish bond △*

*English bond △*

*English cross bond △*

*stack bond △*

*header bond △*

*soldier course △*

### Standard non-modular brick veneer
*Replace* Materials....4.85    Labor .........5.47
*Remove* ....................    Labor .........2.15
▶ Non-modular bricks. Actual dimensions: 3-3/4" thick by 2-1/4" high by 8" long.

| | sf | $2.15 | $10.32 | $12.47 |

### Oversize non-modular brick veneer
*Replace* Materials......4.09    Labor .........5.43
*Remove* ....................    Labor .........2.15
▶ Non-modular bricks. Actual dimensions: 3-3/4" thick by 2-3/4" high by 8" long.

| | sf | $2.15 | $9.52 | $11.67 |

### Three-inch non-modular brick veneer
*Replace* Materials......4.04    Labor .........5.36
*Remove* ....................    Labor .........2.15
▶ Non-modular bricks. Actual dimensions: 3" thick by 2-3/4" high by 9-3/4" long. Three-inch bricks also come in lengths of 9-5/8" and 8-3/4" and widths vary from 2-5/8" to 3". Normally used as a veneer unit.

| | sf | $2.15 | $9.40 | $11.55 |

### Used brick veneer
*Replace* Materials......7.09    Labor .........5.47
*Remove* ....................    Labor .........2.15
▶ Modular bricks. Nominal dimensions: 4" thick by 2-2/3" high by 8" long.

| | sf | $2.15 | $12.56 | $14.71 |

### Standard brick veneer
*Replace* Materials......3.48    Labor .........5.47
*Remove* ....................    Labor .........2.15
▶ Modular bricks. Nominal dimensions: 4" thick by 2-2/3" high by 8" long.

| | sf | $2.15 | $8.95 | $11.10 |

### Engineer brick veneer
*Replace* Materials......3.61    Labor .........4.52
*Remove* ....................    Labor .........2.15
▶ Modular bricks. Nominal dimensions: 4" thick by 3-1/5" high by 8" long.

| | sf | $2.15 | $8.13 | $10.28 |

### Jumbo closure brick veneer
*Replace* Materials......3.60    Labor .........3.88
*Remove* ....................    Labor .........2.15
▶ Also called Economy 8. Modular bricks. Nominal dimensions: 4" thick by 4" high by 8" long.

| | sf | $2.15 | $7.48 | $9.63 |

### Double brick veneer
*Replace* Materials......2.96    Labor .........3.23
*Remove* ....................    Labor .........2.15
▶ Modular bricks. Nominal dimensions: 4" thick by 5-1/3" high by 8" long.

| | sf | $2.15 | $6.19 | $8.34 |

### Roman brick veneer
*Replace* Materials......4.81    Labor .........5.17
*Remove* ....................    Labor .........2.15
▶ Modular bricks. Nominal dimensions: 4" thick by 2" high by 12" long.

| | sf | $2.15 | $9.98 | $12.13 |

### Norman brick veneer
*Replace* Materials......3.94    Labor .........4.18
*Remove* ....................    Labor .........2.15
▶ Modular bricks. Nominal dimensions: 4" thick by 2-2/3" high by 12" long.

| | sf | $2.15 | $8.12 | $10.27 |

### Norwegian brick veneer
*Replace* Materials......3.04    Labor .........3.57
*Remove* ....................    Labor .........2.15
▶ Modular bricks. Nominal dimensions: 4" thick by 3-1/5" high by 12" long.

| | sf | $2.15 | $6.61 | $8.76 |

### Jumbo utility brick veneer
*Replace* Materials......3.85    Labor .........3.31
*Remove* ....................    Labor .........2.15
▶ Also called Economy 12. Modular bricks. Nominal dimensions: 4" thick by 4" high by 12" long.

| | sf | $2.15 | $7.16 | $9.31 |

| Item Description | Unit | Remove | Replace | Total |
|---|---|---|---|---|
| **Triple brick veneer** | sf | $2.15 | $6.28 | $8.43 |

*Replace* Materials........3.16          Labor ...........3.12
*Remove* .....................          Labor ...........2.15
► Modular bricks. Nominal dimensions: 4" thick by 5-1/3" high by 12" long.

| **Add for raked joints** | sf | — | $.22 | $.22 | ◄ **RAKED JOINTS** |
|---|---|---|---|---|---|

*Replace* .....................          Labor ............. .22
► Add for brick walls with raked joints instead of concave.

◄ **ADD FOR OTHER BRICK BONDS**

**Add 16% for common bond**
► Also called American bond. Every sixth course is a full course of full-length headers.

**Add 54% for Flemish bond**
► Each course is made of alternating stretchers and headers.

*sailor course △*

**Add 65% for English bond**
► Alternating full courses made from stretchers and headers. The joints between stretchers in all courses align vertically.

**Add 65% for English cross bond**
► Also called Dutch bond. A variation of English bond. The vertical joints between stretcher bricks, in alternate courses, align vertically with the center of the stretcher brick in the course above and below.

*basketweave △*

**Add 8% for stack bond**
► All vertical and horizontal joints align.

**Add 116% for false all header bond**
► All bricks are laid as headers but bricks are cut in half.

**Add 115% for all header bond**
► All bricks are laid as true headers.

*diagonal △*

**Add 15% for soldier course**
► All bricks are stood on end with edge showing.

**Add 5% for sailor course**
► All bricks are stood on end with face showing.

**Add 122% for basketweave**
► A wide variety of patterns with alternating sections of horizontal and vertical brick.

**Add 125% for herringbone weave**
► Also called diagonal basketweave. Bricks are laid at an angle (usually 45 degree) in alternate sections angling up and down.

*herringbone △*

**Add 90% for diagonal bond**
► All bricks laid at an angle, usually 45 degree.

**Add 70% for coursed ashlar style brick bond with two sizes of bricks**
► A pattern that uses two sizes of bricks to simulate coursed ashlar stone patterns. Usually one size of brick equals two of the second size.

*coursed ashlar style △*

**Add 27% for curved brick walls**

◄ **ADD FOR CURVED INSTALLATION**

| **Add for opening in 4" brick wall per lf of opening** | lf | — | $13.98 | $13.98 | ◄ **ADD FOR OPENING IN MASONRY WALL** |
|---|---|---|---|---|---|

*Replace* Materials........4.10          Labor ............9.88
► Includes angle iron lintel.

*Use only if sf of opening has been deducted from sf price. Includes angle iron lintel.*

| **Add for opening in 6" brick wall per lf of opening** | lf | — | $17.13 | $17.13 |
|---|---|---|---|---|

*Replace* Materials........7.14          Labor ............9.99
► Includes angle iron lintel.

| Item Description | Unit | Remove | Replace | Total |
|---|---|---|---|---|
| **ADD FOR OPENING ▶ IN MASONRY WALL** *continued* | | | | |
| **Add for opening in 8″ brick wall per lf of opening**<br>*Replace* Materials........7.14　　Labor...........10.10<br>▶ Includes angle iron lintel. | lf | — | $17.24 | $17.24 |
| **Add for opening in 10″ brick wall per lf of opening**<br>*Replace* Materials........8.20　　Labor...........10.20<br>▶ Includes angle iron lintel. | lf | — | $18.40 | $18.40 |
| **Add for opening in 12″ brick wall per lf of opening**<br>*Replace* Materials........8.20　　Labor...........10.30<br>▶ Includes angle iron lintel. | lf | — | $18.50 | $18.50 |
| **ADD FOR ▶ BRICK ARCH**  *flat △* **Add for flat brick arch**<br>*Replace* Materials ......12.90　　Labor ..........56.60<br>▶ Also called a Jack arch. Do not use for standard brick wall openings that use a lintel. | lf | — | $69.50 | $69.50 |
| **Add for elliptical brick arch**<br>*Replace* Materials.......15.20　　Labor...........70.30<br>▶ Per lf of arch. | lf | — | $85.50 | $85.50 |
|  *elliptical △* **Add for semi-circular brick arch**<br>*Replace* Materials.......15.20　　Labor...........74.50<br>▶ Per lf of arch. | lf | — | $89.70 | $89.70 |
| **Add to brace existing brick arch from below for repairs**<br>*Replace* Materials.......11.70　　Labor...........21.10<br>▶ 2″ x 6″ or 2″ x 8″ framing members sheathed with plywood that follows curved shape of arch. | lf | — | $32.80 | $32.80 |
|  *semi-circular △* **Minimum charge for arch work**<br>*Replace* Materials ......78.00　　Labor .......380.00 | ea | — | $458.00 | $458.00 |
| **CONCRETE BLOCK ▶ WALL**  **4″ wide concrete block wall**<br>*Replace* Materials........1.86　　Labor ...........3.38<br>*Remove* .....................　　Labor ...........2.28 | sf | $2.28 | $5.24 | $7.52 |
| **6″ wide concrete block wall**<br>*Replace* Materials........2.17　　Labor ...........3.50<br>*Remove* .....................　　Labor ...........2.72 | sf | $2.72 | $5.67 | $8.39 |
| **8″ wide concrete block wall**<br>*Replace* Materials........2.72　　Labor ...........3.69<br>*Remove* .....................　　Labor ...........3.46 | sf | $3.46 | $6.41 | $9.87 |
| **10″ wide concrete block wall**<br>*Replace* Materials........3.35　　Labor ...........3.91<br>*Remove* .....................　　Labor ...........3.90 | sf | $3.90 | $7.26 | $11.16 |
| **12″ wide concrete block wall**<br>*Replace* Materials........4.29　　Labor ...........4.64<br>*Remove* .....................　　Labor ...........4.64 | sf | $4.64 | $8.93 | $13.57 |
| **4″ wide lightweight concrete block wall**<br>*Replace* Materials........1.99　　Labor ...........3.15<br>*Remove* .....................　　Labor ...........2.28 | sf | $2.28 | $5.14 | $7.42 |
| **6″ wide lightweight concrete block wall**<br>*Replace* Materials........2.31　　Labor ...........3.27<br>*Remove* .....................　　Labor ...........2.72 | sf | $2.72 | $5.58 | $8.30 |

**CONCRETE BLOCK WALLS**

Unless otherwise noted all concrete block walls are 8″ x 16″ face block with 3/8″ wide mortar joints.

Cells are grouted 36″ on center and at each corner and include one length of #4 rebar in field cells and 2 lengths in corner cells for an average of 1.4 lengths of rebar per grouted cell.

A horizontal bond beam is also calculated for every 8′ of wall height which includes two lengths of #4 rebar.

continued on next page

| Item Description | Unit | Remove | Replace | Total | |
|---|---|---|---|---|---|
| **8" wide lightweight concrete block wall**<br>*Replace* Materials........2.90  Labor ...........3.46<br>*Remove* ......................  Labor ...........3.46 | sf | $3.46 | $6.36 | $9.82 | **CONCRETE BLOCK WALLS**<br>*continued from prior page*<br> Horizontal wire reinforcing appears in every other course. |
| **10" wide lightweight concrete block wall**<br>*Replace* Materials........3.55  Labor ...........3.69<br>*Remove* ......................  Labor ...........3.90 | sf | $3.90 | $7.24 | $11.14 |  Also includes 4% waste for block and 25% waste for mortar. |
| **12" wide lightweight concrete block wall**<br>*Replace* Materials........4.59  Labor ...........4.33<br>*Remove* ......................  Labor ...........4.64 | sf | $4.64 | $8.92 | $13.56 |  See page 302 for block walls with other types of reinforcing. |
| **4" wide slump block wall**<br>*Replace* Materials........3.10  Labor ...........3.38<br>*Remove* ......................  Labor ...........2.28 | sf | $2.28 | $6.48 | $8.76 | ◄ **SLUMP BLOCK WALL**<br>*4" x 16" face block.* |
| **6" wide slump block wall**<br>*Replace* Materials........3.80  Labor ...........3.50<br>*Remove* ......................  Labor ...........2.72 | sf | $2.72 | $7.30 | $10.02 | |
| **8" wide slump block wall**<br>*Replace* Materials........4.72  Labor ...........3.69<br>*Remove* ......................  Labor ...........3.46 | sf | $3.46 | $8.41 | $11.87 | |
| **10" wide slump block wall**<br>*Replace* Materials........5.62  Labor ...........3.91<br>*Remove* ......................  Labor ...........3.90 | sf | $3.90 | $9.53 | $13.43 | |
| **12" wide slump block wall**<br>*Replace* Materials........7.12  Labor ...........4.64<br>*Remove* ......................  Labor ...........4.64 | sf | $4.64 | $11.76 | $16.40 | |
| **4" wide fluted block wall (fluted one side)**<br>*Replace* Materials........2.66  Labor ...........3.38<br>*Remove* ......................  Labor ...........2.28 | sf | $2.28 | $6.04 | $8.32 | ◄ **FLUTED BLOCK WALL (ONE SIDE)** |
| **6" wide fluted block wall (fluted one side)**<br>*Replace* Materials........3.06  Labor ...........3.50<br>*Remove* ......................  Labor ...........2.72 | sf | $2.72 | $6.56 | $9.28 | |
| **8" wide fluted block wall (fluted one side)**<br>*Replace* Materials........3.84  Labor ...........3.69<br>*Remove* ......................  Labor ...........3.46 | sf | $3.46 | $7.53 | $10.99 | |
| **10" wide fluted block wall (fluted one side)**<br>*Replace* Materials........4.76  Labor ...........3.91<br>*Remove* ......................  Labor ...........3.90 | sf | $3.90 | $8.67 | $12.57 | |
| **12" wide fluted block wall (fluted one side)**<br>*Replace* Materials........6.19  Labor ...........4.64<br>*Remove* ......................  Labor ...........4.64 | sf | $4.64 | $10.83 | $15.47 | |
| **4" wide fluted block wall (fluted two sides)**<br>*Replace* Materials........3.02  Labor ...........3.38<br>*Remove* ......................  Labor ...........2.28 | sf | $2.28 | $6.40 | $8.68 | ◄ **FLUTED BLOCK WALL (TWO SIDES)** |
| **6" wide fluted block wall (fluted two sides)**<br>*Replace* Materials........3.48  Labor ...........3.50<br>*Remove* ......................  Labor ...........2.72 | sf | $2.72 | $6.98 | $9.70 | |

**RELATED ITEMS**

| Item Description | Unit | Remove | Replace | Total |
|---|---|---|---|---|
| **8" wide fluted block wall (fluted two sides)**<br>*Replace* Materials........4.36    Labor ............3.69<br>*Remove* .......................    Labor ............3.46 | sf | $3.46 | $8.05 | $11.51 |
| **10" wide fluted block wall (fluted two sides)**<br>*Replace* Materials........5.40    Labor ............3.91<br>*Remove* .......................    Labor ............3.90 | sf | $3.90 | $9.31 | $13.21 |
| **12" wide fluted block wall (fluted two sides)**<br>*Replace* Materials........7.06    Labor ............4.64<br>*Remove* .......................    Labor ............4.64 | sf | $4.64 | $11.70 | $16.34 |
| **4" wide glazed block wall (glazed one side)**<br>*Replace* Materials ......10.50    Labor ............3.38<br>*Remove* .......................    Labor ............2.28 | sf | $2.28 | $13.88 | $16.16 |
| **6" wide glazed block wall (glazed one side)**<br>*Replace* Materials ......10.90    Labor ............3.50<br>*Remove* .......................    Labor ............2.72 | sf | $2.72 | $14.40 | $17.12 |
| **8" wide glazed block wall (glazed one side)**<br>*Replace* Materials.......11.50    Labor ............3.69<br>*Remove* .......................    Labor ............3.46 | sf | $3.46 | $15.19 | $18.65 |
| **10" wide glazed block wall (glazed one side)**<br>*Replace* Materials ......12.10    Labor ............3.91<br>*Remove* .......................    Labor ............3.90 | sf | $3.90 | $16.01 | $19.91 |
| **12" wide glazed block wall (glazed one side)**<br>*Replace* Materials ......12.70    Labor ............4.64<br>*Remove* .......................    Labor ............4.64 | sf | $4.64 | $17.34 | $21.98 |
| **4" wide glazed block wall (glazed two sides)**<br>*Replace* Materials.......15.20    Labor ............3.38<br>*Remove* .......................    Labor ............2.28 | sf | $2.28 | $18.58 | $20.86 |
| **6" wide glazed block wall (glazed two sides)**<br>*Replace* Materials ......16.40    Labor ............3.50<br>*Remove* .......................    Labor ............2.72 | sf | $2.72 | $19.90 | $22.62 |
| **8" wide glazed block wall (glazed two sides)**<br>*Replace* Materials.......17.20    Labor ............3.69<br>*Remove* .......................    Labor ............3.46 | sf | $3.46 | $20.89 | $24.35 |
| **10" wide glazed block wall (glazed two sides)**<br>*Replace* Materials.......17.80    Labor ............3.91<br>*Remove* .......................    Labor ............3.90 | sf | $3.90 | $21.71 | $25.61 |
| **12" wide glazed block wall (glazed two sides)**<br>*Replace* Materials ......18.30    Labor ............4.64<br>*Remove* .......................    Labor ............4.64 | sf | $4.64 | $22.94 | $27.58 |
| **4" wide split-face block wall**<br>*Replace* Materials........2.86    Labor ............3.38<br>*Remove* .......................    Labor ............2.28 | sf | $2.28 | $6.24 | $8.52 |
| **6" wide split-face block wall**<br>*Replace* Materials........3.43    Labor ............3.50<br>*Remove* .......................    Labor ............2.72 | sf | $2.72 | $6.93 | $9.65 |

**FLUTED BLOCK ▶ WALL (TWO SIDES)**
*continued*

**GLAZED BLOCK ▶ WALL (ONE SIDE)**
*See "Concrete Block Walls" on page 298.*

**GLAZED BLOCK ▶ WALL (TWO SIDES)**
*See "Concrete Block Walls" on page 298.*

**SPLIT-FACE ▶ BLOCK WALL**
*See "Concrete Block Walls" on page 298.*

| Item Description | Unit | Remove | Replace | Total |
|---|---|---|---|---|
| **8" wide split-face block wall**<br>*Replace* Materials........4.52     Labor ...........3.69<br>*Remove* ......................     Labor ...........3.46 | sf | $3.46 | $8.21 | $11.67 |
| **10" wide split-face block wall**<br>*Replace* Materials........5.06     Labor ...........3.91<br>*Remove* ......................     Labor ...........3.90 | sf | $3.90 | $8.97 | $12.87 |
| **12" wide split-face block wall**<br>*Replace* Materials........6.56     Labor ...........4.64<br>*Remove* ......................     Labor ...........4.64 | sf | $4.64 | $11.20 | $15.84 |
| **4" wide split-rib block wall**<br>*Replace* Materials........2.72     Labor ...........3.38<br>*Remove* ......................     Labor ...........2.28 | sf | $2.28 | $6.10 | $8.38 |
| **6" wide split-rib block wall**<br>*Replace* Materials........2.98     Labor ...........3.50<br>*Remove* ......................     Labor ...........2.72 | sf | $2.72 | $6.48 | $9.20 |
| **8" wide split-rib block wall**<br>*Replace* Materials........4.47     Labor ...........3.69<br>*Remove* ......................     Labor ...........3.46 | sf | $3.46 | $8.16 | $11.62 |
| **10" wide split-rib block wall**<br>*Replace* Materials........5.11     Labor ...........3.91<br>*Remove* ......................     Labor ...........3.90 | sf | $3.90 | $9.02 | $12.92 |
| **12" wide split-rib block wall**<br>*Replace* Materials........5.78     Labor ...........4.64<br>*Remove* ......................     Labor ...........4.64 | sf | $4.64 | $10.42 | $15.06 |
| **4" wide screen block, pattern two sides**<br>*Replace* Materials........5.30     Labor ...........3.38<br>*Remove* ......................     Labor ...........2.28 | sf | $2.28 | $8.68 | $10.96 |
| **4" wide screen block, pattern four sides**<br>*Replace* Materials........9.76     Labor ...........3.38<br>*Remove* ......................     Labor ...........2.28 | sf | $2.28 | $13.14 | $15.42 |
| **Add 11% for light ochre colored concrete block**<br>▶ Light tans, browns, yellows, light reddish brown, and so forth. | | | | |
| **Add 17% darker ochre colored concrete block**<br>▶ Light red, blues, specialty grays, darker yellows, mid-tone browns. | | | | |
| **Add 28% for dark or bright colored concrete block**<br>▶ Black, dark blue, terra-cotta red, bright yellow, bright orange, bright red, purple, and so forth. | | | | |
| **Add 15% for interlocking concrete block**<br>▶ Add to the cost of *materials* only. | | | | |
| **Add for polystyrene inserts, 6" block**<br>*Replace* Materials ........ .83 | sf | — | $.83 | $.83 |
| **Add for polystyrene inserts, 8" block**<br>*Replace* Materials ........ .90 | sf | — | $.90 | $.90 |
| **Add for polystyrene inserts, 10" block**<br>*Replace* Materials.......1.00 | sf | — | $1.00 | $1.00 |

**RELATED ITEMS**

◀ **SPLIT-RIB BLOCK WALL**
*See "Concrete Block Walls" on page 298.*

◀ **SCREEN BLOCK**
*12" x 12" face. See "Concrete Block Walls" on page 298.*

◀ **ADD FOR COLORED BLOCK**

◀ **ADD FOR INTERLOCKING BLOCK**

◀ **POLYSTYRENE BLOCK INSERTS**
*Additional cost for block with polystyrene inserts already installed.*

| | Item Description | Unit | Remove | Replace | Total |
|---|---|---|---|---|---|
| **POLYSTYRENE ▶ BLOCK INSERTS** *continued* | **Add for polystyrene inserts, 12" block**<br>*Replace* Materials........1.08 | sf | — | $1.08 | $1.08 |
| **LOOSE BLOCK ▶ INSULATION** *Includes 3% waste.* | **Add for silicone treated perlite or vermiculite loose fill, 6" block**<br>*Replace* Materials ........ .331       Labor............ .15 | sf | — | $.48 | $.48 |
| | **Add for silicone treated perlite or vermiculite loose fill, 8" block**<br>*Replace* Materials ........ .47       Labor............ .17 | sf | — | $.64 | $.64 |
| *block pilaster* ▽ | **Add for silicone treated perlite or vermiculite loose fill, 10" block**<br>*Replace* Materials ........ .60       Labor............ .18 | sf | — | $.78 | $.78 |
| | **Add for silicone treated perlite or vermiculite loose fill, 12" block**<br>*Replace* Materials ........ .86       Labor............ .17 | sf | — | $1.03 | $1.03 |
| **BLOCK PILASTER ▶** *Includes 4% waste.* | **Add for pilaster in block wall (per vertical lf of pilaster)**<br>*Replace* Materials ......12.00       Labor............11.20<br>▶ 16" x 16" pilaster, single piece. For double piece 16" x 20" pilaster add 15%. | lf | — | $23.20 | $23.20 |
| **BLOCK WALL ▶ ADDITIONS & DEDUCTIONS** *Add or deduct from the square foot price of block walls.* | **Deduct for block walls used as backing**<br>*Replace* ........................       Labor.......... −.21<br>▶ For walls finished on one side only. | sf | — | − $.21 | − $.21 |
| | **Deduct for wall with no horizontal wire reinforcement**<br>*Replace* Materials....... −.16       Labor.......... −.04<br>▶ Deduct when ladder or truss style wire reinforcement is not laid between every other course of block. | sf | — | − $.20 | − $.20 |
| | **Deduct for block walls with no vertical reinforcement**<br>*Replace* Materials....... −.55       Labor.......... −.23<br>▶ Deduct when block walls contain no grouted cells. | sf | — | − $.78 | − $.78 |
| | **Deduct for block walls with vertical reinforcement every 48"**<br>*Replace* Materials....... −.16       Labor.......... −.18<br>▶ Deduct when block walls contain grouted cells with rebar every 48" instead of 36". | sf | — | − $.34 | − $.34 |
| | **Add for block walls with vertical reinforcement every 24"**<br>*Replace* Materials ........ .20       Labor............ .20<br>▶ Add when block walls contain grouted cells with rebar every 24" instead of 36". | sf | — | $.40 | $.40 |
| | **Deduct for block walls with no horizontal bond beam reinforcement**<br>*Replace* Materials....... −.37       Labor.......... −.14<br>▶ Deduct when block walls do not contain a bond beam per every 8' of height. | sf | — | − $.51 | − $.51 |
| | **Add for block walls with horizontal bond beam reinforcement 4'**<br>*Replace* Materials ........ .29       Labor............ .22<br>▶ Add when block walls contain horizontal bond beams with rebar for every 4' of wall height instead of every 8'. | sf | — | $.51 | $.51 |
| *high-strength block* ▷ | **Add 19% for high strength concrete block, 3,000 psi**<br>▶ Add to the cost of *materials* only. | | | | |
| | **Add 21% for high strength concrete block, 5,000 psi**<br>▶ Add to the cost of *materials* only. | | | | |
| **BOND BEAM ▶** *Includes two lengths of #4 rebar.* | **6" wide bond beam**<br>*Replace* Materials........1.24       Labor............ .99 | lf | — | $2.23 | $2.23 |
| | **8" wide bond beam**<br>*Replace* Materials........1.44       Labor............1.09 | lf | — | $2.53 | $2.53 |

| Item Description | Unit | Remove | Replace | Total |
|---|---|---|---|---|
| **10" wide bond beam** | lf | — | $2.90 | $2.90 |
| *Replace* Materials........1.71    Labor ...........1.19 | | | | |
| **12" wide bond beam** | lf | — | $3.26 | $3.26 |
| *Replace* Materials........1.97    Labor ...........1.29 | | | | |
| **Parge block foundation wall** | sf | — | $1.05 | $1.05 |
| *Replace* Materials........ .31    Labor............. .74 <br> ► Up to 1/2" thick. | | | | |
| **Add for grade beam cap on 6" wide concrete block wall** | lf | $9.51 | $11.19 | $20.70 |
| *Replace* Materials........7.16    Labor ...........4.03 <br> *Remove* ......................    Labor ...........9.51 | | | | |
| **Add for grade beam cap on 8" wide concrete block wall** | lf | $9.51 | $13.38 | $22.89 |
| *Replace* Materials........9.20    Labor ...........4.18 <br> *Remove* ......................    Labor ...........9.51 | | | | |
| **Add for grade beam cap on 10" wide concrete block wall** | lf | $9.51 | $15.67 | $25.18 |
| *Replace* Materials.......11.30    Labor ...........4.37 <br> *Remove* ......................    Labor ...........9.51 | | | | |
| **Add for grade beam cap on 12" wide concrete block wall** | lf | $9.51 | $17.86 | $27.37 |
| *Replace* Materials.......13.30    Labor ...........4.56 <br> *Remove* ......................    Labor ...........9.51 | | | | |
| **Deduct 8% for concrete block or brick wall installed as fence** <br> ► Includes wall cap (2" block or masonry rowlock) and horizontal wire reinforcing. <br> Does not include footing, bond beam, coping, or cell grouting. | | | | |
| **4" thick clay backing tile** | sf | $2.28 | $8.65 | $10.93 |
| *Replace* Materials........4.39    Labor ...........4.26 <br> *Remove* ......................    Labor ...........2.28 | | | | |
| **6" thick clay backing tile** | sf | $2.72 | $9.23 | $11.95 |
| *Replace* Materials........4.40    Labor ...........4.83 <br> *Remove* ......................    Labor ...........2.72 | | | | |
| **8" thick clay backing tile** | sf | $3.46 | $9.91 | $13.37 |
| *Replace* Materials........4.40    Labor ...........5.51 <br> *Remove* ......................    Labor ...........3.46 | | | | |
| **4" thick structural tile glazed one side** | sf | $2.28 | $13.66 | $15.94 |
| *Replace* Materials........5.91    Labor ...........7.75 <br> *Remove* ......................    Labor ...........2.28 | | | | |
| **4" thick structural tile glazed two sides** | sf | $2.28 | $17.13 | $19.41 |
| *Replace* Materials........9.02    Labor ...........8.11 <br> *Remove* ......................    Labor ...........2.28 | | | | |
| **6" thick structural tile glazed one side** | sf | $2.72 | $17.12 | $19.84 |
| *Replace* Materials........7.85    Labor ...........9.27 <br> *Remove* ......................    Labor ...........2.72 | | | | |
| **6" thick structural tile glazed two sides** | sf | $2.72 | $21.63 | $24.35 |
| *Replace* Materials......12.00    Labor ...........9.63 <br> *Remove* ......................    Labor ...........2.72 | | | | |
| **8" thick structural tile glazed one side** | sf | $3.46 | $20.49 | $23.95 |
| *Replace* Materials......10.50    Labor ...........9.99 <br> *Remove* ......................    Labor ...........3.46 | | | | |

### RELATED ITEMS

Cleaning ......................63
Fences .......................187
Fireplaces...................241
Painting ....................340
Retaining Walls...........391

◄ **PARGETING**
*Up to 1/2" thick.*

◄ **GRADE BEAM FOR BLOCK WALL**
*In some states, concrete block walls are capped with a grade beam. This not only adds strength but also levels the wall top. Because the mason does not take care to maintain a level wall, deduct **25%** from the labor cost for block walls capped with a grade beam. Up to 16" tall with four lengths of #4 rebar. Rebar from grouted cells is also bent into the grade beam.*

◄ **MASONRY FENCE**

◄ **CLAY BACKING TILE WALL**
*12" x 12" face tile with 3/8" wide mortar joints. Includes 4% waste for tile and 25% waste for mortar.*

◄ **STRUCTURAL TILE WALL**
*8" x 16" face tile with 3/8" wide mortar joints. Includes 4% waste for tile and 25% waste for mortar.*

| Item Description | Unit | Remove | Replace | Total |
|---|---|---|---|---|
| **GYPSUM ▶ PARTITION TILE** *12" x 30" face tile with 3/8" wide mortar joints. Includes 4% waste for tile and 25% waste for mortar. (See illustration below.)* | | | | |
| **4" thick gypsum partition tile** *Replace* Materials........1.66    Labor ............2.17  *Remove* .......................    Labor ............2.28 | sf | $2.28 | $3.83 | $6.11 |
| **6" thick gypsum partition tile** *Replace* Materials........2.39    Labor ............3.15  *Remove* .......................    Labor ............3.46 | sf | $3.46 | $5.54 | $9.00 |
| **GLASS BLOCK ▶ WALL** *White mortar with 3/8" wide joints and ladder type wire reinforcing every other course. Includes 4% waste for glass blocks and 25% waste for mortar.* | | | | |
| **4" x 8" thinline smooth-face glass blocks** *Replace* Materials.......19.80    Labor ............12.70  *Remove* .......................    Labor ............2.20 | sf | $2.20 | $32.50 | $34.70 |
| **6" x 6" thinline smooth-face glass blocks** *Replace* Materials ......18.10    Labor ............11.80  *Remove* .......................    Labor ............2.20 | sf | $2.20 | $29.90 | $32.10 |
| **6" x 8" thinline smooth-face glass blocks** *Replace* Materials.......13.70    Labor ............10.10  *Remove* .......................    Labor ............2.20 | sf | $2.20 | $23.80 | $26.00 |
| **4" x 8" smooth-face glass blocks** *Replace* Materials ......24.80    Labor ............12.70  *Remove* .......................    Labor ............2.20 | sf | $2.20 | $37.50 | $39.70 |
| **6" x 6" smooth-face glass blocks** *Replace* Materials ......22.00    Labor ............11.80  *Remove* .......................    Labor ............2.20 | sf | $2.20 | $33.80 | $36.00 |
| **6" x 8" smooth-face glass blocks** *Replace* Materials.......19.80    Labor ............10.10  *Remove* .......................    Labor ............2.20 | sf | $2.20 | $29.90 | $32.10 |
| **8" x 8" smooth-face glass blocks** *Replace* Materials.......15.40    Labor ............7.90  *Remove* .......................    Labor ............2.20 | sf | $2.20 | $23.30 | $25.50 |
| **12" x 12" smooth-face glass blocks** *Replace* Materials ......18.00    Labor ............6.65  *Remove* .......................    Labor ............2.20 | sf | $2.20 | $24.65 | $26.85 |

*gypsum partition tile △*

**other glass block costs ▷**

**Add 80% for solar UV reflective glass block**

**Add 4% for patterned face on glass block**

**Add 12% for tinted glass block**

**Deduct 2% for natural gray mortar in glass block wall**

**Deduct 1% for colored mortar in glass block wall**

| Item | Unit | Remove | Replace | Total |
|---|---|---|---|---|
| **PAVERS ▶** *Pavers on sand base have sand embedded in joints with vibrating compactor. Mortar base pavers have grouted joints. Includes 4% waste for pavers and 25% waste for mortar when used.* | | | | |
| **Natural concrete pavers on sand base** *Replace* Materials........3.68    Labor ............5.59  *Remove* .......................    Labor ............2.20 | sf | $2.20 | $9.27 | $11.47 |
| **Natural concrete pavers on mortar base** *Replace* Materials........3.68    Labor ............6.84  *Remove* .......................    Labor ............3.14 | sf | $3.14 | $10.52 | $13.66 |
| **Adobe pavers on sand base** *Replace* Materials........1.54    Labor ............5.59  *Remove* .......................    Labor ............2.20 | sf | $2.20 | $7.13 | $9.33 |

| Item Description | Unit | Remove | Replace | Total | |
|---|---|---|---|---|---|
| **Adobe pavers on mortar base** | sf | $3.14 | $8.38 | $11.52 | |
| *Replace* Materials........1.54　　Labor ..........6.84 | | | | | |
| *Remove* ......................　　Labor ..........3.14 | | | | | |
| **Brick paver, standard grade, on sand base** | sf | $2.20 | $7.60 | $9.80 | |
| *Replace* Materials........2.01　　Labor ..........5.59 | | | | | |
| *Remove* ......................　　Labor ..........2.20 | | | | | |
| **Brick paver, standard grade, on mortar base** | sf | $3.14 | $8.92 | $12.06 | |
| *Replace* Materials........2.08　　Labor ..........6.84 | | | | | |
| *Remove* ......................　　Labor ..........3.14 | | | | | |
| **Brick paver, high grade, on sand base** | sf | $2.20 | $8.27 | $10.47 | |
| *Replace* Materials........2.68　　Labor ..........5.59 | | | | | |
| *Remove* ......................　　Labor ..........2.20 | | | | | |
| **Brick paver, high grade, on mortar base** | sf | $3.14 | $9.52 | $12.66 | |
| *Replace* Materials........2.68　　Labor ..........6.84 | | | | | |
| *Remove* ......................　　Labor ..........3.14 | | | | | |
| **Brick paver, deluxe grade, on sand base** | sf | $2.20 | $8.85 | $11.05 | |
| *Replace* Materials........3.26　　Labor ..........5.59 | | | | | |
| *Remove* ......................　　Labor ..........2.20 | | | | | |
| **Brick paver, deluxe grade, on mortar base** | sf | $3.14 | $10.17 | $13.31 | |
| *Replace* Materials........3.33　　Labor ..........6.84 | | | | | |
| *Remove* ......................　　Labor ..........3.14 | | | | | |
| **Brick pavers made from full-size bricks, laid face up** | sf | $2.36 | $10.59 | $12.95 | |
| *Replace* Materials........3.56　　Labor ..........7.03 | | | | | |
| *Remove* ......................　　Labor ..........2.36 | | | | | |
| **Brick pavers made from full-size bricks, laid edge up** | sf | $2.36 | $13.35 | $15.71 | |
| *Replace* Materials........5.45　　Labor ..........7.90 | | | | | |
| *Remove* ......................　　Labor ..........2.36 | | | | | |
| **Add for curved edges on pavers** | lf | — | $4.18 | $4.18 | ◁ additional paver costs |
| *Replace* Materials........1.22　　Labor ..........2.96 | | | | | |
| **Add for paver steps installed in mortar over concrete per lf of step** | lf | — | $10.89 | $10.89 | |
| *Replace* Materials........ .59　　Labor ..........10.30 | | | | | |
| **Add for paver steps installed over sand base per lf of step** | lf | — | $11.75 | $11.75 | |
| *Replace* Materials........ .55　　Labor ..........11.20 | | | | | |
| **Add for separate pattern at edges of pavers** | lf | — | $4.09 | $4.09 | |
| *Replace* Materials........1.20　　Labor ..........2.89 | | | | | |
| **Add 17% for non-square pavers with interlocking patterns** | | | | | |
| **Add 8% for pavers installed in diagonal pattern** | | | | | |
| **Add 17% for pavers installed in basketweave pattern** | | | | | |
| **Add 14% for pavers installed in herringbone pattern** | | | | | |
| **Coral stone rubble wall** | cf | $11.50 | $54.20 | $65.70 | ◀ RUBBLE STONE WALL |
| *Replace* Materials......34.50　　Labor ..........19.70 | | | | | |
| *Remove* ......................　　Labor ..........11.50 | | | | | |

RELATED ITEMS
Cleaning ......................63
Fireplaces....................241
Painting ......................340

basketweave △

*continued on next page*

| Item Description | Unit | Remove | Replace | Total |
|---|---|---|---|---|

**RUBBLE STONE ▶ WALL**
*continued*

*Stone walls laid in a variety of rubble patterns, per cubic foot of stone. Includes an average of 1/3 cubic foot of mortar per cubic foot of wall. To estimate by the perch, multiply the cf price by 24.75. (A perch is 16-1/2' long, 1' high and 1-1/2' wide or 24-3/4 cubic feet.) See illustration below.*

| Item Description | Unit | Remove | Replace | Total |
|---|---|---|---|---|
| **Field-stone rubble wall, no mortar**<br>*Replace* Materials ......25.40　　Labor..........18.30<br>*Remove* .....................　　Labor..........6.79 | cf | $6.79 | $43.70 | $50.49 |
| **Field-stone rubble wall**<br>*Replace* Materials ......35.50　　Labor..........19.70<br>*Remove* .....................　　Labor..........11.50 | cf | $11.50 | $55.20 | $66.70 |
| **Lava stone rubble wall**<br>*Replace* Materials ......34.20　　Labor..........19.70<br>*Remove* .....................　　Labor..........11.50 | cf | $11.50 | $53.90 | $65.40 |
| **River stone rubble wall**<br>*Replace* Materials ......36.30　　Labor..........19.70<br>*Remove* .....................　　Labor..........11.50 | cf | $11.50 | $56.00 | $67.50 |

**ASHLAR STONE ▶ WALL**

*Stone walls laid in ashlar patterns, per cf of stone. Stone is 3-1/2" to 6" wide. Lengths and thickness vary. Includes mortar. To estimate by the perch, multiply the cf price by 24.75. (A perch is 16-1/2' long, 1' high and 1-1/2' wide or 24-3/4 cubic feet.)*

*rubble lay △*

*ashlar lay △*

| Item Description | Unit | Remove | Replace | Total |
|---|---|---|---|---|
| **Limestone ashlar wall, natural finish**<br>*Replace* Materials ......28.60　　Labor..........17.90<br>*Remove* .....................　　Labor..........11.50 | cf | $11.50 | $46.50 | $58.00 |
| **Limestone ashlar wall, rough finish**<br>*Replace* Materials ......31.80　　Labor..........17.90<br>*Remove* .....................　　Labor..........11.50 | cf | $11.50 | $49.70 | $61.20 |
| **Limestone ashlar wall, smooth finish**<br>*Replace* Materials ......45.40　　Labor..........17.90<br>*Remove* .....................　　Labor..........11.50 | cf | $11.50 | $63.30 | $74.80 |
| **Marble ashlar wall, natural finish**<br>*Replace* Materials ......65.60　　Labor..........17.90<br>*Remove* .....................　　Labor..........11.50 | cf | $11.50 | $83.50 | $95.00 |
| **Marble ashlar wall, rough finish**<br>*Replace* Materials ......70.60　　Labor..........17.90<br>*Remove* .....................　　Labor..........11.50 | cf | $11.50 | $88.50 | $100.00 |
| **Marble ashlar wall, smooth finish**<br>*Replace* Materials ......87.20　　Labor..........17.90<br>*Remove* .....................　　Labor..........11.50 | cf | $11.50 | $105.10 | $116.60 |
| **Sandstone ashlar wall, natural finish**<br>*Replace* Materials ......27.70　　Labor..........17.90<br>*Remove* .....................　　Labor..........11.50 | cf | $11.50 | $45.60 | $57.10 |
| **Sandstone ashlar wall, rough finish**<br>*Replace* Materials ......30.80　　Labor..........17.90<br>*Remove* .....................　　Labor..........11.50 | cf | $11.50 | $48.70 | $60.20 |
| **Sandstone ashlar wall, smooth finish**<br>*Replace* Materials ......43.80　　Labor..........17.90<br>*Remove* .....................　　Labor..........11.50 | cf | $11.50 | $61.70 | $73.20 |
| **Add for flat arch in stone wall**<br>*Replace* Materials ......67.00　　Labor..........109.00<br>▶ Also called a Jack arch. See illustration on facing page. Do not use for standard stone wall openings that use a lintel. | lf | — | $176.00 | $176.00 |
| **Add for elliptical arch in stone wall**<br>*Replace* Materials ......78.90　　Labor..........136.00<br>▶ Per lf of arch. See illustration on facing page. | lf | — | $214.90 | $214.90 |

**STONE QUALITY**

Stones are quarried within 150 miles of job site.

***Cast stone*** is made from a composite of crushed limestone and quartz sand.

***Granite*** is a good quality gray stone. Add **28%** for light red (pink), light purple, and light brown. Add **88%** for deep green, red, purple, blue, black, charcoal, and brown.

***Limestone*** is standard stock. Add **15%** for select stock and deduct **10%** for rustic stock.

*continued on next page*

| Item Description | Unit | Remove | Replace | Total |
|---|---|---|---|---|
| **Add for semi-circular arch in stone wall** | lf | — | $219.90 | $219.90 |
| *Replace* Materials ......78.90    Labor .........141.00 | | | | |
| ► Per lf of arch.  See illustration below. | | | | |
| **Add 27% for curved stone wall** | | | | |
| **Coral stone rubble veneer** | sf | $2.78 | $20.73 | $23.51 |
| *Replace* Materials......11.50    Labor ...........9.23 | | | | |
| *Remove* ...............    Labor ...........2.78 | | | | |
| **Field stone rubble veneer** | sf | $2.78 | $18.52 | $21.30 |
| *Replace* Materials........9.29    Labor ...........9.23 | | | | |
| *Remove* ...............    Labor ...........2.78 | | | | |
| **Flagstone rubble veneer** | sf | $2.78 | $15.12 | $17.90 |
| *Replace* Materials........5.89    Labor ...........9.23 | | | | |
| *Remove* ...............    Labor ...........2.78 | | | | |
| **Lava stone rubble veneer** | sf | $2.78 | $18.18 | $20.96 |
| *Replace* Materials........8.95    Labor ...........9.23 | | | | |
| *Remove* ...............    Labor ...........2.78 | | | | |
| **River stone rubble veneer** | sf | $2.78 | $18.72 | $21.50 |
| *Replace* Materials........9.49    Labor ...........9.23 | | | | |
| *Remove* ...............    Labor ...........2.78 | | | | |
| **Sandstone rubble veneer** | sf | $2.78 | $22.53 | $25.31 |
| *Replace* Materials.......13.30    Labor ...........9.23 | | | | |
| *Remove* ...............    Labor ...........2.78 | | | | |
| **Flagstone ashlar veneer** | sf | $2.78 | $15.82 | $18.60 |
| *Replace* Materials........6.85    Labor .........8.97 | | | | |
| *Remove* ...............    Labor ...........2.78 | | | | |
| **Limestone ashlar veneer, natural finish** | sf | $2.78 | $16.43 | $19.21 |
| *Replace* Materials........7.46    Labor ...........8.97 | | | | |
| *Remove* ...............    Labor ...........2.78 | | | | |
| **Limestone ashlar veneer, rough finish** | sf | $2.78 | $17.26 | $20.04 |
| *Replace* Materials........8.29    Labor ...........8.97 | | | | |
| *Remove* ...............    Labor ...........2.78 | | | | |
| **Limestone ashlar veneer, smooth finish** | sf | $2.78 | $20.77 | $23.55 |
| *Replace* Materials.......11.80    Labor ...........8.97 | | | | |
| *Remove* ...............    Labor ...........2.78 | | | | |
| **Marble ashlar veneer, natural finish** | sf | $2.78 | $25.87 | $28.65 |
| *Replace* Materials ......16.90    Labor ...........8.97 | | | | |
| *Remove* ...............    Labor ...........2.78 | | | | |
| **Marble ashlar veneer, rough finish** | sf | $2.78 | $27.17 | $29.95 |
| *Replace* Materials ......18.20    Labor ...........8.97 | | | | |
| *Remove* ...............    Labor ...........2.78 | | | | |
| **Marble ashlar veneer, smooth finish** | sf | $2.78 | $31.47 | $34.25 |
| *Replace* Materials ......22.50    Labor ...........8.97 | | | | |
| *Remove* ...............    Labor ...........2.78 | | | | |
| **Sandstone ashlar veneer, natural finish** | sf | $2.78 | $16.19 | $18.97 |
| *Replace* Materials........7.22    Labor ...........8.97 | | | | |
| *Remove* ...............    Labor ...........2.78 | | | | |

*flat arch △*

◄ **RUBBLE STONE**

**STONE QUALITY**

*continued*

**Marble** is grade A, average to high priced. Marble varies widely in price with little relationship to color and often even the quality of the stone. The more expensive grades are Italian.
**Sandstone** is standard grade. Varies from very hard rock to fairly soft. Use for Brownstone work.
**Slate** is standard grade, all colors.

△ *elliptical arch*

◄ **ASHLAR STONE**

△ *semi-circular arch*

**STONE FINISHES**

Stone finishes are generally organized in this book as natural, rough, and smooth. In practice there are many variations of each type of finish.

Stone with **natural** finishes show the cleaving or sawing marks made in the quarry.

**Rough** finishes are applied after the stone is quarried to achieve a specific rough look.

**Smooth** finishes are achieved by polishing the stone. All molded work is finished smooth.

| Item Description | Unit | Remove | Replace | Total |
|---|---|---|---|---|
| **ASHLAR STONE ▶ VENEER** *continued* | | | | |
| **Sandstone ashlar veneer, rough finish** | sf | $2.78 | $16.99 | $19.77 |
| *Replace* Materials........8.02    Labor............8.97 | | | | |
| *Remove* ...................    Labor............2.78 | | | | |
| **Sandstone ashlar veneer, smooth finish** | sf | $2.78 | $20.37 | $23.15 |
| *Replace* Materials.......11.40    Labor............8.97 | | | | |
| *Remove* ...................    Labor............2.78 | | | | |
| **add for arch ▷ Add for flat arch in stone veneer** | lf | — | $83.70 | $83.70 |
| *Replace* Materials.......17.20    Labor..........66.50 | | | | |
| ► Also called a Jack arch. See illustration on previous page. Do not use for standard stone veneer openings that use a lintel. | | | | |
| **Add for elliptical arch in stone veneer** | lf | — | $102.70 | $102.70 |
| *Replace* Materials......20.20    Labor..........82.50 | | | | |
| ► Per lf of arch. See illustration on previous page. | | | | |
| **Add for semi-circular arch in stone veneer** | lf | — | $107.60 | $107.60 |
| *Replace* Materials......20.20    Labor..........87.40 | | | | |
| ► Per lf of arch. See illustration on previous page. | | | | |
| **Add to support arch from below** | lf | — | $32.80 | $32.80 |
| *Replace* Materials......11.70    Labor..........21.10 | | | | |
| ► 2" x 6" or 2" x 8" framing members sheathed with plywood that follows curved shape of arch. | | | | |
| **add for curves ▷ Add 27% for curved stone veneer** | | | | |
| **add for rustication ▷ Add 55% for rusticated stone** | | | | |
| ► Edges of stone rabbeted up to 1" deep. | | | | |
| **KEYSTONE ▶ Keystone, concrete** *For use in stone or brick arches.* | ea | $5.19 | $69.00 | $74.19 |
| *Replace* Materials......46.00    Labor..........23.00 | | | | |
| *Remove* ...................    Labor............5.19 | | | | |
| ► Plain key, recessed key, or winged key. See illustrations on page 322. | | | | |
| **Keystone, cast stone** | ea | $5.19 | $86.00 | $91.19 |
| *Replace* Materials......63.00    Labor..........23.00 | | | | |
| *Remove* ...................    Labor............5.19 | | | | |
| ► Plain key, recessed key, or winged key. See illustrations on page 322. | | | | |
| **Keystone, natural finish** | ea | $5.19 | $122.00 | $127.19 |
| *Replace* Materials......99.00    Labor..........23.00 | | | | |
| *Remove* ...................    Labor............5.19 | | | | |
| ► Plain key, with natural or rough finish. See illustrations on page 322. | | | | |
| **Keystone, with straight patterns** | ea | $5.19 | $151.00 | $156.19 |
| *Replace* Materials.....128.00    Labor..........23.00 | | | | |
| *Remove* ...................    Labor............5.19 | | | | |
| ► Recessed key, or winged key. See illustrations on page 322. | | | | |
| **Keystone, with complex straight patterns (Gothic)** | ea | $5.19 | $186.00 | $191.19 |
| *Replace* Materials.....163.00    Labor..........23.00 | | | | |
| *Remove* ...................    Labor............5.19 | | | | |
| ► Key with Gothic patterns over 1" deep. | | | | |
| **Keystone, with light hand carvings** | ea | $5.19 | $271.00 | $276.19 |
| *Replace* Materials ....248.00    Labor..........23.00 | | | | |
| *Remove* ...................    Labor............5.19 | | | | |
| ► Light carvings, usually less than 3/4" deep. | | | | |

△ *rustication*

| Item Description | Unit | Remove | Replace | Total |
|---|---|---|---|---|
| **Keystone, with medium hand carvings** | ea | $5.19 | $340.00 | $345.19 |
| *Replace* Materials.....317.00    Labor ..........23.00 | | | | |
| *Remove* .......................    Labor ..........5.19 | | | | |
| ► Heavier carvings like vermiculation, Acanthus, and so forth. | | | | |
| **Keystone, with heavy hand carvings** | ea | $5.19 | $467.00 | $472.19 |
| *Replace* Materials....444.00    Labor ..........23.00 | | | | |
| *Remove* .......................    Labor ..........5.19 | | | | |
| ► Heavy and deep carvings including a lion's face, a human face, and so forth. | | | | |
| **Remove keystone for work, then reinstall** | ea | — | $38.80 | $38.80 |
| *Replace* Materials..........    Labor ..........38.80 | | | | |
| **Cast stone quoin** | ea | $5.14 | $107.23 | $112.37 |
| *Replace* Materials.....101.00    Labor ..........6.23 | | | | |
| *Remove* .......................    Labor ..........5.14 | | | | |
| **Limestone quoin** | ea | $5.14 | $121.23 | $126.37 |
| *Replace* Materials .....115.00    Labor ..........6.23 | | | | |
| *Remove* .......................    Labor ..........5.14 | | | | |
| **Sandstone quoin** | ea | $5.14 | $115.23 | $120.37 |
| *Replace* Materials ....109.00    Labor ..........6.23 | | | | |
| *Remove* .......................    Labor ..........5.14 | | | | |
| **Remove quoin for work, then reinstall (per stone)** | ea | — | $16.50 | $16.50 |
| *Replace* Materials..........    Labor ..........16.50 | | | | |
| **Cultured stone veneer panels, smooth finish** | sf | $1.94 | $15.17 | $17.11 |
| *Replace* Materials.......5.18    Labor ..........9.99 | | | | |
| *Remove* .......................    Labor ..........1.94 | | | | |
| **Cultured stone veneer panels, rough finish** | sf | $1.94 | $16.95 | $18.89 |
| *Replace* Materials.......6.96    Labor ..........9.99 | | | | |
| *Remove* .......................    Labor ..........1.94 | | | | |
| **Cultured stone veneer panels, terrazzo style finish** | sf | $1.94 | $25.69 | $27.63 |
| *Replace* Materials.......15.70    Labor ..........9.99 | | | | |
| *Remove* .......................    Labor ..........1.94 | | | | |
| **Ceramic veneer panels** | sf | $1.94 | $22.69 | $24.63 |
| *Replace* Materials .......12.70    Labor ..........9.99 | | | | |
| *Remove* .......................    Labor ..........1.94 | | | | |
| **Granite veneer panels, natural finish** | sf | $1.94 | $34.70 | $36.64 |
| *Replace* Materials ......23.40    Labor ..........11.30 | | | | |
| *Remove* .......................    Labor ..........1.94 | | | | |
| **Granite veneer panels, rough finish** | sf | $1.94 | $36.10 | $38.04 |
| *Replace* Materials ......24.80    Labor ..........11.30 | | | | |
| *Remove* .......................    Labor ..........1.94 | | | | |
| **Granite veneer panels, smooth finish** | sf | $1.94 | $39.80 | $41.74 |
| *Replace* Materials ......28.50    Labor ..........11.30 | | | | |
| *Remove* .......................    Labor ..........1.94 | | | | |
| **Limestone veneer panels, natural finish** | sf | $1.94 | $22.00 | $23.94 |
| *Replace* Materials ......10.70    Labor ..........11.30 | | | | |
| *Remove* .......................    Labor ..........1.94 | | | | |
| **Limestone veneer panels, rough finish** | sf | $1.94 | $27.40 | $29.34 |
| *Replace* Materials ......16.10    Labor ..........11.30 | | | | |
| *Remove* .......................    Labor ..........1.94 | | | | |

◄ **STONE QUOIN**
In brick, stone, or stucco walls. Made from alternate courses of headers and stretchers. Price includes one header and one stretcher (two stones). Quoins are plain, beveled, chamfered, rusticated, or rough tooled.

◄ **CULTURED STONE VENEER PANEL**
3/4" to 1-1/2" thick.

◄ **CERAMIC VENEER PANEL**
Precast panels.

◄ **STONE VENEER PANEL**
Granite, slate, and marble panels are 3/4" to 1-1/2" thick. Limestone and sandstone panels are 2" to 3" thick. See page 307 for more information about quality and finishes.

**RELATED ITEMS**

| Item Description | Unit | Remove | Replace | Total |
|---|---|---|---|---|
| **STONE VENEER ▶ PANELS** *continued* | | | | |
| **Limestone veneer panels, smooth finish** | sf | $1.94 | $32.60 | $34.54 |
| *Replace* Materials ......21.30    Labor ...........11.30 *Remove* ...................    Labor ...........1.94 | | | | |
| **Marble veneer panels, natural finish** | sf | $1.94 | $38.10 | $40.04 |
| *Replace* Materials ......26.80    Labor ...........11.30 *Remove* ...................    Labor ...........1.94 | | | | |
| **Marble veneer panels, rough finish** | sf | $1.94 | $46.40 | $48.34 |
| *Replace* Materials ......35.10    Labor ...........11.30 *Remove* ...................    Labor ...........1.94 | | | | |
| **Marble veneer panels, smooth finish** | sf | $1.94 | $55.20 | $57.14 |
| *Replace* Materials ......43.90    Labor ...........11.30 *Remove* ...................    Labor ...........1.94 | | | | |
| **Sandstone veneer panels, natural finish** | sf | $1.94 | $30.60 | $32.54 |
| *Replace* Materials .......19.30    Labor ...........11.30 *Remove* ...................    Labor ...........1.94 | | | | |
| **Sandstone veneer panels, rough finish** | sf | $1.94 | $32.30 | $34.24 |
| *Replace* Materials ......21.00    Labor ...........11.30 *Remove* ...................    Labor ...........1.94 | | | | |
| **Sandstone veneer panels, smooth finish** | sf | $1.94 | $34.80 | $36.74 |
| *Replace* Materials ......23.50    Labor ...........11.30 *Remove* ...................    Labor ...........1.94 | | | | |
| **Slate veneer panels, natural finish** | sf | $1.94 | $31.10 | $33.04 |
| *Replace* Materials .......19.80    Labor ...........11.30 *Remove* ...................    Labor ...........1.94 | | | | |
| **Slate veneer panels, rough finish** | sf | $1.94 | $32.90 | $34.84 |
| *Replace* Materials ......21.60    Labor ...........11.30 *Remove* ...................    Labor ...........1.94 | | | | |
| **Slate veneer panels, smooth finish** | sf | $1.94 | $35.50 | $37.44 |
| *Replace* Materials ......24.20    Labor ...........11.30 *Remove* ...................    Labor ...........1.94 | | | | |
| **STONE DOOR ▶ ARCHITRAVE**   **Cast stone door architrave, standard grade** | lf | $3.43 | $57.20 | $60.63 |
| *Replace* Materials ......20.00    Labor ...........37.20 *Remove* ...................    Labor ...........3.43 ▶ Simple straight patterns. Cast stone is 6" or less wide. | | | | |
| **Cast stone door architrave, high grade** | lf | $3.43 | $59.10 | $62.53 |
| *Replace* Materials ......21.90    Labor ...........37.20 *Remove* ...................    Labor ...........3.43 ▶ Complex straight patterns (Gothic). Cast stone is 6" or less wide. | | | | |
| **Cast stone door architrave, deluxe grade** | lf | $3.43 | $66.70 | $70.13 |
| *Replace* Materials ......29.50    Labor ...........37.20 *Remove* ...................    Labor ...........3.43 ▶ Cast stone 6" or less wide with complex straight patterns (Gothic) with arched top or flat top with decorative work around corners or center of header. Or simple straight patterns with cast stone up to 10" wide. | | | | |
| **Cast stone door architrave, custom grade** | lf | $3.43 | $73.40 | $76.83 |
| *Replace* Materials ......36.20    Labor ...........37.20 *Remove* ...................    Labor ...........3.43 ▶ Cast stone 6" or less wide with hand carvings on header or up to 10" wide with complex straight patterns (Gothic) with arched top. Or simple straight patterns with cast stone up to 12" wide. | | | | |

| Item Description | Unit | Remove | Replace | Total |
|---|---|---|---|---|
| **Cast stone door architrave, custom deluxe grade** | lf | $3.43 | $83.60 | $87.03 |

*Replace* Materials......46.40          Labor...........37.20
*Remove* .......................          Labor ...........3.43
► Cast stone 6" or less wide with heavy hand carvings on header (e.g. lion's face, human face) or lighter hand carvings throughout or up to 12" wide with complex straight patterns (Gothic). With arched top.

| | | | | |
|---|---|---|---|---|
| **Limestone door architrave, standard grade** | lf | $3.43 | $76.10 | $79.53 |

*Replace* Materials......38.90          Labor...........37.20
*Remove* .......................          Labor ...........3.43
► Simple straight patterns. Stone is 6" or less wide.

| | | | | |
|---|---|---|---|---|
| **Limestone door architrave, high grade** | lf | $3.43 | $108.30 | $111.73 |

*Replace* Materials......71.10          Labor...........37.20
*Remove* .......................          Labor ...........3.43
► Complex straight patterns (Gothic). Stone is 6" or less wide.

| | | | | |
|---|---|---|---|---|
| **Limestone door architrave, deluxe grade** | lf | $3.43 | $139.20 | $142.63 |

*Replace* Materials ....102.00          Labor...........37.20
*Remove* .......................          Labor ...........3.43
► Stone 6" or less wide with complex straight patterns (Gothic) with arched top or flat top with decorative work around corners or center of header. Or simple straight patterns with stone up to 10" wide.

| | | | | |
|---|---|---|---|---|
| **Limestone door architrave, custom grade** | lf | $3.43 | $164.20 | $167.63 |

*Replace* Materials.....127.00          Labor...........37.20
*Remove* .......................          Labor ...........3.43
► Stone 6" or less wide with hand carvings on header or up to 10" wide with complex straight patterns (Gothic) with arched top. Or simple straight patterns with stone up to 12" wide.

| | | | | |
|---|---|---|---|---|
| **Limestone door architrave, custom deluxe grade** | lf | $3.43 | $191.20 | $194.63 |

*Replace* Materials ....154.00          Labor...........37.20
*Remove* .......................          Labor ...........3.43
► Stone 6" or less wide with heavy hand carvings on header (e.g. lion's face, human face) or lighter hand carvings throughout or up to 12" wide with complex straight patterns (Gothic). With arched top.

| | | | | |
|---|---|---|---|---|
| **Marble door architrave, standard grade** | lf | $3.43 | $95.30 | $98.73 |

*Replace* Materials......58.10          Labor...........37.20
*Remove* .......................          Labor ...........3.43
► Simple straight patterns. Stone is 6" or less wide.

| | | | | |
|---|---|---|---|---|
| **Marble door architrave, high grade** | lf | $3.43 | $127.90 | $131.33 |

*Replace* Materials......90.70          Labor...........37.20
*Remove* .......................          Labor ...........3.43
► Complex straight patterns (Gothic). Stone is 6" or less wide.

| | | | | |
|---|---|---|---|---|
| **Marble door architrave, deluxe grade** | lf | $3.43 | $159.20 | $162.63 |

*Replace* Materials ....122.00          Labor...........37.20
*Remove* .......................          Labor ...........3.43
► Stone 6" or less wide with complex straight patterns (Gothic) with arched top or flat top with decorative work around corners or center of header. Or simple straight patterns with stone up to 10" wide.

| | | | | |
|---|---|---|---|---|
| **Marble door architrave, custom grade** | lf | $3.43 | $183.20 | $186.63 |

*Replace* Materials ....146.00          Labor...........37.20
*Remove* .......................          Labor ...........3.43
► Stone 6" or less wide with hand carvings on header or up to 10" wide with complex straight patterns (Gothic) with arched top. Or simple straight patterns with stone up to 12" wide.

| Item Description | Unit | Remove | Replace | Total |
|---|---|---|---|---|
| **STONE DOOR ►** **ARCHITRAVE** *continued* **Marble door architrave, custom deluxe grade** | If | $3.43 | $211.20 | $214.63 |
| *Replace* Materials.....174.00    Labor..........37.20 *Remove* .................    Labor ..........3.43 | | | | |
| ► Stone 6" or less wide with heavy hand carvings on header (e.g. lion's face, human face) or lighter hand carvings throughout or up to 12" wide with complex straight patterns (Gothic). With arched top. | | | | |
| **Sandstone door architrave, standard grade** | If | $3.43 | $71.40 | $74.83 |
| *Replace* Materials......34.20    Labor..........37.20 *Remove* .................    Labor ..........3.43 | | | | |
| ► Simple straight patterns. Stone is 6" or less wide. | | | | |
| **Sandstone door architrave, high grade** | If | $3.43 | $103.70 | $107.13 |
| *Replace* Materials......66.50    Labor..........37.20 *Remove* .................    Labor ..........3.43 | | | | |
| ► Complex straight patterns (Gothic). Stone is 6" or less wide. | | | | |
| **Sandstone door architrave, deluxe grade** | If | $3.43 | $134.90 | $138.33 |
| *Replace* Materials......97.70    Labor..........37.20 *Remove* .................    Labor ..........3.43 | | | | |
| ► Stone 6" or less wide with complex straight patterns (Gothic) with arched top or flat top with decorative work around corners or center of header. Or simple straight patterns with stone up to 10" wide. | | | | |
| **Sandstone door architrave, custom grade** | If | $3.43 | $159.20 | $162.63 |
| *Replace* Materials ....122.00    Labor..........37.20 *Remove* .................    Labor ..........3.43 | | | | |
| ► Stone 6" or less wide with hand carvings on header or up to 10" wide with complex straight patterns (Gothic) with arched top. Or simple straight patterns with stone up to 12" wide. | | | | |
| **Sandstone door architrave, custom deluxe grade** | If | $3.43 | $186.20 | $189.63 |
| *Replace* Materials.....149.00    Labor..........37.20 *Remove* .................    Labor ..........3.43 | | | | |
| ► Stone 6" or less wide with heavy hand carvings on header (e.g. lion's face, human face) or lighter hand carvings throughout or up to 12" wide with complex straight patterns (Gothic). With arched top. | | | | |
| **STONE WINDOW ►** **ARCHITRAVE** **Cast stone window architrave, standard grade** | If | $3.43 | $57.40 | $60.83 |
| *Replace* Materials.......19.40    Labor ..........38.00 *Remove* .................    Labor ..........3.43 | | | | |
| ► Simple straight patterns. Cast stone is 6" or less wide. | | | | |
| **Cast stone window architrave, high grade** | If | $3.43 | $59.30 | $62.73 |
| *Replace* Materials......21.30    Labor ..........38.00 *Remove* .................    Labor ..........3.43 | | | | |
| ► Complex straight patterns (Gothic). Cast stone is 6" or less wide. | | | | |
| **Cast stone window architrave, deluxe grade** | If | $3.43 | $66.80 | $70.23 |
| *Replace* Materials......28.80    Labor ..........38.00 *Remove* .................    Labor ..........3.43 | | | | |
| ► Cast stone 6" or less wide with complex straight patterns (Gothic) with arched top or flat top with decorative work around corners or center of header. Or simple straight patterns with cast stone up to 10" wide. | | | | |
| **Cast stone window architrave, custom grade** | If | $3.43 | $73.20 | $76.63 |
| *Replace* Materials......35.20    Labor ..........38.00 *Remove* .................    Labor ..........3.43 | | | | |
| ► Cast stone 6" or less wide with hand carvings on header or up to 10" wide with complex straight patterns (Gothic) with arched top. Or simple straight patterns with cast stone up to 12" wide. | | | | |

| Item Description | Unit | Remove | Replace | Total |
|---|---|---|---|---|
| **Cast stone window architrave, custom deluxe grade** | If | $3.43 | $83.00 | $86.43 |

*Replace* Materials ......45.00          Labor ..........38.00
*Remove* ........................          Labor ..........3.43
▶ Cast stone 6" or less wide with heavy hand carvings on header (e.g. lion's face, human face) or lighter hand carvings throughout or up to 12" wide with complex straight patterns (Gothic). With arched top.

| | | | | |
|---|---|---|---|---|
| **Limestone window architrave, standard grade** | If | $3.43 | $75.80 | $79.23 |

*Replace* Materials ......37.80          Labor ..........38.00
*Remove* ........................          Labor ..........3.43
▶ Simple straight patterns. Stone is 6" or less wide.

| | | | | |
|---|---|---|---|---|
| **Limestone window architrave, high grade** | If | $3.43 | $107.10 | $110.53 |

*Replace* Materials ......69.10          Labor ..........38.00
*Remove* ........................          Labor ..........3.43
▶ Complex straight patterns (Gothic). Stone is 6" or less wide.

| | | | | |
|---|---|---|---|---|
| **Limestone window architrave, deluxe grade** | If | $3.43 | $137.40 | $140.83 |

*Replace* Materials ......99.40          Labor ..........38.00
*Remove* ........................          Labor ..........3.43
▶ Stone 6" or less wide with complex straight patterns (Gothic) with arched top or flat top with decorative work around corners or center of header. Or simple straight patterns with stone up to 10" wide.

| | | | | |
|---|---|---|---|---|
| **Limestone window architrave, custom grade** | If | $3.43 | $161.00 | $164.43 |

*Replace* Materials .....123.00          Labor ..........38.00
*Remove* ........................          Labor ..........3.43
▶ Stone 6" or less wide with hand carvings on header or up to 10" wide with complex straight patterns (Gothic) with arched top. Or simple straight patterns with stone up to 12" wide.

| | | | | |
|---|---|---|---|---|
| **Limestone window architrave, custom deluxe grade** | If | $3.43 | $188.00 | $191.43 |

*Replace* Materials ....150.00          Labor ..........38.00
*Remove* ........................          Labor ..........3.43
▶ Stone 6" or less wide with heavy hand carvings on header (e.g. lion's face, human face) or lighter hand carvings throughout or up to 12" wide with complex straight patterns (Gothic). With arched top.

| | | | | |
|---|---|---|---|---|
| **Marble window architrave, standard grade** | If | $3.43 | $94.50 | $97.93 |

*Replace* Materials ......56.50          Labor ..........38.00
*Remove* ........................          Labor ..........3.43
▶ Simple straight patterns. Stone is 6" or less wide.

| | | | | |
|---|---|---|---|---|
| **Marble window architrave, high grade** | If | $3.43 | $126.20 | $129.63 |

*Replace* Materials ......88.20          Labor ..........38.00
*Remove* ........................          Labor ..........3.43
▶ Complex straight patterns (Gothic). Stone is 6" or less wide.

| | | | | |
|---|---|---|---|---|
| **Marble window architrave, deluxe grade** | If | $3.43 | $157.00 | $160.43 |

*Replace* Materials .....119.00          Labor ..........38.00
*Remove* ........................          Labor ..........3.43
▶ Stone 6" or less wide with complex straight patterns (Gothic) with arched top or flat top with decorative work around corners or center of header. Or simple straight patterns with stone up to 10" wide.

| | | | | |
|---|---|---|---|---|
| **Marble window architrave, custom grade** | If | $3.43 | $180.00 | $183.43 |

*Replace* Materials .....142.00          Labor ..........38.00
*Remove* ........................          Labor ..........3.43
▶ Stone 6" or less wide with hand carvings on header or up to 10" wide with complex straight patterns (Gothic) with arched top. Or simple straight patterns with stone up to 12" wide.

| Item Description | Unit | Remove | Replace | Total |
|---|---|---|---|---|
| **STONE WINDOW** ▶ **ARCHITRAVE** *continued* **Marble window architrave, custom deluxe grade** | lf | $3.43 | $207.00 | $210.43 |
| *Replace* Materials.....169.00  Labor..........38.00 | | | | |
| *Remove* .......................  Labor...........3.43 | | | | |
| ▶ Stone 6" or less wide with heavy hand carvings on header (e.g. lion's face, human face) or lighter hand carvings throughout or up to 12" wide with complex straight patterns (Gothic). With arched top. | | | | |
| **Sandstone window architrave, standard grade** | lf | $3.43 | $73.40 | $76.83 |
| *Replace* Materials......35.40  Labor..........38.00 | | | | |
| *Remove* .......................  Labor...........3.43 | | | | |
| ▶ Simple straight patterns.  Stone is 6" or less wide. | | | | |
| **Sandstone window architrave, high grade** | lf | $3.43 | $104.70 | $108.13 |
| *Replace* Materials......66.70  Labor..........38.00 | | | | |
| *Remove* .......................  Labor...........3.43 | | | | |
| ▶ Complex straight patterns (Gothic).  Stone is 6" or less wide. | | | | |
| **Sandstone window architrave, deluxe grade** | lf | $3.43 | $134.90 | $138.33 |
| *Replace* Materials......96.90  Labor..........38.00 | | | | |
| *Remove* .......................  Labor...........3.43 | | | | |
| ▶ Stone 6" or less wide with complex straight patterns (Gothic) with arched top or flat top with decorative work around corners or center of header.  Or simple straight patterns with stone up to 10" wide. | | | | |
| **Sandstone window architrave, custom grade** | lf | $3.43 | $159.00 | $162.43 |
| *Replace* Materials.....121.00  Labor..........38.00 | | | | |
| *Remove* .......................  Labor...........3.43 | | | | |
| ▶ Stone 6" or less wide with hand carvings on header or up to 10" wide with complex straight patterns (Gothic) with arched top.  Or simple straight patterns with stone up to 12" wide. | | | | |
| **Sandstone window architrave, custom deluxe grade** | lf | $3.43 | $185.00 | $188.43 |
| *Replace* Materials.....147.00  Labor..........38.00 | | | | |
| *Remove* .......................  Labor...........3.43 | | | | |
| ▶ Stone 6" or less wide with heavy hand carvings on header (e.g. lion's face, human face) or lighter hand carvings throughout or up to 12" wide with complex straight patterns (Gothic).  With arched top. | | | | |
| *add for round window* ▷ **Add 65% for architrave for round or elliptical window** | | | | |
| ▶ Measure perimeter of opening. | | | | |
| *replace section to match* ▷ **Replace section of stone architrave cut to match** | ea | — | $635.00 | $635.00 |
| *Replace* Materials....508.00  Labor.........127.00 | | | | |
| ▶ Includes plaster or clay model with work performed on site or in a shop within 150 miles of the site. | | | | |
| **CUT STONE** ▶ **TRIM OR CORNICE** *Per 4" of width.  Use for friezes, architraves, cornices, string courses, band courses, and so on.* **Cut stone trim or cornice stones, all horizontal patterns** | lf | $2.72 | $26.40 | $29.12 |
| *Replace* Materials ......12.30  Labor..........14.10 | | | | |
| *Remove* .......................  Labor...........2.72 | | | | |
| **Cut stone trim or cornice stones, complex horizontal patterns (Gothic)** | lf | $2.72 | $31.30 | $34.02 |
| *Replace* Materials.......17.20  Labor..........14.10 | | | | |
| *Remove* .......................  Labor...........2.72 | | | | |
| **Cut stone trim or cornice stones with vertical patterns** | lf | $2.72 | $33.20 | $35.92 |
| *Replace* Materials.......19.10  Labor..........14.10 | | | | |
| *Remove* .......................  Labor...........2.72 | | | | |
| **Cut stone trim or cornice stones with light hand carvings** | lf | $2.72 | $40.90 | $43.62 |
| *Replace* Materials......26.80  Labor..........14.10 | | | | |
| *Remove* .......................  Labor...........2.72 | | | | |

| Item Description | Unit | Remove | Replace | Total |
|---|---|---|---|---|
| **Cut stone trim or cornice stones with medium hand carvings**<br>*Replace* Materials......33.40   Labor...........14.10<br>*Remove* ..................   Labor ............2.72 | lf | $2.72 | $47.50 | $50.22 |
| **Cut stone trim or cornice stones with heavy hand carvings**<br>*Replace* Materials......43.50   Labor...........14.10<br>*Remove* ..................   Labor ............2.72 | lf | $2.72 | $57.60 | $60.32 |
| **Limestone trim or cornice stones, all horizontal patterns**<br>*Replace* Materials......18.90   Labor...........14.10<br>*Remove* ..................   Labor ............2.72 | lf | $2.72 | $33.00 | $35.72 |
| **Limestone trim or cornice stones, complex horizontal patterns (Gothic)**<br>*Replace* Materials......35.70   Labor...........14.10<br>*Remove* ..................   Labor ............2.72 | lf | $2.72 | $49.80 | $52.52 |
| **Limestone trim or cornice stones with vertical patterns**<br>*Replace* Materials......68.00   Labor...........14.10<br>*Remove* ..................   Labor ............2.72 | lf | $2.72 | $82.10 | $84.82 |
| **Limestone trim or cornice stones with light hand carvings**<br>*Replace* Materials......99.20   Labor...........14.10<br>*Remove* ..................   Labor ............2.72 | lf | $2.72 | $113.30 | $116.02 |
| **Limestone trim or cornice stones with medium hand carvings**<br>*Replace* Materials.....124.00   Labor...........14.10<br>*Remove* ..................   Labor ............2.72 | lf | $2.72 | $138.10 | $140.82 |
| **Limestone trim or cornice stones with heavy hand carvings**<br>*Replace* Materials.....151.00   Labor...........14.10<br>*Remove* ..................   Labor ............2.72 | lf | $2.72 | $165.10 | $167.82 |
| **Marble trim or cornice stones, all horizontal patterns**<br>*Replace* Materials......35.90   Labor...........14.10<br>*Remove* ..................   Labor ............2.72 | lf | $2.72 | $50.00 | $52.72 |
| **Marble trim or cornice stones, complex horizontal patterns (Gothic)**<br>*Replace* Materials......52.90   Labor...........14.10<br>*Remove* ..................   Labor ............2.72 | lf | $2.72 | $67.00 | $69.72 |
| **Marble trim or cornice stones with vertical patterns**<br>*Replace* Materials......85.60   Labor...........14.10<br>*Remove* ..................   Labor ............2.72 | lf | $2.72 | $99.70 | $102.42 |
| **Marble trim or cornice stones with light hand carvings**<br>*Replace* Materials .....117.00   Labor...........14.10<br>*Remove* ..................   Labor ............2.72 | lf | $2.72 | $131.10 | $133.82 |
| **Marble trim or cornice stones with medium hand carvings**<br>*Replace* Materials.....141.00   Labor...........14.10<br>*Remove* ..................   Labor ............2.72 | lf | $2.72 | $155.10 | $157.82 |
| **Marble trim or cornice stones with heavy hand carvings**<br>*Replace* Materials.....169.00   Labor...........14.10<br>*Remove* ..................   Labor ............2.72 | lf | $2.72 | $183.10 | $185.82 |
| **Sandstone trim or cornice stones, all horizontal patterns**<br>*Replace* Materials.....14.30   Labor...........14.10<br>*Remove* ..................   Labor ............2.72 | lf | $2.72 | $28.40 | $31.12 |

### CUT STONE

**All horizontal patterns** are shallow. Typical depth is 3/4" or less but may be as deep as 1".

**Complex horizontal patterns** are deep Gothic style reliefs that require two passes through the stone planer.

**Vertical patterns** are straight vertical cuts like dentil, meander, or fretwork.

**Light hand carvings** are usually less than 3/4" deep and do not cover the entire face of the stone with detailed work.

**Medium hand carvings** are heavier carvings like vermiculation, Acanthus, and so forth.

**Heavy hand carvings** are heavy and deep carvings including a lion's face, a human face, and so forth.

△ *horizontal patterns*

| | Item Description | Unit | Remove | Replace | Total |
|---|---|---|---|---|---|
| **CUT STONE ▶**<br>**TRIM OR CORNICE**<br>*continued* | **Sandstone trim or cornice stones, complex horizontal patterns (Gothic)**<br>*Replace* Materials......31.20      Labor..........14.10<br>*Remove* ....................      Labor ...........2.72 | lf | $2.72 | $45.30 | $48.02 |
| | **Sandstone trim or cornice stones with vertical patterns**<br>*Replace* Materials......63.40      Labor..........14.10<br>*Remove* ....................      Labor ...........2.72 | lf | $2.72 | $77.50 | $80.22 |
| | **Sandstone trim or cornice stones with light hand carvings**<br>*Replace* Materials ......94.60      Labor..........14.10<br>*Remove* ....................      Labor ...........2.72 | lf | $2.72 | $108.70 | $111.42 |
| | **Sandstone trim or cornice stones with medium hand carvings**<br>*Replace* Materials .....119.00      Labor..........14.10<br>*Remove* ....................      Labor ...........2.72 | lf | $2.72 | $133.10 | $135.82 |
| *△ horizontal patterns* | **Sandstone trim or cornice stones with heavy hand carvings**<br>*Replace* Materials ....146.00      Labor..........14.10<br>*Remove* ....................      Labor ...........2.72 | lf | $2.72 | $160.10 | $162.82 |
| *replace section to match ▷* | **Replace section of stone trim or cornice cut to match**<br>*Replace* Materials .....417.00      Labor..........112.00<br>▶ Includes plaster or clay model with work performed on site or in a shop within 150 miles of the site. | ea | — | $529.00 | $529.00 |
| **CUT STONE SILL ▶**<br>*Up to 10" wide.* | **1-1/2" bluestone window sill or stool**<br>*Replace* Materials ......12.60      Labor..........12.70<br>*Remove* ....................      Labor ...........2.88 | lf | $2.88 | $25.30 | $28.18 |
| *4" ▽* | **4" cast stone window sill**<br>*Replace* Materials........8.70      Labor..........12.70<br>*Remove* ....................      Labor ...........2.88<br>▶ 4" thick at edge.  Up to 6" thick at center or end of sill. | lf | $2.88 | $21.40 | $24.28 |
| | **1-1/2" granite window sill or stool**<br>*Replace* Materials.......13.60      Labor..........12.70<br>*Remove* ....................      Labor ...........2.88 | lf | $2.88 | $26.30 | $29.18 |
| | **4" granite window sill**<br>*Replace* Materials ......24.60      Labor..........12.70<br>*Remove* ....................      Labor ...........2.88<br>▶ 4" thick at edge.  Up to 6" thick at center or end of sill. | lf | $2.88 | $37.30 | $40.18 |
| *△ 1-1/2"* | **1-1/2" limestone window sill or stool**<br>*Replace* Materials ......12.30      Labor..........12.70<br>*Remove* ....................      Labor ...........2.88 | lf | $2.88 | $25.00 | $27.88 |
| | **4" limestone window sill**<br>*Replace* Materials ......22.10      Labor..........12.70<br>*Remove* ....................      Labor ...........2.88<br>▶ 4" thick at edge.  Up to 6" thick at center or end of sill. | lf | $2.88 | $34.80 | $37.68 |
| | **1-1/2" marble window sill or stool**<br>*Replace* Materials ......14.50      Labor..........12.70<br>*Remove* ....................      Labor ...........2.88 | lf | $2.88 | $27.20 | $30.08 |
| | **1-1/2" sandstone window sill or stool**<br>*Replace* Materials........9.00      Labor..........12.70<br>*Remove* ....................      Labor ...........2.88 | lf | $2.88 | $21.70 | $24.58 |

| Item Description | Unit | Remove | Replace | Total |
|---|---|---|---|---|
| **4" sandstone window sill**<br>*Replace* Materials......17.70  Labor..........12.70<br>*Remove* .................  Labor..........2.88<br>► 4" thick at edge. Up to 6" thick at center or end of sill. | lf | $2.88 | $30.40 | $33.28 |
| **1-1/2" slate window sill or stool**<br>*Replace* Materials......14.60  Labor..........12.70<br>*Remove* .................  Labor..........2.88 | lf | $2.88 | $27.30 | $30.18 |
| **10" terra-cotta wall cap**<br>*Replace* Materials......6.62  Labor..........7.03<br>*Remove* .................  Labor..........1.65 | lf | $1.65 | $13.65 | $15.30 |
| **12" terra-cotta wall cap**<br>*Replace* Materials......10.80  Labor..........7.03<br>*Remove* .................  Labor..........1.65 | lf | $1.65 | $17.83 | $19.48 |
| **Aluminum wall cap all wall widths**<br>*Replace* Materials......12.50  Labor..........6.88<br>*Remove* .................  Labor..........50 | lf | $.50 | $19.38 | $19.88 |
| **10" wide concrete coping**<br>*Replace* Materials......13.70  Labor..........6.35<br>*Remove* .................  Labor..........2.72 | lf | $2.72 | $20.05 | $22.77 |
| **12" wide concrete coping**<br>*Replace* Materials......14.40  Labor..........6.35<br>*Remove* .................  Labor..........2.72 | lf | $2.72 | $20.75 | $23.47 |
| **14" wide concrete coping**<br>*Replace* Materials......18.20  Labor..........6.35<br>*Remove* .................  Labor..........2.72 | lf | $2.72 | $24.55 | $27.27 |
| **8" wide granite coping stone**<br>*Replace* Materials......27.50  Labor..........7.03<br>*Remove* .................  Labor..........2.72 | lf | $2.72 | $34.53 | $37.25 |
| **10" wide granite coping stone**<br>*Replace* Materials......31.70  Labor..........7.03<br>*Remove* .................  Labor..........2.72 | lf | $2.72 | $38.73 | $41.45 |
| **12" wide granite coping stone**<br>*Replace* Materials......36.00  Labor..........7.03<br>*Remove* .................  Labor..........2.72 | lf | $2.72 | $43.03 | $45.75 |
| **8" wide limestone coping stone**<br>*Replace* Materials......16.40  Labor..........7.03<br>*Remove* .................  Labor..........2.72 | lf | $2.72 | $23.43 | $26.15 |
| **10" wide limestone coping stone**<br>*Replace* Materials......16.80  Labor..........7.03<br>*Remove* .................  Labor..........2.72 | lf | $2.72 | $23.83 | $26.55 |
| **12" wide limestone coping stone**<br>*Replace* Materials......19.60  Labor..........7.03<br>*Remove* .................  Labor..........2.72 | lf | $2.72 | $26.63 | $29.35 |
| **8" wide marble coping stone**<br>*Replace* Materials......23.20  Labor..........7.03<br>*Remove* .................  Labor..........2.72 | lf | $2.72 | $30.23 | $32.95 |

◄ **WALL CAP**

◄ **WALL COPING**
From 4" to 6" thick at center with straight or curved taper to edges. Widths over 8" include drip grooves on each side as illustrated below.

**RELATED ITEMS**
Cleaning ....................63
Fireplaces....................241
Painting ....................340

| Item Description | Unit | Remove | Replace | Total |
|---|---|---|---|---|
| **WALL COPING ▶** *continued* **10" wide marble coping stone** | lf | $2.72 | $35.73 | $38.45 |
| *Replace* Materials ......28.70    Labor ............7.03 | | | | |
| *Remove* .......................    Labor ............2.72 | | | | |
| **12" wide marble coping stone** | lf | $2.72 | $43.03 | $45.75 |
| *Replace* Materials ......36.00    Labor ............7.03 | | | | |
| *Remove* .......................    Labor ............2.72 | | | | |
| **REPOINT BRICK ▶ WALL** *Tuck pointing. To mask and grout deduct 12%.* **Repoint running bond brick wall** | sf | — | $4.41 | $4.41 |
| *Replace* Materials ........ .31    Labor ............4.10 | | | | |
| **Repoint common bond brick wall** | sf | — | $4.53 | $4.53 |
| *Replace* Materials ........ .31    Labor ............4.22 | | | | |
| ▶ Also called American bond.  Every sixth course is a full course of full-length headers. | | | | |
| **Repoint Flemish bond brick wall** | sf | — | $4.91 | $4.91 |
| *Replace* Materials ........ .31    Labor ............4.60 | | | | |
| ▶ Each course is made of alternating stretchers and headers. | | | | |
| **Repoint English bond brick wall** | sf | — | $5.17 | $5.17 |
| *Replace* Materials ........ .31    Labor ............4.86 | | | | |
| ▶ Alternating full courses made from stretchers and headers.  The joints between stretchers in all courses align vertically. | | | | |
| **Repoint English cross bond brick wall** | sf | — | $5.17 | $5.17 |
| *Replace* Materials ........ .31    Labor ............4.86 | | | | |
| ▶ Also called Dutch bond.  A variation of English bond.  The vertical joints between stretcher bricks, in alternate courses, align vertically with the center of the stretcher brick in the course above and below. | | | | |
| **Repoint stack bond brick wall** | sf | — | $3.43 | $3.43 |
| *Replace* Materials ........ .31    Labor ............3.12 | | | | |
| ▶ All vertical and horizontal joints align. | | | | |
| **Repoint all header bond brick wall** | sf | — | $3.84 | $3.84 |
| *Replace* Materials ........ .31    Labor ............3.53 | | | | |
| ▶ All bricks are laid as headers. | | | | |
| **Repoint soldier course brick wall** | sf | — | $4.34 | $4.34 |
| *Replace* Materials ........ .31    Labor ............4.03 | | | | |
| ▶ All bricks are stood on end with edge showing. | | | | |
| **Repoint sailor course brick wall** | sf | — | $4.07 | $4.07 |
| *Replace* Materials ........ .31    Labor ............3.76 | | | | |
| ▶ All bricks are stood on end with face showing. | | | | |
| **Repoint basketweave brick wall** | sf | — | $6.54 | $6.54 |
| *Replace* Materials ........ .31    Labor ............6.23 | | | | |
| ▶ A wide variety of patterns with alternating sections of horizontal and vertical brick. | | | | |
| **Repoint herringbone weave brick wall** | sf | — | $6.66 | $6.66 |
| *Replace* Materials ........ .31    Labor ............6.35 | | | | |
| ▶ Also called diagonal basketweave.  Bricks are placed at an angle (usually 45 degree) in alternate sections angling up and down. | | | | |
| **Repoint diagonal bond brick wall** | sf | — | $5.78 | $5.78 |
| *Replace* Materials ........ .31    Labor ............5.47 | | | | |
| ▶ All bricks laid at an angle, usually 45 degree. | | | | |

*running bond △*

*common bond △*

*Flemish bond △*

*English bond △*

*English cross bond △*

*stack bond △*

*header bond △*

*soldier course △*

*sailor course △*

*basketweave △*

*diagonal △*

| Item Description | Unit | Remove | Replace | Total | |
|---|---|---|---|---|---|
| **Repoint coursed ashlar style bond brick wall with two sizes of bricks** | sf | — | $4.87 | $4.87 | |
| *Replace* Materials ........ .31        Labor ........... 4.56 | | | | | |
| ▶ A pattern that uses two sizes of bricks to simulate coursed ashlar stone patterns. Usually one size of brick equals two of the second size. | | | | | *herringbone* △ |
| | | | | | ◁ add for hard mortar |
| **Add 12% to repoint brick wall with hard existing mortar** | | | | | |
| **Add 22% to repoint brick wall with very hard existing mortar** | | | | | |
| **Add 18% to repoint brick wall with butter joint mortar** | | | | | *coursed ashlar* △ |
| **Minimum charge to repoint brick wall** | ea | — | $206.00 | $206.00 | ◁ minimum charge |
| *Replace* Materials ...... 16.00        Labor ......... 190.00 | | | | | |
| **Repoint rubble lay stone wall** | sf | — | $12.06 | $12.06 | ◀ **REPOINT STONE WALL** |
| *Replace* Materials ........ 1.46        Labor ........... 10.60 | | | | | |
| **Repoint ashlar lay stone wall** | sf | — | $11.03 | $11.03 | |
| *Replace* Materials ........ 1.15        Labor ........... 9.88 | | | | | |
| **Minimum charge to repoint stone wall** | ea | — | $206.00 | $206.00 | |
| *Replace* Materials ...... 16.00        Labor ......... 190.00 | | | | | *rubble lay* △ |
| **Remove brick veneer, salvage bricks, and re-lay** | sf | — | $34.98 | $34.98 | ◀ **SALVAGE BRICK** |
| *Replace* Materials ........ 1.68        Labor ........... 33.30 | | | | | |
| ▶ Existing bricks are removed and old mortar chipped away. An average of 75% of the bricks are salvaged. To replace the missing bricks, 25% of the salvaged bricks are sawn in half length wise and back filled with mortar to fit. Finish wall includes 50% full bricks and 50% backfilled half bricks. Normally not used for large walls, but on sections of damaged wall where bricks cannot be matched. | | | | | |
| **Replace single brick** | sf | — | $18.35 | $18.35 | ◀ **BRICK WALL REPAIR** |
| *Replace* Materials ........ 1.95        Labor ........... 16.40 | | | | | |
| ▶ A single damaged brick is broken out and replaced. | | | | | |
| **Tooth in brick patch up to 4 sf** | sf | — | $54.90 | $54.90 | |
| *Replace* Materials ...... 35.80        Labor ........... 19.10 | | | | | |
| ▶ A small section of brick (less than 4 sf) is broken out and replaced. | | | | | |
| **Tooth in brick patch, 4 to 20 sf** | sf | — | $24.50 | $24.50 | |
| *Replace* Materials ........ 8.90        Labor ........... 15.60 | | | | | |
| ▶ A small section over 4 sf but less than 20 sf is replaced  Existing bricks remain either above, below, or both.  (Does not include demolition.) | | | | | |
| **Minimum charge to repair brick wall** | ea | — | $495.00 | $495.00 | ◁ minimum charge |
| *Replace* Materials ...... 59.00        Labor ........ 436.00 | | | | | |
| **Replace single stone** | ea | — | $20.96 | $20.96 | ◀ **STONE WALL REPAIR** |
| *Replace* Materials ........ 3.76        Labor ........... 17.20 | | | | | |
| ▶ A single damaged stone is broken out and replaced. | | | | | |
| **Tooth in stone patch up to 4 sf** | ea | — | $90.60 | $90.60 | |
| *Replace* Materials ...... 69.10        Labor ........... 21.50 | | | | | |
| ▶ A small section of stone (less than 4 sf) is broken out and replaced. | | | | | |
| **Tooth in stone patch, 4 to 20 sf** | ea | — | $39.50 | $39.50 | |
| *Replace* Materials ...... 17.30        Labor .......... 22.20 | | | | | |
| ▶ A section of stone veneer is replaced in an area over 4 sf but less than 20 sf. Existing stones remain either above, below, or both.  (Does not include demolition.) | | | | | |

| Item Description | Unit | Remove | Replace | Total |
|---|---|---|---|---|
| **STONE WALL ▶ REPAIR** *continued* | | | | |
| **Remove segment of rubble stone wall and re-lay** | cf | — | $171.17 | $171.17 |
| *Replace* Materials........4.17        Labor .........167.00 | | | | |
| ▶ Existing stones are removed, old mortar is chipped away and wall is re-laid. | | | | |
| **Remove segment of rubble stone veneer and re-lay** | sf | — | $81.69 | $81.69 |
| *Replace* Materials........1.39        Labor ..........80.30 | | | | |
| ▶ Existing stones are removed, old mortar is chipped away and veneer is re-laid. | | | | |
| **Remove segment of ashlar stone wall and re-lay** | cf | — | $164.03 | $164.03 |
| *Replace* Materials........3.03        Labor .........161.00 | | | | |
| ▶ Existing stones are removed, old mortar is chipped away and wall is re-laid. | | | | |
| **Remove segment of ashlar stone veneer and re-lay** | sf | — | $80.00 | $80.00 |
| *Replace* Materials ...... 1.00        Labor...........79.00 | | | | |
| ▶ Existing stones are removed, old mortar is chipped away and veneer is re-laid. | | | | |
| **Minimum charge to repair stone wall** | ea | — | $597.00 | $597.00 |
| *Replace* Materials .....113.00        Labor ........484.00 | | | | |
| **STONE CARVING ▶** *Work performed on site or in a shop within 150 miles of the site. Does not include clay or plaster model.* **Carve stone with light hand carvings** | si | — | $1.53 | $1.53 |
| *Replace* ........................        Labor ............1.53 | | | | |
| ▶ Light carvings usually less than 3/4" deep and do not cover the entire face of the stone with detailed work. | | | | |
| **Carve stone with medium hand carvings** | si | — | $2.25 | $2.25 |
| *Replace* ........................        Labor ............2.25 | | | | |
| ▶ Heavier carvings like vermiculation, Acanthus, and so forth. | | | | |
| △ *vermiculation* **Carve stone with heavy hand carvings** | si | — | $3.17 | $3.17 |
| *Replace* ........................        Labor ............3.17 | | | | |
| ▶ Heavy and deep carvings including a lion's face, a human face, and so forth. | | | | |
| **Add 120% for carving stone to match existing work** | | | | |
| *clay or plaster model* ▷ **Clay or plaster model for stone carvings** | si | — | $1.38 | $1.38 |
| *Replace* Materials........1.38 | | | | |
| ▶ Models for light carvings may run 15% less and models for heavy carvings like faces may run 20% to 45% more. It is not unusual for models to cost as much or more as the actual carving. | | | | |
| **Minimum charge for clay or plaster model for stone carvings** | si | — | $143.00 | $143.00 |
| *Replace* Materials ....143.00 | | | | |
| **CARVED STONE ▶ REPAIR** **Repair carved stone with epoxy** | si | — | $1.27 | $1.27 |
| *Replace* Materials ........ .22        Labor............ 1.05 | | | | |
| ▶ Reattach broken piece of carved stone using epoxy and, when necessary, non-ferrous pins. | | | | |
| **Repair carved stone with stucco** | si | — | $.99 | $.99 |
| *Replace* Materials ........ .03        Labor............. .96 | | | | |
| ▶ Reface damaged or weathered stone with stucco and shape stucco to match carving. | | | | |
| *minimum charge* ▷ **Minimum charge to repair carved stone** | ea | — | $207.00 | $207.00 |
| *Replace* Materials ......33.00        Labor .........174.00 | | | | |
| **STONE REPAIR ▶** **Epoxy repair and pin broken stone** | ea | — | $66.46 | $66.46 |
| *Replace* Materials........8.46        Labor ..........58.00 | | | | |
| ▶ Reattach broken piece of stone using epoxy and, when necessary, non-ferrous pins. | | | | |

| Item Description | Unit | Remove | Replace | Total | |
|---|---|---|---|---|---|
| **Reconstitute delaminating stone with epoxy and reinforcing pins**<br>*Replace* Materials ........ .25        Labor ............ .57<br>► Drill holes and inject epoxy in between layers of delaminating stone.  Non-ferrous reinforcing pins are also added for strength. | si | — | $.82 | $.82 | |
| **Reface damaged stone with grout mixed to match**<br>*Replace* Materials ........ .03        Labor ............6.50<br>► Grout or plaster colored to match stone is applied over the face of damaged or weathered stone and shaped to match. | si | — | $6.53 | $6.53 | |
| **Minimum charge for stone epoxy repair work**<br>*Replace* Materials ......33.00        Labor .........121.00 | ea | — | $154.00 | $154.00 | ◁ minimum charge |
| **Hand clean brick wall**<br>*Replace* Materials ........ .07        Labor ............1.28<br>► With bristle brush and muriatic acid (or similar). | sf | — | $1.35 | $1.35 | ◄ CLEAN MASONRY |
| **Hand clean stone wall**<br>*Replace* Materials ........ .07        Labor ............1.37<br>► With bristle brush and muriatic acid (or similar). | sf | — | $1.44 | $1.44 | |
| **Pressure spray brick wall**<br>*Replace* Materials ........ .09        Labor ............ .34<br>► With water only or with cleaning chemicals. | sf | — | $.43 | $.43 | |
| **Pressure spray stone wall**<br>*Replace* Materials ........ .09        Labor ............ .34<br>► With water only or with cleaning chemicals. | sf | — | $.43 | $.43 | |
| **Steam clean brick wall**<br>*Replace* ...................... Labor ............ .46 | sf | — | $.46 | $.46 | |
| **Steam clean stone wall**<br>*Replace* ...................... Labor ............ .49 | sf | — | $.49 | $.49 | |
| **Wet sandblast brick wall**<br>*Replace* Materials ........ .29        Labor ............1.39 | sf | — | $1.68 | $1.68 | |
| **Wet sandblast stone wall**<br>*Replace* Materials ........ .29        Labor ............1.47 | sf | — | $1.76 | $1.76 | |
| **Cut opening in brick wall to 6" thick**<br>*Replace* ...................... Labor ............7.48 | lf | — | $7.48 | $7.48 | ◄ CUT OPENING IN MASONRY WALL<br>*Cut masonry wall with concrete saw.  See next page for prices to insert lintels into opening.* |
| **Cut opening in brick wall 7" to 12" thick**<br>*Replace* ...................... Labor ............8.36 | lf | — | $8.36 | $8.36 | |
| **Cut opening in brick veneer wall**<br>*Replace* ...................... Labor ............7.19 | lf | — | $7.19 | $7.19 | |
| **Cut opening in stone wall to 6" thick**<br>*Replace* ...................... Labor ............8.36 | lf | — | $8.36 | $8.36 | |
| **Cut opening in stone wall 7" to 12" thick**<br>*Replace* ...................... Labor ............9.49 | lf | — | $9.49 | $9.49 | |
| **Cut opening in stone veneer wall**<br>*Replace* ...................... Labor ............8.03 | lf | — | $8.03 | $8.03 | |

| | Item Description | Unit | Remove | Replace | Total |
|---|---|---|---|---|---|
| **SHORE MASONRY ▶ OPENING** | **Shore masonry opening for work per lf of header** *Replace* Materials.......11.00 Labor...........16.10 ▶ 2" x 6" or 2" x 8" framing members sheathed with plywood. | lf | — | $27.10 | $27.10 |
| | **Shore arched masonry opening for work** *Replace* Materials.......11.70 Labor...........21.10 ▶ 2" x 6" or 2" x 8" framing members sheathed with plywood that follows curved shape of arch. | lf | — | $32.80 | $32.80 |
| **CONCRETE LINTEL ▶** | **Concrete lintel for opening in 4" thick brick or stone** *Replace* Materials........8.90 Labor ............3.26 | lf | — | $12.16 | $12.16 |
| | **Concrete lintel for opening in 6" thick brick or stone** *Replace* Materials.......11.90 Labor ............4.18 | lf | — | $16.08 | $16.08 |
| | **Concrete lintel for opening in 8" thick brick or stone** *Replace* Materials ......12.80 Labor ............4.68 | lf | — | $17.48 | $17.48 |
| | **Concrete lintel for opening in 10" thick brick or stone** *Replace* Materials......22.10 Labor ............5.64 | lf | — | $27.74 | $27.74 |
| | **Concrete lintel for opening in 12" thick brick or stone** *Replace* Materials......29.40 Labor ............6.23 | lf | — | $35.63 | $35.63 |
| | **Add for key cast into lintel** *Replace* Materials......46.00 | ea | — | $46.00 | $46.00 |
| **ANGLE-IRON ▶ LINTEL** | **Angle iron lintel for opening in 4" thick brick or stone** *Replace* Materials........3.57 Labor ............2.55 | lf | — | $6.12 | $6.12 |
| | **Angle iron lintel for opening in 6" thick brick or stone** *Replace* Materials.......7.14 Labor ............2.55 | lf | — | $9.69 | $9.69 |
| | **Angle iron lintel for opening in 8" thick brick or stone** *Replace* Materials.......7.58 Labor ............2.76 | lf | — | $10.34 | $10.34 |
| | **Angle iron lintel for opening in 10" thick brick or stone** *Replace* Materials.......8.51 Labor ............2.80 | lf | — | $11.31 | $11.31 |
| | **Angle iron lintel for opening in 12" thick brick or stone** *Replace* Materials......12.30 Labor ............2.84 | lf | — | $15.14 | $15.14 |

*lintel with plain key* △

*lintel with winged key* △

*lintel with recessed key* △

✍ NOTES: _____

_____

_____

_____

_____

_____

_____

_____

_____

_____

# TIME & MATERIAL CHARTS (selected items)

## Masonry Materials

| DESCRIPTION | MATERIAL PRICE | GROSS COVERAGE | WASTE | NET COVERAGE | UNIT PRICE |
|---|---|---|---|---|---|
| **Rebar** | | | | | |
| #3 (3/8" .376 pound per lf) | $3.32 per 20' bar | 20 | 4% | 19.2 | $.17 lf |
| #4 (1/2" .668 pounds per lf) | $4.24 per 20' bar | 20 | 4% | 19.2 | $.22 lf |
| #5 (5/8" 1.043 pounds per lf) | $6.59 per 20' bar | 20 | 4% | 19.2 | $.34 lf |
| #6 (3/4" 1.502 pounds per lf) | $9.99 per 20' bar | 20 | 4% | 19.2 | $.52 lf |
| **Mortar and grout supplies** | | | | | |
| gypsum cement | $15.20 per bag | 80 | 12% | 70.4 | $.22 lb |
| masonry cement | $6.40 per bag | 70 | 12% | 61.6 | $.10 lb |
| white masonry cement | $19.60 per bag | 70 | 12% | 61.6 | $.32 lb |
| hydrated lime | $6.66 per bag | 50 | 12% | 44 | $.15 lb |
| double hydrated lime | $9.00 per bag | 50 | 12% | 44 | $.20 lb |
| screened and washed sand, delivered | $22.50 per ton | 1 | 0% | 1 | $22.50 ton |
| **Reinforcing wire strip** | | | | | |
| 4" ladder style | $.13 lf | 1 | 2% | .98 | $.13 lf |
| 12" ladder style | $.18 lf | 1 | 2% | .98 | $.18 lf |
| 4" truss style | $.17 lf | 1 | 2% | .98 | $.17 lf |
| 12" truss style | $.22 lf | 1 | 2% | .98 | $.22 lf |
| add **30%** for galvanized | | | | | |
| **Masonry ties** | | | | | |
| galvanized 22 gauge corrugated veneer wall tie | $.17 ea | 1 | 2% | .98 | $.17 ea |
| galvanized 16 gauge corrugated veneer wall tie | $.18 ea | 1 | 2% | .98 | $.18 ea |
| rectangular galvanized wall tie | $.21 ea | 1 | 2% | .98 | $.21 ea |
| galvanized "Z" style cavity wall tie | $.20 ea | 1 | 2% | .98 | $.20 ea |
| **Grout** | | | | | |
| for 6" wide bond beam | $.73 lf | 1 | 11% | .89 | $.82 lf |
| for 8" wide bond beam | $.91 lf | 1 | 11% | .89 | $1.02 lf |
| for 10" wide bond beam | $1.15 lf | 1 | 11% | .89 | $1.29 lf |
| for 12" wide bond beam | $1.38 lf | 1 | 11% | .89 | $1.55 lf |
| for cells in 6" wide concrete block | $.87 lf | 1 | 11% | .89 | $.98 lf |
| for cells in 8" wide concrete block | $1.28 lf | 1 | 11% | .89 | $1.44 lf |
| for cells in 10" wide concrete block | $1.63 lf | 1 | 11% | .89 | $1.83 lf |
| for cells in 12" wide concrete block | $2.06 lf | 1 | 11% | .89 | $2.31 lf |
| **3/8" brick mortar** | | | | | |
| for 4" wide standard non-modular or three-inch | $7.34 cf | 25 | 25% | 18.75 | $.39 sf |
| for 4" wide oversize non-modular | $7.34 cf | 26 | 25% | 19.5 | $.38 sf |
| for 4" wide engineer | $7.34 cf | 27 | 25% | 20.25 | $.36 sf |
| for 4" wide jumbo closure | $7.34 cf | 31 | 25% | 23.25 | $.32 sf |
| for 4" wide double | $7.34 cf | 37 | 25% | 27.75 | $.26 sf |
| for 4" wide Roman | $7.34 cf | 21 | 25% | 15.75 | $.47 sf |
| for 4" wide Norman | $7.34 cf | 26 | 25% | 19.5 | $.38 sf |
| for 4" wide Norwegian | $7.34 cf | 30 | 25% | 22.5 | $.33 sf |
| for 4" wide jumbo utility | $7.34 cf | 36 | 25% | 27 | $.27 sf |
| for 4" wide triple | $7.34 cf | 44 | 25% | 33 | $.22 sf |
| for 6" wide Norwegian | $7.34 cf | 20 | 25% | 15 | $.49 sf |
| for 6" wide Norman | $7.34 cf | 16.8 | 25% | 12.6 | $.58 sf |
| for 6" wide jumbo | $7.34 cf | 24 | 25% | 18 | $.41 sf |
| for 8" wide jumbo | $7.34 cf | 18 | 25% | 13.5 | $.54 sf |
| **3/8" concrete block mortar (8" x 16" face)** | | | | | |
| for 4" wide | $7.34 cf | 40 | 25% | 30 | $.24 sf |
| for 6" wide | $7.34 cf | 30 | 25% | 22.5 | $.33 sf |
| for 8" wide | $7.34 cf | 25 | 25% | 18.75 | $.39 sf |
| for 10" wide | $7.34 cf | 20.5 | 25% | 15.38 | $.48 sf |
| for 12" wide | $7.34 cf | 16.6 | 25% | 12.45 | $.59 sf |

. . . More ➤

## Masonry Materials *continued*

| DESCRIPTION | MATERIAL PRICE | GROSS COVERAGE | WASTE | NET COVERAGE | UNIT PRICE |
|---|---|---|---|---|---|
| **3/8" concrete slump block mortar (4" x 16" face)** | | | | | |
| for 4" wide | $7.34 cf | 34 | 25% | 25.5 | $.29 sf |
| for 6" wide | $7.34 cf | 24 | 25% | 18 | $.41 sf |
| for 8" wide | $7.34 cf | 21 | 25% | 15.75 | $.47 sf |
| for 10" wide | $7.34 cf | 16.5 | 25% | 12.38 | $.59 sf |
| for 12" wide | $7.34 cf | 12.6 | 25% | 9.45 | $.78 sf |
| **3/8" concrete screen block mortar (12" x 12" face)** | | | | | |
| for 4" wide | $7.34 cf | 35.6 | 25% | 26.7 | $.27 sf |
| **3/8" backing tile mortar (12" x 12" face)** | | | | | |
| for 4" thick | $7.34 cf | 35.6 | 25% | 26.7 | $.27 sf |
| for 6" thick | $7.34 cf | 26.5 | 25% | 19.88 | $.37 sf |
| for 8" thick | $7.34 cf | 22.5 | 25% | 16.88 | $.43 sf |
| **3/8" structural tile mortar (8" x 16" face)** | | | | | |
| for 4" thick | $7.34 cf | 40 | 25% | 30 | $.24 sf |
| for 6" thick | $7.34 cf | 30 | 25% | 22.5 | $.33 sf |
| for 8" thick | $7.34 cf | 25 | 25% | 18.75 | $.39 sf |
| **3/8" gypsum partition tile mortar (12" x 30" face)** | | | | | |
| for 4" thick | $7.34 cf | 78 | 25% | 58.5 | $.13 sf |
| for 6" thick | $7.34 cf | 66 | 25% | 49.5 | $.15 sf |
| **3/8" white mortar for glass blocks** | | | | | |
| for block with 4" x 8" face | $9.31 cf | 26 | 25% | 19.5 | $.48 sf |
| for block with 6" x 6" face | $9.31 cf | 29 | 25% | 21.75 | $.43 sf |
| for block with 6" x 8" face | $9.31 cf | 36 | 25% | 27 | $.34 sf |
| for block with 8" x 8" face | $9.31 cf | 44 | 25% | 33 | $.28 sf |
| for block with 12" x 12" face | $9.31 cf | 35.6 | 25% | 26.7 | $.35 sf |
| deduct **22%** for natural gray mortar in glass block wall | | | | | |
| deduct **8%** for colored mortar in glass block wall | | | | | |
| **Mortar for stone walls** | | | | | |
| mortar for rubble stone wall | $7.34 cf | 4.41 | 32% | 3 | $2.45 cf |
| mortar for ashlar stone wall | $7.34 cf | 5.5 | 25% | 4.13 | $1.78 cf |
| mortar for rubble stone veneer | $7.34 cf | 13.2 | 32% | 8.98 | $.82 sf |
| mortar for ashlar stone veneer | $7.34 cf | 16.5 | 25% | 12.38 | $.59 sf |
| **Brick** | | | | | |
| deduct **16%** for common brick | | | | | |
| add **$546.00** per thousand for glazed brick | | | | | |
| 4" wide standard non-modular | $635.00 per thousand | 1,000 | 4% | 960 | $.66 ea |
| 4" wide oversize non-modular | $633.00 per thousand | 1,000 | 4% | 960 | $.66 ea |
| 4" wide three-inch non-modular | $626.00 per thousand | 1,000 | 4% | 960 | $.65 ea |
| 4" wide standard | $505.00 per thousand | 1,000 | 4% | 960 | $.53 ea |
| 4" wide used | $1,100.00 per thousand | 1,000 | 4% | 960 | $1.15 ea |
| 4" wide engineer | $621.00 per thousand | 1,000 | 4% | 960 | $.65 ea |
| 4" wide jumbo closure | $772.00 per thousand | 1,000 | 4% | 960 | $.80 ea |
| 4" wide double | $817.00 per thousand | 1,000 | 4% | 960 | $.85 ea |
| 4" wide Roman | $875.00 per thousand | 1,000 | 4% | 960 | $.91 ea |
| 4" wide Norman | $855.00 per thousand | 1,000 | 4% | 960 | $.89 ea |
| 4" wide Norwegian | $772.00 per thousand | 1,000 | 4% | 960 | $.80 ea |
| 4" wide jumbo utility | $1,250.00 per thousand | 1,000 | 4% | 960 | $1.30 ea |
| 4" wide triple | $1,330.00 per thousand | 1,000 | 4% | 960 | $1.39 ea |
| 6" wide Norwegian | $1,210.00 per thousand | 1,000 | 4% | 960 | $1.26 ea |
| 6" wide Norman | $1,150.00 per thousand | 1,000 | 4% | 960 | $1.20 ea |
| 6" wide jumbo | $1,460.00 per thousand | 1,000 | 4% | 960 | $1.52 ea |
| 8" wide jumbo | $1,940.00 per thousand | 1,000 | 4% | 960 | $2.02 ea |
| **Concrete block** | | | | | |
| 4" wide | $872.00 per thousand | 1,000 | 4% | 960 | $.91 ea |
| 6" wide | $976.00 per thousand | 1,000 | 4% | 960 | $1.02 ea |
| 8" wide | $1,220.00 per thousand | 1,000 | 4% | 960 | $1.27 ea |
| 10" wide | $1,530.00 per thousand | 1,000 | 4% | 960 | $1.59 ea |
| 12" wide | $2,070.00 per thousand | 1,000 | 4% | 960 | $2.16 ea |

*. . . More >*

## Masonry Materials *continued*

| DESCRIPTION | MATERIAL PRICE | GROSS COVERAGE | WASTE | NET COVERAGE | UNIT PRICE |
|---|---|---|---|---|---|
| **Lightweight concrete block** | | | | | |
| 4" wide | $985.00 per thousand | 1,000 | 4% | 960 | $1.03 ea |
| 6" wide | $1,100.00 per thousand | 1,000 | 4% | 960 | $1.15 ea |
| 8" wide | $1,380.00 per thousand | 1,000 | 4% | 960 | $1.44 ea |
| 10" wide | $1,710.00 per thousand | 1,000 | 4% | 960 | $1.78 ea |
| 12" wide | $2,340.00 per thousand | 1,000 | 4% | 960 | $2.44 ea |
| **Slump block** | | | | | |
| 4" wide | $925.00 per thousand | 1,000 | 4% | 960 | $.96 ea |
| 6" wide | $1,120.00 per thousand | 1,000 | 4% | 960 | $1.17 ea |
| 8" wide | $1,390.00 per thousand | 1,000 | 4% | 960 | $1.45 ea |
| 10" wide | $1,640.00 per thousand | 1,000 | 4% | 960 | $1.71 ea |
| 12" wide | $2,100.00 per thousand | 1,000 | 4% | 960 | $2.19 ea |
| **Fluted block (fluted one side)** | | | | | |
| 4" wide | $1,600.00 per thousand | 1,000 | 4% | 960 | $1.67 ea |
| 6" wide | $1,790.00 per thousand | 1,000 | 4% | 960 | $1.86 ea |
| 8" wide | $2,240.00 per thousand | 1,000 | 4% | 960 | $2.33 ea |
| 10" wide | $2,800.00 per thousand | 1,000 | 4% | 960 | $2.92 ea |
| 12" wide | $3,790.00 per thousand | 1,000 | 4% | 960 | $3.95 ea |
| **Fluted block (fluted two sides)** | | | | | |
| 4" wide | $1,930.00 per thousand | 1,000 | 4% | 960 | $2.01 ea |
| 6" wide | $2,160.00 per thousand | 1,000 | 4% | 960 | $2.25 ea |
| 8" wide | $2,710.00 per thousand | 1,000 | 4% | 960 | $2.82 ea |
| 10" wide | $3,390.00 per thousand | 1,000 | 4% | 960 | $3.53 ea |
| 12" wide | $4,580.00 per thousand | 1,000 | 4% | 960 | $4.77 ea |
| **Glazed block (glazed one side)** | | | | | |
| 4" wide | $8,680.00 per thousand | 1,000 | 4% | 960 | $9.04 ea |
| 6" wide | $8,920.00 per thousand | 1,000 | 4% | 960 | $9.29 ea |
| 8" wide | $9,200.00 per thousand | 1,000 | 4% | 960 | $9.58 ea |
| 10" wide | $9,440.00 per thousand | 1,000 | 4% | 960 | $9.83 ea |
| 12" wide | $9,670.00 per thousand | 1,000 | 4% | 960 | $10.10 ea |
| **Glazed block (glazed two sides)** | | | | | |
| 4" wide | $13,000.00 per thousand | 1,000 | 4% | 960 | $13.50 ea |
| 6" wide | $13,800.00 per thousand | 1,000 | 4% | 960 | $14.40 ea |
| 8" wide | $14,300.00 per thousand | 1,000 | 4% | 960 | $14.90 ea |
| 10" wide | $14,600.00 per thousand | 1,000 | 4% | 960 | $15.20 ea |
| 12" wide | $14,800.00 per thousand | 1,000 | 4% | 960 | $15.40 ea |
| **Split-face block** | | | | | |
| 4" wide | $1,780.00 per thousand | 1,000 | 4% | 960 | $1.85 ea |
| 6" wide | $2,120.00 per thousand | 1,000 | 4% | 960 | $2.21 ea |
| 8" wide | $2,850.00 per thousand | 1,000 | 4% | 960 | $2.97 ea |
| 10" wide | $3,080.00 per thousand | 1,000 | 4% | 960 | $3.21 ea |
| 12" wide | $4,130.00 per thousand | 1,000 | 4% | 960 | $4.30 ea |
| **Split-rib block** | | | | | |
| 4" wide | $1,650.00 per thousand | 1,000 | 4% | 960 | $1.72 ea |
| 6" wide | $1,710.00 per thousand | 1,000 | 4% | 960 | $1.78 ea |
| 8" wide | $2,800.00 per thousand | 1,000 | 4% | 960 | $2.92 ea |
| 10" wide | $3,120.00 per thousand | 1,000 | 4% | 960 | $3.25 ea |
| 12" wide | $3,420.00 per thousand | 1,000 | 4% | 960 | $3.56 ea |
| **Screen block** | | | | | |
| 4" wide, pattern two sides | $4,750.00 per thousand | 1,000 | 4% | 960 | $4.95 ea |
| 4" wide, pattern four sides | $9,030.00 per thousand | 1,000 | 4% | 960 | $9.41 ea |
| **Silicone treated perlite or vermiculite loose fill insulation** | | | | | |
| in 6" wide block | $6.66 4 cf bag | 21 | 3% | 20.37 | $.33 sf |
| in 8" wide block | $6.66 4 cf bag | 14.5 | 3% | 14.07 | $.47 sf |
| in 10" wide block | $6.66 4 cf bag | 11.5 | 3% | 11.16 | $.60 sf |
| in 12" wide block | $6.66 4 cf bag | 8 | 3% | 7.76 | $.86 sf |

*. . . More ≽*

## Masonry Materials *continued*

| DESCRIPTION | MATERIAL PRICE | GROSS COVERAGE | WASTE | NET COVERAGE | UNIT PRICE |
|---|---|---|---|---|---|
| **Glass block** | | | | | |
| 4" x 8" thinline smooth-face | $18.50 sf | 1 | 4% | .96 | $19.30 sf |
| 6" x 6" thinline smooth-face | $17.00 sf | 1 | 4% | .96 | $17.70 sf |
| 4" x 8" smooth-face | $23.30 sf | 1 | 4% | .96 | $24.30 sf |
| 6" x 6" smooth-face | $20.70 sf | 1 | 4% | .96 | $21.60 sf |
| 8" x 8" smooth-face | $14.50 sf | 1 | 4% | .96 | $15.10 sf |
| add 83% for solar UV reflective | | | | | |
| add 11% for patterned face | | | | | |
| add 55% for tinted | | | | | |
| **Rubble stone** | | | | | |
| coral-stone rubble | $30.70 cf | 1 | 4% | .96 | $32.00 cf |
| field-stone rubble | $24.40 cf | 1 | 4% | .96 | $25.40 cf |
| flagstone rubble | $14.00 cf | 1 | 4% | .96 | $14.60 cf |
| river stone rubble | $25.00 cf | 1 | 4% | .96 | $26.00 cf |
| lava stone rubble | $23.40 cf | 1 | 4% | .96 | $24.40 cf |
| sandstone rubble | $35.80 cf | 1 | 4% | .96 | $37.30 cf |
| **Ashlar stone** | | | | | |
| flagstone | $14.60 cf | 1 | 4% | .96 | $15.20 cf |
| limestone, natural finish | $19.80 cf | 1 | 4% | .96 | $20.60 cf |
| limestone, rough finish | $22.20 cf | 1 | 4% | .96 | $23.10 cf |
| limestone, smooth finish | $32.20 cf | 1 | 4% | .96 | $33.50 cf |
| marble, natural finish | $47.00 cf | 1 | 4% | .96 | $49.00 cf |
| marble, rough finish | $50.80 cf | 1 | 4% | .96 | $52.90 cf |
| marble, smooth finish | $63.00 cf | 1 | 4% | .96 | $65.60 cf |
| sandstone, natural finish | $19.10 cf | 1 | 4% | .96 | $19.90 cf |
| sandstone, rough finish | $21.40 cf | 1 | 4% | .96 | $22.30 cf |
| sandstone, smooth finish | $31.00 cf | 1 | 4% | .96 | $32.30 cf |
| **Wall coping** | | | | | |
| aluminum, all wall widths | $12.00 lf | 1 | 4% | .96 | $12.50 lf |
| 10" wide concrete | $12.80 lf | 1 | 2% | .98 | $13.10 lf |
| 14" wide concrete | $17.20 lf | 1 | 2% | .98 | $17.60 lf |
| 8" wide granite | $26.40 lf | 1 | 2% | .98 | $26.90 lf |
| 12" wide granite | $34.70 lf | 1 | 2% | .98 | $35.40 lf |
| 8" wide limestone | $15.50 lf | 1 | 2% | .98 | $15.80 lf |
| 12" wide limestone | $18.60 lf | 1 | 2% | .98 | $19.00 lf |
| 8" wide marble | $22.70 lf | 1 | 2% | .98 | $23.20 lf |
| 12" wide marble | $35.30 lf | 1 | 2% | .98 | $36.00 lf |

## Masonry Labor

| LABORER | BASE WAGE | PAID LEAVE | TRUE WAGE | FICA | FUTA | WORKER'S COMP. | UNEMPLOY. INSUR. | HEALTH INSUR. | RETIRE (401k) | LIABILITY INSUR. | COST PER HOUR |
|---|---|---|---|---|---|---|---|---|---|---|---|
| Mason | $23.40 | 1.83 | $25.23 | 1.93 | .20 | 7.50 | 2.20 | 2.54 | .76 | 3.28 | $43.60 |
| Mason's helper | $21.30 | 1.66 | $22.96 | 1.76 | .18 | 6.83 | 2.00 | 2.54 | .69 | 2.98 | $39.90 |
| Hod carrier | $15.90 | 1.24 | $17.14 | 1.31 | .14 | 5.10 | 1.49 | 2.54 | .51 | 2.23 | $30.50 |
| Plasterer | $22.00 | 1.72 | $23.72 | 1.81 | .19 | 6.54 | 2.06 | 2.54 | .71 | 3.08 | $40.70 |
| Stone carver | $56.80 | 4.43 | $61.23 | 4.68 | .49 | 18.21 | 5.33 | 2.54 | 1.84 | 7.96 | $102.30 |
| Demolition laborer | $13.40 | 1.05 | $14.45 | 1.11 | .121 | 4.44 | 1.26 | 2.54 | .43 | 1.88 | $26.20 |

**Paid Leave** is calculated based on two weeks paid vacation, one week sick leave, and seven paid holidays. Employer's matching portion of **FICA** is 7.65 percent. **FUTA** (Federal Unemployment) is .8 percent. **Worker's Compensation** was calculated using a national average of 29.74 percent for masonry workers and .27.58 percent for plastering workers. **Unemployment insurance** was calculated using a national average of 8.7 percent. **Health insurance** was calculated based on a projected national average for 2001 of $505 per employee (and family when applicable) per month. Employer pays 80 percent for a per month cost of $404 per employee. **Retirement** is based on a 401(k) retirement program with employer matching of 50 percent. Employee contributions to the 401(k) plan are an average of 6 percent of the true wage. **Liability insurance** is based on a national average of 12.9 percent.

# Masonry Labor Productivity

| WORK DESCRIPTION | LABORER | COST PER HOUR | PRODUCTIVITY | UNIT PRICE |
|---|---|---|---|---|
| **Demolition** | | | | |
| remove 4" masonry wall | demolition laborer | $26.20 | .087 | $2.28 sf |
| remove 12" masonry wall | demolition laborer | $26.20 | .177 | $4.64 sf |
| remove brick veneer | demolition laborer | $26.20 | .082 | $2.15 sf |
| remove block wall pilaster | demolition laborer | $26.20 | .121 | $3.17 lf |
| remove block wall grade beam cap | demolition laborer | $26.20 | .363 | $9.51 lf |
| remove terra-cotta wall cap | demolition laborer | $26.20 | .063 | $1.65 lf |
| remove coping stone | demolition laborer | $26.20 | .104 | $2.72 lf |
| remove glass block wall | demolition laborer | $26.20 | .084 | $2.20 sf |
| remove pavers on mortar base | demolition laborer | $26.20 | .120 | $3.14 sf |
| remove pavers on sand base | demolition laborer | $26.20 | .084 | $2.20 sf |
| remove stone rubble wall with no mortar | demolition laborer | $26.20 | .259 | $6.79 cf |
| remove stone rubble wall with mortar | demolition laborer | $26.20 | .439 | $11.50 cf |
| remove ashlar wall | demolition laborer | $26.20 | .439 | $11.50 cf |
| remove stone veneer | demolition laborer | $26.20 | .106 | $2.78 sf |
| remove keystone | demolition laborer | $26.20 | .198 | $5.19 ea |
| remove quoin | demolition laborer | $26.20 | .196 | $5.14 ea |
| remove veneer panels | demolition laborer | $26.20 | .074 | $1.94 sf |
| remove door or window architrave | demolition laborer | $26.20 | .131 | $3.43 lf |
| remove trim or cornice stones | demolition laborer | $26.20 | .104 | $2.72 ea |
| remove stone window sill | demolition laborer | $26.20 | .110 | $2.88 lf |
| remove precast concrete lintel | demolition laborer | $26.20 | .120 | $3.14 lf |
| **Masonry crew** | | | | |
| install masonry | mason | $43.60 | | |
| install masonry | mason's helper | $39.90 | | |
| install masonry | hod carrier / laborer | $30.50 | | |
| **install masonry** | **masonry crew** | $38.00 | | |
| **Mason & helper** | | | | |
| install masonry | mason | $43.60 | | |
| install masonry | mason's helper | $39.90 | | |
| **install masonry** | **mason & helper** | $41.80 | | |
| **Install brick wall** | | | | |
| 4" wide standard non-modular | masonry crew | $38.00 | .170 | $6.46 sf |
| 4" wide oversize non-modular | masonry crew | $38.00 | .168 | $6.38 sf |
| 4" wide three-inch non-modular | masonry crew | $38.00 | .167 | $6.35 sf |
| 4" wide standard | masonry crew | $38.00 | .169 | $6.42 sf |
| 4" wide engineer | masonry crew | $38.00 | .141 | $5.36 sf |
| 4" wide jumbo closure | masonry crew | $38.00 | .120 | $4.56 sf |
| 4" wide double | masonry crew | $38.00 | .101 | $3.84 sf |
| 4" wide Roman | masonry crew | $38.00 | .160 | $6.08 sf |
| 4" wide Norman | masonry crew | $38.00 | .130 | $4.94 sf |
| 4" wide Norwegian | masonry crew | $38.00 | .111 | $4.22 sf |
| 4" wide jumbo utility | masonry crew | $38.00 | .102 | $3.88 sf |
| 4" wide triple | masonry crew | $38.00 | .096 | $3.65 sf |
| 6" wide Norwegian | masonry crew | $38.00 | .124 | $4.71 sf |
| 6" wide Norman | masonry crew | $38.00 | .148 | $5.62 sf |
| 6" wide jumbo | masonry crew | $38.00 | .113 | $4.29 sf |
| 8" wide jumbo | masonry crew | $38.00 | .127 | $4.83 sf |
| **Install 8" wide double wythe brick wall** | | | | |
| with standard non-modular brick | masonry crew | $38.00 | .307 | $11.70 sf |
| with oversize non-modular brick | masonry crew | $38.00 | .303 | $11.50 sf |
| with three-inch non-modular brick | masonry crew | $38.00 | .300 | $11.40 sf |
| with standard brick | masonry crew | $38.00 | .305 | $11.60 sf |
| with engineer brick | masonry crew | $38.00 | .253 | $9.61 sf |
| with jumbo closure brick | masonry crew | $38.00 | .216 | $8.21 sf |
| with double brick | masonry crew | $38.00 | .181 | $6.88 sf |
| with Roman brick | masonry crew | $38.00 | .287 | $10.90 sf |
| with Norman brick | masonry crew | $38.00 | .234 | $8.89 sf |
| with Norwegian brick brick | masonry crew | $38.00 | .199 | $7.56 sf |
| with jumbo utility | masonry crew | $38.00 | .184 | $6.99 sf |
| with triple brick | masonry crew | $38.00 | .173 | $6.57 sf |

. . . More ➤

## Masonry Labor Productivity *continued*

| WORK DESCRIPTION | LABORER | COST PER HOUR | PRODUCTIVITY | UNIT PRICE |
|---|---|---|---|---|
| **Install 8" wide wall with 4" wide brick and 4" wide concrete block** | | | | |
| with standard non-modular brick | masonry crew | $38.00 | .233 | $8.85 sf |
| with standard brick | masonry crew | $38.00 | .233 | $8.85 sf |
| with engineer brick | masonry crew | $38.00 | .206 | $7.83 sf |
| with jumbo closure brick | masonry crew | $38.00 | .188 | $7.14 sf |
| with double brick | masonry crew | $38.00 | .170 | $6.46 sf |
| with Roman brick | masonry crew | $38.00 | .224 | $8.51 sf |
| with Norman brick | masonry crew | $38.00 | .197 | $7.49 sf |
| with Norwegian brick | masonry crew | $38.00 | .180 | $6.84 sf |
| with jumbo utility brick | masonry crew | $38.00 | .172 | $6.54 sf |
| with triple brick | masonry crew | $38.00 | .166 | $6.31 sf |
| **Install 10" wide wall with 4" wide brick and 6" wide concrete block** | | | | |
| with standard non-modular brick | masonry crew | $38.00 | .236 | $8.97 sf |
| with standard brick | masonry crew | $38.00 | .235 | $8.93 sf |
| with engineer brick | masonry crew | $38.00 | .209 | $7.94 sf |
| with jumbo brick | masonry crew | $38.00 | .190 | $7.22 sf |
| with double brick | masonry crew | $38.00 | .173 | $6.57 sf |
| with Roman brick | masonry crew | $38.00 | .226 | $8.59 sf |
| with Norman brick | masonry crew | $38.00 | .200 | $7.60 sf |
| with Norwegian brick | masonry crew | $38.00 | .182 | $6.92 sf |
| with jumbo utility brick | masonry crew | $38.00 | .175 | $6.65 sf |
| with triple brick | masonry crew | $38.00 | .170 | $6.46 sf |
| **Install 12" wide wall with 4" wide brick and 8" wide concrete block** | | | | |
| with standard non-modular brick | masonry crew | $38.00 | .240 | $9.12 sf |
| with standard brick | masonry crew | $38.00 | .240 | $9.12 sf |
| with engineer brick | masonry crew | $38.00 | .214 | $8.13 sf |
| with jumbo closure brick | masonry crew | $38.00 | .195 | $7.41 sf |
| with double brick | masonry crew | $38.00 | .178 | $6.76 sf |
| with Roman brick | masonry crew | $38.00 | .231 | $8.78 sf |
| with Norman brick | masonry crew | $38.00 | .204 | $7.75 sf |
| with Norwegian brick | masonry crew | $38.00 | .187 | $7.11 sf |
| with jumbo utility brick | masonry crew | $38.00 | .180 | $6.84 sf |
| with triple brick | masonry crew | $38.00 | .174 | $6.61 sf |
| **Install 12" wide triple wythe wall** | | | | |
| with standard non-modular brick | masonry crew | $38.00 | .433 | $16.50 sf |
| with oversize non-modular brick | masonry crew | $38.00 | .427 | $16.20 sf |
| with three-inch non-modular brick | masonry crew | $38.00 | .424 | $16.10 sf |
| with standard brick | masonry crew | $38.00 | .429 | $16.30 sf |
| with engineer brick | masonry crew | $38.00 | .357 | $13.60 sf |
| with jumbo closure brick | masonry crew | $38.00 | .305 | $11.60 sf |
| with double brick | masonry crew | $38.00 | .255 | $9.69 sf |
| with Roman brick | masonry crew | $38.00 | .407 | $15.50 sf |
| with Norman brick | masonry crew | $38.00 | .330 | $12.50 sf |
| with Norwegian brick | masonry crew | $38.00 | .282 | $10.70 sf |
| with jumbo utility brick | masonry crew | $38.00 | .260 | $9.88 sf |
| with triple brick | masonry crew | $38.00 | .244 | $9.27 sf |
| **Install 10" wide cavity wall with 4" brick and 4" concrete block** | | | | |
| with standard non-modular brick | masonry crew | $38.00 | .244 | $9.27 sf |
| with standard brick | masonry crew | $38.00 | .243 | $9.23 sf |
| with engineer brick | masonry crew | $38.00 | .216 | $8.21 sf |
| with jumbo closure brick | masonry crew | $38.00 | .196 | $7.45 sf |
| with double brick | masonry crew | $38.00 | .178 | $6.76 sf |
| with Roman brick | masonry crew | $38.00 | .234 | $8.89 sf |
| with Norman brick | masonry crew | $38.00 | .206 | $7.83 sf |
| with Norwegian brick | masonry crew | $38.00 | .188 | $7.14 sf |
| with jumbo utility brick | masonry crew | $38.00 | .180 | $6.84 sf |
| with triple brick | masonry crew | $38.00 | .174 | $6.61 sf |
| **Install 10" wide cavity wall with 4" brick on both sides** | | | | |
| with standard non-modular brick | masonry crew | $38.00 | .321 | $12.20 sf |
| with oversize non-modular brick | masonry crew | $38.00 | .317 | $12.00 sf |
| with three-inch non-modular brick | masonry crew | $38.00 | .314 | $11.90 sf |
| with standard brick | masonry crew | $38.00 | .319 | $12.10 sf |

## Masonry Labor Productivity *continued*

| WORK DESCRIPTION | LABORER | COST PER HOUR | PRODUCTIVITY | UNIT PRICE |
|---|---|---|---|---|
| **Install 10" wide cavity wall with 4" brick on both sides** *continued* | | $38.00 | .265 | $10.10 sf |
| with engineer brick | masonry crew | $38.00 | .226 | $8.59 sf |
| with jumbo closure brick | masonry crew | $38.00 | .189 | $7.18 sf |
| with double brick | masonry crew | $38.00 | .301 | $11.40 sf |
| with Roman brick | masonry crew | $38.00 | .245 | $9.31 sf |
| with Norman brick | masonry crew | $38.00 | .209 | $7.94 sf |
| with Norwegian brick | masonry crew | $38.00 | .193 | $7.33 sf |
| with jumbo utility brick | masonry crew | $38.00 | .181 | $6.88 sf |
| with triple brick | masonry crew | $38.00 | | |
| **Install brick veneer** | | | | |
| with standard brick | masonry crew | $38.00 | .144 | $5.47 sf |
| with oversize non-modular brick | masonry crew | $38.00 | .143 | $5.43 sf |
| with three-inch non-modular brick | masonry crew | $38.00 | .141 | $5.36 sf |
| with standard brick | masonry crew | $38.00 | .144 | $5.47 sf |
| with engineer brick | masonry crew | $38.00 | .119 | $4.52 sf |
| with jumbo closure brick | masonry crew | $38.00 | .102 | $3.88 sf |
| with double brick | masonry crew | $38.00 | .085 | $3.23 sf |
| with Roman brick | masonry crew | $38.00 | .136 | $5.17 sf |
| with Norman brick | masonry crew | $38.00 | .110 | $4.18 sf |
| with Norwegian brick | masonry crew | $38.00 | .094 | $3.57 sf |
| with jumbo utility brick | masonry crew | $38.00 | .087 | $3.31 sf |
| with triple brick | masonry crew | $38.00 | .082 | $3.12 sf |
| **Install brick arch** | | | | |
| flat brick arch | masonry crew | $38.00 | 1.49 | $56.60 lf |
| elliptical brick arch | masonry crew | $38.00 | 1.85 | $70.30 lf |
| semi-circular brick arch | masonry crew | $38.00 | 1.96 | $74.50 lf |
| **Install block wall with 8" x 16" face** | | | | |
| 4" wide | masonry crew | $38.00 | .089 | $3.38 sf |
| 6" wide | masonry crew | $38.00 | .092 | $3.50 sf |
| 8" wide | masonry crew | $38.00 | .097 | $3.69 sf |
| 10" wide | masonry crew | $38.00 | .103 | $3.91 sf |
| 12" wide | masonry crew | $38.00 | .122 | $4.64 sf |
| **Install block wall with 4" x 16" face** | | | | |
| 4" wide | masonry crew | $38.00 | .102 | $3.88 sf |
| 6" wide | masonry crew | $38.00 | .106 | $4.03 sf |
| 8" wide | masonry crew | $38.00 | .112 | $4.26 sf |
| 10" wide | masonry crew | $38.00 | .119 | $4.52 sf |
| 12" wide | masonry crew | $38.00 | .140 | $5.32 sf |
| **Install lightweight block wall with 8" x 16" face** | | | | |
| 4" wide | masonry crew | $38.00 | .083 | $3.15 sf |
| 6" wide | masonry crew | $38.00 | .086 | $3.27 sf |
| 8" wide | masonry crew | $38.00 | .091 | $3.46 sf |
| 10" wide | masonry crew | $38.00 | .097 | $3.69 sf |
| 12" wide | masonry crew | $38.00 | .114 | $4.33 sf |
| **Form and pour grade-beam cap on block wall** | | | | |
| 6" wide | masonry crew | $38.00 | .106 | $4.03 lf |
| 12" wide | masonry crew | $38.00 | .120 | $4.56 lf |
| **Install glass block** | | | | |
| 4" x 8" | masonry crew | $38.00 | .333 | $12.70 sf |
| 6" x 8" | masonry crew | $38.00 | .267 | $10.10 sf |
| 8" x 8" | masonry crew | $38.00 | .208 | $7.90 sf |
| 12" x 12" | masonry crew | $38.00 | .175 | $6.65 sf |
| **Install pavers** | | | | |
| on sand base | masonry crew | $38.00 | .147 | $5.59 sf |
| on mortar base | masonry crew | $38.00 | .180 | $6.84 sf |
| full-size bricks, laid face up | masonry crew | $38.00 | .185 | $7.03 sf |
| full-size bricks, laid edge up | masonry crew | $38.00 | .208 | $7.90 sf |
| add for paver steps installed in mortar over concrete | masonry crew | $38.00 | .270 | $10.30 lf |
| add for paver steps installed over sand base | masonry crew | $38.00 | .294 | $11.20 lf |
| add for separate pattern at edges of pavers | masonry crew | $38.00 | .076 | $2.89 lf |

. . . More ➤

## Masonry Labor Productivity *continued*

| WORK DESCRIPTION | LABORER | COST PER HOUR | PRODUCTIVITY | UNIT PRICE |
|---|---|---|---|---|
| **Lay stone wall** | | | | |
| field stone rubble with no mortar | masonry crew | $38.00 | .481 | $18.30 cf |
| rubble wall | masonry crew | $38.00 | .518 | $19.70 cf |
| ashlar wall | masonry crew | $38.00 | .472 | $17.90 cf |
| add to install flat arch | masonry crew | $38.00 | 2.86 | $109.00 lf |
| add to install elliptical arch | masonry crew | $38.00 | 3.57 | $136.00 lf |
| add to install semi-circular arch | masonry crew | $38.00 | 3.70 | $141.00 lf |
| **Lay stone veneer** | | | | |
| rubble | masonry crew | $38.00 | .243 | $9.23 sf |
| ashlar | masonry crew | $38.00 | .236 | $8.97 sf |
| add to install flat arch | masonry crew | $38.00 | 1.75 | $66.50 lf |
| add to install elliptical arch | masonry crew | $38.00 | 2.17 | $82.50 lf |
| add to install semi-circular arch | masonry crew | $38.00 | 2.30 | $87.40 lf |
| **Install veneer panels** | | | | |
| cultured stone | masonry crew | $38.00 | .263 | $9.99 sf |
| natural stone | masonry crew | $38.00 | .298 | $11.30 sf |
| **Install stone architrave** | | | | |
| door | masonry crew | $38.00 | .980 | $37.20 lf |
| window | masonry crew | $38.00 | 1.00 | $38.00 lf |
| **Install trim or cornice stones** | | | | |
| all stone types | masonry crew | $38.00 | .370 | $14.10 lf |
| **Install wall cap or coping** | | | | |
| terra-cotta cap | masonry crew | $38.00 | .185 | $7.03 lf |
| aluminum cap | masonry crew | $38.00 | .181 | $6.88 lf |
| concrete coping | masonry crew | $38.00 | .167 | $6.35 lf |
| stone coping | masonry crew | $38.00 | .185 | $7.03 lf |
| **Salvage brick veneer** | | | | |
| remove, salvage bricks, and re-lay | masonry crew | $38.00 | .877 | $33.30 sf |
| **Repoint brick wall** | | | | |
| running bond | masonry crew | $38.00 | .108 | $4.10 sf |
| common bond (also called American bond) | masonry crew | $38.00 | .111 | $4.22 sf |
| Flemish bond | masonry crew | $38.00 | .121 | $4.60 sf |
| English bond | masonry crew | $38.00 | .128 | $4.86 sf |
| English cross bond (also called Dutch bond) | masonry crew | $38.00 | .128 | $4.86 sf |
| stack bond | masonry crew | $38.00 | .082 | $3.12 sf |
| all header bond | masonry crew | $38.00 | .093 | $3.53 sf |
| soldier course | masonry crew | $38.00 | .106 | $4.03 sf |
| sailor course | masonry crew | $38.00 | .099 | $3.76 sf |
| basketweave | masonry crew | $38.00 | .164 | $6.23 sf |
| herringbone weave | masonry crew | $38.00 | .167 | $6.35 sf |
| diagonal bond | masonry crew | $38.00 | .144 | $5.47 sf |
| coursed ashlar style bond | masonry crew | $38.00 | .120 | $4.56 sf |
| **Repoint stone wall** | | | | |
| rubble | masonry crew | $38.00 | .278 | $10.60 sf |
| ashlar | masonry crew | $38.00 | .260 | $9.88 sf |
| **Stone wall repair** | | | | |
| repair carved stone with epoxy | mason | $43.60 | .024 | $1.05 si |
| repair carved stone with stucco or grout | mason | $43.60 | .022 | $.96 si |
| epoxy repair and pin broken stone | mason | $43.60 | 1.33 | $58.00 ea |
| reconstitute delaminating stone with epoxy | mason | $43.60 | .013 | $.57 si |
| reface stone with grout mixed to match | mason | $43.60 | .149 | $6.50 si |
| remove segment of rubble wall and re-lay | mason & helper | $41.80 | 4.00 | $167.00 cf |
| remove segment of rubble veneer and re-lay | mason & helper | $41.80 | 1.92 | $80.30 sf |
| remove segment of ashlar wall and re-lay | mason & helper | $41.80 | 3.85 | $161.00 cf |
| remove segment of ashlar veneer and re-lay | mason & helper | $41.80 | 1.89 | $79.00 sf |
| **Carve stone** | | | | |
| with light hand carvings | stone carver | $102.30 | .015 | $1.53 si |
| with medium hand carvings | stone carver | $102.30 | .022 | $2.25 si |
| with heavy hand carvings | stone carver | $102.30 | .031 | $3.17 si |

# 25 .................................... *Outbuildings*

| Item Description | Unit | Remove | Replace | Total |
|---|---|---|---|---|
| **8' x 6' metal storage shed**<br>*Replace* Material .....230.00   Labor.........190.00<br>*Remove* .........................   Labor...........65.50 | ea | $65.50 | $420.00 | $485.50 |
| **8' x 10' metal storage shed**<br>*Replace* Material .....309.00   Labor .........204.00<br>*Remove* .........................   Labor...........71.80 | ea | $71.80 | $513.00 | $584.80 |
| **9' x 10' metal storage shed**<br>*Replace* Material .....322.00   Labor .........219.00<br>*Remove* .........................   Labor...........74.90 | ea | $74.90 | $541.00 | $615.90 |
| **10' x 12' metal storage shed**<br>*Replace* Material .....503.00   Labor .........234.00<br>*Remove* .........................   Labor...........79.60 | ea | $79.60 | $737.00 | $816.60 |
| **8' x 6' wood storage shed**<br>*Replace* Material .....532.00   Labor .........204.00<br>*Remove* .........................   Labor...........85.90 | ea | $85.90 | $736.00 | $821.90 |
| **8' x 10' wood storage shed**<br>*Replace* Material ....1250.00   Labor .........219.00<br>*Remove* .........................   Labor.........101.00 | ea | $101.00 | $1,469.00 | $1,570.00 |
| **9' x 10' wood storage shed**<br>*Replace* Material ....1420.00   Labor .........234.00<br>*Remove* .........................   Labor.........112.00 | ea | $112.00 | $1,654.00 | $1,766.00 |
| **10' x 12' wood storage shed**<br>*Replace* Material ....1680.00   Labor .........248.00<br>*Remove* .........................   Labor.........122.00 | ea | $122.00 | $1,928.00 | $2,050.00 |
| **9' gazebo, standard grade**<br>*Replace* Material ....5610.00   Labor .........517.00<br>*Remove* .........................   Labor...........116.00<br>► With cupola, simple fretwork and rails with cross-grain detailing. | ea | $116.00 | $6,127.00 | $6,243.00 |
| **9' gazebo, high grade**<br>*Replace* Material ...6830.00   Labor.........593.00<br>*Remove* .........................   Labor..........116.00<br>► With cupola, fretwork, raised-panel rails. | ea | $116.00 | $7,423.00 | $7,539.00 |
| **9' gazebo, deluxe grade**<br>*Replace* Material ....7740.00   Labor.........691.00<br>*Remove* .........................   Labor..........116.00<br>► With cupola, Queen Anne fretwork, and rails. | ea | $116.00 | $8,431.00 | $8,547.00 |
| **12' gazebo, standard grade**<br>*Replace* Material ...7990.00   Labor.........691.00<br>*Remove* .........................   Labor.........146.00<br>► With cupola, simple fretwork and rails with cross-grain detailing. | ea | $146.00 | $8,681.00 | $8,827.00 |
| **12' gazebo, high grade**<br>*Replace* Material ...9040.00   Labor.........691.00<br>*Remove* .........................   Labor.........146.00<br>► With cupola, fretwork, raised-panel rails. | ea | $146.00 | $9,731.00 | $9,877.00 |

◄ **METAL SHED**
Prefabricated metal storage shed with baked enamel finish and gable roof. Includes assembly. Does not include concrete slab or footings. Add **16%** for gambrel roof. Add **30%** for vinyl covered metal.

◄ **WOOD SHED**
Pre-built and delivered to site. Painted with trim, truss gambrel roof, panel siding, 1/2" roof sheathing, 3/4" tongue and groove floor sheathing with floor skids. Does not include footings or pier blocks. Deduct **12%** for gable roof. Deduct **15%** for gambrel roof on top of walls that are 5' tall or less.

◄ **GAZEBO**
High quality octagonal gazebos priced by diameter. Made from D grade or better kiln-dried western red cedar surfaced four sides. Wood cedar shingles. Prefabricated parts assembled on site. Add **116%** to 15' diameter price for 21' diameter triple roof gazebo. Add **$175** for bench in 9' and 12' diameter gazebos. Add **$200** for bench in 15' diameter gazebo. Add **$475** for bow roof (all sizes). Add **$275** for steps with balustrades. Deduct **25%** for no floor deck. Deduct **17%** if made from select #1 grade western red cedar.

| Item Description | Unit | Remove | Replace | Total |
|---|---|---|---|---|
| **GAZEBO ▶** *continued* | | | | |
| **12′ gazebo, deluxe grade**<br>*Replace* Material..10600.00    Labor.........691.00<br>*Remove*.........................    Labor.........146.00<br>▶ With cupola, Queen Anne fretwork, and rails. | ea | $146.00 | $11,291.00 | $11,437.00 |
| **15′ gazebo, standard grade**<br>*Replace* Material...11100.00    Labor.........830.00<br>*Remove*.........................    Labor.........187.00<br>▶ Double roof with cupola, simple fretwork and rails with cross-grain detailing. | ea | $187.00 | $11,930.00 | $12,117.00 |
| **15′ gazebo, high grade**<br>*Replace* Material..13200.00    Labor.......1040.00<br>*Remove*.........................    Labor.........187.00<br>▶ Double roof with cupola, fretwork, raised-panel rails. | ea | $187.00 | $14,240.00 | $14,427.00 |
| **15′ gazebo, deluxe grade**<br>*Replace* Material..14600.00    Labor.......1040.00<br>*Remove*.........................    Labor.........187.00<br>▶ Double roof with cupola, Queen Anne fretwork, and rails. | ea | $187.00 | $15,640.00 | $15,827.00 |
| **FREE-STANDING ▶ GREENHOUSE** *Residential style, aluminum frame. Automatic electric roof vent.*<br>**8′ x 9′ free-standing greenhouse**<br>*Replace* Material ...4030.00    Labor.........516.00<br>*Remove*.........................    Labor.........79.60 | ea | $79.60 | $4,546.00 | $4,625.60 |
| **8′ x 11′ free-standing greenhouse**<br>*Replace* Material ...4400.00    Labor.........516.00<br>*Remove*.........................    Labor .........90.10 | ea | $90.10 | $4,916.00 | $5,006.10 |
| **8′ x 14′ free-standing greenhouse**<br>*Replace* Material....4580.00    Labor .........602.00<br>*Remove*.........................    Labor.........105.00 | ea | $105.00 | $5,182.00 | $5,287.00 |
| **8′ x 17′ free-standing greenhouse**<br>*Replace* Material ...5480.00    Labor .........602.00<br>*Remove*.........................    Labor..........114.00 | ea | $114.00 | $6,082.00 | $6,196.00 |
| **LEAN-TO ▶ GREENHOUSE** *Residential style, aluminum frame. Manually controlled vents.*<br>**4′ x 8′ lean-to greenhouse**<br>*Replace* Material ....1710.00    Labor.........301.00<br>*Remove*.........................    Labor..........74.90 | ea | $74.90 | $2,011.00 | $2,085.90 |
| **7′ x 14′ lean-to greenhouse**<br>*Replace* Material ...4380.00    Labor.........451.00<br>*Remove*.........................    Labor..........85.90 | ea | $85.90 | $4,831.00 | $4,916.90 |
| **8′ x 16′ lean-to greenhouse**<br>*Replace* Material ...5350.00    Labor .........516.00<br>*Remove*.........................    Labor..........91.70 | ea | $91.70 | $5,866.00 | $5,957.70 |
| **SCREENED ▶ SWIMMING POOL ENCLOSURE**<br>**Screened swimming pool enclosure**<br>*Replace* Material .........5.20    Labor............ .62<br>*Remove*.........................    Labor............ .24<br>▶ Aluminum frame, vinyl screen. | sf | $.24 | $5.82 | $6.06 |
| **CHICKHEE HUT ▶** *Per sf of floor. Typically found in the southern United States.*<br>**Chickhee hut**<br>*Replace* Material........21.00    Labor..........35.90<br>*Remove*.........................    Labor ..........2.62 | sf | $2.62 | $56.90 | $59.52 |
| **Thatched roof for chickhee hut**<br>*Replace* Material .........4.10    Labor ..........22.00<br>*Remove*.........................    Labor........... 1.00<br>▶ Per sf of roof area. | sf | $1.00 | $26.10 | $27.10 |

*single roof △*

*double roof △*

*triple roof △*

# 26 .......................................................................... *Painting*

| Item Description | Unit | prime/stain | 1 Coat | 2 Coats | 3 Coats | |
|---|---|---|---|---|---|---|
| **Minimum charge for painting work** | ea | — | — | — | $59.20 | ◀ MINIMUM |
| *Materials* Minimum ..31.00 | | | | | | |
| *Labor* Minimum .........28.20 | | | | | | |
| **Paint acoustic ceiling texture** | sf | $.70 | $.73 | $1.08 | $1.46 | ◀ ACOUSTIC |
| *Materials* Prime .......... .25  1 Coat........ .28  2 Coats........ .39  3 Coats........ .52 | | | | | | CEILINGS |
| *Labor* Prime ................. .45  1 Coat........ .45  2 Coats........ .69  3 Coats........ .94 | | | | | | |
| **Paint acoustical ceiling tile** | sf | $.70 | $.73 | $1.08 | $1.46 | |
| *Materials* Prime .......... .25  1 Coat........ .28  2 Coats........ .39  3 Coats........ .52 | | | | | | |
| *Labor* Prime ................. .45  1 Coat........ .45  2 Coats........ .69  3 Coats........ .94 | | | | | | |
| **Paint aluminum carport or awning** | sf | $.41 | $.43 | $.67 | $.88 | ◀ AWNINGS AND |
| *Materials* Prime .......... .17  1 Coat........ .19  2 Coats........ .26  3 Coats........ .35 | | | | | | CARPORTS |
| *Labor* Prime ................. .24  1 Coat........ .24  2 Coats........ .41  3 Coats........ .53 | | | | | | |
| **Paint plaster or drywall** | sf | $.36 | $.37 | $.58 | $.76 | ◀ DRYWALL, |
| *Materials* Prime .......... .12  1 Coat........ .13  2 Coats........ .17  3 Coats........ .23 | | | | | | PLASTER AND |
| *Labor* Prime ................. .24  1 Coat........ .24  2 Coats........ .41  3 Coats........ .53 | | | | | | STUCCO |
| **Paint stucco** | sf | $.77 | $.83 | $1.25 | $1.63 | |
| *Materials* Prime .......... .20  1 Coat........ .22  2 Coats........ .31  3 Coats........ .41 | | | | | | |
| *Labor* Prime ................. .57  1 Coat........ .61  2 Coats........ .94  3 Coats ......1.22 | | | | | | |
| **Paint column** | lf | $1.00 | $1.03 | $1.57 | $2.09 | ◀ COLUMNS |
| *Materials* Prime .......... .31  1 Coat........ .34  2 Coats........ .47  3 Coats........ .62 | | | | | | *Deduct **26%** for* |
| *Labor* Prime ................. .69  1 Coat........ .69  2 Coats ......1.10  3 Coats ......1.47 | | | | | | *pilasters, pilaster capitals,* |
| **Stain & varnish column** | lf | $.99 | $1.03 | $1.55 | $2.04 | *pilaster pedestals, and* |
| *Materials* Stain ......... .34  1 Coat........ .38  2 Coats........ .53  3 Coats........ .70 | | | | | | *so on.* |
| *Labor* Stain ............... .65  1 Coat........ .65  2 Coats ......1.02  3 Coats ......1.34 | | | | | | |
| **Paint capital, simple design** | ea | $43.40 | $46.10 | $68.00 | $91.70 | |
| *Materials* Prime ........16.90  1 Coat .....18.80  2 Coats......26.10  3 Coats .....34.70 | | | | | | |
| *Labor* Prime ...............26.50  1 Coat .....27.30  2 Coats......41.90  3 Coats .....57.00 | | | | | | |
| **Paint capital complex design** | ea | $55.90 | $59.30 | $87.70 | $118.00 | |
| *Materials* Prime ........21.80  1 Coat .....24.20  2 Coats .....33.60  3 Coats .....44.70 | | | | | | |
| *Labor* Prime ...............34.10  1 Coat .....35.10  2 Coats .....54.10  3 Coats .....73.30 | | | | | | |
| **Stain & varnish capital, simple design** | ea | $46.00 | $48.90 | $72.00 | $97.00 | |
| *Materials* Stain ........18.70  1 Coat .....20.80  2 Coats......28.90  3 Coats .....38.40 | | | | | | |
| *Labor* Stain ..............27.30  1 Coat .....28.10  2 Coats .....43.10  3 Coats .....58.60 | | | | | | |
| **Stain & varnish capital complex design** | ea | $62.00 | $65.80 | $97.00 | $130.80 | |
| *Materials* Stain ........24.10  1 Coat .....26.80  2 Coats......37.20  3 Coats .....49.40 | | | | | | |
| *Labor* Stain ..............37.90  1 Coat .....39.00  2 Coats .....59.80  3 Coats .....81.40 | | | | | | |
| **Paint column pedestal** | ea | $35.70 | $37.80 | $55.90 | $75.20 | |
| *Materials* Prime ........13.90  1 Coat .....15.40  2 Coats......21.40  3 Coats .....28.40 | | | | | | |
| *Labor* Prime ...............21.80  1 Coat .....22.40  2 Coats .....34.50  3 Coats .....46.80 | | | | | | |
| **Stain & varnish column pedestal** | ea | $39.40 | $41.80 | $61.80 | $83.20 | |
| *Materials* Stain ........15.40  1 Coat......17.10  2 Coats......23.70  3 Coats .....31.50 | | | | | | |
| *Labor* Stain ..............24.00  1 Coat .....24.70  2 Coats .....38.10  3 Coats .....51.70 | | | | | | |
| **Paint concrete floor** | sf | $.49 | $.51 | $.74 | $.98 | ◀ CONCRETE |
| *Materials* Prime .......... .16  1 Coat........ .18  2 Coats........ .25  3 Coats........ .33 | | | | | | |
| *Labor* Prime ................. .33  1 Coat........ .33  2 Coats........ .49  3 Coats........ .65 | | | | | | |

**PAINTING COATS**

Prices for one coat, two coats and three coats do *not* include: the primer coat, sealer coat, or stain.

To estimate painting, add the cost of the primer coat to the number of paint coats.

For example, to estimate the cost to prime a wall then paint with two coats, add the prime price to the two coats price.

To estimate the cost to stain an item then cover with two coats of varnish, add the stain cost to the two coats price (unless otherwise noted).

| Item Description | Unit | prime/stain | 1 Coat | 2 Coats | 3 Coats |
|---|---|---|---|---|---|
| **CONCRETE ►** continued | | | | | |
| **Paint concrete wall** | sf | $.49 | $.51 | $.78 | $1.02 |
| *Materials* Prime .......... .16  1 Coat........ .18  2 Coats........ .25  3 Coats........ .33 | | | | | |
| *Labor* Prime ............... .33  1 Coat .... .33  2 Coats ...... .53  3 Coats........ .69 | | | | | |
| **Paint concrete step (per step)** | ea | $1.44 | $1.54 | $2.29 | $3.08 |
| *Materials* Prime .......... .50  1 Coat........ .56  2 Coats........ .78  3 Coats...... 1.04 | | | | | |
| *Labor* Prime ............... .94  1 Coat....... .98  2 Coats ......1.51  3 Coats ......2.04 | | | | | |
| **DOORS ►** *Unless otherwise noted, does not include jamb and casing. Includes painting both sides of door. Folding and bypassing doors are for both sides of each section. Add **20%** for half-round or elliptical top door.* **Paint folding door** | ea | $26.08 | $27.60 | $40.90 | $54.90 |
| *Materials* Prime..........9.68  1 Coat.......10.80  2 Coats.......15.00  3 Coats.......19.90 | | | | | |
| *Labor* Prime ...............16.40  1 Coat......16.80  2 Coats......25.90  3 Coats......35.00 | | | | | |
| **Stain & varnish folding door** | ea | $39.20 | $41.50 | $61.50 | $82.80 |
| *Materials* Stain .........14.20  1 Coat......15.80  2 Coats......21.90  3 Coats .....29.10 | | | | | |
| *Labor* Stain................25.00  1 Coat .....25.70  2 Coats......39.60  3 Coats .....53.70 | | | | | |
| **folding door ▷** **Paint half-louvered folding door** | ea | $29.20 | $30.90 | $45.80 | $61.60 |
| *Materials* Prime .......10.80  1 Coat......12.00  2 Coats......16.70  3 Coats......22.20 | | | | | |
| *Labor* Prime ...............18.40  1 Coat .....18.90  2 Coats .....29.10  3 Coats......39.40 | | | | | |
| **Stain & varnish half-louvered folding door** | ea | $43.80 | $46.50 | $68.80 | $92.60 |
| *Materials* Stain .........15.80  1 Coat......17.60  2 Coats......24.40  3 Coats......32.40 | | | | | |
| *Labor* Stain................28.00  1 Coat .....28.90  2 Coats .....44.40  3 Coats......60.20 | | | | | |
| **Paint full-louvered folding door** | ea | $32.60 | $34.50 | $51.10 | $69.00 |
| *Materials* Prime .......12.00  1 Coat......13.30  2 Coats......18.50  3 Coats......24.60 | | | | | |
| *Labor* Prime ...............20.60  1 Coat .....21.20  2 Coats......32.60  3 Coats......44.40 | | | | | |
| **Stain & varnish full-louvered folding door** | ea | $49.10 | $52.00 | $76.90 | $103.70 |
| *Materials* Stain .......17.60  1 Coat......19.60  2 Coats......27.20  3 Coats......36.10 | | | | | |
| *Labor* Stain................31.50  1 Coat .....32.40  2 Coats......49.70  3 Coats......67.60 | | | | | |
| **Paint folding panel door** | ea | $28.50 | $30.20 | $44.80 | $60.20 |
| *Materials* Prime .......10.60  1 Coat......11.80  2 Coats......16.40  3 Coats......21.80 | | | | | |
| *Labor* Prime ...............17.90  1 Coat .....18.40  2 Coats......28.40  3 Coats......38.40 | | | | | |
| **Stain & varnish folding panel door** | ea | $43.00 | $45.50 | $67.50 | $90.50 |
| *Materials* Stain .........15.60  1 Coat......17.30  2 Coats......24.00  3 Coats......31.90 | | | | | |
| *Labor* Stain................27.40  1 Coat .....28.20  2 Coats......43.50  3 Coats......58.60 | | | | | |
| **bypassing door ▷** **Paint bypassing door** | ea | $46.00 | $48.40 | $72.60 | $97.50 |
| *Materials* Prime .......12.20  1 Coat......13.60  2 Coats......18.90  3 Coats......25.10 | | | | | |
| *Labor* Prime ...............33.80  1 Coat .....34.80  2 Coats......53.70  3 Coats......72.40 | | | | | |
| **Stain & varnish bypassing door** | ea | $69.60 | $73.20 | $109.40 | $147.70 |
| *Materials* Stain .......17.90  1 Coat......19.90  2 Coats......27.60  3 Coats......36.70 | | | | | |
| *Labor* Stain................51.70  1 Coat .....53.30  2 Coats......81.80  3 Coats......111.00 | | | | | |
| **Paint half-louvered bypassing door** | ea | $51.50 | $54.10 | $81.20 | $109.30 |
| *Materials* Prime .......13.60  1 Coat......15.10  2 Coats......21.00  3 Coats......27.90 | | | | | |
| *Labor* Prime ...............37.90  1 Coat .....39.00  2 Coats......60.20  3 Coats......81.40 | | | | | |
| **Stain & varnish half-louvered bypassing door** | ea | $78.10 | $81.90 | $122.70 | $165.80 |
| *Materials* Stain .......19.90  1 Coat......22.10  2 Coats......30.70  3 Coats......40.80 | | | | | |
| *Labor* Stain................58.20  1 Coat .....59.80  2 Coats......92.00  3 Coats......125.00 | | | | | |
| **Paint full-louvered bypassing door** | ea | $57.80 | $60.80 | $90.90 | $122.20 |
| *Materials* Prime .......15.10  1 Coat......16.80  2 Coats......23.30  3 Coats......31.00 | | | | | |
| *Labor* Prime ...............42.70  1 Coat .....44.00  2 Coats......67.60  3 Coats......91.20 | | | | | |
| **Stain & varnish full-louvered bypassing door** | ea | $87.20 | $91.80 | $137.20 | $185.40 |
| *Materials* Stain .......22.10  1 Coat......24.60  2 Coats......34.20  3 Coats......45.40 | | | | | |
| *Labor* Stain................65.10  1 Coat .....67.20  2 Coats......103.00  3 Coats......140.00 | | | | | |
| **Paint bypassing panel door** | ea | $50.20 | $52.70 | $78.80 | $106.50 |
| *Materials* Prime .......13.60  1 Coat......15.10  2 Coats......21.00  3 Coats......27.90 | | | | | |
| *Labor* Prime ...............36.60  1 Coat .....37.60  2 Coats......57.80  3 Coats......78.60 | | | | | |

| Item Description | Unit | prime/stain | 1 Coat | 2 Coats | 3 Coats | |
|---|---|---|---|---|---|---|
| **Stain & varnish bypassing panel door** | ea | $76.20 | $80.00 | $119.50 | $160.90 | |
| *Materials* Stain ....20.00  1 Coat ....22.20  2 Coats ....30.80  3 Coats ....40.90 | | | | | | |
| *Labor* Stain ....56.20  1 Coat ....57.80  2 Coats ....88.70  3 Coats ....120.00 | | | | | | |
| **Paint interior door** | ea | $21.12 | $22.33 | $33.20 | $45.00 | ◁ interior door |
| *Materials* Prime ....7.32  1 Coat ....8.13  2 Coats ....11.30  3 Coats ....15.30 | | | | | | |
| *Labor* Prime ....13.80  1 Coat ....14.20  2 Coats ....21.90  3 Coats ....29.70 | | | | | | |
| **Stain & varnish interior door** | ea | $32.10 | $34.10 | $50.60 | $67.60 | |
| *Materials* Stain ....11.00  1 Coat ....12.40  2 Coats ....17.10  3 Coats ....22.40 | | | | | | |
| *Labor* Stain ....21.10  1 Coat ....21.70  2 Coats ....33.50  3 Coats ....45.20 | | | | | | |
| **Paint half-louvered door** | ea | $23.64 | $25.04 | $37.20 | $50.00 | |
| *Materials* Prime ....8.14  1 Coat ....9.04  2 Coats ....12.60  3 Coats ....16.70 | | | | | | |
| *Labor* Prime ....15.50  1 Coat ....16.00  2 Coats ....24.60  3 Coats ....33.30 | | | | | | |
| **Stain & varnish half-louvered door** | ea | $35.90 | $38.00 | $56.50 | $76.00 | |
| *Materials* Stain ....12.20  1 Coat ....13.60  2 Coats ....18.90  3 Coats ....25.10 | | | | | | |
| *Labor* Stain ....23.70  1 Coat ....24.40  2 Coats ....37.60  3 Coats ....50.90 | | | | | | |
| **Paint full-louvered door** | ea | $26.45 | $27.95 | $41.60 | $56.00 | |
| *Materials* Prime ....9.05  1 Coat ....10.05  2 Coats ....14.00  3 Coats ....18.60 | | | | | | |
| *Labor* Prime ....17.40  1 Coat ....17.90  2 Coats ....27.60  3 Coats ....37.40 | | | | | | |
| **Stain & varnish full-louvered door** | ea | $40.20 | $42.50 | $63.30 | $84.90 | |
| *Materials* Stain ....13.60  1 Coat ....15.10  2 Coats ....21.00  3 Coats ....27.90 | | | | | | |
| *Labor* Stain ....26.60  1 Coat ....27.40  2 Coats ....42.30  3 Coats ....57.00 | | | | | | |
| **Paint door jamb & casing** | lf | $.60 | $.62 | $.93 | $1.26 | ◁ door jamb and casing |
| *Materials* Prime ....15  1 Coat ....17  2 Coats ....24  3 Coats ....32 | | | | | | |
| *Labor* Prime ....45  1 Coat ....45  2 Coats ....69  3 Coats ....94 | | | | | | |
| **Stain & varnish door jamb & casing** | lf | $.91 | $.93 | $1.39 | $1.86 | |
| *Materials* Stain ....22  1 Coat ....24  2 Coats ....33  3 Coats ....44 | | | | | | |
| *Labor* Stain ....69  1 Coat ....69  2 Coats ....1.06  3 Coats ....1.42 | | | | | | |
| **Paint French door** | ea | $45.80 | $48.10 | $72.20 | $96.80 | ◁ French door |
| *Materials* Prime ....12.50  1 Coat ....13.90  2 Coats ....19.30  3 Coats ....25.60 | | | | | | |
| *Labor* Prime ....33.30  1 Coat ....34.20  2 Coats ....52.90  3 Coats ....71.20 | | | | | | |
| **Stain & varnish French door** | ea | $69.20 | $72.80 | $108.80 | $146.50 | |
| *Materials* Stain ....18.30  1 Coat ....20.30  2 Coats ....28.20  3 Coats ....37.50 | | | | | | |
| *Labor* Stain ....50.90  1 Coat ....52.50  2 Coats ....80.60  3 Coats ....109.00 | | | | | | |
| **Paint full-lite door** | ea | $36.00 | $38.00 | $56.50 | $76.00 | ◁ full-lite door |
| *Materials* Prime ....12.10  1 Coat ....13.40  2 Coats ....18.60  3 Coats ....24.70 | | | | | | |
| *Labor* Prime ....23.90  1 Coat ....24.60  2 Coats ....37.90  3 Coats ....51.30 | | | | | | |
| **Stain & varnish full-lite door** | ea | $54.40 | $57.40 | $85.30 | $115.10 | |
| *Materials* Stain ....17.80  1 Coat ....19.80  2 Coats ....27.50  3 Coats ....36.50 | | | | | | |
| *Labor* Stain ....36.60  1 Coat ....37.60  2 Coats ....57.80  3 Coats ....78.60 | | | | | | |
| **Paint panel door** | ea | $41.90 | $44.30 | $65.80 | $88.90 | ◁ panel door |
| *Materials* Prime ....13.30  1 Coat ....14.80  2 Coats ....20.60  3 Coats ....27.40 | | | | | | |
| *Labor* Prime ....28.60  1 Coat ....29.50  2 Coats ....45.20  3 Coats ....61.50 | | | | | | |
| **Stain & varnish panel door** | ea | $63.50 | $66.90 | $99.30 | $134.00 | |
| *Materials* Stain ....19.50  1 Coat ....21.70  2 Coats ....30.10  3 Coats ....40.00 | | | | | | |
| *Labor* Stain ....44.00  1 Coat ....45.20  2 Coats ....69.20  3 Coats ....94.00 | | | | | | |
| **Paint transom** | ea | $21.16 | $22.23 | $33.25 | $44.70 | ◁ transom |
| *Materials* Prime ....6.06  1 Coat ....6.73  2 Coats ....9.35  3 Coats ....12.40 | | | | | | |
| *Labor* Prime ....15.10  1 Coat ....15.50  2 Coats ....23.90  3 Coats ....32.30 | | | | | | |
| **Stain & varnish transom** | ea | $31.89 | $33.58 | $50.20 | $67.40 | |
| *Materials* Stain ....8.89  1 Coat ....9.88  2 Coats ....13.70  3 Coats ....18.20 | | | | | | |
| *Labor* Stain ....23.00  1 Coat ....23.70  2 Coats ....36.50  3 Coats ....49.20 | | | | | | |

**RELATED ITEMS**

| | Item Description | Unit | prime/stain | 1 Coat | 2 Coats | 3 Coats |
|---|---|---|---|---|---|---|
| storm door ▷ | **Paint storm door** | ea | **$21.79** | **$22.89** | **$34.21** | **$46.10** |
| | *Materials* Prime........6.29  1 Coat.......6.99  2 Coats.......9.71  3 Coats......12.90 | | | | | |
| | *Labor* Prime...............15.50  1 Coat.....15.90  2 Coats.....24.50  3 Coats.....33.20 | | | | | |
| | **Stain & varnish storm door** | ea | **$32.83** | **$34.55** | **$51.60** | **$69.80** |
| | *Materials* Stain........9.23  1 Coat.....10.25  2 Coats......14.20  3 Coats......18.90 | | | | | |
| | *Labor* Stain...............23.60  1 Coat.....24.30  2 Coats.....37.40  3 Coats.....50.90 | | | | | |
| Dutch door ▷ *both sections both sides* | **Paint Dutch door** | ea | **$40.20** | **$42.50** | **$63.40** | **$85.20** |
| | *Materials* Prime ........13.10  1 Coat.....14.60  2 Coats......20.30  3 Coats.....27.00 | | | | | |
| | *Labor* Prime...............27.10  1 Coat.....27.90  2 Coats.....43.10  3 Coats.....58.20 | | | | | |
| | **Stain & varnish Dutch door** | ea | **$60.70** | **$64.00** | **$95.10** | **$128.40** |
| | *Materials* Stain........19.20  1 Coat.....21.30  2 Coats......29.60  3 Coats.....39.30 | | | | | |
| | *Labor* Stain...............41.50  1 Coat.....42.70  2 Coats.....65.50  3 Coats.....89.10 | | | | | |
| entry door ▷ | **Paint steel entry door** | ea | **$37.10** | **$39.10** | **$58.20** | **$78.30** |
| | *Materials* Prime ........11.80  1 Coat......13.10  2 Coats......18.20  3 Coats.....24.20 | | | | | |
| | *Labor* Prime...............25.30  1 Coat.....26.00  2 Coats.....40.00  3 Coats.....54.10 | | | | | |
| | **Paint wood entry door** | ea | **$43.00** | **$44.80** | **$66.60** | **$90.70** |
| | *Materials* Prime ........12.80  1 Coat......13.70  2 Coats......18.60  3 Coats.....26.00 | | | | | |
| | *Labor* Prime...............30.20  1 Coat.....31.10  2 Coats.....48.00  3 Coats.....64.70 | | | | | |
| | **Stain & varnish wood entry door** | ea | **$64.40** | **$67.50** | **$98.90** | **$134.80** |
| | *Materials* Stain........18.40  1 Coat.....19.90  2 Coats......25.60  3 Coats.....35.90 | | | | | |
| | *Labor* Stain...............46.00  1 Coat.....47.60  2 Coats.....73.30  3 Coats.....98.90 | | | | | |
| entry door side lite ▷ | **Paint entry door side lite** | ea | **$37.50** | **$39.30** | **$58.70** | **$79.30** |
| | *Materials* Prime ........10.10  1 Coat......11.20  2 Coats......15.60  3 Coats.....20.70 | | | | | |
| | *Labor* Prime...............27.40  1 Coat.....28.10  2 Coats.....43.10  3 Coats.....58.60 | | | | | |
| | **Stain & varnish entry door side lite** | ea | **$56.70** | **$59.50** | **$89.10** | **$119.80** |
| | *Materials* Stain........14.80  1 Coat.....16.40  2 Coats......22.80  3 Coats.....30.30 | | | | | |
| | *Labor* Stain...............41.90  1 Coat.....43.10  2 Coats.....66.30  3 Coats.....89.50 | | | | | |
| entry door fan lite ▷ | **Paint fan lite** | ea | **$34.76** | **$36.55** | **$54.90** | **$73.70** |
| | *Materials* Prime........8.96  1 Coat.......9.95  2 Coats......13.80  3 Coats.....18.30 | | | | | |
| | *Labor* Prime...............25.80  1 Coat.....26.60  2 Coats.....41.10  3 Coats.....55.40 | | | | | |
| | **Stain & varnish fan lite** | ea | **$52.60** | **$55.30** | **$83.00** | **$111.70** |
| | *Materials* Stain........13.10  1 Coat.....14.60  2 Coats .....20.30  3 Coats.....27.00 | | | | | |
| | *Labor* Stain...............39.50  1 Coat.....40.70  2 Coats.....62.70  3 Coats.....84.70 | | | | | |
| cafe doors ▷ | **Paint cafe doors** | ea | **$34.10** | **$35.90** | **$53.60** | **$72.20** |
| | *Materials* Prime........10.00  1 Coat......11.10  2 Coats......15.40  3 Coats.....20.50 | | | | | |
| | *Labor* Prime...............24.10  1 Coat.....24.80  2 Coats.....38.20  3 Coats......51.70 | | | | | |
| | **Stain & varnish cafe doors** | ea | **$51.50** | **$54.20** | **$80.80** | **$109.00** |
| | *Materials* Stain........14.70  1 Coat.....16.30  2 Coats......22.60  3 Coats.....30.00 | | | | | |
| | *Labor* Stain...............36.80  1 Coat.....37.90  2 Coats.....58.20  3 Coats.....79.00 | | | | | |
| sliding patio door ▷ | **Paint wood sliding patio door** | ea | **$30.56** | **$31.83** | **$48.07** | **$65.33** |
| | *Materials* Prime........4.26  1 Coat.......4.73  2 Coats.......6.57  3 Coats......8.73 | | | | | |
| | *Labor* Prime...............26.30  1 Coat.....27.10  2 Coats.....41.50  3 Coats.....56.60 | | | | | |
| | **Stain & varnish wood sliding patio door** | ea | **$46.45** | **$48.44** | **$73.14** | **$99.10** |
| | *Materials* Stain.........6.25  1 Coat.......6.94  2 Coats.......9.64  3 Coats.....12.80 | | | | | |
| | *Labor* Stain...............40.20  1 Coat.....41.50  2 Coats.....63.50  3 Coats.....86.30 | | | | | |
| garage door ▷ | **Paint garage door** | sf | **$.41** | **$.43** | **$.63** | **$.88** |
| | *Materials* Prime ..........17  1 Coat.......19  2 Coats .......26  3 Coats........35 | | | | | |
| | *Labor* Prime ................24  1 Coat.......24  2 Coats .......37  3 Coats........53 | | | | | |
| | **Stain & varnish garage door** | sf | **$.62** | **$.65** | **$.96** | **$1.29** |
| | *Materials* Stain...........25  1 Coat.......28  2 Coats .......39  3 Coats........52 | | | | | |
| | *Labor* Stain ................37  1 Coat.......37  2 Coats .......57  3 Coats........77 | | | | | |

| Item Description | Unit | prime/stain | 1 Coat | 2 Coats | 3 Coats | |
|---|---|---|---|---|---|---|
| **Paint medicine cabinet** | ea | $19.31 | $20.13 | $30.49 | $41.27 | ◄ MEDICINE CABINET |
| *Materials* Prime........2.91  1 Coat......3.23  2 Coats.......4.49  3 Coats......5.97 | | | | | | |
| *Labor* Prime...............16.40  1 Coat......16.90  2 Coats.....26.00  3 Coats......35.30 | | | | | | |
| **Stain & varnish medicine cabinet** | ea | $29.47 | $30.64 | $46.38 | $62.44 | |
| *Materials* Stain........4.27  1 Coat......4.74  2 Coats.......6.58  3 Coats......8.74 | | | | | | |
| *Labor* Stain...............25.20  1 Coat......25.90  2 Coats.....39.80  3 Coats......53.70 | | | | | | |
| **Paint exterior light-fixture post** | ea | $6.78 | $7.26 | $10.59 | $14.23 | ◄ EXTERIOR LIGHT-FIXTURE POST |
| *Materials* Prime........3.56  1 Coat......3.96  2 Coats.......5.50  3 Coats......7.31 | | | | | | |
| *Labor* Prime...............3.22  1 Coat......3.30  2 Coats.......5.09  3 Coats......6.92 | | | | | | |
| **Paint 4' high wood fence** | lf | $2.87 | $3.04 | $4.52 | $6.06 | ◄ FENCES |
| *Materials* Prime..........79  1 Coat.......88  2 Coats.......1.22  3 Coats......1.62 | | | | | | Wood fence prices are for one side only. Ornamental iron fence prices are for both sides. |
| *Labor* Prime...............2.08  1 Coat......2.16  2 Coats.......3.30  3 Coats......4.44 | | | | | | |
| **Seal or stain 4' high wood fence** | lf | $4.33 | $4.55 | $6.80 | $9.18 | |
| *Materials* Seal/stain ..1.16  1 Coat......1.29  2 Coats.......1.79  3 Coats......2.38 | | | | | | |
| *Labor* Seal/stain ........3.17  1 Coat......3.26  2 Coats.......5.01  3 Coats......6.80 | | | | | | |
| **Paint 6' high wood fence** | lf | $4.29 | $4.51 | $6.76 | $9.10 | |
| *Materials* Prime.......1.16  1 Coat......1.29  2 Coats.......1.79  3 Coats......2.38 | | | | | | |
| *Labor* Prime...............3.13  1 Coat......3.22  2 Coats.......4.97  3 Coats......6.72 | | | | | | |
| **Seal or stain 6' high wood fence** | lf | $6.46 | $6.81 | $10.19 | $13.74 | |
| *Materials* Seal/stain ..1.70  1 Coat......1.89  2 Coats.......2.62  3 Coats......3.48 | | | | | | |
| *Labor* Seal/stain ........4.76  1 Coat......4.92  2 Coats.......7.57  3 Coats......10.26 | | | | | | |
| **Paint 8' high wood fence** | lf | $5.67 | $5.96 | $8.94 | $12.03 | |
| *Materials* Prime.......1.52  1 Coat......1.69  2 Coats.......2.35  3 Coats......3.12 | | | | | | |
| *Labor* Prime...............4.15  1 Coat......4.27  2 Coats.......6.59  3 Coats......8.91 | | | | | | |
| **Seal or stain 8' high wood fence** | lf | $8.58 | $9.03 | $13.49 | $18.17 | |
| *Materials* Seal/stain ..2.23  1 Coat......2.48  2 Coats.......3.44  3 Coats......4.57 | | | | | | |
| *Labor* Seal/stain ........6.35  1 Coat......6.55  2 Coats.......10.05  3 Coats......13.60 | | | | | | |
| **Paint 3' high picket fence** | lf | $2.28 | $2.39 | $3.54 | $4.79 | |
| *Materials* Prime..........61  1 Coat.......68  2 Coats........94  3 Coats......1.25 | | | | | | |
| *Labor* Prime...............1.67  1 Coat......1.71  2 Coats.......2.60  3 Coats......3.54 | | | | | | |
| **Paint 5' high picket fence** | lf | $3.64 | $3.83 | $5.72 | $7.73 | |
| *Materials* Prime..........99  1 Coat......1.10  2 Coats.......1.53  3 Coats......2.03 | | | | | | |
| *Labor* Prime...............2.65  1 Coat......2.73  2 Coats.......4.19  3 Coats......5.70 | | | | | | |
| **Paint 48" high ornamental iron fence** | lf | $4.24 | $4.45 | $6.63 | $8.94 | ◁ ornamental iron |
| *Materials* Prime.......1.11  1 Coat......1.23  2 Coats.......1.71  3 Coats......2.27 | | | | | | |
| *Labor* Prime...............3.13  1 Coat......3.22  2 Coats.......4.92  3 Coats......6.67 | | | | | | |
| **Paint 60" high ornamental iron fence** | lf | $5.40 | $5.65 | $8.46 | $11.41 | |
| *Materials* Prime.......1.49  1 Coat......1.66  2 Coats.......2.31  3 Coats......3.07 | | | | | | |
| *Labor* Prime...............3.91  1 Coat......3.99  2 Coats.......6.15  3 Coats......8.34 | | | | | | |
| **Paint 72" high ornamental iron fence** | lf | $6.76 | $7.11 | $10.62 | $14.32 | |
| *Materials* Prime.......2.08  1 Coat......2.31  2 Coats.......3.21  3 Coats......4.27 | | | | | | |
| *Labor* Prime...............4.68  1 Coat......4.80  2 Coats.......7.41  3 Coats......10.05 | | | | | | |
| **Paint wood trim, simple design** | lf | $.57 | $.58 | $.86 | $1.17 | ◄ FINISH CARPENTRY |
| *Materials* Prime..........12  1 Coat.......13  2 Coats........17  3 Coats........23 | | | | | | ◁ wood trim |
| *Labor* Prime................45  1 Coat.......45  2 Coats........69  3 Coats........94 | | | | | | |
| **Stain & varnish wood trim, simple design** | lf | $.82 | $.82 | $1.23 | $1.65 | |
| *Materials* Stain...........17  1 Coat.......13  2 Coats........17  3 Coats........23 | | | | | | |
| *Labor* Stain.................65  1 Coat.......69  2 Coats.......1.06  3 Coats......1.42 | | | | | | |
| **Paint wood trim, ornate design** | lf | $.68 | $.74 | $1.09 | $1.46 | |
| *Materials* Prime..........15  1 Coat.......17  2 Coats........24  3 Coats........32 | | | | | | |
| *Labor* Prime................53  1 Coat.......57  2 Coats........85  3 Coats......1.14 | | | | | | |

| Item Description | | | | | Unit | prime/stain | 1 Coat | 2 Coats | 3 Coats |
|---|---|---|---|---|---|---|---|---|---|
| **Stain & varnish wood trim, ornate design** | | | | | lf | $1.03 | $1.09 | $1.63 | $2.23 |
| *Materials* Stain .22 | 1 Coat .24 | 2 Coats .33 | 3 Coats .44 | | | | | | |
| *Labor* Stain .81 | 1 Coat .85 | 2 Coats 1.30 | 3 Coats 1.79 | | | | | | |
| **Paint wood trim, very ornate design** | | | | | lf | $.86 | $.88 | $1.32 | $1.77 |
| *Materials* Prime .17 | 1 Coat .19 | 2 Coats .26 | 3 Coats .35 | | | | | | |
| *Labor* Prime .69 | 1 Coat .69 | 2 Coats 1.06 | 3 Coats 1.42 | | | | | | |
| **Stain & varnish wood trim, very ornate design** | | | | | lf | $1.27 | $1.34 | $2.02 | $2.72 |
| *Materials* Stain .25 | 1 Coat .28 | 2 Coats .39 | 3 Coats .52 | | | | | | |
| *Labor* Stain 1.02 | 1 Coat 1.06 | 2 Coats 1.63 | 3 Coats 2.20 | | | | | | |
| **Paint interior architrave, simple design** | | | | | lf | $.78 | $.80 | $1.20 | $1.65 |
| *Materials* Prime .17 | 1 Coat .19 | 2 Coats .26 | 3 Coats .35 | | | | | | |
| *Labor* Prime .61 | 1 Coat .61 | 2 Coats .94 | 3 Coats 1.30 | | | | | | |
| **Stain & varnish interior architrave, simple design** | | | | | lf | $1.19 | $1.22 | $1.86 | $2.47 |
| *Materials* Stain .25 | 1 Coat .28 | 2 Coats .39 | 3 Coats .52 | | | | | | |
| *Labor* Stain .94 | 1 Coat .94 | 2 Coats 1.47 | 3 Coats 1.95 | | | | | | |
| **Paint interior architrave, complex design** | | | | | lf | $1.47 | $1.50 | $2.30 | $3.08 |
| *Materials* Prime .25 | 1 Coat .28 | 2 Coats .39 | 3 Coats .52 | | | | | | |
| *Labor* Prime 1.22 | 1 Coat 1.22 | 2 Coats 1.91 | 3 Coats 2.56 | | | | | | |
| **Stain & varnish interior architrave, complex design** | | | | | lf | $2.20 | $2.32 | $3.50 | $4.71 |
| *Materials* Stain .37 | 1 Coat .41 | 2 Coats .57 | 3 Coats .76 | | | | | | |
| *Labor* Stain 1.83 | 1 Coat 1.91 | 2 Coats 2.93 | 3 Coats 3.95 | | | | | | |
| **Paint exterior architrave, simple design** | | | | | lf | $1.67 | $1.79 | $2.67 | $3.61 |
| *Materials* Prime .33 | 1 Coat .37 | 2 Coats .51 | 3 Coats .68 | | | | | | |
| *Labor* Prime 1.34 | 1 Coat 1.42 | 2 Coats 2.16 | 3 Coats 2.93 | | | | | | |
| **Paint exterior architrave, complex design** | | | | | lf | $3.41 | $3.57 | $5.37 | $7.23 |
| *Materials* Prime .68 | 1 Coat .76 | 2 Coats 1.06 | 3 Coats 1.41 | | | | | | |
| *Labor* Prime 2.73 | 1 Coat 2.81 | 2 Coats 4.31 | 3 Coats 5.82 | | | | | | |
| **Paint exterior door surround, simple design** | | | | | lf | $6.12 | $6.39 | $9.63 | $13.01 |
| *Materials* Prime 1.36 | 1 Coat 1.51 | 2 Coats 2.10 | 3 Coats 2.79 | | | | | | |
| *Labor* Prime 4.76 | 1 Coat 4.88 | 2 Coats 7.53 | 3 Coats 10.22 | | | | | | |
| **Paint exterior door surround, complex design** | | | | | lf | $14.59 | $15.21 | $22.96 | $31.03 |
| *Materials* Prime 2.89 | 1 Coat 3.21 | 2 Coats 4.46 | 3 Coats 5.93 | | | | | | |
| *Labor* Prime 11.70 | 1 Coat 12.00 | 2 Coats 18.50 | 3 Coats 25.10 | | | | | | |
| **Paint exterior window surround, simple design** | | | | | lf | $6.12 | $6.39 | $9.63 | $13.01 |
| *Materials* Prime 1.36 | 1 Coat 1.51 | 2 Coats 2.10 | 3 Coats 2.79 | | | | | | |
| *Labor* Prime 4.76 | 1 Coat 4.88 | 2 Coats 7.53 | 3 Coats 10.22 | | | | | | |
| **Paint exterior window surround, complex design** | | | | | lf | $14.59 | $15.21 | $22.96 | $31.03 |
| *Materials* Prime 2.89 | 1 Coat 3.21 | 2 Coats 4.46 | 3 Coats 5.93 | | | | | | |
| *Labor* Prime 11.70 | 1 Coat 12.00 | 2 Coats 18.50 | 3 Coats 25.10 | | | | | | |
| **Paint closet rod, shelf, and brackets** | | | | | lf | $5.38 | $5.56 | $8.50 | $11.53 |
| *Materials* Prime .21 | 1 Coat .23 | 2 Coats .32 | 3 Coats .43 | | | | | | |
| *Labor* Prime 5.17 | 1 Coat 5.33 | 2 Coats 8.18 | 3 Coats 11.10 | | | | | | |
| **Paint closet organizer system** | | | | | sf | $.69 | $.72 | $1.06 | $1.43 |
| *Materials* Prime .24 | 1 Coat .27 | 2 Coats .37 | 3 Coats .49 | | | | | | |
| *Labor* Prime .45 | 1 Coat .45 | 2 Coats .69 | 3 Coats .94 | | | | | | |
| **Paint bookcase** | | | | | sf | $1.10 | $1.20 | $1.76 | $2.31 |
| *Materials* Prime .53 | 1 Coat .59 | 2 Coats .82 | 3 Coats 1.09 | | | | | | |
| *Labor* Prime .57 | 1 Coat .61 | 2 Coats .94 | 3 Coats 1.22 | | | | | | |
| **Stain & varnish bookcase** | | | | | sf | $1.68 | $1.81 | $2.63 | $3.52 |
| *Materials* Stain .78 | 1 Coat .87 | 2 Coats 1.21 | 3 Coats 1.61 | | | | | | |
| *Labor* Stain .90 | 1 Coat .94 | 2 Coats 1.42 | 3 Coats 1.91 | | | | | | |

Left margin labels:

**FINISH CARPENTRY** *continued*

interior architrave ▷

exterior architrave ▷

exterior door surround ▷

exterior window surround ▷

closets ▷

bookcase ▷

| Item Description | Unit | prime/stain | 1 Coat | 2 Coats | 3 Coats | |
|---|---|---|---|---|---|---|
| **Paint fireplace mantel beam** | lf | $1.00 | $1.03 | $1.56 | $2.11 | ◁ mantel beams and mantels |
| *Materials* Prime .........27  1 Coat.........30  2 Coats........ .42  3 Coats .........56 | | | | | | |
| *Labor* Prime ................73  1 Coat........73  2 Coats...1.14  3 Coats ......1.55 | | | | | | |
| **Stain & varnish mantel beam** | lf | $1.50 | $1.58 | $2.36 | $3.21 | |
| *Materials* Stain ..........40  1 Coat.........44  2 Coats........ .61  3 Coats........ .81 | | | | | | |
| *Labor* Stain...............1.10  1 Coat.....1.14  2 Coats....1.75  3 Coats......2.40 | | | | | | |
| **Paint fireplace mantel** | lf | $1.38 | $1.46 | $2.19 | $2.94 | |
| *Materials* Prime .........36  1 Coat.........40  2 Coats........ .56  3 Coats........ .74 | | | | | | |
| *Labor* Prime ...............1.02  1 Coat.....1.06  2 Coats...1.63  3 Coats......2.20 | | | | | | |
| **Stain & varnish mantel** | lf | $2.08 | $2.18 | $3.30 | $4.43 | |
| *Materials* Stain ..........53  1 Coat.........59  2 Coats........ .82  3 Coats ....1.09 | | | | | | |
| *Labor* Stain...............1.55  1 Coat.....1.59  2 Coats....2.48  3 Coats......3.34 | | | | | | |
| **Paint coffered ceiling, simple design** | sf | $1.11 | $1.20 | $1.75 | $2.37 | ◁ coffered ceiling |
| *Materials* Prime .........42  1 Coat.........47  2 Coats........ .65  3 Coats........ .86 | | | | | | |
| *Labor* Prime ................69  1 Coat........73  2 Coats...1.10  3 Coats......1.51 | | | | | | |
| **Stain & varnish coffered ceiling, simple design** | sf | $1.68 | $1.79 | $2.67 | $3.56 | |
| *Materials* Stain ..........62  1 Coat.........69  2 Coats........ .96  3 Coats ....1.28 | | | | | | |
| *Labor* Stain...............1.06  1 Coat.....1.10  2 Coats....1.71  3 Coats......2.28 | | | | | | |
| **Paint coffered ceiling, complex design** | sf | $2.43 | $2.55 | $3.82 | $5.17 | |
| *Materials* Prime .........76  1 Coat.........84  2 Coats....1.17  3 Coats ....1.55 | | | | | | |
| *Labor* Prime ...............1.67  1 Coat.....1.71  2 Coats....2.65  3 Coats......3.62 | | | | | | |
| **Stain & varnish coffered ceiling, complex design** | sf | $3.68 | $3.80 | $5.79 | $7.78 | |
| *Materials* Stain ........1.12  1 Coat.....1.24  2 Coats....1.72  3 Coats ....2.29 | | | | | | |
| *Labor* Stain...............2.56  1 Coat.....2.56  2 Coats....4.07  3 Coats......5.49 | | | | | | |
| **Paint niche** | ea | $28.84 | $30.21 | $45.30 | $61.00 | ◁ niche |
| *Materials* Prime..........6.94  1 Coat.......7.71  2 Coats...10.70  3 Coats...14.20 | | | | | | |
| *Labor* Prime ..........21.90  1 Coat....22.50  2 Coats....34.60  3 Coats....46.80 | | | | | | |
| **Stain & varnish niche** | ea | $43.68 | $45.70 | $68.60 | $92.50 | |
| *Materials* Stain....10.18  1 Coat......11.30  2 Coats....15.70  3 Coats...20.90 | | | | | | |
| *Labor* Stain..............33.50  1 Coat....34.40  2 Coats....52.90  3 Coats....71.60 | | | | | | |
| **Paint gingerbread running trim** | lf | $2.91 | $3.11 | $4.60 | $6.17 | ◁ running trim |
| *Materials* Prime..........1.08  1 Coat......1.20  2 Coats.......1.67  3 Coats ....2.22 | | | | | | |
| *Labor* Prime ...............1.83  1 Coat.....1.91  2 Coats.......2.93  3 Coats......3.95 | | | | | | |
| **Stain & varnish gingerbread running trim** | lf | $4.39 | $4.65 | $6.92 | $9.26 | |
| *Materials* Stain ........1.58  1 Coat.....1.76  2 Coats....2.44  3 Coats....3.24 | | | | | | |
| *Labor* Stain...............2.81  1 Coat.....2.89  2 Coats....4.48  3 Coats......6.02 | | | | | | |
| **Paint gingerbread bracket** | ea | $15.34 | $15.92 | $24.23 | $32.76 | ◁ bracket |
| *Materials* Prime..........1.64  1 Coat.......1.82  2 Coats......2.53  3 Coats....3.36 | | | | | | |
| *Labor* Prime ..............13.70  1 Coat......14.10  2 Coats....21.70  3 Coats....29.40 | | | | | | |
| **Stain & varnish gingerbread bracket** | ea | $23.41 | $24.28 | $36.92 | $49.74 | |
| *Materials* Stain .........2.41  1 Coat.......2.68  2 Coats.....3.72  3 Coats....4.94 | | | | | | |
| *Labor* Stain..............21.00  1 Coat....21.60  2 Coats....33.20  3 Coats....44.80 | | | | | | |
| **Paint gingerbread corbel** | ea | $15.00 | $15.58 | $23.77 | $32.08 | ◁ corbel |
| *Materials* Prime..........1.60  1 Coat......1.78  2 Coats......2.47  3 Coats....3.28 | | | | | | |
| *Labor* Prime ..............13.40  1 Coat......13.80  2 Coats....21.30  3 Coats....28.80 | | | | | | |
| **Stain & varnish gingerbread corbel** | ea | $22.95 | $23.81 | $36.22 | $48.81 | |
| *Materials* Stain .........2.35  1 Coat.......2.61  2 Coats.....3.62  3 Coats.....4.81 | | | | | | |
| *Labor* Stain..............20.60  1 Coat....21.20  2 Coats....32.60  3 Coats....44.00 | | | | | | |
| **Paint gingerbread door or window header** | lf | $2.73 | $2.83 | $4.28 | $5.77 | ◁ door or window header |
| *Materials* Prime .........53  1 Coat.........59  2 Coats........ .82  3 Coats......1.09 | | | | | | |
| *Labor* Prime ...............2.20  1 Coat.....2.24  2 Coats....3.46  3 Coats......4.68 | | | | | | |

**RELATED ITEMS**
Finish Carpentry..........199

| Item Description | Unit | prime/stain | 1 Coat | 2 Coats | 3 Coats |
|---|---|---|---|---|---|
| **FINISH CARPENTRY** continued | | | | | |
| **Stain & varnish gingerbread door or window header** | lf | $4.12 | $4.29 | $6.50 | $8.77 |
| *Materials* Stain ........ .78  1 Coat ........ .87  2 Coats ....... 1.21  3 Coats ....... 1.61 | | | | | |
| *Labor* Stain ............... 3.34  1 Coat ...... 3.42  2 Coats ....... 5.29  3 Coats ....... 7.16 | | | | | |
| spandrel ▷ **Paint gingerbread spandrel** | lf | $3.61 | $3.75 | $5.70 | $7.69 |
| *Materials* Prime ........ .56  1 Coat ...... .62  2 Coats ...... .86  3 Coats ....... 1.14 | | | | | |
| *Labor* Prime ............... 3.05  1 Coat ...... 3.13  2 Coats ..... 4.84  3 Coats ....... 6.55 | | | | | |
| **Stain & varnish gingerbread spandrel** | lf | $5.50 | $5.71 | $8.67 | $11.72 |
| *Materials* Stain .......... .82  1 Coat ...... .91  2 Coats ...... 1.26  3 Coats ....... 1.67 | | | | | |
| *Labor* Stain ............... 4.68  1 Coat ...... 4.80  2 Coats ...... 7.41  3 Coats ...... 10.05 | | | | | |
| gable ornament ▷ add **51%** to stain & varnish. **Paint gingerbread gable ornament** | ea | $42.10 | $44.20 | $66.10 | $89.20 |
| *Materials* Prime ...... 11.70  1 Coat ....... 13.00  2 Coats .... 18.10  3 Coats ...... 24.10 | | | | | |
| *Labor* Prime ............... 30.40  1 Coat ..... 31.20  2 Coats ..... 48.00  3 Coats ..... 65.10 | | | | | |
| gable finial ▷ add **51%** to stain & varnish. **Paint gingerbread gable finial** | ea | $12.62 | $13.18 | $19.88 | $26.86 |
| *Materials* Prime ........ 2.32  1 Coat ...... 2.58  2 Coats ..... 3.58  3 Coats ...... 4.76 | | | | | |
| *Labor* Prime ............... 10.30  1 Coat ..... 10.60  2 Coats ..... 16.30  3 Coats ..... 22.10 | | | | | |
| porch post ▷ **Paint porch post** | ea | $8.49 | $9.07 | $13.30 | $17.90 |
| *Materials* Prime ........ 3.69  1 Coat ...... 4.10  2 Coats ..... 5.69  3 Coats ....... 7.56 | | | | | |
| *Labor* Prime ............... 4.80  1 Coat ...... 4.97  2 Coats ..... 7.61  3 Coats ..... 10.34 | | | | | |
| **Stain & varnish porch post** | ea | $12.78 | $13.58 | $19.95 | $26.90 |
| *Materials* Stain .......... 5.41  1 Coat ...... 6.01  2 Coats ..... 8.35  3 Coats ...... 11.10 | | | | | |
| *Labor* Stain ............... 7.37  1 Coat ...... 7.57  2 Coats ...... 11.60  3 Coats ..... 15.80 | | | | | |
| **FLOORING** See Flooring for costs to prep wood floors for finish. **Seal stone floor** | sf | $.60 | $.62 | $.93 | $1.26 |
| *Materials* Seal .......... .15  1 Coat ...... .17  2 Coats ...... .24  3 Coats ...... .32 | | | | | |
| *Labor* Seal ............... .45  1 Coat ...... .45  2 Coats ...... .69  3 Coats ...... .94 | | | | | |
| **Paint wood floor** | sf | $.68 | $.70 | $1.06 | $1.45 |
| *Materials* Prime ......... .19  1 Coat ...... .21  2 Coats ...... .29  3 Coats ...... .39 | | | | | |
| *Labor* Prime ............... .49  1 Coat ...... .49  2 Coats ...... .77  3 Coats ...... 1.06 | | | | | |
| **Stain & varnish wood floor** | sf | $1.01 | $1.08 | $1.61 | $2.16 |
| *Materials* Stain .......... .28  1 Coat ...... .31  2 Coats ...... .43  3 Coats ...... .57 | | | | | |
| *Labor* Stain ............... .73  1 Coat ...... .77  2 Coats ...... 1.18  3 Coats ...... 1.59 | | | | | |
| **PANELING** **Paint wall paneling, simple pattern** | sf | $.77 | $.80 | $1.20 | $1.63 |
| *Materials* Prime ......... .28  1 Coat ...... .31  2 Coats ...... .43  3 Coats ...... .57 | | | | | |
| *Labor* Prime ............... .49  1 Coat ...... .49  2 Coats ...... .77  3 Coats ...... 1.06 | | | | | |
| **Stain & varnish wall paneling, simple pattern** | sf | $1.14 | $1.23 | $1.82 | $2.44 |
| *Materials* Stain .......... .41  1 Coat ...... .46  2 Coats ...... .64  3 Coats ...... .85 | | | | | |
| *Labor* Stain ............... .73  1 Coat ...... .77  2 Coats ...... 1.18  3 Coats ...... 1.59 | | | | | |
| **Paint wall paneling, ornate pattern** | sf | $1.07 | $1.11 | $1.68 | $2.24 |
| *Materials* Prime ......... .38  1 Coat ...... .42  2 Coats ...... .58  3 Coats ...... .77 | | | | | |
| *Labor* Prime ............... .69  1 Coat ...... .69  2 Coats ...... 1.10  3 Coats ...... 1.47 | | | | | |
| **Stain & varnish wall paneling, ornate pattern** | sf | $1.62 | $1.72 | $2.53 | $3.42 |
| *Materials* Stain .......... .56  1 Coat ...... .62  2 Coats ...... .86  3 Coats ...... 1.14 | | | | | |
| *Labor* Stain ............... 1.06  1 Coat ...... 1.10  2 Coats ...... 1.67  3 Coats ...... 2.28 | | | | | |
| **Paint wall paneling, very ornate pattern** | sf | $1.60 | $1.69 | $2.50 | $3.38 |
| *Materials* Prime ......... .46  1 Coat ...... .51  2 Coats ...... .71  3 Coats ...... .94 | | | | | |
| *Labor* Prime ............... 1.14  1 Coat ...... 1.18  2 Coats ...... 1.79  3 Coats ...... 2.44 | | | | | |
| **Stain & varnish wall paneling, very ornate pattern** | sf | $2.43 | $2.55 | $3.83 | $5.20 |
| *Materials* Stain .......... .68  1 Coat ...... .76  2 Coats ...... 1.06  3 Coats ...... 1.41 | | | | | |
| *Labor* Stain ............... 1.75  1 Coat ...... 1.79  2 Coats ...... 2.77  3 Coats ...... 3.79 | | | | | |
| **MASONRY** Deduct **26%** for previously painted block or brick. **Paint concrete block** | sf | $.85 | $.92 | $1.37 | $1.79 |
| *Materials* Prime ......... .28  1 Coat ...... .31  2 Coats ...... .43  3 Coats ...... .57 | | | | | |
| *Labor* Prime ............... .57  1 Coat ...... .61  2 Coats ...... .94  3 Coats ...... 1.22 | | | | | |

| Item Description | Unit | prime/stain | 1 Coat | 2 Coats | 3 Coats |
|---|---|---|---|---|---|
| **Paint brick** | sf | $.99 | $1.02 | $1.52 | $2.03 |
| *Materials* Prime .30   1 Coat .33   2 Coats .46   3 Coats .61 | | | | | |
| *Labor* Prime .69   1 Coat .69   2 Coats 1.06   3 Coats 1.42 | | | | | |
| **Paint stone wall** | sf | $.63 | $.65 | $.98 | $1.29 |
| *Materials* Prime .22   1 Coat .24   2 Coats .33   3 Coats .44 | | | | | |
| *Labor* Prime .41   1 Coat .41   2 Coats .65   3 Coats .85 | | | | | |
| **Seal stone wall** | sf | $.63 | $.70 | $.99 | $1.34 |
| *Materials* Seal .30   1 Coat .33   2 Coats .46   3 Coats .61 | | | | | |
| *Labor* Seal .33   1 Coat .37   2 Coats .53   3 Coats .73 | | | | | |
| **Paint metal roofing** | sf | $1.01 | $1.09 | $1.60 | $2.17 |
| *Materials* Prime .32   1 Coat .36   2 Coats .50   3 Coats .66 | | | | | |
| *Labor* Prime .69   1 Coat .73   2 Coats 1.10   3 Coats 1.51 | | | | | |
| **Treat wood shingles or shakes with shingle oil** | sf | $.74 | $.80 | $1.17 | $1.57 |
| *Materials* Treat .21   1 Coat .23   2 Coats .32   3 Coats .43 | | | | | |
| *Labor* Treat .53   1 Coat .57   2 Coats .85   3 Coats 1.14 | | | | | |
| **Seal wall framing** | sf | $.88 | $.90 | $1.38 | $1.87 |
| *Materials* Seal .15   1 Coat .17   2 Coats .24   3 Coats .32 | | | | | |
| *Labor* Seal .73   1 Coat .73   2 Coats 1.14   3 Coats 1.55 | | | | | |
| **Seal floor framing** | sf | $1.10 | $1.16 | $1.73 | $2.32 |
| *Materials* Seal .20   1 Coat .22   2 Coats .31   3 Coats .41 | | | | | |
| *Labor* Seal .90   1 Coat .94   2 Coats 1.42   3 Coats 1.91 | | | | | |
| **Seal roof framing** | sf | $1.39 | $1.46 | $2.18 | $2.92 |
| *Materials* Seal .25   1 Coat .28   2 Coats .39   3 Coats .52 | | | | | |
| *Labor* Seal 1.14   1 Coat 1.18   2 Coats 1.79   3 Coats 2.40 | | | | | |
| **Paint exterior siding** | sf | $.87 | $.89 | $1.35 | $1.79 |
| *Materials* Prime .22   1 Coat .24   2 Coats .33   3 Coats .45 | | | | | |
| *Labor* Prime .65   1 Coat .65   2 Coats 1.02   3 Coats 1.34 | | | | | |
| **Stain exterior siding** | sf | $.97 | $1.01 | $1.50 | $2.04 |
| *Materials* Stain .36   1 Coat .40   2 Coats .56   3 Coats .74 | | | | | |
| *Labor* Stain .61   1 Coat .61   2 Coats .94   3 Coats 1.30 | | | | | |
| **Paint window shutter (per shutter, per side)** | ea | $20.22 | $21.26 | $31.84 | $42.99 |
| *Materials* Prime 4.82   1 Coat 5.36   2 Coats 7.44   3 Coats 9.89 | | | | | |
| *Labor* Prime 15.40   1 Coat 15.90   2 Coats 24.40   3 Coats 33.10 | | | | | |
| **Stain window shutter (per shutter, per side)** | ea | $30.67 | $32.15 | $48.30 | $65.00 |
| *Materials* Stain 7.07   1 Coat 7.85   2 Coats 10.90   3 Coats 14.50 | | | | | |
| *Labor* Stain 23.60   1 Coat 24.30   2 Coats 37.40   3 Coats 50.50 | | | | | |
| **Paint exterior fascia** | lf | $.55 | $.56 | $.84 | $1.14 |
| *Materials* Prime .10   1 Coat .11   2 Coats .15   3 Coats .20 | | | | | |
| *Labor* Prime .45   1 Coat .45   2 Coats .69   3 Coats .94 | | | | | |
| **Stain exterior wood fascia** | lf | $.55 | $.57 | $.87 | $1.14 |
| *Materials* Stain .14   1 Coat .16   2 Coats .22   3 Coats .29 | | | | | |
| *Labor* Stain .41   1 Coat .41   2 Coats .65   3 Coats .85 | | | | | |
| **Paint exterior soffit** | sf | $.67 | $.73 | $1.06 | $1.42 |
| *Materials* Prime .22   1 Coat .24   2 Coats .33   3 Coats .44 | | | | | |
| *Labor* Prime .45   1 Coat .49   2 Coats .73   3 Coats .98 | | | | | |
| **Stain exterior wood soffit** | sf | $.77 | $.80 | $1.20 | $1.63 |
| *Materials* Stain .28   1 Coat .31   2 Coats .43   3 Coats .57 | | | | | |
| *Labor* Stain .49   1 Coat .49   2 Coats .77   3 Coats 1.06 | | | | | |
| **Paint rain gutter or downspout** | lf | $.92 | $.98 | $1.47 | $1.98 |
| *Materials* Prime .19   1 Coat .21   2 Coats .29   3 Coats .39 | | | | | |
| *Labor* Prime .73   1 Coat .77   2 Coats 1.18   3 Coats 1.59 | | | | | |

**RELATED ITEMS**

Finish Carpentry .......... 199
Flooring .......... 257
  *sand, edge & fill*
  *wood floor* .......... 268
Paneling .......... 347
Masonry .......... 287
Roofing .......... 393
Rough Carpentry .......... 409
Siding .......... 455

◄ ROOFING

◄ ROUGH CARPENTRY
◁ seal framing
  *seal smoke-stained*
  *framing for odor control*

◄ SIDING

◁ shutters

◁ fascia

◁ soffit

◁ gutter or downspout

| | Item Description | Unit | prime/stain | 1 Coat | 2 Coats | 3 Coats |
|---|---|---|---|---|---|---|
| **STAIRS ▶** | **Paint stair balustrade** | lf | $10.36 | $10.86 | $16.26 | $22.02 |
| | *Materials* Prime..........2.63  1 Coat.......2.92  2 Coats........4.06  3 Coats........5.42 | | | | | |
| | *Labor* Prime.................7.73  1 Coat.......7.94  2 Coats......12.20  3 Coats.....16.60 | | | | | |
| | **Stain & varnish stair balustrade** | lf | $15.69 | $16.37 | $24.68 | $33.28 |
| | *Materials* Stain .........3.89  1 Coat.......4.27  2 Coats........5.98  3 Coats........7.98 | | | | | |
| | *Labor* Stain ................11.80  1 Coat.....12.10  2 Coats......18.70  3 Coats.....25.30 | | | | | |
| | **Paint stair riser** | ea | $6.76 | $7.12 | $10.59 | $14.28 |
| | *Materials* Prime..........2.20  1 Coat.......2.44  2 Coats........3.39  3 Coats........4.51 | | | | | |
| | *Labor* Prime.................4.56  1 Coat.......4.68  2 Coats........7.20  3 Coats........9.77 | | | | | |
| | **Stain & varnish stair riser** | ea | $10.19 | $10.75 | $15.99 | $21.53 |
| | *Materials* Stain ..........3.23  1 Coat.......3.59  2 Coats........4.99  3 Coats........6.63 | | | | | |
| | *Labor* Stain....................6.96  1 Coat.......7.16  2 Coats......11.00  3 Coats.....14.90 | | | | | |
| | **Paint stair tread** | ea | $7.37 | $7.81 | $11.59 | $15.62 |
| | *Materials* Prime..........2.45  1 Coat.......2.72  2 Coats........3.78  3 Coats........5.02 | | | | | |
| | *Labor* Prime.................4.92  1 Coat.......5.09  2 Coats........7.81  3 Coats.....10.60 | | | | | |
| | **Stain & finish stair tread** | ea | $11.13 | $11.77 | $17.55 | $23.58 |
| | *Materials* Stain ..........3.60  1 Coat.......4.00  2 Coats........5.55  3 Coats........7.38 | | | | | |
| | *Labor* Stain....................7.53  1 Coat.......7.77  2 Coats......12.00  3 Coats.....16.20 | | | | | |
| | **Paint stair bracket** | ea | $5.74 | $6.05 | $8.98 | $12.07 |
| | *Materials* Prime..........2.00  1 Coat.......2.22  2 Coats........3.08  3 Coats........4.09 | | | | | |
| | *Labor* Prime.................3.74  1 Coat.......3.83  2 Coats........5.90  3 Coats........7.98 | | | | | |
| | **Stain & finish stair bracket** | ea | $8.63 | $9.12 | $13.57 | $18.22 |
| | *Materials* Stain ..........2.93  1 Coat.......3.26  2 Coats........4.53  3 Coats........6.02 | | | | | |
| | *Labor* Stain....................5.70  1 Coat.......5.86  2 Coats........9.04  3 Coats.....12.20 | | | | | |
| **WINDOW ▶** | **Paint small window (per side)** | ea | $19.00 | $20.18 | $29.80 | $40.20 |
| | *Materials* Prime..........7.00  1 Coat.......7.78  2 Coats......10.80  3 Coats.....14.40 | | | | | |
| | *Labor* Prime.................12.00  1 Coat.....12.40  2 Coats......19.00  3 Coats.....25.80 | | | | | |
| | **Paint average size window (per side)** | ea | $27.80 | $29.50 | $43.60 | $58.60 |
| | *Materials* Prime........10.70  1 Coat.....11.90  2 Coats......16.50  3 Coats.....21.90 | | | | | |
| | *Labor* Prime.................17.10  1 Coat.....17.60  2 Coats......27.10  3 Coats.....36.70 | | | | | |
| | **Paint large window (per side)** | ea | $35.20 | $37.30 | $55.20 | $74.40 |
| | *Materials* Prime ........13.50  1 Coat.....15.00  2 Coats......20.80  3 Coats.....27.60 | | | | | |
| | *Labor* Prime.................21.70  1 Coat.....22.30  2 Coats......34.40  3 Coats.....46.80 | | | | | |
| | **Paint very large window (per side)** | ea | $46.60 | $49.60 | $73.10 | $98.10 |
| | *Materials* Prime ..........19.40  1 Coat.....21.60  2 Coats......30.00  3 Coats.....39.90 | | | | | |
| | *Labor* Prime.................27.20  1 Coat.....28.00  2 Coats......43.10  3 Coats.....58.20 | | | | | |
| **WALLPAPER ▶** | **Paint wallpaper** | sf | $.62 | $.64 | $.95 | $1.29 |
| | *Materials* Prime ..........17  1 Coat .......19  2 Coats........26  3 Coats.........35 | | | | | |
| | *Labor* Prime .................45  1 Coat .......45  2 Coats.........69  3 Coats.........94 | | | | | |
| **STRIP PAINT ▶** | **Strip paint or varnish from trim, simple design** | lf | $4.59 | $4.90 | $7.18 | $9.69 |
| *Costs to strip paint that does not contain lead.* | *Materials* Strip............1.29  1 Coat.......1.52  2 Coats........2.05  3 Coats........2.69 | | | | | |
| | *Labor* Strip ..................3.30  1 Coat.......3.38  2 Coats........5.13  3 Coats........7.00 | | | | | |
| | **Strip paint or varnish from trim, complex design** | lf | $7.81 | $8.20 | $14.69 | $25.15 |
| | *Materials* Strip............1.58  1 Coat.......1.77  2 Coats........2.79  3 Coats........4.25 | | | | | |
| | *Labor* Strip ..................6.23  1 Coat.......6.43  2 Coats......11.90  3 Coats.....20.90 | | | | | |
| | **Strip paint or varnish from door (slab only)** | ea | $35.50 | $38.70 | $57.80 | $86.50 |
| | *Materials* Strip...........13.90  1 Coat.....16.60  2 Coats......23.40  3 Coats.....34.80 | | | | | |
| | *Labor* Strip .................21.60  1 Coat.....22.10  2 Coats......34.40  3 Coats.....51.70 | | | | | |
| | **Strip paint or varnish from door jamb and casing** | lf | $5.94 | $6.47 | $9.45 | $12.66 |
| | *Materials* Strip...........2.20  1 Coat.......2.60  2 Coats........3.51  3 Coats........4.60 | | | | | |
| | *Labor* Strip .................3.74  1 Coat.......3.87  2 Coats........5.94  3 Coats........8.06 | | | | | |

**RELATED ITEMS**

# TIME & MATERIAL CHARTS (selected items)

## Painting Materials

| DESCRIPTION | APPLIED TO | MATERIAL PRICE | COVERAGE | UNIT PRICE |
|---|---|---|---|---|
| **Prime or seal** | | | | |
| primer or sealer | plaster or drywall | $20.50 gallon | 178 | $.12 sf |
| primer or sealer | interior door | $20.50 gallon | 2.8 | $7.32 ea |
| primer or sealer | entry door | $20.50 gallon | 1.6 | $12.80 ea |
| primer or sealer | wood trim, simple design | $20.50 gallon | 178 | $.12 lf |
| primer or sealer | exterior siding | $20.50 gallon | 94 | $.22 sf |
| primer or sealer | stair balustrade | $20.50 gallon | 7.8 | $2.63 lf |
| **Paint, one coat** | | | | |
| oil or latex paint | plaster or drywall | $26.00 gallon | 205 | $.13 sf |
| oil or latex paint | interior door | $26.00 gallon | 3.2 | $8.13 ea |
| oil or latex paint | entry door | $26.00 gallon | 1.9 | $13.70 ea |
| oil or latex paint | wood trim, simple design | $26.00 gallon | 205 | $.13 lf |
| oil or latex paint | exterior siding | $26.00 gallon | 108 | $.24 sf |
| oil or latex paint | stair balustrade | $26.00 gallon | 8.9 | $2.92 lf |
| **Paint, two coats** | | | | |
| oil or latex paint | plaster or drywall | $26.00 gallon | 151 | $.17 sf |
| oil or latex paint | interior door | $26.00 gallon | 2.3 | $11.30 ea |
| oil or latex paint | entry door | $26.00 gallon | 1.4 | $18.60 ea |
| oil or latex paint | wood trim, simple design | $26.00 gallon | 151 | $.17 lf |
| oil or latex paint | exterior siding | $26.00 gallon | 78 | $.33 sf |
| oil or latex paint | stair balustrade | $26.00 gallon | 6.4 | $4.06 lf |
| **Paint, three coats** | | | | |
| oil or latex paint | plaster or drywall | $26.00 gallon | 113 | $.23 sf |
| oil or latex paint | interior door | $26.00 gallon | 1.7 | $15.30 ea |
| oil or latex paint | entry door | $26.00 gallon | 1 | $26.00 ea |
| oil or latex paint | wood trim, simple design | $26.00 gallon | 113 | $.23 lf |
| oil or latex paint | exterior siding | $26.00 gallon | 58 | $.45 sf |
| oil or latex paint | stair balustrade | $26.00 gallon | 4.8 | $5.42 lf |
| **Stain** | | | | |
| stain | interior door | $27.60 gallon | 2.5 | $11.00 ea |
| stain | entry door | $27.60 gallon | 1.5 | $18.40 ea |
| stain | wood trim, simple design | $27.60 gallon | 159 | $.17 lf |
| stain | exterior siding, one coat | $27.60 gallon | 77 | $.36 sf |
| stain | stair balustrade | $27.60 gallon | 7.1 | $3.89 lf |
| **Varnish, one coat** | | | | |
| varnish, clear | interior door | $35.90 gallon | 2.9 | $12.40 ea |
| varnish, clear | entry door | $35.90 gallon | 1.8 | $19.90 ea |
| varnish, clear | wood trim, simple design | $35.90 gallon | 284 | $.13 lf |
| varnish, clear | stair balustrade | $35.90 gallon | 8.4 | $4.27 lf |
| **Varnish, two coats** | | | | |
| varnish, clear | interior door | $35.90 gallon | 2.1 | $17.10 ea |
| varnish, clear | entry door | $35.90 gallon | 1.4 | $25.60 ea |
| varnish, clear | wood trim, simple design | $35.90 gallon | 208 | $.17 lf |
| varnish, clear | stair balustrade | $35.90 gallon | 6 | $5.98 lf |
| **Varnish, three coats** | | | | |
| varnish, clear | interior door | $35.90 gallon | 1.6 | $22.40 ea |
| varnish, clear | entry door | $35.90 gallon | 1 | $35.90 ea |
| varnish, clear | wood trim, simple design | $35.90 gallon | 156 | $.23 lf |
| varnish, clear | stair balustrade | $35.90 gallon | 4.5 | $7.98 lf |

## Painting Labor

| LABORER | BASE WAGE | PAID LEAVE | TRUE WAGE | FICA | FUTA | WORKER'S COMP. | UNEMPLOY. INSUR. | HEALTH INSUR. | RETIRE (401k) | LIABILITY INSUR. | COST PER HOUR |
|---|---|---|---|---|---|---|---|---|---|---|---|
| Painter | $22.30 | 1.74 | $24.04 | 1.84 | .19 | 6.14 | 2.09 | 2.54 | .72 | 3.13 | $40.70 |

**Paid Leave** is calculated based on two weeks paid vacation, one week sick leave, and seven paid holidays. Employer's matching portion of **FICA** is 7.65 percent. **FUTA** (Federal Unemployment) is .8 percent. **Worker's compensation** for the painting trade was calculated using a national average of 25.52 percent. **Unemployment insurance** was calculated using a national average of 8.7 percent. **Health insurance** was calculated based on a projected national average for 2001 of $505 per employee (and family when applicable) per month. Employer pays 80 percent for a per month cost of $404 per employee. **Retirement** is based on a 401(k) retirement program with employer matching of 50 percent. Employee contributions to the 401(k) plan are an average of 6 percent of the true wage. **Liability insurance** is based on a national average of 12.9 percent.

## Painting Labor Productivity

| WORK DESCRIPTION | LABORER | COST PER HOUR | PRODUCTIVITY | UNIT PRICE |
|---|---|---|---|---|
| **Prime or seal** | | | | |
| acoustic ceiling texture | painter | $40.70 | .011 | $.45 sf |
| plaster or drywall | painter | $40.70 | .006 | $.24 sf |
| masonry, block | painter | $40.70 | .014 | $.57 sf |
| concrete floor | painter | $40.70 | .008 | $.33 sf |
| wood floor | painter | $40.70 | .012 | $.49 sf |
| folding door | painter | $40.70 | .402 | $16.40 ea |
| bypassing door | painter | $40.70 | .830 | $33.80 ea |
| interior door | painter | $40.70 | .340 | $13.80 ea |
| door jamb & casing | painter | $40.70 | .011 | $.45 lf |
| wood entry door | painter | $40.70 | .742 | $30.20 ea |
| wood sliding patio door | painter | $40.70 | .646 | $26.30 ea |
| garage door | painter | $40.70 | .006 | $.24 sf |
| 4' high wood fence (per side) | painter | $40.70 | .051 | $2.08 lf |
| 48" high ornamental iron fence (both sides) | painter | $40.70 | .077 | $3.13 lf |
| wood trim, simple design | painter | $40.70 | .011 | $.45 lf |
| wood trim, very ornate design | painter | $40.70 | .025 | $.69 lf |
| seal smoke-stained frame walls | painter | $40.70 | .018 | $.73 sf |
| seal smoke-stained joists | painter | $40.70 | .022 | $.90 sf |
| seal smoke-stained rafters or trusses | painter | $40.70 | .028 | $1.14 sf |
| siding | painter | $40.70 | .016 | $.65 sf |
| stucco | painter | $40.70 | .014 | $.57 sf |
| stair balustrade | painter | $40.70 | .190 | $7.73 lf |
| small window | painter | $40.70 | .295 | $12.00 ea |
| very large window | painter | $40.70 | .668 | $27.20 ea |
| **Paint, one coat** | | | | |
| acoustic ceiling texture | painter | $40.70 | .011 | $.45 sf |
| plaster or drywall | painter | $40.70 | .006 | $.24 sf |
| masonry, block | painter | $40.70 | .015 | $.61 sf |
| concrete floor | painter | $40.70 | .008 | $.33 sf |
| wood floor | painter | $40.70 | .012 | $.49 sf |
| folding door | painter | $40.70 | .413 | $16.80 ea |
| bypassing door | painter | $40.70 | .854 | $34.80 ea |
| interior door | painter | $40.70 | .349 | $14.20 ea |
| door jamb & casing | painter | $40.70 | .011 | $.45 lf |
| wood entry door | painter | $40.70 | .763 | $31.10 ea |
| wood sliding patio door | painter | $40.70 | .665 | $27.10 sf |
| garage door | painter | $40.70 | .006 | $.24 sf |
| 4' high wood fence (per side) | painter | $40.70 | .053 | $2.16 lf |
| 48" high ornamental iron fence (both sides) | painter | $40.70 | .079 | $3.22 lf |
| wood trim, simple design | painter | $40.70 | .011 | $.45 lf |
| wood trim, very ornate design | painter | $40.70 | .017 | $.69 lf |
| siding | painter | $40.70 | .016 | $.65 sf |
| stucco | painter | $40.70 | .015 | $.61 sf |
| stair balustrade | painter | $40.70 | .195 | $7.94 sf |
| small window | painter | $40.70 | .304 | $12.40 ea |
| very large window | painter | $40.70 | .687 | $28.00 ea |

. . . More ➤

## Painting Labor Productivity *continued*

| WORK DESCRIPTION | LABORER | COST PER HOUR | PRODUCTIVITY | UNIT PRICE |
|---|---|---|---|---|
| **Paint, two coats** | | | | |
| acoustic ceiling texture | painter | $40.70 | .017 | $.69 sf |
| plaster or drywall | painter | $40.70 | .010 | $.41 sf |
| masonry, block | painter | $40.70 | .023 | $.94 sf |
| concrete floor | painter | $40.70 | .012 | $.49 sf |
| wood floor | painter | $40.70 | .019 | $.77 sf |
| folding door | painter | $40.70 | .636 | $25.90 ea |
| bypassing door | painter | $40.70 | 1.32 | $53.70 ea |
| interior door | painter | $40.70 | .538 | $21.90 ea |
| door jamb & casing | painter | $40.70 | .017 | $.69 lf |
| wood entry door | painter | $40.70 | 1.18 | $48.00 ea |
| wood sliding patio door | painter | $40.70 | 1.02 | $41.50 sf |
| garage door | painter | $40.70 | .009 | $.37 sf |
| 4' high wood fence (per side) | painter | $40.70 | .081 | $3.30 lf |
| 48" high ornamental iron fence (both sides) | painter | $40.70 | .121 | $4.92 lf |
| wood trim, simple design | painter | $40.70 | .017 | $.69 lf |
| wood trim, very ornate design | painter | $40.70 | .026 | $1.06 lf |
| siding | painter | $40.70 | .025 | $1.02 sf |
| stucco | painter | $40.70 | .023 | $.94 sf |
| stair balustrade | painter | $40.70 | .300 | $12.20 lf |
| small window | painter | $40.70 | .467 | $19.00 ea |
| very large window | painter | $40.70 | 1.06 | $43.10 ea |
| **Paint, three coats** | | | | |
| acoustic ceiling texture | painter | $40.70 | .023 | $.94 sf |
| plaster or drywall | painter | $40.70 | .013 | $.53 sf |
| masonry, block | painter | $40.70 | .030 | $1.22 sf |
| concrete floor | painter | $40.70 | .016 | $.65 sf |
| wood floor | painter | $40.70 | .026 | $1.06 sf |
| folding door | painter | $40.70 | .861 | $35.00 ea |
| bypassing door | painter | $40.70 | 1.78 | $72.40 ea |
| interior door | painter | $40.70 | .729 | $29.70 ea |
| door jamb & casing | painter | $40.70 | .023 | $.94 lf |
| wood entry door | painter | $40.70 | 1.59 | $64.70 ea |
| wood sliding patio door | painter | $40.70 | 1.39 | $56.60 sf |
| garage door | painter | $40.70 | .013 | $.53 sf |
| 4' high wood fence (per side) | painter | $40.70 | .109 | $4.44 lf |
| 48" high ornamental iron fence (both sides) | painter | $40.70 | .164 | $6.67 lf |
| wood trim, simple design | painter | $40.70 | .023 | $.94 lf |
| wood trim, very ornate design | painter | $40.70 | .035 | $1.42 lf |
| siding | painter | $40.70 | .033 | $1.34 sf |
| stucco | painter | $40.70 | .030 | $1.22 sf |
| stair balustrade | painter | $40.70 | .407 | $16.60 lf |
| small window | painter | $40.70 | .633 | $25.80 ea |
| very large window | painter | $40.70 | 1.43 | $58.20 ea |
| **Stain** | | | | |
| wood floor | painter | $40.70 | .018 | $.73 sf |
| folding door | painter | $40.70 | .614 | $25.00 ea |
| bypassing door | painter | $40.70 | 1.27 | $51.70 ea |
| interior door | painter | $40.70 | .519 | $21.10 ea |
| French door | painter | $40.70 | 1.25 | $50.90 ea |
| panel door | painter | $40.70 | 1.08 | $44.00 ea |
| door jamb & casing | painter | $40.70 | .017 | $.69 lf |
| wood entry door | painter | $40.70 | 1.13 | $46.00 ea |
| wood sliding patio door | painter | $40.70 | .988 | $40.20 ea |
| garage door | painter | $40.70 | .009 | $.37 sf |
| 4' high wood fence (per side) | painter | $40.70 | .078 | $3.17 lf |
| wood trim, simple design | painter | $40.70 | .016 | $.65 lf |
| wood trim, very ornate design | painter | $40.70 | .025 | $1.02 lf |
| wood paneling, simple pattern | painter | $40.70 | .018 | $.73 sf |
| wood paneling, very ornate pattern | painter | $40.70 | .043 | $1.75 sf |
| siding | painter | $40.70 | .015 | $.61 sf |
| stair balustrade | painter | $40.70 | .290 | $11.80 lf |

*. . . More >*

## Painting Labor Productivity *continued*

| WORK DESCRIPTION | LABORER | COST PER HOUR | PRODUCTIVITY | UNIT PRICE |
|---|---|---|---|---|
| **Varnish, one coat** | | | | |
| wood floor | painter | $40.70 | .019 | $.77 sf |
| folding door | painter | $40.70 | .632 | $25.70 ea |
| bypassing door | painter | $40.70 | 1.31 | $53.30 ea |
| interior door | painter | $40.70 | .534 | $21.70 ea |
| French door | painter | $40.70 | 1.29 | $52.50 ea |
| panel door | painter | $40.70 | 1.11 | $45.20 ea |
| door jamb & casing | painter | $40.70 | .017 | $.69 lf |
| wood entry door | painter | $40.70 | 1.17 | $47.60 ea |
| wood sliding patio door | painter | $40.70 | 1.02 | $41.50 ea |
| garage door | painter | $40.70 | .009 | $.37 sf |
| 4' high wood fence (per side) | painter | $40.70 | .080 | $3.26 lf |
| wood trim, simple design | painter | $40.70 | .017 | $.69 lf |
| wood trim, very ornate design | painter | $40.70 | .026 | $1.06 lf |
| wood paneling, simple pattern | painter | $40.70 | .019 | $.77 sf |
| wood paneling, very ornate pattern | painter | $40.70 | .044 | $1.79 sf |
| siding | painter | $40.70 | .015 | $.61 sf |
| stair balustrade | painter | $40.70 | .298 | $12.10 lf |
| **Varnish, two coats** | | | | |
| wood floor | painter | $40.70 | .029 | $1.18 sf |
| folding door | painter | $40.70 | .972 | $39.60 ea |
| bypassing door | painter | $40.70 | 2.01 | $81.80 ea |
| interior door | painter | $40.70 | .822 | $33.50 ea |
| French door | painter | $40.70 | 1.98 | $80.60 ea |
| panel door | painter | $40.70 | 1.70 | $69.20 ea |
| door jamb & casing | painter | $40.70 | .026 | $1.06 lf |
| wood entry door | painter | $24.70 | 1.80 | $73.30 lf |
| wood sliding patio door | painter | $40.70 | 1.56 | $63.50 ea |
| garage door | painter | $40.70 | .014 | $.57 sf |
| 4' high wood fence (per side) | painter | $40.70 | .123 | $5.01 lf |
| wood trim, simple design | painter | $40.70 | .026 | $1.06 lf |
| wood trim, very ornate design | painter | $40.70 | .040 | $1.63 lf |
| wood paneling, simple pattern | painter | $40.70 | .029 | $1.18 sf |
| wood paneling, very ornate pattern | painter | $40.70 | .068 | $2.77 sf |
| siding | painter | $40.70 | .023 | $.94 sf |
| stair balustrade | painter | $40.70 | .459 | $18.70 lf |
| **Varnish, three coats** | | | | |
| wood floor | painter | $40.70 | .039 | $1.59 sf |
| folding door | painter | $40.70 | 1.32 | $53.70 ea |
| bypassing door | painter | $40.70 | 2.72 | $111.00 ea |
| interior door | painter | $40.70 | 1.11 | $45.20 ea |
| French door | painter | $40.70 | 2.68 | $109.00 ea |
| panel door | painter | $40.70 | 2.31 | $94.00 ea |
| door jamb & casing | painter | $40.70 | .035 | $1.42 lf |
| wood entry door | painter | $40.70 | 2.43 | $98.90 ea |
| wood sliding patio door | painter | $40.70 | 2.12 | $86.30 ea |
| garage door | painter | $40.70 | .019 | $.77 sf |
| 4' high wood fence (per side) | painter | $40.70 | .167 | $6.80 lf |
| wood trim, simple design | painter | $40.70 | .035 | $1.42 lf |
| wood trim, very ornate design | painter | $40.70 | .054 | $2.20 lf |
| wood paneling, simple pattern | painter | $40.70 | .039 | $1.59 sf |
| wood paneling, very ornate pattern | painter | $40.70 | .093 | $3.79 sf |
| siding | painter | $40.70 | .032 | $1.30 sf |
| stair balustrade | painter | $40.70 | .621 | $25.30 lf |

NOTES: _____

_____

_____

_____ end

# 27 ............................................................ *Paneling*

| Item Description | Unit | Remove | Replace | Total | |
|---|---|---|---|---|---|
| **Minimum charge for paneling work**<br>*Replace* Materials ......25.00     Labor ..........28.70 | ea | — | $53.70 | $53.70 | ◄ **MINIMUM** |
| **Minimum charge for frame-and-panel wall work**<br>*Replace* Materials ......75.00     Labor ..........138.00 | ea | — | $213.00 | $213.00 | |
| **Hardboard paneling, economy grade**<br>*Replace* Materials ........ .68     Labor ..............1.14<br>*Remove* ......................     Labor ..............18<br>► 1/8" thick. | sf | $.18 | $1.82 | $2.00 | ◄ **HARDBOARD PANELING**<br>*Prefinished. Installed with adhesive and nails. Includes 5% waste.* |
| **Hardboard paneling, standard grade**<br>*Replace* Materials ........ .83     Labor ..............1.14<br>*Remove* ......................     Labor ..............18<br>► 1/4" thick, little or no texture. | sf | $.18 | $1.97 | $2.15 | |
| **Hardboard paneling, high grade**<br>*Replace* Materials ........1.26     Labor ..............1.14<br>*Remove* ......................     Labor ..............18<br>► 1/4" thick, heavy texture or special finish. | sf | $.18 | $2.40 | $2.58 | |
| **Hardboard wall paneling, with simulated brick face**<br>*Replace* Materials ........ .88     Labor ..............1.14<br>*Remove* ......................     Labor ..............18<br>► 1/4" thick. | sf | $.18 | $2.02 | $2.20 | |
| **Hardboard wall paneling, with simulated stone face**<br>*Replace* Materials ........ .94     Labor ..............1.14<br>*Remove* ......................     Labor ..............18<br>► 1/4" thick. | sf | $.18 | $2.08 | $2.26 | |
| **Pegboard**<br>*Replace* Materials ........ .65     Labor ..............1.03<br>*Remove* ......................     Labor ..............18 | sf | $.18 | $1.68 | $1.86 | ◄ **PEGBOARD**<br>*Tempered. Includes 5% waste.* |
| **1/4" ash plywood paneling**<br>*Replace* Materials ........2.89     Labor ..............1.24<br>*Remove* ......................     Labor ..............21 | sf | $.21 | $4.13 | $4.34 | ◄ **PLYWOOD PANELING**<br>*Includes 5% waste. Unfinished with top grade veneer.* |
| **1/4" birch plywood paneling**<br>*Replace* Materials ........1.44     Labor ..............1.24<br>*Remove* ......................     Labor ..............21 | sf | $.21 | $2.68 | $2.89 | |
| **1/4" cherry plywood paneling**<br>*Replace* Materials ........3.27     Labor ..............1.24<br>*Remove* ......................     Labor ..............21 | sf | $.21 | $4.51 | $4.72 | |
| **1/4" hickory plywood paneling**<br>*Replace* Materials ........3.08     Labor ..............1.24<br>*Remove* ......................     Labor ..............21 | sf | $.21 | $4.32 | $4.53 | |
| **1/4" knotty pine plywood paneling**<br>*Replace* Materials ........2.47     Labor ..............1.24<br>*Remove* ......................     Labor ..............21 | sf | $.21 | $3.71 | $3.92 | |

| Item Description | Unit | Remove | Replace | Total |
|---|---|---|---|---|
| **PLYWOOD ▶ PANELING** *continued.* **1/4" mahogany plywood paneling** *Replace* Materials........2.66  Labor ............1.24  *Remove* ......................  Labor............. .21 | sf | $.21 | $3.90 | $4.11 |
| **1/4" white maple plywood paneling** *Replace* Materials........2.16  Labor ............1.24  *Remove* ......................  Labor............. .21 | sf | $.21 | $3.40 | $3.61 |
| **1/4" red or white oak plywood paneling** *Replace* Materials........1.48  Labor ............1.24  *Remove* ......................  Labor............. .21 | sf | $.21 | $2.72 | $2.93 |
| **1/4" quartersawn red or white oak plywood paneling** *Replace* Materials........2.37  Labor ............1.24  *Remove* ......................  Labor............. .21 | sf | $.21 | $3.61 | $3.82 |
| **1/4" walnut plywood paneling** *Replace* Materials........4.21  Labor ............1.24  *Remove* ......................  Labor............. .21 | sf | $.21 | $5.45 | $5.66 |
| **1/4" rough-sawn cedar plywood paneling** *Replace* Materials........2.01  Labor ............1.24  *Remove* ......................  Labor............. .21 | sf | $.21 | $3.25 | $3.46 |

**ADD FOR WALL ▶ MOLDING**
*Includes 6% waste. Add to plywood paneling prices above for moldings that form repeating squares on wall with radius corners. Add 11% for slope-matched wall molding along stairways.*

**Add 44% for wall molding, standard grade**
▶ Simple horizontal pattern moldings.

**Add 53% for wall molding, high grade**
▶ Vertical or embossed pattern moldings.

**Add 70% for wall molding, deluxe grade**
▶ Simple hand-carved moldings.

**Add 84% for wall molding, custom grade**
▶ Ornate hand carved moldings.

| Item Description | Unit | Remove | Replace | Total |
|---|---|---|---|---|
| **PLYWOOD ▶ PANELING WITH GROOVES** *Prefinished. Includes 5% waste.* **1/4" ash plywood paneling with grooves** *Replace* Materials........2.82  Labor ............1.24  *Remove* ......................  Labor............. .21 | sf | $.21 | $4.06 | $4.27 |
| **1/4" birch plywood paneling with grooves** *Replace* Materials........1.41  Labor ............1.24  *Remove* ......................  Labor............. .21 | sf | $.21 | $2.65 | $2.86 |
| **1/4" cherry plywood paneling with grooves** *Replace* Materials........3.19  Labor ............1.24  *Remove* ......................  Labor............. .21 | sf | $.21 | $4.43 | $4.64 |
| **1/4" hickory plywood paneling with grooves** *Replace* Materials........3.00  Labor ............1.24  *Remove* ......................  Labor............. .21 | sf | $.21 | $4.24 | $4.45 |
| **1/4" knotty pine plywood paneling with grooves** *Replace* Materials........2.41  Labor ............1.24  *Remove* ......................  Labor............. .21 | sf | $.21 | $3.65 | $3.86 |
| **1/4" mahogany plywood paneling with grooves** *Replace* Materials........2.60  Labor ............1.24  *Remove* ......................  Labor............. .21 | sf | $.21 | $3.84 | $4.05 |

| Item Description | Unit | Remove | Replace | Total |
|---|---|---|---|---|
| **1/4" white maple plywood paneling with grooves** | sf | $.21 | $3.35 | $3.56 |
| *Replace* Materials........2.11          Labor............1.24 | | | | |
| *Remove* ......................          Labor............. .21 | | | | |
| **1/4" red or white oak plywood paneling with grooves** | sf | $.21 | $2.68 | $2.89 |
| *Replace* Materials........1.44          Labor............1.24 | | | | |
| *Remove* ......................          Labor............. .21 | | | | |
| **1/4" quartersawn red or white oak plywood paneling with grooves** | sf | $.21 | $3.55 | $3.76 |
| *Replace* Materials........2.31          Labor............1.24 | | | | |
| *Remove* ......................          Labor............. .21 | | | | |
| **1/4" walnut plywood paneling with grooves** | sf | $.21 | $5.35 | $5.56 |
| *Replace* Materials........4.11          Labor............1.24 | | | | |
| *Remove* ......................          Labor............. .21 | | | | |
| **1/4" rough-sawn cedar plywood paneling with grooves** | sf | $.21 | $3.20 | $3.41 |
| *Replace* Materials........1.96          Labor............1.24 | | | | |
| *Remove* ......................          Labor............. .21 | | | | |
| **Pine board-on-board paneling** | sf | $.29 | $4.83 | $5.12 |
| *Replace* Materials........3.52          Labor............1.31 | | | | |
| *Remove* ......................          Labor............. .29 | | | | |
| **Pine board-and-batten paneling** | sf | $.29 | $4.89 | $5.18 |
| *Replace* Materials........3.45          Labor............1.44 | | | | |
| *Remove* ......................          Labor............. .29 | | | | |
| **Add 10% for chevron installation** | | | | |
| **Add 18% for herringbone installation** | | | | |
| **Pine tongue-&-groove paneling, simple pattern** | sf | $.29 | $5.27 | $5.56 |
| *Replace* Materials........3.65          Labor............1.62 | | | | |
| *Remove* ......................          Labor............. .29 | | | | |
| ▶ V or bull nose pattern at joints. | | | | |
| **Pine tongue-&-groove paneling, fancy pattern** | sf | $.29 | $5.52 | $5.81 |
| *Replace* Materials........3.90          Labor............1.62 | | | | |
| *Remove* ......................          Labor............. .29 | | | | |
| ▶ V or bull nose pattern at joints with beaded V, nose, or cove in field. | | | | |
| **Pine tongue-&-groove paneling, ornate pattern** | sf | $.29 | $6.17 | $6.46 |
| *Replace* Materials........4.55          Labor............1.62 | | | | |
| *Remove* ......................          Labor............. .29 | | | | |
| ▶ V or bull nose pattern at joints with double beaded V, noses, or coves in field. | | | | |
| **Cedar tongue-&-groove closet lining** | sf | $.29 | $3.69 | $3.98 |
| *Replace* Materials........2.07          Labor............1.62 | | | | |
| *Remove* ......................          Labor............. .29 | | | | |
| **Add 14% for paneling installed as wainscoting** | | | | |
| **Pine frame-and-panel wall, standard grade** | sf | $.50 | $42.70 | $43.20 |
| *Replace* Materials.......17.80          Labor...........24.90 | | | | |
| *Remove* ......................          Labor............. .50 | | | | |
| ▶ Simple crown and base if included, panels are 1/4" plywood with no onlays. | | | | |
| **Pine frame-and-panel wall, high grade** | sf | $.50 | $54.30 | $54.80 |
| *Replace* Materials .......24.40          Labor...........29.90 | | | | |
| *Remove* ......................          Labor............. .50 | | | | |
| ▶ Simple crown and base if included, panels are solid wood, may be raised. | | | | |

---

**RELATED ITEMS**

Cleaning ......................64
Painting ....................340
Siding..........................455

▽ *board-on-board*

*board-and-batten* △

◀ **BOARD-ON-BOARD OR BOARD-AND-BATTEN PANELING**
*Includes 5% waste. Prices for paneling are slightly higher than those for siding because there are more angles indoors.*

◁ add for angled installations

◀ **TONGUE-&-GROOVE PANELING**
*Includes 5% waste.*

◁ add for wainscot installation

◀ **PINE FRAME-AND-PANEL WALL**
*Includes 5% waste. Complete wall systems with furring strips and other backing, moldings between panels, crown and base.*

| Item Description | Unit | Remove | Replace | Total |
|---|---|---|---|---|
| **PINE FRAME-AND-PANEL WALL** *continued* ▶ **Pine frame-and-panel wall, deluxe grade** | sf | $.50 | $64.80 | $65.30 |

*Replace* Materials ......28.70    Labor ..........36.10
*Remove* ........................    Labor.............. .50
▶ Crown and base with vertical patterns if included, panels are solid wood, may be raised, and may have cathedral top.  May have bolection molding around panels.

| **Pine frame-and-panel wall, custom grade** | sf | $.50 | $85.80 | $86.30 |
|---|---|---|---|---|

*Replace* Materials ......42.80    Labor ..........43.00
*Remove* ........................    Labor.............. .50
▶ Crown and base with vertical patterns if included, panels are solid wood, may be raised, and may have cathedral top.  Panels may be linenfold or wall may contain other components that are hand carved.  May also include corbels and pilasters with capitals.

**OAK FRAME-AND-PANEL WALL** ▶

*See pine frame-and-panel items above and on the previous page for explanation of grades. Includes 5% waste. Complete wall systems with furring strips and other backing, moldings between panels, crown and base.*

| **Oak frame-and-panel wall, standard grade** | sf | $.50 | $46.70 | $47.20 |
|---|---|---|---|---|

*Replace* Materials ......21.80    Labor ..........24.90
*Remove* ........................    Labor.............. .50

| **Oak frame-and-panel wall, high grade** | sf | $.50 | $59.80 | $60.30 |
|---|---|---|---|---|

*Replace* Materials ......29.90    Labor ..........29.90
*Remove* ........................    Labor.............. .50

| **Oak frame-and-panel wall, deluxe grade** | sf | $.50 | $71.30 | $71.80 |
|---|---|---|---|---|

*Replace* Materials ......35.20    Labor ..........36.10
*Remove* ........................    Labor.............. .50

| **Oak frame-and-panel wall, custom grade** | sf | $.50 | $95.40 | $95.90 |
|---|---|---|---|---|

*Replace* Materials ......52.40    Labor ..........43.00
*Remove* ........................    Labor.............. .50

**WALNUT FRAME-AND-PANEL WALL** ▶

*See pine frame-and-panel items above and on the previous page for explanation of grades. Includes 5% waste. Complete wall systems with furring strips and other backing, moldings between panels, crown and base.*

| **Walnut frame-and-panel wall, standard grade** | sf | $.50 | $60.80 | $61.30 |
|---|---|---|---|---|

*Replace* Materials ......35.90    Labor ..........24.90
*Remove* ........................    Labor.............. .50

| **Walnut frame-and-panel wall, high grade** | sf | $.50 | $79.00 | $79.50 |
|---|---|---|---|---|

*Replace* Materials ......49.10    Labor ..........29.90
*Remove* ........................    Labor.............. .50

| **Walnut frame-and-panel wall, deluxe grade** | sf | $.50 | $94.00 | $94.50 |
|---|---|---|---|---|

*Replace* Materials ......57.90    Labor ..........36.10
*Remove* ........................    Labor.............. .50

| **Walnut frame-and-panel wall, custom grade** | sf | $.50 | $129.30 | $129.80 |
|---|---|---|---|---|

*Replace* Materials ......86.30    Labor ..........43.00
*Remove* ........................    Labor.............. .50

**ADD FOR OTHER WOOD SPECIES** ▶

*Add to the costs of oak frame-and-panel walls for these wood species.*

**Add 12% for quartersawn oak frame-and-panel wall**

**Add 17% for cherry frame-and-panel wall**

**Add 65% for teak frame-and-panel wall**

**Add 10% for mahogany frame-and-panel wall**

**Add 14% for hickory frame-and-panel wall**

✍ NOTES: _____

_____

_____ end

# TIME & MATERIAL CHARTS (selected items)

## Paneling Materials

| DESCRIPTION | MATERIAL PRICE | GROSS COVERAGE | WASTE | NET COVERAGE | UNIT PRICE |
|---|---|---|---|---|---|
| **Hardboard paneling** | | | | | |
| economy grade | $20.80 sheet | 32 | 5% | 30.4 | $.68 sf |
| high grade | $38.40 sheet | 32 | 5% | 30.4 | $1.26 sf |
| **1/4" plywood paneling** | | | | | |
| rough-sawn cedar | $61.00 sheet | 32 | 5% | 30.4 | $2.01 sf |
| ash | $87.80 sheet | 32 | 5% | 30.4 | $2.89 sf |
| birch | $43.90 sheet | 32 | 5% | 30.4 | $1.44 sf |
| cherry | $99.30 sheet | 32 | 5% | 30.4 | $3.27 sf |
| hickory | $93.50 sheet | 32 | 5% | 30.4 | $3.08 sf |
| knotty pine | $75.10 sheet | 32 | 5% | 30.4 | $2.47 sf |
| mahogany | $80.90 sheet | 32 | 5% | 30.4 | $2.66 sf |
| white maple | $65.60 sheet | 32 | 5% | 30.4 | $2.16 sf |
| red or white oak | $44.90 sheet | 32 | 5% | 30.4 | $1.48 sf |
| quartersawn red or white oak | $72.00 sheet | 32 | 5% | 30.4 | $2.37 sf |
| walnut | $128.00 sheet | 32 | 5% | 30.4 | $4.21 sf |
| **1/4" plywood paneling with grooves** | | | | | |
| rough-sawn cedar | $59.60 sheet | 32 | 5% | 30.4 | $1.96 sf |
| ash | $85.70 sheet | 32 | 5% | 30.4 | $2.82 sf |
| birch | $42.90 sheet | 32 | 5% | 30.4 | $1.41 sf |
| cherry | $97.00 sheet | 32 | 5% | 30.4 | $3.19 sf |
| hickory | $91.30 sheet | 32 | 5% | 30.4 | $3.00 sf |
| knotty pine | $73.30 sheet | 32 | 5% | 30.4 | $2.41 sf |
| mahogany | $79.00 sheet | 32 | 5% | 30.4 | $2.60 sf |
| white maple | $64.10 sheet | 32 | 5% | 30.4 | $2.11 sf |
| red or white oak | $43.90 sheet | 32 | 5% | 30.4 | $1.44 sf |
| quartersawn red or white oak | $70.30 sheet | 32 | 5% | 30.4 | $2.31 sf |
| walnut | $125.00 sheet | 32 | 5% | 30.4 | $4.11 sf |
| **Pine board paneling** | | | | | |
| board-on-board | $3.38 sf | 1 | 4% | .96 | $3.52 sf |
| board-and-batten | $3.31 sf | 1 | 4% | .96 | $3.45 sf |
| tongue-&-groove, simple pattern | $3.50 sf | 1 | 4% | .96 | $3.65 sf |
| tongue-&-groove, ornate pattern | $4.37 sf | 1 | 4% | .96 | $4.55 sf |
| **Frame and panel wall** | | | | | |
| pine, standard grade | $16.70 sf | 1 | 6% | .94 | $17.80 sf |
| pine, custom grade | $40.20 sf | 1 | 6% | .94 | $42.80 sf |
| oak, standard grade | $20.50 sf | 1 | 6% | .94 | $21.80 sf |
| oak, custom grade | $49.30 sf | 1 | 6% | .94 | $52.40 sf |
| walnut, standard grade | $33.70 sf | 1 | 6% | .94 | $35.90 sf |
| walnut, custom grade | $81.10 sf | 1 | 6% | .94 | $86.30 sf |

## Paneling Labor

| LABORER | BASE WAGE | PAID LEAVE | TRUE WAGE | FICA | FUTA | WORKER'S COMP. | UNEMPLOY. INSUR. | HEALTH INSUR. | RETIRE (401K) | LIABILITY INSUR. | COST PER HOUR |
|---|---|---|---|---|---|---|---|---|---|---|---|
| Paneling installer | $22.60 | 1.76 | $24.36 | 1.86 | .19 | 4.56 | 2.12 | 2.54 | .73 | 3.17 | $39.50 |
| Paneling installer's helper | $16.30 | 1.27 | $17.57 | 1.34 | .14 | 3.29 | 1.53 | 2.54 | .53 | 2.28 | $29.20 |
| Demolition laborer | $13.40 | 1.05 | $14.45 | 1.11 | .12 | 4.44 | 1.26 | 2.54 | .43 | 1.88 | $26.20 |

**Paid Leave** is calculated based on two weeks paid vacation, one week sick leave, and seven paid holidays. Employer's matching portion of **FICA** is 7.65 percent. **FUTA** (Federal Unemployment) is .8 percent. **Worker's compensation** for the paneling trade was calculated using a national average of 18.71 percent. **Unemployment insurance** was calculated using a national average of 8.7 percent. **Health insurance** was calculated based on a projected national average for 2001 of $505 per employee (and family when applicable) per month. Employer pays 80 percent for a per month cost of $404 per employee. **Retirement** is based on a 401(k) retirement program with employer matching of 50 percent. Employee contributions to the 401(k) plan are an average of 6 percent of the true wage. **Liability insurance** is based on a national average of 12.9 percent.

## Paneling Labor Productivity

| WORK DESCRIPTION | LABORER | COST PER HOUR | PRODUCTIVITY | UNIT PRICE |
|---|---|---|---|---|
| **Demolition** | | | | |
| remove hardboard paneling | demolition laborer | $26.20 | .007 | $.18 sf |
| remove pegboard | demolition laborer | $26.20 | .007 | $.18 sf |
| remove plywood paneling | demolition laborer | $26.20 | .008 | $.21 sf |
| remove board paneling | demolition laborer | $26.20 | .011 | $.29 sf |
| remove tongue-and-groove paneling | demolition laborer | $26.20 | .011 | $.29 sf |
| remove frame-and-panel wall | demolition laborer | $26.20 | .019 | $.50 sf |
| **Paneling installation crew** | | | | |
| install paneling | paneling installer | $39.50 | | |
| install paneling | paneling installer's helper | $29.20 | | |
| install paneling | **paneling crew** | $34.40 | | |
| **Minimum charge** | | | | |
| for paneling work | paneling crew | $34.40 | .833 | $28.70 ea |
| for frame-and-panel wall work | paneling crew | $34.40 | 4.00 | $138.00 ea |
| **Install paneling** | | | | |
| hardboard | paneling crew | $34.40 | .033 | $1.14 sf |
| pegboard | paneling crew | $34.40 | .030 | $1.03 sf |
| plywood | paneling crew | $34.40 | .036 | $1.24 sf |
| board on board | paneling crew | $34.40 | .038 | $1.31 sf |
| board and batten | paneling crew | $34.40 | .042 | $1.44 sf |
| tongue-&-groove | paneling crew | $34.40 | .047 | $1.62 sf |
| **Install frame-and-panel wall** | | | | |
| standard grade | paneling crew | $34.40 | .725 | $24.90 sf |
| high grade | paneling crew | $34.40 | .870 | $29.90 sf |
| deluxe grade | paneling crew | $34.40 | 1.05 | $36.10 sf |
| custom grade | paneling crew | $34.40 | 1.25 | $43.00 sf |

NOTES:

# 28 Plaster & Stucco

| Item Description | Unit | Remove | Replace | Total | |
|---|---|---|---|---|---|
| **Minimum charge to repair plaster wall or ceiling**<br>*Replace* Materials......50.00        Labor..........80.50 | ea | — | $130.50 | $130.50 | ◄ REPAIR PLASTER |
| **Repair hair-line plaster crack**<br>*Replace* Materials ........ .28        Labor............2.46 | lf | — | $2.74 | $2.74 | |
| **Repair plaster crack less than 1″ wide**<br>*Replace* Materials ........ .42        Labor............3.06 | lf | — | $3.48 | $3.48 | |
| **Patch small plaster hole less than 2″ square**<br>*Replace* Materials........1.27        Labor..........31.80 | ea | — | $33.07 | $33.07 | **FLEXIBLE MOLDS**<br>Cracks to decorative plaster that are larger than a hairline are often repaired using flexible molds. |
| **Patch plaster hole 2″ to 10″ square**<br>*Replace* Materials........5.73        Labor..........40.10 | ea | — | $45.83 | $45.83 | |
| **Patch plaster hole 10″ to 20″ square**<br>*Replace* Materials........9.94        Labor..........49.90 | ea | — | $59.84 | $59.84 | Flexible molds are made by constructing a wood box to fit around the area where the mold will be taken. |
| **Patch plaster section**<br>*Replace* Materials........2.10        Labor............5.90<br>► For plaster repair of an area no greater than 20 sf in size. | sf | — | $8.00 | $8.00 | A release agent is sprayed on the box and the original plaster to help the mold release when dried. |
| **Repair plaster wall outside corner damage**<br>*Replace* Materials........2.70        Labor..........11.00 | lf | — | $13.70 | $13.70 | |
| **Repair plaster wall inside corner damage**<br>*Replace* Materials........2.22        Labor............7.71 | lf | — | $9.93 | $9.93 | Cold-cure silicone is usually used to make the mold, although many professionals use hot-melt mold-making compounds. |
| **Repair section of plaster pilaster or column**<br>*Replace* Materials......18.00        Labor..........34.40 | lf | — | $52.40 | $52.40 | |
| **Repair crack in plaster molding less than 1/4″ wide**<br>*Replace* Materials ........ .28        Labor............2.68 | lf | — | $2.96 | $2.96 | ◄ REPAIR DECORATIVE PLASTER<br>*Repairs to enrichments, moldings, ceiling rose, ceiling medallion, and so on.* |
| **Take flexible mold of plaster molding or decorative plaster**<br>*Replace* Materials......36.30        Labor..........22.20 | ea | — | $58.50 | $58.50 | |
| **Create running mold for plaster molding**<br>*Replace* Materials......47.80        Labor.........151.00 | ea | — | $198.80 | $198.80 | **RELATED ITEMS**<br>Acoustic Ceiling............15<br>Drywall......................133 |
| **Repair section of plaster molding or decorative plaster**<br>*Replace* Materials........5.61        Labor..........48.40<br>► Repair section no greater than 3 lf. | ea | — | $54.01 | $54.01 | Painting......................333<br>Suspended Ceilings.....483 |
| **Minimum charge to repair plaster molding or decorative plaster**<br>*Replace* Materials......23.60        Labor.........135.00 | ea | — | $158.60 | $158.60 | |
| **Two coat acoustical plaster on 3/8″ gypsum lath on wall**<br>*Replace* Materials........1.11        Labor............1.93<br>*Remove* ........................        Labor............. .60 | sf | $.60 | $3.04 | $3.64 | ◄ ACOUSTICAL PLASTER<br>*Includes lathing and plastering with trowel finish.* |
| **Two coat acoustical plaster on 3/8″ gypsum lath on ceiling**<br>*Replace* Materials........1.11        Labor............2.31<br>*Remove* ........................        Labor............. .60 | sf | $.60 | $3.42 | $4.02 | |

| Item Description | Unit | Remove | Replace | Total |
|---|---|---|---|---|
| **ACOUSTICAL ▶ PLASTER** *continued* | | | | |
| **Three coat acoustical plaster on painted metal lath on wall** | sf | $.63 | $3.12 | $3.75 |
| *Replace* Materials ........ .97    Labor ............2.15 | | | | |
| *Remove* ......................    Labor............. .63 | | | | |
| **Three coat acoustical plaster on painted metal lath on ceiling** | sf | $.63 | $3.54 | $4.17 |
| *Replace* Materials ........ .97    Labor ............2.57 | | | | |
| *Remove* ......................    Labor............. .63 | | | | |
| **GYPSUM ▶ PLASTER** *Includes lathing and plastering with trowel finish.* | | | | |
| **Two coat gypsum plaster on 3/8" gypsum lath on wall** | sf | $.60 | $2.94 | $3.54 |
| *Replace* Materials ........ .97    Labor ............1.97 | | | | |
| *Remove* ......................    Labor............. .60 | | | | |
| **Two coat gypsum plaster on 3/8" gypsum lath on ceiling** | sf | $.60 | $3.31 | $3.91 |
| *Replace* Materials ........ .97    Labor ............2.34 | | | | |
| *Remove* ......................    Labor............. .60 | | | | |
| **Three coat gypsum plaster on painted metal lath on wall** | sf | $.63 | $3.02 | $3.65 |
| *Replace* Materials ........ .83    Labor ............2.19 | | | | |
| *Remove* ......................    Labor............. .63 | | | | |
| **Three coat gypsum plaster on painted metal lath on ceiling** | sf | $.63 | $3.44 | $4.07 |
| *Replace* Materials ........ .83    Labor ............2.61 | | | | |
| *Remove* ......................    Labor............. .63 | | | | |
| **PERLITE OR ▶ VERMICULITE PLASTER** *Includes lathing and plastering with trowel finish.* | | | | |
| **Two coat perlite or vermiculite plaster on 3/8" gypsum lath on wall** | sf | $.60 | $3.25 | $3.85 |
| *Replace* Materials ...... 1.02    Labor ............2.23 | | | | |
| *Remove* ......................    Labor............. .60 | | | | |
| **Two coat perlite or vermiculite plaster on 3/8" gypsum lath on ceiling** | sf | $.60 | $3.70 | $4.30 |
| *Replace* Materials ...... 1.02    Labor ............2.68 | | | | |
| *Remove* ......................    Labor............. .60 | | | | |
| **Three coat perlite or vermiculite plaster on painted metal lath on wall** | sf | $.63 | $4.27 | $4.90 |
| *Replace* Materials........1.66    Labor ............2.61 | | | | |
| *Remove* ......................    Labor............. .63 | | | | |
| **Three coat perlite or vermiculite plaster on painted metal lath on ceiling** | sf | $.63 | $4.80 | $5.43 |
| *Replace* Materials........1.66    Labor ............3.14 | | | | |
| *Remove* ......................    Labor............. .63 | | | | |
| **KEENE'S CEMENT ▶ PLASTER** *Includes lathing and plastering with trowel finish.* | | | | |
| **Two coat Keene's cement plaster on 3/8" gypsum lath on wall** | sf | $.60 | $4.05 | $4.65 |
| *Replace* Materials........1.21    Labor ............2.84 | | | | |
| *Remove* ......................    Labor............. .60 | | | | |
| **Two coat Keene's cement plaster on 3/8" gypsum lath on ceiling** | sf | $.60 | $4.61 | $5.21 |
| *Replace* Materials........1.21    Labor ............3.40 | | | | |
| *Remove* ......................    Labor............. .60 | | | | |
| **Three coat Keene's cement plaster on painted metal lath on wall** | sf | $.63 | $4.17 | $4.80 |
| *Replace* Materials........1.07    Labor ............3.10 | | | | |
| *Remove* ......................    Labor............. .63 | | | | |
| **Three coat Keene's cement plaster on painted metal lath on ceiling** | sf | $.63 | $4.59 | $5.22 |
| *Replace* Materials........1.07    Labor ............3.52 | | | | |
| *Remove* ......................    Labor............. .63 | | | | |
| **THIN-COAT ▶ PLASTER** | | | | |
| **Thin-coat plaster on 3/8" thick gypsum lath** | sf | $.55 | $2.02 | $2.57 |
| *Replace* Materials ........ .36    Labor ............1.66 | | | | |
| *Remove* ......................    Labor............. .55 | | | | |
| **Thin-coat plaster on 1/2" thick gypsum lath** | sf | $.55 | $1.91 | $2.46 |
| *Replace* Materials ........ .25    Labor ............1.66 | | | | |
| *Remove* ......................    Labor............. .55 | | | | |

| Item Description | Unit | Remove | Replace | Total | |
|---|---|---|---|---|---|
| **Add 28% for curved wall** | | | | | |
| **Add 60% for plaster installed on old-style wood lath** | | | | | |
| **Square plaster pilaster, plain** | lf | $1.13 | $10.29 | $11.42 | ◄ **PLASTER PILASTER OR COLUMN** Additional costs for plaster pilasters and columns. |
| *Replace* Materials........3.15    Labor ...........7.14 | | | | | |
| *Remove* ......................    Labor ...........1.13 | | | | | |
| **Square plaster pilaster, rusticated** | lf | $1.13 | $11.75 | $12.88 | |
| *Replace* Materials........3.17    Labor ...........8.58 | | | | | |
| *Remove* ......................    Labor ...........1.13 | | | | | |
| **Square plaster column, plain** | lf | $2.02 | $19.31 | $21.33 | |
| *Replace* Materials........6.31    Labor ...........13.00 | | | | | |
| *Remove* ......................    Labor ...........2.02 | | | | | |
| **Square plaster column, rusticated** | lf | $2.02 | $22.74 | $24.76 | |
| *Replace* Materials........6.34    Labor ...........16.40 | | | | | |
| *Remove* ......................    Labor ...........2.02 | | | | | |
| **Add 30% for round pilaster or column** | | | | | |
| **Cast-in-place plaster molding to 3" wide** | lf | — | $64.67 | $64.67 | ◄ **CAST-IN-PLACE PLASTER MOLD** For straight-pattern moldings cast in place on walls and/or ceilings using a running mold. Inside corners require a great deal of handwork by a skilled specialist. Outside corners are less complex. |
| *Replace* Materials........5.67    Labor ...........59.00 | | | | | |
| **Cast-in-place plaster molding 3" to 6" wide** | lf | — | $75.20 | $75.20 | |
| *Replace* Materials.......11.30    Labor ...........63.90 | | | | | |
| **Cast-in-place plaster molding 6" to 14" wide** | lf | — | $92.50 | $92.50 | |
| *Replace* Materials......21.10    Labor ...........71.40 | | | | | |
| **Add for inside corner in cast-in-place plaster molding** | ea | — | $127.73 | $127.73 | |
| *Replace* Materials........5.73    Labor .........122.00 | | | | | |
| **Add for outside corner in cast-in-place plaster molding** | ea | — | $59.73 | $59.73 | |
| *Replace* Materials........1.53    Labor ...........58.20 | | | | | |
| **Production plaster molding to 3" wide** | lf | — | $33.54 | $33.54 | ◄ **PRODUCTION PLASTER MOLD** For moldings available from specialized suppliers in a wide variety of patterns. |
| *Replace* Materials......23.60    Labor ...........9.94 | | | | | |
| **Production plaster molding 3" to 6" wide** | lf | — | $45.20 | $45.20 | |
| *Replace* Materials......35.00    Labor ...........10.20 | | | | | |
| **Production plaster molding to 6" to 14" wide** | lf | — | $67.30 | $67.30 | |
| *Replace* Materials......56.50    Labor ...........10.80 | | | | | |
| **Add for inside corner in production plaster molding** | ea | — | $13.85 | $13.85 | |
| *Replace* Materials........1.25    Labor ...........12.60 | | | | | |
| **Add for outside corner in production plaster molding** | ea | — | $14.03 | $14.03 | |
| *Replace* Materials........1.43    Labor ...........12.60 | | | | | |
| **Plaster enrichment, straight patterns** | lf | — | $31.44 | $31.44 | ◄ **PLASTER ENRICHMENT** Enrichments are placed on walls or ceilings to further accent friezes, cornices, ceiling medallions and so forth. |
| *Replace* Materials......21.50    Labor ...........9.94 | | | | | |
| ► All straight work like scotia, coves, rounds, etc. | | | | | |
| **Plaster enrichment, ornate patterns** | lf | — | $42.60 | $42.60 | |
| *Replace* Materials......32.40    Labor ...........10.20 | | | | | |
| ► Includes fretwork, meander, fluting, Greek key, bead and reel, and simple egg and dart designs. | | | | | |

◄ **ADDITIONAL PLASTER COSTS**

**UNITS OF MEASURE**

In some areas, plaster and stucco are estimated by the square yard.

However, computer estimating systems usually calculate plaster and stucco by the square foot. The square foot method is used in this section.

| | Item Description | Unit | Remove | Replace | Total |
|---|---|---|---|---|---|
| **PLASTER ▶ ENRICHMENT** *continued* | **Plaster enrichment, very ornate patterns** | lf | — | $57.60 | $57.60 |
| | *Replace* Materials......46.80      Labor...........10.80 | | | | |
| | ▶ Very elaborate designs including figures, harps, Acanthus, swags, festoons, leaf and dart, Anthemion patterns and so forth. | | | | |
| **PLASTER FRIEZE ▶** *Usually flat with ornate patterns, plaster friezes can be up to 14" wide.* | **Plaster frieze, straight patterns** | lf | — | $45.74 | $45.74 |
| | *Replace* Materials......35.80      Labor............9.94 | | | | |
| | ▶ All straight work like scotia, coves, rounds, etc. | | | | |
| | **Plaster frieze, ornate patterns** | lf | — | $64.10 | $64.10 |
| | *Replace* Materials......53.90      Labor...........10.20 | | | | |
| | ▶ Includes fretwork, meander, fluting, Greek key, bead and reel, and simple egg and dart style designs. | | | | |
| | **Plaster frieze, very ornate patterns** | lf | — | $88.70 | $88.70 |
| | *Replace* Materials......77.90      Labor...........10.80 | | | | |
| | ▶ Very elaborate designs including figures, harps, Acanthus, swags, festoons, leaf and dart, Anthemion patterns and so forth. | | | | |
| **PLASTER ▶ ARCHITRAVE** *Most complex plaster architraves are production units built by a specialty supplier. See Finish Carpentry, page 206 for more information about architraves.* | **Plaster architrave, plain** | lf | — | $8.34 | $8.34 |
| | *Replace* Materials........2.52      Labor............5.82 | | | | |
| | ▶ Square raised design.  Usually raised 1" to 2" and about 4" to 6" wide. | | | | |
| | **Plaster architrave, rusticated** | lf | — | $9.69 | $9.69 |
| | *Replace* Materials........2.70      Labor............6.99 | | | | |
| | ▶ Same as above with rusticated "stones" shaped into the raised section.  Rusticated architrave may also be much wider and show simulated Jack arch "stone" pattern. | | | | |
| | **Plaster architrave, straight patterns** | lf | — | $21.10 | $21.10 |
| | *Replace* Materials........3.10      Labor...........18.00 | | | | |
| | ▶ Molded straight work like scotia, coves, rounds, etc. | | | | |
| | **Plaster architrave, ornate patterns** | lf | — | $29.59 | $29.59 |
| | *Replace* Materials........3.19      Labor...........26.40 | | | | |
| | ▶ Includes fretwork, fluting, Greek key, bead & reel, egg and dart, Acanthus, urns, pediments, etc.  All or most of the elaborate work will appear on the header. | | | | |
| **PLASTER CEILING ▶ MEDALLION** *Usually round or oval in shape designed for the center of the ceiling.* | **Plaster ceiling medallion, simple pattern** | ea | — | $159.40 | $159.40 |
| | *Replace* Materials.....125.00      Labor...........34.40 | | | | |
| | ▶ Round or oval with some simple raised patterns. | | | | |
| | **Plaster ceiling medallion, ornate pattern** | ea | — | $277.00 | $277.00 |
| | *Replace* Materials.....241.00      Labor...........36.00 | | | | |
| | ▶ Round or oval with elaborate patterns, like scalloped edges, some simple leaf patterns, ridges, fluting, fretwork, and so forth. | | | | |
| | **Plaster ceiling medallion, very ornate pattern** | ea | — | $476.80 | $476.80 |
| | *Replace* Materials....439.00      Labor...........37.80 | | | | |
| | ▶ Very elaborate designs including figures, harps, Acanthus, swags, festoons, leaf and dart, Anthemion patterns and so forth. | | | | |
| **PLASTER ▶ CEILING ROSE** *Very ornate ceiling medallion common to Victorian homes.* | **Plaster small ceiling rose** | ea | — | $247.40 | $247.40 |
| | *Replace* Materials.....213.00      Labor..........34.40 | | | | |
| | **Plaster average size ceiling rose** | ea | — | $363.00 | $363.00 |
| | *Replace* Materials....327.00      Labor..........36.00 | | | | |
| | **Plaster large ceiling rose** | ea | — | $656.80 | $656.80 |
| | *Replace* Materials.....619.00      Labor..........37.80 | | | | |

| Item Description | Unit | Remove | Replace | Total |
|---|---|---|---|---|
| **Three coat Portland cement stucco, sand float finish** | sf | $.71 | $4.50 | $5.21 |
| *Replace* Materials ........ .87      Labor ...........3.63 | | | | |
| *Remove* ......................      Labor ............ .71 | | | | |
| **Three coat Portland cement stucco, sand float finish, on masonry** | sf | $.71 | $3.17 | $3.88 |
| *Replace* Materials ........ .33      Labor ...........2.84 | | | | |
| *Remove* ......................      Labor ............ .71 | | | | |
| **Three coat Portland cement stucco, trowel float finish** | sf | $.71 | $6.25 | $6.96 |
| *Replace* Materials ........ .88      Labor ...........5.37 | | | | |
| *Remove* ......................      Labor ............ .71 | | | | |
| **Three coat Portland cement stucco, trowel float finish, on masonry** | sf | $.71 | $4.92 | $5.63 |
| *Replace* Materials ........ .35      Labor ...........4.57 | | | | |
| *Remove* ......................      Labor ............ .71 | | | | |
| **Add 26% for stucco application on soffits** | | | | |
| **Add 10% for colors** | | | | |
| **Add 19% for white cement** | | | | |
| **Add 32% for pebble dash (rough cast) stucco finish** | | | | |
| ► Colorful aggregate that is "thrown" into the stucco. | | | | |
| **Add 88% for vermiculated stucco finish** | | | | |
| ► Snake-like pattern found on some historical structures, especially around entries. | | | | |
| **Patch single "stone" section in stucco rustication** | ea | — | $33.52 | $33.52 |
| *Replace* Materials........4.42      Labor ..........29.10 | | | | |
| **Add for stucco quoin** | ea | — | $30.48 | $30.48 |
| *Replace* Materials........6.88      Labor ..........23.60 | | | | |
| **Add for stucco key** | ea | — | $51.40 | $51.40 |
| *Replace* Materials ......10.60      Labor ..........40.80 | | | | |
| **Add for stucco raised trim** | lf | — | $8.32 | $8.32 |
| *Replace* Materials........2.69      Labor ...........5.63 | | | | |
| ► For raised trim around doors see architraves on page 357. | | | | |
| **Add for stucco raised curved trim** | lf | — | $12.56 | $12.56 |
| *Replace* Materials........3.11      Labor ...........9.45 | | | | |
| ► Raised, curved trim over doors, windows, and so forth. | | | | |
| **Add for stucco color change** | ea | — | $2.22 | $2.22 |
| *Replace* Materials ........ .18      Labor ...........2.04 | | | | |
| ► Use when stucco changes colors on a wall.  For example, each layer of raised trim may be of a different color. | | | | |
| **Synthetic stucco over 1/2" cement board** | sf | $.71 | $3.62 | $4.33 |
| *Replace* Materials ........ .82      Labor ...........2.80 | | | | |
| *Remove* ......................      Labor ............ .71 | | | | |
| **Synthetic stucco over 1" insulating foam board** | sf | $.71 | $3.46 | $4.17 |
| *Replace* Materials ........ .66      Labor ...........2.80 | | | | |
| *Remove* ......................      Labor ............ .71 | | | | |
| **Synthetic stucco over 2" insulating foam board** | sf | $.71 | $3.50 | $4.21 |
| *Replace* Materials ........ .70      Labor ...........2.80 | | | | |
| *Remove* ......................      Labor ............ .71 | | | | |

◄ **STUCCO**
*Includes felt or building paper, metal lath, and control joint and corner metal.*

◄ **ADDITIONAL STUCCO COSTS**

**RELATED ITEMS**

◄ **SYNTHETIC STUCCO**
*Includes cement board or polystyrene foam insulation board, adhesive primer, color coat stucco, and corner mesh.*

| Item Description | Unit | Remove | Replace | Total |
|---|---|---|---|---|
| **ADDITIONAL ▶ SYNTHETIC STUCCO COSTS** | | | | |
| **Add for synthetic stucco quoin**<br>*Replace* Materials.........3.88          Labor...........35.30 | ea | — | $39.18 | $39.18 |
| **Add for synthetic stucco key**<br>*Replace* Materials........5.98          Labor ..........60.90 | ea | — | $66.88 | $66.88 |
| **Add for synthetic stucco raised trim**<br>*Replace* Materials.......1.52          Labor ............8.43<br>▶ For raised trim around doors see architraves on facing page. | lf | — | $9.95 | $9.95 |
| **Add for synthetic stucco raised curved trim**<br>*Replace* Materials........1.76          Labor...........14.10<br>▶ Raised, curved trim over doors, windows, and so forth. | lf | — | $15.86 | $15.86 |
| **Add for synthetic stucco color change**<br>*Replace* Materials ........ .10          Labor ............3.06<br>▶ Use when stucco changes colors on a wall.  For example, each layer of raised trim may be of a different color. | lf | — | $3.16 | $3.16 |
| **STUCCO REPAIR ▶**<br>*For repair of standard or synthetic stucco.* | | | | |
| **Minimum charge to repair stucco**<br>*Replace* Materials ......49.00          Labor ..........82.00 | ea | — | $131.00 | $131.00 |
| **Repair hair-line stucco crack**<br>*Replace* Materials ........ .29          Labor ............2.49 | lf | — | $2.78 | $2.78 |
| **Repair stucco crack less than 1" wide**<br>*Replace* Materials ........ .43          Labor ............3.14 | lf | — | $3.57 | $3.57 |
| **Patch small stucco hole less than 2" square**<br>*Replace* Materials........1.30          Labor ..........32.30 | ea | — | $33.60 | $33.60 |
| **Patch stucco hole 2" to 10" square**<br>*Replace* Materials........5.86          Labor ..........41.20 | ea | — | $47.06 | $47.06 |
| **Patch stucco hole 10" to 20" square**<br>*Replace* Materials ......10.20          Labor ..........50.30 | ea | — | $60.50 | $60.50 |
| **Patch stucco section**<br>*Replace* Materials........2.15          Labor ............6.01<br>▶ For stucco repair of an area no greater than 20 sf in size. | sf | — | $8.16 | $8.16 |
| **Repair stucco wall outside corner damage per lf of damage**<br>*Replace* Materials........2.76          Labor ...........11.20 | lf | — | $13.96 | $13.96 |
| **Repair stucco wall inside corner damage per lf of damage**<br>*Replace* Materials........2.27          Labor ............7.86 | lf | — | $10.13 | $10.13 |
| **STUCCO PILASTER ▶ OR COLUMN**<br>*Additional costs for stucco pilasters and columns.  For use with standard or synthetic stucco.* | | | | |
| **Square stucco pilaster, plain**<br>*Replace* Materials........3.27          Labor ............7.26<br>*Remove* ......................          Labor ............1.26 | lf | $1.26 | $10.53 | $11.79 |
| **Square stucco pilaster, rusticated**<br>*Replace* Materials........3.29          Labor ............8.69<br>*Remove* ......................          Labor ............1.26 | lf | $1.26 | $11.98 | $13.24 |
| **Square stucco column, plain**<br>*Replace* Materials........6.56          Labor...........13.20<br>*Remove* ......................          Labor ............2.17 | lf | $2.17 | $19.76 | $21.93 |

| Item Description | Unit | Remove | Replace | Total |
|---|---|---|---|---|
| **Square stucco column, rusticated** | lf | $2.17 | $23.29 | $25.46 |
| *Replace* Materials........6.59          Labor...........16.70 | | | | |
| *Remove* .....................          Labor ...........2.17 | | | | |
| | | | | |
| **Add 30% for round stucco pilaster or column** | | | | |
| | | | | |
| **Repair section of stucco pilaster or column** | ea | — | $54.00 | $54.00 |
| *Replace* Materials.......19.00          Labor...........35.00 | | | | |
| ▶ Repair section by hand or by pouring into mold then patching into architrave. | | | | |
| | | | | |
| **Minimum charge to repair stucco pilaster or column** | ea | — | $71.20 | $71.20 |
| *Replace* Materials......33.00          Labor .........38.20 | | | | |
| | | | | |
| **Stucco architrave, plain** | lf | — | $8.53 | $8.53 |
| *Replace* Materials........2.63          Labor ...........5.90 | | | | |
| ▶ Square raised design.  Usually raised 1" to 2" and about 4" to 6" wide. | | | | |
| | | | | |
| **Stucco architrave, rusticated** | lf | — | $9.76 | $9.76 |
| *Replace* Materials........2.65          Labor ...........7.11 | | | | |
| ▶ Same as above with rusticated "stones" shaped into the raised section.  Rusticated architrave may also be much wider and show simulated Jack arch "stone" pattern. | | | | |
| | | | | |
| **Stucco architrave, straight patterns** | lf | — | $21.11 | $21.11 |
| *Replace* Materials........2.81          Labor...........18.30 | | | | |
| ▶ Molded straight work like scotia, coves, rounds, etc. | | | | |
| | | | | |
| **Stucco architrave, ornate patterns** | lf | — | $30.03 | $30.03 |
| *Replace* Materials........3.23          Labor...........26.80 | | | | |
| ▶ Includes fretwork, fluting, Greek key, bead & reel, egg and dart, Acanthus, urns, pediments, etc.  All or most of the elaborate work will appear on the header. | | | | |
| | | | | |
| **Take flexible mold of existing stucco architrave** | ea | — | $58.80 | $58.80 |
| *Replace* Materials......36.30          Labor .........22.50 | | | | |
| | | | | |
| **Create mold for stucco architrave** | ea | — | $198.80 | $198.80 |
| *Replace* Materials......47.80          Labor .........151.00 | | | | |
| | | | | |
| **Repair section of stucco architrave** | ea | — | $56.86 | $56.86 |
| *Replace* Materials........5.86          Labor...........51.00 | | | | |
| ▶ Repair section by hand or by pouring into mold then patching into architrave. | | | | |
| | | | | |
| **Minimum charge to repair stucco architrave** | ea | — | $163.60 | $163.60 |
| *Replace* Materials......23.60          Labor...........140.00 | | | | |

◀ **STUCCO ARCHITRAVE**
*Most complex stucco architraves are production units built by a specialty supplier.*

**RELATED ITEMS**
Acoustic Ceiling .............15
Drywall.......................133
Finish Carpentry...........199
  *architrave*...................206
Masonry......................287
  *stone architrave*..............310
  *cut stone trim*................314
Painting.......................333
Suspended Ceilings .....483

# TIME & MATERIAL CHARTS *(selected items)*

**Plaster & Stucco Materials**

| DESCRIPTION | MATERIAL PRICE | GROSS COVERAGE | WASTE | NET COVERAGE | UNIT PRICE |
|---|---|---|---|---|---|
| **Plaster and stucco materials** | | | | | |
| *gauging plaster* | $20.20 *100 lb. bag* | 1 | 21% | .79 | $25.60 *ea* |
| *gypsum plaster* | $15.90 *80 lb. bag* | 1 | 21% | .79 | $20.10 *ea* |
| *thin-coat plaster* | $11.00 *50 lb. bag* | 1 | 21% | .79 | $13.90 *ea* |
| *Keene's cement* | $23.10 *100 lb. bag* | 1 | 21% | .79 | $29.20 *ea* |
| *perlite or vermiculite plaster* | $15.50 *100 lb. bag* | 1 | 21% | .79 | $19.60 *ea* |
| *3/8" perforated gypsum lath* | $15.40 *sheet* | 32 | 4% | 30.72 | $.50 *sf* |
| *1/2" perforated gypsum lath* | $16.30 *sheet* | 32 | 4% | 30.72 | $.53 *sf* |
| *painted metal lath* | $.25 *sf* | 1 | 4% | .96 | $.26 *sf* |
| *painted stucco mesh* | $.38 *sf* | 1 | 4% | .96 | $.40 *ea* |

## Plaster & Stucco Labor

| LABORER | BASE WAGE | PAID LEAVE | TRUE WAGE | FICA | FUTA | WORKER'S COMP. | UNEMPLOY. INSUR. | HEALTH INSUR. | RETIRE (401K) | LIABILITY INSUR. | COST PER HOUR |
|---------|-----------|------------|-----------|------|------|----------------|------------------|---------------|---------------|------------------|---------------|
| Plasterer | $22.00 | 1.72 | $23.72 | 1.81 | .19 | 6.54 | 2.06 | 2.54 | .71 | 3.08 | $40.70 |
| Plasterer's helper | $18.60 | 1.45 | $20.05 | 1.53 | .16 | 5.53 | 1.74 | 2.54 | .60 | 2.61 | $34.80 |
| Demolition laborer | $13.40 | 1.05 | $14.45 | 1.11 | .12 | 4.44 | 1.26 | 2.54 | .43 | 1.88 | $26.20 |

**Paid Leave** is calculated based on two weeks paid vacation, one week sick leave, and seven paid holidays. Employer's matching portion of **FICA** is 7.65 percent. **FUTA** (Federal Unemployment) is .8 percent. **Worker's compensation** for the plaster and stucco trade was calculated using a national average of 27.58 percent. **Unemployment insurance** was calculated using a national average of 8.7 percent. **Health insurance** was calculated based on a projected national average for 2001 of $505 per employee (and family when applicable) per month. Employer pays 80 percent for a per month cost of $404 per employee. **Retirement** is based on a 401(k) retirement program with employer matching of 50 percent. Employee contributions to the 401(k) plan are an average of 6 percent of the true wage. **Liability insurance** is based on a national average of 12.9 percent.

## Plaster & Stucco Labor Productivity

| WORK DESCRIPTION | LABORER | COST PER HOUR | PRODUCTIVITY | UNIT PRICE |
|------------------|---------|---------------|--------------|------------|
| **Demolition** | | | | |
| remove plaster on gypsum lath | demolition laborer | $26.20 | .023 | $.60 sf |
| remove plaster on metal lath | demolition laborer | $26.20 | .024 | $.63 sf |
| remove thin-coat plaster on gypsum | demolition laborer | $26.20 | .021 | $.55 sf |
| remove plaster pilaster | demolition laborer | $26.20 | .043 | $1.13 lf |
| remove plaster column | demolition laborer | $26.20 | .077 | $2.02 lf |
| remove stucco | demolition laborer | $26.20 | .027 | $.71 sf |
| remove synthetic stucco on cement board | demolition laborer | $26.20 | .027 | $.71 sf |
| remove stucco pilaster | demolition laborer | $26.20 | .048 | $1.26 lf |
| remove stucco column | demolition laborer | $26.20 | .083 | $2.17 lf |
| **Plaster installation crew** | | | | |
| install plaster | plasterer | $40.70 | | |
| install plaster | plasterer's helper | $34.80 | | |
| install plaster | **plastering crew** | $37.80 | | |
| **Install acoustical plaster** | | | | |
| two coat on 3/8" gypsum lath on wall | plastering crew | $37.80 | .051 | $1.93 sf |
| two coat on 3/8" gypsum lath on ceiling | plastering crew | $37.80 | .061 | $2.31 sf |
| three coat on painted metal lath on wall | plastering crew | $37.80 | .057 | $2.15 sf |
| three coat on painted metal lath on ceiling | plastering crew | $37.80 | .068 | $2.57 sf |
| **Install gypsum plaster** | | | | |
| two coat on 3/8" gypsum lath on wall | plastering crew | $37.80 | .052 | $1.97 sf |
| two coat on 3/8" gypsum lath on ceiling | plastering crew | $37.80 | .062 | $2.34 sf |
| three coat on painted metal lath on wall | plastering crew | $37.80 | .058 | $2.19 sf |
| three coat on painted metal lath on ceiling | plastering crew | $37.80 | .069 | $2.61 sf |
| **Install perlite or vermiculite plaster** | | | | |
| two coat on 3/8" gypsum lath on wall | plastering crew | $37.80 | .059 | $2.23 sf |
| two coat on 3/8" gypsum lath on ceiling | plastering crew | $37.80 | .071 | $2.68 sf |
| three coat on painted metal lath on wall | plastering crew | $37.80 | .069 | $2.61 sf |
| three coat on painted metal lath on ceiling | plastering crew | $37.80 | .083 | $3.14 sf |
| **Install Keene's cement plaster** | | | | |
| two coat on 3/8" gypsum lath on wall | plastering crew | $37.80 | .075 | $2.84 sf |
| two coat on 3/8" gypsum lath on ceiling | plastering crew | $37.80 | .090 | $3.40 sf |
| three coat on painted metal lath on wall | plastering crew | $37.80 | .082 | $3.10 sf |
| three coat on painted metal lath on ceiling | plastering crew | $37.80 | .093 | $3.52 sf |
| **Install thin-coat plaster** | | | | |
| on 3/8" thick gypsum lath | plastering crew | $37.80 | .044 | $1.66 sf |
| on 1/2" thick gypsum lath | plastering crew | $37.80 | .044 | $1.66 sf |
| **Install three-coat Portland cement stucco** | | | | |
| sand float finish | plastering crew | $37.80 | .096 | $3.63 sf |
| sand float finish, on masonry | plastering crew | $37.80 | .075 | $2.84 sf |
| trowel float finish | plastering crew | $37.80 | .142 | $5.37 sf |
| trowel float finish, on masonry | plastering crew | $37.80 | .121 | $4.57 sf |
| **Install synthetic stucco** | | | | |
| all applications | plastering crew | $37.80 | .074 | $2.80 sf |

# 29 .......................................................... *Plumbing*

| Item Description | Unit | Remove | Replace | Total | |
|---|---|---|---|---|---|
| **Minimum charge for plumbing work**<br>*Replace* Materials......40.00    Labor..........56.70 | ea | — | $96.70 | $96.70 | ◄ **MINIMUM** |
| **1/2" diameter black steel supply pipe**<br>*Replace* Materials........2.08    Labor..........5.41 | lf | — | $7.49 | $7.49 | ◄ **BLACK STEEL PIPE**<br>*Field threaded with fitting or coupling every 8.5 lf and hanger every 10 lf.* |
| **3/4" diameter black steel supply pipe**<br>*Replace* Materials........2.24    Labor..........5.79 | lf | — | $8.03 | $8.03 | |
| **1" diameter black steel supply pipe**<br>*Replace* Materials........2.98    Labor..........6.73 | lf | — | $9.71 | $9.71 | |
| **2" diameter black steel supply pipe**<br>*Replace* Materials........5.79    Labor..........9.84 | lf | — | $15.63 | $15.63 | |
| **Replace section of black steel supply pipe**<br>*Replace* Materials......24.60    Labor..........43.50<br>► Includes cut-out in typical drywall wall, replacement section and couplings. Does not include wall repair (see *Drywall* page 136) | ea | — | $68.10 | $68.10 | |
| **1/2" diameter brass water supply pipe**<br>*Replace* Materials........6.19    Labor..........7.33 | lf | — | $13.52 | $13.52 | ◄ **BRASS WATER SUPPLY PIPE**<br>*Field threaded with fitting or coupling every 8.5 lf and hanger every 10 lf.* |
| **3/4" diameter brass water supply pipe**<br>*Replace* Materials........8.21    Labor..........7.67 | lf | — | $15.88 | $15.88 | |
| **1" diameter brass water supply pipe**<br>*Replace* Materials......10.90    Labor..........8.18 | lf | — | $19.08 | $19.08 | |
| **2" diameter brass water supply pipe**<br>*Replace* Materials......27.10    Labor..........8.95 | lf | — | $36.05 | $36.05 | |
| **Replace section of brass water supply pipe**<br>*Replace* Materials......50.00    Labor..........59.20<br>► Includes cut-out in typical drywall wall, replacement section and couplings. Does not include wall repair. | ea | — | $109.20 | $109.20 | ◁ replace section |
| **1/2" diameter type K copper water supply pipe**<br>*Replace* Materials........2.14    Labor..........4.43 | lf | — | $6.57 | $6.57 | ◄ **COPPER WATER SUPPLY PIPE TYPE K**<br>*With sweated fitting or coupling every 8.5 lf and hanger every 10 lf.* |
| **3/4" diameter type K copper water supply pipe**<br>*Replace* Materials........2.20    Labor..........4.64 | lf | — | $6.84 | $6.84 | |
| **1" diameter type K copper water supply pipe**<br>*Replace* Materials........4.11    Labor..........5.20 | lf | — | $9.31 | $9.31 | |
| **2" diameter type K copper water supply pipe**<br>*Replace* Materials........9.66    Labor..........8.61 | lf | — | $18.27 | $18.27 | |
| **1/2" diameter type L copper water supply pipe**<br>*Replace* Materials........1.86    Labor..........4.43 | lf | — | $6.29 | $6.29 | ◄ **COPPER WATER SUPPLY PIPE TYPE L**<br>*With sweated fitting or coupling every 8.5 lf and hanger every 10 lf.* |
| **3/4" diameter type L copper water supply pipe**<br>*Replace* Materials........2.01    Labor..........4.64 | lf | — | $6.65 | $6.65 | |

**RELATED ITEMS**
Bathroom Hardware......41
Cleaning .....................64

| | Item Description | Unit | Remove | Replace | Total |
|---|---|---|---|---|---|
| **COPPER WATER** ▶ SUPPLY PIPE TYPE L *continued* | **1″ diameter type L copper water supply pipe** *Replace* Materials........3.55     Labor ............5.20 | lf | — | $8.75 | $8.75 |
| | **2″ diameter type L copper water supply pipe** *Replace* Materials........8.73     Labor ............8.61 | lf | — | $17.34 | $17.34 |
| **COPPER WATER** ▶ SUPPLY PIPE TYPE M *With sweated fitting or coupling every 8.5 lf and hanger every 10 lf.* | **1/2″ diameter type M copper water supply pipe** *Replace* Materials........1.53     Labor ............4.43 | lf | — | $5.96 | $5.96 |
| | **3/4″ diameter type M copper water supply pipe** *Replace* Materials........2.01     Labor ............4.64 | lf | — | $6.65 | $6.65 |
| | **1″ diameter type M copper water supply pipe** *Replace* Materials........2.79     Labor ............5.20 | lf | — | $7.99 | $7.99 |
| replace section ▷ | **Replace section of copper water supply pipe** *Replace* Materials.......17.60     Labor............35.20 ▶ Includes cut-out in typical drywall wall, replacement section and couplings. Does not include wall repair (see *Drywall* page 136). | ea | — | $52.80 | $52.80 |
| **GALVANIZED** ▶ STEEL WATER SUPPLY PIPE *Field threaded with fitting or coupling every 8.5 lf and hanger every 10 lf.* | **1/2″ diameter galvanized steel water supply pipe** *Replace* Materials........2.52     Labor ............5.50 | lf | — | $8.02 | $8.02 |
| | **3/4″ diameter galvanized steel water supply pipe** *Replace* Materials........2.73     Labor ............5.79 | lf | — | $8.52 | $8.52 |
| | **1″ diameter galvanized steel water supply pipe** *Replace* Materials........3.91     Labor ............6.60 | lf | — | $10.51 | $10.51 |
| | **2″ diameter galvanized steel water supply pipe** *Replace* Materials........7.19     Labor ............9.84 | lf | — | $17.03 | $17.03 |
| replace section ▷ | **Replace section of galvanized steel water supply pipe** *Replace* Materials......30.30     Labor..........44.30 ▶ Includes cut-out in typical drywall wall, replacement section and couplings. Does not include wall repair (see *Drywall* page 136). | ea | — | $74.60 | $74.60 |
| **CPVC WATER** ▶ SUPPLY PIPE *With fitting or coupling every 8.5 lf and hanger every 3.5 lf.* | **1/2″ diameter CPVC schedule 40 water supply pipe** *Replace* Materials........3.27     Labor ............6.52 | lf | — | $9.79 | $9.79 |
| | **3/4″ diameter CPVC schedule 40 water supply pipe** *Replace* Materials........3.97     Labor ............6.90 | lf | — | $10.87 | $10.87 |
| | **1″ diameter CPVC schedule 40 water supply pipe** *Replace* Materials........4.84     Labor ............8.05 | lf | — | $12.89 | $12.89 |
| **PVC WATER** ▶ SUPPLY PIPE *With fitting or coupling every 8.5 lf and hanger every 3.5 lf.* | **1/2″ diameter PVC schedule 40 cold water supply pipe** *Replace* Materials........1.89     Labor ............6.52 | lf | — | $8.41 | $8.41 |
| | **3/4″ diameter PVC schedule 40 cold water supply pipe** *Replace* Materials........1.94     Labor ............6.90 | lf | — | $8.84 | $8.84 |
| | **1″ diameter PVC schedule 40 cold water supply pipe** *Replace* Materials........2.27     Labor ............8.05 | lf | — | $10.32 | $10.32 |
| **REPLACE SECTION** ▶ OF PVC OR CPVC SUPPLY PIPE | **Replace section of PVC or CPVC water supply pipe** *Replace* Materials ......14.80     Labor..........52.40 ▶ Includes cut-out in typical drywall wall, replacement section and couplings. Does not include wall repair (see *Drywall* page 136). | ea | — | $67.20 | $67.20 |

| Item Description | Unit | Remove | Replace | Total | |
|---|---|---|---|---|---|
| **Minimum charge for supply pipe work**<br>*Replace* Materials......40.00   Labor .........77.50 | ea | — | $117.50 | $117.50 | ◄ **MINIMUM SUPPLY PIPE** |
| **2" cast-iron DWV pipe**<br>*Replace* Materials........5.35   Labor...........10.00 | lf | — | $15.35 | $15.35 | ◄ **CAST-IRON DWV PIPE**<br>*Lead and oakum joints with fitting every 9.5 lf.* |
| **3" cast-iron DWV pipe**<br>*Replace* Materials........7.33   Labor...........10.60 | lf | — | $17.93 | $17.93 | |
| **4" cast-iron DWV pipe**<br>*Replace* Materials........9.76   Labor ...........11.50 | lf | — | $21.26 | $21.26 | |
| **5" cast-iron DWV pipe**<br>*Replace* Materials ......12.80   Labor...........13.00 | lf | — | $25.80 | $25.80 | |
| **6" cast-iron DWV pipe**<br>*Replace* Materials.......15.60   Labor...........13.50 | lf | — | $29.10 | $29.10 | |
| **Replace section of cast-iron DWV pipe**<br>*Replace* Materials......92.00   Labor........71.10<br>► Includes cut-out in typical drywall wall, replacement section and couplings. Does not include wall repair (see *Drywall* page 136). | ea | — | $163.10 | $163.10 | ◁ replace section |
| **Repack cast-iron DWV pipe joint with oakum and caulk**<br>*Replace* Materials.......11.00   Labor............7.71 | ea | — | $18.71 | $18.71 | ◁ repack |
| **2" cast-iron no-hub DWV pipe**<br>*Replace* Materials........6.33   Labor............8.95 | lf | — | $15.28 | $15.28 | ◄ **CAST-IRON NO-HUB DWV PIPE**<br>*With fitting or coupling every 9.5 lf.* |
| **3" cast-iron no-hub DWV pipe**<br>*Replace* Materials........8.52   Labor............9.46 | lf | — | $17.98 | $17.98 | |
| **4" cast-iron no-hub DWV pipe**<br>*Replace* Materials......10.60   Labor...........10.30 | lf | — | $20.90 | $20.90 | |
| **5" cast-iron no-hub DWV pipe**<br>*Replace* Materials.......15.30   Labor...........11.60 | lf | — | $26.90 | $26.90 | |
| **6" cast-iron no-hub DWV pipe**<br>*Replace* Materials.......17.90   Labor...........12.10 | lf | — | $30.00 | $30.00 | |
| **Replace section of cast-iron no-hub DWV pipe**<br>*Replace* Materials......70.40   Labor..........63.50<br>► Includes cut-out in typical drywall wall, replacement section and couplings. Does not include wall repair (see *Drywall* page 136). | ea | — | $133.90 | $133.90 | ◁ replace section |
| **Repair pin-hole leak in cast-iron DWV pipe with epoxy**<br>*Replace* Materials........7.74   Labor ..........23.10 | ea | — | $30.84 | $30.84 | ◁ repair pin-hole leak |
| **1-1/4" PVC DWV pipe**<br>*Replace* Materials........2.51   Labor ...........8.43 | lf | — | $10.94 | $10.94 | ◄ **PVC DWV PIPE**<br>*With fitting or coupling every 8.5 lf and hanger every 10 lf.* |
| **1-1/2" PVC DWV pipe**<br>*Replace* Materials........2.79   Labor ...........9.80 | lf | — | $12.59 | $12.59 | |
| **2" PVC DWV pipe**<br>*Replace* Materials........2.97   Labor...........10.70 | lf | — | $13.67 | $13.67 | |
| **3" PVC DWV pipe**<br>*Replace* Materials........4.36   Labor...........12.00 | lf | — | $16.36 | $16.36 | |

| Item Description | Unit | Remove | Replace | Total |
|---|---|---|---|---|
| **PVC DWV PIPE** ▶ continued **4" PVC DWV pipe** *Replace* Materials........5.57   Labor...........13.20 | lf | — | $18.77 | $18.77 |
| **5" PVC DWV pipe** *Replace* Materials........7.64   Labor...........14.70 | lf | — | $22.34 | $22.34 |
| **6" PVC DWV pipe** *Replace* Materials .....10.80   Labor...........16.20 | lf | — | $27.00 | $27.00 |
| replace section ▷ **Replace section of PVC DWV pipe** *Replace* Materials......34.50   Labor...........61.80 ▶ Includes cut-out in typical drywall wall, replacement section and couplings. Does not include wall repair (see *Drywall* page 136). | ea | — | $96.30 | $96.30 |
| **MINIMUM** ▶ **DWV PIPE** **Minimum charge for DWV line work** *Replace* Materials......56.00   Labor...........65.60 | ea | — | $121.60 | $121.60 |
| **EXTERIOR LINES** ▶ *Includes excavation up to 8' deep, backfill, laying pipe, pipe, and fittings. Does not include mobilization or shoring. Also see Excavation, page 178.* **4" diameter exterior sewer lines** *Replace* Materials......22.70   Labor...........69.90 | lf | — | $92.60 | $92.60 |
| **6" diameter exterior sewer lines** *Replace* Materials......32.70   Labor...........72.00 | lf | — | $104.70 | $104.70 |
| **1" diameter exterior water supply line** *Replace* Materials.......15.40   Labor...........69.90 | lf | — | $85.30 | $85.30 |
| **1-1/2" diameter exterior water supply line** *Replace* Materials ......18.10   Labor...........72.00 | lf | — | $90.10 | $90.10 |
| minimum ▷ **Minimum charge for exterior line work** *Replace* Materials......92.00   Labor......426.00 | ea | — | $518.00 | $518.00 |
| **SHUT-OFF AND** ▶ **PRESSURE VALVES** **Interior water supply shut-off valve with pressure valve,1-1/2" line** *Replace* Materials....360.00   Labor ..........46.90 | ea | — | $406.90 | $406.90 |
| **Interior water supply shut-off valve with pressure valve, 2" line** *Replace* Materials....464.00   Labor ..........46.90 | ea | — | $510.90 | $510.90 |
| **REPAIR UNDER-** ▶ **GROUND LINE** *Includes excavation to specified depth, backfill, laying pipe, pipe, and fittings. Does not include mobilization or shoring. Also see Excavation, page 178.* **Excavate and repair underground line 4' deep or less** *Replace* Materials......48.60   Labor...........71.10 | lf | — | $119.70 | $119.70 |
| **Excavate and repair underground line 4' to 8' deep** *Replace* Materials......48.60   Labor...........92.40 | lf | — | $141.00 | $141.00 |
| **Excavate and repair underground line 8' to 12' deep** *Replace* Materials......48.60   Labor.........129.00 | lf | — | $177.60 | $177.60 |
| **Excavate and repair underground line 12' to 16' deep** *Replace* Materials......48.60   Labor.........185.00 | lf | — | $233.60 | $233.60 |
| **BREAK-OUT** ▶ **CONCRETE &** **INSTALL PIPE** **Install pipe underneath existing concrete slab** *Replace* Materials.......15.80   Labor...........94.60 ▶ Saw concrete slab and break-out, hand excavate, lay pipe, hand back fill, and patch concrete. Includes sand bed for pipe as necessary. | lf | — | $110.40 | $110.40 |
| minimum ▷ **Minimum charge to install pipe underneath existing concrete slab** *Replace* Materials......99.00   Labor ........533.00 | ea | — | $632.00 | $632.00 |

| Item Description | Unit | Remove | Replace | Total | |
|---|---|---|---|---|---|
| **Complete supply lines, waste lines & finish fixtures, economy grade**<br>*Replace* Materials........2.00          Labor............3.45<br>► With PVC drain, waste, and vent lines, CPVC hot water lines, PVC cold water lines. | sf | — | $5.45 | $5.45 | ◄ **COMPLETE HOUSE ROUGH & FINISH PLUMBING**<br>*Grades refer to quality of plumbing fixtures. For residential structures only. See page 369 for information about plumbing fixture quality.* |
| **Complete supply lines, waste lines, & finish fixtures, standard grade**<br>*Replace* Materials........3.21          Labor............3.62<br>► With PVC drain, waste, and vent lines, copper water supply lines. | sf | — | $6.83 | $6.83 | |
| **Complete supply lines, waste lines, & finish fixtures, high grade**<br>*Replace* Materials........3.48          Labor............3.66<br>► With PVC drain, waste, and vent lines, copper water supply lines. | sf | — | $7.14 | $7.14 | |
| **Complete supply lines, waste lines, & finish fixtures, deluxe grade**<br>*Replace* Materials........4.00          Labor............3.88<br>► With cast-iron drain, waste, and vent lines, copper water supply lines. | sf | — | $7.88 | $7.88 | |
| **Complete supply lines, waste lines, & finish fixtures, custom deluxe grade**<br>*Replace* Materials........4.41          Labor............3.92<br>► With cast-iron drain, waste, and vent lines, copper water supply lines. | sf | — | $8.33 | $8.33 | |
| **Complete house rough plumbing (no fixtures), economy grade**<br>*Replace* Materials........ .53          Labor............1.62<br>► PVC drain, waste, and vent lines, CPVC hot water lines, PVC cold water lines. | sf | — | $2.15 | $2.15 | ◄ **COMPLETE HOUSE ROUGH PLUMBING** |
| **Complete house rough plumbing (no fixtures) standard grade**<br>*Replace* Materials........ .77          Labor............1.79<br>► PVC drain, waste, and vent lines, copper water supply lines. | sf | — | $2.56 | $2.56 | |
| **Complete house rough plumbing (no fixtures) high grade**<br>*Replace* Materials........1.11          Labor............1.92<br>► Cast-iron drain, waste, and vent lines, copper water supply lines. | sf | — | $3.03 | $3.03 | |
| **Complete house plumbing fixtures, economy grade**<br>*Replace* Materials........1.47          Labor............1.83 | sf | — | $3.30 | $3.30 | ◄ **COMPLETE HOUSE FINISH PLUMBING (FIXTURES)**<br>*See page 369 for information about plumbing fixture quality.* |
| **Complete house plumbing fixtures, standard grade**<br>*Replace* Materials........2.44          Labor............1.87 | sf | — | $4.31 | $4.31 | |
| **Complete house plumbing fixtures, high grade**<br>*Replace* Materials........2.71          Labor............1.87 | sf | — | $4.58 | $4.58 | |
| **Complete house plumbing fixtures, deluxe grade**<br>*Replace* Materials........2.89          Labor............1.92 | sf | — | $4.81 | $4.81 | |
| **Complete house plumbing fixtures, custom deluxe grade**<br>*Replace* Materials........3.30          Labor............1.96 | sf | — | $5.26 | $5.26 | |
| **Rough plumbing, two fixture bathroom, plastic supply, plastic DWV**<br>*Replace* Materials....300.00          Labor.........835.00 | ea | — | $1,135.00 | $1,135.00 | ◄ **ROUGH PLUMBING TWO FIXTURE BATHROOM**<br>*Typically rough plumbing for one toilet and one sink. Does not include fixtures.* |
| **Rough plumbing, two fixture bathroom, copper supply, plastic DWV**<br>*Replace* Materials....360.00          Labor.........869.00 | ea | — | $1,229.00 | $1,229.00 | |
| **Rough plumbing, two fixture bathroom, copper supply, cast-iron DWV**<br>*Replace* Materials.....415.00          Labor.........907.00 | ea | — | $1,322.00 | $1,322.00 | |

**RELATED ITEMS**

| Item Description | Unit | Remove | Replace | Total |
|---|---|---|---|---|
| **ROUGH PLUMBING ▶ THREE FIXTURE BATHROOM** *Typically rough plumbing for one toilet, one sink and a shower or bathtub. Does not include fixtures.* | | | | |
| **Rough plumbing, three fixture bathroom, plastic supply, plastic DWV** *Replace* Materials ....390.00  Labor .......1070.00 | ea | — | $1,460.00 | $1,460.00 |
| **Rough plumbing, three fixture bathroom, copper supply, plastic DWV** *Replace* Materials .....470.00  Labor ........1120.00 | ea | — | $1,590.00 | $1,590.00 |
| **Rough plumbing, three fixture bathroom, copper supply, cast-iron DWV** *Replace* Materials ....535.00  Labor .......1220.00 | ea | — | $1,755.00 | $1,755.00 |
| **ROUGH PLUMBING ▶ FOUR FIXTURE BATHROOM** *Typically rough plumbing for one toilet, one sink one shower and a bathtub. Does not include fixtures.* | | | | |
| **Rough plumbing, four fixture bathroom, plastic supply, plastic DWV** *Replace* Materials ....480.00  Labor .......1420.00 | ea | — | $1,900.00 | $1,900.00 |
| **Rough plumbing, four fixture bathroom, copper supply, plastic DWV** *Replace* Materials ....580.00  Labor .......1520.00 | ea | — | $2,100.00 | $2,100.00 |
| **Rough plumbing, four fixture bathroom, copper supply, cast-iron DWV** *Replace* Materials ....660.00  Labor .......1640.00 | ea | — | $2,300.00 | $2,300.00 |
| **ROUGH PLUMBING ▶ FIVE FIXTURE BATHROOM** *Typically rough plumbing for one toilet, two sinks one shower and a bathtub. Does not include fixtures.* | | | | |
| **Rough plumbing, five fixture bathroom, plastic supply, plastic DWV** *Replace* Materials ....580.00  Labor .......1780.00 | ea | — | $2,360.00 | $2,360.00 |
| **Rough plumbing, five fixture bathroom, copper supply, plastic DWV** *Replace* Materials ....700.00  Labor .......1850.00 | ea | — | $2,550.00 | $2,550.00 |
| **Rough plumbing, five fixture bathroom, copper supply, cast-iron DWV** *Replace* Materials ....795.00  Labor .......1940.00 | ea | — | $2,735.00 | $2,735.00 |
| **ROUGH PLUMBING ▶ LAUNDRY ROOM** *Includes supply valves and recessed wall box.* | | | | |
| **Rough plumbing, laundry room, plastic supply, plastic DWV** *Replace* Materials ....130.00  Labor .........276.00 | ea | — | $406.00 | $406.00 |
| **Rough plumbing, laundry room, copper supply, plastic DWV** *Replace* Materials .....155.00  Labor ........290.00 | ea | — | $445.00 | $445.00 |
| **Rough plumbing, laundry room, copper supply, cast-iron DWV** *Replace* Materials ....180.00  Labor ........306.00 | ea | — | $486.00 | $486.00 |
| **ROUGH PLUMBING ▶ LAUNDRY ROOM WITH SINK** *Includes supply valves, recessed wall box, and plumbing for one or two hole laundry sink.* | | | | |
| **Rough plumbing, laundry room with sink, plastic supply, plastic DWV** *Replace* Materials ....305.00  Labor .........541.00 | ea | — | $846.00 | $846.00 |
| **Rough plumbing, laundry room with sink, copper supply, plastic DWV** *Replace* Materials ....365.00  Labor ........554.00 | ea | — | $919.00 | $919.00 |
| **Rough plumbing, laundry room with sink, copper supply, cast-iron DWV** *Replace* Materials ....420.00  Labor ........567.00 | ea | — | $987.00 | $987.00 |
| **ROUGH PLUMBING ▶ KITCHEN** *Rough plumbing for one, two or three hole kitchen sink. With ice maker includes line from sink to refrigerator ice maker or water dispenser.* | | | | |
| **Rough plumbing, kitchen, plastic supply, plastic DWV** *Replace* Materials ...220.00  Labor .........349.00 | ea | — | $569.00 | $569.00 |
| **Rough plumbing, kitchen, copper supply, plastic DWV** *Replace* Materials ....245.00  Labor .......364.00 | ea | — | $609.00 | $609.00 |
| **Rough plumbing, kitchen, copper supply, cast-iron DWV** *Replace* Materials ....270.00  Labor .........374.00 | ea | — | $644.00 | $644.00 |
| **Rough plumbing, kitchen with ice maker, plastic supply, plastic DWV** *Replace* Materials ....250.00  Labor .........417.00 | ea | — | $667.00 | $667.00 |
| **Rough plumbing, kitchen with ice maker, copper supply, plastic DWV** *Replace* Materials ....275.00  Labor .......430.00 | ea | — | $705.00 | $705.00 |

| Item Description | Unit | Remove | Replace | Total | |
|---|---|---|---|---|---|
| **Rough plumbing, kitchen with icemaker, copper supply, cast-iron DWV**<br>*Replace* Materials....300.00    Labor........443.00 | ea | — | $743.00 | $743.00 | |
| **Rough plumbing, wet bar sink, plastic supply, plastic DWV**<br>*Replace* Materials.....115.00    Labor.........316.00 | ea | — | $431.00 | $431.00 | **◄ ROUGH PLUMBING WET BAR SINK**<br>*Rough plumbing for one hole bar sink. For feeds only see page 375. For wet bar sink faucets see page 370 and 384. For wet bar sinks see page 374.* |
| **Rough plumbing, wet bar sink, copper supply, plastic DWV**<br>*Replace* Materials.....135.00    Labor.........328.00 | ea | — | $463.00 | $463.00 | |
| **Rough plumbing, wet bar sink, copper supply, cast-iron DWV**<br>*Replace* Materials....155.00    Labor........338.00 | ea | — | $493.00 | $493.00 | |
| **Rough plumbing, bathroom sink, plastic supply, plastic DWV**<br>*Replace* Materials.....115.00    Labor.........316.00 | ea | — | $431.00 | $431.00 | **◄ ROUGH PLUMBING BATHROOM SINK**<br>*Rough plumbing for one hole bathroom sink. For feeds only see page 375. For bathroom sink faucets see page 368 and 384. For bathroom sinks see page 371 and 385.* |
| **Rough plumbing, bathroom sink, copper supply, plastic DWV**<br>*Replace* Materials....140.00    Labor........328.00 | ea | — | $468.00 | $468.00 | |
| **Rough plumbing, bathroom sink, copper supply, cast-iron DWV**<br>*Replace* Materials.....160.00    Labor........338.00 | ea | — | $498.00 | $498.00 | |
| **Rough plumbing, kitchen sink, plastic supply, plastic DWV**<br>*Replace* Materials.....195.00    Labor........349.00 | ea | — | $544.00 | $544.00 | **◄ ROUGH PLUMBING KITCHEN SINK**<br>*Rough plumbing for one, two or three hole kitchen sink. For feeds only see page 375. For kitchen sink faucets see page 369 and 384. For kitchen sinks see page 373.* |
| **Rough plumbing, kitchen sink, copper supply, plastic DWV**<br>*Replace* Materials....220.00    Labor........364.00 | ea | — | $584.00 | $584.00 | |
| **Rough plumbing, kitchen sink, copper supply, cast-iron DWV**<br>*Replace* Materials.....245.00    Labor........374.00 | ea | — | $619.00 | $619.00 | |
| **Rough plumbing, laundry sink, plastic supply, plastic DWV**<br>*Replace* Materials.....115.00    Labor........276.00 | ea | — | $391.00 | $391.00 | **◄ ROUGH PLUMBING LAUNDRY SINK**<br>*For one or two hole laundry sink. For feeds only see page 375. For laundry sink faucets see page 369. For laundry sinks see page 374.* |
| **Rough plumbing, laundry sink, copper supply, plastic DWV**<br>*Replace* Materials.....135.00    Labor........290.00 | ea | — | $425.00 | $425.00 | |
| **Rough plumbing, laundry sink, copper supply, cast-iron DWV**<br>*Replace* Materials.....155.00    Labor........306.00 | ea | — | $461.00 | $461.00 | |
| **Rough plumbing, bathtub or shower, plastic supply, plastic DWV**<br>*Replace* Materials.....165.00    Labor........294.00 | ea | — | $459.00 | $459.00 | **◄ ROUGH PLUMBING BATHTUB OR SHOWER**<br>*For bathtub and shower faucets see page 370 and 384-385. For bathtubs see page 377 and 387. For showers see page 387.* |
| **Rough plumbing, bathtub or shower, copper supply, plastic DWV**<br>*Replace* Materials....205.00    Labor........309.00 | ea | — | $514.00 | $514.00 | |
| **Rough plumbing, bathtub or shower, copper supply, cast-iron DWV**<br>*Replace* Materials....230.00    Labor........323.00 | ea | — | $553.00 | $553.00 | |
| **Rough plumbing, toilet, plastic supply & plastic DWV**<br>*Replace* Materials.....145.00    Labor.........249.00 | ea | — | $394.00 | $394.00 | **◄ ROUGH PLUMBING TOILET**<br>*For toilets see page 376 and 386.* |
| **Rough plumbing, toilet, copper supply & plastic DWV**<br>*Replace* Materials....180.00    Labor........265.00 | ea | — | $445.00 | $445.00 | |
| **Rough plumbing, toilet, copper supply & cast-iron DWV**<br>*Replace* Materials....200.00    Labor........275.00 | ea | — | $475.00 | $475.00 | **RELATED ITEMS**<br>Bathroom Hardware......41<br>Cleaning ......................64 |
| **Rough plumbing, bidet, plastic supply & plastic DWV**<br>*Replace* Materials.....160.00    Labor........276.00 | ea | — | $436.00 | $436.00 | **◄ ROUGH PLUMBING BIDET**<br>*For bidets see page 376.* |

| | Item Description | Unit | Remove | Replace | Total |
|---|---|---|---|---|---|
| **ROUGH PLUMBING ▶** **BIDET** *continued* | **Rough plumbing, bidet, copper supply & plastic DWV** *Replace* Materials....200.00      Labor.........294.00 | ea | — | $494.00 | $494.00 |
| | **Rough plumbing, bidet, copper supply & cast iron DWV** *Replace* Materials....225.00      Labor........304.00 | ea | — | $529.00 | $529.00 |
| **ROUGH PLUMBING ▶** **CLOTHES WASHER** *Includes supply valves and recessed wall box. For clothes washers see page 31.* | **Rough plumbing, clothes washer, plastic supply & plastic DWV** *Replace* Materials.....120.00      Labor........309.00 | ea | — | $429.00 | $429.00 |
| | **Rough plumbing, clothes washer, copper supply & plastic DWV** *Replace* Materials ....140.00      Labor........320.00 | ea | — | $460.00 | $460.00 |
| | **Rough plumbing, clothes washer, copper supply & cast iron DWV** *Replace* Materials.....160.00      Labor........330.00 | ea | — | $490.00 | $490.00 |
| **ROUGH PLUMBING ▶** **DISHWASHER** *Connection from kitchen sink (see previous page) to dishwasher. For dishwashers see page 26.* | **Rough plumbing, dishwasher, plastic supply & plastic DWV** *Replace* Materials......20.00      Labor...........59.20 | ea | — | $79.20 | $79.20 |
| | **Rough plumbing, dishwasher, copper supply & plastic DWV** *Replace* Materials......25.00      Labor..........63.50 | ea | — | $88.50 | $88.50 |
| | **Rough plumbing, dishwasher, copper supply & cast iron DWV** *Replace* Materials......30.00      Labor..........67.70 | ea | — | $97.70 | $97.70 |
| **ROUGH PLUMBING ▶** **HOSE BIBB** *Freeze-proof hose bibb.* | **Cold water plastic supply line for exterior hose bibb** *Replace* Materials ......67.00      Labor.........151.00 | ea | — | $218.00 | $218.00 |
| | **Cold water copper supply line for exterior hose bibb** *Replace* Materials ......91.00      Labor.........150.00 | ea | — | $241.00 | $241.00 |
| **ROUGH PLUMBING ▶** **EVAP. COOLER** | **Cold water copper supply line for evaporative cooler** *Replace* Materials ......48.00      Labor..........114.00 | ea | — | $162.00 | $162.00 |
| **ROUGH PLUMBING ▶** **ICE MAKER** *Supply lines only. For supply line installation including hookup see Appliances on page 31.* | **Cold water plastic supply line for refrigerator ice maker** *Replace* Materials.......13.00      Labor ..........89.50 | ea | — | $102.50 | $102.50 |
| | **Cold water copper supply line for refrigerator ice maker** *Replace* Materials ......32.00      Labor...........94.10 | ea | — | $126.10 | $126.10 |
| **ROUGH PLUMBING ▶** **FLOOR DRAIN** | **Drain lines for in-floor French drain** *Replace* Materials ......95.00      Labor..........138.00 ▶ Includes drain, up to 12 lf drain pipe, and two cubic yard gravel drain field. Does not include excavation or backfill. | ea | — | $233.00 | $233.00 |
| | **Drain lines for in-floor drain connected to sewer** *Replace* Materials ....230.00      Labor.........224.00 ▶ Includes drain, up to 32 lf drain pipe. Does not include excavation or backfill. | ea | — | $454.00 | $454.00 |
| **BATHROOM SINK ▶** **FAUCET** *For antique style faucets see page 384. For bathroom sink rough plumbing see page 367. For bathroom sinks see page 371 and 385.* | **Bathroom sink faucet, economy grade** *Replace* Materials ......85.00      Labor .........23.70 *Remove* ........................      Labor ...........9.35 | ea | $9.35 | $108.70 | $118.05 |
| | **Bathroom sink faucet, standard grade** *Replace* Materials.....160.00      Labor ..........23.70 *Remove* ........................      Labor ...........9.35 | ea | $9.35 | $183.70 | $193.05 |
| | **Bathroom sink faucet, high grade** *Replace* Materials ....300.00      Labor ..........23.70 *Remove* ........................      Labor ...........9.35 | ea | $9.35 | $323.70 | $333.05 |

| Item Description | Unit | Remove | Replace | Total |
|---|---|---|---|---|
| **Bathroom sink faucet, deluxe grade** | ea | $9.35 | $543.70 | $553.05 |
| *Replace* Materials ....520.00    Labor ..........23.70 | | | | |
| *Remove* .....................    Labor ..........9.35 | | | | |
| **Remove bathroom sink faucet for work, then reinstall** | ea | — | $35.50 | $35.50 |
| *Replace* .....................    Labor..........35.50 | | | | |
| **Bidet faucet, standard grade** | ea | $9.35 | $285.30 | $294.65 |
| *Replace* Materials ....260.00    Labor ..........25.30 | | | | |
| *Remove* .....................    Labor ..........9.35 | | | | |
| **Bidet faucet, high grade** | ea | $9.35 | $440.30 | $449.65 |
| *Replace* Materials .....415.00    Labor ..........25.30 | | | | |
| *Remove* .....................    Labor ..........9.35 | | | | |
| **Bidet faucet, deluxe grade** | ea | $9.35 | $705.30 | $714.65 |
| *Replace* Materials ....680.00    Labor ..........25.30 | | | | |
| *Remove* .....................    Labor ..........9.35 | | | | |
| **Remove bidet faucet for work, then reinstall** | ea | — | $37.10 | $37.10 |
| *Replace* .....................    Labor..........37.10 | | | | |
| **Kitchen sink faucet, economy grade** | ea | $9.35 | $123.90 | $133.25 |
| *Replace* Materials ....100.00    Labor ..........23.90 | | | | |
| *Remove* .....................    Labor ..........9.35 | | | | |
| **Kitchen sink faucet, standard grade** | ea | $9.35 | $198.90 | $208.25 |
| *Replace* Materials .....175.00    Labor ..........23.90 | | | | |
| *Remove* .....................    Labor ..........9.35 | | | | |
| **Kitchen sink faucet, high grade** | ea | $9.35 | $363.90 | $373.25 |
| *Replace* Materials ....340.00    Labor ..........23.90 | | | | |
| *Remove* .....................    Labor ..........9.35 | | | | |
| **Kitchen sink faucet, deluxe grade** | ea | $9.35 | $603.90 | $613.25 |
| *Replace* Materials ....580.00    Labor ..........23.90 | | | | |
| *Remove* .....................    Labor ..........9.35 | | | | |
| **Remove kitchen sink faucet for work, then reinstall** | ea | — | $36.10 | $36.10 |
| *Replace* .....................    Labor ..........36.10 | | | | |
| **Laundry sink faucet, economy grade** | ea | $9.35 | $78.30 | $87.65 |
| *Replace* Materials ......55.00    Labor ..........23.30 | | | | |
| *Remove* .....................    Labor ..........9.35 | | | | |
| **Laundry sink faucet, standard grade** | ea | $9.35 | $118.30 | $127.65 |
| *Replace* Materials ......95.00    Labor ..........23.30 | | | | |
| *Remove* .....................    Labor ..........9.35 | | | | |
| **Laundry sink faucet, high grade** | ea | $9.35 | $158.30 | $167.65 |
| *Replace* Materials .....135.00    Labor ..........23.30 | | | | |
| *Remove* .....................    Labor ..........9.35 | | | | |
| **Laundry sink faucet, deluxe grade** | ea | $9.35 | $258.30 | $267.65 |
| *Replace* Materials ....235.00    Labor ..........23.30 | | | | |
| *Remove* .....................    Labor ..........9.35 | | | | |
| **Remove laundry sink faucet for work, then reinstall** | ea | — | $34.90 | $34.90 |
| *Replace* .....................    Labor ..........34.90 | | | | |

**RELATED ITEMS**

Bathroom Hardware......41
Cleaning ....................64

◁ remove & reinstall

◀ **BIDET FAUCET**
*For rough plumbing see page 367. For bidets see page 376.*

◁ remove & reinstall

◀ **KITCHEN SINK FAUCET**
*For antique style faucets see page 384. For rough plumbing see page 367. For kitchen sinks see page 373.*

◁ remove & reinstall

◀ **LAUNDRY SINK FAUCET**
*For rough plumbing see page 367. For laundry sinks see page 374.*

**FAUCET QUALITY**

Some faucet quality rules of thumb:

**Economy:** Light gauge metal, chrome plated. May have some plastic components. Little or no pattern.

**Standard:** Heavier gauge metal, chrome or brass plated with little or no pattern or with wood handles made of ash or oak.

*continued on next page*

| Item Description | Unit | Remove | Replace | Total |
|---|---|---|---|---|

**SHOWER FAUCET ▶**
*For rough plumbing see page 367. For shower stalls and bathtub surrounds see page 378 and page 491.*

**FAUCET QUALITY**
*continued*
**High:** Brass, chrome over brass, or nickel over brass with minimal detail or plated hardware with ornate detail, or with European style plastic or porcelain components.
**Deluxe:** Brass, chrome over brass, or nickel over brass with ornate detail.

**BATHTUB FAUCET ▶**
*For antique style faucets see page 384. For rough plumbing see page 367. For bathtubs see page 377 and page 386.*

**remove & reinstall ▷**

**BATHUB WITH ▶ SHOWER FAUCET**
*For antique style faucets see page 384. For rough plumbing see page 367. For bathtubs see page 377 and page 386.*

**remove & reinstall ▷**

**WET BAR SINK ▶ FAUCET**
*For rough plumbing see page 367. For wet bar sink see page 374.*

| Item Description | Unit | Remove | Replace | Total |
|---|---|---|---|---|
| **Shower faucet, economy grade** <br> *Replace* Materials.....120.00    Labor..........24.50 <br> *Remove* ....................    Labor ..........9.35 | ea | $9.35 | $144.50 | $153.85 |
| **Shower faucet, standard grade** <br> *Replace* Materials.....215.00    Labor..........24.50 <br> *Remove* ....................    Labor ..........9.35 | ea | $9.35 | $239.50 | $248.85 |
| **Shower faucet, high grade** <br> *Replace* Materials ....365.00    Labor..........24.50 <br> *Remove* ....................    Labor ..........9.35 | ea | $9.35 | $389.50 | $398.85 |
| **Shower faucet, deluxe grade** <br> *Replace* Materials....540.00    Labor..........24.50 <br> *Remove* ....................    Labor ..........9.35 | ea | $9.35 | $564.50 | $573.85 |
| **Remove shower faucet for work, then reinstall** <br> *Replace* ....................    Labor..........37.70 | ea | — | $37.70 | $37.70 |
| **Bathtub faucet, economy grade** <br> *Replace* Materials ....130.00    Labor..........24.20 <br> *Remove* ....................    Labor ..........9.35 | ea | $9.35 | $154.20 | $163.55 |
| **Bathtub faucet, standard grade** <br> *Replace* Materials ....240.00    Labor..........24.20 <br> *Remove* ....................    Labor ..........9.35 | ea | $9.35 | $264.20 | $273.55 |
| **Bathtub faucet, high grade** <br> *Replace* Materials....405.00    Labor..........24.20 <br> *Remove* ....................    Labor ..........9.35 | ea | $9.35 | $429.20 | $438.55 |
| **Bathtub faucet, deluxe grade** <br> *Replace* Materials....600.00    Labor..........24.20 <br> *Remove* ....................    Labor ..........9.35 | ea | $9.35 | $624.20 | $633.55 |
| **Remove bathtub faucet for work, then reinstall** <br> *Replace* ....................    Labor..........37.40 | ea | — | $37.40 | $37.40 |
| **Bathtub with shower faucet, economy grade** <br> *Replace* Materials.....145.00    Labor ..........25.80 <br> *Remove* ....................    Labor..........10.50 | ea | $10.50 | $170.80 | $181.30 |
| **Bathtub with shower faucet, standard grade** <br> *Replace* Materials ....260.00    Labor ..........25.80 <br> *Remove* ....................    Labor..........10.50 | ea | $10.50 | $285.80 | $296.30 |
| **Bathtub with shower faucet, high grade** <br> *Replace* Materials ....445.00    Labor ..........25.80 <br> *Remove* ....................    Labor..........10.50 | ea | $9.88 | $470.80 | $481.30 |
| **Bathub with shower faucet, deluxe grade** <br> *Replace* Materials ....660.00    Labor ..........25.80 <br> *Remove* ....................    Labor..........10.50 | ea | $10.50 | $685.80 | $696.30 |
| **Remove bathtub with shower faucet for work, then reinstall** <br> *Replace* ....................    Labor ..........38.40 | ea | — | $38.40 | $38.40 |
| **Wet bar sink faucet, economy grade** <br> *Replace* Materials ......75.00    Labor..........23.00 <br> *Remove* ....................    Labor ..........9.35 | ea | $9.35 | $98.00 | $107.35 |

| Item Description | Unit | Remove | Replace | Total | |
|---|---|---|---|---|---|
| **Wet bar sink faucet, standard grade**<br>*Replace* Materials ....140.00  Labor ..........23.00<br>*Remove* ................... Labor ..........9.35 | ea | $9.35 | $163.00 | $172.35 | |
| **Wet bar sink faucet, high grade**<br>*Replace* Materials ....270.00  Labor ..........23.00<br>*Remove* ................... Labor ..........9.35 | ea | $9.35 | $293.00 | $302.35 | |
| **Wet bar sink faucet, deluxe grade**<br>*Replace* Materials....460.00  Labor ..........23.00<br>*Remove* ................... Labor ..........9.35 | ea | $9.35 | $483.00 | $492.35 | |
| **Remove wet bar sink faucet for work, then reinstall**<br>*Replace* ................... Labor ..........34.10 | ea | — | $34.10 | $34.10 | ◁ remove & reinstall |
| **Refurbish and repack faucet**<br>*Replace* Materials.......15.00  Labor ..........19.40 | ea | — | $34.40 | $34.40 | ◀ **REPACK FAUCET** |
| **Bathroom oval sink, wall-hung porcelain-enamel cast iron**<br>*Replace* Materials ....385.00  Labor ..........37.40<br>*Remove* ................... Labor ..........9.59 | ea | $9.59 | $422.40 | $431.99 | ◀ **BATHROOM SINK** With visible plumbing including water feeds, P trap, escutcheons, and so forth, to wall or floor. Does not include faucet. For rough plumbing see page 367. For bathroom sink faucets see page 368. |
| **Bathroom round sink, wall-hung porcelain-enamel cast iron**<br>*Replace* Materials....380.00  Labor ..........37.40<br>*Remove* ................... Labor ..........9.59 | ea | $9.59 | $417.40 | $426.99 | |
| **Bathroom hexagonal sink, wall-hung porcelain-enamel cast iron**<br>*Replace* Materials.....415.00  Labor ..........37.40<br>*Remove* ................... Labor ..........9.59 | ea | $9.59 | $452.40 | $461.99 | ◁ wall-hung |
| **Bathroom oval sink, wall-hung porcelain-enamel steel**<br>*Replace* Materials ....320.00  Labor ..........37.40<br>*Remove* ................... Labor ..........9.59 | ea | $9.59 | $357.40 | $366.99 | |
| **Bathroom round sink, wall-hung porcelain-enamel steel**<br>*Replace* Materials.....315.00  Labor ..........37.40<br>*Remove* ................... Labor ..........9.59 | ea | $9.59 | $352.40 | $361.99 | |
| **Bathroom hexagonal sink, wall-hung porcelain-enamel steel**<br>*Replace* Materials ....345.00  Labor ..........37.40<br>*Remove* ................... Labor ..........9.59 | ea | $9.59 | $382.40 | $391.99 | |
| **Bathroom oval sink, wall-hung vitreous china**<br>*Replace* Materials.....310.00  Labor ..........37.40<br>*Remove* ................... Labor ..........9.59 | ea | $9.59 | $347.40 | $356.99 | |
| **Bathroom oval sink, wall-hung vitreous china with pattern**<br>*Replace* Materials.....410.00  Labor ..........37.40<br>*Remove* ................... Labor ..........9.59 | ea | $9.59 | $447.40 | $456.99 | |
| **Bathroom round sink, wall-hung vitreous china**<br>*Replace* Materials....305.00  Labor ..........37.40<br>*Remove* ................... Labor ..........9.59 | ea | $9.59 | $342.40 | $351.99 | |
| **Bathroom round sink, wall-hung vitreous china with pattern**<br>*Replace* Materials....405.00  Labor ..........37.40<br>*Remove* ................... Labor ..........9.59 | ea | $9.59 | $442.40 | $451.99 | |
| **Bathroom hexagonal sink, wall-hung vitreous china**<br>*Replace* Materials......315.00  Labor ..........37.40<br>*Remove* ................... Labor ..........9.59 | ea | $9.59 | $352.40 | $361.99 | |

**RELATED ITEMS**

| | Item Description | | Unit | Remove | Replace | Total |
|---|---|---|---|---|---|---|
| **BATHROOM SINK ▶** *continued* | **Remove wall-hung bathroom sink for work, then reinstall** | | ea | — | $46.40 | $46.40 |
| | *Replace* .................... | Labor ..........46.40 | | | | |
| self-rimming ▷ | **Bathroom oval sink, self-rimming vitreous china** | | ea | $9.59 | $318.70 | $328.29 |
| | *Replace* Materials ....280.00 | Labor ..........38.70 | | | | |
| | *Remove* ..................... | Labor ..........9.59 | | | | |
| | **Bathroom oval sink, self-rimming vitreous china with pattern** | | ea | $9.59 | $408.70 | $418.29 |
| | *Replace* Materials ....370.00 | Labor ..........38.70 | | | | |
| | *Remove* ..................... | Labor ..........9.59 | | | | |
| | **Bathroom round sink, self-rimming vitreous china** | | ea | $9.59 | $313.70 | $323.29 |
| | *Replace* Materials ....275.00 | Labor ..........38.70 | | | | |
| | *Remove* ..................... | Labor ..........9.59 | | | | |
| | **Bathroom round sink, self-rimming vitreous china with pattern** | | ea | $9.59 | $403.70 | $413.29 |
| | *Replace* Materials ....365.00 | Labor ..........38.70 | | | | |
| | *Remove* ..................... | Labor ..........9.59 | | | | |
| | **Bathroom hexagonal sink, self-rimming vitreous china** | | ea | $9.59 | $323.70 | $333.29 |
| | *Replace* Materials ....285.00 | Labor ..........38.70 | | | | |
| | *Remove* ..................... | Labor ..........9.59 | | | | |
| | **Bathroom oval sink, self-rimming stainless steel** | | ea | $9.59 | $338.70 | $348.29 |
| | *Replace* Materials ....300.00 | Labor ..........38.70 | | | | |
| | *Remove* ..................... | Labor ..........9.59 | | | | |
| | **Bathroom oval sink, self-rimming scalloped stainless steel** | | ea | $9.59 | $383.70 | $393.29 |
| | *Replace* Materials ....345.00 | Labor ..........38.70 | | | | |
| | *Remove* ..................... | Labor ..........9.59 | | | | |
| | **Bathroom oval sink, self-rimming polished brass** | | ea | $9.59 | $373.70 | $383.29 |
| | *Replace* Materials ....335.00 | Labor ..........38.70 | | | | |
| | *Remove* ..................... | Labor ..........9.59 | | | | |
| | **Bathroom oval sink, self-rimming hammered finish brass** | | ea | $9.59 | $418.70 | $428.29 |
| | *Replace* Materials ....380.00 | Labor ..........38.70 | | | | |
| | *Remove* ..................... | Labor ..........9.04 | | | | |
| | **Bathroom oval sink, self-rimming scalloped polished brass** | | ea | $9.59 | $453.70 | $463.29 |
| | *Replace* Materials .....415.00 | Labor ..........38.70 | | | | |
| | *Remove* ..................... | Labor ..........9.59 | | | | |
| | **Remove self-rimming bathroom sink for work, then reinstall** | | ea | — | $48.60 | $48.60 |
| | *Replace* ..................... | Labor ..........48.60 | | | | |
| under-counter ▷ | **Bathroom oval sink, under-counter vitreous china** | | ea | $9.59 | $330.60 | $340.19 |
| | *Replace* Materials ....290.00 | Labor ..........40.60 | | | | |
| | *Remove* ..................... | Labor ..........9.59 | | | | |
| | **Bathroom oval sink, under-counter vitreous china with pattern** | | ea | $9.59 | $425.60 | $435.19 |
| | *Replace* Materials ....385.00 | Labor ..........40.60 | | | | |
| | *Remove* ..................... | Labor ..........9.59 | | | | |
| | **Bathroom round sink, under-counter vitreous china** | | ea | $9.59 | $330.60 | $340.19 |
| | *Replace* Materials ....290.00 | Labor ..........40.60 | | | | |
| | *Remove* ..................... | Labor ..........9.59 | | | | |
| | **Bathroom round sink, under-counter vitreous china with pattern** | | ea | $9.59 | $420.60 | $430.19 |
| | *Replace* Materials ....380.00 | Labor ..........40.60 | | | | |
| | *Remove* ..................... | Labor ..........9.59 | | | | |

| Item Description | Unit | Remove | Replace | Total |
|---|---|---|---|---|
| **Bathroom hexagonal sink, under-counter vitreous china**<br>*Replace* Materials ....295.00    Labor ..........40.60<br>*Remove* .......................    Labor ...........9.59 | ea | $9.59 | $335.60 | $345.19 |
| **Remove under-counter bathroom sink for work, then reinstall**<br>*Replace* .......................    Labor ..........50.30 | ea | — | $50.30 | $50.30 |
| **24" by 21" single-bowl porcelain-enamel, cast-iron kitchen sink**<br>*Replace* Materials ....305.00    Labor ..........39.40<br>*Remove* .......................    Labor ...........9.67 | ea | $9.67 | $344.40 | $354.07 |
| **30" by 21" single-bowl porcelain-enamel, cast-iron kitchen sink**<br>*Replace* Materials ....375.00    Labor ..........39.40<br>*Remove* .......................    Labor ...........9.67 | ea | $9.67 | $414.40 | $424.07 |
| **32" by 21" double-bowl porcelain-enamel, cast-iron kitchen sink**<br>*Replace* Materials ....450.00    Labor ..........39.40<br>*Remove* .......................    Labor ...........9.67 | ea | $9.67 | $489.40 | $499.07 |
| **42" by 21" triple-bowl porcelain-enamel, cast-iron kitchen sink**<br>*Replace* Materials ....985.00    Labor ..........39.40<br>*Remove* .......................    Labor ...........9.67 | ea | $9.67 | $1,024.40 | $1,034.07 |
| **24" by 21" single-bowl porcelain-enamel, steel kitchen sink**<br>*Replace* Materials.....155.00    Labor ..........39.40<br>*Remove* .......................    Labor ...........9.67 | ea | $9.67 | $194.40 | $204.07 |
| **30" by 21" single-bowl porcelain-enamel, steel kitchen sink**<br>*Replace* Materials ....180.00    Labor ..........39.40<br>*Remove* .......................    Labor ...........9.67 | ea | $9.67 | $219.40 | $229.07 |
| **32" by 21" double-bowl porcelain-enamel, steel kitchen sink**<br>*Replace* Materials.....185.00    Labor ..........39.40<br>*Remove* .......................    Labor ...........9.67 | ea | $9.67 | $224.40 | $234.07 |
| **42" by 21" triple-bowl porcelain-enamel, steel kitchen sink**<br>*Replace* Materials ....835.00    Labor ..........39.40<br>*Remove* .......................    Labor ...........9.67 | ea | $9.67 | $874.40 | $884.07 |
| **19" by 18" single-bowl stainless steel kitchen sink**<br>*Replace* Materials ....230.00    Labor ..........39.40<br>*Remove* .......................    Labor ...........9.67 | ea | $9.67 | $269.40 | $279.07 |
| **25" by 22" single-bowl stainless steel kitchen sink**<br>*Replace* Materials ....250.00    Labor ..........39.40<br>*Remove* .......................    Labor ...........9.67 | ea | $9.67 | $289.40 | $299.07 |
| **33" by 22" double-bowl stainless steel kitchen sink**<br>*Replace* Materials ....335.00    Labor ..........39.40<br>*Remove* .......................    Labor ...........9.67 | ea | $9.67 | $374.40 | $384.07 |
| **43" by 22" double-bowl stainless steel kitchen sink**<br>*Replace* Materials ....355.00    Labor ..........39.40<br>*Remove* .......................    Labor ...........9.67 | ea | $9.67 | $394.40 | $404.07 |
| **43" by 22" triple-bowl stainless steel kitchen sink**<br>*Replace* Materials.....475.00    Labor ..........39.40<br>*Remove* .......................    Labor ...........9.67 | ea | $9.67 | $514.40 | $524.07 |
| **Remove kitchen sink for work, then reinstall**<br>*Replace* .......................    Labor...........47.30 | ea | — | $47.30 | $47.30 |

---

**RELATED ITEMS**

Bathroom Hardware......41
Cleaning .......................64

---

◄ **KITCHEN SINK**

*With visible plumbing including water feeds, P trap, escutcheons, and so forth, to wall or floor. Does not include faucet. For rough plumbing see page 367. For kitchen sink faucets see page 369.*

◁ remove & reinstall

| Item Description | Unit | Remove | Replace | Total |
|---|---|---|---|---|
| **LAUNDRY SINK** ▶ **22" x 17" single-bowl stainless steel laundry sink in countertop** | ea | $9.67 | $368.40 | $378.07 |
| *Replace* Materials ....330.00   Labor ..........38.40 | | | | |
| *Remove* ..................   Labor ..........9.67 | | | | |
| **19" x 22" single-bowl stainless steel laundry sink in countertop** | ea | $9.67 | $388.40 | $398.07 |
| *Replace* Materials ....350.00   Labor ..........38.40 | | | | |
| *Remove* ..................   Labor ..........9.67 | | | | |
| **33" x 22" double-bowl stainless steel laundry sink in countertop** | ea | $9.67 | $401.40 | $410.51 |
| *Replace* Materials ....365.00   Labor ..........36.40 | | | | |
| *Remove* ..................   Labor ..........9.11 | | | | |
| porcelain-enamel ▷ **24" x 20" single-bowl porcelain-enamel, cast-iron laundry sink on iron frame** | ea | $9.67 | $495.50 | $505.17 |
| *Replace* Materials ....460.00   Labor ..........35.50 | | | | |
| *Remove* ..................   Labor ..........9.67 | | | | |
| **24" x 23" single-bowl porcelain-enamel, cast-iron laundry sink on iron frame** | ea | $9.67 | $535.50 | $545.17 |
| *Replace* Materials ....500.00   Labor ..........35.50 | | | | |
| *Remove* ..................   Labor ..........9.67 | | | | |
| plastic ▷ **18" x 23" single-bowl plastic laundry sink on plastic legs** | ea | $9.67 | $160.50 | $170.17 |
| *Replace* Materials .....125.00   Labor ..........35.50 | | | | |
| *Remove* ..................   Labor ..........9.67 | | | | |
| **20" x 24" single-bowl plastic laundry sink on plastic legs** | ea | $9.67 | $195.50 | $205.17 |
| *Replace* Materials .....160.00   Labor ..........35.50 | | | | |
| *Remove* ..................   Labor ..........9.67 | | | | |
| **36" x 23" double-bowl plastic laundry sink on plastic legs** | ea | $9.67 | $225.50 | $235.17 |
| *Replace* Materials .....190.00   Labor ..........35.50 | | | | |
| *Remove* ..................   Labor ..........9.67 | | | | |
| **40" x 24" double-bowl plastic laundry sink on plastic legs** | ea | $9.67 | $300.50 | $310.17 |
| *Replace* Materials ....265.00   Labor ..........35.50 | | | | |
| *Remove* ..................   Labor ..........9.67 | | | | |
| remove & reinstall ▷ **Remove laundry sink for work, then reinstall** | ea | — | $47.70 | $47.70 |
| *Replace* ..................   Labor ..........47.70 | | | | |
| **WET BAR SINK** ▶ **Wet bar sink, self-rimming vitreous china** | ea | $9.38 | $483.70 | $493.08 |
| *Replace* Materials ....445.00   Labor ..........38.70 | | | | |
| *Remove* ..................   Labor ..........9.38 | | | | |
| **Wet bar sink, self-rimming vitreous china with pattern** | ea | $9.38 | $573.70 | $583.08 |
| *Replace* Materials ....535.00   Labor ..........38.70 | | | | |
| *Remove* ..................   Labor ..........9.38 | | | | |
| self-rimming ▷ **Wet bar sink, self-rimming porcelain-enamel cast iron** | ea | $9.38 | $433.70 | $443.08 |
| *Replace* Materials ....395.00   Labor ..........38.70 | | | | |
| *Remove* ..................   Labor ..........9.38 | | | | |
| **Wet bar sink, self-rimming porcelain-enamel steel** | ea | $9.38 | $263.70 | $273.08 |
| *Replace* Materials ....225.00   Labor ..........38.70 | | | | |
| *Remove* ..................   Labor ..........9.38 | | | | |
| **Wet bar sink, self-rimming stainless steel** | ea | $9.38 | $208.70 | $218.08 |
| *Replace* Materials .....170.00   Labor ..........38.70 | | | | |
| *Remove* ..................   Labor ..........9.38 | | | | |
| **Wet bar sink, self-rimming scalloped stainless steel** | ea | $9.38 | $283.70 | $293.08 |
| *Replace* Materials .....245.00   Labor ..........38.70 | | | | |
| *Remove* ..................   Labor ..........9.38 | | | | |

*LAUNDRY SINK — With visible plumbing including water feeds, P trap, escutcheons, and so forth, to wall or floor. Does not include faucet. For rough plumbing see page 367. For laundry sink faucet see page 369.*

*WET BAR SINK — With visible plumbing including water feeds, P trap, escutcheons, and so forth to wall or floor. Does not include faucet. For rough plumbing see page 367. For wet bar sink faucet see page 370.*

| Item Description | Unit | Remove | Replace | Total | |
|---|---|---|---|---|---|
| **Wet bar sink, self-rimming polished brass**<br>*Replace* Materials.....340.00    Labor ..........38.70<br>*Remove* ......................    Labor ..........9.38 | ea | $9.38 | $378.70 | $388.08 | **RELATED ITEMS**<br>Bathroom Hardware......41<br>Cleaning ......................64 |
| **Wet bar sink, self-rimming hammered finish brass**<br>*Replace* Materials.....390.00    Labor ..........38.70<br>*Remove* ......................    Labor ..........9.38 | ea | $9.38 | $428.70 | $438.08 | |
| **Wet bar sink, self-rimming scalloped polished brass**<br>*Replace* Materials.....435.00    Labor ..........38.70<br>*Remove* ......................    Labor ..........9.38 | ea | $9.38 | $473.70 | $483.08 | |
| **Remove self-rimming wet bar sink for work, then reinstall**<br>*Replace* ......................    Labor ..........48.60 | ea | — | $48.60 | $48.60 | |
| **Wet bar sink, under-counter vitreous china**<br>*Replace* Materials.....310.00    Labor ..........40.60<br>*Remove* ......................    Labor ..........9.38 | ea | $9.38 | $350.60 | $359.98 | ◁ under-counter |
| **Wet bar sink, under-counter vitreous china with pattern**<br>*Replace* Materials.....400.00    Labor ..........40.60<br>*Remove* ......................    Labor ..........9.38 | ea | $9.38 | $440.60 | $449.98 | |
| **Wet bar sink, under-counter porcelain enamel cast iron**<br>*Replace* Materials ....385.00    Labor ..........40.60<br>*Remove* ......................    Labor ..........9.38 | ea | $9.38 | $425.60 | $434.98 | |
| **Wet bar sink, under-counter porcelain enamel steel**<br>*Replace* Materials ....220.00    Labor ..........40.60<br>*Remove* ......................    Labor ..........9.38 | ea | $9.38 | $260.60 | $269.98 | |
| **Wet bar sink, under-counter stainless steel**<br>*Replace* Materials.....165.00    Labor ..........40.60<br>*Remove* ......................    Labor ..........9.38 | ea | $9.38 | $205.60 | $214.98 | |
| **Wet bar sink, under-counter scalloped stainless steel**<br>*Replace* Materials ....240.00    Labor ..........40.60<br>*Remove* ......................    Labor ..........8.84 | ea | $9.38 | $280.60 | $289.98 | |
| **Wet bar sink, under-counter polished brass**<br>*Replace* Materials....330.00    Labor ..........40.60<br>*Remove* ......................    Labor ..........9.38 | ea | $9.38 | $370.60 | $379.98 | |
| **Wet bar sink, under-counter hammered finish brass**<br>*Replace* Materials....380.00    Labor ..........40.60<br>*Remove* ......................    Labor ..........9.38 | ea | $9.38 | $420.60 | $429.98 | |
| **Wet bar sink, under-counter scalloped polished brass**<br>*Replace* Materials ....425.00    Labor ..........40.60<br>*Remove* ......................    Labor ..........9.38 | ea | $9.38 | $465.60 | $474.98 | |
| **Remove under-counter wet bar sink for work, then reinstall**<br>*Replace* ......................    Labor ..........50.30 | ea | — | $50.30 | $50.30 | |
| **Add for brass supply and waste lines** | ea | — | $121.00 | $121.00 | ◀ **ADDITIONAL**<br>**SINK COSTS** |
| **Add 33% for almond colored porcelain enamel** | | | | | |
| **Add 65% for colored porcelain enamel** | | | | | |
| **Sink plumbing, chrome**<br>*Replace* Materials ....105.00    Labor ..........20.30 | ea | — | $125.30 | $125.30 | ◀ **SINK PLUMBING**<br>*continued on next page* |

| Item Description | | Unit | Remove | Replace | Total |
|---|---|---|---|---|---|
| **SINK PLUMBING** ▶ With visible plumbing including water feeds, P trap, escutcheons, and so forth, to wall or floor. Does not include faucet. | **Sink plumbing, brass** *Replace* Materials.....170.00    Labor ..........20.30 | ea | — | $190.30 | $190.30 |
| | **Sink plumbing, chrome-plated brass** *Replace* Materials.....215.00    Labor ..........20.30 | ea | — | $235.30 | $235.30 |
| **TOILET PLUMBING** ▶ Includes cold water supply, shut-off valve, wax ring, and toilet bolts. | **Toilet plumbing, chrome** *Replace* Materials ......70.00    Labor ..........14.70 | ea | — | $84.70 | $84.70 |
| | **Toilet plumbing, brass** *Replace* Materials .....115.00    Labor ..........14.70 | ea | — | $129.70 | $129.70 |
| **BIDET** ▶ Includes water supply lines with shut-off valves. For rough plumbing see page 367. For bidet faucet see page 369. | **Bidet, standard grade** *Replace* Materials ....360.00    Labor ..........62.60 *Remove* .....................    Labor ..........9.46 | ea | $9.46 | $422.60 | $432.06 |
| | **Bidet, deluxe grade** *Replace* Materials ....525.00    Labor ..........62.60 *Remove* .....................    Labor ..........9.46 | ea | $9.46 | $587.60 | $597.06 |
| remove & reinstall ▷ | **Remove bidet for work, then reinstall** *Replace* Materials........1.75    Labor .........101.00 | ea | — | $102.75 | $102.75 |
| **TOILET** ▶ Economy grade toilets are typically white with round bowls. Standard grade toilets are typically white with elongated bowls. High and deluxe grades are typically low-tank toilets, in a variety of colors, with elongated bowls. Deluxe grade may also be "jet" toilets which combine low-water consumption with a direct-fed jet, siphon-assisted blow out action. For rough plumbing see page 367. For antique styles see page 386. | **Toilet, economy grade** *Replace* Materials ....140.00    Labor ..........56.70 *Remove* .....................    Labor ..........9.07 | ea | $9.07 | $196.70 | $205.77 |
| | **Toilet, standard grade** *Replace* Materials.....165.00    Labor ..........56.70 *Remove* .....................    Labor ..........9.07 | ea | $9.07 | $221.70 | $230.77 |
| | **Toilet, high grade** *Replace* Materials.....245.00    Labor ..........56.70 *Remove* .....................    Labor ..........9.07 | ea | $9.07 | $301.70 | $310.77 |
| | **Toilet, deluxe grade** *Replace* Materials.....420.00    Labor ..........56.70 *Remove* .....................    Labor ..........9.07 | ea | $9.07 | $476.70 | $485.77 |
| | **Remove toilet for work, then reinstall** *Replace* Materials........1.75    Labor ..........92.40 | ea | — | $94.15 | $94.15 |
| **TOILET SEAT** ▶ | **Toilet seat, plain round** *Replace* Materials......20.00    Labor ..........9.46 *Remove* .....................    Labor ..........3.64 | ea | $3.64 | $29.46 | $33.10 |
| | **Toilet seat, hardwood** *Replace* Materials......25.00    Labor ..........9.46 *Remove* .....................    Labor ..........3.64 | ea | $3.64 | $34.46 | $38.10 |
| | **Toilet seat, with pattern** *Replace* Materials......35.00    Labor ..........9.46 *Remove* .....................    Labor ..........3.64 | ea | $3.64 | $44.46 | $48.10 |
| | **Toilet seat, elongated** *Replace* Materials.....50.00    Labor ..........9.46 *Remove* .....................    Labor ..........3.64 | ea | $3.64 | $59.46 | $63.10 |
| | **Toilet seat, padded** *Replace* Materials......40.00    Labor ..........9.46 *Remove* .....................    Labor ..........3.64 | ea | $3.64 | $49.46 | $53.10 |

| Item Description | Unit | Remove | Replace | Total |
|---|---|---|---|---|
| **Remove toilet seat for work, then reinstall** | ea | — | $13.80 | $13.80 |
| *Replace* ................ Labor..........13.80 | | | | |
| **48" long by 44" deep cast-iron corner bathtub** | ea | $42.20 | $1,725.00 | $1,767.20 |
| *Replace* Materials ..1600.00 Labor.........125.00 | | | | |
| *Remove* ................ Labor..........42.20 | | | | |
| **48" long by 44" deep acrylic fiberglass corner bathtub** | ea | $26.70 | $726.30 | $753.00 |
| *Replace* Materials.....650.00 Labor.........76.30 | | | | |
| *Remove* ................ Labor..........26.70 | | | | |
| **60" long by 32" deep acrylic fiberglass bathtub** | ea | $26.70 | $376.30 | $403.00 |
| *Replace* Materials.....300.00 Labor.........76.30 | | | | |
| *Remove* ................ Labor..........26.70 | | | | |
| **60" long by 32" deep porcelain-enamel, cast-iron bathtub** | ea | $42.20 | $855.00 | $897.20 |
| *Replace* Materials.....730.00 Labor.........125.00 | | | | |
| *Remove* ................ Labor..........42.20 | | | | |
| **60" long by 32" deep porcelain-enamel, steel bathtub** | ea | $42.20 | $420.00 | $462.20 |
| *Replace* Materials.....295.00 Labor.........125.00 | | | | |
| *Remove* ................ Labor..........42.20 | | | | |
| **72" long by 36" deep acrylic fiberglass bathtub** | ea | $26.70 | $686.30 | $713.00 |
| *Replace* Materials.....610.00 Labor.........76.30 | | | | |
| *Remove* ................ Labor..........26.70 | | | | |
| **72" long by 36" deep porcelain-enamel, cast-iron bathtub** | ea | $42.20 | $1,625.00 | $1,667.20 |
| *Replace* Materials ..1500.00 Labor.........125.00 | | | | |
| *Remove* ................ Labor..........42.20 | | | | |
| **72" long by 36" deep porcelain-enamel, steel bathtub** | ea | $42.20 | $580.00 | $622.20 |
| *Replace* Materials.....455.00 Labor.........125.00 | | | | |
| *Remove* ................ Labor..........42.20 | | | | |
| **Remove fiberglass bathtub for work, then reinstall** | ea | — | $147.00 | $147.00 |
| *Replace* ................ Labor .........147.00 | | | | |
| **Remove cast-iron or steel bathtub for work, then reinstall** | ea | — | $224.00 | $224.00 |
| *Replace* ................ Labor.........224.00 | | | | |
| **60" long by 32" deep acrylic fiberglass bathtub with whirlpool jets** | ea | $38.00 | $1,697.00 | $1,735.00 |
| *Replace* Materials...1550.00 Labor .......147.00 | | | | |
| *Remove* ................ Labor .........38.00 | | | | |
| **60" long by 32" deep porcelain-enamel, cast-iron bathtub with whirlpool jets** | ea | $55.80 | $3,870.00 | $3,925.80 |
| *Replace* Materials ..3700.00 Labor.........170.00 | | | | |
| *Remove* ................ Labor..........55.80 | | | | |
| **72" long by 36" deep acrylic fiberglass bathtub with whirlpool jets** | ea | $38.00 | $3,347.00 | $3,385.00 |
| *Replace* Materials ..3200.00 Labor .......147.00 | | | | |
| *Remove* ................ Labor .........38.00 | | | | |
| **72" long by 36" deep porcelain-enamel, cast-iron bathtub with whirlpool jets** | ea | $55.80 | $7,870.00 | $7,925.80 |
| *Replace* Materials ..7700.00 Labor.........170.00 | | | | |
| *Remove* ................ Labor...........55.80 | | | | |
| **66" long by 48" deep fiberglass bathtub with whirlpool jets** | ea | $38.00 | $2,997.00 | $3,035.00 |
| *Replace* Materials ..2850.00 Labor .........147.00 | | | | |
| *Remove* ................ Labor ..........38.00 | | | | |

◄ **BATHTUB**
*Includes standard chrome drain and overflow assembly. Does not include faucet. For rough plumbing see page 367. For bathtub faucets see page 370. For antique style bathtubs see page 386. For antique style faucets see page 384.*

◁ remove & reinstall

◄ **BATHTUB WITH WHIRLPOOL JETS**
*Includes standard chrome drain and overflow assembly and jets and electrical pump hookup. Does not include faucet or electrical rough wiring. For rough plumbing see page 367. For bathtub faucets see page 370. For antique style bathtubs see page 386. For antique style faucets see page 384.*

| | Item Description | Unit | Remove | Replace | Total |
|---|---|---|---|---|---|
| **BATHTUB WITH ▶ WHIRLPOOL JETS** *continued* | **72" long by 36" deep fiberglass bathtub with whirlpool jets** *Replace* Materials ..2700.00    Labor .........147.00  *Remove* .....................    Labor .........38.00 | ea | $38.00 | $2,847.00 | $2,885.00 |
| | **60" long by 30" deep fiberglass bathtub with whirlpool jets** *Replace* Materials...2150.00    Labor .........147.00  *Remove* .....................    Labor .........38.00 | ea | $38.00 | $2,297.00 | $2,335.00 |
| | **72" long by 42" deep fiberglass bathtub with whirlpool jets** *Replace* Materials..3400.00    Labor .........147.00  *Remove* .....................    Labor .........38.00 | ea | $38.00 | $3,547.00 | $3,585.00 |
| | **83" long by 65" deep fiberglass bathtub with whirlpool jets** *Replace* Materials..5850.00    Labor .........147.00  *Remove* .....................    Labor .........38.00 | ea | $38.00 | $5,997.00 | $6,035.00 |
| *remove & reinstall* ▷ | **Remove fiberglass bathtub with whirlpool jets for work, then reinstall** *Replace* .....................    Labor ........284.00 | ea | — | $284.00 | $284.00 |
| | **Remove cast iron bathtub with whirlpool jets for work, then reinstall** *Replace* .....................    Labor..........387.00 | ea | — | $387.00 | $387.00 |
| **BATHTUB & ▶ SHOWER** *Does not include faucet. High and deluxe quality usually indicates thicker fiberglass with glossier finishes and more ornate soap and wash cloth compartments. For rough plumbing see page 367. For bathtub faucets see page 370. For antique style bath- tubs see page 386. For antique style faucets see page 384.* | **Acrylic fiberglass bathtub & shower combination, standard grade** *Replace* Materials.....410.00    Labor.........138.00  *Remove* .....................    Labor .........44.30 | ea | $44.30 | $548.00 | $592.30 |
| | **Acrylic fiberglass bathtub & shower combination, high grade** *Replace* Materials ....650.00    Labor.........138.00  *Remove* .....................    Labor .........44.30 | ea | $44.30 | $788.00 | $832.30 |
| | **Acrylic fiberglass bathtub & shower combination, deluxe grade** *Replace* Materials ....825.00    Labor.........138.00  *Remove* .....................    Labor .........44.30 | ea | $44.30 | $963.00 | $1,007.30 |
| | **Remove fiberglass bathtub & shower combination for work, then reinstall** *Replace* .....................    Labor..........237.00 | ea | — | $237.00 | $237.00 |
| **SHOWER STALL ▶** *Includes concrete rein- forcement under base. Does not include faucet.* | **32" wide by 32" deep acrylic fiberglass shower stall** *Replace* Materials ....340.00    Labor..........115.00  *Remove* .....................    Labor .........32.00 | ea | $32.00 | $455.00 | $487.00 |
| | **32" wide by 32" deep acrylic fiberglass shower stall with terrazzo base** *Replace* Materials.....410.00    Labor..........115.00  *Remove* .....................    Labor .........32.00 | ea | $32.00 | $525.00 | $557.00 |
| | **32" wide by 32" deep metal shower stall** *Replace* Materials.....160.00    Labor..........115.00  *Remove* .....................    Labor .........32.00 | ea | $32.00 | $275.00 | $307.00 |
| | **48" wide by 35" deep acrylic fiberglass shower stall** *Replace* Materials ....385.00    Labor..........115.00  *Remove* .....................    Labor .........32.00 | ea | $32.00 | $500.00 | $532.00 |
| | **60" wide by 35" deep acrylic fiberglass shower stall** *Replace* Materials ....430.00    Labor..........115.00  *Remove* .....................    Labor .........32.00 | ea | $32.00 | $545.00 | $577.00 |
| *remove & reinstall* ▷ | **Remove fiberglass shower stall for work, then reinstall** *Replace* .....................    Labor .........185.00 | ea | — | $185.00 | $185.00 |
| **SHOWER PAN ▶** *Pan and drain for tile shower.* | **Shower pan, typical size** *Replace* Materials......50.00    Labor ..........43.50 | ea | — | $93.50 | $93.50 |

| Item Description | Unit | Remove | Replace | Total | |
|---|---|---|---|---|---|
| **Shower pan, large size** | ea | — | $118.50 | $118.50 | |
| *Replace* Materials ......75.00     Labor .........43.50 | | | | | |
| **Shower base, fiberglass** | ea | — | $154.70 | $154.70 | ◄ SHOWER BASE |
| *Replace* Materials .....110.00     Labor .........44.70 | | | | | *Prefabricated* |
| **Shower base, terrazzo style** | ea | — | $444.70 | $444.70 | |
| *Replace* Materials ....400.00     Labor .........44.70 | | | | | |
| **Corner entry shower base, fiberglass** | ea | — | $174.70 | $174.70 | |
| *Replace* Materials ....130.00     Labor .........44.70 | | | | | |
| **Corner entry shower base, terrazzo style** | ea | — | $484.70 | $484.70 | |
| *Replace* Materials ....440.00     Labor .........44.70 | | | | | |
| **Cultured stone bathtub surround** | ea | $23.40 | $615.20 | $638.60 | ◄ BATHTUB SURROUND |
| *Replace* Materials ....530.00     Labor...........85.20 | | | | | *Three walls surrounding* |
| *Remove* ......................     Labor .........23.40 | | | | | *bathtub: two widths and* |
| **Fiberglass bathtub surround, standard grade** | ea | $23.40 | $375.60 | $399.00 | *one length. See* |
| *Replace* Materials .....310.00     Labor...........65.60 | | | | | *bathtubs on page 377.* |
| *Remove* ......................     Labor .........23.40 | | | | | *For bathtub rough plumb-* |
| **Fiberglass bathtub surround, high grade** | ea | $23.40 | $550.60 | $574.00 | *ing see page 367. For* |
| *Replace* Materials ....485.00     Labor...........65.60 | | | | | *bathtub faucets see page* |
| *Remove* ......................     Labor .........23.40 | | | | | *370. For antique style* |
| **Fiberglass bathtub surround, deluxe grade** | ea | $23.40 | $760.60 | $784.00 | *bathtubs see page 386.* |
| *Replace* Materials .....695.00     Labor...........65.60 | | | | | *For antique style faucets* |
| *Remove* ......................     Labor .........23.40 | | | | | *see page 384.* |
| **Remove bathtub surround for work, then reinstall** | ea | — | $112.00 | $112.00 | ◁ remove & reinstall |
| *Replace* ......................     Labor..........112.00 | | | | | |
| **Glass shower, with cultured stone slabs on walls, standard grade** | ea | $32.00 | $794.30 | $826.30 | ◄ GLASS SHOWER |
| *Replace* Materials .....695.00     Labor ..........99.30 | | | | | *Cultured stone slabs or* |
| *Remove* ......................     Labor ..........32.00 | | | | | *fiberglass panels on two* |
| **Glass shower, with cultured stone slabs on walls, high grade** | ea | $32.00 | $864.30 | $896.30 | *walls, glass on one wall,* |
| *Replace* Materials .....765.00     Labor ..........99.30 | | | | | *and a glass door on one* |
| *Remove* ......................     Labor ..........32.00 | | | | | *wall. Corner entry* |
| **Corner entry glass shower, cultured stone slabs on walls, standard grade** | ea | $32.00 | $1,020.00 | $1,052.00 | *showers have two glass* |
| *Replace* Materials ....905.00     Labor..........115.00 | | | | | *walls and a corner entry* |
| *Remove* ......................     Labor ..........32.00 | | | | | *door.* |
| **Corner entry glass shower, cultured slabs on walls, high grade** | ea | $32.00 | $1,110.00 | $1,142.00 | |
| *Replace* Materials ....995.00     Labor..........115.00 | | | | | |
| *Remove* ......................     Labor ..........32.00 | | | | | |
| **Glass shower, fiberglass panels on walls, standard grade** | ea | $32.00 | $718.60 | $750.60 | |
| *Replace* Materials ....630.00     Labor ..........88.60 | | | | | |
| *Remove* ......................     Labor ..........32.00 | | | | | |
| **Glass shower, fiberglass panels on walls, high grade** | ea | $32.00 | $783.60 | $815.60 | |
| *Replace* Materials .....695.00     Labor ..........88.60 | | | | | |
| *Remove* ......................     Labor ..........32.00 | | | | | |
| **Corner entry glass shower, fiberglass panels on walls, standard grade** | ea | $32.00 | $929.00 | $961.00 | |
| *Replace* Materials .....825.00     Labor.........104.00 | | | | | |
| *Remove* ......................     Labor ..........32.00 | | | | | |

| Item Description | Unit | Remove | Replace | Total |
|---|---|---|---|---|
| **GLASS SHOWER ▶** *continued*    **Corner entry glass shower, fiberglass panels on walls, high grade**<br>*Replace* Materials....905.00    Labor.........104.00<br>*Remove* .......................    Labor .........32.00 | ea | $32.00 | $1,009.00 | $1,041.00 |
| **remove & reinstall ▷**    **Remove glass shower for work, then reinstall**<br>*Replace* .......................    Labor.........133.00 | ea | — | $133.00 | $133.00 |
| **SLIDING BATHTUB ▶ DOOR** *See tubs on page 377.*    **Sliding glass bathtub door, mill finish trim**<br>*Replace* Materials....200.00    Labor .........58.40<br>*Remove* .......................    Labor .........13.50 | ea | $13.50 | $258.40 | $271.90 |
| **Sliding glass bathtub door, mill finish trim with fancy glass**<br>*Replace* Materials....250.00    Labor .........58.40<br>*Remove* .......................    Labor .........13.50 | ea | $13.50 | $308.40 | $321.90 |
| **Sliding glass bathtub door, gold finish trim**<br>*Replace* Materials.....245.00    Labor .........58.40<br>*Remove* .......................    Labor .........13.50 | ea | $13.50 | $303.40 | $316.90 |
| **Sliding glass bathtub door, gold finish trim with fancy glass**<br>*Replace* Materials....305.00    Labor .........58.40<br>*Remove* .......................    Labor .........13.50 | ea | $13.50 | $363.40 | $376.90 |
| **Sliding glass bathtub door, brass trim**<br>*Replace* Materials....460.00    Labor .........58.40<br>*Remove* .......................    Labor .........13.50 | ea | $13.50 | $518.40 | $531.90 |
| **Sliding glass bathtub door, brass trim with etched glass**<br>*Replace* Materials ....570.00    Labor .........58.40<br>*Remove* .......................    Labor .........13.50 | ea | $13.50 | $628.40 | $641.90 |
| **remove & reinstall ▷**    **Remove sliding glass bathtub door for work, then reinstall**<br>*Replace* .......................    Labor..........97.20 | ea | — | $97.20 | $97.20 |
| **FOLDING BATHTUB ▶ DOOR** *See tubs on page 377.*    **Folding plastic bathtub doors**<br>*Replace* Materials.....195.00    Labor ..........53.30<br>*Remove* .......................    Labor ..........13.10 | ea | $13.10 | $248.30 | $261.40 |
| **remove & reinstall ▷**    **Remove folding plastic bathtub door for work, then reinstall**<br>*Replace* .......................    Labor..........72.00 | ea | — | $72.00 | $72.00 |
| **SHOWER DOOR ▶** *See showers on page 378 and below.*    **Shower door, solid glass**<br>*Replace* Materials ....235.00    Labor..........51.10<br>*Remove* .......................    Labor..........12.70 | ea | $12.70 | $286.10 | $298.80 |
| **Shower door, mill finish trim with fancy glass**<br>*Replace* Materials ....265.00    Labor..........51.10<br>*Remove* .......................    Labor..........12.70 | ea | $12.70 | $316.10 | $328.80 |
| **Shower door, gold finish trim**<br>*Replace* Materials ....265.00    Labor..........51.10<br>*Remove* .......................    Labor..........12.70 | ea | $12.70 | $316.10 | $328.80 |
| **Shower door, gold finish trim with fancy glass**<br>*Replace* Materials ....295.00    Labor..........51.10<br>*Remove* .......................    Labor..........12.70 | ea | $12.70 | $346.10 | $358.80 |
| **Shower door, brass finish trim**<br>*Replace* Materials ....445.00    Labor..........51.10<br>*Remove* .......................    Labor..........12.70 | ea | $12.70 | $496.10 | $508.80 |

| Item Description | Unit | Remove | Replace | Total | RELATED ITEMS |
|---|---|---|---|---|---|
| **Shower doors, brass trim with etched glass**<br>*Replace* Materials ....495.00    Labor..........51.10<br>*Remove* .................    Labor..........12.70 | ea | $12.70 | $546.10 | $558.80 | Bathroom Hardware......41<br>Cleaning ......................64 |
| **Remove shower door for work, then reinstall**<br>*Replace* ......................    Labor..........69.90 | ea | — | $69.90 | $69.90 | ◁ remove & reinstall |
| **10 gallon gas water heater**<br>*Replace* Materials....280.00    Labor ..........142.00<br>*Remove* .................    Labor ..........29.10 | ea | $29.10 | $422.00 | $451.10 | ◀ **GAS WATER HEATER** |
| **20 gallon gas water heater**<br>*Replace* Materials....305.00    Labor ..........142.00<br>*Remove* .................    Labor ..........29.10 | ea | $29.10 | $447.00 | $476.10 | |
| **30 gallon gas water heater**<br>*Replace* Materials....345.00    Labor ..........142.00<br>*Remove* .................    Labor ..........29.10 | ea | $29.10 | $487.00 | $516.10 | |
| **40 gallon gas water heater**<br>*Replace* Materials....360.00    Labor ..........142.00<br>*Remove* .................    Labor ..........29.10 | ea | $29.10 | $502.00 | $531.10 | |
| **50 gallon gas water heater**<br>*Replace* Materials.....415.00    Labor ..........142.00<br>*Remove* .................    Labor ..........29.10 | ea | $29.10 | $557.00 | $586.10 | |
| **75 gallon gas water heater**<br>*Replace* Materials....740.00    Labor ..........142.00<br>*Remove* .................    Labor ..........29.10 | ea | $29.10 | $882.00 | $911.10 | |
| **Remove gas water heater for work, then reinstall**<br>*Replace* ......................    Labor..........213.00 | ea | — | $213.00 | $213.00 | ◁ remove & reinstall |
| **10 gallon electric water heater**<br>*Replace* Materials....220.00    Labor..........133.00<br>*Remove* .................    Labor..........27.80 | ea | $27.80 | $353.00 | $380.80 | ◀ **ELECTRIC WATER HEATER** |
| **20 gallon electric water heater**<br>*Replace* Materials....280.00    Labor..........133.00<br>*Remove* .................    Labor..........27.80 | ea | $27.80 | $413.00 | $440.80 | |
| **30 gallon electric water heater**<br>*Replace* Materials....320.00    Labor..........133.00<br>*Remove* .................    Labor..........27.80 | ea | $27.80 | $453.00 | $480.80 | |
| **40 gallon electric water heater**<br>*Replace* Materials....340.00    Labor..........133.00<br>*Remove* .................    Labor..........27.80 | ea | $27.80 | $473.00 | $500.80 | |
| **50 gallon electric water heater**<br>*Replace* Materials....405.00    Labor..........133.00<br>*Remove* .................    Labor..........27.80 | ea | $27.80 | $538.00 | $565.80 | |
| **75 gallon electric water heater**<br>*Replace* Materials....750.00    Labor..........133.00<br>*Remove* .................    Labor..........27.80 | ea | $27.80 | $883.00 | $910.80 | |
| **Replace element in electric water heater**<br>*Replace* Materials......80.00    Labor..........54.50 | ea | — | $134.50 | $134.50 | ◁ replace element |
| **Remove electric water heater for work, then reinstall**<br>*Replace* ......................    Labor........203.00 | ea | — | $203.00 | $203.00 | |

| | Item Description | Unit | Remove | Replace | Total |
|---|---|---|---|---|---|
| **WATER SOFTENER** ▶ | **Water softener, automatic two tank up to 30 grains per gallon**<br>*Replace* Materials....500.00     Labor.........142.00<br>*Remove* ......................     Labor...........10.70 | ea | $10.70 | $642.00 | $652.70 |
| | **Water softener, automatic two tank up to 100 grains per gallon**<br>*Replace* Materials...1100.00     Labor.........142.00<br>*Remove* ......................     Labor...........10.70 | ea | $10.70 | $1,242.00 | $1,252.70 |
| remove & reinstall ▷ | **Remove water softener for work, then reinstall**<br>*Replace* ......................     Labor.........224.00 | ea | — | $224.00 | $224.00 |
| **SEPTIC TANK** ▶<br>**WITH LEACH FIELD**<br>*Includes mobilization, excavation, backfill, gravel, crushed stone, pipe, couplings, connectors, building paper, tank, and distribution box.* | **1,000 gallon concrete septic tank with 1,000 sf leach field**<br>*Replace* Materials..2300.00     Labor.......3310.00 | ea | — | $5,610.00 | $5,610.00 |
| | **1,000 gallon concrete septic tank with 2,000 sf leach field**<br>*Replace* Materials..3300.00     Labor.......4770.00 | ea | — | $8,070.00 | $8,070.00 |
| | **1,250 gallon concrete septic tank with 1,000 sf leach field**<br>*Replace* Materials...2450.00     Labor......3400.00 | ea | — | $5,850.00 | $5,850.00 |
| | **1,250 gallon concrete septic tank with 2,000 sf leach field**<br>*Replace* Materials ..3450.00     Labor ......4860.00 | ea | — | $8,310.00 | $8,310.00 |
| | **1,500 gallon concrete septic tank with 1,000 sf leach field**<br>*Replace* Materials ..2600.00     Labor ......3440.00 | ea | — | $6,040.00 | $6,040.00 |
| | **1,500 gallon concrete septic tank with 2,000 sf leach field**<br>*Replace* Materials ..3600.00     Labor.......4900.00 | ea | — | $8,500.00 | $8,500.00 |
| | **1,000 gallon fiberglass septic tank with 1,000 sf leach field**<br>*Replace* Materials ..2250.00     Labor ......3300.00 | ea | — | $5,550.00 | $5,550.00 |
| | **1,000 gallon fiberglass septic tank with 2,000 sf leach field**<br>*Replace* Materials ..3200.00     Labor ......4770.00 | ea | — | $7,970.00 | $7,970.00 |
| | **1,250 gallon fiberglass septic tank with 1,000 sf leach field**<br>*Replace* Materials ..2400.00     Labor ......3380.00 | ea | — | $5,780.00 | $5,780.00 |
| | **1,250 gallon fiberglass septic tank with 2,000 sf leach field**<br>*Replace* Materials ..3350.00     Labor ......4860.00 | ea | — | $8,210.00 | $8,210.00 |
| | **1,500 gallon fiberglass septic tank with 1,000 sf leach field**<br>*Replace* Materials ..2550.00     Labor ......3430.00 | ea | — | $5,980.00 | $5,980.00 |
| | **1,500 gallon fiberglass septic tank with 2,000 sf leach field**<br>*Replace* Materials ..3500.00     Labor.......4900.00 | ea | — | $8,400.00 | $8,400.00 |
| | **1,000 gallon polyethylene septic tank with 1,000 sf leach field**<br>*Replace* Materials ..2050.00     Labor ......3300.00 | ea | — | $5,350.00 | $5,350.00 |
| | **1,000 gallon polyethylene septic tank with 2,000 sf leach field**<br>*Replace* Materials ..3050.00     Labor.......4770.00 | ea | — | $7,820.00 | $7,820.00 |
| | **1,250 gallon polyethylene septic tank with 1,000 sf leach field**<br>*Replace* Materials ..2200.00     Labor ......3380.00 | ea | — | $5,580.00 | $5,580.00 |
| | **1,250 gallon polyethylene septic tank with 2,000 sf leach field**<br>*Replace* Materials ..3200.00     Labor ......4860.00 | ea | — | $8,060.00 | $8,060.00 |

| Item Description | Unit | Remove | Replace | Total |
|---|---|---|---|---|
| **1,500 gallon polyethylene septic tank with 1,000 sf leach field**<br>*Replace* Materials ..2350.00    Labor ......3430.00 | ea | — | $5,780.00 | $5,780.00 |
| **1,500 gallon polyethylene septic tank with 2,000 sf leach field**<br>*Replace* Materials ..3350.00    Labor......4900.00 | ea | — | $8,250.00 | $8,250.00 |
| **Submersible 1/2 hp water pump**<br>*Replace* Materials ....485.00   Labor........235.00<br>*Remove* .................   Labor..........45.90 | ea | $45.90 | $720.00 | $765.90 |
| **Submersible 3/4 hp water pump**<br>*Replace* Materials ....530.00   Labor........235.00<br>*Remove* .................   Labor..........45.90 | ea | $45.90 | $765.00 | $810.90 |
| **Submersible 1 hp water pump**<br>*Replace* Materials ....540.00   Labor........235.00<br>*Remove* .................   Labor..........45.90 | ea | $45.90 | $775.00 | $820.90 |
| **Submersible 1-1/2 hp water pump**<br>*Replace* Materials .....670.00   Labor........235.00<br>*Remove* .................   Labor..........45.90 | ea | $45.90 | $905.00 | $950.90 |
| **Submersible 2 hp water pump**<br>*Replace* Materials ....740.00   Labor........235.00<br>*Remove* .................   Labor..........45.90 | ea | $45.90 | $975.00 | $1,020.90 |
| **Submersible 3 hp water pump**<br>*Replace* Materials ....960.00   Labor........235.00<br>*Remove* .................   Labor..........45.90 | ea | $45.90 | $1,195.00 | $1,240.90 |
| **Submersible 5 hp water pump**<br>*Replace* Materials ...1100.00   Labor........235.00<br>*Remove* .................   Labor..........45.90 | ea | $45.90 | $1,335.00 | $1,380.90 |
| **Remove submersible pump for work then reinstall**<br>*Replace* .................   Labor........328.00 | ea | — | $328.00 | $328.00 |
| **1/4 hp automatic plastic sump pump**<br>*Replace* Materials ....180.00   Labor..........59.20<br>*Remove* .................   Labor..........14.70 | ea | $14.70 | $239.20 | $253.90 |
| **1/3 hp automatic plastic sump pump**<br>*Replace* Materials ....220.00   Labor..........59.20<br>*Remove* .................   Labor..........14.70 | ea | $14.70 | $279.20 | $293.90 |
| **1/2 hp automatic plastic sump pump**<br>*Replace* Materials ....285.00   Labor..........59.20<br>*Remove* .................   Labor..........14.70 | ea | $14.70 | $344.20 | $358.90 |
| **1/4 hp automatic cast-iron sump pump**<br>*Replace* Materials ....220.00   Labor..........59.20<br>*Remove* .................   Labor..........14.70 | ea | $14.70 | $279.20 | $293.90 |
| **1/3 hp automatic cast-iron sump pump**<br>*Replace* Materials ....250.00   Labor..........59.20<br>*Remove* .................   Labor..........14.70 | ea | $14.70 | $309.20 | $323.90 |
| **1/2 hp automatic cast-iron sump pump**<br>*Replace* Materials ....320.00   Labor..........59.20<br>*Remove* .................   Labor..........14.70 | ea | $14.70 | $379.20 | $393.90 |
| **Remove sump pump for work, then reinstall**<br>*Replace* .................   Labor.........104.00 | ea | — | $104.00 | $104.00 |

**RELATED ITEMS**
Bathroom Hardware......41
Cleaning ......................64

◄ **SUBMERSIBLE WATER PUMP** *Includes wiring and placement for well up to 100' deep.*

◁ remove & reinstall

◄ **SUMP PUMP** *Basement style installation, includes up to 45 lf 1-1/2" PVC pipe and wiring hookup. Does not include rough electrical.*

◁ remove & reinstall

| Item Description | Unit | Remove | Replace | Total |
|---|---|---|---|---|
| **Antique style sink faucet, standard grade**<br>*Replace* Materials.....160.00    Labor ..........23.70<br>*Remove* .....................    Labor ............9.35 | ea | $9.35 | $183.70 | $193.05 |
| **Antique style sink faucet, high grade**<br>*Replace* Materials ....270.00    Labor ..........23.70<br>*Remove* .....................    Labor ............9.35 | ea | $9.35 | $293.70 | $303.05 |
| **Antique style sink faucet, deluxe grade**<br>*Replace* Materials ....365.00    Labor ..........23.70<br>*Remove* .....................    Labor ............9.35 | ea | $9.35 | $388.70 | $398.05 |
| **Antique style sink faucet, custom grade**<br>*Replace* Materials ....535.00    Labor ..........23.70<br>*Remove* .....................    Labor ............9.35 | ea | $9.35 | $558.70 | $568.05 |
| **Antique style sink faucet, custom deluxe grade**<br>*Replace* Materials ....760.00    Labor ..........23.70<br>*Remove* .....................    Labor ............9.35 | ea | $9.35 | $783.70 | $793.05 |
| **Remove antique style sink faucet for work, then reinstall**<br>*Replace* .....................    Labor..........35.50 | ea | — | $35.50 | $35.50 |
| **Claw-foot bathtub faucet, economy grade**<br>*Replace* Materials ....205.00    Labor ..........38.00<br>*Remove* .....................    Labor ............9.46 | ea | $9.46 | $243.00 | $252.46 |
| **Claw-foot bathtub faucet, standard grade**<br>*Replace* Materials ....350.00    Labor ..........38.00<br>*Remove* .....................    Labor ............9.46 | ea | $9.46 | $388.00 | $397.46 |
| **Claw-foot bathtub faucet, high grade**<br>*Replace* Materials .....470.00    Labor ..........38.00<br>*Remove* .....................    Labor ............9.46 | ea | $9.46 | $508.00 | $517.46 |
| **Claw-foot bathtub faucet, deluxe grade**<br>*Replace* Materials ....690.00    Labor ..........38.00<br>*Remove* .....................    Labor ............9.46 | ea | $9.46 | $728.00 | $737.46 |
| **Claw-foot bathtub faucet, custom grade**<br>*Replace* Materials ....980.00    Labor ..........38.00<br>*Remove* .....................    Labor ............9.46 | ea | $9.46 | $1,018.00 | $1,027.46 |
| **Remove claw-foot bathtub faucet for work, then reinstall**<br>*Replace* .....................    Labor ..........48.60 | ea | — | $48.60 | $48.60 |
| **Claw-foot bathtub faucet with hand-held shower, standard grade**<br>*Replace* Materials ....320.00    Labor...........42.20<br>*Remove* .....................    Labor ............9.48 | ea | $9.48 | $362.20 | $371.68 |
| **Claw-foot bathtub faucet with hand-held shower, high grade**<br>*Replace* Materials ....545.00    Labor...........42.20<br>*Remove* .....................    Labor ............9.48 | ea | $9.48 | $587.20 | $596.68 |
| **Claw-foot bathtub faucet with hand-held shower, deluxe grade**<br>*Replace* Materials ....730.00    Labor...........42.20<br>*Remove* .....................    Labor ............9.48 | ea | $9.48 | $772.20 | $781.68 |
| **Claw-foot bathtub faucet with hand-held shower, custom grade**<br>*Replace* Materials ..1050.00    Labor...........42.20<br>*Remove* .....................    Labor ............9.48 | ea | $9.48 | $1,092.20 | $1,101.68 |

**ANTIQUE STYLE ▶ SINK FAUCET**
*See page 369 for information about faucet quality. Antique style faucets are usually brass, chrome over brass, or nickel over brass with ornate detail. Often used in homes that are not historical. For standard faucets see page 368 and 369.*

remove & reinstall ▷

**ANTIQUE STYLE ▶ BATHTUB FAUCET**
*See page 369 for information about faucet quality. Antique style are usually brass, chrome over brass, or nickel over brass with ornate detail. Often used in homes that are not historical. For standard faucets see page 370.*

remove & reinstall ▷

**ANTIQUE STYLE ▶ BATHTUB FAUCET WITH HAND–HELD SHOWER**
*See page 369 for information about faucet quality. Antique style faucets are usually brass, chrome over brass, or nickel over brass with ornate detail. Often used in homes that are not historical. For standard faucets see page 370.*

| Item Description | Unit | Remove | Replace | Total | |
|---|---|---|---|---|---|
| Remove claw-foot bathtub faucet with hand-held shower for work, then reinstall | ea | — | $50.70 | $50.70 | ◁ remove & reinstall |
| Replace ......... Labor ........50.70 | | | | | |
| Claw-foot bathtub faucet with shower conversion, standard grade | ea | $13.20 | $502.40 | $515.60 | ◄ ANTIQUE STYLE BATHTUB FAUCET WITH SHOWER CONVERSION |
| Replace Materials.....410.00 Labor .........92.40 | | | | | With exposed shower supply pipe and circular shower curtain rod. See standard faucets on page 370. |
| Remove ................... Labor .........13.20 | | | | | |
| Claw-foot bathtub faucet with shower conversion, high grade | ea | $13.20 | $682.40 | $695.60 | |
| Replace Materials ....590.00 Labor .........92.40 | | | | | |
| Remove ................... Labor .........13.20 | | | | | |
| Claw-foot bathtub faucet with shower conversion, deluxe grade | ea | $13.20 | $812.40 | $825.60 | |
| Replace Materials ....720.00 Labor .........92.40 | | | | | |
| Remove ................... Labor .........13.20 | | | | | |
| Claw-foot bathtub faucet with shower conversion, custom grade | ea | $13.20 | $1,112.40 | $1,125.60 | |
| Replace Materials ..1020.00 Labor .........92.40 | | | | | |
| Remove ................... Labor.........13.20 | | | | | |
| Remove claw-foot bathtub faucet with shower conversion, for work, then reinstall | ea | — | $133.00 | $133.00 | |
| Replace ......... Labor.........133.00 | | | | | |
| Claw-foot bathtub supply lines, chrome-plated brass | ea | $11.20 | $207.70 | $218.90 | ◄ ANTIQUE STYLE TUB SUPPLY LINES |
| Replace Materials.....160.00 Labor........47.70 | | | | | Exposed lines used on antique style bathtubs. |
| Remove ................... Labor .........11.20 | | | | | |
| Claw-foot bathtub supply lines, brass | ea | $11.20 | $187.70 | $198.90 | |
| Replace Materials ....140.00 Labor........47.70 | | | | | |
| Remove ................... Labor...........11.20 | | | | | |
| Claw-foot bathtub drain, chrome-plated brass | ea | $10.60 | $199.00 | $209.60 | ◄ ANTIQUE STYLE BATHTUB DRAIN |
| Replace Materials ....150.00 Labor........49.00 | | | | | |
| Remove ................... Labor...........10.60 | | | | | |
| Claw-foot bathtub drain, brass | ea | $10.60 | $169.00 | $179.60 | |
| Replace Materials.....120.00 Labor...........49.00 | | | | | |
| Remove ................... Labor...........10.60 | | | | | |
| Free-standing water feeds for claw-foot or slipper bathtub, chrome-plated brass | ea | $11.40 | $282.00 | $293.40 | ◄ ANTIQUE STYLE FREE-STANDING SUPPLY LINES |
| Replace Materials....230.00 Labor...........52.00 | | | | | Exposed lines used on antique style bathtubs that do not rely on the bathtub for support. |
| Remove ................... Labor ...........11.40 | | | | | |
| Free-standing water feeds for claw-foot or slipper bathtub, brass | ea | $11.40 | $327.00 | $338.40 | |
| Replace Materials ....275.00 Labor...........52.00 | | | | | |
| Remove ................... Labor ...........11.40 | | | | | |
| Pedestal sink, economy grade | ea | $12.70 | $412.00 | $424.70 | ◄ PEDESTAL SINK Antique or contemporary style. See standard sinks on page 371. |
| Replace Materials....360.00 Labor...........52.00 | | | | | |
| Remove ................... Labor...........12.70 | | | | | |
| Pedestal sink, standard grade | ea | $12.70 | $472.00 | $484.70 | |
| Replace Materials ....420.00 Labor...........52.00 | | | | | |
| Remove ................... Labor........12.70 | | | | | |
| Pedestal sink, high grade | ea | $12.70 | $612.00 | $624.70 | |
| Replace Materials....560.00 Labor...........52.00 | | | | | |
| Remove ................... Labor........12.70 | | | | | |
| Pedestal sink, deluxe grade | ea | $12.70 | $1,022.00 | $1,034.70 | |
| Replace Materials ....970.00 Labor...........52.00 | | | | | |
| Remove ................... Labor........12.70 | | | | | |

**RELATED ITEMS**
Bathroom Hardware......41
Cleaning ....................64

| | Item Description | Unit | Remove | Replace | Total |
|---|---|---|---|---|---|
| **PEDESTAL SINK ▶**<br>*continued* | **Pedestal sink, custom grade**<br>*Replace* Materials ..1400.00    Labor............52.00<br>*Remove* ......................    Labor...........12.70 | ea | $12.70 | $1,452.00 | $1,464.70 |
| | **Pedestal sink, custom deluxe grade**<br>*Replace* Materials ..1800.00    Labor............52.00<br>*Remove* ......................    Labor...........12.70 | ea | $12.70 | $1,852.00 | $1,864.70 |
| remove & reinstall ▷ | **Remove pedestal sink for work, then reinstall**<br>*Replace* ......................    Labor ..........90.70 | ea | — | $90.70 | $90.70 |
| **ANTIQUE STYLE ▶**<br>**PILLBOX TOILET**<br>*Round tank with beaded rim. See standard toilets on page 376.* | **Antique style pillbox toilet**<br>*Replace* Materials...1750.00    Labor...........94.60<br>*Remove* ......................    Labor ..........11.20 | ea | $11.20 | $1,844.60 | $1,855.80 |
| | **Remove antique style pillbox toilet for work, then reinstall**<br>*Replace* ......................    Labor ..........147.00 | ea | — | $147.00 | $147.00 |
| **ANTIQUE STYLE ▶**<br>**LOW-TANK TOILET**<br>*Identifiable by pipe (usually brass) running from tank to bowl. See standard toilets on page 376.* | **Antique style low-tank toilet with porcelain tank**<br>*Replace* Materials....920.00    Labor...........94.60<br>*Remove* ......................    Labor ..........11.20 | ea | $11.20 | $1,014.60 | $1,025.80 |
| | **Antique style low-tank toilet with oak tank**<br>*Replace* Materials.....765.00    Labor...........94.60<br>*Remove* ......................    Labor ..........11.20 | ea | $11.20 | $859.60 | $870.80 |
| | **Remove antique style low-tank toilet for work, then reinstall**<br>*Replace* Materials........1.75    Labor .........147.00 | ea | — | $148.75 | $148.75 |
| **ANTIQUE STYLE ▶**<br>**HIGH-TANK TOILET**<br>*Tank mounted high on wall. Includes brass pipe and connectors, pull chain, hardwood toilet seat, brass tank support brackets. Wood tanks include plastic liner.* | **Antique style high-tank toilet with porcelain tank**<br>*Replace* Materials ...1150.00    Labor...........112.00<br>*Remove* ......................    Labor ..........15.80 | ea | $15.80 | $1,262.00 | $1,277.80 |
| | **Antique style high-tank toilet with oak tank**<br>*Replace* Materials ....995.00    Labor...........112.00<br>*Remove* ......................    Labor ..........15.80 | ea | $15.80 | $1,107.00 | $1,122.80 |
| | **Remove antique style high-tank toilet for work, then reinstall**<br>*Replace* Materials........1.68    Labor .........158.00 | ea | — | $159.75 | $159.75 |
| **ANTIQUE BATHTUB ▶**<br>*Claw-foot or ball-foot. Does not include supply lines or faucet. Includes $90 for crating and $260 for shipping. See standard bathtubs on page 377.* | **60" antique claw-foot or ball-foot cast-iron bathtub (as is condition)**<br>*Replace* Materials.....670.00    Labor...........224.00<br>*Remove* ......................    Labor ..........47.70 | ea | $47.70 | $894.00 | $941.70 |
| | **66" antique claw-foot or ball-foot cast-iron bathtub (as is condition)**<br>*Replace* Materials ....740.00    Labor...........237.00<br>*Remove* ......................    Labor ..........47.70 | ea | $47.70 | $977.00 | $1,024.70 |
| **REFINISHED ▶**<br>**ANTIQUE BATHTUB**<br>*Claw-foot or ball-foot. Interior and lip refinished exterior surfaces painted. Does not include visible supply lines or faucet. Includes $90 for crating and $260 for shipping. See standard bathtubs on page 377.* | **48" refinished antique claw-foot or ball-foot cast-iron bathtub**<br>*Replace* Materials ..2050.00    Labor...........203.00<br>*Remove* ......................    Labor ..........47.70 | ea | $47.70 | $2,253.00 | $2,300.70 |
| | **52" refinished antique claw-foot or ball-foot cast-iron bathtub**<br>*Replace* Materials ..1950.00    Labor ..........213.00<br>*Remove* ......................    Labor...........47.70 | ea | $47.70 | $2,163.00 | $2,210.70 |
| | **60" refinished antique claw-foot or ball-foot cast-iron bathtub**<br>*Replace* Materials ..1750.00    Labor...........224.00<br>*Remove* ......................    Labor...........47.70 | ea | $47.70 | $1,974.00 | $2,021.70 |

| Item Description | Unit | Remove | Replace | Total |
|---|---|---|---|---|
| **66" refinished antique claw-foot or ball-foot cast-iron bathtub**<br>*Replace* Materials ..1800.00  Labor.........237.00<br>*Remove* ..................  Labor.........47.70 | ea | $47.70 | $2,037.00 | $2,084.70 |
| **60" antique reproduction claw-foot or ball-foot cast-iron bathtub**<br>*Replace* Materials ..1400.00  Labor.........224.00<br>*Remove* ..................  Labor.........47.70 | ea | $47.70 | $1,624.00 | $1,671.70 |
| **66" antique reproduction claw-foot or ball-foot cast-iron bathtub**<br>*Replace* Materials ..1750.00  Labor.........237.00<br>*Remove* ..................  Labor.........47.70 | ea | $47.70 | $1,987.00 | $2,034.70 |
| **60" antique reproduction fiberglass claw-foot or ball-foot bathtub**<br>*Replace* Materials ..1950.00  Labor.........133.00<br>*Remove* ..................  Labor.........38.00 | ea | $38.00 | $2,083.00 | $2,121.00 |
| **66" antique reproduction fiberglass claw-foot or ball-foot bathtub**<br>*Replace* Materials ..2650.00  Labor.........142.00<br>*Remove* ..................  Labor.........38.00 | ea | $38.00 | $2,792.00 | $2,830.00 |
| **Remove antique (or antique style) bathtub for work, then reinstall**<br>*Replace* ..................  Labor.........237.00 | ea | — | $237.00 | $237.00 |
| **60" antique cast-iron slipper bathtub**<br>*Replace* Materials ..2500.00  Labor.........224.00<br>*Remove* ..................  Labor.........47.70 | ea | $47.70 | $2,724.00 | $2,771.70 |
| **66" antique reproduction fiberglass slipper bathtub**<br>*Replace* Materials ..4600.00  Labor.........237.00<br>*Remove* ..................  Labor.........38.00 | ea | $38.00 | $4,837.00 | $4,875.00 |
| **Add for solid brass legs**<br>*Replace* Materials ......80.00 | ea | — | $80.00 | $80.00 |
| **Add for brass-plated legs**<br>*Replace* Materials ......50.00 | ea | — | $50.00 | $50.00 |
| **Add for oak trim around lip of antique bathtub**<br>*Replace* Materials ..1400.00 | ea | — | $1,400.00 | $1,400.00 |

**RELATED ITEMS**

Bathroom Hardware......41
Cleaning .......................64

◄ **REPRODUCTION ANTIQUE BATHTUB**
*Claw-foot or ball-foot. New tubs built in the antique style. Does not include supply lines or faucet. Includes $90 for crating and $260 for shipping. ($150 shipping for fiberglass tubs.) See standard tubs on page 377.*

*slipper bathtub* △

◄ **REMOVE ANTIQUE BATHTUB & REINSTALL**

◄ **REPRODUCTION SLIPPER BATHTUB**
*Claw-foot or ball-foot. Does not include supply lines or faucet. Includes $90 for crating and $260 for shipping. ($150 shipping for fiberglass tubs.) See standard tubs on page 377.*

◄ **ADDITIONAL ANTIQUE BATHTUB COSTS**

# TIME & MATERIAL CHARTS *(selected items)*

## Plumbing Materials

| DESCRIPTION | UNIT PRICE |
|---|---|
| **Black steel pipe** | $1.07 lf |
| 1/2" pipe | $1.28 lf |
| 3/4" pipe | $1.81 lf |
| 1" pipe | $5.77 lf |
| 2" pipe | |
| **Brass pipe** | $3.65 lf |
| 1/2" pipe | $4.85 lf |
| 3/4" pipe | $7.93 lf |
| 1" pipe | $12.40 lf |
| 2" pipe | |
| **Type K copper pipe** | $1.98 lf |
| 1/2" pipe | $2.63 lf |
| 3/4" pipe | $3.41 lf |
| 1" pipe | $8.26 lf |
| 2" pipe | |

. . . More ➤

## Plumbing Materials *continued*

| DESCRIPTION | UNIT PRICE |
|---|---|
| **Type L copper pipe** | |
| 1/2" pipe | $1.17 lf |
| 3/4" pipe | $1.93 lf |
| 1" pipe | $2.63 lf |
| 2" pipe | $6.38 lf |
| **Type M copper pipe** | |
| 1/2" pipe | $.90 lf |
| 3/4" pipe | $1.48 lf |
| 1" pipe | $2.00 lf |
| **Galvanized steel pipe** | |
| 1/2" pipe | $1.31 lf |
| 3/4" pipe | $1.56 lf |
| 1" pipe | $2.21 lf |
| 2" pipe | $7.05 lf |
| **CPVC pipe** | |
| 1/2" pipe | $.73 lf |
| 3/4" pipe | $.90 lf |
| 1" pipe | $1.08 lf |
| **PVC pipe** | |
| 1/2" pipe | $.46 lf |
| 3/4" pipe | $.49 lf |
| 1" pipe | $.55 lf |
| 1-1/2" pipe | $.73 lf |
| 2" pipe | $.89 lf |
| 3" pipe | $1.28 lf |
| 4" pipe | $1.68 lf |
| 5" pipe | $2.41 lf |
| 6" pipe | $2.87 lf |
| **Cast-iron pipe** | |
| 2" pipe | $4.72 lf |
| 3" pipe | $6.48 lf |
| 4" pipe | $9.14 lf |
| 5" pipe | $26.20 lf |
| 6" pipe | $33.50 lf |
| **No-hub cast-iron pipe** | |
| 2" pipe | $6.53 lf |
| 3" pipe | $8.36 lf |
| 4" pipe | $10.80 lf |
| 5" pipe | $15.80 lf |

## Plumbing Labor

| LABORER | BASE WAGE | PAID LEAVE | TRUE WAGE | FICA | FUTA | WORKER'S COMP. | UNEMPLOY. INSUR. | HEALTH INSUR. | RETIRE (401k) | LIABILITY INSUR. | COST PER HOUR |
|---|---|---|---|---|---|---|---|---|---|---|---|
| Plumber | $24.90 | 1.94 | $26.84 | 2.05 | .21 | 4.30 | 2.34 | 2.54 | .81 | 3.49 | $42.60 |
| Plumber's helper | $20.90 | 1.63 | $22.53 | 1.72 | .18 | 3.61 | 1.96 | 2.54 | .68 | 2.93 | $36.20 |
| Demolition laborer | $13.40 | 1.05 | $14.45 | 1.11 | .12 | 4.44 | 1.26 | 2.54 | .43 | 1.88 | $26.20 |

**Paid Leave** is calculated based on two weeks paid vacation, one week sick leave, and seven paid holidays. Employer's matching portion of **FICA** is 7.65 percent. **FUTA** (Federal Unemployment) is .8 percent. **Worker's compensation** for the plumbing trade was calculated using a national average of 16.02 percent. **Unemployment insurance** was calculated using a national average of 8.7 percent. **Health insurance** was calculated based on a projected national average for 2001 of $505 per employee (and family when applicable) per month. Employer pays 80 percent for a per month cost of $404 per employee. **Retirement** is based on a 401(k) retirement program with employer matching of 50 percent. Employee contributions to the 401(k) plan are an average of 6 percent of the true wage. **Liability insurance** is based on a national average of 12.9 percent.

# Plumbing Labor Productivity

| WORK DESCRIPTION | LABORER | COST PER HOUR | PRODUCTIVITY | UNIT PRICE |
|---|---|---|---|---|
| **Demolition** | | | | |
| remove faucet | demolition laborer | $26.20 | .357 | $9.35 ea |
| remove bathroom sink | demolition laborer | $26.20 | .366 | $9.59 ea |
| remove kitchen or laundry sink | demolition laborer | $26.20 | .369 | $9.67 ea |
| remove wet bar sink | demolition laborer | $26.20 | .358 | $9.38 ea |
| remove toilet | demolition laborer | $26.20 | .346 | $9.07 ea |
| remove fiberglass bathtub | demolition laborer | $26.20 | 1.02 | $26.70 ea |
| remove cast-iron or steel bathtub | demolition laborer | $26.20 | 1.61 | $42.20 |
| remove fiberglass bathtub with whirlpool jets | demolition laborer | $26.20 | 1.45 | $38.00 |
| remove cast-iron or steel tub with whirlpool jets | demolition laborer | $26.20 | 2.13 | $55.80 ea |
| remove glass shower | demolition laborer | $26.20 | 1.22 | $32.00 |
| remove bathtub and shower combination | demolition laborer | $26.20 | 1.69 | $44.30 ea |
| remove shower stall | demolition laborer | $26.20 | 1.22 | $32.00 ea |
| remove bathtub surround | demolition laborer | $26.20 | .893 | $23.40 ea |
| remove sliding glass bathtub door | demolition laborer | $26.20 | .515 | $13.50 ea |
| remove shower door | demolition laborer | $26.20 | .485 | $12.70 ea |
| remove gas water heater | demolition laborer | $26.20 | 1.11 | $29.10 ea |
| remove electric water heater | demolition laborer | $26.20 | 1.06 | $27.80 ea |
| remove water softener | demolition laborer | $26.20 | .408 | $10.70 ea |
| remove submersible pump | demolition laborer | $26.20 | 1.75 | $45.90 ea |
| remove sump pump | demolition laborer | $26.20 | .562 | $14.70 ea |
| remove antique style sink faucet | demolition laborer | $26.20 | .357 | $9.35 ea |
| remove antique style bathtub faucet | demolition laborer | $26.20 | .361 | $9.46 ea |
| remove claw-foot bathtub supply lines | demolition laborer | $26.20 | .429 | $11.20 ea |
| remove claw-foot bathtub drain | demolition laborer | $26.20 | .403 | $10.60 ea |
| remove free-standing water feeds | demolition laborer | $26.20 | .437 | $11.40 ea |
| remove pedestal sink | demolition laborer | $26.20 | .483 | $12.70 ea |
| remove antique style pillbox toilet | demolition laborer | $26.20 | .429 | $11.20 ea |
| remove antique style low-tank toilet | demolition laborer | $26.20 | .429 | $11.20 ea |
| remove antique style high-tank toilet | demolition laborer | $26.20 | .602 | $15.80 ea |
| remove cast-iron claw-foot bathtub | demolition laborer | $26.20 | 1.82 | $47.70 ea |
| remove fiberglass claw-foot bathtub | demolition laborer | $26.20 | 1.45 | $38.00 ea |
| **Install field threaded pipe** | | | | |
| 1/2" | plumber | $42.60 | .127 | $5.41 lf |
| 3/4" | plumber | $42.60 | .136 | $5.79 lf |
| 1" | plumber | $42.60 | .158 | $6.73 lf |
| 2" | plumber | $42.60 | .231 | $9.84 lf |
| **Install copper pipe** | | | | |
| 1/2" | plumber | $42.60 | .104 | $4.43 lf |
| 3/4" | plumber | $42.60 | .109 | $4.64 lf |
| 1" | plumber | $42.60 | .122 | $5.20 lf |
| 2" | plumber | $42.60 | .202 | $8.61 lf |
| **Install plastic pipe** | | | | |
| 1/2" | plumber | $42.60 | .153 | $6.52 lf |
| 3/4" | plumber | $42.60 | .162 | $6.90 lf |
| 1" | plumber | $42.60 | .189 | $8.05 lf |
| 2" | plumber | $42.60 | .251 | $10.70 lf |
| 3" | plumber | $42.60 | .281 | $12.00 lf |
| 4" | plumber | $42.60 | .311 | $13.20 lf |
| 5" | plumber | $42.60 | .346 | $14.70 lf |
| 6" | plumber | $42.60 | .380 | $16.20 lf |
| **Install cast-iron pipe** | | | | |
| 2" | plumber | $42.60 | .235 | $10.00 lf |
| 3" | plumber | $42.60 | .248 | $10.60 lf |
| 4" | plumber | $42.60 | .270 | $11.50 lf |
| 5" | plumber | $42.60 | .305 | $13.00 lf |
| 6" | plumber | $42.60 | .317 | $13.50 lf |
| **Install no-hub cast-iron pipe** | | | | |
| 2" | plumber | $42.60 | .210 | $8.95 lf |
| 3" | plumber | $42.60 | .222 | $9.46 lf |
| 4" | plumber | $42.60 | .242 | $10.30 lf |
| 6" | plumber | $42.60 | .283 | $12.10 lf |

*. . . More ➤*

## Plumbing Labor Productivity *continued*

| WORK DESCRIPTION | LABORER | COST PER HOUR | PRODUCTIVITY | UNIT PRICE |
|---|---|---|---|---|
| **Install faucet** | | | | |
| bathroom sink | plumber | $42.60 | .556 | $23.70 ea |
| kitchen sink | plumber | $42.60 | .562 | $23.90 ea |
| laundry sink | plumber | $42.60 | .546 | $23.30 ea |
| shower | plumber | $42.60 | .575 | $24.50 ea |
| bathtub | plumber | $42.60 | .568 | $24.20 ea |
| bathtub with shower | plumber | $42.60 | .606 | $25.80 ea |
| **Install bathroom sink** | | | | |
| wall-hung | plumber | $42.60 | .877 | $37.40 ea |
| self-rimming | plumber | $42.60 | .909 | $38.70 ea |
| under-counter | plumber | $42.60 | .952 | $40.60 ea |
| **Install kitchen sink** | | | | |
| install | plumber | $42.60 | .926 | $39.40 ea |
| **Install laundry sink** | | | | |
| in countertop | plumber | $42.60 | .901 | $38.40 ea |
| on legs or frame | plumber | $42.60 | .833 | $35.50 ea |
| **Install wet bar sink** | | | | |
| self-rimming | plumber | $42.60 | .909 | $38.70 ea |
| under-counter | plumber | $42.60 | 1.14 | $48.60 ea |
| **Install fixtures** | | | | |
| toilet | plumber | $42.60 | 1.33 | $56.70 ea |
| cast-iron or steel bathtub | plumber | $42.60 | 2.94 | $125.00 ea |
| fiberglass bathtub | plumber | $42.60 | 1.79 | $76.30 ea |
| cast-iron or steel bathtub with whirlpool jets | plumber | $42.60 | 4.00 | $170.00 ea |
| fiberglass bathtub with whirlpool jets | plumber | $42.60 | 3.45 | $147.00 ea |
| fiberglass bathtub & shower combination | plumber | $42.60 | 3.23 | $138.00 ea |
| shower stall | plumber | $42.60 | 2.70 | $115.00 ea |
| **Install shower / bathtub door** | | | | |
| sliding bathtub door | plumber | $42.60 | 1.37 | $58.40 ea |
| shower door | plumber | $42.60 | 1.20 | $51.10 ea |
| **Install water heater** | | | | |
| gas | plumber | $42.60 | 3.33 | $142.00 ea |
| electric | plumber | $42.60 | 3.13 | $133.00 ea |
| **Install water softener** | | | | |
| install | plumber | $42.60 | 3.33 | $142.00 ea |
| **Install septic system** | | | | |
| with concrete tank | | | | |
| 1,000 gallon with 1,000 sf leach field | plumber | $42.60 | 77.8 | $3,310.00 ea |
| 1,000 gallon with 2,000 sf leach field | plumber | $42.60 | 112 | $4,770.00 ea |
| with fiberglass tank | | | | |
| 1,000 gallon with 1,000 sf leach field | plumber | $42.60 | 77.5 | $3,300.00 ea |
| 1,000 gallon with 2,000 sf leach field | plumber | $42.60 | 112 | $4,770.00 ea |
| with polyethylene tank | | | | |
| 1,000 gallon with 1,000 sf leach field | plumber | $42.60 | 77.5 | $3,300.00 ea |
| 1,000 gallon with 2,000 sf leach field | plumber | $42.60 | 112 | $4,770.00 ea |
| **Install water pump** | | | | |
| submersible | plumber | $42.60 | 5.52 | $235.00 ea |
| automatic sump | plumber | $42.60 | 1.39 | $59.20 ea |
| **Install claw-foot bathtub faucet** | | | | |
| faucet | plumber | $42.60 | .893 | $38.00 ea |
| faucet with shower conversion | plumber | $42.60 | 2.17 | $92.40 ea |
| **Install pedestal sink** | | | | |
| install | plumber | $42.60 | 1.22 | $52.00 ea |
| **Install antique style toilet** | | | | |
| pillbox or low tank | plumber | $42.60 | 2.22 | $94.60 ea |
| high-tank | plumber | $42.60 | 2.63 | $112.00 ea |
| **Install antique style bathtub** | | | | |
| 52" cast-iron | plumber | $42.60 | 5.00 | $213.00 ea |
| 60" cast-iron | plumber | $42.60 | 5.26 | $224.00 ea |
| 66" cast-iron | plumber | $42.60 | 5.56 | $237.00 ea |
| 60" reproduction fiberglass | plumber | $42.60 | 3.13 | $133.00 ea |
| 66" reproduction fiberglass | plumber | $42.60 | 3.33 | $142.00 ea |

# 30 Retaining Walls

| Item Description | Unit | Remove | Replace | Total | |
|---|---|---|---|---|---|
| **Minimum charge for retaining wall work**<br>*Replace* Materials ....150.00   Labor........96.00   Equipment ........96.80 | ea | — | $342.80 | $342.80 | ◄ **MINIMUM** |
| **Concrete retaining wall**<br>*Replace* Materials........6.86   Labor ..........8.72   Equipment...........2.46<br>*Remove* ..............Labor ..........9.04<br>► Includes 4" perforated pipe drain line at inside base that is set in gravel. | sf | $9.04 | $18.04 | $27.08 | ◄ **CONCRETE**<br>See Masonry, page 296 for brick veneer and page 317 for wall caps and wall coping. |
| **Wood pile retaining wall with wood lagging**<br>*Replace* Materials........5.28   Labor ..........3.65   Equipment...........1.44<br>*Remove* ..............Labor ..........4.85 | sf | $4.85 | $10.37 | $15.22 | ◄ **PILE WITH LAGGING** |
| **Steel pile retaining wall with wood lagging**<br>*Replace* Materials........5.49   Labor ..........3.99   Equipment...........1.44<br>*Remove* ..............Labor ..........5.34 | sf | $5.34 | $10.92 | $16.26 | |
| **Add for anchored tieback**<br>*Replace* Materials ....105.00   Labor ........93.70   Equipment..........28.50<br>*Remove* ..............Labor ........47.70 | ea | $47.70 | $227.20 | $274.90 | ◄ **ANCHORED TIEBACK**<br>For all retaining wall types. |
| **Railroad tie retaining wall with tie tiebacks**<br>*Replace* Materials........5.40   Labor ..........9.37   Equipment...........1.39<br>*Remove* ..............Labor ..........5.24 | sf | $5.24 | $16.16 | $21.40 | ◄ **RAILROAD TIE** |
| **Railroad tie retaining wall without tie tiebacks**<br>*Replace* Materials........4.88   Labor ..........6.41   Equipment...........1.24<br>*Remove* ..............Labor ..........4.95 | sf | $4.95 | $12.53 | $17.48 | |
| **Cedar tie retaining wall with tie tiebacks**<br>*Replace* Materials........6.86   Labor ..........9.60   Equipment...........1.29<br>*Remove* ..............Labor ..........4.93 | sf | $4.93 | $17.75 | $22.68 | ◄ **CEDAR TIE** |
| **Cedar tie retaining wall without tie tiebacks**<br>*Replace* Materials........6.57   Labor ..........6.49   Equipment...........1.20<br>*Remove* ..............Labor ..........4.66 | sf | $4.66 | $14.26 | $18.92 | |
| **Random stone retaining wall, dry set**<br>*Replace* Materials........15.50   Labor ........16.80   Equipment...........1.44<br>*Remove* ..............Labor ........10.10 | sf | $10.10 | $33.74 | $43.84 | ◄ **STONE**<br>Includes 4" perforated pipe drain line at inside base set in gravel. |
| **Random stone retaining wall, mortar set**<br>*Replace* Materials......16.10   Labor ........14.50   Equipment...........1.44<br>*Remove* ..............Labor ........10.10 | sf | $10.10 | $32.04 | $42.14 | |
| **Cut stone retaining wall, dry set**<br>*Replace* Materials......19.60   Labor ........14.30   Equipment...........1.44<br>*Remove* ..............Labor ........10.10 | sf | $10.10 | $35.34 | $45.44 | |
| **Cut stone retaining wall, mortar set**<br>*Replace* Materials......20.20   Labor ........14.10   Equipment...........1.44<br>*Remove* ..............Labor ........10.10 | sf | $10.10 | $35.74 | $45.84 | |
| **Interlocking masonry block retaining wall**<br>*Replace* Materials........9.47   Labor ........12.00   Equipment...........1.44<br>*Remove* ..............Labor ..........8.72 | sf | $8.72 | $22.91 | $31.63 | ◄ **INTERLOCKING BLOCK** |

**RETAINING WALLS**

Retaining walls include excavation and backfill. Measure sf of surface area. Includes sand and/or gravel base and 2' to 3' of walls buried beneath exposed surface.

| Item Description | Unit | Remove | Replace | Total |
|---|---|---|---|---|
| **INTERLOCKING BLOCK** *continued* — **Add for solid cap on interlocking masonry block retaining wall** *Replace* Materials........4.61  Labor...........1.84  ► 4" high by 16" wide by 10" deep. Per lf of wall. | lf | — | $6.45 | $6.45 |
| **Add for knock-out cap on interlocking masonry block retaining wall** *Replace* Materials........5.35  Labor...........1.84  ► Same as above except 3" to 4" back the cap is cut out to about half its thickness to allow soil and vegetation to overlap the top of the wall. Per lf of wall. | lf | — | $7.19 | $7.19 |
| **ADD FOR FABRIC REINFORCEMENT** *One common brand name is called GeoGrid. Fabric ties retaining walls into hillside.* — **Add for 4-1/2' deep reinforced fabric, one row every 2' of wall height** *Replace* Materials........3.47  Labor............27 | sf | — | $3.74 | $3.74 |
| **Add for 4-1/2' deep reinforced fabric, one row every 3' of wall height** *Replace* Materials........2.32  Labor............19 | sf | — | $2.51 | $2.51 |
| **Add for 6' deep reinforced fabric, one row every 2' of wall height** *Replace* Materials........4.21  Labor............27 | sf | — | $4.48 | $4.48 |
| **Add for 6' deep reinforced fabric, one row every 3' of wall height** *Replace* Materials........2.81  Labor............19 | sf | — | $3.00 | $3.00 |
| **SHOTCRETE** ► **Shotcrete slope stabilization with wire mesh (per inch deep)** *Replace* Materials........1.59  Labor...........3.99  Equipment ...........23 | sf | — | $5.81 | $5.81 |

# TIME & MATERIAL CHARTS *(selected items)*

## Retaining Walls Materials

See *Retaining Walls* material prices with the line items and other information in the **QuickFinder** column.

## Retaining Walls Labor

| LABORER | BASE WAGE | PAID LEAVE | TRUE WAGE | FICA | FUTA | WORKER'S COMP. | UNEMPLOY. INSUR. | HEALTH INSUR. | RETIRE (401K) | LIABILITY INSUR. | COST PER HOUR |
|---|---|---|---|---|---|---|---|---|---|---|---|
| Retaining wall installer | $22.20 | 1.73 | $23.93 | 1.83 | .19 | 3.99 | 2.08 | 2.54 | .72 | 3.11 | $38.40 |
| Mason | $23.40 | 1.83 | $25.23 | 1.93 | .20 | 7.50 | 2.20 | 2.54 | .76 | 3.28 | $43.60 |
| Equipment operator | $28.70 | 2.24 | $30.94 | 2.37 | .25 | 5.36 | 2.69 | 2.54 | .93 | 4.02 | $49.10 |
| Demolition laborer | $13.40 | 1.05 | $14.45 | 1.11 | .12 | 4.44 | 1.26 | 2.54 | .43 | 1.88 | $26.20 |

**Paid Leave** is calculated based on two weeks paid vacation, one week sick leave, and seven paid holidays. Employer's matching portion of **FICA** is 7.65 percent. **FUTA** (Federal Unemployment) is .8 percent. **Worker's Compensation** was calculated using a national average of 16.66 percent for the retaining wall installer; 29.74 percent for the mason, and 17.31 percent for the equipment operator. **Unemployment insurance** was calculated using a national average of 8.7 percent. **Health insurance** was calculated based on a projected national average for 2001 of $505 per employee (and family when applicable) per month. Employer pays 80 percent for a per month cost of $404 per employee. **Retirement** is based on a 401(k) retirement program with employer matching of 50 percent. Employee contributions to the 401(k) plan are an average of 6 percent of the true wage. **Liability insurance** is based on a national average of 12.9 percent.

## Retaining Walls Labor Productivity

| WORK DESCRIPTION | LABORER | COST PER HOUR | PRODUCTIVITY | UNIT PRICE |
|---|---|---|---|---|
| **Install retaining wall** | | | | |
| concrete | retaining wall installer | $38.40 | .227 | $8.72 sf |
| railroad tie with tie tiebacks | retaining wall installer | $38.40 | .244 | $9.37 sf |
| railroad tie, no tie tiebacks | retaining wall installer | $38.40 | .167 | 6.41 sf |
| cedar tie with tie tiebacks | retaining wall installer | $38.40 | .250 | $9.60 sf |
| cedar tie, no tie tiebacks | retaining wall installer | $38.40 | .169 | $6.49 sf |
| interlocking masonry block | retaining wall installer | $38.40 | .313 | $12.00 sf |

# 31 .......... *Roofing*

| Item Description | Unit | Remove | Replace | Total | |
|---|---|---|---|---|---|
| **Minimum charge for roofing work**<br>*Replace* Materials......60.00     Labor.........52.40 | ea | — | $112.40 | $112.40 | ◄ **MINIMUM** |
| **Add 35% for steep roofs 6-12 to 8-12 slope** | | | | | ◄ **ADD FOR STEEP & COMPLEX ROOFS** *Cut-up roofs contain four to six intersecting roof lines. Very cut-up roofs contain seven or more.* |
| **Add 50% for steep roofs greater than 8-12 slope** | | | | | |
| **Add 30% for cut-up roof** | | | | | |
| **Add 50% for very cut-up roof** | | | | | |
| **Aluminum shingles, .02" thick, natural finish**<br>*Replace* Materials.....242.00     Labor..........46.30<br>*Remove* ....................     Labor..........27.20 | sq | $27.20 | $288.30 | $315.50 | ◄ **ALUMINUM SHINGLES** *See **Roofing** box on page 394.* |
| **Aluminum shingles, .03" thick, natural finish**<br>*Replace* Materials....263.00     Labor..........46.30<br>*Remove* ....................     Labor..........27.20 | sq | $27.20 | $309.30 | $336.50 | |
| **Add 20% for colored aluminum shingles (all colors)** | | | | | ◁ add for colored finish |
| **Galvanized steel shingles, 26 gauge, natural finish**<br>*Replace* Materials.....179.00     Labor..........48.50<br>*Remove* ....................     Labor..........27.20 | sq | $27.20 | $227.50 | $254.70 | ◄ **GALVANIZED STEEL SHINGLES** *See **Roofing** box on page 394.* |
| **Galvanized steel shingles, 24 gauge, natural finish**<br>*Replace* Materials ....189.00     Labor..........48.50<br>*Remove* ....................     Labor..........27.20 | sq | $27.20 | $237.50 | $264.70 | |
| **Galvanized steel shingles, 22 gauge, natural finish**<br>*Replace* Materials.....211.00     Labor..........48.50<br>*Remove* ....................     Labor..........27.20 | sq | $27.20 | $259.50 | $286.70 | |
| **Add 21% for galvanized steel shingles with baked enamel factory finish** | | | | | ◁ add for colored finish |
| **Add 10% for metal shingles with 1" polystyrene insulation** | | | | | ◁ add for insulation |
| **Minimum charge for metal shingle roof repair**<br>*Replace* Materials......40.00     Labor..........87.40 | ea | — | $127.40 | $127.40 | ◄ **MINIMUM METAL SHINGLES** |
| **20 year asphalt shingles (210 to 230 lb)**<br>*Replace* Materials......38.30     Labor..........54.20<br>*Remove* ....................     Labor..........26.70 | sq | $26.70 | $92.50 | $119.20 | ◄ **ASPHALT SHINGLES** *See **Roofing** box on page 394. Prices are for standard three tab shingles. Add **14%** for 4 to 6 tab. Add **16%** for thatch style edge. Add **15%** for shingles with cut-outs. Add **10%** for textured shingles.* |
| **25 year asphalt shingles (220 to 240 lb)**<br>*Replace* Materials.....51.10     Labor..........54.20<br>*Remove* ....................     Labor..........26.70 | sq | $26.70 | $105.30 | $132.00 | |
| **30 year asphalt shingles (240 to 260 lb)**<br>*Replace* Materials ......69.40     Labor..........55.50<br>*Remove* ....................     Labor..........26.70 | sq | $26.70 | $124.90 | $151.60 | |
| **40 year asphalt shingles (260 to 300 lb)**<br>*Replace* Materials......83.90     Labor..........55.50<br>*Remove* ....................     Labor..........26.70 | sq | $26.70 | $139.40 | $166.10 | |

**RELATED ITEMS**

| Item Description | Unit | Remove | Replace | Total |
|---|---|---|---|---|
| **LAMINATED ASPHALT SHINGLES** *See Roofing box below.* **Laminated asphalt shingles, standard grade (250 to 300 lb)** | sq | $26.70 | $162.90 | $189.60 |
| *Replace* Materials ......72.90    Labor ..........90.00  *Remove* ......................    Labor...........26.70 | | | | |
| **Laminated asphalt shingles, standard grade (300 to 390 lb)** | sq | $26.70 | $179.20 | $205.90 |
| *Replace* Materials ......89.20    Labor ..........90.00  *Remove* ......................    Labor...........26.70 | | | | |
| **Laminated asphalt shingles, high grade (260 to 300 lb)** | sq | $26.70 | $193.40 | $220.10 |
| *Replace* Materials ......86.40    Labor ..........107.00  *Remove* ......................    Labor...........26.70 | | | | |
| **Laminated asphalt shingles, high grade (300 to 400 lb)** | sq | $26.70 | $209.00 | $235.70 |
| *Replace* Materials ....102.00    Labor ..........107.00  *Remove* ......................    Labor...........26.70 | | | | |
| **T-LOCK, DIAMOND & HEXAGONAL** *See Roofing box below.* **T-lock asphalt shingles (210 to 230 lb)** | sq | $26.70 | $91.90 | $118.60 |
| *Replace* Materials ......36.40    Labor..........55.50  *Remove* ......................    Labor...........26.70 | | | | |
| **Diamond asphalt shingles (210 to 230 lb)** | sq | $26.70 | $92.80 | $119.50 |
| *Replace* Materials ......37.30    Labor..........55.50  *Remove* ......................    Labor...........26.70 | | | | |
| **Hexagonal asphalt shingles (210 to 230 lb)** | sq | $26.70 | $93.70 | $120.40 |
| *Replace* Materials ......38.20    Labor..........55.50  *Remove* ......................    Labor...........26.70 | | | | |
| **MINIMUM ASPHALT SHINGLES** **Minimum charge for asphalt shingle roof repair** | ea | — | $117.40 | $117.40 |
| *Replace* Materials ......30.00    Labor...........87.40 | | | | |
| **ROLL ROOFING** *Add 82% for double selvage lay.* **90 lb roll roofing** | sq | $19.30 | $54.60 | $73.90 |
| *Replace* Materials ......26.40    Labor ..........28.20  *Remove* ......................    Labor..........19.30 | | | | |
| **110 lb roll roofing** | sq | $19.30 | $73.70 | $93.00 |
| *Replace* Materials ......45.50    Labor ..........28.20  *Remove* ......................    Labor ..........19.30 | | | | |
| **140 lb roll roofing** | sq | $19.30 | $97.20 | $116.50 |
| *Replace* Materials ......69.00    Labor ..........28.20  *Remove* ......................    Labor ..........19.30 | | | | |
| **SLATE** *See Roofing box below.* unfading ▷ **Vermont unfading green slate, clear** | sq | $96.90 | $824.00 | $920.90 |
| *Replace* Materials ...649.00    Labor ..........175.00  *Remove* ......................    Labor...........96.90 | | | | |
| **Vermont unfading purple slate, clear** | sq | $96.90 | $836.00 | $932.90 |
| *Replace* Materials.....661.00    Labor ..........175.00  *Remove* ......................    Labor...........96.90 | | | | |
| **Vermont unfading variegated purple slate, clear** | sq | $96.90 | $920.00 | $1,016.90 |
| *Replace* Materials.....745.00    Labor ..........175.00  *Remove* ......................    Labor...........96.90 | | | | |
| **Vermont unfading dark gray or black slate, clear** | sq | $96.90 | $858.00 | $954.90 |
| *Replace* Materials ....683.00    Labor ..........175.00  *Remove* ......................    Labor...........96.90 | | | | |
| **Vermont unfading red slate, clear** | sq | $96.90 | $1,815.00 | $1,911.90 |
| *Replace* Materials ..1640.00    Labor ..........175.00  *Remove* ......................    Labor...........96.90 | | | | |

**ROOFING**

Roofing costs are based on a typical 2,550 sf house with a 6 in 12 slope roof or less. Roof height is less than 16' so ropes and other safety equipment are not required.

Includes costs for ridges and rakes. Typical roof has an intersecting or L-shaped roof and two dormers. Also includes boots and flashing.

| Item Description | Unit | Remove | Replace | Total | |
|---|---|---|---|---|---|
| **Pennsylvania black weathering slate, clear**<br>*Replace* Materials ....635.00   Labor .........175.00<br>*Remove* .................   Labor...........96.90 | sq | $96.90 | $810.00 | $906.90 | ◁ weathering slate |
| **Vermont weathering green slate, clear**<br>*Replace* Materials .....615.00   Labor .........175.00<br>*Remove* .................   Labor...........96.90 | sq | $96.90 | $790.00 | $886.90 | |
| **Deduct 15% for slate with ribbons of foreign color** | | | | | ◁ deduct for lower grade |
| **Minimum charge for slate roof repair**<br>*Replace* Materials ....225.00   Labor .........175.00 | ea | — | $400.00 | $400.00 | ◁ minimum |
| **Replace single slate**<br>*Replace* Materials ......20.00   Labor...........16.80 | ea | — | $36.80 | $36.80 | ◁ replace single slate |
| **16" blue label cedar shingles (Royals)**<br>*Replace* Materials ....243.00   Labor .........125.00<br>*Remove* .................   Labor...........31.40 | sq | $31.40 | $368.00 | $399.40 | ◀ **WOOD SHINGLES**<br>See *Roofing* box on facing page. |
| **18" blue label cedar shingles (Perfections)**<br>*Replace* Materials ....257.00   Labor..........112.00<br>*Remove* .................   Labor...........31.40 | sq | $31.40 | $369.00 | $400.40 | |
| **16" red label cedar shingles (Royals)**<br>*Replace* Materials ....235.00   Labor .........125.00<br>*Remove* .................   Labor...........31.40 | sq | $31.40 | $360.00 | $391.40 | |
| **18" red label cedar shingles (Perfections)**<br>*Replace* Materials ....248.00   Labor..........112.00<br>*Remove* .................   Labor...........31.40 | sq | $31.40 | $360.00 | $391.40 | |
| **Minimum charge for wood shingle repair**<br>*Replace* Materials ......60.00   Labor...........87.40 | ea | — | $147.40 | $147.40 | ◁ minimum |
| **Replace single wood shingle**<br>*Replace* Materials .......15.00   Labor ............9.09 | ea | — | $24.09 | $24.09 | ◁ replace single shingle |
| **Deduct 6% for black label shingles** | | | | | ◁ additional costs |
| **Add 20% for 16" wood shingles with 4" exposure** | | | | | |
| **Deduct 17% for 16" wood shingles with 5-1/2" exposure** | | | | | |
| **Deduct 20% for 16" wood shingles with 6" exposure** | | | | | |
| **Add 18% for wood shingles treated with fire retardant** | | | | | |
| **Add 16% for wood shingles treated with mildew retardant** | | | | | |
| **Add 16% for wood shingle staggered installation** | | | | | |
| **Add 26% for wood shingle thatch installation** | | | | | |
| **Add 24% for wood shingle serrated installation** | | | | | |
| **Add 38% for wood shingle Dutch weave installation** | | | | | |
| **Add 45% for wood shingle pyramid installation** | | | | | |
| **18" medium handsplit and resawn shakes**<br>*Replace* Materials .....159.00   Labor .........146.00<br>*Remove* .................   Labor...........31.40 | sq | $31.40 | $305.00 | $336.40 | ◀ **WOOD SHAKES**<br>See *Roofing* box on facing page. |

**RELATED ITEMS**

Rough Carpentry
chimney cricket .............444

*thatch* △

*serrated* △

*Dutch weave* △

*pyramid* △

| | Item Description | Unit | Remove | Replace | Total |
|---|---|---|---|---|---|
| **WOOD SHAKES** ▶ continued handsplit and resawn ▷ | **18" heavy handsplit and resawn shakes**<br>*Replace* Materials.....174.00     Labor.........146.00<br>*Remove* ......................     Labor.........31.40 | sq | $31.40 | $320.00 | $351.40 |
| | **24" medium handsplit and resawn shakes**<br>*Replace* Materials.....212.00     Labor.........125.00<br>*Remove* ......................     Labor.........31.40 | sq | $31.40 | $337.00 | $368.40 |
| | **24" heavy handsplit and resawn shakes**<br>*Replace* Materials....235.00     Labor.........125.00<br>*Remove* ......................     Labor.........31.40 | sq | $31.40 | $360.00 | $391.40 |
| taper split ▷ | **24" tapersplit shakes**<br>*Replace* Materials.....166.00     Labor.........125.00<br>*Remove* ......................     Labor.........31.40 | sq | $31.40 | $291.00 | $322.40 |
| straight split ▷ | **18" straight split shakes**<br>*Replace* Materials ....143.00     Labor.........146.00<br>*Remove* ......................     Labor.........31.40 | sq | $31.40 | $289.00 | $320.40 |
| | **24" straight split shakes**<br>*Replace* Materials.....151.00     Labor.........125.00<br>*Remove* ......................     Labor.........31.40 | sq | $31.40 | $276.00 | $307.40 |
| other exposures ▷ | **Add 20% for 8" shake exposure**<br><br>**Deduct 20% for 12" shake exposure** | | | | |
| staggered installation ▷ | **Add 16% for staggered shake installation** | | | | |
| minimum charge ▷ | **Minimum charge for shake roof repair**<br>*Replace* Materials......60.00     Labor...........87.40 | ea | — | $147.40 | $147.40 |
| replace single shake ▷ | **Replace single shake**<br>*Replace* Materials......10.00     Labor ...........9.09 | ea | — | $19.09 | $19.09 |
| **FIBER AND CEMENT** ▶ **SHINGLES** *Older style shingles may contain asbestos. This is a hazardous material which requires special techniques and equipment to remove.* | **Fiber and cement shingles, weathering shake**<br>*Replace* Materials......80.40     Labor.........104.00<br>*Remove* ......................     Labor .........29.10 | sq | $29.10 | $184.40 | $213.50 |
| | **Fiber and cement shingles, Spanish tile**<br>*Replace* Materials.....101.00     Labor.........109.00<br>*Remove* ......................     Labor .........29.10 | sq | $29.10 | $210.00 | $239.10 |
| minimum ▷ | **Minimum charge for fiber and cement shingle roof repair**<br>*Replace* Materials ......31.30     Labor...........67.30 | sq | — | $98.60 | $98.60 |
| **GRANULAR** ▶ **COATED METAL TILE** *See Roofing box on page 394.* | **Granular coated metal tile, simple pattern**<br>*Replace* Materials ....267.00     Labor.........187.00<br>*Remove* ......................     Labor...........27.20 | sq | $27.20 | $454.00 | $481.20 |
| | **Granular coated metal tile, complex pattern**<br>*Replace* Materials ....323.00     Labor.........187.00<br>*Remove* ......................     Labor...........27.20 | sq | $27.20 | $510.00 | $537.20 |
| **FLAT CLAY TILE** ▶ *See Roofing box on page 394. Old style clay tile shingles.* | **Flat clay tile shingle, terra-cotta red**<br>*Replace* Materials ......94.00     Labor .........141.00<br>*Remove* ......................     Labor .........90.40 | sq | $90.40 | $235.00 | $325.40 |
| | **Flat clay tile shingle, glazed red**<br>*Replace* Materials.....192.00     Labor .........141.00<br>*Remove* ......................     Labor .........90.40 | sq | $90.40 | $333.00 | $423.40 |

| Item Description | Unit | Remove | Replace | Total | |
|---|---|---|---|---|---|
| **Mission tile, terra-cotta red**<br>*Replace* Materials ....182.00    Labor.........243.00<br>*Remove* ......................    Labor ..........90.40 | sq | $90.40 | $425.00 | $515.40 | ◄ **MISSION TILE**<br>See *Roofing* box on page 394. Includes 30 lb felt underlayment, doubled felt on rakes and eaves, bird stop, booster tiles, ridge and rake tiles. |
| **Mission tile, peach**<br>*Replace* Materials....208.00    Labor.........243.00<br>*Remove* ......................    Labor ..........90.40 | sq | $90.40 | $451.00 | $541.40 | |
| **Mission tile, white**<br>*Replace* Materials ....243.00    Labor.........243.00<br>*Remove* ......................    Labor ..........90.40 | sq | $90.40 | $486.00 | $576.40 | |
| **Mission tile, color blends**<br>*Replace* Materials ....229.00    Labor.........243.00<br>*Remove* ......................    Labor ..........90.40 | sq | $90.40 | $472.00 | $562.40 | |
| **Mission tile, glazed white**<br>*Replace* Materials ....243.00    Labor ..............<br>*Remove* ......................    Labor ..........90.40 | sq | $90.40 | $829.40 | $496.00 | |
| **Mission tile, glazed gray**<br>*Replace* Materials....501.00    Labor.........243.00<br>*Remove* ......................    Labor ..........90.40 | sq | $90.40 | $744.00 | $834.40 | |
| **Mission tile, glazed burgundy**<br>*Replace* Materials....504.00    Labor.........243.00<br>*Remove* ......................    Labor ..........90.40 | sq | $90.40 | $747.00 | $837.40 | |
| **Mission tile, glazed terra-cotta red**<br>*Replace* Materials....502.00    Labor.........243.00<br>*Remove* ......................    Labor ..........90.40 | sq | $90.40 | $745.00 | $835.40 | |
| **Mission tile, glazed teal**<br>*Replace* Materials....630.00    Labor.........243.00<br>*Remove* ......................    Labor ..........90.40 | sq | $90.40 | $873.00 | $963.40 | |
| **Mission tile, glazed blue**<br>*Replace* Materials ....647.00    Labor.........243.00<br>*Remove* ......................    Labor ..........90.40 | sq | $90.40 | $890.00 | $980.40 | |
| **Add for vertical furring strips under all cap tiles**<br>*Replace* Materials ......97.00    Labor.........143.00 | sq | — | $240.00 | $240.00 | ◁ **add for vertical strips** |
| **Add for Mission tiles attached with wire**<br>*Replace* Materials ......16.40    Labor...........97.00 | sq | — | $113.40 | $113.40 | ◁ **add for other attachment** |
| **Add for Mission tiles attached with stainless steel nails**<br>*Replace* Materials ......22.60 | sq | — | $22.60 | $22.60 | |
| **Add for Mission tiles attached with brass or copper nails**<br>*Replace* Materials ......30.20 | sq | — | $30.20 | $30.20 | |
| **Add for Mission tiles with wire attached to braided wire runners**<br>*Replace* Materials ......29.20    Labor...........94.80 | sq | — | $124.00 | $124.00 | |
| **Add for Mission tiles attached with hurricane clips or wind locks**<br>*Replace* Materials.......19.80    Labor .........132.00 | sq | — | $151.80 | $151.80 | |
| **Add for adhesive between Mission tiles**<br>*Replace* Materials.......15.60    Labor ...........6.60 | sq | — | $22.20 | $22.20 | |

**RELATED ITEMS**

| Item Description | Unit | Remove | Replace | Total |
|---|---|---|---|---|
| **SPANISH TILE ▶** *See Roofing box on page 394. Includes 30 lb felt underlayment, doubled felt on rakes and eaves, bird stop, ridge and rake tiles.* | | | | |
| **Spanish tile, terra-cotta red** *Replace* Materials .....115.00  Labor.........146.00  *Remove* .....................  Labor .........90.40 | sq | $90.40 | $261.00 | $351.40 |
| **Spanish tile, peach** *Replace* Materials.....142.00  Labor.........146.00  *Remove* .....................  Labor .........90.40 | sq | $90.40 | $288.00 | $378.40 |
| **Spanish tile, white** *Replace* Materials.....175.00  Labor.........146.00  *Remove* .....................  Labor .........90.40 | sq | $90.40 | $321.00 | $411.40 |
| **Spanish tile, color blends** *Replace* Materials .....161.00  Labor.........146.00  *Remove* .....................  Labor .........90.40 | sq | $90.40 | $307.00 | $397.40 |
| **Spanish tile, glazed white** *Replace* Materials .....450.00  Labor.........146.00  *Remove* .....................  Labor .........90.40 | sq | $90.40 | $596.00 | $686.40 |
| **Spanish tile, glazed gray** *Replace* Materials.....452.00  Labor.........146.00  *Remove* .....................  Labor .........90.40 | sq | $90.40 | $598.00 | $688.40 |
| **Spanish tile, glazed burgundy** *Replace* Materials ....569.00  Labor.........146.00  *Remove* .....................  Labor .........90.40 | sq | $90.40 | $715.00 | $805.40 |
| **Spanish tile, glazed terra-cotta red** *Replace* Materials ....454.00  Labor.........146.00  *Remove* .....................  Labor .........90.40 | sq | $90.40 | $600.00 | $690.40 |
| **Spanish tile, glazed teal** *Replace* Materials.....574.00  Labor.........146.00  *Remove* .....................  Labor .........90.40 | sq | $90.40 | $720.00 | $810.40 |
| **Spanish tile, glazed blue** *Replace* Materials .....593.00  Labor.........146.00  *Remove* .....................  Labor .........90.40 | sq | $90.40 | $739.00 | $829.40 |
| **add for other ▷ attachment** **Add for Spanish tiles attached with wire** *Replace* Materials.....13.70  Labor...........76.50 | sq | — | $90.20 | $90.20 |
| **Add for Spanish tiles attached with stainless steel nails** *Replace* Materials.......19.10 | sq | — | $19.10 | $19.10 |
| **Add for Spanish tiles attached with brass or copper nails** *Replace* Materials.......25.40 | sq | — | $25.40 | $25.40 |
| **Add for Spanish tiles with wire attached to braided wire runners** *Replace* Materials ......24.10  Labor...........64.20 | sq | — | $88.30 | $88.30 |
| **Add for Spanish tiles attached with hurricane clips or wind locks** *Replace* Materials.......15.10  Labor...........79.50 | sq | — | $94.60 | $94.60 |
| **Add for Spanish tiles attached using mortar set method** *Replace* Materials......44.50  Labor.........115.00 | sq | — | $159.50 | $159.50 |
| **Add for adhesive between Spanish tiles** *Replace* Materials.......15.60  Labor ...........5.90 | sq | — | $21.50 | $21.50 |

| Item Description | Unit | Remove | Replace | Total | |
|---|---|---|---|---|---|
| **Deduct 5% for ASTM grade 2 moderate weathering tiles** | | | | | ◄ **OTHER CLAY TILE GRADES** *Deduct from the cost of Spanish or mission tiles.* |
| **Deduct 11% for ASTM grade 3 negligible weathering tiles** | | | | | |
| **Deduct 12% for low profile Spanish or Mission tiles** | | | | | |
| **Furring strips for roofing tiles, vertically laid only** *Replace* Materials ......18.50   Labor..........26.50  *Remove* ........................   Labor..........12.50 | sq | $12.50 | $45.00 | $57.50 | ◄ **FURRING STRIPS** *See Roofing box on page 394.* |
| **Furring strips for roofing tiles, vertically and horizontally laid** *Replace* Materials......30.30   Labor..........38.30  *Remove* ........................   Labor..........22.00 | sq | $22.00 | $68.60 | $90.60 | |
| **Corrugated concrete tile, natural gray** *Replace* Materials......93.90   Labor..........137.00  *Remove* ........................   Labor..........101.00 | sq | $101.00 | $230.90 | $331.90 | ◄ **CONCRETE TILE** *See Roofing box on page 394.* |
| **Corrugated concrete tile, black** *Replace* Materials ....106.00   Labor..........137.00  *Remove* ........................   Labor..........101.00 | sq | $101.00 | $243.00 | $344.00 | |
| **Corrugated concrete tile, browns and terra-cotta reds** *Replace* Materials .....113.00   Labor..........137.00  *Remove* ........................   Labor..........101.00 | sq | $101.00 | $250.00 | $351.00 | |
| **Corrugated concrete tile, bright reds** *Replace* Materials.....121.00   Labor..........137.00  *Remove* ........................   Labor..........101.00 | sq | $101.00 | $258.00 | $359.00 | |
| **Corrugated concrete tile, greens** *Replace* Materials.....131.00   Labor..........137.00  *Remove* ........................   Labor..........101.00 | sq | $101.00 | $268.00 | $369.00 | |
| **Corrugated concrete tile, blues** *Replace* Materials.....137.00   Labor..........137.00  *Remove* ........................   Labor..........101.00 | sq | $101.00 | $274.00 | $375.00 | |
| **Flat concrete tile, natural gray** *Replace* Materials......86.00   Labor..........132.00  *Remove* ........................   Labor..........101.00 | sq | $101.00 | $218.00 | $319.00 | ◁ flat |
| **Flat concrete tile, black** *Replace* Materials ......97.90   Labor..........132.00  *Remove* ........................   Labor..........101.00 | sq | $101.00 | $229.90 | $330.90 | |
| **Flat concrete tile, browns and terra-cotta reds** *Replace* Materials ....104.00   Labor..........132.00  *Remove* ........................   Labor..........101.00 | sq | $101.00 | $236.00 | $337.00 | |
| **Flat concrete tile, bright reds** *Replace* Materials .....111.00   Labor..........132.00  *Remove* ........................   Labor..........101.00 | sq | $101.00 | $243.00 | $344.00 | |
| **Flat concrete tile, greens** *Replace* Materials.....121.00   Labor..........132.00  *Remove* ........................   Labor..........101.00 | sq | $101.00 | $253.00 | $354.00 | |
| **Flat concrete tile, blues** *Replace* Materials.....126.00   Labor..........132.00  *Remove* ........................   Labor..........101.00 | sq | $101.00 | $258.00 | $359.00 | **RELATED ITEMS** **Rough Carpentry** *chimney cricket* .............444 |

| Item Description | Unit | Remove | Replace | Total |
|---|---|---|---|---|
| **CONCRETE TILE** continued additional costs ▷ Add 2% for glazed concrete tiles | | | | |
| Add 5% for painted concrete tiles | | | | |
| **ALUMINUM SHEET CORRUGATED** See **Roofing** box on page 394. .016" thick corrugated aluminum roofing, natural finish  Replace Materials ........ .84  Labor ............ 1.05  Remove .....................  Labor ............. .26 | sf | $.26 | $1.89 | $2.15 |
| .019" thick corrugated aluminum roofing, natural finish  Replace Materials ........ .92  Labor ............ 1.05  Remove .....................  Labor ............. .26 | sf | $.26 | $1.97 | $2.23 |
| colored finish ▷ .016" thick corrugated aluminum roofing, colored finish  Replace Materials ....... 1.04  Labor ............1.05  Remove .....................  Labor ............. .26 | sf | $.26 | $2.09 | $2.35 |
| .019" thick corrugated aluminum roofing, colored finish  Replace Materials ....... 1.14  Labor ............1.05  Remove .....................  Labor ............. .26 | sf | $.26 | $2.19 | $2.45 |
| **ALUMINUM SHEET RIBBED** See **Roofing** box on page 394. .016" thick ribbed aluminum roofing, natural finish  Replace Materials ........ .88  Labor ............1.14  Remove .....................  Labor ............. .26 | sf | $.26 | $2.02 | $2.28 |
| .019" thick ribbed aluminum roofing, natural finish  Replace Materials ....... 1.19  Labor ............1.14  Remove .....................  Labor ............. .26 | sf | $.26 | $2.33 | $2.59 |
| .032" thick ribbed aluminum roofing, natural finish  Replace Materials ....... 1.71  Labor ............1.14  Remove .....................  Labor ............. .26 | sf | $.26 | $2.85 | $3.11 |
| .04" thick ribbed aluminum roofing, natural finish  Replace Materials ....... 2.24  Labor ............1.14  Remove .....................  Labor ............. .26 | sf | $.26 | $3.38 | $3.64 |
| .05" thick ribbed aluminum roofing, natural finish  Replace Materials ....... 2.63  Labor ............1.14  Remove .....................  Labor ............. .26 | sf | $.26 | $3.77 | $4.03 |
| colored finish ▷ .016" thick ribbed aluminum roofing, colored finish  Replace Materials ....... 1.04  Labor ............1.14  Remove .....................  Labor ............. .26 | sf | $.26 | $2.18 | $2.44 |
| .019" thick ribbed aluminum roofing, colored finish  Replace Materials ....... 1.16  Labor ............1.14  Remove .....................  Labor ............. .26 | sf | $.26 | $2.30 | $2.56 |
| .032" thick ribbed aluminum roofing, colored finish  Replace Materials ....... 1.75  Labor ............1.14  Remove .....................  Labor ............. .26 | sf | $.26 | $2.89 | $3.15 |
| .04" thick ribbed aluminum roofing, colored finish  Replace Materials ....... 2.97  Labor ............1.14  Remove .....................  Labor ............. .26 | sf | $.26 | $4.11 | $4.37 |
| .05" thick ribbed aluminum roofing, colored finish  Replace Materials ....... 3.40  Labor ............1.14  Remove .....................  Labor ............. .26 | sf | $.26 | $4.54 | $4.80 |
| **FIBERGLASS CORRUGATED** See **Roofing** page 394. 8 ounce corrugated fiberglass roofing  Replace Materials ....... 2.25  Labor ............1.05  Remove .....................  Labor ............. .24 | sf | $.24 | $3.30 | $3.54 |

| Item Description | Unit | Remove | Replace | Total | |
|---|---|---|---|---|---|
| **12 ounce corrugated fiberglass roofing**<br>*Replace* Materials........2.99    Labor............1.05<br>*Remove* .....................    Labor............ .24 | sf | $.24 | $4.04 | $4.28 | |
| **30 gauge galvanized steel corrugated roofing**<br>*Replace* Materials........ .84    Labor............1.09<br>*Remove* .....................    Labor............ .26 | sf | $.26 | $1.93 | $2.19 | ◀ **GALVANIZED STEEL CORRUGATED**<br>See *Roofing* box on page 394. |
| **28 gauge galvanized steel corrugated roofing**<br>*Replace* Materials........ .88    Labor............1.09<br>*Remove* .....................    Labor............ .26 | sf | $.26 | $1.97 | $2.23 | |
| **26 gauge galvanized steel corrugated roofing**<br>*Replace* Materials........ .93    Labor............1.09<br>*Remove* .....................    Labor............ .26 | sf | $.26 | $2.02 | $2.28 | |
| **24 gauge galvanized steel corrugated roofing**<br>*Replace* Materials........1.03    Labor............1.09<br>*Remove* .....................    Labor............ .26 | sf | $.26 | $2.12 | $2.38 | |
| **30 gauge galvanized steel ribbed roofing**<br>*Replace* Materials........ .87    Labor............1.14<br>*Remove* .....................    Labor............ .26 | sf | $.26 | $2.01 | $2.27 | ◀ **GALVANIZED STEEL RIBBED**<br>See *Roofing* box on page 394. |
| **28 gauge galvanized steel ribbed roofing**<br>*Replace* Materials........ .92    Labor............1.14<br>*Remove* .....................    Labor............ .26 | sf | $.26 | $2.06 | $2.32 | |
| **26 gauge galvanized steel ribbed roofing**<br>*Replace* Materials........ .97    Labor............1.14<br>*Remove* .....................    Labor............ .26 | sf | $.26 | $2.11 | $2.37 | |
| **24 gauge galvanized steel ribbed roofing**<br>*Replace* Materials........1.07    Labor............1.14<br>*Remove* .....................    Labor............ .26 | sf | $.26 | $2.21 | $2.47 | |
| **30 gauge galvanized steel ribbed roofing with colored finish**<br>*Replace* Materials........1.19    Labor............1.14<br>*Remove* .....................    Labor............ .26 | sf | $.26 | $2.33 | $2.59 | ◁ **colored finish** |
| **28 gauge galvanized steel ribbed roofing with colored finish**<br>*Replace* Materials........1.27    Labor............1.14<br>*Remove* .....................    Labor............ .26 | sf | $.26 | $2.41 | $2.67 | |
| **26 gauge galvanized steel ribbed roofing with colored finish**<br>*Replace* Materials........1.34    Labor............1.14<br>*Remove* .....................    Labor............ .26 | sf | $.26 | $2.48 | $2.74 | |
| **24 gauge galvanized steel ribbed roofing with colored finish**<br>*Replace* Materials........1.47    Labor............1.14<br>*Remove* .....................    Labor............ .26 | sf | $.26 | $2.61 | $2.87 | |
| **16 ounce copper standing seam roofing**<br>*Replace* Materials....528.00    Labor........291.00<br>*Remove* .....................    Labor...........27.00 | sq | $27.00 | $819.00 | $846.00 | ◀ **COPPER**<br>See *Roofing* box on page 394.<br>◁ **standing seam** |
| **18 ounce copper standing seam roofing**<br>*Replace* Materials....586.00    Labor........312.00<br>*Remove* .....................    Labor...........27.00 | sq | $27.00 | $898.00 | $925.00 | |
| **20 ounce copper standing seam roofing**<br>*Replace* Materials.....670.00    Labor........336.00<br>*Remove* .....................    Labor...........27.00 | sq | $27.00 | $1,006.00 | $1,033.00 | **RELATED ITEMS**<br>**Rough Carpentry**<br>*chimney cricket*.............444 |

| Item Description | Unit | Remove | Replace | Total |
|---|---|---|---|---|
| **COPPER ►** *continued* **batten seam ►** | | | | |
| **16 ounce copper batten seam roofing**<br>*Replace* Materials....539.00    Labor........336.00<br>*Remove* ..................    Labor..........27.00 | sq | $27.00 | $875.00 | $902.00 |
| **18 ounce copper batten seam roofing**<br>*Replace* Materials....600.00    Labor........364.00<br>*Remove* ..................    Labor..........27.00 | sq | $27.00 | $964.00 | $991.00 |
| **20 ounce copper batten seam roofing**<br>*Replace* Materials....686.00    Labor........397.00<br>*Remove* ..................    Labor..........27.00 | sq | $27.00 | $1,083.00 | $1,110.00 |
| **flat seam ►** **16 ounce copper flat seam roofing**<br>*Replace* Materials....484.00    Labor........312.00<br>*Remove* ..................    Labor..........27.00 | sq | $27.00 | $796.00 | $823.00 |
| **18 ounce copper flat seam roofing**<br>*Replace* Materials....540.00    Labor........336.00<br>*Remove* ..................    Labor..........27.00 | sq | $27.00 | $876.00 | $903.00 |
| **20 ounce copper flat seam roofing**<br>*Replace* Materials....605.00    Labor........364.00<br>*Remove* ..................    Labor..........27.00 | sq | $27.00 | $969.00 | $996.00 |
| **LEAD ►** See **Roofing** box on page 394. **3 lb batten seam lead roof**<br>*Replace* Materials....623.00    Labor........312.00<br>*Remove* ..................    Labor..........27.00 | sq | $27.00 | $935.00 | $962.00 |
| **3 lb flat seam lead roof**<br>*Replace* Materials....561.00    Labor........336.00<br>*Remove* ..................    Labor..........27.00 | sq | $27.00 | $897.00 | $924.00 |
| **STAINLESS STEEL ►** See **Roofing** box on page 394. **standing seam ►** **28 gauge stainless steel standing seam roof**<br>*Replace* Materials....404.00    Labor........312.00<br>*Remove* ..................    Labor..........27.00 | sq | $27.00 | $716.00 | $743.00 |
| **26 gauge stainless steel standing seam roof**<br>*Replace* Materials....450.00    Labor........291.00<br>*Remove* ..................    Labor..........27.00 | sq | $27.00 | $741.00 | $768.00 |
| **batten seam ►** **28 gauge stainless steel batten seam roof**<br>*Replace* Materials.....415.00    Labor........336.00<br>*Remove* ..................    Labor..........27.00 | sq | $27.00 | $751.00 | $778.00 |
| **26 gauge stainless steel batten seam roof**<br>*Replace* Materials....463.00    Labor........312.00<br>*Remove* ..................    Labor..........27.00 | sq | $27.00 | $775.00 | $802.00 |
| **flat seam ►** **28 gauge stainless steel flat seam roof**<br>*Replace* Materials....384.00    Labor........312.00<br>*Remove* ..................    Labor..........27.00 | sq | $27.00 | $696.00 | $723.00 |
| **26 gauge stainless steel flat seam roof**<br>*Replace* Materials....429.00    Labor........291.00<br>*Remove* ..................    Labor..........27.00 | sq | $27.00 | $720.00 | $747.00 |
| **coated finish ►** **Add 13% for terne coated stainless steel** | | | | |
| **Add 14% for lead coated stainless steel** | | | | |
| **TERNE ►** See **Roofing** box on page 394. **40 lb terne standing seam roof**<br>*Replace* Materials.....915.00    Labor........364.00<br>*Remove* ..................    Labor..........27.00 | sq | $27.00 | $1,279.00 | $1,306.00 |

| Item Description | Unit | Remove | Replace | Total |
|---|---|---|---|---|
| **40 lb terne batten seam roof** | sq | $27.00 | $1,269.00 | $1,296.00 |
| *Replace* Materials....933.00　　Labor........336.00 | | | | |
| *Remove* ....................　　Labor........27.00 | | | | |
| **40 lb terne flat seam roof** | sq | $27.00 | $1,272.00 | $1,299.00 |
| *Replace* Materials....875.00　　Labor........397.00 | | | | |
| *Remove* ....................　　Labor........27.00 | | | | |
| **Solder patch into metal roof (less than 1' square)** | ea | — | $87.30 | $87.30 |
| *Replace* Materials......40.00　　Labor.........47.30 | | | | |
| **Minimum charge for seamed metal roof repair** | ea | — | $218.00 | $218.00 |
| *Replace* Materials....100.00　　Labor........118.00 | | | | |
| **Built-up 3 ply roofing** | sq | $63.90 | $205.11 | $269.01 |
| *Replace* Materials......49.80　　Labor....146.00　　Equipment....9.31 | | | | |
| *Remove* ....................　　Labor........63.90 | | | | |
| **Built-up 4 ply roofing** | sq | $79.40 | $255.08 | $334.48 |
| *Replace* Materials......69.70　　Labor....175.00　　Equipment....10.38 | | | | |
| *Remove* ....................　　Labor........79.40 | | | | |
| **Built-up 5 ply roofing** | sq | $101.00 | $323.50 | $424.50 |
| *Replace* Materials....104.00　　Labor....208.00　　Equipment....11.50 | | | | |
| *Remove* ....................　　Labor........101.00 | | | | |
| **Minimum charge for roofing work requiring hot asphalt** | ea | — | $378.00 | $378.00 |
| *Replace* Materials....160.00　　Labor....218.00 | | | | |
| **Add for built-up roofing gravel surface embedded in flood coat** | sq | $22.20 | $31.33 | $53.53 |
| *Replace* Materials......12.40　　Labor....17.50　　Equipment....1.43 | | | | |
| *Remove* ....................　　Labor........22.20 | | | | |
| **Add for flood coat** | sq | — | $50.72 | $50.72 |
| *Replace* Materials......15.70　　Labor....31.20　　Equipment....3.82 | | | | |
| **Add to paint built-up roof with aluminum UV coating** | sq | — | $51.50 | $51.50 |
| *Replace* Materials......15.10　　Labor....36.40 | | | | |
| **Add to paint built-up roof with aluminum UV coating with fiber** | sq | — | $55.10 | $55.10 |
| *Replace* Materials......18.70　　Labor....36.40 | | | | |
| **Add for mineral faced cap sheet** | sq | — | $15.70 | $15.70 |
| *Replace* Materials......15.70 | | | | |
| **Remove gravel, flood coat, then replace gravel** | sq | — | $156.90 | $156.90 |
| *Replace* Materials......33.50　　Labor....108.00　　Equipment....15.40 | | | | |
| **Add per lf of parapet wall on built-up roof** | lf | — | $19.50 | $19.50 |
| *Replace* Materials......8.90　　Labor....9.92　　Equipment.....68 | | | | |
| **45 mil SCPE elastomeric roofing, loose laid and ballasted with stone** | sq | $53.40 | $198.43 | $251.83 |
| *Replace* Materials....152.00　　Labor....43.70　　Equipment....2.73 | | | | |
| *Remove* ....................　　Labor........53.40 | | | | |
| **45 mil SCPE elastomeric roofing, attached at seams with batten strips** | sq | $25.70 | $201.77 | $227.47 |
| *Replace* Materials....161.00　　Labor....36.40　　Equipment....4.37 | | | | |
| *Remove* ....................　　Labor........25.70 | | | | |
| **45 mil SCPE elastomeric roofing, fully attached to deck** | sq | $40.90 | $220.73 | $261.63 |
| *Replace* Materials....167.00　　Labor....45.40　　Equipment....8.33 | | | | |
| *Remove* ....................　　Labor........40.90 | | | | |

◄ **TERNE**
Terne is short for Terneplate. Terneplate is sheet iron or steel that is plated with an alloy that is one part tin and three to four parts lead.

◄ **SEAMED METAL ROOF REPAIR**
For repairs to standing seam, batten seam, or flat seam metal roofs.

◄ **BUILT-UP**
Does not include finish coat or wrap up parapet wall (see below).

◁ minimum

◁ surface finish

**RELATED ITEMS**
Rough Carpentry
chimney cricket.............444

◁ replace gravel

◁ add for parapet wall
Includes cant strip and roofing wrap up wall.

◄ **SCPE ELASTOMERIC**
Chlorosulfonated polyethylene-hypalon roofing is abbreviated SCPE. Ballasted roofs contain 1/2 ton of stone per square.

| Item Description | Unit | Remove | Replace | Total |
|---|---|---|---|---|
| **EPDM ▶** | | | | |
| **ELASTOMERIC** | | | | |
| **45 mil EPDM elastomeric roofing, loose laid & ballasted with stone** | sq | $53.40 | $194.83 | $248.23 |
| *Replace* Materials ......85.10    Labor..........107.00    Equipment............2.73 | | | | |
| *Remove* ........................    Labor ..........53.40 | | | | |
| **45 mil EPDM elastomeric roofing, attached to deck at seams** | sq | $25.70 | $164.87 | $190.57 |
| *Replace* Materials ......73.10    Labor..........87.40    Equipment............4.37 | | | | |
| *Remove* ........................    Labor ..........25.70 | | | | |
| **45 mil EPDM elastomeric roofing, fully attached to deck** | sq | $40.90 | $235.33 | $276.23 |
| *Replace* Materials ....102.00    Labor..........125.00    Equipment............8.33 | | | | |
| *Remove* ........................    Labor ..........40.90 | | | | |
| **55 mil EPDM elastomeric roofing, loose laid & ballasted with stone** | sq | $53.40 | $210.13 | $263.53 |
| *Replace* Materials ......98.40    Labor..........109.00    Equipment............2.73 | | | | |
| *Remove* ........................    Labor ..........53.40 | | | | |
| **55 mil EPDM elastomeric roofing, attached to deck at seams** | sq | $25.70 | $179.87 | $205.57 |
| *Replace* Materials ......86.40    Labor ..........89.10    Equipment............4.37 | | | | |
| *Remove* ........................    Labor ..........25.70 | | | | |
| **55 mil EPDM elastomeric roofing, fully attached to deck** | sq | $40.90 | $252.33 | $293.23 |
| *Replace* Materials .....116.00    Labor..........128.00    Equipment............8.33 | | | | |
| *Remove* ........................    Labor ..........40.90 | | | | |
| **60 mil EPDM elastomeric roofing, loose laid & ballasted with stone** | sq | $53.40 | $219.73 | $273.13 |
| *Replace* Materials ....105.00    Labor..........112.00    Equipment............2.73 | | | | |
| *Remove* ........................    Labor ..........53.40 | | | | |
| **60 mil EPDM elastomeric roofing, attached to deck at seams** | sq | $25.70 | $184.37 | $210.07 |
| *Replace* Materials ......89.10    Labor..........90.90    Equipment............4.37 | | | | |
| *Remove* ........................    Labor ..........25.70 | | | | |
| **60 mil EPDM elastomeric roofing, fully attached to deck** | sq | $40.90 | $259.33 | $300.23 |
| *Replace* Materials ....119.00    Labor..........132.00    Equipment............8.33 | | | | |
| *Remove* ........................    Labor ..........40.90 | | | | |
| **PVC ▶** | | | | |
| **45 mil PVC elastomeric roofing, loose laid & ballasted with stone** | sq | $53.40 | $130.43 | $183.83 |
| *Replace* Materials ....102.00    Labor..........25.70    Equipment............2.73 | | | | |
| *Remove* ........................    Labor ..........53.40 | | | | |
| **45 mil PVC elastomeric roofing, attached to deck at seams** | sq | $25.70 | $172.07 | $197.77 |
| *Replace* Materials.....128.00    Labor..........39.70    Equipment............4.37 | | | | |
| *Remove* ........................    Labor ..........25.70 | | | | |
| **45 mil PVC elastomeric roofing, fully attached to deck** | sq | $40.90 | $204.43 | $245.33 |
| *Replace* Materials.....138.00    Labor..........58.10    Equipment............8.33 | | | | |
| *Remove* ........................    Labor ..........40.90 | | | | |
| **Add 22% for 45 mil reinforced PVC elastomeric roofing** | | | | |
| **48 mil PVC elastomeric roofing, loose laid & ballasted with stone** | sq | $53.40 | $140.03 | $193.43 |
| *Replace* Materials .....110.00    Labor..........27.30    Equipment............2.73 | | | | |
| *Remove* ........................    Labor ..........53.40 | | | | |
| **48 mil PVC elastomeric roofing, attached to deck at seams** | sq | $25.70 | $181.07 | $206.77 |
| *Replace* Materials.....133.00    Labor ..........43.70    Equipment............4.37 | | | | |
| *Remove* ........................    Labor ..........25.70 | | | | |
| **48 mil PVC elastomeric roofing, fully attached to deck** | sq | $40.90 | $212.33 | $253.23 |
| *Replace* Materials.....145.00    Labor..........59.00    Equipment............8.33 | | | | |
| *Remove* ........................    Labor ..........40.90 | | | | |

Side labels:

**EPDM ▶ ELASTOMERIC**
*Ethylene propylene diene monomer roofing is abbreviated EPDM. Ballasted roofs contain 1/2 ton of stone per square.*

55 mil ▷

60 mil ▷

**PVC ▶**
*Polyvinyl chloride roofing is abbreviated PVC. Ballasted roofs contain 1/2 ton of stone per square.*

45 mil ▷

add for reinforced ▷

48 mil ▷

| Item Description | Unit | Remove | Replace | Total | |
|---|---|---|---|---|---|
| **60 mil PVC elastomeric roofing, loose laid & ballasted with stone** | sq | $53.40 | $183.83 | $237.23 | ◁ 60 mil |
| *Replace* Materials.....152.00     Labor..........29.10     Equipment............2.73 <br> *Remove* ......................     Labor ..........53.40 | | | | | |
| **60 mil PVC elastomeric roofing, attached to deck at seams** | sq | $25.70 | $210.97 | $236.67 | |
| *Replace* Materials.....162.00     Labor..........44.60     Equipment............4.37 <br> *Remove* ......................     Labor ..........25.70 | | | | | |
| **60 mil PVC elastomeric roofing, fully attached to deck** | sq | $40.90 | $253.03 | $293.93 | |
| *Replace* Materials ....184.00     Labor..........60.70     Equipment............8.33 <br> *Remove* ......................     Labor ..........40.90 | | | | | |
| **120 mil modified bitumen roofing, loose laid & ballasted with stone** | sq | $53.40 | $127.23 | $180.63 | ◀ **MODIFIED BITUMEN** *Comes in hot-mop or torch-down styles.* |
| *Replace* Materials......77.10     Labor..........43.30     Equipment............6.83 <br> *Remove* ......................     Labor ..........53.40 | | | | | |
| **120 mil modified bitumen roofing, attached to deck at seams** | sq | $25.70 | $130.23 | $155.93 | ◁ 120 mil |
| *Replace* Materials......73.10     Labor..........50.30     Equipment............6.83 <br> *Remove* ......................     Labor ..........25.70 | | | | | |
| **120 mil modified bitumen roofing, fully attached to deck with torch** | sq | $40.90 | $145.09 | $185.99 | |
| *Replace* Materials......71.80     Labor..........65.10     Equipment............8.19 <br> *Remove* ......................     Labor ..........40.90 | | | | | |
| **120 mil modified bitumen roofing, fully attached with hot asphalt** | sq | $40.90 | $155.80 | $196.70 | |
| *Replace* Materials......79.80     Labor..........65.10     Equipment............10.90 <br> *Remove* ......................     Labor ..........40.90 | | | | | |
| **150 mil modified bitumen roofing, loose laid & ballasted with stone** | sq | $53.40 | $132.93 | $186.33 | ◁ 150 mil |
| *Replace* Materials......82.40     Labor..........43.70     Equipment............6.83 <br> *Remove* ......................     Labor ..........53.40 | | | | | |
| **150 mil modified bitumen roofing, attached to deck at seams** | sq | $25.70 | $135.53 | $161.23 | |
| *Replace* Materials......77.10     Labor..........51.60     Equipment............6.83 <br> *Remove* ......................     Labor ..........25.70 | | | | | |
| **150 mil modified bitumen roofing, fully attached to deck** | sq | $40.90 | $150.39 | $191.29 | |
| *Replace* Materials......75.80     Labor..........66.40     Equipment............8.19 <br> *Remove* ......................     Labor ..........40.90 | | | | | |
| **150 mil modified bitumen roofing, fully attached with hot asphalt** | sq | $40.90 | $162.80 | $203.70 | |
| *Replace* Materials......83.70     Labor..........68.20     Equipment..........10.90 <br> *Remove* ......................     Labor ..........40.90 | | | | | |
| **160 mil modified bitumen roofing, loose laid & ballasted with stone** | sq | $53.40 | $135.13 | $188.53 | ◁ 160 mil |
| *Replace* Materials......83.70     Labor..........44.60     Equipment............6.83 <br> *Remove* ......................     Labor ..........53.40 | | | | | |
| **160 mil modified bitumen roofing, attached to deck at seams** | sq | $25.70 | $139.03 | $164.73 | |
| *Replace* Materials......79.80     Labor..........52.40     Equipment............6.83 <br> *Remove* ......................     Labor ..........25.70 | | | | | |
| **160 mil modified bitumen roofing, fully attached to deck** | sq | $40.90 | $153.99 | $194.89 | |
| *Replace* Materials......78.50     Labor..........67.30     Equipment............8.19 <br> *Remove* ......................     Labor ..........40.90 | | | | | |
| **160 mil modified bitumen roofing, fully attached with hot asphalt** | sq | $40.90 | $172.20 | $213.10 | |
| *Replace* Materials......91.80     Labor..........69.50     Equipment..........10.90 <br> *Remove* ......................     Labor ..........40.90 | | | | | |
| **15-pound roofing felt** | sq | $3.90 | $7.70 | $11.60 | ◀ **ROOFING FELT** |
| *Replace* Materials........3.99     Labor ............3.71 <br> *Remove* ......................     Labor ............3.90 | | | | | |

**RELATED ITEMS**
Rough Carpentry
*chimney cricket* ............444

| Item Description | Unit | Remove | Replace | Total |
|---|---|---|---|---|
| **ROOFING FELT ►** *continued* **30-pound roofing felt** *Replace* Materials.......7.18  Labor ..........3.71  *Remove* ....................... Labor ..........3.90 | sq | $3.90 | $10.89 | $14.79 |
| **ICE AND WATER ► SHIELD** **Ice and water shield** *Replace* Materials ........ .46  Labor............ .35 | sf | — | $.81 | $.81 |
| **DRIP EDGE ►** **Drip edge** *Replace* Materials ........ .44  Labor............ .26  *Remove* ....................... Labor............ .13 | lf | $.13 | $.70 | $.83 |
| **GRAVEL STOP ►** **Gravel stop** *Replace* Materials ........ .76  Labor............ .26  *Remove* ....................... Labor............ .13 | lf | $.13 | $1.02 | $1.15 |
| **STEP FLASHING ►** **Step flashing** *Replace* Materials.......1.24  Labor ..........1.75 | lf | — | $2.99 | $2.99 |
| **CHIMNEY SAW- ► KERF FLASHING** **Chimney saw-kerf flashing** *Replace* Materials.......6.10  Labor ..........6.90 | lf | — | $13.00 | $13.00 |
| **Minimum charge for chimney saw-kerf flashing** *Replace* Materials ......36.50  Labor ..........43.70 | ea | — | $80.20 | $80.20 |
| **VALLEY METAL ►** **Valley metal (galvanized or aluminum)** *Replace* Materials........1.64  Labor............ .74  *Remove* ....................... Labor............ .26 | lf | $.26 | $2.38 | $2.64 |
| **Copper valley metal** *Replace* Materials........6.60  Labor............ .70  *Remove* ....................... Labor............ .26 | lf | $.26 | $7.30 | $7.56 |
| **PIPE JACK ►** **Pipe jack** *Replace* Materials.......7.94  Labor ..........7.65  *Remove* ....................... Labor ..........8.96 | ea | $8.96 | $15.59 | $24.55 |
| **ROOF VENT ►** **Roof vent, turbine** *Replace* Materials......30.60  Labor ..........12.90  *Remove* ....................... Labor ..........11.10 | ea | $11.10 | $43.50 | $54.60 |
| **Roof vent, turtle** *Replace* Materials ......14.60  Labor ..........11.10  *Remove* ....................... Labor ..........11.10 | ea | $11.10 | $25.70 | $36.80 |
| **Roof vent, gable** *Replace* Materials ......18.70  Labor ..........11.20  *Remove* ....................... Labor ..........11.10 | ea | $11.10 | $29.90 | $41.00 |
| **Remove roof vent for work, then reinstall** *Replace* ....................... Labor..........21.40 | ea | — | $21.40 | $21.40 |
| **FURNACE VENT ►** **Furnace vent cap** *Replace* Materials ......10.60  Labor ..........8.96  *Remove* ....................... Labor ..........11.20 | ea | $11.20 | $19.56 | $30.76 |
| **Remove vent cap for work, then reinstall** *Replace* ....................... Labor..........15.50 | ea | — | $15.50 | $15.50 |
| **REPAIR LEAK ► WITH MASTIC** **Repair roof leak with mastic** *Replace* Materials.......2.89  Labor..........19.80 | ea | — | $22.69 | $22.69 |
| **Repair flashing leak with mastic** *Replace* Materials.......2.89  Labor..........19.00 | ea | — | $21.89 | $21.89 |

# TIME & MATERIAL CHARTS (selected items)

## Roofing Materials

See **Roofing** material prices with the line items and other information in the **QuickFinder** column.

## Roofing Labor

| LABORER | BASE WAGE | PAID LEAVE | TRUE WAGE | FICA | FUTA | WORKER'S COMP. | UNEMPLOY. INSUR. | HEALTH INSUR. | RETIRE (401K) | LIABILITY INSUR. | COST PER HOUR |
|---------|-----------|------------|-----------|------|------|----------------|------------------|---------------|---------------|------------------|---------------|
| Roofer / slater | $22.00 | 1.72 | $23.72 | 1.81 | .19 | 13.14 | 2.06 | 2.54 | .71 | 3.08 | $47.30 |
| Roofer's helper | $18.40 | 1.44 | $19.84 | 1.52 | .16 | 10.99 | 1.73 | 2.54 | .60 | 2.58 | $40.00 |
| Demolition laborer | $13.40 | 1.05 | $14.45 | 1.11 | .12 | 4.44 | 1.26 | 2.54 | .43 | 1.88 | $26.20 |

**Paid Leave** is calculated based on two weeks paid vacation, one week sick leave, and seven paid holidays. Employer's matching portion of **FICA** is 7.65 percent. **FUTA** (Federal Unemployment) is .8 percent. **Worker's compensation** for the roofing trade was calculated using a national average of 55.38 percent. **Unemployment insurance** was calculated using a national average of 8.7 percent. **Health insurance** was calculated based on a projected national average for 2001 of $505 per employee (and family when applicable) per month. Employer pays 80 percent for a per month cost of $404 per employee. **Retirement** is based on a 401(k) retirement program with employer matching of 50 percent. Employee contributions to the 401(k) plan are an average of 6 percent of the true wage. **Liability insurance** is based on a national average of 12.9 percent.

## Roofing Labor Productivity

| WORK DESCRIPTION | LABORER | COST PER HOUR | PRODUCTIVITY | UNIT PRICE |
|------------------|---------|---------------|--------------|------------|
| **Demolition** | | | | |
| remove metal shingles | demolition laborer | $26.20 | 1.04 | $27.20 sq |
| remove asphalt shingles | demolition laborer | $26.20 | 1.02 | $26.70 sq |
| remove roll roofing | demolition laborer | $26.20 | .735 | $19.30 sq |
| remove slate shingles | demolition laborer | $26.20 | 3.70 | $96.90 sq |
| remove wood shingles or shakes | demolition laborer | $26.20 | 1.20 | $31.40 sq |
| remove fiber and cement shingles | demolition laborer | $26.20 | 1.11 | $29.10 sq |
| remove mission or Spanish tile shingles | demolition laborer | $26.20 | 3.45 | $90.40 sq |
| remove vertically laid furring strips | demolition laborer | $26.20 | .478 | $12.50 sq |
| remove vertically & horizontally laid furring strips | demolition laborer | $26.20 | .840 | $22.00 sq |
| remove concrete shingles | demolition laborer | $26.20 | 3.85 | $101.00 sq |
| remove preformed metal roofing | demolition laborer | $26.20 | .010 | $.26 sf |
| remove preformed fiberglass roofing | demolition laborer | $26.20 | .009 | $.24 sf |
| remove seamed metal roofing | demolition laborer | $26.20 | 1.03 | $27.00 sq |
| remove built-up 3 ply roofing | demolition laborer | $26.20 | 2.44 | $63.90 sq |
| remove built-up 4 ply roofing | demolition laborer | $26.20 | 3.03 | $79.40 sq |
| remove built-up 5 ply roofing | demolition laborer | $26.20 | 3.85 | $101.00 sq |
| add to remove built-up roof with ballast | demolition laborer | $26.20 | .847 | $22.20 sq |
| remove single ply roof partially adhered | demolition laborer | $26.20 | .980 | $25.70 sq |
| remove single ply roof fully adhered | demolition laborer | $26.20 | 1.56 | $40.90 sq |
| remove single ply roof with ballast | demolition laborer | $26.20 | 2.04 | $53.40 sq |
| **Roofing crew** | | | | |
| install roofing | roofer | $47.30 | | |
| install roofing | roofer's helper | $40.00 | | |
| install roofing | **roofing crew** | $43.70 | | |
| **Install shingles** | | | | |
| aluminum shingles | roofing crew | $43.70 | 1.06 | $46.30 sq |
| galvanized steel shingles | roofing crew | $43.70 | 1.11 | $48.50 sq |
| 20 year to 25 year asphalt | roofing crew | $43.70 | 1.24 | $54.20 sq |
| 30 year to 40 year asphalt | roofing crew | $43.70 | 1.27 | $55.50 sq |
| standard grade laminated asphalt | roofing crew | $43.70 | 2.06 | $90.00 sq |
| high grade laminated asphalt | roofing crew | $43.70 | 2.45 | $107.00 sq |
| T-lock asphalt | roofing crew | $43.70 | 1.27 | $55.50 sq |
| hexagonal asphalt | roofing crew | $43.70 | 1.27 | $55.50 sq |
| diamond asphalt | roofing crew | $43.70 | 1.27 | $55.50 sq |

*. . . More* ➢

## Roofing Labor Productivity *continued*

| WORK DESCRIPTION | LABORER | COST PER HOUR | PRODUCTIVITY | UNIT PRICE |
|---|---|---|---|---|
| **Install roll roofing** | | | | |
| all weights | roofing crew | $43.70 | .645 | $28.20 sq |
| **Install slate** | | | | |
| typical | roofing crew | $43.70 | 4.00 | $175.00 sq |
| replace single slate shingle | roofing crew | $43.70 | .385 | $16.80 ea |
| **Install wood shingles** | | | | |
| 16″ | roofing crew | $43.70 | 2.86 | $125.00 sq |
| 24″ | roofing crew | $43.70 | 2.00 | $87.40 sq |
| replace single wood shingle | roofing crew | $43.70 | .208 | $9.09 ea |
| **Install wood shakes** | | | | |
| 18″ | roofing crew | $43.70 | 3.33 | $146.00 sq |
| 24″ | roofing crew | $43.70 | 2.86 | $125.00 sq |
| replace single shake | roofing crew | $43.70 | .208 | $9.09 ea |
| **Install fiber and cement shingles** | | | | |
| weathering shake style | roofing crew | $43.70 | 2.38 | $104.00 sq |
| Spanish tile style | roofing crew | $43.70 | 2.50 | $109.00 sq |
| **Install clay tile** | | | | |
| flat | roofing crew | $43.70 | 3.23 | $141.00 sq |
| Mission tile | roofing crew | $43.70 | 5.56 | $243.00 sq |
| Spanish tile | roofing crew | $43.70 | 3.33 | $146.00 sq |
| **Install tile furring strips** | | | | |
| vertically laid only | roofing crew | $43.70 | .606 | $26.50 sq |
| vertically and horizontally laid | roofing crew | $43.70 | .877 | $38.30 sq |
| **Install concrete tile** | | | | |
| corrugated | roofing crew | $43.70 | 3.13 | $137.00 sq |
| flat | roofing crew | $43.70 | 3.03 | $132.00 sq |
| **Install pre-formed roofing** | | | | |
| corrugated aluminum or fiberglass | roofing crew | $43.70 | .024 | $1.05 sf |
| corrugated galvanized steel | roofing crew | $43.70 | .025 | $1.09 sf |
| ribbed (all types) | roofing crew | $43.70 | .026 | $1.14 sf |
| **Install standing seam metal roofing** | | | | |
| 16 ounce copper | roofing crew | $43.70 | 6.67 | $291.00 sq |
| 20 ounce copper | roofing crew | $43.70 | 7.69 | $336.00 sq |
| 28 gauge stainless steel | roofing crew | $43.70 | 7.14 | $312.00 sq |
| 40 lb terne | roofing crew | $43.70 | 8.33 | $364.00 sq |
| **Install batten seam metal roofing** | | | | |
| 16 ounce copper | roofing crew | $43.70 | 7.69 | $336.00 sq |
| 20 ounce copper | roofing crew | $43.70 | 9.09 | $397.00 sq |
| 28 gauge stainless steel | roofing crew | $43.70 | 7.69 | $336.00 sq |
| 26 gauge stainless steel | roofing crew | $43.70 | 7.14 | $312.00 sq |
| 3 lb lead | roofing crew | $43.70 | 7.14 | $312.00 sq |
| 40 lb terne | roofing crew | $43.70 | 7.69 | $336.00 sq |
| **Install flat seam metal roofing** | | | | |
| 16 ounce copper | roofing crew | $43.70 | 7.14 | $312.00 sq |
| 20 ounce copper | roofing crew | $43.70 | 8.33 | $364.00 sq |
| 28 gauge stainless steel | roofing crew | $43.70 | 7.14 | $312.00 sq |
| 26 gauge stainless steel | roofing crew | $43.70 | 6.67 | $291.00 sq |
| 3 lb lead | roofing crew | $43.70 | 7.69 | $336.00 sq |
| 40 lb terne | roofing crew | $43.70 | 9.09 | $397.00 sq |
| **Seamed metal roofing repair** | | | | |
| solder patch (less than 1′ square) | roofer | $47.30 | 1.00 | $47.30 ea |
| **Install built-up roof** | | | | |
| 3 ply | roofing crew | $43.70 | 3.33 | $146.00 sq |
| 4 ply | roofing crew | $43.70 | 4.00 | $175.00 sq |
| 5 ply | roofing crew | $43.70 | 4.76 | $208.00 sq |

✍ NOTES: _____

_____ end

# 32 ......................... *Rough Carpentry*

| Item Description | Unit | Remove | Replace | Total | |
|---|---|---|---|---|---|
| **Minimum charge for rough carpentry work**<br>*Replace* Materials......50.00    Labor..........45.80 | ea | — | $95.80 | $95.80 | ◄ **MINIMUM** |
| **2" x 4" interior partition wall 8' tall 16" on center**<br>*Replace* Materials.......7.46   Labor.........8.29<br>*Remove*.....................   Labor ..........1.18 | lf | $1.18 | $15.75 | $16.93 | ◄ **PER LF**<br>**INTERIOR**<br>**PARTITION WALL**<br>*Includes 5% waste.*<br>*Based on an average wall*<br>*with 4 openings and 5* |
| **2" x 4" interior partition wall 8' tall 24" on center**<br>*Replace* Materials.......6.24   Labor.........7.05<br>*Remove*.....................   Labor ..........1.18 | lf | $1.18 | $13.29 | $14.47 | *corners per 56 lf of wall.*<br>*A net of 2.2 studs is*<br>*added for each corner and* |
| **2" x 4" interior partition wall 10' tall 16" on center**<br>*Replace* Materials.......8.88   Labor.........8.39<br>*Remove* .....................   Labor ..........1.49 | lf | $1.49 | $17.27 | $18.76 | *opening. All walls have*<br>*two top plates and a*<br>*single bottom plate.* |
| **2" x 4" interior partition wall 10' tall 24" on center**<br>*Replace* Materials.......7.34   Labor.........7.12<br>*Remove* .....................   Labor ..........1.49 | lf | $1.49 | $14.46 | $15.95 | |
| **2" x 6" interior partition wall 8' tall 16" on center**<br>*Replace* Materials......10.70   Labor.........8.39<br>*Remove*.....................   Labor ..........1.26 | lf | $1.26 | $19.09 | $20.35 |  |
| **2" x 6" interior partition wall 8' tall 24" on center**<br>*Replace* Materials......8.98   Labor .........7.12<br>*Remove*.....................   Labor ..........1.26 | lf | $1.26 | $16.10 | $17.36 | |
| **2" x 6" interior partition wall 10' tall 16" on center**<br>*Replace* Materials ......12.70   Labor ..........8.50<br>*Remove*.....................   Labor ..........1.57 | lf | $1.57 | $21.20 | $22.77 | |
| **2" x 6" interior partition wall 10' tall 24" on center**<br>*Replace* Materials......10.50   Labor ..........7.19<br>*Remove*.....................   Labor ..........1.57 | lf | $1.57 | $17.69 | $19.26 | **LUMBER PRICES**<br>Some lumber prices,<br>such as oak timbers,<br>vary by as much as 60% |
| **2" x 8" interior partition wall 8' tall 16" on center**<br>*Replace* Materials ......14.00   Labor ..........8.50<br>*Remove* .....................   Labor ..........1.28 | lf | $1.28 | $22.50 | $23.78 | depending on the region.<br>These prices will be 15%<br>to 30% lower in the<br>Northeast, South, and |
| **2" x 8" interior partition wall 8' tall 24" on center**<br>*Replace* Materials.......11.80   Labor ..........7.19<br>*Remove* .....................   Labor ..........1.28 | lf | $1.28 | $18.99 | $20.27 | most Great Lake states<br>and provinces. In many<br>areas of the western mid-<br>west and mountain states |
| **2" x 8" interior partition wall 10' tall 16" on center**<br>*Replace* Materials ......16.60   Labor ..........8.60<br>*Remove* .....................   Labor ..........1.60 | lf | $1.60 | $25.20 | $26.80 | and provinces, oak tim-<br>bers are not available<br>unless specially shipped<br>for a particular job. |
| **2" x 8" interior partition wall 10' tall 24" on center**<br>*Replace* Materials.......13.80   Labor ..........7.26<br>*Remove* .....................   Labor ..........1.60 | lf | $1.60 | $21.06 | $22.66 | For the most accurate<br>results, compare your<br>local prices with the<br>prices found in the mate-<br>rial charts for this section<br>starting on page 445 and<br>create a materials factor. |
| **2" x 4" interior bearing wall 8' tall 12" on center**<br>*Replace* Materials ......10.80   Labor...........10.60<br>*Remove*.....................   Labor ..........1.18 | lf | $1.18 | $21.40 | $22.58 | ◄ **PER LF**<br>**INTERIOR**<br>**BEARING WALL** |
| **2" x 4" interior bearing wall 8' tall 16" on center**<br>*Replace* Materials ......9.60   Labor ..........8.98<br>*Remove*.....................   Labor ..........1.18 | lf | $1.18 | $18.58 | $19.76 | *continued on next page* |

| Item Description | Unit | Remove | Replace | Total |
|---|---|---|---|---|

**PER LF ▶**
**INTERIOR**
**BEARING WALL**
*continued*

*Includes 5% waste. Based on an average wall with 4 openings and 5 corners per 56 lf of wall. A net of 2.2 studs is added for each corner and opening. (Four openings are, two 3' wide, one 4' wide, and one 5' wide for a total of 15 lf.) Headers in openings are made from sandwiched 2" x 10" boards with 1/2" CDX plywood stiffeners between. All walls have two top plates and a single bottom plate.*

| Item Description | Unit | Remove | Replace | Total |
|---|---|---|---|---|
| **2" x 4" interior bearing wall 10' tall 12" on center** *Replace* Materials ......12.60  Labor..........10.70  *Remove* ........................  Labor ...........1.49 | lf | $1.49 | $23.30 | $24.79 |
| **2" x 4" interior bearing wall 10' tall 16" on center** *Replace* Materials.......11.00  Labor ...........9.12  *Remove* ........................  Labor ...........1.49 | lf | $1.49 | $20.12 | $21.61 |
| **2" x 6" interior bearing wall 8' tall 12" on center** *Replace* Materials ......18.30  Labor..........10.70  *Remove* ........................  Labor ...........1.26 | lf | $1.26 | $29.00 | $30.26 |
| **2" x 6" interior bearing wall 8' tall 16" on center** *Replace* Materials ......16.60  Labor ...........9.05  *Remove*........................  Labor ...........1.26 | lf | $1.26 | $25.65 | $26.91 |
| **2" x 6" interior bearing wall 10' tall 12" on center** *Replace* Materials ......20.80  Labor..........10.80  *Remove* ........................  Labor ...........1.57 | lf | $1.57 | $31.60 | $33.17 |
| **2" x 6" interior bearing wall 10' tall 16" on center** *Replace* Materials ......18.60  Labor ...........9.18  *Remove*........................  Labor ...........1.57 | lf | $1.57 | $27.78 | $29.35 |
| **2" x 8" interior bearing wall 8' tall 12" on center** *Replace* Materials ......24.00  Labor..........10.80  *Remove* ........................  Labor ...........1.28 | lf | $1.28 | $34.80 | $36.08 |
| **2" x 8" interior bearing wall 8' tall 16" on center** *Replace* Materials ......21.80  Labor ...........9.15  *Remove* ........................  Labor ...........1.28 | lf | $1.28 | $30.95 | $32.23 |
| **2" x 8" interior bearing wall 10' tall 12" on center** *Replace* Materials ......27.10  Labor..........10.90  *Remove* ........................  Labor ...........1.60 | lf | $1.60 | $38.00 | $39.60 |
| **2" x 8" interior bearing wall 10' tall 16" on center** *Replace* Materials ......24.30  Labor ...........9.29  *Remove* ........................  Labor ...........1.60 | lf | $1.60 | $33.59 | $35.19 |

**PER LF ▶**
**EXTERIOR WALL**

*Includes 5% waste. Based on an average wall with 4 openings and 5 corners per 56 lf of wall. A net of 2.2 studs is added for each corner and opening. (Four openings are, two 3' wide, one 4' wide, and one 5' wide for a total of 15 lf.) Headers in openings are made from sandwiched 2" x 10" boards with 1/2" CDX plywood stiffeners between boards. Includes 4 metal let-in braces for every 56 lf of wall. All walls have two top plates and a single bottom plate. Does not include exterior sheathing.*

| Item Description | Unit | Remove | Replace | Total |
|---|---|---|---|---|
| **2" x 4" exterior wall 8' tall 12" on center** *Replace* Materials.......11.06  Labor..........10.80  *Remove*........................  Labor ...........1.18 | lf | $1.18 | $21.86 | $23.04 |
| **2" x 4" exterior wall 8' tall 16" on center** *Replace* Materials.......9.84  Labor ...........9.18  *Remove*........................  Labor ...........1.18 | lf | $1.18 | $19.02 | $20.20 |
| **2" x 4" exterior wall 8' tall 24" on center** *Replace* Materials.......8.61  Labor ...........7.43  *Remove*........................  Labor ...........1.18 | lf | $1.18 | $16.04 | $17.22 |
| **2" x 4" exterior wall 10' tall 12" on center** *Replace* Materials ......12.80  Labor..........10.90  *Remove* ........................  Labor ...........1.49 | lf | $1.49 | $23.70 | $25.19 |
| **2" x 4" exterior wall 10' tall 16" on center** *Replace* Materials.......11.30  Labor ...........9.29  *Remove* ........................  Labor ...........1.49 | lf | $1.49 | $20.59 | $22.08 |
| **2" x 4" exterior wall 10' tall 24" on center** *Replace* Materials.......9.71  Labor ...........7.50  *Remove* ........................  Labor ...........1.49 | lf | $1.49 | $17.21 | $18.70 |

| Item Description | Unit | Remove | Replace | Total | |
|---|---|---|---|---|---|
| **2" x 6" exterior wall 8' tall 12" on center**<br>*Replace* Materials ......18.60  Labor..........10.90<br>*Remove* ......................  Labor ...........1.18 | lf | $1.18 | $29.50 | $30.68 | ◁ **2" x 6"** |
| **2" x 6" exterior wall 8' tall 16" on center**<br>*Replace* Materials ......16.80  Labor ...........9.29<br>*Remove*......................  Labor ...........1.18 | lf | $1.18 | $26.09 | $27.27 | |
| **2" x 6" exterior wall 8' tall 24" on center**<br>*Replace* Materials......15.00  Labor ...........7.50<br>*Remove*......................  Labor ...........1.18 | lf | $1.18 | $22.50 | $23.68 | |
| **2" x 6" exterior wall 10' tall 12" on center**<br>*Replace* Materials ......21.00  Labor ...........11.00<br>*Remove*......................  Labor ...........1.49 | lf | $1.49 | $32.00 | $33.49 | |
| **2" x 6" exterior wall 10' tall 16" on center**<br>*Replace* Materials ......18.80  Labor ...........9.39<br>*Remove*......................  Labor ...........1.49 | lf | $1.49 | $28.19 | $29.68 | |
| **2" x 6" exterior wall 10' tall 24" on center**<br>*Replace* Materials ......16.60  Labor ...........7.60<br>*Remove*......................  Labor ...........1.49 | lf | $1.49 | $24.20 | $25.69 | |
| **2" x 8" exterior wall 8' tall 12" on center**<br>*Replace* Materials......24.20  Labor ...........11.00<br>*Remove* ......................  Labor ...........1.18 | lf | $1.18 | $35.20 | $36.38 | ◁ **2" x 8"** |
| **2" x 8" exterior wall 8' tall 16" on center**<br>*Replace* Materials......22.00  Labor ...........9.36<br>*Remove* ......................  Labor ...........1.18 | lf | $1.18 | $31.36 | $32.54 | |
| **2" x 8" exterior wall 8' tall 24" on center**<br>*Replace* Materials........19.80  Labor ...........7.57<br>*Remove* ......................  Labor ...........1.18 | lf | $1.18 | $27.37 | $28.55 | |
| **2" x 8" exterior wall 10' tall 12" on center**<br>*Replace* Materials......27.30  Labor ...........11.10<br>*Remove* ......................  Labor ...........1.49 | lf | $1.49 | $38.40 | $39.89 | |
| **2" x 8" exterior wall 10' tall 16" on center**<br>*Replace* Materials ......24.60  Labor ...........9.46<br>*Remove* ......................  Labor ...........1.49 | lf | $1.49 | $34.06 | $35.55 | |
| **2" x 8" exterior wall 10' tall 24" on center**<br>*Replace* Materials ......21.80  Labor ...........7.67<br>*Remove* ......................  Labor ...........1.49 | lf | $1.49 | $29.47 | $30.96 | |
| **2" x 4" interior partition wall 16" on center**<br>*Replace* Materials ........ .93  Labor........... 1.03<br>*Remove*......................  Labor ............. .16 | sf | $.16 | $1.96 | $2.12 | ◀ **PER SF**<br>**INTERIOR** |
| **2" x 4" interior partition wall 24" on center**<br>*Replace* Materials ........ .78  Labor............. .89<br>*Remove* ......................  Labor ............. .16 | sf | $.16 | $1.67 | $1.83 | **PARTITION WALL**<br>*Includes 5% waste.*<br>*Based on an average* |
| **2" x 6" interior partition wall 16" on center**<br>*Replace* Materials........1.34  Labor........... 1.03<br>*Remove* ......................  Labor ............. .16 | sf | $.16 | $2.37 | $2.53 | *wall with 4 openings and*<br>*5 corners per 448 sf of*<br>*wall. A net of 2.2 studs*<br>*is added for each corner* |
| **2" x 6" interior partition wall 24" on center**<br>*Replace* Materials........1.12  Labor............. .89<br>*Remove* ......................  Labor ............. .16 | sf | $.16 | $2.01 | $2.17 | *and opening. All walls*<br>*have two top plates and*<br>*a single bottom plate.* |

| Item Description | Unit | Remove | Replace | Total |
|---|---|---|---|---|
| **PER SF ▶** **INTERIOR PARTITION WALL** *continued* | | | | |
| **2" x 8" interior partition wall 16" on center** <br> *Replace* Materials........3.39    Labor ...........1.07 <br> *Remove* .........................    Labor............ .16 | sf | $.16 | $4.46 | $4.62 |
| **2" x 8" interior partition wall 24" on center** <br> *Replace* Materials........3.04    Labor............ .89 <br> *Remove* .........................    Labor............ .16 | sf | $.16 | $3.93 | $4.09 |
| **PER SF ▶** **SLOPING INTERIOR PARTITION WALL** *Includes 5% waste. Based on an average wall with one 3' wide opening, two 4'6" wide openings, and 2 corners per 24 lf of wall. A net of 2.4 studs is added per corner or opening. All walls have two top plates and a single bottom plate.* | | | | |
| **2" x 4" sloping interior partition wall 16" on center** <br> *Replace* Materials ........ .74    Labor ...........1.41 <br> *Remove*.........................    Labor............ .16 | sf | $.16 | $2.15 | $2.31 |
| **2" x 4" sloping interior partition wall 24" on center** <br> *Replace* Materials ........ .62    Labor ...........1.20 <br> *Remove*.........................    Labor............ .16 | sf | $.16 | $1.82 | $1.98 |
| **2" x 6" sloping interior partition wall 16" on center** <br> *Replace* Materials........1.05    Labor ...........1.44 <br> *Remove* .........................    Labor............ .16 | sf | $.16 | $2.49 | $2.65 |
| **2" x 6" sloping interior partition wall 24" on center** <br> *Replace* Materials ........ .89    Labor ...........1.24 <br> *Remove* .........................    Labor............ .16 | sf | $.16 | $2.13 | $2.29 |
| **2" x 8" sloping interior partition wall 16" on center** <br> *Replace* Materials........1.36    Labor ...........1.44 <br> *Remove* .........................    Labor............ .16 | sf | $.16 | $2.80 | $2.96 |
| **2" x 8" sloping interior partition wall 24" on center** <br> *Replace* Materials........1.16    Labor ...........1.24 <br> *Remove* .........................    Labor............ .16 | sf | $.16 | $2.40 | $2.56 |
| **PER SF ▶** **SLOPING INTERIOR BEARING WALL** *Includes 5% waste. Based on an average wall with one 3' wide opening, two 4'6" wide openings, and 2 corners per 24 lf of wall. A net of 2.4 studs is added per corner or opening. Headers in openings are made from sandwiched 2" x 10" boards with 1/2" CDX plywood stiffeners between boards. All walls have two top plates and a single bottom plate.* | | | | |
| **2" x 4" sloping interior bearing wall 12" on center** <br> *Replace* Materials........1.08    Labor ...........2.03 <br> *Remove* .........................    Labor............ .16 | sf | $.16 | $3.11 | $3.27 |
| **2" x 4" sloping interior bearing wall 16" on center** <br> *Replace* Materials ........ .96    Labor ...........1.72 <br> *Remove* .........................    Labor............ .16 | sf | $.16 | $2.68 | $2.84 |
| **2" x 6" sloping interior bearing wall 12" on center** <br> *Replace* Materials........1.45    Labor ...........2.03 <br> *Remove* .........................    Labor............ .16 | sf | $.16 | $3.48 | $3.64 |
| **2" x 6" sloping interior bearing wall 16" on center** <br> *Replace* Materials........1.28    Labor ...........1.72 <br> *Remove* .........................    Labor............ .16 | sf | $.16 | $3.00 | $3.16 |
| **2" x 8" sloping interior bearing wall 12" on center** <br> *Replace* Materials........1.80    Labor ...........2.06 <br> *Remove* .........................    Labor............ .16 | sf | $.16 | $3.86 | $4.02 |
| **2" x 8" sloping interior bearing wall 16" on center** <br> *Replace* Materials........1.59    Labor ...........1.75 <br> *Remove* .........................    Labor............ .16 | sf | $.16 | $3.34 | $3.50 |
| **PER SF ▶** **INTERIOR BEARING WALL** *Includes 5% waste. Based on an average wall with 4 openings and 5 corners per 56 lf.* | | | | |
| **2" x 4" interior bearing wall 12" on center** <br> *Replace* Materials........1.35    Labor ...........1.31 <br> *Remove*.........................    Labor............ .16 | sf | $.16 | $2.66 | $2.82 |
| **2" x 4" interior bearing wall 16" on center** <br> *Replace* Materials........1.20    Labor ...........1.14 <br> *Remove*.........................    Labor............ .16 | sf | $.16 | $2.34 | $2.50 |

*continued on next page*

| Item Description | Unit | Remove | Replace | Total |
|---|---|---|---|---|
| **2" x 6" interior bearing wall 12" on center**<br>*Replace* Materials........2.29  Labor...........1.34<br>*Remove* .....................  Labor.............16 | sf | $.16 | $3.63 | $3.79 |
| **2" x 6" interior bearing wall 16" on center**<br>*Replace* Materials........2.08  Labor...........1.14<br>*Remove* .....................  Labor.............16 | sf | $.16 | $3.22 | $3.38 |
| **2" x 8" interior bearing wall 12" on center**<br>*Replace* Materials........3.00  Labor...........1.34<br>*Remove* .....................  Labor.............16 | sf | $.16 | $4.34 | $4.50 |
| **2" x 8" interior bearing wall 16" on center**<br>*Replace* Materials........2.73  Labor...........1.14<br>*Remove* .....................  Labor.............16 | sf | $.16 | $3.87 | $4.03 |
| **2" x 4" exterior wall 12" on center**<br>*Replace* Materials........1.38  Labor...........1.38<br>*Remove*.....................  Labor.............16 | sf | $.16 | $2.76 | $2.92 |
| **2" x 4" exterior wall 16" on center**<br>*Replace* Materials........1.23  Labor...........1.17<br>*Remove*.....................  Labor.............16 | sf | $.16 | $2.40 | $2.56 |
| **2" x 4" exterior wall 24" on center**<br>*Replace* Materials........1.08  Labor.............93<br>*Remove*.....................  Labor.............16 | sf | $.16 | $2.01 | $2.17 |
| **2" x 6" exterior wall 12" on center**<br>*Replace* Materials........2.33  Labor...........1.38<br>*Remove* .....................  Labor.............16 | sf | $.16 | $3.71 | $3.87 |
| **2" x 6" exterior wall 16" on center**<br>*Replace* Materials........2.10  Labor...........1.17<br>*Remove* .....................  Labor.............16 | sf | $.16 | $3.27 | $3.43 |
| **2" x 6" exterior wall 24" on center**<br>*Replace* Materials........1.88  Labor.............93<br>*Remove* .....................  Labor.............16 | sf | $.16 | $2.81 | $2.97 |
| **2" x 8" exterior wall 12" on center**<br>*Replace* Materials........3.03  Labor...........1.38<br>*Remove* .....................  Labor.............16 | sf | $.16 | $4.41 | $4.57 |
| **2" x 8" exterior wall 16" on center**<br>*Replace* Materials........2.75  Labor...........1.17<br>*Remove* .....................  Labor.............16 | sf | $.16 | $3.92 | $4.08 |
| **2" x 8" exterior wall 24" on center**<br>*Replace* Materials........2.48  Labor.............96<br>*Remove* .....................  Labor.............16 | sf | $.16 | $3.44 | $3.60 |
| **2" x 4" sloping exterior wall 12" on center**<br>*Replace* Materials........1.25  Labor...........1.86<br>*Remove*.....................  Labor.............16 | sf | $.16 | $3.11 | $3.27 |
| **2" x 4" sloping exterior wall 16" on center**<br>*Replace* Materials........1.12  Labor...........1.58<br>*Remove*.....................  Labor.............16 | sf | $.16 | $2.70 | $2.86 |
| **2" x 4" sloping exterior wall 24" on center**<br>*Replace* Materials........ .99  Labor...........1.31<br>*Remove*.....................  Labor.............16 | sf | $.16 | $2.30 | $2.46 |

◄ **PER SF INTERIOR BEARING WALL** *continued*

A net of 2.2 studs is added for each corner and opening. Openings are two 3' wide, one 4' wide, and one 5' wide for a total of 15 lf. Headers are made from sandwiched 2" x 10" boards with 1/2" CDX plywood stiffeners. All walls have two top plates and a single bottom plate.

◄ **PER SF EXTERIOR WALL** Includes 5% waste. Based on an average wall with 4 openings and 5 corners per 56 lf of wall. A net of 2.2 studs is added for each corner and opening. Openings are two 3' wide, one 4' wide, and one 5' wide for a total of 15 lf. Headers in openings are made from sandwiched 2" x 10" boards with 1/2" CDX plywood stiffeners between boards. Includes 4 metal let-in braces for every 56 lf of wall. All walls have two top plates and a single bottom plate. Does not include exterior sheathing.

◁ **2" x 8"**

**RELATED ITEMS**

◄ **PER SF SLOPING EXTERIOR WALL** Includes 5% waste. Based on an average wall with one 3' wide opening, two 4'6" openings, and 2 corners per 24 lf. A net of 2.4 studs is added per corner or opening.

continued on next page

| Item Description | Unit | Remove | Replace | Total |
|---|---|---|---|---|
| **PER SF ►**<br>**SLOPING EXTERIOR WALL** *continued*<br><br>*Headers in openings are made from sandwiched 2" x 10" boards with 1/2" CDX plywood stiffeners between boards. Includes 3 metal let-in braces for every 24 lf of wall. All walls have two top plates and a single bottom plate.* | | | | |
| **2" x 6" sloping exterior wall 12" on center**<br>*Replace* Materials........1.65      Labor ............1.86<br>*Remove* .....................      Labor............ .16 | sf | $.16 | $3.51 | $3.67 |
| **2" x 6" sloping exterior wall 16" on center**<br>*Replace* Materials........1.47      Labor ............1.58<br>*Remove* .....................      Labor............ .16 | sf | $.16 | $3.05 | $3.21 |
| **2" x 6" sloping exterior wall 24" on center**<br>*Replace* Materials........1.29      Labor ............1.31<br>*Remove* .....................      Labor............ .16 | sf | $.16 | $2.60 | $2.76 |
| **2" x 8" sloping exterior wall 12" on center**<br>*Replace* Materials........2.04      Labor ............1.89<br>*Remove* .....................      Labor............ .16 | sf | $.16 | $3.93 | $4.09 |
| **2" x 8" sloping exterior wall 16" on center**<br>*Replace* Materials........1.81      Labor ............1.62<br>*Remove* .....................      Labor............ .16 | sf | $.16 | $3.43 | $3.59 |
| **2" x 8" sloping exterior wall 24" on center**<br>*Replace* Materials........1.58      Labor ............1.31<br>*Remove* .....................      Labor............ .16 | sf | $.16 | $2.89 | $3.05 |
| **ADDITIONAL ►**<br>**WALL FRAMING COSTS** | | | | |
| **Add for beam pocket in exterior or bearing wall**<br>*Replace* Materials ......37.00      Labor .........38.20 | ea | — | $75.20 | $75.20 |
| **Add to frame round- or elliptical-top door or window per lf of opening**<br>*Replace* Materials........2.99      Labor .........20.20 | lf | — | $23.19 | $23.19 |
| **Add to frame round window per diameter of opening**<br>*Replace* Materials........3.46      Labor.........21.90 | lf | — | $25.36 | $25.36 |
| **Add to frame bay window per lf of wall**<br>*Replace* Materials........3.46      Labor .........20.00 | lf | — | $23.46 | $23.46 |
| **Add to frame bow window per lf of wall**<br>*Replace* Materials........3.46      Labor .........22.30 | lf | — | $25.76 | $25.76 |
| **ADDITIONAL ►**<br>**COST FOR CEC BRACING**<br>*Additional cost to nail, brace, and shear panel to California Earthquake Code standards. Per sf of wall.* | | | | |
| **Add for CEC bracing and shear paneling of interior bearing wall**<br>*Replace* Materials ........ .25      Labor............ .38 | sf | — | $.63 | $.63 |
| **Add for CEC bracing and shear paneling of sloping interior wall**<br>*Replace* Materials ........ .28      Labor............ .48 | sf | — | $.76 | $.76 |
| **Add for CEC bracing and shear paneling of exterior wall**<br>*Replace* Materials ........ .31      Labor............ .38 | sf | — | $.69 | $.69 |
| **Add for CEC bracing and shear paneling of sloping exterior wall**<br>*Replace* Materials ........ .35      Labor............ .52 | sf | — | $.87 | $.87 |
| **PER BF ►**<br>**WALL FRAMING**<br>*Includes 7% waste.* | | | | |
| **Interior wall per bf**<br>*Replace* Materials ........ .99      Labor ............1.17<br>*Remove* .....................      Labor............ .18 | bf | $.18 | $2.16 | $2.34 |
| **Sloping interior wall per bf**<br>*Replace* Materials........1.05      Labor ............1.62<br>*Remove* .....................      Labor............ .18 | bf | $.18 | $2.67 | $2.85 |
| **Exterior wall per bf**<br>*Replace* Materials........1.21      Labor ............1.27<br>*Remove* .....................      Labor............ .18 | bf | $.18 | $2.48 | $2.66 |

*CEC = California Earthquake Code.*

| Item Description | Unit | Remove | Replace | Total |
|---|---|---|---|---|
| **Sloping exterior wall per bf** | bf | $.18 | $3.04 | $3.22 |
| *Replace* Materials........1.29　　　Labor............1.75 | | | | |
| *Remove* ......................　　　Labor............18 | | | | |
| **2″ x 4″ top plate** | lf | $.34 | $1.23 | $1.57 |
| *Replace* Materials........ .65　　　Labor.............58 | | | | |
| *Remove* ......................　　　Labor............34 | | | | |
| **2″ x 6″ top plate** | lf | $.34 | $1.55 | $1.89 |
| *Replace* Materials........ .93　　　Labor.............62 | | | | |
| *Remove* ......................　　　Labor............34 | | | | |
| **2″ x 8″ top plate** | lf | $.34 | $1.98 | $2.32 |
| *Replace* Materials........1.36　　　Labor.............62 | | | | |
| *Remove* ......................　　　Labor............34 | | | | |
| **2″ x 4″ treated-wood foundation sill plate** | lf | $1.18 | $3.37 | $4.55 |
| *Replace* Materials........1.07　　　Labor............2.30 | | | | |
| *Remove* ......................　　　Labor............1.18 | | | | |
| **2″ x 6″ treated-wood foundation sill plate** | lf | $1.18 | $3.89 | $5.07 |
| *Replace* Materials........1.59　　　Labor............2.30 | | | | |
| *Remove* ......................　　　Labor............1.18 | | | | |
| **2″ x 8″ treated-wood foundation sill plate** | lf | $1.18 | $4.45 | $5.63 |
| *Replace* Materials........2.11　　　Labor............2.34 | | | | |
| *Remove* ......................　　　Labor............1.18 | | | | |
| **2″ x 4″ con common redwood foundation sill plate** | lf | $1.18 | $3.50 | $4.68 |
| *Replace* Materials........1.26　　　Labor............2.24 | | | | |
| *Remove* ......................　　　Labor............1.18 | | | | |
| **2″ x 6″ con common redwood foundation sill plate** | lf | $1.18 | $3.83 | $5.01 |
| *Replace* Materials........1.59　　　Labor............2.24 | | | | |
| *Remove* ......................　　　Labor............1.18 | | | | |
| **2″ x 8″ con common redwood foundation sill plate** | lf | $1.18 | $4.48 | $5.66 |
| *Replace* Materials........2.21　　　Labor............2.27 | | | | |
| *Remove* ......................　　　Labor............1.18 | | | | |
| **4″ x 6″ header beam** | lf | $1.05 | $5.96 | $7.01 |
| *Replace* Materials........4.58　　　Labor............1.38 | | | | |
| *Remove* ......................　　　Labor............1.05 | | | | |
| ▶ For 2″ x 4″. Doubled 2″ x 6″ with 1/2″ CDX plywood stiffener. | | | | |
| **4″ x 8″ header beam** | lf | $1.05 | $6.61 | $7.66 |
| *Replace* Materials........5.17　　　Labor............1.44 | | | | |
| *Remove* ......................　　　Labor............1.05 | | | | |
| ▶ For 2″ x 4″ wall. Doubled 2″ x 8″ with 1/2″ CDX plywood stiffener. | | | | |
| **4″ x 10″ header beam** | lf | $1.05 | $8.73 | $9.78 |
| *Replace* Materials........7.25　　　Labor............1.48 | | | | |
| *Remove* ......................　　　Labor............1.05 | | | | |
| ▶ For 2″ x 4″ wall. Doubled 2″ x 10″ with 1/2″ CDX plywood stiffener. | | | | |
| **4″ x 12″ header beam** | lf | $1.05 | $10.33 | $11.38 |
| *Replace* Materials........8.78　　　Labor............1.55 | | | | |
| *Remove* ......................　　　Labor............1.05 | | | | |
| ▶ For 2″ x 4″ wall. Doubled 2″ x 12″ with 1/2″ CDX plywood stiffener. | | | | |
| **6″ x 6″ header beam** | lf | $1.05 | $10.33 | $11.38 |
| *Replace* Materials........8.23　　　Labor............2.10 | | | | |
| *Remove* ......................　　　Labor............1.05 | | | | |
| ▶ For 2″ x 6″ wall. Three 2″ x 6″ with two 1/2″ CDX plywood stiffeners. | | | | |

◀ **TOP PLATE**
Includes 5% waste. Cost to remove and replace a damaged top plate on an existing wall.

◀ **FOUNDATION SILL PLATE**
Includes foam sealer strip, hole drilling for anchor bolts, and fastening.

**CALIFORNIA EARTHQUAKE CODE**

Items that include "CEC" in the description are priced according to California earthquake code requirements.

Although these *Universal Building Code* standards are also required in other areas, they are most commonly associated with efforts initiated in California to improve the construction and engineering of structures in quake zones.

◀ **WALL HEADER**
Includes 5% waste.
◁ for 2″ x 4″ wall

◁ for 2″ x 6″ wall

| Item Description | Unit | Remove | Replace | Total |
|---|---|---|---|---|
| **WALL HEADER ▶** *continued*    **6" x 8" header beam** <br> *Replace* Materials........9.18    Labor ............2.24 <br> *Remove* ...................    Labor ............1.05 <br> ▶ For 2" x 6" wall. Three 2" x 8" with two 1/2" CDX plywood stiffeners. | lf | $1.05 | $11.42 | $12.47 |
| **6" x 10" header beam** <br> *Replace* Materials ......12.70    Labor ............2.37 <br> *Remove* ...................    Labor ............1.05 <br> ▶ For 2" x 6" wall. Three 2" x 10" with two 1/2" CDX plywood stiffeners. | lf | $1.05 | $15.07 | $16.12 |
| **6" x 12" header beam** <br> *Replace* Materials.......15.50    Labor ............2.55 <br> *Remove* ...................    Labor ............1.05 <br> ▶ For 2" x 6" wall. Three 2" x 12" with two 1/2" CDX plywood stiffeners. | lf | $1.05 | $18.05 | $19.10 |
| for 2" x 8" wall ▷    **8" x 6" header beam** <br> *Replace* Materials.......11.90    Labor ............2.51 <br> *Remove* ...................    Labor ............1.05 <br> ▶ For 2" x 8" wall. Four 2" x 6" with three 1/2" CDX plywood stiffeners. | lf | $1.05 | $14.41 | $15.46 |
| **8" x 8" header beam** <br> *Replace* Materials.......13.20    Labor ............2.68 <br> *Remove* ...................    Labor ............1.05 <br> ▶ For 2" x 8" wall. Four 2" x 8" with three 1/2" CDX plywood stiffeners. | lf | $1.05 | $15.88 | $16.93 |
| **8" x 10" header beam** <br> *Replace* Materials ......14.50    Labor ............2.92 <br> *Remove* ...................    Labor ............1.05 <br> ▶ For 2" x 8" wall. Four 2" x 10" with three 1/2" CDX plywood stiffeners. | lf | $1.05 | $17.42 | $18.47 |
| **8" x 12" header beam** <br> *Replace* Materials ......22.10    Labor ............3.20 <br> *Remove* ...................    Labor ............1.05 <br> ▶ For 2" x 8" wall. Four 2" x 12" with three 1/2" CDX plywood stiffeners. | lf | $1.05 | $25.30 | $26.35 |
| **POSTS ▶** *Includes 4% waste.* <br> **4" x 4" ▷**    **4" x 4" pine post** <br> *Replace* Materials........2.59    Labor ............1.44 <br> *Remove* ...................    Labor ............1.55 | lf | $1.55 | $4.03 | $5.58 |
| **4" x 4" con common redwood post** <br> *Replace* Materials........3.14    Labor ............1.44 <br> *Remove* ...................    Labor ............1.55 | lf | $1.55 | $4.58 | $6.13 |
| **4" x 4" treated pine post** <br> *Replace* Materials........3.37    Labor ............1.44 <br> *Remove* ...................    Labor ............1.55 | lf | $1.55 | $4.81 | $6.36 |
| **4" x 6" ▷**    **4" x 6" pine post** <br> *Replace* Materials........3.01    Labor ............1.48 <br> *Remove* ...................    Labor ............1.55 | lf | $1.55 | $4.49 | $6.04 |
| **4" x 6" con common redwood post** <br> *Replace* Materials........3.36    Labor ............1.48 <br> *Remove* ...................    Labor ............1.55 | lf | $1.55 | $4.84 | $6.39 |
| **4" x 6" treated pine post** <br> *Replace* Materials........3.91    Labor ............1.48 <br> *Remove* ...................    Labor ............1.55 | lf | $1.55 | $5.39 | $6.94 |
| **4" x 8" ▷**    **4" x 8" pine post** <br> *Replace* Materials........4.80    Labor ............1.48 <br> *Remove* ...................    Labor ............1.55 | lf | $1.55 | $6.28 | $7.83 |

| Item Description | Unit | Remove | Replace | Total |
|---|---|---|---|---|
| **4" x 8" con common redwood post**<br>*Replace* Materials........4.84     Labor ............1.48<br>*Remove* ......................     Labor ...........1.55 | lf | $1.55 | $6.32 | $7.87 |
| **4" x 8" treated pine post**<br>*Replace* Materials........6.25     Labor ............1.48<br>*Remove* ......................     Labor ...........1.55 | lf | $1.55 | $7.73 | $9.28 |
| **6" x 6" pine post**<br>*Replace* Materials........6.30     Labor ...........1.51<br>*Remove* ......................     Labor ...........1.55 | lf | $1.55 | $7.81 | $9.36 |
| **6" x 6" con common redwood post**<br>*Replace* Materials........5.44     Labor ...........1.51<br>*Remove* ......................     Labor ...........1.55 | lf | $1.55 | $6.95 | $8.50 |
| **6" x 6" treated pine post**<br>*Replace* Materials........8.19     Labor ...........1.51<br>*Remove* ......................     Labor ...........1.55 | lf | $1.55 | $9.70 | $11.25 |
| **6" x 8" pine post**<br>*Replace* Materials........8.41     Labor ...........1.55<br>*Remove* ......................     Labor ...........1.55 | lf | $1.55 | $9.96 | $11.51 |
| **6" x 8" con common redwood post**<br>*Replace* Materials........7.25     Labor ............1.55<br>*Remove* ......................     Labor ...........1.55 | lf | $1.55 | $8.80 | $10.35 |
| **6" x 8" treated pine post**<br>*Replace* Materials ......10.90     Labor ...........1.55<br>*Remove* ......................     Labor ...........1.55 | lf | $1.55 | $12.45 | $14.00 |
| **6" x 10" pine post**<br>*Replace* Materials ......10.50     Labor ...........1.62<br>*Remove* ......................     Labor ...........1.55 | lf | $1.55 | $12.12 | $13.67 |
| **6" x 10" con common redwood post**<br>*Replace* Materials........9.08     Labor ...........1.62<br>*Remove* ......................     Labor ...........1.55 | lf | $1.55 | $10.70 | $12.25 |
| **6" x 10" treated pine post**<br>*Replace* Materials.......13.70     Labor ............1.62<br>*Remove* ......................     Labor ............1.55 | lf | $1.55 | $15.32 | $16.87 |
| **8" x 8" pine post**<br>*Replace* Materials.......11.20     Labor ...........1.65<br>*Remove* ......................     Labor ...........1.55 | lf | $1.55 | $12.85 | $14.40 |
| **8" x 8" con common redwood post**<br>*Replace* Materials........9.67     Labor ...........1.65<br>*Remove* ......................     Labor ...........1.55 | lf | $1.55 | $11.32 | $12.87 |
| **8" x 8" treated pine post**<br>*Replace* Materials ......14.60     Labor ...........1.65<br>*Remove* ......................     Labor ...........1.55 | lf | $1.55 | $16.25 | $17.80 |
| **Pre-cast concrete pier**<br>*Replace* Materials.......17.50     Labor ...........8.98<br>*Remove* ......................     Labor ...........7.07 | ea | $7.07 | $26.48 | $33.55 |
| **51" to 90" adjustable steel jackpost to 13,000 pound load**<br>*Replace* Materials ......47.20     Labor...........12.30<br>*Remove* ......................     Labor ...........8.20 | ea | $8.20 | $59.50 | $67.70 |

RELATED ITEMS

◁ 6" x 6"

◁ 6" x 8"

◁ 6" x 10"

◁ 8" x 8"

◀ PRECAST PIER

◀ JACKPOST

| Item Description | Unit | Remove | Replace | Total |
|---|---|---|---|---|
| **JACKPOST** ▶ *continued* — 20" to 36" adjustable steel jackpost to 16,000 pound load<br>*Replace* Materials......30.90  Labor ............8.36<br>*Remove* ..................  Labor ............8.20 | ea | $8.20 | $39.26 | $47.46 |
| 48" to 100" adjustable steel jackpost to 16,000 pound load<br>*Replace* Materials......53.30  Labor............13.20<br>*Remove* ................  Labor............8.20 | ea | $8.20 | $66.50 | $74.70 |
| 37" to 60" adjustable steel jackpost to 17,500 pound load<br>*Replace* Materials......38.90  Labor ............9.36<br>*Remove* ..................  Labor ............8.20 | ea | $8.20 | $48.26 | $56.46 |
| 56" to 96" adjustable steel jackpost to 25,000 pound load<br>*Replace* Materials......60.80  Labor............12.10<br>*Remove* ..................  Labor ............8.20 | ea | $8.20 | $72.90 | $81.10 |
| **LALLY COLUMN** ▶ 3-1/2" diameter concrete-filled lally column, 6' to 8'<br>*Replace* Materials ......74.40  Labor............18.10<br>*Remove* ..................  Labor ............9.35 | ea | $9.35 | $92.50 | $101.85 |
| 3-1/2" diameter concrete-filled lally column, 8' to 10'<br>*Replace* Materials......83.10  Labor............19.10<br>*Remove* ..................  Labor ............9.35 | ea | $9.35 | $102.20 | $111.55 |
| 3-1/2" diameter concrete-filled lally column, 10' to 12'<br>*Replace* Materials......103.20  Labor ............20.20<br>*Remove* ..................  Labor ............9.35 | ea | $9.35 | $123.40 | $132.75 |
| **GLUE-LAMINATED BEAM PER BF** *Includes 3% waste.* — Glue-laminated beam per bf<br>*Replace* Materials........4.25  Labor............2.06  Equipment ............33<br>*Remove* ..................  Labor ............66 | bf | $.66 | $6.64 | $7.30 |
| **GLUE-LAMINATED BEAM PER LF** *Includes 3% waste.* 3-1/8" wide ▷ — 3-1/8" x 7-1/2" glue-laminated beam<br>*Replace* Materials........8.28  Labor............4.99  Equipment ............62<br>*Remove* ..................  Labor ............5.82 | lf | $5.82 | $13.89 | $19.71 |
| 3-1/8" x 9" glue-laminated beam<br>*Replace* Materials........9.96  Labor ............5.02  Equipment ............62<br>*Remove* ..................  Labor ............5.82 | lf | $5.82 | $15.60 | $21.42 |
| 3-1/8" x 10-1/2" glue-laminated beam<br>*Replace* Materials.......11.60  Labor ............5.92  Equipment ............62<br>*Remove* ..................  Labor ............5.82 | lf | $5.82 | $18.14 | $23.96 |
| 3-1/8" x 12" glue-laminated beam<br>*Replace* Materials.......13.30  Labor ............6.50  Equipment ............62<br>*Remove* ..................  Labor ............5.82 | lf | $5.82 | $20.42 | $26.24 |
| 3-1/8" x 13-1/2" glue-laminated beam<br>*Replace* Materials ......14.90  Labor ............7.26  Equipment ............62<br>*Remove* ..................  Labor ............5.82 | lf | $5.82 | $22.78 | $28.60 |
| 3-1/8" x 15" glue-laminated beam<br>*Replace* Materials ......16.60  Labor ............7.29  Equipment ............62<br>*Remove* ..................  Labor ............5.82 | lf | $5.82 | $24.51 | $30.33 |
| 3-1/8" x 16-1/2" glue-laminated beam<br>*Replace* Materials ......18.20  Labor ............7.36  Equipment ............62<br>*Remove* ..................  Labor ............5.82 | lf | $5.82 | $26.18 | $32.00 |
| 3-1/8" x 18" glue-laminated beam<br>*Replace* Materials.......19.90  Labor ............7.43  Equipment ............62<br>*Remove* ..................  Labor ............5.82 | lf | $5.82 | $27.95 | $33.77 |

| Item Description | | Unit | Remove | Replace | Total | |
|---|---|---|---|---|---|---|
| **3-1/2" x 9" glue-laminated beam**<br>*Replace* Materials......11.10    Labor ............5.02    Equipment ............ .62<br>*Remove* .....................    Labor ............5.82 | | lf | $5.82 | $16.74 | $22.56 | ◁ 3-1/2" wide |
| **3-1/2" x 12" glue-laminated beam**<br>*Replace* Materials ......14.80    Labor ............5.99    Equipment ............ .62<br>*Remove* .....................    Labor ............5.82 | | lf | $5.82 | $21.41 | $27.23 | |
| **3-1/2" x 15" glue-laminated beam**<br>*Replace* Materials ......18.60    Labor ............6.67    Equipment ............ .62<br>*Remove* .....................    Labor ............5.82 | | lf | $5.82 | $25.89 | $31.71 | |
| **3-1/2" x 19-1/2" glue-laminated beam**<br>*Replace* Materials ......24.10    Labor ............7.60    Equipment ............ .62<br>*Remove* .....................    Labor ............5.82 | | lf | $5.82 | $32.32 | $38.14 | |
| **3-1/2" x 21" glue-laminated beam**<br>*Replace* Materials ......26.00    Labor ............7.67    Equipment ............ .62<br>*Remove* .....................    Labor ............5.82 | | lf | $5.82 | $34.29 | $40.11 | |
| **5-1/8" x 7-1/2" glue-laminated beam**<br>*Replace* Materials......13.60    Labor ............5.95    Equipment ............ .62<br>*Remove* .....................    Labor ............5.82 | | lf | $5.82 | $20.17 | $25.99 | ◁ 5-1/8" wide |
| **5-1/8" x 9" glue-laminated beam**<br>*Replace* Materials ......16.30    Labor ............6.02    Equipment ............ .62<br>*Remove* .....................    Labor ............5.82 | | lf | $5.82 | $22.94 | $28.76 | |
| **5-1/8" x 10-1/2" glue-laminated beam**<br>*Replace* Materials......19.10    Labor ............6.67    Equipment ............ .62<br>*Remove* .....................    Labor ............5.82 | | lf | $5.82 | $26.39 | $32.21 | |
| **5-1/8" x 12" glue-laminated beam**<br>*Replace* Materials ......22.20    Labor ............7.50    Equipment ............ .62<br>*Remove* .....................    Labor ............5.82 | | lf | $5.82 | $30.32 | $36.14 | |
| **5-1/8" x 13-1/2" glue-laminated beam**<br>*Replace* Materials ......24.50    Labor ............7.60    Equipment ............ .62<br>*Remove* .....................    Labor ............5.82 | | lf | $5.82 | $32.72 | $38.54 | |
| **5-1/8" x 15" glue-laminated beam**<br>*Replace* Materials ......27.20    Labor ............7.71    Equipment ............ .62<br>*Remove* .....................    Labor ............5.82 | | lf | $5.82 | $35.53 | $41.35 | |
| **5-1/8" x 16-1/2" glue-laminated beam**<br>*Replace* Materials......29.90    Labor ............7.81    Equipment ............ .62<br>*Remove* .....................    Labor ............5.82 | | lf | $5.82 | $38.33 | $44.15 | |
| **5-1/8" x 18" glue-laminated beam**<br>*Replace* Materials......32.70    Labor ............7.95    Equipment ............ .62<br>*Remove* .....................    Labor ............5.82 | | lf | $5.82 | $41.27 | $47.09 | |
| **5-1/8" x 19-1/2" glue-laminated beam**<br>*Replace* Materials ......35.40    Labor ............8.05    Equipment ............ .62<br>*Remove* .....................    Labor ............5.82 | | lf | $5.82 | $44.07 | $49.89 | |
| **5-1/8" x 21" glue-laminated beam**<br>*Replace* Materials......38.10    Labor ............8.19    Equipment ............ .62<br>*Remove* .....................    Labor ............5.82 | | lf | $5.82 | $46.91 | $52.73 | |
| **5-1/8" x 22-1/2" glue-laminated beam**<br>*Replace* Materials......40.80    Labor ............8.32    Equipment ............ .62<br>*Remove* .....................    Labor ............5.82 | | lf | $5.82 | $49.74 | $55.56 | |

| Item Description | Unit | Remove | Replace | Total |
|---|---|---|---|---|
| **GLUE-LAMINATED BEAM** *continued* — **5-1/8" x 24" glue-laminated beam** <br> *Replace* Materials......43.50  Labor ...........8.43  Equipment ...........62 <br> *Remove* ........................ Labor ...........5.82 | lf | $5.82 | $52.55 | $58.37 |
| **6-3/4" wide** ▷ **6-3/4" x 18" glue-laminated beam** <br> *Replace* Materials......43.00  Labor ...........8.39  Equipment ...........62 <br> *Remove* ........................ Labor ...........5.82 | lf | $5.82 | $52.01 | $57.83 |
| **6-3/4" x 19-1/2" glue-laminated beam** <br> *Replace* Materials......46.60  Labor ...........8.60  Equipment ...........62 <br> *Remove* ........................ Labor ...........5.82 | lf | $5.82 | $55.82 | $61.64 |
| **6-3/4" x 24" glue-laminated beam** <br> *Replace* Materials......57.30  Labor ...........9.18  Equipment ...........62 <br> *Remove* ........................ Labor ...........5.82 | lf | $5.82 | $67.10 | $72.92 |
| **MICRO-LAMINATED BEAM** *Includes 4% waste.* — **1-3/4" x 7-1/4" micro-laminated beam** <br> *Replace* Materials........4.85  Labor ...........1.65 <br> *Remove* ........................ Labor ...........2.78 | lf | $2.78 | $6.50 | $9.28 |
| **1-3/4" x 9-1/2" micro-laminated beam** <br> *Replace* Materials........6.36  Labor ...........1.72 <br> *Remove* ........................ Labor ...........2.78 | lf | $2.78 | $8.08 | $10.86 |
| **1-3/4" x 11-7/8" micro-laminated beam** <br> *Replace* Materials........7.96  Labor ...........1.82 <br> *Remove* ........................ Labor ...........2.78 | lf | $2.78 | $9.78 | $12.56 |
| **1-3/4" x 14" micro-laminated beam** <br> *Replace* Materials........9.39  Labor ...........1.93 <br> *Remove* ........................ Labor ...........2.78 | lf | $2.78 | $11.32 | $14.10 |
| **1-3/4" x 16" micro-laminated beam** <br> *Replace* Materials......10.70  Labor ...........2.03 <br> *Remove* ........................ Labor ...........2.78 | lf | $2.78 | $12.73 | $15.51 |
| **1-3/4" x 18" micro-laminated beam** <br> *Replace* Materials ......12.10  Labor ...........2.17 <br> *Remove* ........................ Labor ...........2.78 | lf | $2.78 | $14.27 | $17.05 |
| **PINE BEAM** *Includes 4% waste. Deduct 12% for #1 and better grade pine. Rough sawn. Installed as posts, beams, joists, and purlins. Pine species vary by region. Western coastal areas: Douglas fir, hemlock fir; Mountain states and provinces: spruce, pine, Douglas fir, South: southern yellow pine; Midwest: spruce, pine, Douglas fir, southern yellow pine; Southwest: southern yellow pine; Northeast: spruce, pine, Douglas fir, and hemlock fir.* — **4" x 6" pine beam, select structural grade** <br> *Replace* Materials......3.54  Labor ...........2.68  Equipment ...........62 <br> *Remove* ........................ Labor ...........5.82 | lf | $5.82 | $6.84 | $12.66 |
| **4" x 8" pine beam, select structural grade** <br> *Replace* Materials......4.72  Labor ...........3.16  Equipment ...........62 <br> *Remove* ........................ Labor ...........5.82 | lf | $5.82 | $8.50 | $14.32 |
| **4" x 10" pine beam, select structural grade** <br> *Replace* Materials......5.91  Labor ...........3.92  Equipment ...........62 <br> *Remove* ........................ Labor ...........5.82 | lf | $5.82 | $10.45 | $16.27 |
| **4" x 12" pine beam, select structural grade** <br> *Replace* Materials......7.08  Labor ...........5.13  Equipment ...........62 <br> *Remove* ........................ Labor ...........5.82 | lf | $5.82 | $12.83 | $18.65 |
| **4" x 14" pine beam, select structural grade** <br> *Replace* Materials......8.26  Labor ...........6.12  Equipment ...........62 <br> *Remove* ........................ Labor ...........5.82 | lf | $5.82 | $15.00 | $20.82 |
| **4" x 16" pine beam, select structural grade** <br> *Replace* Materials......9.45  Labor ...........6.19  Equipment ...........62 <br> *Remove* ........................ Labor ...........5.82 | lf | $5.82 | $16.26 | $22.08 |

| Item Description | | Unit | Remove | Replace | Total | |
|---|---|---|---|---|---|---|
| **6" x 6" pine beam, select structural grade**<br>*Replace* Materials........5.31    Labor ...........3.51<br>*Remove* .....................    Labor ..........5.82 | Equipment ...........62 | lf | $5.82 | $9.44 | $15.26 | ◁ 6" wide |
| **6" x 8" pine beam, select structural grade**<br>*Replace* Materials........7.08    Labor ...........3.96<br>*Remove* .....................    Labor ..........5.82 | Equipment ...........62 | lf | $5.82 | $11.66 | $17.48 | |
| **6" x 10" pine beam, select structural grade**<br>*Replace* Materials........8.85    Labor ...........4.54<br>*Remove* .....................    Labor ..........5.82 | Equipment ...........62 | lf | $5.82 | $14.01 | $19.83 | |
| **6" x 12" pine beam, select structural grade**<br>*Replace* Materials ......10.60    Labor ...........5.30<br>*Remove* .....................    Labor ..........5.82 | Equipment ...........62 | lf | $5.82 | $16.52 | $22.34 | |
| **6" x 14" pine beam, select structural grade**<br>*Replace* Materials ......12.40    Labor ...........5.81<br>*Remove* .....................    Labor ..........5.82 | Equipment ...........62 | lf | $5.82 | $18.83 | $24.65 | |
| **6" x 16" pine beam, select structural grade**<br>*Replace* Materials ......14.20    Labor ...........6.50<br>*Remove* .....................    Labor ..........5.82 | Equipment ...........62 | lf | $5.82 | $21.32 | $27.14 | |
| **8" x 8" pine beam, select structural grade**<br>*Replace* Materials........9.44    Labor ...........4.78<br>*Remove* .....................    Labor ..........5.82 | Equipment ...........62 | lf | $5.82 | $14.84 | $20.66 | ◁ 8" wide |
| **8" x 10" pine beam, select structural grade**<br>*Replace* Materials.......11.80    Labor ...........5.37<br>*Remove* .....................    Labor ..........5.82 | Equipment ...........62 | lf | $5.82 | $17.79 | $23.61 | |
| **8" x 12" pine beam, select structural grade**<br>*Replace* Materials ......14.20    Labor ...........6.26<br>*Remove* .....................    Labor ..........5.82 | Equipment ...........62 | lf | $5.82 | $21.08 | $26.90 | |
| **8" x 14" pine beam, select structural grade**<br>*Replace* Materials ......16.60    Labor ...........6.64<br>*Remove* .....................    Labor ..........5.82 | Equipment ...........62 | lf | $5.82 | $23.86 | $29.68 | |
| **8" x 16" pine beam, select structural grade**<br>*Replace* Materials ......18.90    Labor ...........6.85<br>*Remove* .....................    Labor ..........5.82 | Equipment ...........62 | lf | $5.82 | $26.37 | $32.19 | |
| **10" x 10" pine beam, select structural grade**<br>*Replace* Materials ......14.80    Labor ...........6.05<br>*Remove* .....................    Labor ..........5.82 | Equipment ...........62 | lf | $5.82 | $21.47 | $27.29 | ◁ 10" wide |
| **10" x 12" pine beam, select structural grade**<br>*Replace* Materials.......17.70    Labor ...........6.74<br>*Remove* .....................    Labor ..........5.82 | Equipment ...........62 | lf | $5.82 | $25.06 | $30.88 | |
| **10" x 14" pine beam, select structural grade**<br>*Replace* Materials ......20.60    Labor ...........6.98<br>*Remove* .....................    Labor ..........5.82 | Equipment ...........62 | lf | $5.82 | $28.20 | $34.02 | |
| **10" x 16" pine beam, select structural grade**<br>*Replace* Materials ......23.60    Labor ...........7.22<br>*Remove* .....................    Labor ..........5.82 | Equipment ...........62 | lf | $5.82 | $31.44 | $37.26 | |
| **12" x 12" pine beam, select structural grade**<br>*Replace* Materials ......21.30    Labor ...........7.02<br>*Remove* .....................    Labor ..........5.82 | Equipment ...........62 | lf | $5.82 | $28.94 | $34.76 | ◁ 12" wide |

| Item Description | | Unit | Remove | Replace | Total |
|---|---|---|---|---|---|
| **PINE BEAM ▶** *continued* | **12" x 14" pine beam, select structural grade**<br>*Replace* Materials .....24.80   Labor ............7.33   Equipment ...........62<br>*Remove* ....................   Labor ............5.82 | If | $5.82 | $32.75 | $38.57 |
| | **12" x 16" pine beam, select structural grade**<br>*Replace* Materials ......28.30   Labor ............7.64   Equipment ...........62<br>*Remove* ....................   Labor ............5.82 | If | $5.82 | $36.56 | $42.38 |
| **OAK BEAM ▶** *Includes 4% waste. Installed as posts, beams, joists, and purlins.* | **4" x 6" oak beam, select structural grade**<br>*Replace* Materials ........7.73   Labor ............2.68   Equipment ...........62<br>*Remove* ....................   Labor ............5.82 | If | $5.82 | $11.03 | $16.85 |
| | **4" x 8" oak beam, select structural grade**<br>*Replace* Materials ......10.30   Labor ............3.16   Equipment ...........62<br>*Remove* ....................   Labor ............5.82 | If | $5.82 | $14.08 | $19.90 |
| | **4" x 10" oak beam, select structural grade**<br>*Replace* Materials ......12.90   Labor ............3.92   Equipment ...........62<br>*Remove* ....................   Labor ............5.82 | If | $5.82 | $17.44 | $23.26 |
| | **4" x 12" oak beam, select structural grade**<br>*Replace* Materials ......15.40   Labor ............5.13   Equipment ...........62<br>*Remove* ....................   Labor ............5.82 | If | $5.82 | $21.15 | $26.97 |
| | **4" x 14" oak beam, select structural grade**<br>*Replace* Materials ......18.00   Labor ............6.12   Equipment ...........62<br>*Remove* ....................   Labor ............5.82 | If | $5.82 | $24.74 | $30.56 |
| | **4" x 16" oak beam, select structural grade**<br>*Replace* Materials ......20.60   Labor ............6.19   Equipment ...........62<br>*Remove* ....................   Labor ............5.82 | If | $5.82 | $27.41 | $33.23 |
| **6" wide ▷** | **6" x 6" oak beam, select structural grade**<br>*Replace* Materials .......11.60   Labor ............3.51   Equipment ...........62<br>*Remove* ....................   Labor ............5.82 | If | $5.82 | $15.73 | $21.55 |
| | **6" x 8" oak beam, select structural grade**<br>*Replace* Materials ......16.00   Labor ............3.96   Equipment ...........62<br>*Remove* ....................   Labor ............5.82 | If | $5.82 | $20.58 | $26.40 |
| | **6" x 10" oak beam, select structural grade**<br>*Replace* Materials .....19.40   Labor ............4.54   Equipment ...........62<br>*Remove* ....................   Labor ............5.82 | If | $5.82 | $24.56 | $30.38 |
| | **6" x 12" oak beam, select structural grade**<br>*Replace* Materials ......23.20   Labor ............5.30   Equipment ...........62<br>*Remove* ....................   Labor ............5.82 | If | $5.82 | $29.12 | $34.94 |
| | **6" x 14" oak beam, select structural grade**<br>*Replace* Materials ......27.10   Labor ............5.81   Equipment ...........62<br>*Remove* ....................   Labor ............5.82 | If | $5.82 | $33.53 | $39.35 |
| | **6" x 16" oak beam, select structural grade**<br>*Replace* Materials ......30.90   Labor ............6.50   Equipment ...........62<br>*Remove* ....................   Labor ............5.82 | If | $5.82 | $38.02 | $43.84 |
| **8" wide ▷** | **8" x 8" oak beam, select structural grade**<br>*Replace* Materials ......20.60   Labor ............4.78   Equipment ...........62<br>*Remove* ....................   Labor ............5.82 | If | $5.82 | $26.00 | $31.82 |
| | **8" x 10" oak beam, select structural grade**<br>*Replace* Materials ......25.70   Labor ............5.37   Equipment ...........62<br>*Remove* ....................   Labor ............5.82 | If | $5.82 | $31.69 | $37.51 |

| Item Description | Unit | Remove | Replace | Total |
|---|---|---|---|---|
| **8" x 12" oak beam, select structural grade**<br>*Replace* Materials......30.90　　Labor ..........6.26　　Equipment ...........62<br>*Remove* .......................　　Labor ..........5.82 | lf | $5.82 | $37.78 | $43.60 |
| **8" x 14" oak beam, select structural grade**<br>*Replace* Materials......36.00　　Labor ..........6.64　　Equipment ...........62<br>*Remove* .......................　　Labor ..........5.82 | lf | $5.82 | $43.26 | $49.08 |
| **8" x 16" oak beam, select structural grade**<br>*Replace* Materials ......41.30　　Labor ..........6.85　　Equipment ...........62<br>*Remove* .......................　　Labor ..........5.82 | lf | $5.82 | $48.77 | $54.59 |
| **10" x 10" oak beam, select structural grade**<br>*Replace* Materials......32.20　　Labor ..........6.05　　Equipment ...........62<br>*Remove* .......................　　Labor ..........5.82 | lf | $5.82 | $38.87 | $44.69 |
| **10" x 12" oak beam, select structural grade**<br>*Replace* Materials......38.60　　Labor ..........6.74　　Equipment ...........62<br>*Remove* .......................　　Labor ..........5.82 | lf | $5.82 | $45.96 | $51.78 |
| **10" x 14" oak beam, select structural grade**<br>*Replace* Materials ......45.10　　Labor ..........6.98　　Equipment ...........62<br>*Remove* .......................　　Labor ..........5.82 | lf | $5.82 | $52.70 | $58.52 |
| **10" x 16" oak beam, select structural grade**<br>*Replace* Materials ......51.60　　Labor ..........7.22　　Equipment ...........62<br>*Remove* .......................　　Labor ..........5.82 | lf | $5.82 | $59.44 | $65.26 |
| **12" x 12" oak beam, select structural grade**<br>*Replace* Materials......46.40　　Labor ..........7.02　　Equipment ...........62<br>*Remove* .......................　　Labor ..........5.82 | lf | $5.82 | $54.04 | $59.86 |
| **12" x 14" oak beam, select structural grade**<br>*Replace* Materials......54.10　　Labor ..........7.33　　Equipment ...........62<br>*Remove* .......................　　Labor ..........5.82 | lf | $5.82 | $62.05 | $67.87 |
| **12" x 16" oak beam, select structural grade**<br>*Replace* Materials......61.90　　Labor ..........7.64　　Equipment ...........62<br>*Remove* .......................　　Labor ..........5.82 | lf | $5.82 | $70.16 | $75.98 |
| **Add for hand-hewn pine beam per square inch of surface**<br>*Replace* Materials ........ .02 | si | — | $.02 | $.02 |
| **Add for curved pine framing member in post & beam framing**<br>*Replace* .......................　　Labor ..........39.00 | lf | — | $39.00 | $39.00 |
| **Add for hand-hewn oak beam per square inch of surface**<br>*Replace* Materials ........ .04 | si | — | $.04 | $.04 |
| **Add for curved oak framing member in post & beam framing**<br>*Replace* .......................　　Labor..........51.50 | lf | — | $51.50 | $51.50 |
| **Pine post & beam single-story bent with simple truss**<br>*Replace* Materials.......3.01　　Labor ..........22.60　　Equipment ...........37<br>*Remove* .......................　　Labor ..........1.86 | sf | $1.86 | $25.98 | $27.84 |
| **Pine post & beam single-story bent with king post truss**<br>*Replace* Materials.......3.35　　Labor ..........24.40　　Equipment ...........37<br>*Remove* .......................　　Labor ..........1.86 | sf | $1.86 | $28.12 | $29.98 |
| **Pine post & beam single-story bent with king post & struts truss**<br>*Replace* Materials.......3.76　　Labor..........26.50　　Equipment ...........37<br>*Remove* .......................　　Labor ..........1.86 | sf | $1.86 | $30.63 | $32.49 |

◁ 10" wide

◁ 12" wide

◀ **ADDITIONAL BEAM COSTS**

◀ **PINE POST & BEAM BENT WITH TRUSS**
*With pine posts and beams, per sf of bent. Post & beam framing styles are nearly unlimited. The following styles are representative.*

**PINE POST & ▶**
**BEAM BENT WITH**
**TRUSS**
*continued*

simple truss △

king post truss △

king post & struts truss △

queen post truss △

hammer beam truss △

scissors truss △

| Item Description | Unit | Remove | Replace | Total |
|---|---|---|---|---|
| **Pine post & beam single-story bent with queen post truss** | sf | $1.86 | $30.08 | $31.94 |
| *Replace* Materials........3.51     Labor...........26.20     Equipment ............ .37 | | | | |
| *Remove* .......................     Labor ...........1.86 | | | | |
| **Pine post & beam single-story bent with hammer beam truss** | sf | $1.86 | $49.07 | $50.93 |
| *Replace* Materials........3.70     Labor...........45.00     Equipment ............ .37 | | | | |
| *Remove* .......................     Labor ...........1.86 | | | | |
| **Pine post & beam single-story bent with scissors truss** | sf | $1.86 | $46.76 | $48.62 |
| *Replace* Materials........3.89     Labor...........42.50     Equipment ............ .37 | | | | |
| *Remove* .......................     Labor ...........1.86 | | | | |
| **Pine post & beam two-story bent with simple truss** | sf | $1.86 | $27.64 | $29.50 |
| *Replace* Materials........2.77     Labor...........24.50     Equipment ............ .37 | | | | |
| *Remove* .......................     Labor ...........1.86 | | | | |
| **Pine post & beam two-story bent with king post truss** | sf | $1.86 | $29.95 | $31.81 |
| *Replace* Materials........2.98     Labor...........26.60     Equipment ............ .37 | | | | |
| *Remove* .......................     Labor ...........1.86 | | | | |
| **Pine post & beam two-story bent with king post & struts truss** | sf | $1.86 | $32.80 | $34.66 |
| *Replace* Materials........3.23     Labor...........29.20     Equipment ............ .37 | | | | |
| *Remove* .......................     Labor ...........1.86 | | | | |
| **Pine post & beam two-story bent with queen post truss** | sf | $1.86 | $32.25 | $34.11 |
| *Replace* Materials........3.08     Labor ...........28.80     Equipment ............ .37 | | | | |
| *Remove* .......................     Labor ...........1.86 | | | | |

knee brace

bent plate

purlin

bent girt

overhang drop

connecting girt

post

joist

△ post & beam framing

| Item Description | Unit | Remove | Replace | Total | |
|---|---|---|---|---|---|
| **Pine post & beam two-story bent with hammer beam truss**<br>*Replace* Materials.......3.33   Labor..........44.60   Equipment............37<br>*Remove* ......................   Labor...........1.86 | sf | $1.86 | $48.30 | $50.16 | |
| **Pine post & beam two-story bent with scissors truss**<br>*Replace* Materials.......3.33   Labor..........44.60   Equipment............37<br>*Remove* ......................   Labor...........1.86 | sf | $1.86 | $48.30 | $50.16 | |
| **Add for overhang drop in pine two-story bent**<br>*Replace* Materials.....168.00   Labor........858.00   Equipment............37 | ea | — | $1,026.37 | $1,026.37 | ◁ add for overhang |
| **Pine connecting members between single-story bents and trusses**<br>*Replace* Materials.......5.27   Labor..........47.60<br>*Remove* ......................   Labor...........5.61 | sf | $5.61 | $52.87 | $58.48 | ◀ **PINE CONNECTING MEMBERS BETWEEN BENTS**<br>*Pine. Includes floor joists, roof purlins, diagonal braces, and beams. Per sf of area beneath roof. Measure only one floor.* |
| **Pine connecting members between two-story bents and trusses**<br>*Replace* Materials.......7.88   Labor..........79.40<br>*Remove* ......................   Labor...........7.49 | sf | $7.49 | $87.28 | $94.77 | |
| **Oak post & beam single-story bent with simple truss**<br>*Replace* Materials.......6.55   Labor..........22.60   Equipment............37<br>*Remove* ......................   Labor...........1.86 | sf | $1.86 | $29.52 | $31.38 | ◀ **OAK POST & BEAM BENT WITH TRUSS**<br>*With oak posts and beams, per sf of bent. Post & beam framing styles are nearly unlimited. The following styles are representative.* |
| **Oak post & beam single-story bent with king post truss**<br>*Replace* Materials.......7.30   Labor..........24.40   Equipment............37<br>*Remove* ......................   Labor...........1.86 | sf | $1.86 | $32.07 | $33.93 | |
| **Oak post & beam single-story bent with king post & struts truss**<br>*Replace* Materials.......8.18   Labor..........26.50   Equipment............37<br>*Remove* ......................   Labor...........1.75 | sf | $1.86 | $35.05 | $36.91 | |
| **Oak post & beam single-story bent with queen post truss**<br>*Replace* Materials.......7.62   Labor..........26.20   Equipment............37<br>*Remove* ......................   Labor...........1.86 | sf | $1.86 | $34.19 | $36.05 | |
| **Oak post & beam single-story bent with hammer beam truss**<br>*Replace* Materials.......8.06   Labor..........45.00   Equipment............37<br>*Remove* ......................   Labor...........1.86 | sf | $1.86 | $53.43 | $55.29 | |
| **Oak post & beam single-story bent with scissors truss**<br>*Replace* Materials.......8.50   Labor..........42.50   Equipment............37<br>*Remove* ......................   Labor...........1.86 | sf | $1.86 | $51.37 | $53.23 | |

| Item Description | Unit | Remove | Replace | Total |
|---|---|---|---|---|
| **OAK POST & BEAM BENT WITH TRUSS** continued ▶ **Oak post & beam two-story bent with simple truss** | sf | $1.86 | $30.90 | $32.76 |
| *Replace* Materials........6.03 Labor...........24.50 Equipment ............ .37 *Remove* ..................... Labor ............1.86 | | | | |
| **Oak post & beam two-story bent with king post truss** | sf | $1.86 | $33.47 | $35.33 |
| *Replace* Materials........6.50 Labor...........26.60 Equipment ............ .37 *Remove* ..................... Labor ............1.86 | | | | |
| △ sill corner half-lap **Oak post & beam two-story bent with king post & struts truss** | sf | $1.86 | $36.63 | $38.49 |
| *Replace* Materials........7.06 Labor.........29.20 Equipment ............ .37 *Remove* ..................... Labor ............1.86 | | | | |
| △ sill corner half-lap with through tenon **Oak post & beam two-story bent with queen post truss** | sf | $1.86 | $35.88 | $37.74 |
| *Replace* Materials........6.71 Labor.........28.80 Equipment ............ .37 *Remove* ..................... Labor ............1.86 | | | | |
| **Oak post & beam two-story bent with hammer beam truss** | sf | $1.86 | $60.95 | $62.81 |
| *Replace* Materials........6.98 Labor.........53.60 Equipment ............ .37 *Remove* ..................... Labor ............1.86 | | | | |
| sill corner dovetail △ **Oak post & beam two-story bent with scissors truss** | sf | $1.86 | $52.22 | $54.08 |
| *Replace* Materials........7.25 Labor..........44.60 Equipment ............ .37 *Remove* ..................... Labor ............1.86 | | | | |
| **add for overhang** ▷ see framed overhang illustration on facing page **Add for overhang drop in oak two-story bent** | ea | — | $1,187.37 | $1,187.37 |
| *Replace* Materials ....329.00 Labor.........858.00 Equipment ............ .37 | | | | |
| **OAK CONNECTING MEMBERS BETWEEN BENTS** ▶ Includes floor joists, roof purlins, diagonal braces, and beams. Per sf of area beneath roof. Measure only one floor. **Oak connecting members between single-story bents and trusses** | sf | $5.61 | $59.10 | $64.71 |
| *Replace* Materials........11.50 Labor...........47.60 *Remove* ..................... Labor ............5.61 | | | | |
| **Oak connecting members between two-story bents and trusses** | sf | $7.49 | $96.50 | $103.99 |
| *Replace* Materials........17.10 Labor...........79.40 *Remove* ..................... Labor ............7.49 | | | | |
| **minimum p & b** ▷ **Minimum charge for post & beam framing work** | ea | — | $1,675.00 | $1,675.00 |
| *Replace* Materials ....342.00 Labor.........858.00 Equipment ........475.00 | | | | |
| **P & B JOINTS** ▶ Includes cutting, drilling, and joining with pegs. **Sill corner half-lap joint** | ea | — | $55.30 | $55.30 |
| *Replace* ........................ Labor...........55.30 ▶ Joint connects two timbers that form the sill and intersect at a 90 degree angle. | | | | |
| **Sill corner half-lap joint with through tenon** | ea | — | $140.00 | $140.00 |
| *Replace* ........................ Labor.........140.00 ▶ Joint connects three timbers. Two level timbers form the sill and intersect at a 90 degree angle. A mortise is also cut at the corner. The third member is the plumb corner post with a tenon on the bottom. | | | | |
| sill corner dovetail △ with through tenon **Sill corner dovetail joint** | ea | — | $101.00 | $101.00 |
| *Replace* ........................ Labor.........101.00 ▶ Joint connects two timbers that form the sill and intersect at a 90 degree angle. | | | | |
| **Sill corner dovetail joint with through tenon** | ea | — | $194.00 | $194.00 |
| *Replace* ........................ Labor .........194.00 ▶ Joint connects three timbers. Two level timbers form the sill and intersect at a 90 degree angle. A mortise is also cut at the corner. The third member is the plumb corner post with a tenon on the bottom. | | | | |
| sill corner tongue & fork △ **Sill corner tongue & fork joint** | ea | — | $90.00 | $90.00 |
| *Replace* ........................ Labor ..........90.00 ▶ Joint connects two timbers that form the sill and intersect at a 90 degree angle. | | | | |

sill corner tongue & fork △ with through tenon

| Item Description | Unit | Remove | Replace | Total | |
|---|---|---|---|---|---|
| **Sill corner tongue & fork joint with through tenon** | ea | — | $174.00 | $174.00 | |
| *Replace* .................... Labor .........174.00 | | | | | |
| ► Joint connects three timbers. Two level timbers form the sill and intersect at a 90 degree angle. A mortise is also cut at the corner. The third member is the plumb corner post with a tenon on the bottom. | | | | | *lapped dovetail* △ |
| **Lapped dovetail joint** | ea | — | $103.00 | $103.00 | |
| *Replace* .................... Labor.........103.00 | | | | | |
| ► Joint connects two timbers that intersect at a 90 degree angle. Usually the connection between a purlin and a rafter or a joist and a summer beam. | | | | | *housed lapped dovetail* △ |
| **Housed lapped dovetail joint** | ea | — | $129.00 | $129.00 | |
| *Replace* .................... Labor.........129.00 | | | | | |
| ► Joint connects two timbers that intersect at a 90 degree angle. Usually the connection between a purlin and a rafter or a joist and a summer beam. | | | | | *tusk tenon* △ |
| **Tusk tenon joint** | ea | — | $140.00 | $140.00 | |
| *Replace* .................... Labor.........140.00 | | | | | |
| ► Joint connects two timbers that intersect at a 90 degree angle. Usually the connection between a purlin and a rafter or a joist and a summer beam. | | | | | |
| **Half-lap joint** | ea | — | $54.30 | $54.30 | |
| *Replace* .................... Labor .........54.30 | | | | | *half-lap* △ |
| ► Joint connects two timbers that intersect at a 90 degree angle. Usually the connection between a purlin and a rafter or a joist and a summer beam. | | | | | |
| **Through mortise & tenon with shoulders joint** | ea | — | $114.00 | $114.00 | |
| *Replace* .................... Labor.........114.00 | | | | | *through mortise & tenon* △ |
| ► Joint connects two timbers that intersect at a 90 degree angle. Usually the connection between beam and a post. The level shouldered beam connects into a mortise in the plumb post. | | | | | |
| **Housed mortise & tenon joint** | ea | — | $120.00 | $120.00 | |
| *Replace* .................... Labor.........120.00 | | | | | *housed mortise & tenon* △ |
| ► Joint connects two timbers that intersect at a 90 degree angle. Usually the connection between beam and a post. The level beam connects into a mortise in the plumb post. | | | | | |
| **Shouldered mortise & tenon joint** | ea | — | $117.00 | $117.00 | *shouldered* △ |
| *Replace* .................... Labor..........117.00 | | | | | *mortise & tenon* |
| ► Joint connects two timbers that intersect at a 90 degree angle. Usually the connection between beam and a post. The level beam connects into a mortise in the plumb post. | | | | | |
| **Wedged dovetail mortise & tenon joint** | ea | — | $120.00 | $120.00 | *wedged dovetail* △ |
| *Replace* .................... Labor.........120.00 | | | | | *mortise & tenon* |
| ► Joint connects two timbers that intersect at a 90 degree angle. Usually the connection between beam and a post. The level beam connects into a mortise in the plumb post. | | | | | |
| **Mortise & tenon joint (90 degree intersection)** | ea | — | $62.90 | $62.90 | *mortise & tenon* △ |
| *Replace* .................... Labor..........62.90 | | | | | |
| ► Joint connects two timbers that intersect at a 90 degree angle. A beam or post connects into a mortise in the second beam or post. | | | | | |
| **Anchor-beam joint** | ea | — | $148.00 | $148.00 | |
| *Replace* .................... Labor.........148.00 | | | | | |
| ► Joint connects two level beams to opposite sides of a post. The post and beams intersect at 90 degree angles. Each level shouldered beam connects into a mortise in the plumb post. | | | | | *anchor beam* △ |
| **Framed overhang joint** | ea | — | $503.00 | $503.00 | |
| *Replace* .................... Labor .........503.00 | | | | | |
| ► Includes decorative cutting of the "acorn" on the free-hanging post. Three mortises are cut into the post. One for the cantilevered level beam and two for connecting beams on each side of the post. All three beams are cut with shouldered tenons. | | | | | *framed overhang* △ |

| Item Description | Unit | Remove | Replace | Total |
|---|---|---|---|---|
| **P&B JOINTS ▶** *continued* | | | | |
| **Through half-lap joint** | ea | — | **$60.40** | **$60.40** |
| *Replace* .................. Labor..........60.40 | | | | |
| ▶ Used when two members cross and neither member terminates at the joint. Both members overlap and continue. | | | | |
| **Mortise & tenon knee brace joint (45 degree intersection)** | ea | — | **$78.50** | **$78.50** |
| *Replace* .................. Labor..........78.50 | | | | |
| ▶ Used for diagonal corner braces. Knee brace connects into a post on the bottom and a beam on the top. A mortise is cut into both the post and beam. Tenons are cut at a 45 degree angle in the knee brace. Price is for mortise and tenon on one end only. For a complete knee brace installation use this price twice. | | | | |
| **Collar tie lapped half dovetail joint** | ea | — | **$98.60** | **$98.60** |
| *Replace* .................. Labor..........98.60 | | | | |
| ▶ Used for connecting collar ties to rafters. Collar tie is plumb and intersects with rafters at an angle dictated by the slope of the roof. Price is for joint on one side of the collar tie only. For a complete collar tie use this price twice. | | | | |
| **Stopped splayed scarf joint** | ea | — | **$162.00** | **$162.00** |
| *Replace* .................. Labor..........162.00 | | | | |
| ▶ Used to splice two level beams together. | | | | |
| **Stopped splayed scarf joint with through tenon** | ea | — | **$252.00** | **$252.00** |
| *Replace* .................. Labor..........252.00 | | | | |
| ▶ Used to splice two level beams together. A mortise is cut through the center of the joint. A tenon is cut at the top of the plumb post that supports the beam. | | | | |
| **Bladed scarf joint** | ea | — | **$123.00** | **$123.00** |
| *Replace* .................. Labor..........123.00 | | | | |
| ▶ Used to splice two level beams together. | | | | |
| **Bladed scarf joint with through tenon** | ea | — | **$219.00** | **$219.00** |
| *Replace* .................. Labor..........219.00 | | | | |
| ▶ Used to splice two level beams together. A mortise is cut through the center of the joint. A tenon is cut at the top of the plumb post that supports the beam. | | | | |
| **Rafter foot housed bird's mouth joint** | ea | — | **$69.90** | **$69.90** |
| *Replace* .................. Labor..........69.90 | | | | |
| ▶ Bird's mouth is cut at foot of rafter. Top plate is cut to receive inside of bird's mouth. | | | | |
| **Rafter foot beveled shoulder bird's mouth joint** | ea | — | **$65.40** | **$65.40** |
| *Replace* .................. Labor..........65.40 | | | | |
| ▶ Bird's mouth is cut at foot of rafter. Top plate is bevel-cut to receive inside of bird's mouth. | | | | |
| **Rafter foot bird's mouth, purlin, and post joint** | ea | — | **$157.00** | **$157.00** |
| *Replace* .................. Labor..........157.00 | | | | |
| ▶ Bird's mouth is cut at foot of rafter. The rafter connects to the timber that is the bottom chord of the truss. A relief for the bird's mouth is cut into the bottom chord. Price also includes the mortise and tenon joint between the bottom chord and the post. | | | | |
| **Rafter foot bird's mouth joint** | ea | — | **$50.30** | **$50.30** |
| *Replace* .................. Labor..........50.30 | | | | |
| ▶ Bird's mouth is cut at foot of rafter. Rafter connects to beam that forms wall plate. No cut is made in the beam. | | | | |
| **Rafter foot bird's mouth with tenon joint** | ea | — | **$144.00** | **$144.00** |
| *Replace* .................. Labor..........144.00 | | | | |
| ▶ Direct connection between rafter and a post. (Does not connect with a beam.) Bird's mouth with a tenon is cut at foot of rafter. A mortise is cut in the post. (See illustration on top of facing page.) | | | | |

Left margin labels (with diagrams):
*through half-lap △*
*mortise & tenon △ knee brace*
*collar tie lapped △ half dovetail*
*stopped splayed scarf △*
*stopped splayed scarf △ with through tenon*
*bladed scarf △*
*bladed scarf △ with through tenon*
*rafter foot housed △ bird's mouth*
*rafter foot beveled △ shoulder bird's mouth*
*rafter foot bird's △ mouth, purlin, and post*
*rafter foot bird's mouth △*

| Item Description | Unit | Remove | Replace | Total |
|---|---|---|---|---|
| **Rafter peak tongue & fork joint** | ea | — | $90.00 | $90.00 |
| *Replace* .................. Labor ..........90.00 | | | | |
| ► The connection between rafters at the peak. One rafter end is cut with a tongue and the other is cut with a fork. The angle of the joint varies with the slope of the roof. (See illustration lower right.) | | | | |
| **2" x 6" joist system for a deck with support beam & posts** | sf | $.34 | $4.34 | $4.68 |
| *Replace* Materials........2.04    Labor ............2.30 | | | | |
| *Remove* ...................... Labor ............ .34 | | | | |
| **2" x 8" joist system for a deck with support beam & posts** | sf | $.34 | $4.70 | $5.04 |
| *Replace* Materials........2.26    Labor ............2.44 | | | | |
| *Remove* ...................... Labor ............ .34 | | | | |
| **2" x 10" joist system for a deck with support beam & posts** | sf | $.34 | $5.53 | $5.87 |
| *Replace* Materials........2.88    Labor ............2.65 | | | | |
| *Remove* ...................... Labor ............ .34 | | | | |
| **2" x 12" joist system for a deck with support beam & posts** | sf | $.34 | $6.01 | $6.35 |
| *Replace* Materials........3.15    Labor ............2.86 | | | | |
| *Remove* ...................... Labor ............ .34 | | | | |
| **2" x 4" redwood decking, con common** | sf | $.68 | $5.38 | $6.06 |
| *Replace* Materials........4.00    Labor ............1.38 | | | | |
| *Remove* ...................... Labor ............ .68 | | | | |
| **2" x 4" redwood decking, con heart** | sf | $.68 | $6.02 | $6.70 |
| *Replace* Materials........4.64    Labor ............1.38 | | | | |
| *Remove* ...................... Labor ............ .68 | | | | |
| **2" x 6" redwood deck, con common** | sf | $.68 | $4.47 | $5.15 |
| *Replace* Materials........3.20    Labor ............1.27 | | | | |
| *Remove* ...................... Labor ............ .68 | | | | |
| **2" x 6" redwood deck, con heart** | sf | $.68 | $4.99 | $5.67 |
| *Replace* Materials........3.72    Labor ............1.27 | | | | |
| *Remove* ...................... Labor ............ .68 | | | | |
| **2" x 8" redwood deck, con common** | sf | $.68 | $4.57 | $5.25 |
| *Replace* Materials........3.43    Labor ............1.14 | | | | |
| *Remove* ...................... Labor ............ .68 | | | | |
| **2" x 8" redwood deck, con heart** | sf | $.68 | $5.11 | $5.79 |
| *Replace* Materials........3.97    Labor ............1.14 | | | | |
| *Remove* ...................... Labor ............ .68 | | | | |
| **2" x 4" treated wood deck** | sf | $.68 | $4.80 | $5.48 |
| *Replace* Materials........3.42    Labor ............1.38 | | | | |
| *Remove* ...................... Labor ............ .68 | | | | |
| **2" x 6" treated wood deck** | sf | $.68 | $4.59 | $5.27 |
| *Replace* Materials........3.32    Labor ............1.27 | | | | |
| *Remove* ...................... Labor ............ .68 | | | | |
| **2" x 8" treated wood deck** | sf | $.68 | $4.41 | $5.09 |
| *Replace* Materials........3.27    Labor ............1.14 | | | | |
| *Remove* ...................... Labor ............ .68 | | | | |
| **Redwood deck railing, con common** | lf | $.89 | $16.63 | $17.52 |
| *Replace* Materials........7.20    Labor ............9.43 | | | | |
| *Remove* ...................... Labor ............ .89 | | | | |
| **Redwood deck railing, con heart** | lf | $.89 | $17.77 | $18.66 |
| *Replace* Materials........8.34    Labor ............9.43 | | | | |
| *Remove* ...................... Labor ............ .89 | | | | |

*rafter foot bird's △ mouth with tenon*

◄ **EXTERIOR DECK JOIST SYSTEM**
Includes 5% waste. Complete joist system. Does not include decking, railing, or stairs. Includes footings, excavation for footings, column stirrups and connectors, posts, and beams on outside edge of deck, connection with joist hangers against house, and joists.

◄ **EXTERIOR DECKING**
Includes 5% waste. Deduct **14%** for 5/4 treated wood decking (decking that is 1-1/4" thick instead of 1-1/2" thick).

*rafter peak △ tongue & fork*

**RELATED ITEMS**

◄ **EXTERIOR DECK RAILING**
Includes 5% waste. With 2" x 2" balusters placed approximately 4" on center.

| Item Description | Unit | Remove | Replace | Total |
|---|---|---|---|---|
| **EXTERIOR DECK** ▶ **RAILING** *continued* — **Treated wood deck railing** <br> *Replace* Materials........7.07    Labor ............9.43 <br> *Remove* .....................    Labor............ .89 | lf | $.89 | $16.50 | $17.39 |
| **EXTERIOR** ▶ **DECK STAIRS** — **2' 6" wide con common redwood deck stairs with railing** <br> *Replace* Materials......30.10    Labor............18.60 <br> *Remove* .....................    Labor............1.60 | ea | $1.60 | $48.70 | $50.30 |
| **2' 6" wide con heart redwood deck stairs with railing** <br> *Replace* Materials......32.40    Labor............18.60 <br> *Remove* .....................    Labor............1.60 | ea | $1.60 | $51.00 | $52.60 |
| **2' 6" wide treated wood deck stairs with railing** <br> *Replace* Materials......29.80    Labor............18.60 <br> *Remove* .....................    Labor............1.60 | ea | $1.60 | $48.40 | $50.00 |
| **3' wide con common redwood deck stairs with railing** <br> *Replace* Materials......32.00    Labor............20.20 <br> *Remove* .....................    Labor............1.60 | ea | $1.60 | $52.20 | $53.80 |
| **3' wide con heart redwood deck stairs with railing** <br> *Replace* Materials......34.30    Labor............20.20 <br> *Remove* .....................    Labor............1.60 | ea | $1.60 | $54.50 | $56.10 |
| **3' wide treated wood deck stairs with railing** <br> *Replace* Materials......31.70    Labor............20.20 <br> *Remove* .....................    Labor............1.60 | ea | $1.60 | $51.90 | $53.50 |
| **EXTERIOR** ▶ **DECK LANDING** — **Redwood deck stairway landing, con common decking** <br> *Replace* Materials......10.70    Labor............2.55 <br> *Remove* .....................    Labor............ .39 | sf | $.39 | $13.25 | $13.64 |
| **Redwood deck stairway landing, con heart decking** <br> *Replace* Materials......11.80    Labor............2.55 <br> *Remove* .....................    Labor............ .39 | sf | $.39 | $14.35 | $14.74 |
| **Treated wood deck stairway landing** <br> *Replace* Materials......10.50    Labor............2.55 <br> *Remove* .....................    Labor............ .39 | sf | $.39 | $13.05 | $13.44 |
| **FURRING STRIPS** ▶ — **1" x 2" furring strips applied to wood 12" on center** <br> *Replace* Materials........ .18    Labor............ .52 <br> *Remove* .....................    Labor............ .29 | sf | $.29 | $.70 | $.99 |
| **1" x 2" furring strips applied to wood 16" on center** <br> *Replace* Materials........ .15    Labor............ .45 <br> *Remove* .....................    Labor............ .29 | sf | $.29 | $.60 | $.89 |
| **1" x 2" furring strips applied to wood 24" on center** <br> *Replace* Materials........ .11    Labor............ .38 <br> *Remove* .....................    Labor............ .29 | sf | $.29 | $.49 | $.78 |
| **1" x 2" furring strips applied to masonry or concrete 12" on center** <br> *Replace* Materials........ .18    Labor............ .69 <br> *Remove* .....................    Labor............ .31 | sf | $.31 | $.87 | $1.18 |
| **1" x 2" furring strips applied to masonry or concrete 16" on center** <br> *Replace* Materials........ .15    Labor............ .55 <br> *Remove* .....................    Labor............ .31 | sf | $.31 | $.70 | $1.01 |
| **1" x 2" furring strips applied to masonry or concrete 24" on center** <br> *Replace* Materials........ .11    Labor............ .48 <br> *Remove* .....................    Labor............ .31 | sf | $.31 | $.59 | $.90 |

**EXTERIOR DECK STAIRS**
Per step. Includes 5% waste. With three stringers made from 2" x 12" lumber. Each step has up to three 2" x 4" treads. Balusters are approximately 4" on center.

**EXTERIOR DECK LANDING**
Includes 5% waste. 2" x 10" joist system with beams, posts, stirrups, footings, excavation for footings, and all fasteners.

**FURRING STRIPS**
Includes 5% waste.
1" x 2" ▷

| Item Description | Unit | Remove | Replace | Total | |
|---|---|---|---|---|---|
| **2" x 2" furring strips applied to wood 12" on center**<br>*Replace* Materials ........ .43     Labor............. .52<br>*Remove* .....................     Labor............. .29 | sf | $.29 | $.95 | $1.24 | ◁ 2"x 2" |
| **2" x 2" furring strips applied to wood 16" on center**<br>*Replace* Materials ........ .35     Labor............. .45<br>*Remove* .....................     Labor............. .29 | sf | $.29 | $.80 | $1.09 | |
| **2" x 2" furring strips applied to wood 24" on center**<br>*Replace* Materials ........ .27     Labor............. .38<br>*Remove* .....................     Labor............. .29 | sf | $.29 | $.65 | $.94 | |
| **2" x 2" furring strips applied to masonry or concrete 12" on center**<br>*Replace* Materials ........ .43     Labor............. .69<br>*Remove* .....................     Labor............. .31 | sf | $.31 | $1.12 | $1.43 | |
| **2" x 2" furring strips applied to masonry or concrete 16" on center**<br>*Replace* Materials ........ .35     Labor............. .55<br>*Remove* .....................     Labor............. .31 | sf | $.31 | $.90 | $1.21 | |
| **2" x 2" furring strips applied to masonry or concrete 24" on center**<br>*Replace* Materials ........ .27     Labor............. .48<br>*Remove* .....................     Labor............. .31 | sf | $.31 | $.75 | $1.06 | |
| **2" x 4" joist system 12" on center with blocking**<br>*Replace* Materials ........ .81     Labor............. .62<br>*Remove* .....................     Labor............. .37 | sf | $.37 | $1.43 | $1.80 | |
| **2" x 4" joist system 16" on center with blocking**<br>*Replace* Materials ........ .65     Labor............. .48<br>*Remove* .....................     Labor............. .37 | sf | $.37 | $1.13 | $1.50 | |
| **2" x 4" joist system 24" on center with blocking**<br>*Replace* Materials ........ .46     Labor............. .38<br>*Remove* .....................     Labor............. .37 | sf | $.37 | $.84 | $1.21 | |
| **2" x 6" joist system 12" on center with blocking and cross bracing**<br>*Replace* Materials ........1.18     Labor............. .86<br>*Remove* .....................     Labor............. .37 | sf | $.37 | $2.04 | $2.41 | ◁ 2"x 6" |
| **2" x 6" joist system 16" on center with blocking and cross bracing**<br>*Replace* Materials ........ .95     Labor............. .65<br>*Remove* .....................     Labor............. .37 | sf | $.37 | $1.60 | $1.97 | |
| **2" x 6" joist system 24" on center with blocking and cross bracing**<br>*Replace* Materials ........ .68     Labor............. .45<br>*Remove* .....................     Labor............. .37 | sf | $.37 | $1.13 | $1.50 | |
| **2" x 8" joist system 12" on center with blocking and cross bracing**<br>*Replace* Materials ........1.45     Labor............1.00<br>*Remove* .....................     Labor............. .37 | sf | $.37 | $2.45 | $2.82 | ◁ 2"x 8" |
| **2" x 8" joist system 16" on center with blocking and cross bracing**<br>*Replace* Materials ........1.15     Labor............. .83<br>*Remove* .....................     Labor............. .37 | sf | $.37 | $1.98 | $2.35 | |
| **2" x 8" joist system 24" on center with blocking and cross bracing**<br>*Replace* Materials ........ .82     Labor............. .62<br>*Remove* .....................     Labor............. .37 | sf | $.37 | $1.44 | $1.81 | |
| **2" x 10" joist system 12" on center with blocking and cross bracing**<br>*Replace* Materials ........2.18     Labor.............1.24<br>*Remove* .....................     Labor............. .37 | sf | $.37 | $3.42 | $3.79 | ◁ 2"x 10" |

**RELATED ITEMS**

◀ **JOIST SYSTEM PER SF**
Includes 5% waste. All joist systems include joists, rim joists, blocking, and steel X braces at center span. (Except 2" x 4" joists which include solid blocking at center of span.)

| Item Description | Unit | Remove | Replace | Total |
|---|---|---|---|---|
| **JOIST SYSTEM ▶** *continued* | | | | |
| **2" x 10" joist system 16" on center with blocking and cross bracing** | sf | $.37 | $2.72 | $3.09 |
| *Replace* Materials....1.72    Labor.......... 1.00 | | | | |
| *Remove* .....................    Labor.............. .37 | | | | |
| **2" x 10" joist system 24" on center with blocking and cross bracing** | sf | $.37 | $1.95 | $2.32 |
| *Replace* Materials........1.19    Labor.............. .76 | | | | |
| *Remove* .....................    Labor.............. .37 | | | | |
| **2" x 12" ▷** **2" x 12" joist system 12" on center with blocking and cross bracing** | sf | $.37 | $4.03 | $4.40 |
| *Replace* Materials........2.48    Labor ...........1.55 | | | | |
| *Remove* .....................    Labor.............. .37 | | | | |
| **2" x 12" joist system 16" on center with blocking and cross bracing** | sf | $.37 | $3.09 | $3.46 |
| *Replace* Materials........1.95    Labor ...........1.14 | | | | |
| *Remove* .....................    Labor.............. .37 | | | | |
| **2" x 12" joist system 24" on center with blocking and cross bracing** | sf | $.37 | $2.35 | $2.72 |
| *Replace* Materials........1.35    Labor.......... 1.00 | | | | |
| *Remove* .....................    Labor.............. .37 | | | | |
| **joists per bf ▷** **Joist system per bf** | bf | $.16 | $1.89 | $2.05 |
| *Replace* Materials........1.17    Labor.............. .72 | | | | |
| *Remove* .....................    Labor.............. .16 | | | | |
| **LAMINATED ▶ I JOIST** *Includes 3% waste. The lf price includes I joist, rim joists, blocking, and steel X braces at center span.* **Laminated lumber I joist with 1-3/4" flange, 9-1/2" deep** | lf | $.37 | $3.37 | $3.74 |
| *Replace* Materials........2.20    Labor ...........1.17 | | | | |
| *Remove* .....................    Labor.............. .37 | | | | |
| **Laminated lumber I joist with 1-3/4" flange, 11-7/8" deep** | lf | $.37 | $3.91 | $4.28 |
| *Replace* Materials........2.67    Labor ...........1.24 | | | | |
| *Remove* .....................    Labor.............. .37 | | | | |
| **Laminated lumber I joist with 1-3/4" flange, 14" deep** | lf | $.37 | $4.54 | $4.91 |
| *Replace* Materials........3.27    Labor ...........1.27 | | | | |
| *Remove* .....................    Labor.............. .37 | | | | |
| **2-5/16" wide ▷** **Laminated lumber I joist with 2-5/16" flange, 11-7/8" deep** | lf | $.37 | $5.02 | $5.39 |
| *Replace* Materials........3.78    Labor ...........1.24 | | | | |
| *Remove* .....................    Labor.............. .37 | | | | |
| **Laminated lumber I joist with 2-5/16" flange, 14" deep** | lf | $.37 | $5.94 | $6.31 |
| *Replace* Materials........4.63    Labor ...........1.31 | | | | |
| *Remove* .....................    Labor.............. .37 | | | | |
| **Laminated lumber I joist with 2-5/16" flange, 16" deep** | lf | $.37 | $6.81 | $7.18 |
| *Replace* Materials........5.47    Labor ...........1.34 | | | | |
| *Remove* .....................    Labor.............. .37 | | | | |
| **FLOOR TRUSS ▶** *The lf price includes cat walks, diagonal braces, fasteners and rim materials.* **Floor truss** | lf | $.37 | $6.98 | $7.35 |
| *Replace* Materials........3.85    Labor ...........3.13 | | | | |
| *Remove* .....................    Labor.............. .37 | | | | |
| **Floor truss designed for heavy loading** | lf | $.37 | $7.40 | $7.77 |
| *Replace* Materials........4.17    Labor ...........3.23 | | | | |
| *Remove* .....................    Labor.............. .37 | | | | |
| **HAND-FRAMED ROOF ▶** *Gable roof. Includes 5% waste. Measure the sf of area beneath roof.* **Hand-framed roof 4 in 12 slope with 2" x 4" rafters** | sf | $.42 | $1.74 | $2.16 |
| *Replace* Materials ........ .57    Labor ...........1.17 | | | | |
| *Remove* .....................    Labor.............. .42 | | | | |
| **Hand-framed roof 6 in 12 slope with 2" x 4" rafters** | sf | $.45 | $1.84 | $2.29 |
| *Replace* Materials ........ .60    Labor ...........1.24 | | | | |
| *Remove* .....................    Labor.............. .45 | | | | |

*continued on next page*

| Item Description | Unit | Remove | Replace | Total |
|---|---|---|---|---|
| **Hand-framed roof 8 in 12 slope with 2" x 4" rafters**<br>*Replace* Materials ........ .62  Labor ............1.38<br>*Remove* ........................  Labor ............. .50 | sf | $.50 | $2.00 | $2.50 |
| **Hand-framed roof 10 in 12 slope with 2" x 4" rafters**<br>*Replace* Materials ........ .66  Labor ............1.51<br>*Remove* ........................  Labor ............. .63 | sf | $.63 | $2.17 | $2.80 |
| **Hand-framed roof 12 in 12 slope with 2" x 4" rafters**<br>*Replace* Materials ........ .72  Labor ............1.69<br>*Remove* ........................  Labor ............. .84 | sf | $.84 | $2.41 | $3.25 |
| **Hand-framed roof 14 in 12 slope with 2" x 4" rafters**<br>*Replace* Materials ........ .76  Labor ............1.86<br>*Remove* ........................  Labor ............ 1.00 | sf | $1.00 | $2.62 | $3.62 |
| **Hand-framed roof 16 in 12 slope with 2" x 4" rafters**<br>*Replace* Materials ........ .81  Labor ............2.06<br>*Remove* ........................  Labor ............1.31 | sf | $1.31 | $2.87 | $4.18 |
| **Hand-framed roof 18 in 12 slope with 2" x 4" rafters**<br>*Replace* Materials ........ .88  Labor ............2.30<br>*Remove* ........................  Labor ............2.02 | sf | $2.02 | $3.18 | $5.20 |
| **Hand-framed roof 4 in 12 slope with 2" x 6" rafters**<br>*Replace* Materials ........ .81  Labor ............1.20<br>*Remove* ........................  Labor ............. .42 | sf | $.42 | $2.01 | $2.43 |
| **Hand-framed roof 6 in 12 slope with 2" x 6" rafters**<br>*Replace* Materials ........ .85  Labor ............1.31<br>*Remove* ........................  Labor ............. .45 | sf | $.45 | $2.16 | $2.61 |
| **Hand-framed roof 8 in 12 slope with 2" x 6" rafters**<br>*Replace* Materials ........ .90  Labor ............1.44<br>*Remove* ........................  Labor ............. .50 | sf | $.50 | $2.34 | $2.84 |
| **Hand-framed roof 10 in 12 slope with 2" x 6" rafters**<br>*Replace* Materials ........ .96  Labor ............1.58<br>*Remove* ........................  Labor ............. .63 | sf | $.63 | $2.54 | $3.17 |
| **Hand-framed roof 12 in 12 slope with 2" x 6" rafters**<br>*Replace* Materials ...... 1.02  Labor ............1.75<br>*Remove* ........................  Labor ............. .84 | sf | $.84 | $2.77 | $3.61 |
| **Hand-framed roof 14 in 12 slope with 2" x 6" rafters**<br>*Replace* Materials ........1.09  Labor ............1.93<br>*Remove* ........................  Labor ............ 1.00 | sf | $1.00 | $3.02 | $4.02 |
| **Hand-framed roof 16 in 12 slope with 2" x 6" rafters**<br>*Replace* Materials ........1.17  Labor ............2.13<br>*Remove* ........................  Labor ............1.31 | sf | $1.31 | $3.30 | $4.61 |
| **Hand-framed roof 18 in 12 slope with 2" x 6" rafters**<br>*Replace* Materials ........1.25  Labor ............2.41<br>*Remove* ........................  Labor ............2.02 | sf | $2.02 | $3.66 | $5.68 |
| **Hand-framed roof 4 in 12 slope with 2" x 8" rafters**<br>*Replace* Materials ........1.17  Labor ............1.24<br>*Remove* ........................  Labor ............. .42 | sf | $.42 | $2.41 | $2.83 |
| **Hand-framed roof 6 in 12 slope with 2" x 8" rafters**<br>*Replace* Materials ........1.22  Labor ............1.34<br>*Remove* ........................  Labor ............. .45 | sf | $.45 | $2.56 | $3.01 |

◄ **HAND-FRAMED ROOF**
*continued*
(The sf of bottom floor plus sf under overhangs.) Do not measure the sf of roof. Includes rafters, collar ties, a ridge board that is 2" wider than the rafter (except for 2" x 12" rafters which have a ridge made from a 1-1/2" x 11-7/8" micro-laminated beam), rough fascia board, blocking, and wall fasteners. If roof has a hip or a Dutch hip see page 435. There is no additional charge for a Dutch gable. (see illustrations on page 435.)

◁ **2"x 6"**

**RELATED ITEMS**

◁ **2"x 8"**

| | Item Description | Unit | Remove | Replace | Total |
|---|---|---|---|---|---|
| **HAND-FRAMED ▶ ROOF** *continued* | **Hand-framed roof 8 in 12 slope with 2" x 8" rafters**<br>*Replace* Materials........1.29      Labor ............1.48<br>*Remove* .......................      Labor............. .50 | sf | $.50 | $2.77 | $3.27 |
| | **Hand-framed roof 10 in 12 slope with 2" x 8" rafters**<br>*Replace* Materials........1.37      Labor ............1.62<br>*Remove* .......................      Labor............. .63 | sf | $.63 | $2.99 | $3.62 |
| | **Hand-framed roof 12 in 12 slope with 2" x 8" rafters**<br>*Replace* Materials........1.48      Labor ............1.79<br>*Remove* .......................      Labor............. .84 | sf | $.84 | $3.27 | $4.11 |
| | **Hand-framed roof 14 in 12 slope with 2" x 8" rafters**<br>*Replace* Materials........1.57      Labor ............2.00<br>*Remove* .......................      Labor............ 1.00 | sf | $1.00 | $3.57 | $4.57 |
| | **Hand-framed roof 16 in 12 slope with 2" x 8" rafters**<br>*Replace* Materials........1.67      Labor ............2.20<br>*Remove* .......................      Labor............1.31 | sf | $1.31 | $3.87 | $5.18 |
| | **Hand-framed roof 18 in 12 slope with 2" x 8" rafters**<br>*Replace* Materials........1.79      Labor ............2.48<br>*Remove* .......................      Labor............2.02 | sf | $2.02 | $4.27 | $6.29 |
| **2" x 10" ▷** | **Hand-framed roof 4 in 12 slope with 2" x 10" rafters**<br>*Replace* Materials........1.52      Labor ............1.27<br>*Remove* .......................      Labor............ .42 | sf | $.42 | $2.79 | $3.21 |
| | **Hand-framed roof 6 in 12 slope with 2" x 10" rafters**<br>*Replace* Materials........1.58      Labor ............1.38<br>*Remove* .......................      Labor............ .45 | sf | $.45 | $2.96 | $3.41 |
| | **Hand-framed roof 8 in 12 slope with 2" x 10" rafters**<br>*Replace* Materials........1.67      Labor ............1.51<br>*Remove* .......................      Labor............ .50 | sf | $.50 | $3.18 | $3.68 |
| | **Hand-framed roof 10 in 12 slope with 2" x 10" rafters**<br>*Replace* Materials........1.79      Labor ............1.69<br>*Remove* .......................      Labor............ .63 | sf | $.63 | $3.48 | $4.11 |
| | **Hand-framed roof 12 in 12 slope with 2" x 10" rafters**<br>*Replace* Materials........1.93      Labor ............1.86<br>*Remove* .......................      Labor............ .84 | sf | $.84 | $3.79 | $4.63 |
| | **Hand-framed roof 14 in 12 slope with 2" x 10" rafters**<br>*Replace* Materials........2.06      Labor ............2.03<br>*Remove* .......................      Labor............1.00 | sf | $1.00 | $4.09 | $5.09 |
| | **Hand-framed roof 16 in 12 slope with 2" x 10" rafters**<br>*Replace* Materials........2.21      Labor ............2.27<br>*Remove* .......................      Labor............1.31 | sf | $1.31 | $4.48 | $5.79 |
| | **Hand-framed roof 18 in 12 slope with 2" x 10" rafters**<br>*Replace* Materials........2.37      Labor ............2.58<br>*Remove* .......................      Labor............2.02 | sf | $2.02 | $4.95 | $6.97 |
| **2" x 12" ▷** | **Hand-framed roof 4 in 12 slope with 2" x 12" rafters**<br>*Replace* Materials........2.06      Labor ............1.31<br>*Remove* .......................      Labor............ .42 | sf | $.42 | $3.37 | $3.79 |
| | **Hand-framed roof 6 in 12 slope with 2" x 12" rafters**<br>*Replace* Materials........2.14      Labor ............1.44<br>*Remove* .......................      Labor............ .45 | sf | $.45 | $3.58 | $4.03 |

| Item Description | Unit | Remove | Replace | Total | |
|---|---|---|---|---|---|
| **Hand-framed roof 8 in 12 slope with 2″ x 12″ rafters**<br>*Replace* Materials........2.25    Labor ...........1.58<br>*Remove* .....................    Labor............. .50 | sf | $.50 | $3.83 | $4.33 | *gable* △ |
| **Hand-framed roof 10 in 12 slope with 2″ x 12″ rafters**<br>*Replace* Materials........2.38    Labor ...........1.72<br>*Remove* .....................    Labor............. .63 | sf | $.63 | $4.10 | $4.73 | *hip* △ |
| **Hand-framed roof 12 in 12 slope with 2″ x 12″ rafters**<br>*Replace* Materials........2.53    Labor ...........1.93<br>*Remove* .....................    Labor............. .84 | sf | $.84 | $4.46 | $5.30 | *mansard* △ |
| **Hand-framed roof 14 in 12 slope with 2″ x 12″ rafters**<br>*Replace* Materials........2.68    Labor ...........2.10<br>*Remove* .....................    Labor............. 1.00 | sf | $1.00 | $4.78 | $5.78 | *gambrel* △ |
| **Hand-framed roof 16 in 12 slope with 2″ x 12″ rafters**<br>*Replace* Materials........2.86    Labor ...........2.34<br>*Remove* .....................    Labor...........1.31 | sf | $1.31 | $5.20 | $6.51 | *Dutch gable* △ |
| **Hand-framed roof 18 in 12 slope with 2″ x 12″ rafters**<br>*Replace* Materials........3.04    Labor ...........2.65<br>*Remove* .....................    Labor...........2.02 | sf | $2.02 | $5.69 | $7.71 | |
| **Add for each lf of valley in hand-framed roof**<br>*Replace* Materials ......12.20    Labor...........27.10<br>▶ Includes additional labor, materials, and waste to frame a valley. | lf | — | $39.30 | $39.30 | ◀ **ADDITIONAL COSTS FOR HAND-FRAMED ROOFS** |
| **For a hand-framed hip roof add for each lf of width**<br>*Replace* Materials........1.93    Labor ...........7.30<br>▶ Includes additional labor, materials, and waste to frame a hip.  Per lf of hip.  (For a hip on both ends of a roof measure the lf of both sides.) | lf | — | $9.23 | $9.23 | *Dutch hip* △ |
| **For a hand-framed Dutch hip roof add for each lf of width**<br>*Replace* Materials........2.13    Labor ...........7.88<br>▶ Includes additional labor, materials, and waste to frame a Dutch hip.  Per lf of hip. (For a Dutch hip on both ends of a roof measure the lf of both sides.) | lf | — | $10.01 | $10.01 | |
| **Hand-framed mansard roof with 2″ x 4″ rafters**<br>*Replace* Materials ........ .09    Labor............. .17<br>*Remove* .....................    Labor............. .05 | cf | $.05 | $.26 | $.31 | ◀ **HAND-FRAMED MANSARD ROOF**<br>*Includes 7% waste.  Roof area equals roof system width times height times length.  Includes rafters, collar ties, ridge boards, hip rafters, rough fascia board, blocking, and wall fasteners.* |
| **Hand-framed mansard roof with 2″ x 6″ rafters**<br>*Replace* Materials ........ .14    Labor............. .17<br>*Remove* .....................    Labor............. .05 | cf | $.05 | $.31 | $.36 | |
| **Hand-framed mansard roof with 2″ x 8″ rafters**<br>*Replace* Materials ........ .19    Labor............. .17<br>*Remove* .....................    Labor............. .05 | cf | $.05 | $.36 | $.41 | |
| **Hand-framed mansard roof with 2″ x 10″ rafters**<br>*Replace* Materials ........ .24    Labor............. .17<br>*Remove* .....................    Labor............. .05 | cf | $.05 | $.41 | $.46 | |
| **Hand-framed mansard roof with 2″ x 12″ rafters**<br>*Replace* Materials ........ .28    Labor............. .21<br>*Remove* .....................    Labor............. .05 | cf | $.05 | $.49 | $.54 | |
| **Add for each lf of valley in hand-framed mansard roof**<br>*Replace* Materials ......14.60    Labor...........37.20<br>▶ Includes additional labor, materials, and waste to frame a valley. | lf | — | $51.80 | $51.80 | ◁ *mansard roof valley* |
| **Hand-framed gambrel roof with 2″ x 4″ rafters**<br>*Replace* Materials ........ .12    Labor............. .14<br>*Remove* .....................    Labor............. .05 | cf | $.05 | $.26 | $.31 | ◀ **HAND FRAMED GAMBREL ROOF**<br>*continued on next page* |

| Item Description | Unit | Remove | Replace | Total |
|---|---|---|---|---|
| **HAND-FRAMED GAMBREL ROOF** *continued*<br><br>*Includes 7% waste. Roof area equals roof system width times height times length. Includes rafters, collar ties, ridge boards, valley rafters, rough fascia board, blocking, and wall fasteners. Does not include wall that must be built at the intersection of the top and bottom sloping roof sections.* | | | | |
| **Hand-framed gambrel roof with 2″ x 6″ rafters**<br>*Replace* Materials ........ .18     Labor............ .17<br>*Remove* ......................     Labor............ .05 | cf | $.05 | $.35 | $.40 |
| **Hand-framed gambrel roof with 2″ x 8″ rafters**<br>*Replace* Materials ........ .25     Labor............ .17<br>*Remove* ......................     Labor............ .05 | cf | $.05 | $.42 | $.47 |
| **Hand-framed gambrel roof with 2″ x 10″ rafters**<br>*Replace* Materials ........ .32     Labor............ .17<br>*Remove* ......................     Labor............ .05 | cf | $.05 | $.49 | $.54 |
| **Hand-framed gambrel roof with 2″ x 12″ rafters**<br>*Replace* Materials ........ .37     Labor............ .21<br>*Remove* ......................     Labor............ .05 | cf | $.05 | $.58 | $.63 |
| **gambrel roof valley** ▷ | | | | |
| **Add for each lf of valley in hand-framed gambrel roof**<br>*Replace* Materials.......15.20     Labor .........39.20<br>▶ Includes additional labor, materials, and waste to frame a valley in a gambrel roof. | lf | — | $54.40 | $54.40 |
| **HAND-FRAMED ROOF PER BF** *Includes 5% waste.* | | | | |
| **Hand-framed gable roof per bf**<br>*Replace* Materials ........ .97     Labor............ .79<br>*Remove* ......................     Labor............ .18 | bf | $.18 | $1.76 | $1.94 |
| **Hand-framed hip roof per bf**<br>*Replace* Materials........1.07     Labor............ .79<br>*Remove* ......................     Labor............ .18 | bf | $.18 | $1.86 | $2.04 |
| **Hand-framed Dutch hip roof per bf**<br>*Replace* Materials........1.09     Labor............ .83<br>*Remove* ......................     Labor............ .18 | bf | $.18 | $1.92 | $2.10 |
| **Hand-framed mansard roof per bf**<br>*Replace* Materials........1.18     Labor............ .89<br>*Remove* ......................     Labor............ .18 | bf | $.18 | $2.07 | $2.25 |
| **Hand-framed gambrel roof per bf**<br>*Replace* Materials........1.25     Labor............ .86<br>*Remove* ......................     Labor............ .18 | bf | $.18 | $2.11 | $2.29 |
| **MINIMUM FOR ROOF FRAMING** | | | | |
| **Minimum charge for roof framing**<br>*Replace* Materials......50.00     Labor .........43.00 | ea | — | $93.00 | $93.00 |
| **HAND-FRAMED SHED DORMER** *Includes 7% waste. Complete dormer including all side walls and roof framing.* | | | | |
| **Shed dormer 4 in 12 slope (length x width of dormer)**<br>*Replace* Materials ........ .96     Labor............1.55<br>*Remove* ......................     Labor............ .45 | sf | $.45 | $2.51 | $2.96 |
| **Shed dormer 6 in 12 slope (length x width of dormer)**<br>*Replace* Materials ...... 1.00     Labor............1.62<br>*Remove* ......................     Labor............ .47 | sf | $.47 | $2.62 | $3.09 |
| **Shed dormer 8 in 12 slope (length x width of dormer)**<br>*Replace* Materials........1.06     Labor............1.69<br>*Remove* ......................     Labor............ .52 | sf | $.52 | $2.75 | $3.27 |
| **Shed dormer 10 in 12 slope (length x width of dormer)**<br>*Replace* Materials........1.13     Labor............1.86<br>*Remove* ......................     Labor............ .66 | sf | $.66 | $2.99 | $3.65 |
| **Shed dormer 12 in 12 slope (length x width of dormer)**<br>*Replace* Materials........1.20     Labor............2.06<br>*Remove* ......................     Labor............ .86 | sf | $.86 | $3.26 | $4.12 |

| Item Description | Unit | Remove | Replace | Total |
|---|---|---|---|---|
| **Shed dormer 14 in 12 slope (length x width of dormer)** | sf | $1.05 | $3.42 | $4.47 |
| *Replace* Materials........1.29     Labor ...........2.13 | | | | |
| *Remove* .....................     Labor ...........1.05 | | | | |
| **Shed dormer 16 in 12 slope (length x width of dormer)** | sf | $1.39 | $3.58 | $4.97 |
| *Replace* Materials........1.38     Labor ...........2.20 | | | | |
| *Remove* .....................     Labor ...........1.39 | | | | |
| **Shed dormer 18 in 12 slope (length x width of dormer)** | sf | $2.12 | $3.78 | $5.90 |
| *Replace* Materials........1.48     Labor ...........2.30 | | | | |
| *Remove* .....................     Labor ...........2.12 | | | | |
| **Gable dormer 4 in 12 slope (length of ridge x width of dormer)** | sf | $.45 | $2.69 | $3.14 |
| *Replace* Materials........1.07     Labor ...........1.62 | | | | |
| *Remove* .....................     Labor ............ .45 | | | | |
| **Gable dormer 6 in 12 slope (length of ridge x width of dormer)** | sf | $.47 | $2.81 | $3.28 |
| *Replace* Materials........1.12     Labor ...........1.69 | | | | |
| *Remove* .....................     Labor ............ .47 | | | | |
| **Gable dormer 8 in 12 slope (length of ridge x width of dormer)** | sf | $.52 | $2.94 | $3.46 |
| *Replace* Materials........1.19     Labor ...........1.75 | | | | |
| *Remove* .....................     Labor ............ .52 | | | | |
| **Gable dormer 10 in 12 slope (length of ridge x width of dormer)** | sf | $.66 | $3.20 | $3.86 |
| *Replace* Materials........1.27     Labor ...........1.93 | | | | |
| *Remove* .....................     Labor ............ .66 | | | | |
| **Gable dormer 12 in 12 slope (length of ridge x width of dormer)** | sf | $.86 | $3.48 | $4.34 |
| *Replace* Materials........1.35     Labor ...........2.13 | | | | |
| *Remove* .....................     Labor ............ .86 | | | | |
| **Gable dormer 14 in 12 slope (length of ridge x width of dormer)** | sf | $1.05 | $3.68 | $4.73 |
| *Replace* Materials........1.44     Labor ...........2.24 | | | | |
| *Remove* .....................     Labor ...........1.05 | | | | |
| **Gable dormer 16 in 12 slope (length of ridge x width of dormer)** | sf | $1.39 | $3.84 | $5.23 |
| *Replace* Materials........1.54     Labor ...........2.30 | | | | |
| *Remove* .....................     Labor ...........1.39 | | | | |
| **Gable dormer 18 in 12 slope (length of ridge x width of dormer)** | sf | $2.12 | $4.06 | $6.18 |
| *Replace* Materials........1.65     Labor ...........2.41 | | | | |
| *Remove* .....................     Labor ...........2.12 | | | | |
| **Hip dormer 4 in 12 slope (length x width of dormer)** | sf | $.45 | $2.79 | $3.24 |
| *Replace* Materials........1.10     Labor ...........1.69 | | | | |
| *Remove* .....................     Labor ............ .45 | | | | |
| **Hip dormer 6 in 12 slope (length x width of dormer)** | sf | $.47 | $2.91 | $3.38 |
| *Replace* Materials........1.16     Labor ...........1.75 | | | | |
| *Remove* .....................     Labor ............ .47 | | | | |
| **Hip dormer 8 in 12 slope (length x width of dormer)** | sf | $.52 | $3.04 | $3.56 |
| *Replace* Materials........1.22     Labor ...........1.82 | | | | |
| *Remove* .....................     Labor ............ .52 | | | | |
| **Hip dormer 10 in 12 slope (length x width of dormer)** | sf | $.66 | $3.31 | $3.97 |
| *Replace* Materials........1.31     Labor ...........2.00 | | | | |
| *Remove* .....................     Labor ............ .66 | | | | |
| **Hip dormer 12 in 12 slope (length x width of dormer)** | sf | $.86 | $3.63 | $4.49 |
| *Replace* Materials........1.39     Labor ...........2.24 | | | | |
| *Remove* .....................     Labor ............ .86 | | | | |

◄ **HAND-FRAMED GABLE DORMER**
*Includes 7% waste. Complete dormer including all side walls and roof framing.*

◄ **HAND-FRAMED HIP DORMER**
*Includes 7% waste. Complete dormer including all side walls and roof framing.*

| Item Description | Unit | Remove | Replace | Total |
|---|---|---|---|---|
| **HAND-FRAMED HIP DORMER** continued | | | | |
| **Hip dormer 14 in 12 slope (length x width of dormer)** | sf | $1.05 | $3.78 | $4.83 |
| *Replace* Materials........1.48   Labor ...........2.30 | | | | |
| *Remove* .....................   Labor ...........1.05 | | | | |
| **Hip dormer 16 in 12 slope (length x width of dormer)** | sf | $1.39 | $4.00 | $5.39 |
| *Replace* Materials........1.59   Labor ...........2.41 | | | | |
| *Remove* .....................   Labor ...........1.39 | | | | |
| **Hip dormer 18 in 12 slope (length x width of dormer)** | sf | $2.12 | $4.21 | $6.33 |
| *Replace* Materials........1.70   Labor ...........2.51 | | | | |
| *Remove* .....................   Labor ...........2.12 | | | | |
| **HAND-FRAMED DUTCH-HIP DORMER** Includes 7% waste. Complete dormer including all side walls and roof framing. | | | | |
| **Dutch-hip dormer 4 in 12 slope (length x width of dormer)** | sf | $.45 | $2.88 | $3.33 |
| *Replace* Materials........1.13   Labor ...........1.75 | | | | |
| *Remove* .....................   Labor .............45 | | | | |
| **Dutch-hip dormer 6 in 12 slope (length x width of dormer)** | sf | $.47 | $2.98 | $3.45 |
| *Replace* Materials........1.19   Labor ...........1.79 | | | | |
| *Remove* .....................   Labor .............47 | | | | |
| **Dutch-hip dormer 8 in 12 slope (length x width of dormer)** | sf | $.52 | $3.12 | $3.64 |
| *Replace* Materials........1.26   Labor ...........1.86 | | | | |
| *Remove* .....................   Labor .............52 | | | | |
| **Dutch-hip dormer 10 in 12 slope (length x width of dormer)** | sf | $.66 | $3.40 | $4.06 |
| *Replace* Materials........1.34   Labor ...........2.06 | | | | |
| *Remove* .....................   Labor .............66 | | | | |
| **Dutch-hip dormer 12 in 12 slope (length x width of dormer)** | sf | $.86 | $3.73 | $4.59 |
| *Replace* Materials........1.43   Labor ...........2.30 | | | | |
| *Remove* .....................   Labor .............86 | | | | |
| **Dutch-hip dormer 14 in 12 slope (length x width of dormer)** | sf | $1.05 | $3.90 | $4.95 |
| *Replace* Materials........1.53   Labor ...........2.37 | | | | |
| *Remove* .....................   Labor ...........1.05 | | | | |
| **Dutch-hip dormer 16 in 12 slope (length x width of dormer)** | sf | $1.39 | $4.12 | $5.51 |
| *Replace* Materials........1.64   Labor ...........2.48 | | | | |
| *Remove* .....................   Labor ...........1.39 | | | | |
| **Dutch-hip dormer 18 in 12 slope (length x width of dormer)** | sf | $2.12 | $4.30 | $6.42 |
| *Replace* Materials........1.75   Labor ...........2.55 | | | | |
| *Remove* .....................   Labor ...........2.12 | | | | |
| **HAND-FRAMED GAMBREL DORMER** Includes 7% waste. | | | | |
| **Gambrel dormer (length x width of dormer)** | sf | $.45 | $3.19 | $3.64 |
| *Replace* Materials........1.16   Labor ...........2.03 | | | | |
| *Remove* .....................   Labor .............45 | | | | |
| **HAND-FRAMED ROOF DORMER PER BF** | | | | |
| **Shed dormer per bf** | bf | $.26 | $2.74 | $3.00 |
| *Replace* Materials........1.57   Labor ...........1.17 | | | | |
| *Remove* .....................   Labor .............26 | | | | |
| **Gable dormer per bf** | bf | $.45 | $2.85 | $3.30 |
| *Replace* Materials........1.65   Labor ...........1.20 | | | | |
| *Remove* .....................   Labor .............45 | | | | |
| **Hip dormer per bf** | bf | $.47 | $2.93 | $3.40 |
| *Replace* Materials........1.69   Labor ...........1.24 | | | | |
| *Remove* .....................   Labor .............47 | | | | |
| **Dutch-hip dormer per bf** | bf | $.50 | $3.06 | $3.56 |
| *Replace* Materials........1.75   Labor ...........1.31 | | | | |
| *Remove* .....................   Labor .............50 | | | | |

| Item Description | Unit | Remove | Replace | Total |
|---|---|---|---|---|
| **Gambrel dormer per bf**<br>*Replace* Materials .......1.79  Labor ............1.27<br>*Remove* .................. Labor ............ .60 | bf | $.60 | $3.06 | $3.66 |
| **Flat roof truss**<br>*Replace* Materials .......3.84  Labor ............ .79  Equipment ............ .16<br>*Remove* .................. Labor ............1.10 | lf | $1.10 | $4.79 | $5.89 |
| **4 in 12 slope truss**<br>*Replace* Materials .......4.05  Labor ............ .79  Equipment ............ .16<br>*Remove* .................. Labor ............1.10 | lf | $1.10 | $5.00 | $6.10 |
| **6 in 12 slope truss**<br>*Replace* Materials .......4.37  Labor ............ .79  Equipment ............ .16<br>*Remove* .................. Labor ............1.10 | lf | $1.10 | $5.32 | $6.42 |
| **8 in 12 slope truss**<br>*Replace* Materials .......5.90  Labor ............ .83  Equipment ............ .16<br>*Remove* .................. Labor ............1.10 | lf | $1.10 | $6.89 | $7.99 |
| **10 in 12 slope truss**<br>*Replace* Materials .......6.78  Labor ............ .83  Equipment ............ .16<br>*Remove* .................. Labor ............1.10 | lf | $1.10 | $7.77 | $8.87 |
| **12 in 12 slope truss**<br>*Replace* Materials .......7.89  Labor ............ .83  Equipment ............ .16<br>*Remove* .................. Labor ............1.10 | lf | $1.10 | $8.88 | $9.98 |
| **14 in 12 slope truss**<br>*Replace* Materials .......8.36  Labor ............ .86  Equipment ............ .16<br>*Remove* .................. Labor ............1.10 | lf | $1.10 | $9.38 | $10.48 |
| **16 in 12 slope truss**<br>*Replace* Materials .......9.00  Labor ............ .89  Equipment ............ .16<br>*Remove* .................. Labor ............1.10 | lf | $1.10 | $10.05 | $11.15 |
| **17 in 12 slope truss**<br>*Replace* Materials .......9.72  Labor ............ .961  Equipment ............ .16<br>*Remove* .................. Labor ............1.10 | lf | $1.10 | $10.84 | $11.94 |
| **Flat roof truss designed for slate or tile roofing**<br>*Replace* Materials .......4.08  Labor ............ .79  Equipment ............ .16<br>*Remove* .................. Labor ............1.10 | lf | $1.10 | $5.03 | $6.13 |
| **4 in 12 slope truss designed for slate or tile roofing**<br>*Replace* Materials .......4.37  Labor ............ .79  Equipment ............ .16<br>*Remove* .................. Labor ............1.10 | lf | $1.10 | $5.32 | $6.42 |
| **6 in 12 slope truss designed for slate or tile roofing**<br>*Replace* Materials .......4.64  Labor ............ .79  Equipment ............ .16<br>*Remove* .................. Labor ............1.10 | lf | $1.10 | $5.59 | $6.69 |
| **8 in 12 slope truss designed for slate or tile roofing**<br>*Replace* Materials .......6.20  Labor ............ .83  Equipment ............ .16<br>*Remove* .................. Labor ............1.10 | lf | $1.10 | $7.19 | $8.29 |
| **10 in 12 slope truss designed for slate or tile roofing**<br>*Replace* Materials .......7.10  Labor ............ .83  Equipment ............ .16<br>*Remove* .................. Labor ............1.10 | lf | $1.10 | $8.09 | $9.19 |
| **12 in 12 slope truss designed for slate or tile roofing**<br>*Replace* Materials .......8.20  Labor ............ .83  Equipment ............ .16<br>*Remove* .................. Labor ............1.10 | lf | $1.10 | $9.19 | $10.29 |

◄ **ROOF TRUSS PER LF**
*Add 10% for treated trusses. Per lf of truss bottom chord. The lf price includes cat walks, diagonal braces, fasteners and rough fascia.*

◄ **ROOF TRUSS FOR HEAVY LOAD PER LF**
*Add 10% for treated trusses. Per lf of truss bottom chord. The lf price includes cat walks, diagonal braces, fasteners and rough fascia.*

| | Item Description | Unit | Remove | Replace | Total |
|---|---|---|---|---|---|
| **ROOF TRUSS FOR ►**<br>**HEAVY LOAD**<br>**PER LF**<br>*continued* | **14 in 12 slope truss designed for slate or tile roofing**<br>*Replace* Materials........8.69　　Labor............ .86　　Equipment ............ .16<br>*Remove* ...................　　Labor............1.10 | lf | $1.10 | $9.71 | $10.81 |
| | **16 in 12 slope truss designed for slate or tile roofing**<br>*Replace* Materials........9.35　　Labor............ .89　　Equipment ............ .16<br>*Remove* ...................　　Labor............1.10 | lf | $1.10 | $10.40 | $11.50 |
| | **17 in 12 slope truss designed for slate or tile roofing**<br>*Replace* Materials......10.10　　Labor............ .96　　Equipment ............ .16<br>*Remove* ...................　　Labor............1.10 | lf | $1.10 | $11.22 | $12.32 |
| **ROOF TRUSS ►**<br>**PER SF**<br>Add **10%** *for treated*<br>*trusses. Per sf of area*<br>*underneath the roof. For*<br>*roofs with asphalt, metal,*<br>*or wood roofing.*<br>*Includes cat walks,*<br>*diagonal braces, fasteners*<br>*and rough fascia.* | **Truss roof system 4 in 12 slope**<br>*Replace* Materials........2.35　　Labor............ .41　　Equipment ............ .09<br>*Remove* ...................　　Labor............ .45 | sf | $.45 | $2.85 | $3.30 |
| | **Truss roof system 6 in 12 slope**<br>*Replace* Materials........2.53　　Labor............ .41　　Equipment ............ .09<br>*Remove* ...................　　Labor............ .47 | sf | $.47 | $3.03 | $3.50 |
| | **Truss roof system 8 in 12 slope**<br>*Replace* Materials........3.42　　Labor............ .41　　Equipment ............ .09<br>*Remove* ...................　　Labor............ .55 | sf | $.55 | $3.92 | $4.47 |
| | **Truss roof system 10 in 12 slope**<br>*Replace* Materials........3.93　　Labor............ .45　　Equipment ............ .09<br>*Remove* ...................　　Labor............ .66 | sf | $.66 | $4.47 | $5.13 |
| | **Truss roof system 12 in 12 slope**<br>*Replace* Materials........4.58　　Labor............ .45　　Equipment ............ .09<br>*Remove* ...................　　Labor............ .89 | sf | $.89 | $5.12 | $6.01 |
| | **Truss roof system 14 in 12 slope**<br>*Replace* Materials........4.85　　Labor............ .45　　Equipment ............ .09<br>*Remove* ...................　　Labor............1.05 | sf | $1.05 | $5.39 | $6.44 |
| | **Truss roof system 16 in 12 slope**<br>*Replace* Materials........5.22　　Labor............ .45　　Equipment ............ .09<br>*Remove* ...................　　Labor............1.39 | sf | $1.39 | $5.76 | $7.15 |
| | **Truss roof system 17 in 12 slope**<br>*Replace* Materials........5.64　　Labor............ .45　　Equipment ............ .09<br>*Remove* ...................　　Labor............2.15 | sf | $2.15 | $6.18 | $8.33 |
| **ROOF TRUSS ►**<br>**FOR HEAVY LOAD**<br>**PER SF**<br>Add **10%** *for treated*<br>*trusses. Per sf of area*<br>*underneath the roof. For*<br>*roofs with slate, tile, or*<br>*other heavy roofing.*<br>*Includes cat walks,*<br>*diagonal braces, fasteners*<br>*and rough fascia.* | **Truss roof system 4 in 12 slope designed for slate or tile roofing**<br>*Replace* Materials........2.53　　Labor............ .41　　Equipment ............ .09<br>*Remove* ...................　　Labor............ .45 | sf | $.45 | $3.03 | $3.48 |
| | **Truss roof system 6 in 12 slope designed for slate or tile roofing**<br>*Replace* Materials........2.69　　Labor............ .41　　Equipment ............ .09<br>*Remove* ...................　　Labor............ .47 | sf | $.47 | $3.19 | $3.66 |
| | **Truss roof system 8 in 12 slope designed for slate or tile roofing**<br>*Replace* Materials........3.60　　Labor............ .41　　Equipment ............ .09<br>*Remove* ...................　　Labor............ .55 | sf | $.55 | $4.10 | $4.65 |
| | **Truss roof system 10 in 12 slope designed for slate or tile roofing**<br>*Replace* Materials........4.12　　Labor............ .45　　Equipment ............ .09<br>*Remove* ...................　　Labor............ .66 | sf | $.66 | $4.66 | $5.32 |
| | **Truss roof system 12 in 12 slope designed for slate or tile roofing**<br>*Replace* Materials........4.76　　Labor............ .45　　Equipment ............ .09<br>*Remove* ...................　　Labor............ .89 | sf | $.89 | $5.30 | $6.19 |

| Item Description | Unit | Remove | Replace | Total |
|---|---|---|---|---|
| **Truss roof system 14 in 12 slope designed for slate or tile roofing** | sf | $1.05 | $5.58 | $6.63 |
| *Replace* Materials.......5.04    Labor.............45    Equipment ............09 | | | | |
| *Remove* .....................    Labor............1.05 | | | | |
| **Truss roof system 16 in 12 slope designed for slate or tile roofing** | sf | $1.39 | $5.96 | $7.35 |
| *Replace* Materials.......5.42    Labor.............45    Equipment ............09 | | | | |
| *Remove* .....................    Labor............1.39 | | | | |
| **Truss roof system 17 in 12 slope designed for slate or tile roofing** | sf | $2.15 | $6.40 | $8.55 |
| *Replace* Materials.......5.86    Labor.............45    Equipment ............09 | | | | |
| *Remove* .....................    Labor............2.15 | | | | |
| **Add for each lf of valley in truss roof** | lf | — | $52.20 | $52.20 |
| *Replace* Materials ......24.20    Labor...........28.00 | | | | |
| ▶ Includes materials and labor for "California" fill between truss roofs with ridge board and jack rafters.  Does not include sheathing. | | | | |
| **Add for each lf of width in a hip truss roof** | lf | — | $34.20 | $34.20 |
| *Replace* Materials ......21.80    Labor...........12.40 | | | | |
| ▶ Includes additional cost for trusses designed to create a hip.  Add per lf of hip. | | | | |
| **Add for each lf of width in a Dutch hip truss roof** | lf | — | $37.80 | $37.80 |
| *Replace* Materials ......23.80    Labor...........14.00 | | | | |
| ▶ Includes additional cost for trusses designed to create a hip.  The Dutch hip is stacked and hand framed.  Add per lf of Dutch hip. | | | | |
| **Truss mansard roof system** | cf | $.16 | $.47 | $.63 |
| *Replace* Materials ........ .37    Labor.............10 | | | | |
| *Remove* .....................    Labor.............16 | | | | |
| **Truss mansard roof system designed for slate or tile roofing** | cf | $.16 | $.52 | $.68 |
| *Replace* Materials ........ .42    Labor.............10 | | | | |
| *Remove* .....................    Labor.............16 | | | | |
| **Add for each lf of valley in trussed mansard roof** | lf | — | $56.60 | $56.60 |
| *Replace* Materials ......23.90    Labor...........32.70 | | | | |
| ▶ Includes materials and labor to fill between truss roofs with ridge boards and jack rafters.  Does not include sheathing. | | | | |
| **Truss gambrel roof system** | cf | $.16 | $.56 | $.72 |
| *Replace* Materials ........ .46    Labor.............10 | | | | |
| *Remove* .....................    Labor.............16 | | | | |
| **Truss gambrel roof system designed for slate or tile roofing** | cf | $.16 | $.62 | $.78 |
| *Replace* Materials ........ .52    Labor.............10 | | | | |
| *Remove* .....................    Labor.............16 | | | | |
| **Add for each lf of valley in trussed gambrel roof** | lf | — | $64.10 | $64.10 |
| *Replace* Materials ......24.20    Labor...........39.90 | | | | |
| ▶ Includes materials and labor to fill between truss roofs with ridge boards and jack rafters.  Does not include sheathing. | | | | |
| **Remove truss for work, then reinstall** | lf | — | $3.13 | $3.13 |
| *Replace* .....................    Labor............3.13 | | | | |
| **1/2" fiberboard sheathing** | sf | $.34 | $.94 | $1.28 |
| *Replace* Materials ........ .42    Labor.............52 | | | | |
| *Remove* .....................    Labor.............34 | | | | |
| **3/4" fiberboard sheathing** | sf | $.34 | $1.09 | $1.43 |
| *Replace* Materials ........ .57    Labor.............52 | | | | |
| *Remove* .....................    Labor.............34 | | | | |

**RELATED ITEMS**

◀ **ADDITIONAL TRUSS ROOF COSTS**

◀ **TRUSS MANSARD ROOF**
Add **10%** for treated trusses.  Roof area equals the roof system width times height times length.  Includes cat walks, diagonal braces, fasteners and rough fascia.

◀ **TRUSS GAMBREL ROOF**
Add **10%** for treated trusses.  Roof area equals the roof system width times height times length.  Includes cat walks, diagonal braces, fasteners and rough fascia.

◀ **REMOVE TRUSS THEN REINSTALL**

◀ **WALL OR ROOF SHEATHING**
Includes 4% waste.

| Item Description | | Unit | Remove | Replace | Total |
|---|---|---|---|---|---|
| **WALL OR ROOF ▶** **SHEATHING** *continued* | **1/2" sound-deadening fiberboard** <br> *Replace* Materials ........ .41  Labor............. .52 <br> *Remove* .....................  Labor............. .34 | sf | $.34 | $.93 | $1.27 |
| | **1/2" foil-faced foam sheathing** <br> *Replace* Materials ........ .48  Labor............. .52 <br> *Remove* .....................  Labor............. .34 | sf | $.34 | $1.00 | $1.34 |
| | **3/4" foil-faced foam sheathing** <br> *Replace* Materials ........ .64  Labor............. .52 <br> *Remove* .....................  Labor............. .34 | sf | $.34 | $1.16 | $1.50 |
| | **1" foil-faced foam sheathing** <br> *Replace* Materials ........ .82  Labor............. .55 <br> *Remove* .....................  Labor............. .34 | sf | $.34 | $1.37 | $1.71 |
| | **3/8" CDX plywood sheathing** <br> *Replace* Materials ........ .61  Labor............. .55 <br> *Remove* .....................  Labor............. .34 | sf | $.34 | $1.16 | $1.50 |
| | **1/2" CDX plywood sheathing** <br> *Replace* Materials ........ .57  Labor............. .55 <br> *Remove* .....................  Labor............. .34 | sf | $.34 | $1.12 | $1.46 |
| | **1/2" treated plywood sheathing** <br> *Replace* Materials ........ .65  Labor............. .55 <br> *Remove* .....................  Labor............. .34 | sf | $.34 | $1.20 | $1.54 |
| | **1/2" waferboard sheathing** <br> *Replace* Materials ........ .53  Labor............. .55 <br> *Remove* .....................  Labor............. .34 | sf | $.34 | $1.08 | $1.42 |
| | **1/2" oriented strand board (OSB) sheathing** <br> *Replace* Materials ........ .60  Labor............. .55 <br> *Remove* .....................  Labor............. .34 | sf | $.34 | $1.15 | $1.49 |
| | **5/8" CDX plywood sheathing** <br> *Replace* Materials ........ .84  Labor............. .55 <br> *Remove* .....................  Labor............. .34 | sf | $.34 | $1.39 | $1.73 |
| | **5/8" treated plywood sheathing** <br> *Replace* Materials ........ .98  Labor............. .55 <br> *Remove* .....................  Labor............. .34 | sf | $.34 | $1.53 | $1.87 |
| | **5/8" waferboard sheathing** <br> *Replace* Materials ........ .92  Labor............. .55 <br> *Remove* .....................  Labor............. .34 | sf | $.34 | $1.47 | $1.81 |
| | **5/8" oriented strand board (OSB) sheathing** <br> *Replace* Materials ........ .93  Labor............. .55 <br> *Remove* .....................  Labor............. .34 | sf | $.34 | $1.48 | $1.82 |
| | **3/4" CDX plywood sheathing** <br> *Replace* Materials ...... 1.03  Labor............. .55 <br> *Remove* .....................  Labor............. .34 | sf | $.34 | $1.58 | $1.92 |
| | **3/4" tongue-&-groove plywood sheathing** <br> *Replace* Materials ...... 1.04  Labor............. .55 <br> *Remove* .....................  Labor............. .34 | sf | $.34 | $1.59 | $1.93 |
| | **3/4" treated plywood sheathing** <br> *Replace* Materials........1.21  Labor............. .55 <br> *Remove* .....................  Labor............. .34 | sf | $.34 | $1.76 | $2.10 |

| Item Description | Unit | Remove | Replace | Total | RELATED ITEMS |
|---|---|---|---|---|---|
| **3/4" tongue-&-groove waferboard sheathing**<br>*Replace* Materials........1.09    Labor............. .55<br>*Remove* ......................    Labor............. .34 | sf | $.34 | $1.64 | $1.98 | |
| **3/4" tongue-&-groove oriented strand board (OSB) sheathing**<br>*Replace* Materials........1.10    Labor............. .55<br>*Remove* ......................    Labor............. .34 | sf | $.34 | $1.65 | $1.99 | |
| **1" x 6" sheathing**<br>*Replace* Materials........2.00    Labor............. .58<br>*Remove* ......................    Labor............. .37 | sf | $.37 | $2.58 | $2.95 | |
| **1" x 6" tongue-&-groove sheathing**<br>*Replace* Materials........3.13    Labor............. .58<br>*Remove* ......................    Labor............. .37 | sf | $.37 | $3.71 | $4.08 | |
| **2" x 6" tongue-&-groove sheathing**<br>*Replace* Materials........7.40    Labor............. .58<br>*Remove* ......................    Labor............. .42 | sf | $.42 | $7.98 | $8.40 | |
| **2" x 8" tongue-&-groove sheathing**<br>*Replace* Materials........4.81    Labor............. .58<br>*Remove* ......................    Labor............. .39 | sf | $.39 | $5.39 | $5.78 | |
| **Add for shear-panel sheathing installation**<br>*Replace* ......................    Labor............. .10<br>► Includes shear paneling installed with nailing patterns and splicing according to code specifications for a shear panel. | sf | — | $.10 | $.10 | ◁ shear-panel install |
| **Frame interior soffit (two sides)**<br>*Replace* Materials........5.05    Labor............2.03<br>*Remove* ......................    Labor............1.18 | lf | $1.18 | $7.08 | $8.26 | ◄ **INTERIOR SOFFIT FRAMING** |
| **Frame interior soffit with recess for indirect lighting (two sides)**<br>*Replace* Materials........7.35    Labor............3.44<br>*Remove* ......................    Labor............1.18 | lf | $1.18 | $10.79 | $11.97 | |
| **Frame interior soffit (three sides)**<br>*Replace* Materials........6.70    Labor............2.75<br>*Remove* ......................    Labor............1.18 | lf | $1.18 | $9.45 | $10.63 | |
| **Frame interior soffit with recess for indirect lighting (three sides)**<br>*Replace* Materials........8.00    Labor............4.44<br>*Remove* ......................    Labor............1.18 | lf | $1.18 | $12.44 | $13.62 | |
| **6" thick factory designed & fabricated structural wall panel**<br>*Replace* Materials........5.01    Labor............1.75    Equipment............ .30<br>*Remove* ......................    Labor............. .18 | sf | $.18 | $7.06 | $7.24 | ◄ **FACTORY BUILT PANELS**<br>*Often called stress-skin panels. Wall panels are installed with dimensional lumber top and bottom plates. Roof and floor panels must be installed between structural members. Does not include the cost for these structural members.* |
| **8" thick factory designed & fabricated structural wall panel**<br>*Replace* Materials........5.64    Labor............1.79    Equipment............ .30<br>*Remove* ......................    Labor............. .18 | sf | $.18 | $7.73 | $7.91 | |
| **10" thick factory designed & fabricated structural wall panel**<br>*Replace* Materials........6.15    Labor............1.86    Equipment............ .30<br>*Remove* ......................    Labor............. .18 | sf | $.18 | $8.31 | $8.49 | |
| **12" thick factory designed & fabricated structural wall panel**<br>*Replace* Materials........6.82    Labor............1.86    Equipment............ .30<br>*Remove* ......................    Labor............. .18 | sf | $.18 | $8.98 | $9.16 | |
| **6" thick factory designed & fabricated structural floor panel**<br>*Replace* Materials........5.39    Labor............1.75    Equipment............ .30<br>*Remove* ......................    Labor............. .21 | sf | $.21 | $7.44 | $7.65 | |

| Item Description | Unit | Remove | Replace | Total |
|---|---|---|---|---|
| **FACTORY BUILT ▶ PANELS** *continued* | | | | |
| **8" thick factory designed & fabricated structural floor panel** | sf | $.21 | $8.07 | $8.28 |
| *Replace* Materials........6.02   Labor ............1.75   Equipment ............ .30 | | | | |
| *Remove* ......................   Labor............. .21 | | | | |
| **10" thick factory designed & fabricated structural floor panel** | sf | $.21 | $8.74 | $8.95 |
| *Replace* Materials........6.62   Labor ............1.82   Equipment ............ .30 | | | | |
| *Remove* ......................   Labor............. .21 | | | | |
| **12" thick factory designed & fabricated structural floor panel** | sf | $.21 | $9.45 | $9.66 |
| *Replace* Materials........7.29   Labor ............1.86   Equipment ............ .30 | | | | |
| *Remove* ......................   Labor............. .21 | | | | |
| **6" thick factory designed & fabricated structural roof panel** | sf | $.39 | $8.59 | $8.98 |
| *Replace* Materials........6.19   Labor ............2.10   Equipment ............ .30 | | | | |
| *Remove* ......................   Labor............. .39 | | | | |
| **8" thick factory designed & fabricated structural roof panel** | sf | $.39 | $9.44 | $9.83 |
| *Replace* Materials........7.01   Labor ............2.13   Equipment ............ .30 | | | | |
| *Remove* ......................   Labor............. .39 | | | | |
| **10" thick factory designed & fabricated structural roof panel** | sf | $.39 | $10.09 | $10.48 |
| *Replate* Materials........7.62   Labor ............2.17   Equipment ............ .30 | | | | |
| *Remove* ......................   Labor............. .39 | | | | |
| **12" thick factory designed & fabricated structural roof panel** | sf | $.39 | $10.99 | $11.38 |
| *Replace* Materials........8.42   Labor ............2.27   Equipment ............ .30 | | | | |
| *Remove* ......................   Labor............. .39 | | | | |
| **CHIMNEY CRICKET ▶** *Includes 5% waste.* **Wood-frame chimney cricket (length x width)** | sf | $.50 | $4.32 | $4.82 |
| *Replace* Materials........1.46   Labor ............2.86 | | | | |
| *Remove* ......................   Labor............. .50 | | | | |
| **MAIL BOX ▶** *Mail box is standard rural style. Black, white, or gray.* **Mail box** | sf | $2.10 | $17.66 | $19.76 |
| *Replace* Materials.......11.30   Labor ............6.36 | | | | |
| *Remove* ......................   Labor............2.10 | | | | |
| **Mail-box post** | sf | $11.80 | $49.90 | $61.70 |
| *Replace* Materials......27.50   Labor ............22.40 | | | | |
| *Remove* ......................   Labor............11.80 | | | | |
| **Mail box with post** | sf | $15.10 | $67.60 | $82.70 |
| *Replace* Materials......38.80   Labor ............28.80 | | | | |
| *Remove* ......................   Labor............15.10 | | | | |
| **Remove mail box for work, then reinstall** | sf | — | $10.15 | $10.15 |
| *Replace* Materials........ .31   Labor ............9.84 | | | | |

✍ NOTES: _____

_____

_____

_____

_____

_____

_____

_____

_____ end

# TIME & MATERIAL CHARTS (selected items)

## Rough Carpentry Materials

| DESCRIPTION | MATERIAL PRICE | GROSS COVERAGE | WASTE | NET COVERAGE | UNIT PRICE |
|---|---|---|---|---|---|
| **Lumber, random lengths per 1,000 bf** | | | | | |
| #2 pine or better 2" wide framing lumber | $930.00 per mbf | 1,000 | 7% | 930 | $1.00 bf |
| #2 pine or better 1" wide framing lumber | $1,130.00 per mbf | 1,000 | 7% | 930 | $1.22 bf |
| #2 treated pine or better 2" wide framing lumber | $1,160.00 per mbf | 1,000 | 7% | 930 | $1.25 bf |
| redwood con common 2" wide framing lumber | $1,880.00 per mbf | 1,000 | 7% | 930 | $2.02 bf |
| redwood con heart 2" wide framing lumber | $2,180.00 per mbf | 1,000 | 7% | 930 | $2.34 bf |
| heavy oak timber | $3,710.00 per mbf | 1,000 | 7% | 930 | $3.99 bf |
| heavy pine timber | $1,700.00 per mbf | 1,000 | 7% | 930 | $1.83 bf |
| **Fasteners and metal braces** | | | | | |
| 16d gun nails | $63.00 per box | 2,500 | 5% | 2375 | $.03 ea |
| 12d gun nails | $59.00 per box | 2,500 | 5% | 2375 | $.05 ea |
| 2" gun staples | $99.00 per box | 10,000 | 5% | 9500 | $.01 ea |
| construction adhesive per 29 ounce tube | $6.60 per tube | 75 | 5% | 71.25 | $.09 lf |
| metal let-in brace with V-shape for saw kerf | $6.50 per 11.5' stick | | | | $6.50 ea |
| metal X bracing for between joists | $1.77 per 24" oc | | | | $1.77 ea |
| **Furring strips** | | | | | |
| 1" x 2" x 8' #2 or better pine | $1.31 ea | 8 | 5% | 7.6 | $.17 lf |
| 2" x 2" x 8' #2 or better pine | $3.05 ea | 8 | 5% | 7.6 | $.40 lf |
| 2" x 2" x 8' con heart redwood | $4.55 ea | 8 | 5% | 7.6 | $.60 lf |
| 2" x 2" x 8' con common redwood | $3.93 ea | 8 | 5% | 7.6 | $.52 lf |
| **#2 or better pine framing lumber** | | | | | |
| 2" x 4", random lengths | $4.90 ea | 8 | 5% | 7.6 | $.64 lf |
| 2" x 6", random lengths | $7.07 ea | 8 | 5% | 7.6 | $.93 lf |
| 2" x 8", random lengths | $8.84 ea | 8 | 5% | 7.6 | $1.16 lf |
| 2" x 10", random lengths | $13.80 ea | 8 | 5% | 7.6 | $1.82 lf |
| 2" x 12", random lengths | $16.00 ea | 8 | 5% | 7.6 | $2.11 lf |
| **Redwood framing lumber** | | | | | |
| 2" x 4" con heart, random lengths | $11.00 ea | 8 | 5% | 7.6 | $1.45 lf |
| 2" x 6" con heart, random lengths | $12.90 ea | 8 | 5% | 7.6 | $1.70 lf |
| 2" x 8" con heart, random lengths | $19.40 ea | 8 | 5% | 7.6 | $2.55 lf |
| 2" x 4" con common, random lengths | $9.50 ea | 8 | 5% | 7.6 | $1.25 lf |
| 2" x 6" con common, random lengths | $11.10 ea | 8 | 5% | 7.6 | $1.46 lf |
| 2" x 8" con common, random lengths | $16.70 ea | 8 | 5% | 7.6 | $2.20 lf |
| **Treated framing lumber** | | | | | |
| 2" x 4", random lengths | $8.10 ea | 8 | 5% | 7.6 | $1.07 lf |
| 2" x 6" random lengths | $12.10 ea | 8 | 5% | 7.6 | $1.59 lf |
| 2" x 8", random lengths | $20.00 ea | 8 | 5% | 7.6 | $2.63 lf |
| **Posts** | | | | | |
| **4" x 4"** | | | | | |
| #2 or better pine | $19.90 8' post | 8 | 4% | 7.68 | $2.59 lf |
| con common redwood | $24.10 8' post | 8 | 4% | 7.68 | $3.14 lf |
| treated pine | $25.90 8' post | 8 | 4% | 7.68 | $3.37 lf |
| **4" x 6"** | | | | | |
| #2 or better pine | $23.10 8' post | 8 | 4% | 7.68 | $3.01 lf |
| con common redwood | $25.80 8' post | 8 | 4% | 7.68 | $3.36 lf |
| treated pine | $30.00 8' post | 8 | 4% | 7.68 | $3.91 lf |
| **6" x 6"** | | | | | |
| #2 or better pine | $48.40 8' post | 8 | 4% | 7.68 | $6.30 lf |
| con common redwood | $41.80 8' post | 8 | 4% | 7.68 | $5.44 lf |
| treated pine | $62.90 8' post | 8 | 4% | 7.68 | $8.19 lf |
| **8" x 8"** | | | | | |
| #2 or better pine | $86.20 8' post | 8 | 4% | 7.68 | $11.20 lf |
| con common redwood | $74.30 8' post | 8 | 4% | 7.68 | $9.67 lf |
| treated pine | $112.00 8' post | 8 | 4% | 7.68 | $14.60 lf |

. . . More ➤

## Rough Carpentry Materials *continued*

| DESCRIPTION | MATERIAL PRICE | GROSS COVERAGE | WASTE | NET COVERAGE | UNIT PRICE |
|---|---|---|---|---|---|
| **Adjustable steel jack post** | | | | | |
| 51" to 90" to 13,000 pound load | $47.20 *ea* | | | | **$47.20** *ea* |
| 20" to 36" to 16,000 pound load | $30.90 *ea* | | | | **$30.90** *ea* |
| 37" to 60" to 17,500 pound load | $38.90 *ea* | | | | **$38.90** *ea* |
| 56" to 96" to 25,000 pound load | $60.80 *ea* | | | | **$60.80** *ea* |
| **Lally column** | | | | | |
| 3 1/2" diameter, 6' to 8' | $69.00 *ea* | | | | **$69.00** *ea* |
| 3 1/2" diameter, 8' to 10' | $77.70 *ea* | | | | **$77.70** *ea* |
| 3 1/2" diameter, 10' to 12' | $97.80 *ea* | | | | **$97.80** *ea* |
| **Glue-laminated beam** | | | | | |
| per bf | 4.12 *bf* | 1 | 3% | .97 | **$4.25** *bf* |
| **Micro-laminated beam** | | | | | |
| 1-3/4" x 9-1/2" | $6.11 *lf* | 1 | 4% | .96 | **$6.36** *lf* |
| 1-3/4" x 11-7/8" | $7.64 *lf* | 1 | 4% | .96 | **$7.96** *lf* |
| 1-3/4" x 14" | $9.01 *lf* | 1 | 4% | .96 | **$9.39** *lf* |
| 1-3/4" x 18" | $11.60 *lf* | 1 | 4% | .96 | **$12.10** *lf* |
| **Beams, select structural grade, per bf** | | | | | |
| pine | $1.70 *bf* | 1 | 4% | .96 | **$1.77** *bf* |
| oak | $3.71 *bf* | 1 | 4% | .96 | **$3.86** *bf* |
| **Laminated lumber I joist** | | | | | |
| 1-3/4" flange, 9-1/2" deep | $2.13 *lf* | 1 | 3% | .97 | **$2.20** *lf* |
| 1-3/4" flange, 11-7/8" deep | $2.59 *lf* | 1 | 3% | .97 | **$2.67** *lf* |
| 1-3/4" flange, 14" deep | $3.17 *lf* | 1 | 3% | .97 | **$3.27** *lf* |
| 2-5/16" flange, 11-7/8" deep | $3.67 *lf* | 1 | 3% | .97 | **$3.78** *lf* |
| **Floor truss** | | | | | |
| typical loading | $3.85 *lf* | | | | **$3.85** *lf* |
| heavy loading | $4.17 *lf* | | | | **$4.17** *lf* |
| **Roof truss** | | | | | |
| flat | $3.84 *lf* | | | | **$3.84** *lf* |
| 4 in 12 slope | $4.05 *lf* | | | | **$4.05** *lf* |
| 8 in 12 slope | $5.90 *lf* | | | | **$5.90** *lf* |
| 12 in 12 slope | $7.89 *lf* | | | | **$7.89** *lf* |
| 17 in 12 slope | $9.72 *lf* | | | | **$9.72** *lf* |
| **Roof or wall sheathing** | | | | | |
| 1/2" fiberboard | $12.80 *8' sheet* | 32 | 4% | 30.72 | **$.42** *sf* |
| 3/4" fiberboard | $17.40 *8' sheet* | 32 | 4% | 30.72 | **$.57** *sf* |
| 1/2" foil-faced foam | $14.60 *8' sheet* | 32 | 4% | 30.72 | **$.48** *sf* |
| 3/4" foil-faced foam | $19.60 *8' sheet* | 32 | 4% | 30.72 | **$.64** *sf* |
| 1" foil-faced foam | $25.30 *8' sheet* | 32 | 4% | 30.72 | **$.82** *sf* |
| 1/2" cdx plywood | $17.50 *8' sheet* | 32 | 4% | 30.72 | **$.57** *sf* |
| 1/2" waferboard | $16.30 *8' sheet* | 32 | 4% | 30.72 | **$.53** *sf* |
| 1/2" oriented strand board (OSB) | $18.40 *8' sheet* | 32 | 4% | 30.72 | **$.60** *sf* |
| 5/8" cdx plywood | $25.70 *8' sheet* | 32 | 4% | 30.72 | **$.84** *sf* |
| 5/8" waferboard | $28.40 *8' sheet* | 32 | 4% | 30.72 | **$.92** *sf* |
| 5/8" oriented strand board (OSB) | $28.50 *8' sheet* | 32 | 4% | 30.72 | **$.93** *sf* |
| 3/4" cdx plywood | $31.50 *8' sheet* | 32 | 4% | 30.72 | **$1.03** *sf* |
| 3/4" tongue-&-groove plywood | $31.80 *8' sheet* | 32 | 4% | 30.72 | **$1.04** *sf* |
| 3/4" tongue-&-groove waferboard | $33.50 *8' sheet* | 32 | 4% | 30.72 | **$1.09** *sf* |
| 3/4" tongue-&-groove oriented strand board (OSB) | $33.80 *8' sheet* | 32 | 4% | 30.72 | **$1.10** *sf* |
| 1" x 6" tongue-&-groove sheathing | $1.50 *lf* | .50 | 4% | .48 | **$3.13** *sf* |
| 2" x 6" tongue-&-groove sheathing | $3.55 *lf* | .50 | 4% | .48 | **$7.40** *sf* |
| **Factory designed and fabricated building panel** | | | | | |
| 6" thick wall panel | $5.01 *sf* | | | | **$5.01** *sf* |
| 8" thick wall panel | $5.64 *sf* | | | | **$5.64** *sf* |
| 10" thick floor panel | $6.62 *sf* | | | | **$6.62** *sf* |
| 12" thick floor panel | $7.29 *sf* | | | | **$7.29** *sf* |
| 6" thick roof panel | $6.19 *sf* | | | | **$6.19** *sf* |
| 8" thick roof panel | $7.01 *sf* | | | | **$7.01** *sf* |

## Rough Carpentry Labor

| LABORER | BASE WAGE | PAID LEAVE | TRUE WAGE | FICA | FUTA | WORKER'S COMP. | UNEMPLOY. INSUR. | HEALTH INSUR. | RETIRE (401k) | LIABILITY INSUR. | COST PER HOUR |
|---|---|---|---|---|---|---|---|---|---|---|---|
| Carpenter | $22.60 | 1.76 | $24.36 | 1.86 | .19 | 4.56 | 2.12 | 2.54 | .73 | 3.17 | $39.50 |
| Carpenter's helper | $16.30 | 1.27 | $17.57 | 1.34 | .14 | 3.29 | 1.53 | 2.54 | .53 | 2.28 | $29.20 |
| Post & beam carpenter | $29.20 | 2.28 | $31.48 | 2.41 | .25 | 5.89 | 2.74 | 2.54 | .94 | 4.09 | $50.30 |
| P & B carpenter's helper | $20.10 | 1.57 | $21.67 | 1.66 | .17 | 4.05 | 1.89 | 2.54 | .65 | 2.82 | $35.50 |
| Equipment operator | $28.70 | 2.24 | $30.94 | 2.37 | .25 | 5.36 | 2.69 | 2.54 | .93 | 4.02 | $49.10 |
| Demolition laborer | $13.40 | 1.05 | $14.45 | 1.11 | .12 | 4.44 | 1.26 | 2.54 | .43 | 1.88 | $26.20 |

**Paid Leave** is calculated based on two weeks paid vacation, one week sick leave, and seven paid holidays. Employer's matching portion of **FICA** is 7.65 percent. **FUTA** (Federal Unemployment) is .8 percent. **Worker's Compensation** for the rough carpentry trade was calculated using a national average of 18.71 percent. **Unemployment insurance** was calculated using a national average of 8.7 percent. **Health insurance** was calculated based on a projected national average for 2001 of $505 per employee (and family when applicable) per month. Employer pays 80 percent for a per month cost of $404 per employee. **Retirement** is based on a 401(k) retirement program with employer matching of 50 percent. Employee contributions to the 401(k) plan are an average of 6 percent of the true wage. **Liability insurance** is based on a national average of 12.9 percent.

## Rough Carpentry Labor Productivity

| WORK DESCRIPTION | LABORER | COST PER HOUR | PRODUCTIVITY | UNIT PRICE |
|---|---|---|---|---|
| **Demolition** | | | | |
| remove 2" x 4" wall 8' tall | demolition laborer | $26.20 | .045 | $1.18 lf |
| remove 2" x 6" wall 8' tall | demolition laborer | $26.20 | .048 | $1.26 lf |
| remove 2" x 8" wall 8' tall | demolition laborer | $26.20 | .049 | $1.28 lf |
| remove wood post | demolition laborer | $26.20 | .059 | $1.55 lf |
| remove glue-laminated beam | demolition laborer | $26.20 | .222 | $5.82 lf |
| remove micro-laminated beam | demolition laborer | $26.20 | .106 | $2.78 lf |
| remove sheathing | demolition laborer | $26.20 | .012 | $.31 sf |
| remove beam | demolition laborer | $26.20 | .222 | $5.82 lf |
| remove deck planking | demolition laborer | $26.20 | .026 | $.68 sf |
| remove deck railing | demolition laborer | $26.20 | .034 | $.89 lf |
| remove deck stairway per step | demolition laborer | $26.20 | .061 | $1.60 ea |
| remove furring strips applied to wood | demolition laborer | $26.20 | .011 | $.29 sf |
| remove joist system | demolition laborer | $26.20 | .014 | $.37 lf |
| remove floor truss system | demolition laborer | $26.20 | .014 | $.37 lf |
| remove hand-framed roof 4 in 12 slope | demolition laborer | $26.20 | .016 | $.42 sf |
| remove hand-framed roof 8 in 12 slope | demolition laborer | $26.20 | .019 | $.50 sf |
| remove hand-framed roof 12 in 12 slope | demolition laborer | $26.20 | .032 | $.84 sf |
| remove hand-framed roof 16 in 12 slope | demolition laborer | $26.20 | .050 | $1.31 sf |
| remove hand-framed roof 18 in 12 slope | demolition laborer | $26.20 | .077 | $2.02 sf |
| remove flat roof truss | demolition laborer | $26.20 | .016 | $.42 sf |
| remove truss roof 4 in 12 slope | demolition laborer | $26.20 | .017 | $.45 sf |
| remove truss roof 8 in 12 slope | demolition laborer | $26.20 | .021 | $.55 sf |
| remove truss roof 12 in 12 slope | demolition laborer | $26.20 | .034 | $.89 sf |
| remove truss roof 16 in 12 slope | demolition laborer | $26.20 | .053 | $1.39 sf |
| remove truss roof 17 in 12 slope | demolition laborer | $26.20 | .082 | $2.15 sf |
| remove hand-framed dormer, 4 in 12 slope | demolition laborer | $26.20 | .017 | $.45 sf |
| remove hand-framed dormer, 10 in 12 slope | demolition laborer | $26.20 | .025 | $.66 sf |
| remove hand-framed dormer, 18 in 12 slope | demolition laborer | $26.20 | .081 | $2.12 sf |
| remove pre-fabricated structural wall panel | demolition laborer | $26.20 | .007 | $.18 sf |
| remove pre-fabricated structural floor panel | demolition laborer | $26.20 | .008 | $.21 sf |
| remove pre-fabricated structural roof panel | demolition laborer | $26.20 | .015 | $.39 sf |
| **Framing crew** | | | | |
| rough carpentry | carpenter | $39.50 | | |
| rough carpentry | carpenter's helper | $29.20 | | |
| **rough carpentry** | **framing crew** | $34.40 | | |
| **Post & beam framing crew** | | | | |
| post & beam framing | post & beam carpenter | $50.30 | | |
| post & beam framing | post & beam carpenter's helper | $35.50 | | |
| **post & beam framing** | **post & beam crew** | $42.90 | | |

... More ➤

## Rough Carpentry Labor Productivity *continued*

| WORK DESCRIPTION | LABORER | COST PER HOUR | PRODUCTIVITY | UNIT PRICE |
|---|---|---|---|---|
| **Build interior partition wall** | | | | |
| 2" x 4" 8' tall 16" on center | framing crew | $34.40 | .241 | $8.29 lf |
| 2" x 4" 10' tall 16" on center | framing crew | $34.40 | .244 | $8.39 lf |
| 2" x 6" 8' tall 16" on center | framing crew | $34.40 | .244 | $8.39 lf |
| 2" x 6" 10' tall 16" on center | framing crew | $34.40 | .247 | $8.50 lf |
| 2" x 8" 8' tall 16" on center | framing crew | $34.40 | .247 | $8.50 lf |
| 2" x 8" 10' tall 16" on center | framing crew | $34.40 | .250 | $8.60 lf |
| **Build interior bearing wall** | | | | |
| 2" x 4" 8' tall 16" on center | framing crew | $34.40 | .261 | $8.98 lf |
| 2" x 4" 10' tall 16" on center | framing crew | $34.40 | .265 | $9.12 lf |
| 2" x 6" 8' tall 16" on center | framing crew | $34.40 | .263 | $9.05 lf |
| 2" x 6" 10' tall 16" on center | framing crew | $34.40 | .267 | $9.18 lf |
| 2" x 8" 8' tall 16" on center | framing crew | $34.40 | .266 | $9.15 lf |
| 2" x 8" 10' tall 16" on center | framing crew | $34.40 | .270 | $9.29 lf |
| **Build exterior wall** | | | | |
| 2" x 4" 8' tall 16" on center | framing crew | $34.40 | 9.18 | $9.18 lf |
| 2" x 4" 10' tall 16" on center | framing crew | $34.40 | .270 | $9.29 lf |
| 2" x 6" 8' tall 16" on center | framing crew | $34.40 | .270 | $9.29 lf |
| 2" x 6" 10' tall 16" on center | framing crew | $34.40 | .273 | $9.39 lf |
| 2" x 8" 8' tall 16" on center | framing crew | $34.40 | .272 | $9.36 lf |
| 2" x 8" 10' tall 16" on center | framing crew | $34.40 | .275 | $9.46 lf |
| **Build interior partition wall per sf** | | | | |
| 2" x 4" 16" on center | framing crew | $34.40 | .030 | $1.03 sf |
| 2" x 6" 16" on center | framing crew | $34.40 | .030 | $1.03 sf |
| 2" x 8" 16" on center | framing crew | $34.40 | .031 | $1.07 sf |
| **Build sloping interior partition wall per sf** | | | | |
| 2" x 4" 16" on center | framing crew | $34.40 | .041 | $1.41 sf |
| 2" x 6" 16" on center | framing crew | $34.40 | .042 | $1.44 sf |
| 2" x 8" 16" on center | framing crew | $34.40 | .042 | $1.44 sf |
| **Build sloping interior bearing wall per sf** | | | | |
| 2" x 4" 16" on center | framing crew | $34.40 | .050 | $1.72 sf |
| 2" x 6" 16" on center | framing crew | $34.40 | .050 | $1.72 sf |
| 2" x 8" 16" on center | framing crew | $34.40 | .051 | $1.75 sf |
| **Build interior bearing wall per sf** | | | | |
| 2" x 4" 16" on center | framing crew | $34.40 | .033 | $1.14 sf |
| 2" x 6" 16" on center | framing crew | $34.40 | .033 | $1.14 sf |
| 2" x 8" 16" on center | framing crew | $34.40 | .033 | $1.14 sf |
| **Build exterior wall per sf** | | | | |
| 2" x 4" 16" on center | framing crew | $34.40 | .034 | $1.17 sf |
| 2" x 6" 16" on center | framing crew | $34.40 | .034 | $1.17 sf |
| 2" x 8" 16" on center | framing crew | $34.40 | .034 | $1.17 sf |
| **Build sloping exterior wall per sf** | | | | |
| 2" x 4" 16" on center | framing crew | $34.40 | .046 | $1.58 sf |
| 2" x 6" 16" on center | framing crew | $34.40 | .046 | $1.58 sf |
| 2" x 8" 16" on center | framing crew | $34.40 | .047 | $1.62 sf |
| **Build walls per bf** | | | | |
| interior wall | framing crew | $34.40 | .034 | $1.17 bf |
| sloping interior wall | framing crew | $34.40 | .047 | $1.62 bf |
| exterior wall | framing crew | $34.40 | .037 | $1.27 bf |
| sloping exterior wall | framing crew | $34.40 | .051 | $1.75 bf |
| **Build and install wall header** *Made from 2" x dimension lumber and 1/2" cdx plywood* | | | | |
| 4" x 10" header | framing crew | $34.40 | .043 | $1.48 lf |
| 4" x 12" header | framing crew | $34.40 | .045 | $1.55 lf |
| 6" x 10" header | framing crew | $34.40 | .069 | $2.37 lf |
| 6" x 12" header | framing crew | $34.40 | .074 | $2.55 lf |
| **Install posts** | | | | |
| 4" x 4" post | framing crew | $34.40 | .042 | $1.44 lf |
| 6" x 6" post | framing crew | $34.40 | .044 | $1.51 lf |
| 8" x 8" post | framing crew | $34.40 | .048 | $1.65 lf |

. . . More ➤

## Rough Carpentry Labor Productivity *continued*

| WORK DESCRIPTION | LABORER | COST PER HOUR | PRODUCTIVITY | UNIT PRICE |
|---|---|---|---|---|
| **Install adjustable steel jackpost** | | | | |
| 20" to 36" adjustable | framing crew | $34.40 | .243 | $8.36 ea |
| 37" to 60" adjustable | framing crew | $34.40 | .272 | $9.36 ea |
| 48" to 100" adjustable | framing crew | $34.40 | .385 | $13.20 ea |
| 56" to 96" adjustable | framing crew | $34.40 | .351 | $12.10 ea |
| **Install lally column** | | | | |
| 3-1/2" diameter, 6' to 8' | framing crew | $34.40 | .526 | $18.10 ea |
| 3-1/2" diameter, 8' to 10' | framing crew | $34.40 | .556 | $19.10 ea |
| 3-1/2" diameter, 10' to 12' | framing crew | $34.40 | .588 | $20.20 ea |
| **Install glue-laminated beam** | | | | |
| per bf | framing crew | $34.40 | .060 | $2.06 bf |
| **Install micro-laminated beam** | | | | |
| 1-3/4" x 7-1/4" | framing crew | $34.40 | .048 | $1.65 lf |
| 1-3/4" x 9-1/2" | framing crew | $34.40 | .050 | $1.72 lf |
| 1-3/4" x 11-7/8" | framing crew | $34.40 | .053 | $1.82 lf |
| 1-3/4" x 14" | framing crew | $34.40 | .056 | $1.93 lf |
| 1-3/4" x 18" | framing crew | $34.40 | .063 | $2.17 lf |
| **Install beam** | | | | |
| 4" x 10" | framing crew | $34.40 | .114 | $3.92 lf |
| 4" x 12" | framing crew | $34.40 | .149 | $5.13 lf |
| 6" x 10" | framing crew | $34.40 | .132 | $4.54 lf |
| 6" x 12" | framing crew | $34.40 | .154 | $5.30 lf |
| 8" x 10" | framing crew | $34.40 | .156 | $5.37 lf |
| 8" x 12" | framing crew | $34.40 | .182 | $6.26 lf |
| 10" x 10" | framing crew | $34.40 | .176 | $6.05 lf |
| 10" x 12" | framing crew | $34.40 | .196 | $6.74 lf |
| 12" x 12" | framing crew | $34.40 | .204 | $7.02 lf |
| 12" x 16" | framing crew | $34.40 | .222 | $7.64 lf |
| **Post & beam framing** | | | | |
| **Cut and assemble bent with truss** | | | | |
| single-story with simple truss | post & beam crew | $42.90 | .526 | $22.60 sf |
| two-story with simple truss | post & beam crew | $42.90 | .571 | $24.50 sf |
| single-story with king post truss | post & beam crew | $42.90 | .568 | $24.40 sf |
| two-story with king post truss | post & beam crew | $42.90 | .621 | $26.60 sf |
| single-story with king post & struts truss | post & beam crew | $42.90 | .617 | $26.50 sf |
| two-story with king post & struts truss | post & beam crew | $42.90 | .680 | $29.20 sf |
| single-story with queen post truss | post & beam crew | $42.90 | .610 | $26.20 sf |
| two-story with queen post truss | post & beam crew | $42.90 | .671 | $28.80 sf |
| single-story with hammer beam truss | post & beam crew | $42.90 | 1.05 | $45.00 sf |
| two-story with hammer beam truss | post & beam crew | $42.90 | 1.25 | $53.60 sf |
| single-story with scissors truss | post & beam crew | $42.90 | .990 | $42.50 sf |
| two-story with scissors truss | post & beam crew | $42.90 | 1.04 | $44.60 sf |
| add for overhang drop in two-story bent | post & beam crew | $42.90 | 20.0 | $858.00 ea |
| **Cut and assemble connecting members between bents** *per sf of area beneath* | | | | |
| between single-story bents | post & beam crew | $42.90 | 1.11 | $47.60 sf |
| **Cut post & beam framing joint and join timbers** | | | | |
| sill corner half-lap | p & b carpenter | $50.30 | 1.10 | $55.30 ea |
| sill corner half-lap with through tenon | p & b carpenter | $50.30 | 2.78 | $140.00 ea |
| sill corner dovetail | p & b carpenter | $50.30 | 2.00 | $101.00 ea |
| sill corner dovetail with through tenon | p & b carpenter | $50.30 | 3.85 | $194.00 ea |
| sill corner tongue & fork | p & b carpenter | $50.30 | 1.79 | $90.00 ea |
| sill corner tongue & fork with through tenon | p & b carpenter | $50.30 | 3.45 | $174.00 ea |
| lapped dovetail | p & b carpenter | $50.30 | 2.04 | $103.00 ea |
| housed lapped dovetail | p & b carpenter | $50.30 | 2.56 | $129.00 ea |
| tusk tenon | p & b carpenter | $50.30 | 2.78 | $140.00 ea |
| half-lap | p & b carpenter | $50.30 | 1.08 | $54.30 ea |
| through mortise & tenon with shoulders | p & b carpenter | $50.30 | 2.27 | $114.00 ea |
| housed mortise & tenon | p & b carpenter | $50.30 | 2.38 | $120.00 ea |
| shouldered mortise & tenon | p & b carpenter | $50.30 | 2.33 | $117.00 ea |
| wedged dovetail mortise & tenon | p & b carpenter | $50.30 | 2.38 | $120.00 ea |
| mortise & tenon (90 degree) | p & b carpenter | $50.30 | 1.25 | $62.90 ea |

*. . . More* ➤

## Rough Carpentry Labor Productivity *continued*

| WORK DESCRIPTION | LABORER | COST PER HOUR | PRODUCTIVITY | UNIT PRICE |
|---|---|---|---|---|
| **Post & beam framing** *continued* | | | | |
| **Cut post & beam framing joint and join timbers** *continued* | | | | |
| anchor-beam | p & b carpenter | $50.30 | 2.94 | **$148.00** *ea* |
| framed overhang | p & b carpenter | $50.30 | 10.0 | **$503.00** *ea* |
| through half-lap | p & b carpenter | $50.30 | 1.20 | **$60.40** *ea* |
| mortise & tenon knee brace (45 degree) | p & b carpenter | $50.30 | 1.56 | **$78.50** *ea* |
| collar tie lapped half dovetail | p & b carpenter | $50.30 | 1.96 | **$98.60** *ea* |
| stopped splayed scarf | p & b carpenter | $50.30 | 3.23 | **$162.00** *ea* |
| stopped splayed scarf with through tenon | p & b carpenter | $50.30 | 5.00 | **$252.00** *ea* |
| bladed scarf | p & b carpenter | $50.30 | 2.44 | **$123.00** *ea* |
| bladed scarf with through tenon | p & b carpenter | $50.30 | 4.35 | **$219.00** *ea* |
| rafter foot housed bird's mouth | p & b carpenter | $50.30 | 1.39 | **$69.90** *ea* |
| rafter foot beveled shoulder bird's mouth | p & b carpenter | $50.30 | 1.30 | **$65.40** *ea* |
| rafter foot bird's mouth, purlin, & post joint | p & b carpenter | $50.30 | 3.13 | **$157.00** *ea* |
| rafter foot bird's mouth joint | p & b carpenter | $50.30 | 1.00 | **$50.30** *ea* |
| rafter foot bird's mouth with tenon | p & b carpenter | $50.30 | 2.86 | **$144.00** *ea* |
| rafter peak tongue & fork | p & b carpenter | $50.30 | 1.79 | **$90.00** *ea* |
| **Build joist system for outdoor deck** *with support beams, posts and concrete footing* | | | | |
| 2" x 8" joists | framing crew | $34.40 | .071 | **$2.44** *sf* |
| 2" x 10" joists | framing crew | $34.40 | .077 | **$2.65** *sf* |
| 2" x 12" joists | framing crew | $34.40 | .083 | **$2.86** *sf* |
| **Install outdoor deck planking per sf** | | | | |
| 2" x 4" | framing crew | $34.40 | .040 | **$1.38** *sf* |
| 2" x 6" | framing crew | $34.40 | .037 | **$1.27** *sf* |
| 2" x 8" | framing crew | $34.40 | .033 | **$1.14** *sf* |
| **Install deck railing and stairs** | | | | |
| deck railing | framing crew | $34.40 | .274 | **$9.43** *lf* |
| 3' wide deck stairs with balustrades | framing crew | $34.40 | .588 | **$20.20** *ea* |
| deck stairway landing per sf | framing crew | $34.40 | .074 | **$2.55** *sf* |
| **Install furring strips** | | | | |
| on wood 16" on center | framing crew | $34.40 | .013 | **$.45** *sf* |
| on wood 24" on center | framing crew | $34.40 | .011 | **$.38** *sf* |
| on masonry or concrete 16" on center | framing crew | $34.40 | .016 | **$.55** *sf* |
| on masonry or concrete 24" on center | framing crew | $34.40 | .014 | **$.48** *sf* |
| **Build joist systems with blocking and cross bracing** | | | | |
| per bf | framing crew | $34.40 | .021 | **$.72** *bf* |
| **Install laminated lumber I truss** | | | | |
| 1-3/4" flange, 11-7/8" deep | framing crew | $34.40 | .036 | **$1.24** *lf* |
| 1-3/4" flange, 14" deep | framing crew | $34.40 | .037 | **$1.27** *lf* |
| 2-5/16" flange, 11-7/8" deep | framing crew | $34.40 | .036 | **$1.24** *lf* |
| 2-5/16" flange, 14" deep | framing crew | $34.40 | .038 | **$1.31** *lf* |
| 2-5/16" flange, 16" deep | framing crew | $34.40 | .039 | **$1.34** *lf* |
| **Install floor truss** | | | | |
| typical | framing crew | $34.40 | .091 | **$3.13** *lf* |
| **Hand-frame roof, 24" on center** | | | | |
| **with 2" x 4" rafters** | | | | |
| 4 in 12 slope | framing crew | $34.40 | .034 | **$1.17** *sf* |
| 8 in 12 slope | framing crew | $34.40 | .040 | **$1.38** *sf* |
| 12 in 12 slope | framing crew | $34.40 | .049 | **$1.69** *sf* |
| 16 in 12 slope | framing crew | $34.40 | .060 | **$2.06** *sf* |
| **with 2" x 6" rafters** | | | | |
| 4 in 12 slope | framing crew | $34.40 | .035 | **$1.20** *sf* |
| 8 in 12 slope | framing crew | $34.40 | .042 | **$1.44** *sf* |
| 12 in 12 slope | framing crew | $34.40 | .051 | **$1.75** *sf* |
| 16 in 12 slope | framing crew | $34.40 | .062 | **$2.13** *sf* |
| **with 2" x 8" rafters** | | | | |
| 4 in 12 slope | framing crew | $34.40 | .036 | **$1.24** *sf* |
| 8 in 12 slope | framing crew | $34.40 | .043 | **$1.48** *sf* |
| 12 in 12 slope | framing crew | $34.40 | .052 | **$1.79** *sf* |
| 16 in 12 slope | framing crew | $34.40 | .064 | **$2.20** *sf* |

... More ➤

## Rough Carpentry Labor Productivity *continued*

| WORK DESCRIPTION | LABORER | COST PER HOUR | PRODUCTIVITY | UNIT PRICE |
|---|---|---|---|---|
| **Hand-frame roof, 24" on center** *continued* | | | | |
| **with 2" x 10" rafters** | | | | |
| 4 in 12 slope | framing crew | $34.40 | .037 | $1.27 sf |
| 8 in 12 slope | framing crew | $34.40 | .044 | $1.51 sf |
| 12 in 12 slope | framing crew | $34.40 | .054 | $1.86 sf |
| 16 in 12 slope | framing crew | $34.40 | .066 | $2.27 sf |
| **with 2" x 12" rafters** | | | | |
| 4 in 12 slope | framing crew | $34.40 | .038 | $1.31 sf |
| 8 in 12 slope | framing crew | $34.40 | .046 | $1.58 sf |
| 12 in 12 slope | framing crew | $34.40 | .056 | $1.93 sf |
| 16 in 12 slope | framing crew | $34.40 | .068 | $2.34 sf |
| **additional hand-framed roof labor costs** | | | | |
| add for each lf of valley | framing crew | $34.40 | .787 | $27.10 lf |
| add for each lf of hip width | framing crew | $34.40 | .211 | $7.30 lf |
| add for each lf of Dutch hip width | framing crew | $34.40 | .229 | $7.88 lf |
| **Hand-frame mansard roof, 24" on center** *per cf of roof* | | | | |
| 2" x 4" rafters | framing crew | $34.40 | .005 | $.17 cf |
| 2" x 8" rafters | framing crew | $34.40 | .005 | $.17 cf |
| 2" x 12" rafters | framing crew | $34.40 | .006 | $.21 cf |
| add for each lf of valley | framing crew | $34.40 | 1.08 | $37.20 lf |
| **Hand-frame gambrel roof, 24" on center** *per cf of roof* | | | | |
| 2" x 4" rafters | framing crew | $34.40 | .004 | $.14 cf |
| 2" x 8" rafters | framing crew | $34.40 | .005 | $.17 cf |
| 2" x 12" rafters | framing crew | $34.40 | .006 | $.21 cf |
| add for each lf of valley | framing crew | $34.40 | 1.14 | $39.20 lf |
| **Hand-frame roof per bf** | | | | |
| gable roof | framing crew | $34.40 | .023 | $.79 bf |
| hip roof | framing crew | $34.40 | .023 | $.79 bf |
| Dutch hip roof | framing crew | $34.40 | .024 | $.83 bf |
| mansard roof | framing crew | $34.40 | .026 | $.89 bf |
| gambrel roof | framing crew | $34.40 | .025 | $.86 bf |
| **Hand-frame dormer, 24" on center** | | | | |
| **shed dormer** | | | | |
| 4 in 12 slope | framing crew | $34.40 | .045 | $1.55 sf |
| 8 in 12 slope | framing crew | $34.40 | .049 | $1.69 sf |
| 12 in 12 slope | framing crew | $34.40 | .060 | $2.06 sf |
| 16 in 12 slope | framing crew | $34.40 | .064 | $2.20 sf |
| **gable dormer** | | | | |
| 4 in 12 slope | framing crew | $34.40 | .047 | $1.62 sf |
| 8 in 12 slope | framing crew | $34.40 | .051 | $1.75 sf |
| 12 in 12 slope | framing crew | $34.40 | .062 | $2.13 sf |
| 16 in 12 slope | framing crew | $34.40 | .067 | $2.30 sf |
| **hip dormer** | | | | |
| 4 in 12 slope | framing crew | $34.40 | 1.69 | $1.69 sf |
| 8 in 12 slope | framing crew | $34.40 | .053 | $1.82 sf |
| 12 in 12 slope | framing crew | $34.40 | .065 | $2.24 sf |
| 16 in 12 slope | framing crew | $34.40 | .070 | $2.41 sf |
| **Dutch hip dormer** | | | | |
| 4 in 12 slope | framing crew | $34.40 | .051 | $1.75 sf |
| 8 in 12 slope | framing crew | $34.40 | .054 | $1.86 sf |
| 12 in 12 slope | framing crew | $34.40 | .067 | $2.30 sf |
| 16 in 12 slope | framing crew | $34.40 | .072 | $2.48 sf |
| **gambrel dormer** | | | | |
| per length of ridge x width of dormer | framing crew | $34.40 | .059 | $2.03 sf |
| **Hand-frame dormer, per bf** | | | | |
| shed dormer | framing crew | $34.40 | .034 | $1.17 bf |
| gable dormer | framing crew | $34.40 | .035 | $1.20 bf |
| hip dormer | framing crew | $34.40 | .036 | $1.24 bf |
| Dutch-hip dormer | framing crew | $34.40 | .038 | $1.31 bf |
| gambrel dormer | framing crew | $34.40 | .037 | $1.27 bf |

. . . More ➤

## Rough Carpentry Labor Productivity *continued*

| WORK DESCRIPTION | LABORER | COST PER HOUR | PRODUCTIVITY | UNIT PRICE |
|---|---|---|---|---|
| **Install roof truss** | | | | |
| flat roof | framing crew | $34.40 | .023 | **$.79** lf |
| 4 in 12 slope | framing crew | $34.40 | .023 | **$.79** lf |
| 8 in 12 slope | framing crew | $34.40 | .023 | **$.79** lf |
| 12 in 12 slope | framing crew | $34.40 | .024 | **$.83** lf |
| 16 in 12 slope | framing crew | $34.40 | .026 | **$.89** lf |
| **Install truss system, 24" on center, per sf** | | | | |
| 4 in 12 slope | framing crew | $34.40 | .012 | **$.41** sf |
| 8 in 12 slope | framing crew | $34.40 | .012 | **$.41** sf |
| 12 in 12 slope | framing crew | $34.40 | .013 | **$.45** sf |
| 16 in 12 slope | framing crew | $34.40 | .013 | **$.45** sf |
| **Additional truss roof costs** | | | | |
| add labor for each lf of valley | framing crew | $34.40 | .813 | **$28.00** lf |
| add labor for each lf of width in a hip | framing crew | $34.40 | .360 | **$12.40** lf |
| add labor for each lf of width in a Dutch hip | framing crew | $34.40 | .408 | **$14.00** lf |
| **Install mansard truss system, 24" on center, per cf** | | | | |
| per width x height x length | framing crew | $34.40 | .003 | **$.10** cf |
| add labor for each lf of valley | framing crew | $34.40 | .952 | **$32.70** lf |
| **Install gambrel truss system, 24" on center, per cf** | | | | |
| per width x height x length | framing crew | $34.40 | .003 | **$.10** cf |
| add labor for each lf of valley | framing crew | $34.40 | 1.16 | **$39.90** lf |
| **Install wall or floor sheathing** | | | | |
| builder board | framing crew | $34.40 | .015 | **$.52** lf |
| plywood, waferboard, or OSB | framing crew | $34.40 | .016 | **$.55** sf |
| 1" x 6" sheathing | framing crew | $34.40 | .017 | **$.58** sf |
| 1" x 6" tongue-&-groove | framing crew | $34.40 | .017 | **$.58** sf |
| 2" x 6" tongue-&-groove | framing crew | $34.40 | .017 | **$.58** sf |
| 2" x 8" tongue-&-groove | framing crew | $34.40 | .017 | **$.58** sf |
| add labor for shear-panel installation | framing crew | $34.40 | .003 | **$.10** sf |
| **Build interior soffit** | | | | |
| two sides | framing crew | $34.40 | .059 | **$2.03** lf |
| two sides with recess for indirect lighting | framing crew | $34.40 | .100 | **$3.44** lf |
| three sides | framing crew | $34.40 | .080 | **$2.75** lf |
| three sides with recess for indirect lighting | framing crew | $34.40 | .129 | **$4.44** lf |
| **Install factory designed and fabricated structural panel** | | | | |
| 6" thick wall panel | framing crew | $34.40 | .051 | **$1.75** sf |
| 8" thick wall panel | framing crew | $34.40 | .052 | **$1.79** sf |
| 10" thick wall panel | framing crew | $34.40 | .054 | **$1.86** sf |
| 12" thick wall panel | framing crew | $34.40 | .054 | **$1.86** sf |
| 6" thick floor panel | framing crew | $34.40 | .051 | **$1.75** sf |
| 8" thick floor panel | framing crew | $34.40 | .051 | **$1.75** sf |
| 10" thick floor panel | framing crew | $34.40 | .053 | **$1.82** sf |
| 12" thick floor panel | framing crew | $34.40 | .054 | **$1.86** sf |
| 6" thick roof panel | framing crew | $34.40 | .061 | **$2.10** sf |
| 8" thick roof panel | framing crew | $34.40 | .062 | **$2.13** sf |
| 10" thick roof panel | framing crew | $34.40 | .063 | **$2.17** sf |
| 12" thick roof panel | framing crew | $34.40 | .066 | **$2.27** sf |
| **Wood-frame chimney cricket** | | | | |
| length of ridge x width | framing crew | $34.40 | .083 | **$2.86** sf |

✍ NOTES: _____

_____

_____

_____

_____

_____

_____ **end**

# 33 .................. *Security Systems*

| Item Description | Unit | Remove | Replace | Total | |
|---|---|---|---|---|---|
| **Minimum charge for security system work**<br>*Replace* Materials......25.00     Labor...........37.00 | ea | — | $62.00 | $62.00 | ◄ **MINIMUM** |
| **Add 37% for security system installed in finished structure** | | | | | ◄ **IN EXISTING BUILDING** |
| **Security system control panel, standard grade**<br>*Replace* Materials.....310.00     Labor.........182.00<br>*Remove* ....................     Labor ...........6.55<br>► Controls audio alarms and lights. | ea | $6.55 | $492.00 | $498.55 | ◄ **CONTROL PANEL**<br>*Includes up to 50 lf of wiring.* |
| **Security system control panel, high grade**<br>*Replace* Materials....390.00     Labor.........242.00<br>*Remove* ....................     Labor ...........6.55<br>► Controls audio alarms and lights. Digital read-out reports location of security breach and automatically calls security center. | ea | $6.55 | $632.00 | $638.55 | |
| **Security system key pad**<br>*Replace* Materials.....160.00     Labor ..........46.10<br>*Remove* ....................     Labor ............5.24<br>► Shows armed / unarmed status with lights, usually red and green. | ea | $5.24 | $206.10 | $211.34 | ◄ **KEY PAD**<br>*Includes up to 50 lf of wiring.* |
| **Security system key pad with LED read-out**<br>*Replace* Materials....200.00     Labor ..........46.10<br>*Remove* ....................     Labor ............5.24<br>► Shows armed / unarmed status with LED read-out that also reports location of security breach. | ea | $5.24 | $246.10 | $251.34 | |
| **Security system outside key control**<br>*Replace* Materials ......95.00     Labor...........41.40<br>*Remove* ....................     Labor ............3.75<br>► Shows armed / unarmed status with lights, usually red and green. | ea | $3.75 | $136.40 | $140.15 | ◄ **KEY CONTROL**<br>*Includes up to 50 lf of wiring.* |
| **Security system mechanical contact per opening**<br>*Replace* Materials......53.00     Labor ..........34.60<br>*Remove* ....................     Labor ............3.75 | ea | $3.75 | $87.60 | $91.35 | ◄ **CONTACT**<br>*Includes up to 50 lf of wiring.* |
| **Security system magnetic contact per opening**<br>*Replace* Materials ......65.00     Labor...........49.70<br>*Remove* ....................     Labor ............4.38 | ea | $4.38 | $114.70 | $119.08 | |
| **Security system sound detector**<br>*Replace* Materials.....145.00     Labor ..........56.60<br>*Remove* ....................     Labor ............4.38 | ea | $4.38 | $201.60 | $205.98 | ◄ **SOUND DETECTOR**<br>*Includes up to 50 lf of wiring.* |
| **Security system motion detector**<br>*Replace* Materials ....275.00     Labor ..........54.10<br>*Remove* ....................     Labor ............4.38 | ea | $4.38 | $329.10 | $333.48 | ◄ **MOTION DETECTOR**<br>*Includes up to 50 lf of wiring.* |
| **Security system pressure mat detector**<br>*Replace* Materials ......45.00     Labor...........55.20<br>*Remove* ....................     Labor ............4.85 | lf | $4.85 | $100.20 | $105.05 | ◄ **PRESSURE MAT**<br>*Includes up to 50 lf of wiring.* |

| Item Description | | Unit | Remove | Replace | Total |
|---|---|---|---|---|---|
| **SMOKE DETECTOR ▶** Includes up to 50 lf of wiring. | **Security system smoke detector**<br>*Replace* Materials.....175.00 Labor .........54.10<br>*Remove* ...................... Labor .........4.38<br>▶ For smoke detectors that are not connected to an alarm system see *Electrical* on page 149. For wiring see page 140. | ea | $4.38 | $229.10 | $233.48 |
| **HORN OR SIREN ▶** Includes up to 50 lf of wiring. | **Security system horn or siren**<br>*Replace* Materials ......55.00 Labor .........46.50<br>*Remove* ...................... Labor ...........3.75<br>▶ Exterior or interior. | ea | $3.75 | $101.50 | $105.25 |
| **PANIC BUTTON ▶** Includes up to 50 lf of wiring. | **Security system panic button**<br>*Replace* Materials ......45.00 Labor .........23.40<br>*Remove* ...................... Labor ...........3.28 | ea | $3.28 | $68.40 | $71.68 |

# TIME & MATERIAL CHARTS (selected items)

## Security Systems Materials

See **Security Systems** material prices with the line items and other information in the **QuickFinder** column.

## Security Systems Labor

| LABORER | BASE WAGE | PAID LEAVE | TRUE WAGE | FICA | FUTA | WORKER'S COMP. | UNEMPLOY. INSUR. | HEALTH INSUR. | RETIRE (401K) | LIABILITY INSUR. | COST PER HOUR |
|---|---|---|---|---|---|---|---|---|---|---|---|
| Security system installer | $21.70 | 1.69 | $23.39 | 1.79 | .19 | 2.66 | 2.03 | 2.54 | .70 | 3.04 | $36.30 |
| Demolition laborer | $13.40 | 1.05 | $14.45 | 1.11 | .12 | 4.44 | 1.26 | 2.54 | .43 | 1.88 | $26.20 |

**Paid Leave** is calculated based on two weeks paid vacation, one week sick leave, and seven paid holidays. Employer's matching portion of **FICA** is 7.65 percent. **FUTA** (Federal Unemployment) is .8 percent. **Worker's compensation** for the security systems trade was calculated using a national average of 11.36 percent. **Unemployment insurance** was calculated using a national average of 8.7 percent. **Health insurance** was calculated based on a projected national average for 2001 of $505 per employee (and family when applicable) per month. Employer pays 80 percent for a per month cost of $404 per employee. **Retirement** is based on a 401(k) retirement program with employer matching of 50 percent. Employee contributions to the 401(k) plan are an average of 6 percent of the true wage. **Liability insurance** is based on a national average of 12.9 percent.

## Security Systems Labor Productivity

| WORK DESCRIPTION | LABORER | COST PER HOUR | PRODUCTIVITY | UNIT PRICE |
|---|---|---|---|---|
| **Demolition** | | | | |
| remove control panel | demolition laborer | $26.20 | .250 | $6.55 ea |
| remove exterior key pad | demolition laborer | $26.20 | .200 | $5.24 ea |
| remove contact | demolition laborer | $26.20 | .143 | $3.75 ea |
| remove detector (all types) | demolition laborer | $26.20 | .167 | $4.38 ea |
| remove pressure mat detector | demolition laborer | $26.20 | .185 | $4.85 ea |
| remove horn or siren | demolition laborer | $26.20 | .143 | $3.75 ea |
| remove panic button | demolition laborer | $26.20 | .125 | $3.28 ea |
| **Install security system** | | | | |
| control panel, standard grade | security system installer | $36.30 | 5.00 | $182.00 ea |
| control panel, high grade | security system installer | $36.30 | 6.67 | $242.00 ea |
| key pad | security system installer | $36.30 | 1.27 | $46.10 ea |
| outside key control | security system installer | $36.30 | 1.14 | $41.40 ea |
| mechanical contact per opening | security system installer | $36.30 | 1.14 | $41.40 ea |
| magnetic contact per opening | security system installer | $36.30 | .952 | $34.60 ea |
| sound detector | security system installer | $36.30 | 1.37 | $49.70 ea |
| motion detector | security system installer | $36.30 | 1.56 | $56.60 ea |
| pressure mat detector | security system installer | $36.30 | 1.49 | $54.10 ea |
| smoke detector | security system installer | $36.30 | 1.52 | $55.20 lf |
| horn or siren | security system installer | $36.30 | 1.49 | $54.10 ea |
| panic button | security system installer | $36.30 | .645 | $23.40 ea |

# 34 ......................................................... *Siding*

| Item Description | Unit | Remove | Replace | Total | |
|---|---|---|---|---|---|
| **Minimum charge for siding work** | ea | — | $78.00 | $78.00 | ◄ **MINIMUM** |
| *Replace* Materials......44.00    Labor ..........34.00 | | | | | |
| **Fiberglass corrugated siding, 6 ounce** | sf | $.18 | $2.78 | $2.96 | ◄ **FIBERGLASS CORRUGATED SIDING** |
| *Replace* Materials........1.83    Labor..............95 | | | | | *Greenhouse style.* |
| *Remove* ......................    Labor..............18 | | | | | *Includes purlins with* |
| **Fiberglass corrugated siding, 8 ounce** | sf | $.18 | $2.92 | $3.10 | *corrugated pattern and* |
| *Replace* Materials........1.97    Labor..............95 | | | | | *4% waste. Weights are* |
| *Remove* ......................    Labor..............18 | | | | | *per sf.* |
| **Fiberglass corrugated siding, 12 ounce** | sf | $.18 | $3.68 | $3.86 | |
| *Replace* Materials........2.73    Labor..............95 | | | | | |
| *Remove* ......................    Labor..............18 | | | | | |
| **Aluminum siding, standard grade** | sf | $.21 | $2.52 | $2.73 | ◄ **ALUMINUM SIDING** |
| *Replace* Materials........1.36    Labor ..........1.16 | | | | | *Includes 4% waste.* |
| *Remove* ......................    Labor..............21 | | | | | |
| ► .019" to .021" thick. Lightly embossed wood patterns. | | | | | |
| **Aluminum siding, high grade** | sf | $.21 | $2.76 | $2.97 | |
| *Replace* Materials........1.60    Labor ..........1.16 | | | | | |
| *Remove* ......................    Labor..............21 | | | | | |
| ► .024" thick. Embossed patterns with fancy detail work around openings, porches, or in gables. | | | | | |
| **Aluminum siding, deluxe grade** | sf | $.21 | $3.07 | $3.28 | |
| *Replace* Materials........1.91    Labor ..........1.16 | | | | | |
| *Remove* ......................    Labor..............21 | | | | | |
| ► .024" thick. Board-and-batten, board-on-board, or similar embossed patterns. | | | | | |
| **Aluminum siding, custom grade** | sf | $.21 | $3.92 | $4.13 | |
| *Replace* Materials........2.76    Labor ..........1.16 | | | | | |
| *Remove* ......................    Labor..............21 | | | | | |
| ► .024" thick. Shake shingle, or similar embossed patterns. | | | | | |
| **Add for insulated aluminum siding** | sf | — | $.38 | $.38 | ◁ add for insulation |
| *Replace* Materials ........ .38 | | | | | |
| ► Add for R-3 to R-4 insulation integrated into siding. | | | | | |
| **Cement fiber shingle siding, standard grade** | sf | $.34 | $2.73 | $3.07 | ◄ **CEMENT FIBER SHINGLE SIDING** |
| *Replace* Materials........1.20    Labor ..........1.53 | | | | | *Includes 4% waste. Also* |
| *Remove* ......................    Labor..............34 | | | | | *called asbestos cement.* |
| ► 1/8" to 1/4" thick, lightly embossed shingles with square edges. | | | | | *Some older styles contain* |
| **Cement fiber shingle siding, high grade** | sf | $.34 | $3.03 | $3.37 | *dangerous asbestos which* |
| *Replace* Materials........1.50    Labor ..........1.53 | | | | | *must be removed using* |
| *Remove* ......................    Labor..............34 | | | | | *hazardous material* |
| ► 1/8" to 1/4" thick, heavily embossed shingles with patterned edges. | | | | | *removal techniques.* |
| **Replace single cement fiber shingle** | sf | — | $18.70 | $18.70 | ◁ single shingle |
| *Replace* Materials........2.50    Labor..........16.20 | | | | | |
| **Minimum charge to repair cement fiber siding** | ea | — | $70.00 | $70.00 | ◁ minimum |
| *Replace* Materials......36.00    Labor ..........34.00 | | | | | |

**RELATED ITEMS**

Finish Carpentry..........199
Paneling.....................347
Rough Carpentry ........409

| Item Description | Unit | Remove | Replace | Total |
|---|---|---|---|---|
| **SHAKE OR ▶ WOOD SHINGLE SIDING** *Includes 4% waste.* | | | | |
| **Shake or wood shingle siding, standard grade** | sf | $.37 | $2.51 | $2.88 |
| *Replace* Materials ........ .98        Labor ............1.53 | | | | |
| *Remove* ......................        Labor ............. .37 | | | | |
| ▶ #2 red label wood shingles, straight overlap installation. | | | | |
| **Shake or wood shingle siding, high grade** | sf | $.37 | $2.64 | $3.01 |
| *Replace* Materials........1.11        Labor ............1.53 | | | | |
| *Remove* ......................        Labor ............. .37 | | | | |
| ▶ #1 shakes or #1 blue label wood shingles, straight overlap installation; or #2 red label wood shingles staggered installation. | | | | |
| **Shake or wood shingle siding, deluxe grade** | sf | $.37 | $2.86 | $3.23 |
| *Replace* Materials........1.33        Labor ............1.53 | | | | |
| *Remove* ......................        Labor ............. .37 | | | | |
| ▶ #1 shakes or #1 blue wood shingles, staggered installation; or #2 red label wood shingles double coursed installation. | | | | |
| **Shake or wood shingle siding, custom grade (fancy cut)** | sf | $.37 | $3.33 | $3.70 |
| *Replace* Materials........1.80        Labor ............1.53 | | | | |
| *Remove* ......................        Labor ............. .37 | | | | |
| ▶ #1 shakes or #1 blue fancy cut wood shingle. | | | | |
| **single shake or shingle ▷ Replace single shake or wood shingle** | ea | — | $16.78 | $16.78 |
| *Replace* Materials........2.88        Labor ............13.90 | | | | |
| **minimum ▷ Minimum charge to repair shake or wood shingle siding** | ea | — | $74.00 | $74.00 |
| *Replace* Materials......40.00        Labor ..........34.00 | | | | |
| **VINYL SIDING ▶** *Includes 4% waste.* **Vinyl siding, standard grade** | sf | $.18 | $2.88 | $3.06 |
| *Replace* Materials........1.72        Labor ............1.16 | | | | |
| *Remove* ......................        Labor ............. .18 | | | | |
| ▶ Lightly embossed wood patterns. | | | | |
| **Vinyl siding, high grade** | sf | $.18 | $3.13 | $3.31 |
| *Replace* Materials........1.97        Labor ............1.16 | | | | |
| *Remove* ......................        Labor ............. .18 | | | | |
| ▶ Heavy embossed patterns such as board-and-batten, board-on-board or similar patterns, with fancy detail work around openings, porches, or in gables. | | | | |
| **Vinyl siding, deluxe grade** | sf | $.18 | $4.13 | $4.31 |
| *Replace* Materials........2.97        Labor ............1.16 | | | | |
| *Remove* ......................        Labor ............. .18 | | | | |
| ▶ Shake shingle, gable fans, or similar embossed patterns. | | | | |
| **add for insulation ▷ Add for insulated vinyl siding** | sf | — | $.47 | $.47 |
| *Replace* Materials ........ .47 | | | | |
| ▶ Add for R-3 to R-4 insulation integrated into siding. | | | | |
| **HARDBOARD ▶ SIDING** *Includes 4% waste.* **7/16" thick hardboard siding, standard grade** | sf | $.24 | $1.46 | $1.70 |
| *Replace* Materials ........ .64        Labor ............. .82 | | | | |
| *Remove* ......................        Labor ............. .24 | | | | |
| **7/16" thick hardboard siding, painted-board finish** | sf | $.24 | $1.53 | $1.77 |
| *Replace* Materials ........ .71        Labor ............. .82 | | | | |
| *Remove* ......................        Labor ............. .24 | | | | |
| **7/16" thick hardboard siding, stained-board finish** | sf | $.24 | $1.81 | $2.05 |
| *Replace* Materials ........ .99        Labor ............. .82 | | | | |
| *Remove* ......................        Labor ............. .24 | | | | |

| Item Description | Unit | Remove | Replace | Total | |
|---|---|---|---|---|---|
| **7/16" thick hardboard siding, simulated stucco finish**<br>*Replace* Materials ...... .78     Labor............. .82<br>*Remove* ..................... Labor............. .24 | sf | $.24 | $1.60 | $1.84 | |
| **Hardboard lap siding**<br>*Replace* Materials ....... .74     Labor............. .88<br>*Remove* ..................... Labor............. .26 | sf | $.26 | $1.62 | $1.88 | ◁ lap |
| **5/8" thick plywood siding, texture 1-11, cedar face**<br>*Replace* Materials.......1.23     Labor............. .85<br>*Remove* ..................... Labor............. .26 | sf | $.26 | $2.08 | $2.34 | ◀ **PLYWOOD T1-11** SIDING<br>*Includes 5% waste.* |
| **5/8" thick plywood siding, texture 1-11, rough-sawn cedar face**<br>*Replace* Materials.......1.51     Labor............. .85<br>*Remove* ..................... Labor............. .26 | sf | $.26 | $2.36 | $2.62 | |
| **5/8" thick plywood siding, texture 1-11, fir face**<br>*Replace* Materials.......1.09     Labor............. .85<br>*Remove* ..................... Labor............. .26 | sf | $.26 | $1.94 | $2.20 | |
| **5/8" thick plywood siding, texture 1-11, rough-sawn fir face**<br>*Replace* Materials.......1.24     Labor............. .85<br>*Remove* ..................... Labor............. .26 | sf | $.26 | $2.09 | $2.35 | |
| **5/8" thick plywood siding, texture 1-11, Southern yellow pine face**<br>*Replace* Materials ....... .90     Labor............. .85<br>*Remove* ..................... Labor............. .26 | sf | $.26 | $1.75 | $2.01 | |
| **5/8" thick plywood siding, texture 1-11, redwood face**<br>*Replace* Materials.......2.05     Labor............. .85<br>*Remove* ..................... Labor............. .26 | sf | $.26 | $2.90 | $3.16 | |
| **Add for factory stained plywood siding**<br>*Replace* Materials ....... .16 | sf | — | $.16 | $.16 | ◁ add for factory stain |
| **1/2" plywood with 1" x 4" stained cedar boards**<br>*Replace* Materials.......3.13     Labor............1.94<br>*Remove* ..................... Labor............. .48 | sf | $.48 | $5.07 | $5.55 | ◀ **BOARD OVER PLYWOOD SIDING**<br>*Includes 4% waste.* |
| **5/8" plywood with 1" x 4" stained cedar boards**<br>*Replace* Materials.......3.20     Labor............1.94<br>*Remove* ..................... Labor............. .48 | sf | $.48 | $5.14 | $5.62 | |
| **Pine board-and-batten siding, select grade**<br>*Replace* Materials.......3.23     Labor............1.26<br>*Remove* ..................... Labor............. .29 | sf | $.29 | $4.49 | $4.78 | ◀ **BOARD-AND-BATTEN SIDING**<br>*Includes 4% waste.*<br>*Deduct **9%** for next lower grade, deduct **14%** for third grade.* |
| **Cedar board-and-batten siding, A grade**<br>*Replace* Materials.......3.39     Labor............1.26<br>*Remove* ..................... Labor............. .29 | sf | $.29 | $4.65 | $4.94 | |
| **Pine board-on-board siding, select grade**<br>*Replace* Materials.......3.29     Labor............1.16<br>*Remove* ..................... Labor............. .29 | sf | $.29 | $4.45 | $4.74 | ◀ **BOARD-ON-BOARD SIDING**<br>*Includes 4% waste.*<br>*Deduct **9%** for next lower grade, deduct **14%** for third grade.* |
| **Cedar board-on-board siding, A grade**<br>*Replace* Materials.......3.45     Labor............1.16<br>*Remove* ..................... Labor............. .29 | sf | $.29 | $4.61 | $4.90 | |
| **Pine channel rustic siding, select grade**<br>*Replace* Materials.......3.31     Labor............1.33<br>*Remove* ..................... Labor............. .29 | sf | $.29 | $4.64 | $4.93 | ◀ **CHANNEL RUSTIC SIDING**<br>*Includes 4% waste.* |

**RELATED ITEMS**
Finish Carpentry...........199
Paneling.......................347
Rough Carpentry .........409

| | Item Description | Unit | Remove | Replace | Total |
|---|---|---|---|---|---|
| **CHANNEL RUSTIC** ▶ **SIDING** *continued* *Deduct 9% for next lower grade, deduct 14% for third grade.* | **Cedar channel rustic siding, A grade**<br>*Replace* Materials........4.16    Labor ............1.33<br>*Remove* .....................    Labor............ .29 | sf | $.29 | $5.49 | $5.78 |
| | **Redwood channel rustic siding, clear all heart grade**<br>*Replace* Materials........8.63    Labor ............1.33<br>*Remove* .....................    Labor............ .29 | sf | $.29 | $9.96 | $10.25 |
| **SHIPLAP SIDING** ▶ *Includes 4% waste. Deduct 9% for next lower grade, deduct 14% for third grade.* | **Pine shiplap siding, select grade**<br>*Replace* Materials........3.35    Labor ............1.33<br>*Remove* .....................    Labor............ .29 | sf | $.29 | $4.68 | $4.97 |
| | **Cedar shiplap siding, A grade**<br>*Replace* Materials........4.21    Labor ............1.33<br>*Remove* .....................    Labor............ .29 | sf | $.29 | $5.54 | $5.83 |
| | **Redwood shiplap siding, clear all heart grade**<br>*Replace* Materials........8.73    Labor ............1.33<br>*Remove* .....................    Labor............ .29 | sf | $.29 | $10.06 | $10.35 |
| **TONGUE-&-** ▶ **GROOVE SIDING** ▶ *Includes 4% waste. Deduct 9% for next lower grade, deduct 14% for third grade.* | **Pine tongue-&-groove siding, simple pattern, select grade**<br>*Replace* Materials........3.43    Labor ............1.33<br>*Remove* .....................    Labor............ .29 | sf | $.29 | $4.76 | $5.05 |
| | **Pine tongue-&-groove siding, fancy pattern, select grade**<br>*Replace* Materials........3.66    Labor ............1.33<br>*Remove* .....................    Labor............ .29 | sf | $.29 | $4.99 | $5.28 |
| ▽ *simple pattern* | **Cedar tongue-&-groove siding, simple pattern, A grade**<br>*Replace* Materials........4.30    Labor ............1.33<br>*Remove* .....................    Labor............ .29 | sf | $.29 | $5.63 | $5.92 |
| | **Cedar tongue-&-groove siding, fancy pattern, A grade**<br>*Replace* Materials........4.58    Labor ............1.33<br>*Remove* .....................    Labor............ .29 | sf | $.29 | $5.91 | $6.20 |
| *fancy pattern* △ | **Redwood tongue-&-groove siding, simple pattern, clear all heart grade**<br>*Replace* Materials........8.93    Labor ............1.33<br>*Remove* .....................    Labor............ .29 | sf | $.29 | $10.26 | $10.55 |
| | **Redwood tongue-&-groove siding, fancy pattern, clear all heart grade**<br>*Replace* Materials........9.51    Labor ............1.33<br>*Remove* .....................    Labor............ .29 | sf | $.29 | $10.84 | $11.13 |
| **CLAPBOARD** ▶ **SIDING** *True clapboard. Based on grades marketed by Donnell's Clapboard Mill of Sedgwick, Maine.* | **Radially sawn clapboard siding, eastern pine, #1 premium clear**<br>*Replace* Materials........4.85    Labor ............1.87<br>*Remove* .....................    Labor............ .29 | sf | $.29 | $6.72 | $7.01 |
| | **Radially sawn clapboard siding, eastern pine, #1 New England Cape**<br>*Replace* Materials........4.24    Labor ............1.87<br>*Remove* .....................    Labor............ .29 | sf | $.29 | $6.11 | $6.40 |
| **BEVELED SIDING** ▶ *Siding that looks like clapboard but is not radially sawn. (The grain in radially sawn board runs at a consistent 90 degree angle to the board face. In resawn boards grain orientation is inconsistent.)* | **Pine resawn beveled siding, select grade**<br>*Replace* Materials........1.79    Labor ............1.39<br>*Remove* .....................    Labor............ .29 | sf | $.29 | $3.18 | $3.47 |
| | **Cedar resawn beveled siding, select grade**<br>*Replace* Materials........2.25    Labor ............1.39<br>*Remove* .....................    Labor............ .29 | sf | $.29 | $3.64 | $3.93 |

| Item Description | Unit | Remove | Replace | Total | |
|---|---|---|---|---|---|
| **Redwood resawn beveled siding, clear all heart grade**<br>*Replace* Materials.......4.67    Labor ...........1.39<br>*Remove* ..................    Labor............ .29 | sf | $.29 | $6.06 | $6.35 | |
| **Pine bungalow siding, select grade**<br>*Replace* Materials.......2.42    Labor ...........1.33<br>*Remove* ..................    Labor............ .29 | sf | $.29 | $3.75 | $4.04 | ◀ **BUNGALOW SIDING** *Tapered siding that is thicker and wider than beveled siding. Includes 4% waste. Deduct **9%** for next lower grade, deduct **14%** for third grade.* |
| **Cedar bungalow siding, select grade**<br>*Replace* Materials.......3.03    Labor ...........1.33<br>*Remove* ..................    Labor............ .29 | sf | $.29 | $4.36 | $4.65 | |
| **Redwood bungalow siding, clear all heart grade**<br>*Replace* Materials.......6.29    Labor ...........1.33<br>*Remove* ..................    Labor............ .29 | sf | $.29 | $7.62 | $7.91 | |
| **Pine Dolly Varden siding, select grade**<br>*Replace* Materials.......2.59    Labor ...........1.33<br>*Remove* ..................    Labor............ .29 | sf | $.29 | $3.92 | $4.21 | ◀ **DOLLY VARDEN SIDING** *Includes 4% waste. Deduct **9%** for next lower grade, deduct **14%** for third grade.* |
| **Cedar Dolly Varden siding, select grade**<br>*Replace* Materials.......3.25    Labor ...........1.33<br>*Remove* ..................    Labor............ .29 | sf | $.29 | $4.58 | $4.87 | |
| **Redwood Dolly Varden siding, clear all heart grade**<br>*Replace* Materials.......6.74    Labor ...........1.33<br>*Remove* ..................    Labor............ .29 | sf | $.29 | $8.07 | $8.36 | |
| **Pine log cabin siding, select grade**<br>*Replace* Materials.......2.43    Labor ...........1.33<br>*Remove* ..................    Labor............ .29 | sf | $.29 | $3.76 | $4.05 | ◀ **LOG CABIN SIDING** *Includes 4% waste. Deduct **9%** for next lower grade, deduct **14%** for third grade.* |
| **Cedar log cabin siding, select grade**<br>*Replace* Materials.......3.04    Labor ...........1.33<br>*Remove* ..................    Labor............ .29 | sf | $.29 | $4.37 | $4.66 | |
| **Add for one coat factory stain**<br>*Replace* Materials ........ .37 | sf | — | $.37 | $.37 | ◀ **ADD FOR FACTORY STAINED SIDING** |
| **Add for two coat factory stain**<br>*Replace* Materials ........ .54 | sf | — | $.54 | $.54 | |
| **Replace section of wood siding**<br>*Replace* Materials......19.00    Labor ..........28.10 | ea | — | $47.10 | $47.10 | ◀ **SIDING REPAIR** |
| **Minimum charge to repair wood siding**<br>*Replace* Materials......53.00    Labor ..........34.00 | ea | — | $87.00 | $87.00 | ◁ minimum |
| **Aluminum fascia to 6" wide**<br>*Replace* Materials.......1.51    Labor ...........1.16<br>*Remove* ..................    Labor............ .16 | lf | $.16 | $2.67 | $2.83 | ◀ **FASCIA** *Includes 4% waste.* |
| **Aluminum fascia 6" to 12" wide**<br>*Replace* Materials.......2.03    Labor ...........1.16<br>*Remove* ..................    Labor............ .16 | lf | $.16 | $3.19 | $3.35 | |
| **Vinyl fascia to 6" wide**<br>*Replace* Materials.......2.21    Labor ...........1.16<br>*Remove* ..................    Labor............ .16 | lf | $.16 | $3.37 | $3.53 | |

**RELATED ITEMS**
Finish Carpentry...........199
Paneling.....................347
Rough Carpentry ........409

| | Item Description | Unit | Remove | Replace | Total |
|---|---|---|---|---|---|
| **FASCIA** ▶<br>*continued* | **Vinyl fascia 6" to 12" wide**<br>*Replace* Materials........3.07    Labor.............1.16<br>*Remove* ........................    Labor..............16 | lf | $.16 | $4.23 | $4.39 |
| | **Cedar fascia to 6" wide**<br>*Replace* Materials........1.86    Labor.............1.26<br>*Remove* ........................    Labor..............18 | lf | $.18 | $3.12 | $3.30 |
| | **Cedar fascia 6" to 12" wide**<br>*Replace* Materials........2.49    Labor.............1.26<br>*Remove* ........................    Labor..............18 | lf | $.18 | $3.75 | $3.93 |
| | **Redwood fascia to 6" wide**<br>*Replace* Materials........3.61    Labor.............1.26<br>*Remove* ........................    Labor..............18 | lf | $.18 | $4.87 | $5.05 |
| | **Redwood fascia 6" to 12" wide**<br>*Replace* Materials........4.82    Labor.............1.26<br>*Remove* ........................    Labor..............18 | lf | $.18 | $6.08 | $6.26 |
| minimum ▷ | **Minimum charge for soffit & fascia work**<br>*Replace* Materials......57.00    Labor.........34.00 | ea | — | $91.00 | $91.00 |
| **SOFFIT** ▶<br>*Includes 4% waste.* | **Aluminum soffit**<br>*Replace* Materials........2.55    Labor.............1.67<br>*Remove* ........................    Labor..............24 | sf | $.24 | $4.22 | $4.46 |
| | **Vinyl soffit**<br>*Replace* Materials........3.78    Labor.............1.67<br>*Remove* ........................    Labor..............24 | sf | $.24 | $5.45 | $5.69 |
| | **Cedar plywood soffit**<br>*Replace* Materials........1.76    Labor.............1.77<br>*Remove* ........................    Labor..............26 | sf | $.26 | $3.53 | $3.79 |
| | **Cedar rough-sawn plywood soffit**<br>*Replace* Materials........1.79    Labor.............1.77<br>*Remove* ........................    Labor..............26 | sf | $.26 | $3.56 | $3.82 |
| | **Fir plywood soffit**<br>*Replace* Materials........1.56    Labor.............1.77<br>*Remove* ........................    Labor..............26 | sf | $.26 | $3.33 | $3.59 |
| | **Fir rough-sawn plywood soffit**<br>*Replace* Materials........1.60    Labor.............1.77<br>*Remove* ........................    Labor..............26 | sf | $.26 | $3.37 | $3.63 |
| | **Redwood plywood soffit**<br>*Replace* Materials........3.69    Labor.............1.77<br>*Remove* ........................    Labor..............26 | sf | $.26 | $5.46 | $5.72 |
| | **Redwood rough-sawn plywood soffit**<br>*Replace* Materials........3.74    Labor.............1.77<br>*Remove* ........................    Labor..............26 | sf | $.26 | $5.51 | $5.77 |
| tongue-&-groove soffit ▷ | **Cedar tongue-&-groove soffit, simple pattern**<br>*Replace* Materials........3.39    Labor.............2.07<br>*Remove* ........................    Labor..............31 | sf | $.31 | $5.46 | $5.77 |
| | **Cedar tongue-&-groove soffit, fancy pattern**<br>*Replace* Materials........4.06    Labor.............2.07<br>*Remove* ........................    Labor..............31 | sf | $.31 | $6.13 | $6.44 |

| Item Description | Unit | Remove | Replace | Total |
|---|---|---|---|---|
| **Fir tongue-&-groove soffit, simple pattern** | sf | $.31 | $5.22 | $5.53 |
| *Replace* Materials........3.15    Labor ............2.07 | | | | |
| *Remove* ......................    Labor ............. .31 | | | | |
| **Fir tongue-&-groove soffit, fancy pattern** | sf | $.31 | $5.38 | $5.69 |
| *Replace* Materials........3.31    Labor ............2.07 | | | | |
| *Remove* ......................    Labor ............. .31 | | | | |
| **Redwood tongue-&-groove soffit, simple pattern** | sf | $.31 | $7.62 | $7.93 |
| *Replace* Materials........5.55    Labor ............2.07 | | | | |
| *Remove* ......................    Labor ............. .31 | | | | |
| **Redwood tongue-&-groove soffit, fancy pattern** | sf | $.31 | $8.11 | $8.42 |
| *Replace* Materials........6.04    Labor ............2.07 | | | | |
| *Remove* ......................    Labor ............. .31 | | | | |
| **Aluminum rain gutter** | lf | $.29 | $5.01 | $5.30 |
| *Replace* Materials........3.62    Labor ............1.39 | | | | |
| *Remove* ......................    Labor ............. .29 | | | | |
| **Copper built-in box rain gutter** | lf | $.68 | $90.80 | $91.48 |
| *Replace* Materials......33.30    Labor............57.50 | | | | |
| *Remove* ......................    Labor ............. .68 | | | | |
| ► Includes additional framing material and labor costs for a typical rain gutter integrated into the roof system and flashed with copper. Removal costs include only copper flashing. | | | | |
| **Copper rain gutter** | lf | $.29 | $19.79 | $20.08 |
| *Replace* Materials......18.40    Labor ............1.39 | | | | |
| *Remove* ......................    Labor ............. .29 | | | | |
| **Galvanized steel rain gutter** | lf | $.29 | $10.51 | $10.80 |
| *Replace* Materials........9.12    Labor ............1.39 | | | | |
| *Remove* ......................    Labor ............. .29 | | | | |
| **Plastic rain gutter** | lf | $.29 | $4.32 | $4.61 |
| *Replace* Materials........2.93    Labor ............1.39 | | | | |
| *Remove* ......................    Labor ............. .29 | | | | |
| **Redwood rain gutter** | lf | $.29 | $33.59 | $33.88 |
| *Replace* Materials......32.20    Labor ............1.39 | | | | |
| *Remove* ......................    Labor ............. .29 | | | | |
| **Tin built-in box rain gutter** | lf | $.68 | $80.90 | $81.58 |
| *Replace* Materials......23.40    Labor............57.50 | | | | |
| *Remove* ......................    Labor ............. .68 | | | | |
| ► Includes additional framing material and labor costs for a typical rain gutter integrated into the roof system and flashed with 40 pound terne tin. Removal costs include only copper flashing. | | | | |
| **Tin rain gutter** | lf | $.29 | $17.69 | $17.98 |
| *Replace* Materials......16.30    Labor ............1.39 | | | | |
| *Remove* ......................    Labor ............. .29 | | | | |
| **Aluminum rain gutter downspout** | lf | $.24 | $5.71 | $5.95 |
| *Replace* Materials........4.42    Labor ............1.29 | | | | |
| *Remove* ......................    Labor ............. .24 | | | | |
| **Copper built-in box rain gutter downspout** | lf | $.24 | $40.00 | $40.24 |
| *Replace* Materials......20.90    Labor ............19.10 | | | | |
| *Remove* ......................    Labor ............. .24 | | | | |
| ► Includes additional framing material and labor costs for an enclosed, concealed downspout. Also includes PVC pipe and excavation to drain field. | | | | |

---

**RELATED ITEMS**

◄ **RAIN GUTTER**
*Includes 3% waste.*

*built-in box* △

◄ **RAIN GUTTER DOWNSPOUT**
*Includes 3% waste.*

| Item Description | Unit | Remove | Replace | Total |
|---|---|---|---|---|
| **RAIN GUTTER DOWNSPOUT** *continued* | | | | |
| **Copper rain gutter downspout** | lf | $.24 | $23.79 | $24.03 |
| *Replace* Materials......22.50    Labor............1.29 | | | | |
| *Remove* .....................    Labor.............24 | | | | |
| **Galvanized steel rain gutter downspout** | lf | $.24 | $12.39 | $12.63 |
| *Replace* Materials.......11.10    Labor............1.29 | | | | |
| *Remove* .....................    Labor.............24 | | | | |
| **Plastic rain gutter downspout** | lf | $.24 | $4.87 | $5.11 |
| *Replace* Materials........3.58    Labor............1.29 | | | | |
| *Remove* .....................    Labor.............24 | | | | |
| **Tin built-in box rain gutter downspout** | lf | $.24 | $17.19 | $17.43 |
| *Replace* Materials.......15.90    Labor............1.29 | | | | |
| *Remove* .....................    Labor.............24 | | | | |
| ▶ Includes additional framing material and labor costs for an enclosed, concealed downspout. Also includes PVC pipe and excavation to drain field. | | | | |
| **Tin rain gutter downspout** | lf | $.24 | $39.00 | $39.24 |
| *Replace* Materials.......19.90    Labor...........19.10 | | | | |
| *Remove* .....................    Labor.............24 | | | | |
| **DOWNSPOUT CONDUCTOR** | | | | |
| **Copper downspout conductor, standard grade** | ea | — | $60.20 | $60.20 |
| *Replace* Materials ......45.50    Labor...........14.70 | | | | |
| ▶ Simple or clear decorative work. | | | | |
| *high grade* △ | | | | |
| **Copper downspout conductor, high grade** | ea | — | $101.20 | $101.20 |
| *Replace* Materials ......86.50    Labor...........14.70 | | | | |
| ▶ Decorative embossed design. | | | | |
| **Galvanized steel downspout conductor, standard grade** | ea | — | $51.10 | $51.10 |
| *Replace* Materials ......36.40    Labor...........14.70 | | | | |
| ▶ Simple or clear decorative work. | | | | |
| **Galvanized steel downspout conductor, high grade** | ea | — | $84.10 | $84.10 |
| *Replace* Materials ......69.40    Labor...........14.70 | | | | |
| ▶ Decorative embossed design. | | | | |
| *high grade* △ | | | | |
| **POLYPROPYLENE SHUTTER** Per 16" wide pair. For 12" wide deduct 42%; for 18" wide add 8%; for 20" wide add 14%; for 24" wide add 26%. | | | | |
| **24" tall polypropylene fixed shutter** | ea | $4.09 | $43.90 | $47.99 |
| *Replace* Materials ......32.90    Labor............11.00 | | | | |
| *Remove* .....................    Labor............4.09 | | | | |
| **48" tall polypropylene fixed shutter** | ea | $4.09 | $62.00 | $66.09 |
| *Replace* Materials ......51.00    Labor............11.00 | | | | |
| *Remove* .....................    Labor............4.09 | | | | |
| **60" tall polypropylene fixed shutter** | ea | $4.09 | $70.10 | $74.19 |
| *Replace* Materials ......59.10    Labor............11.00 | | | | |
| *Remove* .....................    Labor............4.09 | | | | |
| **66" tall polypropylene fixed shutter** | ea | $4.09 | $79.50 | $83.59 |
| *Replace* Materials ......68.50    Labor............11.00 | | | | |
| *Remove* .....................    Labor............4.09 | | | | |
| **WOOD SHUTTER** Per 16" wide pair. For 12" wide deduct 6%; for 18" wide add 10%; for 20" wide add 52%; for 24" wide add 78%. | | | | |
| **36" tall wood fixed shutter** | ea | $4.09 | $118.00 | $122.09 |
| *Replace* Materials .....107.00    Labor............11.00 | | | | |
| *Remove* .....................    Labor............4.09 | | | | |
| **48" tall wood fixed shutter** | ea | $4.09 | $132.00 | $136.09 |
| *Replace* Materials .....121.00    Labor............11.00 | | | | |
| *Remove* .....................    Labor............4.09 | | | | |

| Item Description | Unit | Remove | Replace | Total |
|---|---|---|---|---|
| **60" tall wood fixed shutter**<br>*Replace* Materials.....136.00   Labor ...........11.00<br>*Remove* ...................   Labor ...........4.09 | ea | $4.09 | $147.00 | $151.09 |
| **72" tall wood fixed shutter**<br>*Replace* Materials.....149.00   Labor ...........11.00<br>*Remove* ...................   Labor ...........4.09 | ea | $4.09 | $160.00 | $164.09 |
| **36" tall wood moveable shutter**<br>*Replace* Materials.....169.00   Labor ...........11.30<br>*Remove* ...................   Labor ...........4.14 | ea | $4.14 | $180.30 | $184.44 |
| **48" tall wood moveable shutter**<br>*Replace* Materials.....197.00   Labor ...........11.30<br>*Remove* ...................   Labor ...........4.14 | ea | $4.14 | $208.30 | $212.44 |
| **60" tall wood moveable shutter**<br>*Replace* Materials....229.00   Labor ...........11.30<br>*Remove* ...................   Labor ...........4.14 | ea | $4.14 | $240.30 | $244.44 |
| **72" tall wood moveable shutter**<br>*Replace* Materials....283.00   Labor ...........11.30<br>*Remove* ...................   Labor ...........4.14 | ea | $4.14 | $294.30 | $298.44 |
| **Remove shutter for work, then reinstall**<br>*Replace* ...................   Labor ...........15.30 | ea | — | $15.30 | $15.30 |

**RELATED ITEMS**

Finish Carpentry...........199
Paneling.....................347
Rough Carpentry .......409

◄ **WOOD MOVEABLE SHUTTER** Per 16" wide pair including hardware. For 12" wide deduct **15%**; for 18" wide add **7%**; for 20" wide add **14%**; for 24" wide add **27%**. For fixed half circle top add **$120** per pair. For moveable louvers with half-circle top add **$210** per pair. For raised panel shutter with half-circle top add **$130** per pair. For Gothic peaked top (Gothic arch) add **$210** per pair.

NOTES: _____

_____ end

# TIME & MATERIAL CHARTS *(selected items)*

## Siding Materials

See **Siding** material prices with the line items and waste information in the **QuickFinder** column.

## Siding Labor

| LABORER | BASE WAGE | PAID LEAVE | TRUE WAGE | FICA | FUTA | WORKER'S COMP. | UNEMPLOY. INSUR. | HEALTH INSUR. | RETIRE (401k) | LIABILITY INSUR. | COST PER HOUR |
|---|---|---|---|---|---|---|---|---|---|---|---|
| Siding installer | $22.40 | 1.75 | $24.15 | 1.85 | .19 | 4.44 | 2.10 | 2.54 | .73 | 3.14 | $39.10 |
| Siding installer's helper | $16.10 | 1.26 | $17.36 | 1.33 | .14 | 3.19 | 1.51 | 2.54 | .52 | 2.26 | $28.90 |
| Demolition laborer | $13.40 | 1.05 | $14.45 | 1.11 | .12 | 4.44 | 1.26 | 2.54 | .43 | 1.88 | $26.20 |

**Paid Leave** is calculated based on two weeks paid vacation, one week sick leave, and seven paid holidays. Employer's matching portion of **FICA** is 7.65 percent. **FUTA** (Federal Unemployment) is .8 percent. **Worker's compensation** for the siding trade was calculated using a national average of 18.39 percent. **Unemployment insurance** was calculated using a national average of 8.7 percent. **Health insurance** was calculated based on a projected national average for 2001 of $505 per employee (and family when applicable) per month. Employer pays 80 percent for a per month cost of $404 per employee. **Retirement** is based on a 401(k) retirement program with employer matching of 50 percent. Employee contributions to the 401(k) plan are an average of 6 percent of the true wage. **Liability insurance** is based on a national average of 12.9 percent.

## Siding Labor Productivity

| WORK DESCRIPTION | LABORER | COST PER HOUR | PRODUCTIVITY | UNIT PRICE |
|---|---|---|---|---|
| **Demolition** | | | | |
| remove fiberglass corrugated siding | demolition laborer | $26.20 | .007 | $.18 sf |
| remove aluminum siding | demolition laborer | $26.20 | .008 | $.21 sf |
| remove cement fiber shingle siding | demolition laborer | $26.20 | .013 | $.34 sf |
| remove shake or wood shingle siding | demolition laborer | $26.20 | .014 | $.37 sf |
| remove vinyl siding | demolition laborer | $26.20 | .007 | $.18 sf |
| remove hardboard siding | demolition laborer | $26.20 | .009 | $.24 sf |
| remove hardboard beveled siding | demolition laborer | $26.20 | .010 | $.26 sf |
| remove plywood siding | demolition laborer | $26.20 | .010 | $.26 sf |
| remove wood siding | demolition laborer | $26.20 | .011 | $.29 sf |
| remove aluminum or vinyl fascia | demolition laborer | $26.20 | .006 | $.16 lf |
| remove wood fascia | demolition laborer | $26.20 | .007 | $.18 lf |
| remove aluminum or vinyl soffit | demolition laborer | $26.20 | .009 | $.24 sf |
| remove plywood soffit | demolition laborer | $26.20 | .010 | $.26 sf |
| remove tongue-&-groove soffit | demolition laborer | $26.20 | .012 | $.31 lf |
| remove rain gutter | demolition laborer | $26.20 | .011 | $.29 lf |
| remove built-in box rain gutter | demolition laborer | $26.20 | .026 | $.68 lf |
| remove downspout | demolition laborer | $26.20 | .009 | $.24 lf |
| remove fixed shutter | demolition laborer | $26.20 | .156 | $4.09 ea |
| remove moveable shutter | demolition laborer | $26.20 | .158 | $4.14 ea |
| **Siding installation crew** | | | | |
| install siding | siding installer | $39.10 | | |
| install siding | siding installer's helper | $28.90 | | |
| **install siding** | **siding crew** | **$34.00** | | |
| **Install siding** | | | | |
| fiberglass corrugated | siding crew | $34.00 | .028 | $.95 sf |
| aluminum | siding crew | $34.00 | .034 | $1.16 sf |
| cement fiber shingle | siding crew | $34.00 | .045 | $1.53 sf |
| shake or wood shingle | siding crew | $34.00 | .045 | $1.53 sf |
| vinyl | siding crew | $34.00 | .034 | $1.16 sf |
| 7/16" thick hardboard | siding crew | $34.00 | .024 | $.82 sf |
| hardboard lap | siding crew | $34.00 | .026 | $.88 sf |
| 5/8" thick plywood | siding crew | $34.00 | .025 | $.85 sf |
| plywood with 1" x 4" boards | siding crew | $34.00 | .057 | $1.94 sf |
| board-and-batten | siding crew | $34.00 | .037 | $1.26 sf |
| board-on-board | siding crew | $34.00 | .034 | $1.16 sf |
| drop siding | siding crew | $34.00 | .039 | $1.33 sf |
| clapboard | siding crew | $34.00 | .055 | $1.87 sf |
| bevel | siding crew | $34.00 | .041 | $1.39 sf |
| **Install fascia** | | | | |
| aluminum or vinyl | siding crew | $34.00 | .034 | $1.16 lf |
| wood fascia | siding crew | $34.00 | .037 | $1.26 lf |
| **Install soffit** | | | | |
| aluminum or vinyl | siding crew | $34.00 | .049 | $1.67 sf |
| plywood | siding crew | $34.00 | .052 | $1.77 sf |
| tongue-&-groove | siding crew | $34.00 | .061 | $2.07 sf |
| **Install rain gutter** | | | | |
| typical | siding crew | $34.00 | .041 | $1.39 lf |
| built-in box | siding crew | $34.00 | 1.69 | $57.50 lf |
| **Install rain gutter downspout** | | | | |
| typical | siding crew | $34.00 | .038 | $1.29 lf |
| built-in box | siding crew | $34.00 | .562 | $19.10 lf |
| **Install downspout conductor** | | | | |
| typical | siding crew | $34.00 | .431 | $14.70 ea |
| **Install shutter** | | | | |
| fixed | siding crew | $34.00 | .323 | $11.00 ea |
| moveable | siding crew | $34.00 | .333 | $11.30 ea |

NOTES: _____

_____

_____ end

# 35 ............................................. *Stairs*

| Item Description | Unit | Remove | Replace | Total |
|---|---|---|---|---|
| **3' wide utility stairs** | st | $2.65 | $30.60 | $33.25 |
| *Replace* Materials ......16.30   Labor...........14.30 | | | | |
| *Remove*........................   Labor...........2.65 | | | | |
| ► Includes three 2" x 12" stringers and 2" dimensional lumber treads. | | | | |
| **3' wide enclosed stairs for covered treads & risers** | st | $3.20 | $48.30 | $51.50 |
| *Replace* Materials ......29.60   Labor...........18.70 | | | | |
| *Remove*........................   Labor...........3.20 | | | | |
| ► Treads and risers are plywood or particleboard with pine risers. Treads and risers will be completely covered by carpeting or other flooring. | | | | |
| **3' wide enclosed stairs with false oak tread & riser** | st | $3.20 | $84.20 | $87.40 |
| *Replace* Materials ......62.20   Labor...........22.00 | | | | |
| *Remove*........................   Labor...........3.20 | | | | |
| ► Particleboard treads with pine risers covered with two wall end false red oak tread and riser assemblies. (Carpet runs between false treads.) | | | | |
| **3' wide enclosed stairs with oak treads & paint-grade risers** | st | $3.20 | $81.60 | $84.80 |
| *Replace* Materials ......62.90   Labor...........18.70 | | | | |
| *Remove*........................   Labor...........3.20 | | | | |
| ► Treads are red oak and risers are paint-grade pine. | | | | |
| **3' wide enclosed stairs with oak treads & oak risers** | st | $3.20 | $86.00 | $89.20 |
| *Replace* Materials ......67.30   Labor...........18.70 | | | | |
| *Remove*........................   Labor...........3.20 | | | | |
| ► Treads and risers are red oak. | | | | |
| **3' wide stairs, one side open, for covered treads & risers** | st | $3.20 | $48.80 | $52.00 |
| *Replace* Materials ......29.60   Labor...........19.20 | | | | |
| *Remove*........................   Labor...........3.20 | | | | |
| ► Particleboard treads and pine risers. Treads and risers will be completely covered by carpeting or other flooring. | | | | |
| **3' wide stairs, one side open, with false oak tread & riser** | st | $3.20 | $98.70 | $101.90 |
| *Replace* Materials ......76.20   Labor...........22.50 | | | | |
| *Remove*........................   Labor...........3.20 | | | | |
| ► Particleboard treads with pine risers covered with one open end and one wall end false red oak tread and riser assemblies. (Carpet runs between false treads.) | | | | |
| **3' wide stairs, one side open, with oak treads & paint-grade risers** | st | $3.20 | $82.10 | $85.30 |
| *Replace* Materials ......62.90   Labor...........19.20 | | | | |
| *Remove*........................   Labor...........3.20 | | | | |
| ► Treads are red oak with easing on open side and 1/2" red oak cove trim beneath tread. Risers are paint-grade pine. | | | | |
| **3' wide stairs, one side open, with oak treads & oak risers** | st | $3.20 | $86.50 | $89.70 |
| *Replace* Materials ......67.30   Labor...........19.20 | | | | |
| *Remove*........................   Labor...........3.20 | | | | |
| ► Treads are red oak with easing on open side and 1/2" red oak cove trim beneath tread. Risers are red oak. | | | | |
| **3' wide stairs, two sides open, for covered treads & risers** | st | $3.20 | $50.10 | $53.30 |
| *Replace* Materials ......29.60   Labor...........20.50 | | | | |
| *Remove*........................   Labor...........3.20 | | | | |
| ► Particleboard tread and pine risers. Treads and risers will be completely covered by carpeting or other flooring. | | | | |

◄ **UTILITY STAIRS**
*Per step. Does not include railing.*

◄ **STRAIGHT STAIRS**
*Per step. Each stair system includes four 2" x 12" stringers reinforced with plywood or waferboard. Does not include balustrade.*

◁ enclosed

◁ one side open

**RELATED ITEMS**
Columns ........................71
Finish Carpentry...........199
*porch posts*...................231
Rough Carpentry ........409
*exterior deck stairs*.........430

◁ two sides open

| Item Description | Unit | Remove | Replace | Total |
|---|---|---|---|---|

**STRAIGHT STAIRS** ▶
*continued*

**3' wide stairs, two sides open, with false oak tread & riser** | st | $3.20 | $114.00 | $117.20
*Replace* Materials......90.20    Labor..........23.80
*Remove*........................    Labor..........3.20
▶ Particleboard treads with pine risers covered with two open end false red oak tread and riser assemblies. (Carpet runs between false treads.)

**3' wide stairs, two sides open, with oak treads & paint-grade risers** | st | $3.20 | $83.40 | $86.60
*Replace* Materials......62.90    Labor..........20.50
*Remove*........................    Labor..........3.20
▶ Treads are red oak with easing on both sides and 1/2" red oak cove trim beneath tread. Risers are paint-grade pine.

**3' wide stairs, two sides open, with oak treads & oak risers** | st | $3.20 | $87.80 | $91.00
*Replace* Materials......67.30    Labor..........20.50
*Remove*........................    Labor..........3.20
▶ Treads are red oak with easing on both sides and 1/2" red oak cove trim beneath tread. Risers are red oak.

**1/4 TURN STAIRS** ▶
*Per step.*
*Ten step minimum.*
*L-shaped stair system*
*with 3' by 3' landing.*
*Includes bearing walls*
*beneath landing as*
*indicated, 2" x 8" joists,*
*headers, and 3/4"*
*tongue-&-groove*
*sheathing. Each stair*
*system includes four*
*2" x 12" stringers*
*reinforced with plywood*
*or waferboard. Does*
*not include balustrade.*

*enclosed* ▷

**3' wide enclosed 1/4 turn stairs for covered treads & risers** | st | $3.54 | $70.70 | $74.24
*Replace* Materials......38.10    Labor..........32.60
*Remove*........................    Labor..........3.54
▶ 6 lf of landing bearing wall. Particleboard treads and pine risers or plywood treads and risers. Treads, risers, and landing will be covered by the flooring.

**3' wide enclosed 1/4 turn stairs with false oak tread & riser** | st | $3.54 | $120.30 | $123.84
*Replace* Materials......74.50    Labor..........45.80
*Remove*........................    Labor..........3.54
▶ 6 lf of landing bearing wall. Particleboard treads with pine risers covered with two wall end false red oak tread and riser assemblies. (Carpet runs between false treads.) Landing covered with oak flooring with stair edged trimmed with landing nose.

**3' wide enclosed 1/4 turn stairs with oak treads & paint-grade risers** | st | $3.54 | $119.30 | $122.84
*Replace* Materials......79.00    Labor..........40.30
*Remove*........................    Labor..........3.54
▶ 6 lf of landing bearing wall. Treads are red oak and risers are paint-grade pine. Landing covered with oak flooring with stair edge trimmed with landing nose.

**3' wide enclosed 1/4 turn stairs with oak treads & oak risers** | st | $3.54 | $123.70 | $127.24
*Replace* Materials......83.40    Labor..........40.30
*Remove*........................    Labor..........3.54
▶ 6 lf of landing bearing wall. Treads and risers are red oak. Landing covered with oak flooring with stair edge trimmed with landing nose.

*one side open* ▷

**3' wide 1/4 turn stairs, one side open, for covered treads & risers** | st | $3.54 | $71.90 | $75.44
*Replace* Materials......38.10    Labor..........33.80
*Remove*........................    Labor..........3.54
▶ 6 lf of landing bearing wall. Particleboard treads and pine risers. Treads, risers, and landing will be completely covered by carpeting or other flooring.

**3' wide 1/4 turn stairs, one side open, with false oak tread & riser** | st | $3.54 | $135.90 | $139.44
*Replace* Materials......88.50    Labor..........47.40
*Remove*........................    Labor..........3.54
▶ 6 lf of landing bearing wall. Particleboard treads with pine risers covered with one open end and one wall end false red oak tread and riser assemblies. (Carpet runs between false treads.) Landing covered with oak flooring with stair edge trimmed with landing nose.

**3' wide 1/4 turn stairs, one side open, with oak treads & paint-grade risers** | st | $3.54 | $120.10 | $123.64
*Replace* Materials......79.00    Labor..........41.10
*Remove*........................    Labor..........3.54
▶ 6 lf of landing bearing wall. Treads are red oak with easing on open side and 1/2" red oak cove trim beneath tread. Risers are paint-grade pine. Landing covered with oak flooring with stair edge trimmed with landing nose.

| Item Description | Unit | Remove | Replace | Total |
|---|---|---|---|---|
| **3' wide 1/4 turn stairs, one side open, with oak treads & oak risers** | st | $3.54 | $124.50 | $128.04 |
| *Replace* Materials......83.40      Labor...........41.10<br>*Remove*........................      Labor ...........3.54 | | | | |
| ► 6 lf of landing bearing wall. Treads are red oak with easing on open side and 1/2" red oak cove trim beneath tread. Risers are red oak. Landing covered with oak flooring with stair edge trimmed with landing nose. | | | | |
| **3' wide 1/4 turn stairs, two sides open, for covered treads & risers** | st | $3.54 | $73.10 | $76.64 |
| *Replace* Materials......38.10      Labor...........35.00<br>*Remove*........................      Labor ...........3.54 | | | | |
| ► 12 lf of landing bearing wall. Particleboard treads and pine risers or plywood treads and risers. Treads, risers, and landing will be completely covered by flooring. | | | | |
| **3' wide 1/4 turn stairs, two sides open, with false oak tread & riser** | st | $3.54 | $151.10 | $154.64 |
| *Replace* Materials....102.50      Labor ..........48.60<br>*Remove*........................      Labor ...........3.54 | | | | |
| ► 12 lf of landing bearing wall. Particleboard treads with pine risers covered with two open end false red oak tread and riser assemblies. (Space is left for carpet to run between treads.) Landing covered with oak flooring with stair edge trimmed with landing nose. | | | | |
| **3' wide 1/4 turn stairs, two sides open, with oak treads & paint-grade risers** | st | $3.54 | $120.50 | $124.04 |
| *Replace* Materials......79.00      Labor...........41.50<br>*Remove*........................      Labor ...........3.54 | | | | |
| ► 12 lf of landing bearing wall. Treads are red oak with easing on both sides and 1/2" red oak cove trim beneath tread. Risers are paint-grade pine. Landing covered with oak flooring with stair edge trimmed with landing nose. | | | | |
| **3' wide 1/4 turn stairs, two sides open, with oak treads & oak risers** | st | $3.54 | $124.90 | $128.44 |
| *Replace* Materials......83.40      Labor...........41.50<br>*Remove*........................      Labor ...........3.54 | | | | |
| ► 12 lf of landing bearing wall. Treads are red oak with easing on both sides and 1/2" red oak cove trim beneath tread. Risers are red oak. Landing covered with oak flooring with stair edge trimmed with landing nose. | | | | |
| **3' wide enclosed 1/2 turn stairs for covered treads and risers** | st | $3.93 | $82.50 | $86.43 |
| *Replace* Materials......46.60      Labor...........35.90<br>*Remove*........................      Labor ...........3.93 | | | | |
| ► 9 lf of landing bearing wall. Particleboard treads and pine risers or plywood treads and risers. Treads, risers, and landing will be completely covered by flooring. | | | | |
| **3' wide enclosed 1/2 turn stairs with false oak tread and riser** | st | $3.93 | $136.50 | $140.43 |
| *Replace* Materials......86.80      Labor...........49.70<br>*Remove*........................      Labor ...........3.93 | | | | |
| ► 9 lf of landing bearing wall. Particleboard treads with pine risers covered with two wall end false red oak tread and riser assemblies. (Carpet runs between false treads.) Landing covered with oak flooring with stair edged trimmed with landing nose. | | | | |
| **3' wide enclosed 1/2 turn stairs with oak treads & paint-grade risers** | st | $3.93 | $135.50 | $139.43 |
| *Replace* Materials......91.30      Labor ..........44.20<br>*Remove*........................      Labor ...........3.93 | | | | |
| ► 9 lf of landing bearing wall. Treads are red oak and risers are paint-grade pine. Landing covered with oak flooring with stair edge trimmed with landing nose. | | | | |
| **3' wide enclosed 1/2 turn stairs with oak treads & oak risers** | st | $3.93 | $139.90 | $143.83 |
| *Replace* Materials......95.70      Labor ..........44.20<br>*Remove*........................      Labor ...........3.93 | | | | |
| ► 9 lf of landing bearing wall. Treads and risers are red oak. Landing covered with oak flooring with stair edge trimmed with landing nose. | | | | |

### RELATED ITEMS

Columns ..........................71
**Finish Carpentry** ...........199
  *porch posts* ...................231
**Rough Carpentry** ........409
  *exterior deck stairs* .........430

◁ two sides open

◄ **1/2 TURN STAIRS**
*Per step. Ten step minimum. U shaped stair system with 6' by 3' landing. Includes bearing walls beneath landing as indicated, 2" x 8" joists, headers, and 3/4" tongue-&-groove sheathing. Each stair system includes four 2" x 12" stringers reinforced with plywood or waferboard.*

◁ enclosed

| Item Description | Unit | Remove | Replace | Total |
|---|---|---|---|---|
| **1/2 TURN STAIRS ▶** *continued* **one side open** ▷ | | | | |
| **3' wide 1/2 turn stairs, one side open, for covered treads & risers** | st | $3.93 | $83.80 | $87.73 |
| *Replace* Materials ......46.60  Labor...........37.20 | | | | |
| *Remove*.........................  Labor ............3.93 | | | | |
| ▶ 9 lf of landing bearing wall. Particleboard treads and pine risers. Treads and risers will be completely covered by carpeting or other flooring. | | | | |
| **3' wide 1/2 turn stairs, one side open, with false oak tread & riser** | st | $3.93 | $166.70 | $170.63 |
| *Replace* Materials .....115.00  Labor...........51.70 | | | | |
| *Remove*.........................  Labor ............3.93 | | | | |
| ▶ 9 lf of landing bearing wall. Particleboard treads with pine risers covered with one open end and one wall end false red oak tread and riser assemblies. (Space is left for carpet to run between treads.) Landing covered with oak flooring with stair edge trimmed with landing nose. | | | | |
| **3' wide 1/2 turn stairs, one side open, with oak treads & paint-grade risers** | st | $3.93 | $136.70 | $140.63 |
| *Replace* Materials ......91.30  Labor...........45.40 | | | | |
| *Remove*.........................  Labor ............3.93 | | | | |
| ▶ 9 lf of landing bearing wall. Treads are red oak with easing on open side and 1/2" red oak cove trim beneath tread. Risers are paint-grade pine. Landing covered with oak flooring with stair edge trimmed with landing nose. | | | | |
| **3' wide 1/2 turn stairs, one side open, with oak treads & oak risers** | st | $3.93 | $141.10 | $145.03 |
| *Replace* Materials ......95.70  Labor...........45.40 | | | | |
| *Remove*.........................  Labor ............3.93 | | | | |
| ▶ 9 lf of landing bearing wall. Treads are red oak with easing on open side and 1/2" red oak cove trim beneath tread. Risers are red oak. Landing covered with oak flooring with stair edge trimmed with landing nose. | | | | |
| **two sides open** ▷ **3' wide 1/2 turn stairs, two sides open, for covered treads & risers** | st | $3.93 | $85.00 | $88.93 |
| *Replace* Materials ......46.60  Labor ...........38.40 | | | | |
| *Remove*.........................  Labor ............3.93 | | | | |
| ▶ 18 lf of landing bearing wall. Particleboard treads and pine risers or plywood treads and risers. Treads, risers, and landing will be completely covered by flooring. | | | | |
| **3' wide 1/2 turn stairs, two sides open, with false oak tread & riser** | st | $3.93 | $167.90 | $171.83 |
| *Replace* Materials .....115.00  Labor...........52.90 | | | | |
| *Remove*.........................  Labor ............3.93 | | | | |
| ▶ 18 lf of landing bearing wall. Particleboard treads with pine risers covered with two open end false red oak tread and riser assemblies. (Space is left for carpet to run between treads.) Landing covered with oak flooring with stair edge trimmed with landing nose. | | | | |
| **3' wide 1/2 turn stairs, two sides open, with oak treads & paint-grade risers** | st | $3.93 | $137.10 | $141.03 |
| *Replace* Materials ......91.30  Labor...........45.80 | | | | |
| *Remove*.........................  Labor ............3.93 | | | | |
| ▶ 18 lf of landing bearing wall. Treads are red oak with easing on both sides and 1/2" red oak cove trim beneath tread. Risers are paint-grade pine. Landing covered with oak flooring with stair edge trimmed with landing nose. | | | | |
| **3' wide 1/2 turn stairs, two sides open, with oak treads & oak risers** | st | $3.93 | $141.50 | $145.43 |
| *Replace* Materials ......95.70  Labor...........45.80 | | | | |
| *Remove*.........................  Labor ............3.93 | | | | |
| ▶ 18 lf of landing bearing wall. Treads and risers are red oak with easing on both sides and 1/2" red oak cove trim beneath tread. Landing covered with oak flooring with stair edge trimmed with landing nose. | | | | |
| **CIRCULAR STAIRS ▶** *Circular stairs usually form half of a circle or less. Based on 9' radius.* | | | | |
| **3' wide enclosed circular stairs for covered treads and risers** | st | $4.14 | $645.00 | $649.14 |
| *Replace* Materials ......187.00  Labor..........458.00 | | | | |
| *Remove*.........................  Labor ............4.14 | | | | |
| ▶ Treads and risers are plywood or particleboard treads with pine risers. Treads and risers will be completely covered by carpeting or other flooring. | | | | |

continued on next page

| Item Description | Unit | Remove | Replace | Total | |
|---|---|---|---|---|---|
| **3' wide enclosed circular stairs with false oak tread and riser**<br>*Replace* Materials....220.00      Labor........465.00<br>*Remove*.........................      Labor ...........4.14<br>▶ Particleboard treads with pine risers covered with two wall end false red oak tread and riser assemblies. (Carpet runs between false treads.) | st | $4.14 | $685.00 | $689.14 | ◀ **CIRCULAR STAIRS** *Labor prices are for hand-framed open or closed stringer stairs. Overall these prices also apply to purchase and installation of prefabricated circular stairs. Does not include balustrade.* |
| **3' wide enclosed circular stairs with oak treads and paint-grade risers**<br>*Replace* Materials....220.00      Labor........458.00<br>*Remove*.........................      Labor ...........4.14<br>▶ Treads are red oak and risers are paint-grade pine. | st | $4.14 | $678.00 | $682.14 | |
| **3' wide enclosed circular stairs with oak treads and oak risers**<br>*Replace* Materials....225.00      Labor........458.00<br>*Remove*.........................      Labor ...........4.14<br>▶ Treads and risers are red oak. | st | $4.14 | $683.00 | $687.14 | |
| **3' wide circular stairs, one side open, for covered treads and risers**<br>*Replace* Materials.....187.00      Labor ........466.00<br>*Remove*.........................      Labor ...........4.14<br>▶ Particleboard treads and pine risers. Treads and risers will be completely covered by carpeting or other flooring. | st | $4.14 | $653.00 | $657.14 | ◁ **one side open** |
| **3' wide circular stairs, one side open, with false oak tread and riser**<br>*Replace* Materials....234.00      Labor........473.00<br>*Remove*.........................      Labor ...........4.14<br>▶ Particleboard treads with pine risers covered with one open end and one wall end false red oak tread and riser assemblies. (Carpet runs between treads.) | st | $4.14 | $707.00 | $711.14 | |
| **3' wide circular stairs, one side open, with oak treads and paint-grade risers**<br>*Replace* Materials....220.00      Labor ........466.00<br>*Remove*.........................      Labor ...........4.14<br>▶ Treads are red oak with easing on open side and 1/2" red oak cove trim beneath tread. Risers are paint-grade pine. | st | $4.14 | $686.00 | $690.14 | |
| **3' wide circular stairs, one side open, with oak treads and oak risers**<br>*Replace* Materials....225.00      Labor ........466.00<br>*Remove*.........................      Labor ...........4.14<br>▶ Treads are red oak with easing on open side and 1/2" red oak cove trim beneath tread. Risers are paint-grade pine. | st | $4.14 | $691.00 | $695.14 | |
| **3' wide circular stairs, two sides open, for covered treads and risers**<br>*Replace* Materials.....187.00      Labor........470.00<br>*Remove*.........................      Labor ...........4.14<br>▶ Particleboard tread and pine risers. Treads and risers will be completely covered by carpeting or other flooring. | st | $4.14 | $657.00 | $661.14 | ◁ **two sides open** |
| **3' wide circular stairs, two sides open, with false oak tread and riser**<br>*Replace* Materials....248.00      Labor........477.00<br>*Remove*.........................      Labor ...........4.14<br>▶ Particleboard treads with pine risers covered with two open end false red oak tread and riser assemblies. (Carpet runs between false treads.) | st | $4.14 | $725.00 | $729.14 | |
| **3' wide circular stairs, two sides open, with oak treads and paint-grade risers**<br>*Replace* Materials....220.00      Labor........470.00<br>*Remove*.........................      Labor ...........4.14<br>▶ Treads are red oak with easing on both sides and 1/2" red oak cove trim beneath tread. Risers are paint-grade pine. | st | $4.14 | $690.00 | $694.14 | |
| **3' wide circular stairs, two sides open, with oak treads and oak risers**<br>*Replace* Materials....225.00      Labor........470.00<br>*Remove*.........................      Labor ...........4.14<br>▶ Treads are red oak with easing on both sides and 1/2" red oak cove trim beneath tread. Risers are red oak. | st | $4.14 | $695.00 | $699.14 | |

| Item Description | Unit | Remove | Replace | Total |
|---|---|---|---|---|
| **ADD FOR 4' WIDE STAIRS**    **Add 12% for 4' wide stairs** | | | | |
| ► For 4' wide straight, 1/4 turn, or 1/2 turn stairs containing the same number of stringers as 3' wide stairs (4) with wider treads and risers. 1/4 turn stair landing is 4' x 4' and 1/2 turn stair landing is 8' x 4'. Add **16%** for 4' wide circular stairs. | | | | |
| **ADD FOR STAIR WINDERS**    **Add for winder with particleboard tread, paint-grade riser** | ea | — | $59.10 | $59.10 |
| *Replace* Materials......43.30    Labor...........15.80 | | | | |
| ► For use with 1/4 turn and 1/2 turn stairs. Winders are pie-shaped stair treads, usually placed on top of the landing. Each winder is a box made from 2" x 8" boards ripped to the height of the riser. Additional ripped 2" x 8" boards are placed 12" on center inside the box for reinforcement. (Add **3%** for risers over 7-3/8" made from ripped 2" x 10" boards.) Winders are stacked on top of each other. | | | | |
| **Add for winder with oak tread, paint-grade riser** | ea | — | $92.40 | $92.40 |
| *Replace* Materials ......76.60    Labor...........15.80 | | | | |
| ► For details see above. | | | | |
| **Add for winder with oak tread, oak riser** | ea | — | $96.80 | $96.80 |
| *Replace* Materials ......81.00    Labor...........15.80 | | | | |
| ► For details see above. | | | | |
| **ADD FOR MITERED STEPS**    **Add for mitered corners on bottom three treads** | ea | — | $209.00 | $209.00 |
| *Replace* Materials .....117.00    Labor..........92.00 | | | | |
| ► For stairs where the bottom three steps turn at a 45 degree angle (or less) making three steps from the side and front. The three steps on the side are made from stacked boxes made from 2" x 8" boards ripped to the riser height, sheathed with 3/4" plywood then capped with the tread and riser material. Cost per side. (For example, for stairs with mitered corners on both sides, use this price twice.) | | | | |
| **ADD FOR BULL NOSE ON STARTING STEP**    **Add for starting step with bull nose one side, standard grade** | ea | — | $233.50 | $233.50 |
| *Replace* Materials.....214.00    Labor...........19.50 | | | | |
| ► Red oak up to 4' wide. | | | | |
| **Add for starting step with bull nose one side, high grade** | ea | — | $278.50 | $278.50 |
| *Replace* Materials ....259.00    Labor...........19.50 | | | | |
| ► Red oak up to 5' wide. | | | | |
| **Add for starting step with bull nose two sides, standard grade** | ea | — | $314.50 | $314.50 |
| *Replace* Materials ....295.00    Labor...........19.50 | | | | |
| ► Red oak up to 4' wide. | | | | |
| **Add for starting step with bull nose two sides, high grade** | ea | — | $376.50 | $376.50 |
| *Replace* Materials ....357.00    Labor...........19.50 | | | | |
| ► Red oak up to 5' wide. | | | | |
| **SPIRAL STAIRS** ► *Per step. Prefabricated spiral stairs assembled and installed by carpenter on site. Includes balustrade.*    **Prefabricated spiral stairs, economy grade** | st | $3.22 | $206.80 | $210.02 |
| *Replace* Materials.....173.00    Labor ..........33.80 | | | | |
| *Remove*........................    Labor ............3.22 | | | | |
| ► 48" to 54" diameter. Balusters are made from straight wood, steel, or aluminum with matching hand rail. One baluster per tread. Treads are made from aluminum, steel, or waferboard (for carpet). Add **$50** per lf for landing or balcony railing to match. | | | | |
| **Prefabricated spiral stairs, standard grade** | st | $3.22 | $338.80 | $342.02 |
| *Replace* Materials....305.00    Labor ..........33.80 | | | | |
| *Remove*........................    Labor ............3.22 | | | | |
| ► 48" to 54" diameter. Balusters are made from turned wood, twisted steel, or aluminum with steel or laminated wood hand rail. One baluster per tread. Treads are made from aluminum, steel, or waferboard (for carpet). Add **$70** per lf for landing or balcony railing to match. | | | | |

| Item Description | Unit | Remove | Replace | Total |
|---|---|---|---|---|
| **Prefabricated spiral stairs, high grade** | st | $3.22 | $369.80 | $373.02 |
| *Replace* Materials....336.00        Labor .........33.80 | | | | |
| *Remove*........................        Labor ............3.22 | | | | |
| ▶ 55" to 66" diameter. Balusters made from ornate wood or octagonal wood, twisted steel with decorative wrought iron work, or aluminum with matching hand rail. Two balusters per tread. Treads are made from aluminum, steel, or waferboard (for carpet). Add **$80** per lf for landing or balcony railing to match. | | | | |
| **Prefabricated spiral stairs, custom grade** | st | $3.22 | $400.80 | $404.02 |
| *Replace* Materials....367.00        Labor .........33.80 | | | | |
| *Remove*........................        Labor ............3.22 | | | | |
| ▶ 55" to 66" diameter. Balusters made from spiral wood or octagonal wood, steel or cast iron with decorative wrought iron work including brass elements with matching hand rail. Two balusters per tread. Treads are made from aluminum, steel, decorative cast iron, or waferboard (for carpet). Add **$90** per lf for landing or balcony railing to match. | | | | |
| **Prefabricated spiral stairs, deluxe grade** | st | $3.22 | $476.80 | $480.02 |
| *Replace* Materials....443.00        Labor .........33.80 | | | | |
| *Remove*........................        Labor ............3.22 | | | | |
| ▶ 67" to 72" diameter. Balusters made from ornate wood or octagonal wood, twisted steel with decorative wrought iron work with matching hand rail. Two balusters per tread. Treads are made from aluminum, steel, decorative cast iron or waferboard (for carpet). Add **$100** per lf for landing or balcony railing to match. | | | | |
| **Prefabricated spiral stairs, custom deluxe grade** | st | $3.22 | $517.80 | $521.02 |
| *Replace* Materials....484.00        Labor .........33.80 | | | | |
| *Remove*........................        Labor ............3.22 | | | | |
| ▶ 67" to 72" diameter. Balusters made from spiral wood or octagonal wood, steel or cast iron with decorative wrought iron work including brass elements with matching hand rail. Two balusters per tread. Treads are made from aluminum, steel, decorative cast iron, or waferboard (for carpet). Add **$120** per lf for landing or balcony railing to match. | | | | |
| **Disappearing attic stairs, standard grade** | ea | $7.07 | $415.00 | $422.07 |
| *Replace* Materials ....321.00        Labor...........94.00 | | | | |
| *Remove*........................        Labor ............7.07 | | | | |
| ▶ Pine components with stain-grade panel door. | | | | |
| **Disappearing attic stairs, high grade** | ea | $7.07 | $633.00 | $640.07 |
| *Replace* Materials....539.00        Labor...........94.00 | | | | |
| *Remove*........................        Labor ............7.07 | | | | |
| ▶ Pine components with stain-grade panel door, spring loaded, heavier quality side rails and treads. | | | | |
| **Disappearing attic stairs, deluxe grade** | ea | $7.07 | $1,005.00 | $1,012.07 |
| *Replace* Materials.....911.00        Labor...........94.00 | | | | |
| *Remove*........................        Labor ............7.07 | | | | |
| ▶ Pine components with stain-grade panel door, spring loaded, heavy duty side rails and treads. | | | | |
| **Remove disappearing attic stairs for work, then reinstall** | ea | — | $132.00 | $132.00 |
| *Replace* ........................        Labor..........132.00 | | | | |
| **Pine stair balustrade with 1-1/2" balusters** | lf | $1.39 | $77.10 | $78.49 |
| *Replace* Materials......25.00        Labor...........52.10 | | | | |
| *Remove*........................        Labor ............1.39 | | | | |
| **Pine stair balustrade with 1-1/2" fluted balusters** | lf | $1.39 | $82.10 | $83.49 |
| *Replace* Materials.....30.00        Labor...........52.10 | | | | |
| *Remove*........................        Labor ............1.39 | | | | |

**RELATED ITEMS**

Columns .....................71
Finish Carpentry ..........199
porch posts...................231
Rough Carpentry .........409
exterior deck stairs.........430

◀ **DISAPPEARING ATTIC STAIRS**
*Fold-up attic access stairs with side rails.*

◁ **remove & reinstall**

◀ **PINE STAIR BALUSTRADE**
*Includes newel post. Add* **9%** *for red oak rail and newel in pine balustrade. Add* **85%** *for installation on curved stair. Deduct* **10%** *for balustrade installed on porch or other level application.*

| Item Description | Unit | Remove | Replace | Total |
|---|---|---|---|---|
| **PINE STAIR** ▶ **BALUSTRADE** *continued* | | | | |
| **Pine stair balustrade with 1-1/2" spiral balusters** | If | $1.39 | $98.80 | $100.19 |
| *Replace* Materials......46.70       Labor...........52.10 | | | | |
| *Remove*.......................       Labor............1.39 | | | | |
| **Pine stair balustrade with 2-1/2" balusters** | If | $1.39 | $80.70 | $82.09 |
| *Replace* Materials......28.20       Labor...........52.50 | | | | |
| *Remove*.......................       Labor............1.39 | | | | |
| **Pine stair balustrade with 2-1/2" fluted balusters** | If | $1.39 | $86.50 | $87.89 |
| *Replace* Materials......34.00       Labor...........52.50 | | | | |
| *Remove*.......................       Labor............1.39 | | | | |
| **Pine stair balustrade with 2-1/2" spiral balusters** | If | $1.39 | $105.20 | $106.59 |
| *Replace* Materials......52.70       Labor...........52.50 | | | | |
| *Remove*.......................       Labor............1.39 | | | | |
| **Pine stair balustrade with 3-1/2" balusters** | If | $1.39 | $87.60 | $88.99 |
| *Replace* Materials......34.30       Labor...........53.30 | | | | |
| *Remove*.......................       Labor............1.39 | | | | |
| **Pine stair balustrade with 3-1/2" fluted balusters** | If | $1.39 | $94.50 | $95.89 |
| *Replace* Materials......41.20       Labor...........53.30 | | | | |
| *Remove*.......................       Labor............1.39 | | | | |
| **Pine stair balustrade with 3-1/2" spiral balusters** | If | $1.39 | $117.40 | $118.79 |
| *Replace* Materials......64.10       Labor...........53.30 | | | | |
| *Remove*.......................       Labor............1.39 | | | | |
| **Pine stair balustrade with 5-1/2" balusters** | If | $1.39 | $110.50 | $111.89 |
| *Replace* Materials......54.80       Labor...........55.70 | | | | |
| *Remove*.......................       Labor............1.39 | | | | |
| **Pine stair balustrade with 5-1/2" fluted balusters** | If | $1.39 | $120.50 | $121.89 |
| *Replace* Materials......64.80       Labor...........55.70 | | | | |
| *Remove*.......................       Labor............1.39 | | | | |
| **Pine stair balustrade with 5-1/2" spiral balusters** | If | $1.39 | $152.60 | $153.99 |
| *Replace* Materials......96.90       Labor...........55.70 | | | | |
| *Remove*.......................       Labor............1.39 | | | | |
| **Poplar stair balustrade with 1-1/2" balusters** | If | $1.39 | $93.70 | $95.09 |
| *Replace* Materials......41.60       Labor...........52.10 | | | | |
| *Remove*.......................       Labor............1.39 | | | | |
| **Poplar stair balustrade with 1-1/2" fluted balusters** | If | $1.39 | $102.40 | $103.79 |
| *Replace* Materials......50.30       Labor...........52.10 | | | | |
| *Remove*.......................       Labor............1.39 | | | | |
| **Poplar stair balustrade with 1-1/2" spiral balusters** | If | $1.39 | $131.80 | $133.19 |
| *Replace* Materials......79.70       Labor...........52.10 | | | | |
| *Remove*.......................       Labor............1.39 | | | | |
| **Poplar stair balustrade with 2-1/2" balusters** | If | $1.39 | $99.50 | $100.89 |
| *Replace* Materials......47.00       Labor...........52.50 | | | | |
| *Remove*.......................       Labor............1.39 | | | | |
| **Poplar stair balustrade with 2-1/2" fluted balusters** | If | $1.39 | $109.30 | $110.69 |
| *Replace* Materials......56.80       Labor...........52.50 | | | | |
| *Remove*.......................       Labor............1.39 | | | | |
| **Poplar stair balustrade with 2-1/2" spiral balusters** | If | $1.39 | $142.30 | $143.69 |
| *Replace* Materials......89.80       Labor...........52.50 | | | | |
| *Remove*.......................       Labor............1.39 | | | | |

with 2-1/2" balusters ▷

with 3-1/2" balusters ▷

with 5-1/2" balusters ▷

**POPLAR STAIR** ▶ **BALUSTRADE**
*Includes newel post. Add **9%** for red oak rail and newel in poplar balustrade. Add **85%** for installation on curved stair. Deduct **10%** for balustrade installed on porch or other level application.*

with 2-1/2" balusters ▷

| Item Description | Unit | Remove | Replace | Total | |
|---|---|---|---|---|---|
| **Poplar stair balustrade with 3-1/2" balusters**<br>*Replace* Materials ......57.20    Labor ..........53.30<br>*Remove*.....................    Labor ...........1.39 | If | $1.39 | $110.50 | $111.89 | ◁ **with 3-1/2" balusters** |
| **Poplar stair balustrade with 3-1/2" fluted balusters**<br>*Replace* Materials ......69.20    Labor ..........53.30<br>*Remove*.....................    Labor ...........1.39 | If | $1.39 | $122.50 | $123.89 | |
| **Poplar stair balustrade with 3-1/2" spiral balusters**<br>*Replace* Materials .....110.00    Labor ..........53.30<br>*Remove*.....................    Labor ...........1.39 | If | $1.39 | $163.30 | $164.69 | |
| **Poplar stair balustrade with 5-1/2" balusters**<br>*Replace* Materials .....89.70    Labor..........55.70<br>*Remove*.....................    Labor ...........1.39 | If | $1.39 | $145.40 | $146.79 | ◁ **with 5-1/2" balusters** |
| **Poplar stair balustrade with 5-1/2" fluted balusters**<br>*Replace* Materials .....107.00    Labor..........55.70<br>*Remove*.....................    Labor ...........1.39 | If | $1.39 | $162.70 | $164.09 | |
| **Poplar stair balustrade with 5-1/2" spiral balusters**<br>*Replace* Materials ....164.00    Labor..........55.70<br>*Remove*.....................    Labor ...........1.39 | If | $1.39 | $219.70 | $221.09 | |
| **Redwood stair balustrade with 1-1/2" balusters**<br>*Replace* Materials ......46.50    Labor..........52.10<br>*Remove*.....................    Labor ...........1.39 | If | $1.39 | $98.60 | $99.99 | ◀ **REDWOOD STAIR BALUSTRADE**<br>*Includes newel post. Add* **85%** *for installation on curved stair. Deduct* **10%** *for balustrade installed on porch or other level application.* |
| **Redwood stair balustrade with 1-1/2" fluted balusters**<br>*Replace* Materials ......56.10    Labor..........52.10<br>*Remove*.....................    Labor ...........1.39 | If | $1.39 | $108.20 | $109.59 | |
| **Redwood stair balustrade with 1-1/2" spiral balusters**<br>*Replace* Materials ......89.00    Labor..........52.10<br>*Remove*.....................    Labor ...........1.39 | If | $1.39 | $141.10 | $142.49 | |
| **Redwood stair balustrade with 2-1/2" balusters**<br>*Replace* Materials ......52.50    Labor..........52.50<br>*Remove*.....................    Labor ...........1.39 | If | $1.39 | $105.00 | $106.39 | ◁ **with 2-1/2" balusters** |
| **Redwood stair balustrade with 2-1/2" fluted balusters**<br>*Replace* Materials ......63.50    Labor..........52.50<br>*Remove*.....................    Labor ...........1.39 | If | $1.39 | $116.00 | $117.39 | |
| **Redwood stair balustrade with 2-1/2" spiral balusters**<br>*Replace* Materials ....100.20    Labor..........52.50<br>*Remove*.....................    Labor ...........1.39 | If | $1.39 | $152.70 | $154.09 | |
| **Redwood stair balustrade with 3-1/2" balusters**<br>*Replace* Materials ......63.90    Labor ..........53.30<br>*Remove*.....................    Labor ...........1.39 | If | $1.39 | $117.20 | $118.59 | ◁ **with 3-1/2" balusters** |
| **Redwood stair balustrade with 3-1/2" fluted balusters**<br>*Replace* Materials ......77.40    Labor ..........53.30<br>*Remove*.....................    Labor ...........1.39 | If | $1.39 | $130.70 | $132.09 | |
| **Redwood stair balustrade with 3-1/2" spiral balusters**<br>*Replace* Materials ....122.00    Labor ..........53.30<br>*Remove*.....................    Labor ...........1.39 | If | $1.39 | $175.30 | $176.69 | |
| **Redwood stair balustrade with 5-1/2" balusters**<br>*Replace* Materials ....100.00    Labor..........55.70<br>*Remove*.....................    Labor ...........1.39 | If | $1.39 | $155.70 | $157.09 | ◁ **with 5-1/2" balusters** |

**RELATED ITEMS**

Columns .........................71
Finish Carpentry...........199
  *porch posts*...................231
Rough Carpentry ........409
  *exterior deck stairs*.........430

| Item Description | Unit | Remove | Replace | Total |
|---|---|---|---|---|
| **REDWOOD STAIR ▶ BALUSTRADE** *continued* | | | | |
| **Redwood stair balustrade with 5-1/2″ fluted balusters** | lf | $1.39 | $175.70 | $177.09 |
| *Replace* Materials.....120.00  Labor..........55.70 | | | | |
| *Remove*........................  Labor ...........1.39 | | | | |
| **Redwood stair balustrade with 5-1/2″ spiral balusters** | lf | $1.39 | $238.70 | $240.09 |
| *Replace* Materials ....183.00  Labor..........55.70 | | | | |
| *Remove*........................  Labor ...........1.39 | | | | |
| **RED OAK STAIR ▶ BALUSTRADE** *Includes newel post. Add 85% for installation on curved stair. Deduct 10% for balustrade installed on porch or other level application.* | | | | |
| **Red oak stair balustrade with 1-1/2″ balusters** | lf | $1.39 | $110.70 | $112.09 |
| *Replace* Materials......58.60  Labor..........52.10 | | | | |
| *Remove*........................  Labor ...........1.39 | | | | |
| **Red oak stair balustrade with 1-1/2″ fluted balusters** | lf | $1.39 | $122.70 | $124.09 |
| *Replace* Materials.......70.60  Labor..........52.10 | | | | |
| *Remove*........................  Labor ...........1.39 | | | | |
| **Red oak stair balustrade with 1-1/2″ spiral balusters** | lf | $1.39 | $162.10 | $163.49 |
| *Replace* Materials.....110.00  Labor..........52.10 | | | | |
| *Remove*........................  Labor ...........1.39 | | | | |
| **Red oak stair balustrade with 1-1/2″ hand-carved balusters** | lf | $1.39 | $276.10 | $277.49 |
| *Replace* Materials ....224.00  Labor..........52.10 | | | | |
| *Remove*........................  Labor ...........1.39 | | | | |
| **Red oak stair balustrade with 1-1/2″ heavy hand-carved balusters** | lf | $1.39 | $292.10 | $293.49 |
| *Replace* Materials ....240.00  Labor..........52.10 | | | | |
| *Remove*........................  Labor ...........1.39 | | | | |
| with 2-1/2″ balusters ▷ **Red oak stair balustrade with 2-1/2″ balusters** | lf | $1.39 | $118.30 | $119.69 |
| *Replace* Materials......65.80  Labor..........52.50 | | | | |
| *Remove*........................  Labor ...........1.39 | | | | |
| **Red oak stair balustrade with 2-1/2″ fluted balusters** | lf | $1.39 | $131.70 | $133.09 |
| *Replace* Materials......79.20  Labor..........52.50 | | | | |
| *Remove*........................  Labor ...........1.39 | | | | |
| **Red oak stair balustrade with 2-1/2″ spiral balusters** | lf | $1.39 | $175.50 | $176.89 |
| *Replace* Materials.....123.00  Labor..........52.50 | | | | |
| *Remove*........................  Labor ...........1.39 | | | | |
| **Red oak stair balustrade with 2-1/2″ hand-carved balusters** | lf | $1.39 | $279.50 | $280.89 |
| *Replace* Materials ....227.00  Labor..........52.50 | | | | |
| *Remove*........................  Labor ...........1.39 | | | | |
| **Red oak stair balustrade with 2-1/2″ heavy hand-carved balusters** | lf | $1.39 | $296.50 | $297.89 |
| *Replace* Materials ....244.00  Labor..........52.50 | | | | |
| *Remove*........................  Labor ...........1.39 | | | | |
| with 3-1/2″ balusters ▷ **Red oak stair balustrade with 3-1/2″ balusters** | lf | $1.39 | $133.30 | $134.69 |
| *Replace* Materials......80.00  Labor..........53.30 | | | | |
| *Remove*........................  Labor ...........1.39 | | | | |
| **Red oak stair balustrade with 3-1/2″ fluted balusters** | lf | $1.39 | $149.70 | $151.09 |
| *Replace* Materials......96.40  Labor..........53.30 | | | | |
| *Remove*........................  Labor ...........1.39 | | | | |
| **Red oak stair balustrade with 3-1/2″ spiral balusters** | lf | $1.39 | $203.30 | $204.69 |
| *Replace* Materials ....150.00  Labor..........53.30 | | | | |
| *Remove*........................  Labor ...........1.39 | | | | |
| **Red oak stair balustrade with 3-1/2″ hand-carved balusters** | lf | $1.39 | $331.30 | $332.69 |
| *Replace* Materials ....278.00  Labor..........53.30 | | | | |
| *Remove*........................  Labor ...........1.39 | | | | |

| Item Description | Unit | Remove | Replace | Total | |
|---|---|---|---|---|---|
| **Red oak stair balustrade with 3-1/2" heavy hand-carved balusters** <br> *Replace* Materials....302.00    Labor..........53.30 <br> *Remove*......................    Labor ...........1.39 | lf | $1.39 | $355.30 | $356.69 | |
| **Red oak stair balustrade with 5-1/2" balusters** <br> *Replace* Materials.....127.00    Labor..........55.70 <br> *Remove*......................    Labor ...........1.39 | lf | $1.39 | $182.70 | $184.09 | ◁ with 5-1/2" balusters |
| **Red oak stair balustrade with 5-1/2" fluted balusters** <br> *Replace* Materials.....151.00    Labor..........55.70 <br> *Remove*......................    Labor ...........1.39 | lf | $1.39 | $206.70 | $208.09 | |
| **Red oak stair balustrade with 5-1/2" spiral balusters** <br> *Replace* Materials....226.00    Labor..........55.70 <br> *Remove*......................    Labor ...........1.39 | lf | $1.39 | $281.70 | $283.09 | |
| **Red oak stair balustrade with 5-1/2" hand-carved balusters** <br> *Replace* Materials....272.00    Labor..........55.70 <br> *Remove*......................    Labor ...........1.39 | lf | $1.39 | $327.70 | $329.09 | |
| **Red oak stair balustrade with 5-1/2" heavy hand-carved balusters** <br> *Replace* Materials....300.00    Labor..........55.70 <br> *Remove*......................    Labor ...........1.39 | lf | $1.39 | $355.70 | $357.09 | |
| **Pine stair balustrade with sawn balusters** <br> *Replace* Materials ......41.80    Labor..........52.10 <br> *Remove*......................    Labor ...........1.39 | lf | $1.39 | $93.90 | $95.29 | ◀ **SAWN STAIR BALUSTRADE** *Includes newel post Deduct* **10%** *for balustrade installed on porch or other level application.* |
| **Pine stair balustrade with sawn baluster panels** <br> *Replace* Materials ......70.70    Labor..........52.10 <br> *Remove*......................    Labor ...........1.39 | lf | $1.39 | $122.80 | $124.19 | |
| **Poplar stair balustrade with sawn balusters** <br> *Replace* Materials ......57.00    Labor..........52.10 <br> *Remove*......................    Labor ...........1.39 | lf | $1.39 | $109.10 | $110.49 | |
| **Poplar stair balustrade with sawn baluster panels** <br> *Replace* Materials ......86.60    Labor..........52.10 <br> *Remove*......................    Labor ...........1.39 | lf | $1.39 | $138.70 | $140.09 | △ sawn balusters |
| **Add for red oak rail & newel in paint-grade sawn stair balustrade** <br> *Replace* Materials.......11.60 | lf | — | $11.60 | $11.60 | |
| **Redwood stair balustrade with sawn balusters** <br> *Replace* Materials ......85.40    Labor..........52.10 <br> *Remove*......................    Labor ...........1.39 | lf | $1.39 | $137.50 | $138.89 | |
| **Redwood stair balustrade with sawn baluster panels** <br> *Replace* Materials .....135.00    Labor..........52.10 <br> *Remove*......................    Labor ...........1.39 | lf | $1.39 | $187.10 | $188.49 | △ sawn baluster panels |
| **Red oak stair balustrade with sawn balusters** <br> *Replace* Materials ......77.80    Labor..........52.10 <br> *Remove*......................    Labor ...........1.39 | lf | $1.39 | $129.90 | $131.29 | |
| **Red oak stair balustrade with sawn baluster panels** <br> *Replace* Materials .....116.00    Labor..........52.10 <br> *Remove*......................    Labor ...........1.39 | lf | $1.39 | $168.10 | $169.49 | |
| **Remove stair balustrade for work, then reinstall** <br> *Replace* ......................    Labor...........94.00 | lf | — | $94.00 | $94.00 | ◀ **REMOVE & REINSTALL BALUSTRADE** |

**RELATED ITEMS**

| | Item Description | Unit | Remove | Replace | Total |
|---|---|---|---|---|---|
| **ADDITIONAL BALUSTRADE COSTS** | **Add for volute end**<br>*Replace* Materials ....237.00  Labor.........120.00<br>▶ Oak, poplar, or pine.  Includes additional balusters and labor to install volute end with circled balusters and newel.  Usually not used on stairs with balusters larger than 2-1/2". | ea | — | $357.00 | $357.00 |
| | **Add for goose neck**<br>*Replace* Materials ....271.00  Labor...........96.40<br>▶ Oak, poplar, or pine. | ea | — | $367.40 | $367.40 |
| | **Add for 1/4 turn in stair rail**<br>*Replace* Materials .....83.70  Labor ...........89.70<br>▶ Oak, poplar, or pine.  90 degree turn slopes up on one side and down on the other. | ea | — | $173.40 | $173.40 |
| | **Add for 1/2 turn in stair rail**<br>*Replace* Materials.....192.00  Labor...........96.40<br>▶ Oak, poplar, or pine.  180 degree turn slopes up on one side and down on the other. | ea | — | $288.40 | $288.40 |
| **STAIR BRACKET**<br>*Brackets installed beneath open end of tread.* | **Stair bracket, standard grade**<br>*Replace* Materials........9.35  Labor ............3.59<br>*Remove*........................  Labor ............1.41<br>▶ Paint-grade.  No inside pattern. | ea | $1.41 | $12.94 | $14.35 |
| | **Stair bracket, high grade**<br>*Replace* Materials .....10.90  Labor ............3.59<br>*Remove*........................  Labor ............1.41<br>▶ Poplar or red oak.  Simple inside pattern. | ea | $1.41 | $14.49 | $15.90 |
| | **Stair bracket, deluxe grade**<br>*Replace* Materials.......13.00  Labor ............3.59<br>*Remove*........................  Labor ............1.41<br>▶ Poplar or red oak.  Ornate inside pattern. | ea | $1.41 | $16.59 | $18.00 |
| | **Stair bracket, custom grade**<br>*Replace* Materials ......14.60  Labor ............3.59<br>*Remove*........................  Labor ............1.41<br>▶ Poplar or red oak.  Very ornate inside pattern. | ea | $1.41 | $18.19 | $19.60 |
| | **Remove stair bracket for work, then reinstall**<br>*Replace* ........................  Labor ............5.89 | ea | — | $5.89 | $5.89 |
| **STAIR TREAD TRIM**<br>*Up to 3/4" cove, quarter-round, cove, or similar installed beneath the open end of the tread.* | **Pine molding trim beneath tread**<br>*Replace* Materials ........ .54  Labor ............4.27<br>*Remove*........................  Labor ............. .50 | ea | $.50 | $4.81 | $5.31 |
| | **Red oak molding trim beneath tread**<br>*Replace* Materials ........ .86  Labor ............4.27<br>*Remove*........................  Labor ............. .50 | ea | $.50 | $5.13 | $5.63 |
| **PINE NEWEL**<br>for 1-1/2" balusters ▷<br>*newel is 3-1/2" to 4" wide* | **Pine newel post for 1-1/2" balusters**<br>*Replace* Materials ......42.70  Labor ..........38.00<br>*Remove*........................  Labor ............4.93 | ea | $4.93 | $80.70 | $85.63 |
| | **Pine fluted newel post for 1-1/2" balusters**<br>*Replace* Materials.....56.70  Labor ..........38.00<br>*Remove*........................  Labor ............4.93 | ea | $4.93 | $94.70 | $99.63 |
| | **Pine spiral newel post for 1-1/2" balusters**<br>*Replace* Materials.....58.20  Labor ..........38.00<br>*Remove*........................  Labor ............4.93 | ea | $4.93 | $96.20 | $101.13 |

| Item Description | Unit | Remove | Replace | Total | |
|---|---|---|---|---|---|
| **Pine newel post for 2-1/2″ balusters**<br>*Replace* Materials ......51.30　　Labor ..........38.00<br>*Remove*.....................　　Labor ...........4.93 | ea | $4.93 | $89.30 | $94.23 | ◁ **for 2-1/2″ balusters**<br>newel is 4″ to<br>4-1/2″ wide. |
| **Pine fluted newel post for 2-1/2″ balusters**<br>*Replace* Materials ......68.00　　Labor ..........38.00<br>*Remove*.....................　　Labor ...........4.93 | ea | $4.93 | $106.00 | $110.93 | |
| **Pine spiral newel post for 2-1/2″ balusters**<br>*Replace* Materials ......69.80　　Labor ..........38.00<br>*Remove*.....................　　Labor ...........4.93 | ea | $4.93 | $107.80 | $112.73 | |
| **Pine newel post for 3-1/2″ balusters**<br>*Replace* Materials .......61.20　　Labor ..........38.00<br>*Remove*.....................　　Labor ...........4.93 | ea | $4.93 | $99.20 | $104.13 | ◁ **for 3-1/2″ balusters**<br>newel is 4-1/2″<br>to 5″ wide. |
| **Pine fluted newel post for 3-1/2″ balusters**<br>*Replace* Materials ......81.60　　Labor ..........38.00<br>*Remove*.....................　　Labor ...........4.93 | ea | $4.93 | $119.60 | $124.53 | |
| **Pine spiral newel post for 3-1/2″ balusters**<br>*Replace* Materials ......83.70　　Labor ..........38.00<br>*Remove*.....................　　Labor ...........4.93 | ea | $4.93 | $121.70 | $126.63 | |
| **Pine newel post for 5-1/2″ balusters**<br>*Replace* Materials ......97.80　　Labor ..........38.00<br>*Remove*.....................　　Labor ...........4.93 | ea | $4.93 | $135.80 | $140.73 | ◁ **for 5-1/2″ balusters**<br>newel is 6″ to 7″ wide. |
| **Pine fluted newel post for 5-1/2″ balusters**<br>*Replace* Materials ....130.00　　Labor ..........38.00<br>*Remove*.....................　　Labor ...........4.93 | ea | $4.93 | $168.00 | $172.93 | |
| **Pine spiral newel post for 5-1/2″ balusters**<br>*Replace* Materials .....133.00　　Labor ..........38.00<br>*Remove*.....................　　Labor ...........4.93 | ea | $4.93 | $171.00 | $175.93 | |
| **Poplar newel post for 1-1/2″ balusters**<br>*Replace* Materials ......71.20　　Labor ..........38.00<br>*Remove*.....................　　Labor ...........4.93 | ea | $4.93 | $109.20 | $114.13 | ◀ **POPLAR NEWEL**<br>◁ **for 1-1/2″ balusters**<br>newel is 3-1/2″<br>to 4″ wide. |
| **Poplar fluted newel post for 1-1/2″ balusters**<br>*Replace* Materials ......94.50　　Labor ..........38.00<br>*Remove*.....................　　Labor ...........4.93 | ea | $4.93 | $132.50 | $137.43 | |
| **Poplar spiral newel post for 1-1/2″ balusters**<br>*Replace* Materials ......96.90　　Labor ..........38.00<br>*Remove*.....................　　Labor ...........4.93 | ea | $4.93 | $134.90 | $139.83 | |
| **Poplar newel post for 2-1/2″ balusters**<br>*Replace* Materials ......85.40　　Labor ..........38.00<br>*Remove*.....................　　Labor ...........4.93 | ea | $4.93 | $123.40 | $128.33 | ◁ **for 2-1/2″ balusters**<br>newel is 4″ to<br>4-1/2″ wide. |
| **Poplar fluted newel post for 2-1/2″ balusters**<br>*Replace* Materials .....113.00　　Labor ..........38.00<br>*Remove*.....................　　Labor ...........4.93 | ea | $4.93 | $151.00 | $155.93 | |
| **Poplar spiral newel post for 2-1/2″ balusters**<br>*Replace* Materials .....116.00　　Labor ..........38.00<br>*Remove*.....................　　Labor ...........4.93 | ea | $4.93 | $154.00 | $158.93 | |
| **Poplar newel post for 3-1/2″ balusters**<br>*Replace* Materials ....102.00　　Labor ..........38.00<br>*Remove*.....................　　Labor ...........4.93 | ea | $4.93 | $140.00 | $144.93 | ◁ **for 3-1/2″ balusters**<br>newel is 4-1/2″<br>to 5″ wide. |

477

| | Item Description | Unit | Remove | Replace | Total |
|---|---|---|---|---|---|
| **POPLAR NEWEL** ▶ *continued* | **Poplar fluted newel post for 3-1/2" balusters** <br> *Replace* Materials.....136.00    Labor .........38.00 <br> *Remove*........................    Labor ..........4.93 | ea | $4.93 | $174.00 | $178.93 |
| | **Poplar spiral newel post for 3-1/2" balusters** <br> *Replace* Materials ....140.00    Labor .........38.00 <br> *Remove*........................    Labor ..........4.93 | ea | $4.93 | $178.00 | $182.93 |
| for 5-1/2" balusters ▷ *newel is 6" to 8" wide* | **Poplar newel post for 5-1/2" balusters** <br> *Replace* Materials.....163.00    Labor .........38.00 <br> *Remove*........................    Labor ..........4.93 | ea | $4.93 | $201.00 | $205.93 |
| | **Poplar fluted newel post for 5-1/2" balusters** <br> *Replace* Materials.....216.00    Labor .........38.00 <br> *Remove*........................    Labor ..........4.93 | ea | $4.93 | $254.00 | $258.93 |
| | **Poplar spiral newel post for 5-1/2" balusters** <br> *Replace* Materials ....222.00    Labor .........38.00 <br> *Remove*........................    Labor ..........4.93 | ea | $4.93 | $260.00 | $264.93 |
| **REDWOOD NEWEL** ▶ <br> for 1-1/2" balusters ▷ *newel is 3-1/2" to 4" wide* | **Redwood newel post for 1-1/2" balusters** <br> *Replace* Materials......80.50    Labor .........38.00 <br> *Remove*........................    Labor ..........4.93 | ea | $4.93 | $118.50 | $123.43 |
| | **Redwood fluted newel post for 1-1/2" balusters** <br> *Replace* Materials.....107.00    Labor .........38.00 <br> *Remove*........................    Labor ..........4.93 | ea | $4.93 | $145.00 | $149.93 |
| | **Redwood spiral newel post for 1-1/2" balusters** <br> *Replace* Materials.....110.00    Labor .........38.00 <br> *Remove*........................    Labor ..........4.93 | ea | $4.93 | $148.00 | $152.93 |
| for 2-1/2" balusters ▷ *newel is 4" to 4-1/2" wide* | **Redwood newel post for 2-1/2" balusters** <br> *Replace* Materials.....96.50    Labor .........38.00 <br> *Remove*........................    Labor ..........4.93 | ea | $4.93 | $134.50 | $139.43 |
| | **Redwood fluted newel post for 2-1/2" balusters** <br> *Replace* Materials.....128.00    Labor .........38.00 <br> *Remove*........................    Labor ..........4.93 | ea | $4.93 | $166.00 | $170.93 |
| | **Redwood spiral newel post for 2-1/2" balusters** <br> *Replace* Materials.....131.00    Labor .........38.00 <br> *Remove*........................    Labor ..........4.93 | ea | $4.93 | $169.00 | $173.93 |
| for 3-1/2" balusters ▷ *newel is 4-1/2" to 5" wide.* | **Redwood newel post for 3-1/2" balusters** <br> *Replace* Materials .....116.00    Labor .........38.00 <br> *Remove*........................    Labor ..........4.93 | ea | $4.93 | $154.00 | $158.93 |
| | **Redwood fluted newel post for 3-1/2" balusters** <br> *Replace* Materials ....154.00    Labor .........38.00 <br> *Remove*........................    Labor ..........4.93 | ea | $4.93 | $192.00 | $196.93 |
| | **Redwood spiral newel post for 3-1/2" balusters** <br> *Replace* Materials.....158.00    Labor .........38.00 <br> *Remove*........................    Labor ..........4.93 | ea | $4.93 | $196.00 | $200.93 |
| for 5-1/2" balusters ▷ *newel is 6" to 8" wide* | **Redwood newel post for 5-1/2" balusters** <br> *Replace* Materials ....184.00    Labor .........38.00 <br> *Remove*........................    Labor ..........4.93 | ea | $4.93 | $222.00 | $226.93 |
| | **Redwood fluted newel post for 5-1/2" balusters** <br> *Replace* Materials ....244.00    Labor .........38.00 <br> *Remove*........................    Labor ..........4.93 | ea | $4.93 | $282.00 | $286.93 |

| Item Description | Unit | Remove | Replace | Total | |
|---|---|---|---|---|---|
| **Redwood spiral newel post for 5-1/2" balusters**<br>*Replace* Materials....250.00    Labor .........38.00<br>*Remove*.......................    Labor ...........4.93 | ea | $4.93 | $288.00 | $292.93 | |
| **Red oak newel post for 1-1/2" balusters**<br>*Replace* Materials ....105.00    Labor .........38.00<br>*Remove*.......................    Labor ...........4.93 | ea | $4.93 | $143.00 | $147.93 | ◄ **RED OAK NEWEL**<br>◁ **for 1-1/2" balusters**<br>*newel is 3-1/2"<br>to 4" wide.* |
| **Red oak fluted newel post for 1-1/2" balusters**<br>*Replace* Materials.....139.00    Labor .........38.00<br>*Remove*.......................    Labor ...........4.93 | ea | $4.93 | $177.00 | $181.93 | |
| **Red oak spiral newel post for 1-1/2" balusters**<br>*Replace* Materials ....143.00    Labor .........38.00<br>*Remove*.......................    Labor ...........4.93 | ea | $4.93 | $181.00 | $185.93 | |
| **Red oak hand-carved newel post for 1-1/2" balusters**<br>*Replace* Materials.....191.00    Labor .........38.00<br>*Remove*.......................    Labor ...........4.93 | ea | $4.93 | $229.00 | $233.93 | |
| **Red oak heavy hand-carved newel post for 1-1/2" balusters**<br>*Replace* Materials....206.00    Labor .........38.00<br>*Remove*.......................    Labor ...........4.93 | ea | $4.93 | $244.00 | $248.93 | |
| **Red oak newel post for 2-1/2" balusters**<br>*Replace* Materials .....119.00    Labor .........38.00<br>*Remove*.......................    Labor ...........4.93 | ea | $4.93 | $157.00 | $161.93 | ◁ **for 2-1/2" balusters**<br>*newel is 4" to<br>4-1/2" wide.* |
| **Red oak fluted newel post for 2-1/2" balusters**<br>*Replace* Materials .....158.00    Labor .........38.00<br>*Remove*.......................    Labor ...........4.93 | ea | $4.93 | $196.00 | $200.93 | |
| **Red oak spiral newel post for 2-1/2" balusters**<br>*Replace* Materials.....162.00    Labor .........38.00<br>*Remove*.......................    Labor ...........4.93 | ea | $4.93 | $200.00 | $204.93 | |
| **Red oak hand-carved newel post for 2-1/2" balusters**<br>*Replace* Materials.....217.00    Labor .........38.00<br>*Remove*.......................    Labor ...........4.93 | ea | $4.93 | $255.00 | $259.93 | |
| **Red oak heavy hand-carved newel post for 2-1/2" balusters**<br>*Replace* Materials....234.00    Labor .........38.00<br>*Remove*.......................    Labor ...........4.93 | ea | $4.93 | $272.00 | $276.93 | |
| **Red oak newel post for 3-1/2" balusters**<br>*Replace* Materials ....143.00    Labor .........38.00<br>*Remove*.......................    Labor ...........4.93 | ea | $4.93 | $181.00 | $185.93 | ◁ **for 3-1/2" balusters**<br>*newel is 4-1/2"<br>to 5" wide.* |
| **Red oak fluted newel post for 3-1/2" balusters**<br>*Replace* Materials.....190.00    Labor .........38.00<br>*Remove*.......................    Labor ...........4.93 | ea | $4.93 | $228.00 | $232.93 | |
| **Red oak spiral newel post for 3-1/2" balusters**<br>*Replace* Materials.....194.00    Labor .........38.00<br>*Remove*.......................    Labor ...........4.93 | ea | $4.93 | $232.00 | $236.93 | |
| **Red oak hand-carved newel post for 3-1/2" balusters**<br>*Replace* Materials ....237.00    Labor .........38.00<br>*Remove*.......................    Labor ...........4.93 | ea | $4.93 | $275.00 | $279.93 | |
| **Red oak heavy hand-carved newel post for 3-1/2" balusters**<br>*Replace* Materials.....253.00    Labor .........38.00<br>*Remove*.......................    Labor ...........4.93 | ea | $4.93 | $291.00 | $295.93 | |

| Item Description | | Unit | Remove | Replace | Total |
|---|---|---|---|---|---|
| **RED OAK NEWEL ▶** *continued* **for 5-1/2" balusters ▷** *newel is 6" to 8" wide* | **Red oak newel post for 5-1/2" balusters** *Replace* Materials....227.00    Labor ..........38.00 *Remove*.....................    Labor ............4.93 | ea | $4.93 | $265.00 | $269.93 |
| | **Red oak fluted newel post for 5-1/2" balusters** *Replace* Materials....302.00    Labor ..........38.00 *Remove*.....................    Labor ............4.93 | ea | $4.93 | $340.00 | $344.93 |
| | **Red oak spiral newel post for 5-1/2" balusters** *Replace* Materials....308.00    Labor ..........38.00 *Remove*.....................    Labor ............4.93 | ea | $4.93 | $346.00 | $350.93 |
| | **Red oak hand-carved newel post for 5-1/2" balusters** *Replace* Materials ....423.00    Labor ..........38.00 *Remove*.....................    Labor ............4.93 | ea | $4.93 | $461.00 | $465.93 |
| | **Red oak heavy hand-carved newel post for 5-1/2" balusters** *Replace* Materials....454.00    Labor ..........38.00 *Remove*.....................    Labor ............4.93 | ea | $4.93 | $492.00 | $496.93 |
| | **Remove newel post for work, then reinstall** *Replace* .....................    Labor..........55.70 | ea | — | $55.70 | $55.70 |
| **ADD FOR OTHER ▶ WOOD SPECIES** *Add to the cost of poplar stair components.* | **Add 24% for mahogany** **Add 43% for cherry** **Add 11% for maple** **Add 2% for birch** | | | | |

# TIME & MATERIAL CHARTS *(selected items)*

## Stairs Materials

See **Stairs** material prices with the line items and waste information in the **QuickFinder** column.

## Stairs Labor

| LABORER | BASE WAGE | PAID LEAVE | TRUE WAGE | FICA | FUTA | WORKER'S COMP. | UNEMPLOY. INSUR. | HEALTH INSUR. | RETIRE (401K) | LIABILITY INSUR. | COST PER HOUR |
|---|---|---|---|---|---|---|---|---|---|---|---|
| Carpenter | $22.60 | 1.76 | $24.36 | 1.86 | .19 | 4.56 | 2.12 | 2.54 | .73 | 3.17 | $39.50 |
| Demolition laborer | $13.40 | 1.05 | $14.45 | 1.11 | .12 | 4.44 | 1.26 | 2.54 | .43 | 1.88 | $26.20 |

**Paid Leave** is calculated based on two weeks paid vacation, one week sick leave, and seven paid holidays. Employer's matching portion of **FICA** is 7.65 percent. **FUTA** (Federal Unemployment) is .8 percent. **Worker's compensation** for the stairs trade was calculated using a national average of 18.71 percent. **Unemployment insurance** was calculated using a national average of 8.7 percent. **Health insurance** was calculated based on a projected national average for 2001 of $505 per employee (and family when applicable) per month. Employer pays 80 percent for a per month cost of $404 per employee. **Retirement** is based on a 401(k) retirement program with employer matching of 50 percent. Employee contributions to the 401(k) plan are an average of 6 percent of the true wage. **Liability insurance** is based on a national average of 12.9 percent.

## Stairs Labor Productivity

| WORK DESCRIPTION | LABORER | COST PER HOUR | PRODUCTIVITY | UNIT PRICE |
|---|---|---|---|---|
| **Demolition** | | | | |
| remove utility stairs | demolition laborer | $26.20 | .101 | $2.65 st |
| remove stairs | demolition laborer | $26.20 | .122 | $3.20 st |
| remove 1/4 turn stairs | demolition laborer | $26.20 | .135 | $3.54 st |
| remove 1/2 turn stairs | demolition laborer | $26.20 | .150 | $3.93 st |
| remove circular stairs | demolition laborer | $26.20 | .158 | $4.14 st |
| remove spiral stairs | demolition laborer | $26.20 | .123 | $3.22 st |
| remove disappearing attic stairs | demolition laborer | $26.20 | .270 | $7.07 ea |
| remove stair balustrade | demolition laborer | $26.20 | .053 | $1.39 lf |
| remove stair bracket | demolition laborer | $26.20 | .054 | $1.41 ea |
| remove newel post | demolition laborer | $26.20 | .188 | $4.93 ea |
| **Build 3' wide stairs with three stringers** | | | | |
| utility stairs | finish carpenter | $39.50 | .361 | $14.30 st |
| **Build 3' wide straight stairs with four stringers** | | | | |
| 3' wide enclosed | finish carpenter | $39.50 | .474 | $18.70 st |
| 3' wide, one side open | finish carpenter | $39.50 | .485 | $19.20 st |
| 3' wide, two sides open | finish carpenter | $39.50 | .518 | $20.50 st |
| **Build 3' wide 1/4 turn stairs with four stringers, 3' x 3' landing** | | | | |
| 3' wide enclosed | finish carpenter | $39.50 | .826 | $32.60 st |
| 3' wide enclosed & oak plank on landing | finish carpenter | $39.50 | 1.02 | $40.30 st |
| 3' wide, one side open | finish carpenter | $39.50 | .855 | $33.80 st |
| 3' wide, one side open & oak plank on landing | finish carpenter | $39.50 | 1.04 | $41.10 st |
| 3' wide, two sides open | finish carpenter | $39.50 | .885 | $35.00 st |
| 3' wide, two sides open & oak plank on landing | finish carpenter | $39.50 | 1.05 | $41.50 st |
| **Build 3' wide 1/2 turn stairs with four stringers, 6' x 3' landing** | | | | |
| 3' wide enclosed | finish carpenter | $39.50 | .909 | $35.90 st |
| 3' wide enclosed with oak plank on landing | finish carpenter | $39.50 | 1.12 | $44.20 st |
| 3' wide, one side open | finish carpenter | $39.50 | .943 | $37.20 st |
| 3' wide, one side open & oak plank on landing | finish carpenter | $39.50 | 1.15 | $45.40 st |
| 3' wide, two sides open | finish carpenter | $39.50 | .971 | $38.40 st |
| 3' wide, two sides open & oak plank on landing | finish carpenter | $39.50 | 1.16 | $45.80 st |
| **Additional stair costs** | | | | |
| add to build platform winders | finish carpenter | $39.50 | .400 | $15.80 st |
| add to build mitered corner on bottom step | finish carpenter | $39.50 | 2.33 | $92.00 ea |
| add to install bull-nose starting step | finish carpenter | $39.50 | .493 | $19.50 ea |
| **Install false treads and risers** | | | | |
| closed end | finish carpenter | $39.50 | .070 | $2.77 ea |
| open end | finish carpenter | $39.50 | .090 | $3.56 ea |
| **Build 3' wide circular stairs** | | | | |
| enclosed | finish carpenter | $39.50 | 11.6 | $458.00 st |
| one side open | finish carpenter | $39.50 | 11.8 | $466.00 st |
| two sides open | finish carpenter | $39.50 | 11.9 | $470.00 st |
| **Install prefabricated spiral stairs** | | | | |
| all grades | finish carpenter | $39.50 | .855 | $33.80 st |
| **Install disappearing attic stairs** | | | | |
| all grades | finish carpenter | $39.50 | 2.38 | $94.00 ea |
| remove for work, then reinstall | finish carpenter | $39.50 | 3.33 | $132.00 ea |
| **Install wood stair balustrade** | | | | |
| with 1-1/2" balusters | finish carpenter | $39.50 | 1.32 | $52.10 lf |
| with 2-1/2" balusters | finish carpenter | $39.50 | 1.33 | $52.50 lf |
| with 3-1/2" balusters | finish carpenter | $39.50 | 1.35 | $53.30 lf |
| with 5-1/2" balusters | finish carpenter | $39.50 | 1.41 | $55.70 lf |
| remove for work, then reinstall | finish carpenter | $39.50 | 2.38 | $94.00 lf |
| **Install newel post** | | | | |
| install | finish carpenter | $39.50 | .962 | $38.00 ea |
| remove for work, then reinstall | finish carpenter | $39.50 | 1.41 | $55.70 ea |

NOTES: _____

_____

_____

_____

_____

_____

_____

_____

_____

_____

_____

_____

_____

_____

_____

_____

_____

_____

_____

_____

_____

_____

_____

_____

_____

_____

_____

_____

_____

_____

_____

_____

_____

_____

_____

_____

_____

_____

_____

_____

_____

_____ end

# 36 ......... *Suspended Ceilings*

| Item Description | Unit | Remove | Replace | Total | |
|---|---|---|---|---|---|
| **12" x 12" concealed grid suspended ceiling tile, smooth face** | sf | $.16 | $1.70 | $1.86 | ◄ **12" X 12"** TILE |
| *Replace* Materials........1.09    Labor.............61 | | | | | Prices are for tile and |
| **Remove** ......................    Labor.............16 | | | | | installation only. For |
| **12" x 12" concealed grid suspended ceiling tile, fissured face** | sf | $.16 | $1.90 | $2.06 | concealed grid systems, |
| *Replace* Materials........1.29    Labor.............61 | | | | | see below. |
| **Remove** ......................    Labor.............16 | | | | | |
| **12" x 12" concealed grid suspended ceiling tile, textured face** | sf | $.16 | $2.08 | $2.24 | |
| *Replace* Materials........1.47    Labor.............61 | | | | | |
| **Remove** ......................    Labor.............16 | | | | | |
| **12" x 12" concealed grid suspended ceiling tile, patterned face** | sf | $.16 | $2.20 | $2.36 | |
| *Replace* Materials........1.59    Labor.............61 | | | | | |
| **Remove** ......................    Labor.............16 | | | | | |
| **Grid for 12" x 12" concealed grid system** | sf | $.16 | $1.82 | $1.98 | ◄ **12" X 12"** GRID |
| *Replace* Materials........1.18    Labor.............64 | | | | | |
| **Remove** ......................    Labor.............16 | | | | | |
| ► Includes main runners, cross tees, wires, and eyelet screws. Does not include tiles. | | | | | |
| **Access panel in 12" x 12" concealed grid system** | ea | $2.50 | $78.20 | $80.70 | |
| *Replace* Materials......55.00    Labor .........23.20 | | | | | |
| **Remove** ......................    Labor ...........2.50 | | | | | |
| **Re-level sagging 12" x 12" concealed suspended grid** | sf | — | $.63 | $.63 | ◁ re-level |
| *Replace* Materials..........    Labor.............63 | | | | | |
| **2' x 4' suspended ceiling tile, smooth face** | sf | $.13 | $.78 | $.91 | ◄ **2' X 4'** TILES |
| *Replace* Materials ........ .48    Labor.............30 | | | | | |
| **Remove** ......................    Labor...........13 | | | | | |
| **2' x 4' suspended ceiling tile, fissured face** | sf | $.13 | $.93 | $1.06 | |
| *Replace* Materials ........ .63    Labor.............30 | | | | | |
| **Remove** ......................    Labor.............13 | | | | | |
| **2' x 4' suspended ceiling tile, textured face** | sf | $.13 | $1.13 | $1.26 | |
| *Replace* Materials ........ .83    Labor.............30 | | | | | |
| **Remove** ......................    Labor.............13 | | | | | |
| **2' x 4' suspended ceiling tile, patterned face** | sf | $.13 | $1.36 | $1.49 | |
| *Replace* Materials........1.06    Labor.............30 | | | | | |
| **Remove** ......................    Labor.............13 | | | | | |
| **Add for fire-rated 2' x 4' suspended ceiling tile installed with clips** | sf | — | $.62 | $.62 | ◁ add for fire-rated tile |
| *Replace* Materials ........ .35    Labor.............27 | | | | | |
| **2' x 4' polystyrene cracked-ice or mist-white luminous panel** | sf | $.13 | $1.43 | $1.56 | ◄ **2' X 4'** LUMINOUS PANEL |
| *Replace* Materials........1.16    Labor.............27 | | | | | |
| **Remove** ......................    Labor.............13 | | | | | |
| **2' x 4' acrylic cracked-ice or mist-white luminous panel** | sf | $.13 | $2.50 | $2.63 | |
| *Replace* Materials........2.23    Labor.............27 | | | | | |
| **Remove** ......................    Labor.............13 | | | | | |

**RELATED ITEMS**
Acoustic Ceilings.............15
Drywall......................133
Electrical
*drop-in fixtures*................166

| Item Description | | | Unit | Remove | Replace | Total |
|---|---|---|---|---|---|---|
| **2' x 4' polystyrene egg crate luminous panel** | | | sf | $.13 | $1.40 | $1.53 |
| *Replace* Materials........1.13 | Labor...............27 | | | | | |
| *Remove* ...................... | Labor...............13 | | | | | |
| **2' x 4' acrylic egg crate luminous panel** | | | sf | $.13 | $4.41 | $4.54 |
| *Replace* Materials........4.14 | Labor...............27 | | | | | |
| *Remove* ...................... | Labor...............13 | | | | | |
| **2' x 4' acrylic egg crate luminous panel with stainless-steel finish** | | | sf | $.13 | $4.79 | $4.92 |
| *Replace* Materials........4.52 | Labor...............27 | | | | | |
| *Remove* ...................... | Labor...............13 | | | | | |
| **2' x 4' acrylic egg crate luminous panel with brass finish** | | | sf | $.13 | $4.84 | $4.97 |
| *Replace* Materials........4.57 | Labor...............27 | | | | | |
| *Remove* ...................... | Labor...............13 | | | | | |
| **2' x 4' square crate polystyrene luminous panel** | | | sf | $.13 | $1.38 | $1.51 |
| *Replace* Materials........1.11 | Labor...............27 | | | | | |
| *Remove* ...................... | Labor...............13 | | | | | |
| **2' x 4' square crate acrylic luminous panel** | | | sf | $.13 | $4.18 | $4.31 |
| *Replace* Materials........3.91 | Labor...............27 | | | | | |
| *Remove* ...................... | Labor...............13 | | | | | |
| **2' x 4' square crate acrylic luminous panel with stainless-steel finish** | | | sf | $.13 | $4.67 | $4.80 |
| *Replace* Materials........4.40 | Labor...............27 | | | | | |
| *Remove* ...................... | Labor...............13 | | | | | |
| **2' x 4' square crate acrylic luminous panel with brass finish** | | | sf | $.13 | $4.74 | $4.87 |
| *Replace* Materials........4.47 | Labor...............27 | | | | | |
| *Remove* ...................... | Labor...............13 | | | | | |
| **2' x 4' suspended grid** | | | sf | $.10 | $.85 | $.95 |
| *Replace* Materials ........ .43 | Labor...............42 | | | | | |
| *Remove* ...................... | Labor...............10 | | | | | |
| **2' x 4' colored suspended grid** | | | sf | $.10 | $.92 | $1.02 |
| *Replace* Materials ........ .50 | Labor...............42 | | | | | |
| *Remove* ...................... | Labor...............10 | | | | | |
| **2' x 4' brass finish suspended grid** | | | sf | $.10 | $1.10 | $1.20 |
| *Replace* Materials ........ .68 | Labor...............42 | | | | | |
| *Remove* ...................... | Labor...............10 | | | | | |
| **2' x 4' stainless steel finish suspended grid** | | | sf | $.10 | $1.27 | $1.37 |
| *Replace* Materials ........ .85 | Labor...............42 | | | | | |
| *Remove* ...................... | Labor...............10 | | | | | |
| **Add for fire-rated 2' x 4' suspended grid** | | | sf | — | $.29 | $.29 |
| *Replace* Materials ........ .29 | | | | | | |
| **2' x 4' narrow suspended grid** | | | sf | $.10 | $.89 | $.99 |
| *Replace* Materials ........ .47 | Labor...............42 | | | | | |
| *Remove* ...................... | Labor...............10 | | | | | |
| **2' x 4' colored narrow suspended grid** | | | sf | $.10 | $.89 | $.99 |
| *Replace* Materials ........ .47 | Labor...............42 | | | | | |
| *Remove* ...................... | Labor...............10 | | | | | |
| **2' x 4' brass finish narrow suspended grid** | | | sf | $.10 | $1.24 | $1.34 |
| *Replace* Materials ........ .82 | Labor...............42 | | | | | |
| *Remove* ...................... | Labor...............10 | | | | | |

**2' x 4'**
**LUMINOUS PANEL**
*continued*

**2' x 4' GRID**
*Includes main runners 4' on center. Cross tees, wire, and eyelet screws. Does not include tiles or luminous panels.*

add for fire-rated grid

**2' x 4'**
**NARROW GRID**
*Includes main runners 4' on center. Cross tees, wire, and eyelet screws. Does not include tiles or luminous panels.*

| Item Description | Unit | Remove | Replace | Total | |
|---|---|---|---|---|---|
| **2' x 4' stainless steel finish narrow suspended grid** | sf | $.10 | $1.27 | $1.37 | |
| *Replace* Materials ........ .85     Labor.............. .42 | | | | | |
| *Remove* .......................     Labor.............. .10 | | | | | |
| **Add for fire-rated 2' x 4' narrow suspended grid** | sf | — | $.75 | $.75 | ◁ add for fire-rated grid |
| *Replace* Materials ........ .33     Labor.............. .42 | | | | | |
| **Re-level sagging 2' x 4' suspended grid** | sf | — | $.44 | $.44 | ◀ RE-LEVEL 2' x 4' GRID |
| *Replace* .......................     Labor.............. .44 | | | | | |
| **Remove 2' x 4' tiles for work, then reinstall** | sf | — | $.34 | $.34 | ◀ REMOVE 2' x 4' TILES & REINSTALL |
| *Replace* .......................     Labor.............. .34 | | | | | |
| **Remove 2' x 4' tiles & blanket or insulation for work, then reinstall** | sf | — | $.42 | $.42 | |
| *Replace* .......................     Labor.............. .42 | | | | | |
| **2' x 2' suspended ceiling tile, smooth face** | sf | $.10 | $.87 | $.97 | ◀ 2' x 2' TILES |
| *Replace* Materials ........ .57     Labor.............. .30 | | | | | |
| *Remove* .......................     Labor.............. .10 | | | | | |
| **2' x 2' suspended ceiling tile, fissured face** | sf | $.10 | $1.24 | $1.34 | |
| *Replace* Materials ........ .94     Labor.............. .30 | | | | | |
| *Remove* .......................     Labor.............. .10 | | | | | |
| **2' x 2' suspended ceiling tile, textured face** | sf | $.10 | $1.29 | $1.39 | |
| *Replace* Materials ........ .99     Labor.............. .30 | | | | | |
| *Remove* .......................     Labor.............. .10 | | | | | |
| **2' x 2' suspended ceiling tile, patterned face** | sf | $.10 | $1.58 | $1.68 | |
| *Replace* Materials........1.28     Labor.............. .30 | | | | | |
| *Remove* .......................     Labor.............. .10 | | | | | |
| **Add for fire-rated 2' x 2' suspended ceiling tile installed with clips** | sf | — | $.71 | $.71 | ◁ add for fire-rated tile |
| *Replace* Materials ........ .41     Labor.............. .30 | | | | | |
| **2' x 2' recessed edge suspended ceiling tile, smooth face** | sf | $.10 | $.96 | $1.06 | ◀ RECESSED 2' x 2' TILES |
| *Replace* Materials ........ .66     Labor.............. .30 | | | | | |
| *Remove* .......................     Labor.............. .10 | | | | | |
| **2' x 2' recessed edge suspended ceiling tile, fissured face** | sf | $.10 | $1.16 | $1.26 | |
| *Replace* Materials ........ .86     Labor.............. .30 | | | | | |
| *Remove* .......................     Labor.............. .10 | | | | | |
| **2' x 2' recessed edge suspended ceiling tile, textured face** | sf | $.10 | $1.44 | $1.54 | |
| *Replace* Materials........1.14     Labor.............. .30 | | | | | |
| *Remove* .......................     Labor.............. .10 | | | | | |
| **2' x 2' recessed edge suspended ceiling tile, patterned face** | sf | $.10 | $1.77 | $1.87 | |
| *Replace* Materials........1.47     Labor.............. .30 | | | | | |
| *Remove* .......................     Labor.............. .10 | | | | | |
| **Add for fire-rated 2' x 2' recessed edge tile installed with clips** | sf | — | $.33 | $.33 | ◁ add for fire-rated tile |
| *Replace* Materials ........ .03     Labor.............. .30 | | | | | |
| **2' x 2' polystyrene cracked-ice or mist-white luminous panel** | sf | $.10 | $1.54 | $1.64 | ◀ 2' x 2' LUMINOUS PANEL |
| *Replace* Materials........1.38     Labor.............. .16 | | | | | |
| *Remove* .......................     Labor.............. .10 | | | | | |
| **2' x 2' acrylic cracked-ice or mist-white luminous panel** | sf | $.10 | $2.84 | $2.94 | |
| *Replace* Materials........2.68     Labor.............. .16 | | | | | |
| *Remove* .......................     Labor.............. .10 | | | | | |

**RELATED ITEMS**

Acoustic Ceilings............15
Drywall.......................133
Electrical
  drop in fixtures.............166

| Item Description | Unit | Remove | Replace | Total |
|---|---|---|---|---|
| **2' x 2' LUMINOUS PANEL** *continued* | | | | |
| **2' x 2' polystyrene egg crate luminous panel** | sf | $.10 | $1.51 | $1.61 |
| *Replace* Materials........1.35    Labor............ .16 | | | | |
| *Remove* ........................    Labor............ .10 | | | | |
| **2' x 2' acrylic egg crate luminous panel** | sf | $.10 | $5.13 | $5.23 |
| *Replace* Materials........4.97    Labor............ .16 | | | | |
| *Remove* ........................    Labor............ .10 | | | | |
| **2' x 2' acrylic egg crate luminous panel with stainless steel finish** | sf | $.10 | $5.58 | $5.68 |
| *Replace* Materials........5.42    Labor............ .16 | | | | |
| *Remove* ........................    Labor............ .10 | | | | |
| **2' x 2' acrylic egg crate luminous panel with brass finish** | sf | $.10 | $5.65 | $5.75 |
| *Replace* Materials........5.49    Labor............ .16 | | | | |
| *Remove* ........................    Labor............ .10 | | | | |
| **2' x 2' square crate polystyrene luminous panel** | sf | $.10 | $1.49 | $1.59 |
| *Replace* Materials........1.33    Labor............ .16 | | | | |
| *Remove* ........................    Labor............ .10 | | | | |
| **2' x 2' square crate acrylic luminous panel** | sf | $.10 | $4.85 | $4.95 |
| *Replace* Materials........4.69    Labor............ .16 | | | | |
| *Remove* ........................    Labor............ .10 | | | | |
| **2' x 2' square crate acrylic luminous panel with stainless-steel finish** | sf | $.10 | $5.45 | $5.55 |
| *Replace* Materials........5.29    Labor............ .16 | | | | |
| *Remove* ........................    Labor............ .10 | | | | |
| **2' x 2' square crate acrylic luminous panel with brass finish** | sf | $.10 | $5.52 | $5.62 |
| *Replace* Materials........5.36    Labor............ .16 | | | | |
| *Remove* ........................    Labor............ .10 | | | | |
| **2' x 2' GRID** *Includes main runners 4' on center. Cross tees, wire, and eyelet screws. Does not include tiles or luminous panels.* | | | | |
| **2' x 2' suspended grid** | sf | $.10 | $1.11 | $1.21 |
| *Replace* Materials ........ .69    Labor............ .42 | | | | |
| *Remove* ........................    Labor............ .10 | | | | |
| **2' x 2' colored suspended grid** | sf | $.10 | $1.21 | $1.31 |
| *Replace* Materials ........ .79    Labor............ .42 | | | | |
| *Remove* ........................    Labor............ .10 | | | | |
| **2' x 2' brass finish suspended grid** | sf | $.10 | $1.45 | $1.55 |
| *Replace* Materials........1.03    Labor............ .42 | | | | |
| *Remove* ........................    Labor............ .10 | | | | |
| **2' x 2' stainless steel finish suspended grid** | sf | $.10 | $1.49 | $1.59 |
| *Replace* Materials........1.07    Labor............ .42 | | | | |
| *Remove* ........................    Labor............ .10 | | | | |
| **add for fire-rated grid** ▷ **Add for fire-rated 2' x 2' suspended grid** | sf | — | $.59 | $.59 |
| *Replace* Materials ........ .59 | | | | |
| **2' x 2' NARROW GRID** *Includes main runners 4' on center. Cross tees, wire, and eyelet screws. Does not include tiles or luminous panels.* | | | | |
| **2' x 2' narrow suspended grid** | sf | $.10 | $1.15 | $1.25 |
| *Replace* Materials ........ .73    Labor............ .42 | | | | |
| *Remove* ........................    Labor............ .10 | | | | |
| **2' x 2' colored narrow suspended grid** | sf | $.10 | $1.17 | $1.27 |
| *Replace* Materials ........ .75    Labor............ .42 | | | | |
| *Remove* ........................    Labor............ .10 | | | | |
| **2' x 2' brass finish narrow suspended grid** | sf | $.10 | $1.45 | $1.55 |
| *Replace* Materials........1.03    Labor............ .42 | | | | |
| *Remove* ........................    Labor............ .10 | | | | |

Insurance Repair Estimator

| Item Description | Unit | Remove | Replace | Total | |
|---|---|---|---|---|---|
| **2' x 2' stainless steel finish suspended grid**<br>*Replace* Materials........1.31　　Labor............ .42<br>*Remove* ......................　　Labor............ .10 | sf | $.10 | $1.73 | $1.83 | |
| **Add for fire-rated 2' x 2' narrow suspended grid**<br>*Replace* Materials ........ .59 | sf | — | $.59 | $.59 | ◁ add for fire-rated grid |
| **Re-level sagging 2' x 2' suspended grid**<br>*Replace* Materials ..........　Labor............ .52 | sf | — | $.52 | $.52 | ◀ **RE-LEVEL 2' x 2' GRID** |
| **Remove 2' x 2' tiles for work, then reinstall**<br>*Replace* Materials ..........　Labor............ .37 | sf | — | $.37 | $.37 | ◀ **REMOVE 2' x 2' TILES & REINSTALL** |
| **Remove 2' x 2' tiles & blanket for work, then reinstall**<br>*Replace* Materials ..........　Labor............ .45 | sf | — | $.45 | $.45 | |
| **Minimum charge for suspended ceiling work**<br>*Replace* Materials......50.00　Labor.........56.50 | ea | — | $106.50 | $106.50 | ◀ **MINIMUM CHARGE** |
| **Suspended ceiling cold-air return panel**<br>*Replace* Materials ......45.00　Labor............19.50<br>*Remove* ......................　Labor............3.54 | ea | 3.54 | $64.50 | $68.04 | ◀ **DROP-IN HVAC PANELS** |
| **Suspended ceiling air diffuser panel**<br>*Replace* Materials ......45.00　Labor............19.50<br>*Remove* ......................　Labor............3.54 | ea | 3.54 | $64.50 | $68.04 | |
| **2" sound absorbing blanket above suspended grid system**<br>*Replace* Materials ........ .40　labor............ .30<br>*Remove* ......................　Labor............ .21 | sf | $.21 | $.70 | $.91 | ◀ **SOUND BLANKET**<br>*Sound absorbing blanket installed above grid.* |
| **3" sound absorbing blanket above suspended grid system**<br>*Replace* Materials ........ .61　labor............ .30<br>*Remove* ......................　Labor............ .24 | sf | $.24 | $.91 | $1.15 | |

**RELATED ITEMS**
Acoustic Ceilings............15
Drywall....................133
Electrical
　drop in fixtures..............166

✍ NOTES: _____

_____ end

# TIME & MATERIAL CHARTS *(selected items)*

### Suspended Ceilings Materials

| DESCRIPTION | PRICE | GROSS COVERAGE | WASTE | NET COVERAGE | UNIT PRICE |
|---|---|---|---|---|---|
| **Suspended ceiling with concealed grid** | | | | | |
| wall angle | $5.60 per 12' stick | 83 | 4% | 79.68 | $.07 sf |
| main tee | $7.10 per 12' stick | 15.00 | 4% | 14.40 | $.49 sf |
| cross tee (12" x 12" installation) | $.68 per 1' stick | 1.14 | 4% | 1.09 | $.62 sf |
| **Suspended ceiling grid baked enamel finish** | | | | | |
| wall angle | $4.30 per 12' stick | 43.20 | 4% | 41.47 | $.10 sf |
| main tee | $7.10 per 12' stick | 27.48 | 4% | 26.38 | $.27 sf |
| cross tee in 2' x 4' installation | $2.40 per 4' stick | 41.60 | 4% | 39.94 | $.06 sf |
| cross tee in 2' x 2' installation | $1.40 per 2' stick | 4.58 | 4% | 4.40 | $.32 sf |

*. . . More ➤*

## Suspended Ceilings Materials *continued*

| DESCRIPTION | MATERIAL PRICE | | GROSS COVERAGE | WASTE | NET COVERAGE | UNIT PRICE |
|---|---|---|---|---|---|---|
| **12" x 12" suspended tile for concealed grid system** | | | | | | |
| smooth face | $1.04 | per tile | 1 | 5% | .95 | $1.09 sf |
| patterned face | $1.51 | per tile | 1 | 5% | .95 | $1.59 sf |
| add for fire rating | $.38 | per tile | 1 | 5% | .95 | $.40 sf |
| **2' x 4' suspended tile** | | | | | | |
| smooth face | $3.61 | per tile | 8 | 5% | 7.6 | $.48 sf |
| patterned face | $8.09 | per tile | 8 | 5% | 7.6 | $1.06 sf |
| add for 2' x 4' tile with fire rating | $2.35 | per tile | 8 | 5% | 7.6 | $.31 sf |
| **2' x 4' luminous panel** | | | | | | |
| polystyrene cracked-ice or mist-white | $8.90 | per panel | 8 | 4% | 7.68 | $1.16 sf |
| acrylic mist-white | $17.10 | per panel | 8 | 4% | 7.68 | $2.23 sf |
| polystyrene egg crate | $8.70 | per panel | 8 | 4% | 7.68 | $1.13 sf |
| acrylic egg crate | $31.80 | per panel | 8 | 4% | 7.68 | $4.14 sf |
| acrylic egg crate with stainless-steel finish | $34.70 | per panel | 8 | 4% | 7.68 | $4.52 sf |
| acrylic egg crate with brass finish | $35.10 | per panel | 8 | 4% | 7.68 | $4.57 sf |

## Suspended Ceiling Labor

| LABORER | BASE WAGE | PAID LEAVE | TRUE WAGE | FICA | FUTA | WORKER'S COMP. | UNEMPLOY. INSUR. | HEALTH INSUR. | RETIRE (401K) | LIABILITY INSUR. | COST PER HOUR |
|---|---|---|---|---|---|---|---|---|---|---|---|
| Installer | $22.00 | 1.72 | $23.72 | 1.81 | .19 | 2.82 | 2.06 | 2.54 | .71 | 3.08 | $36.90 |
| Installer's helper | $15.90 | 1.24 | $17.14 | 1.31 | .14 | 2.04 | 1.49 | 2.54 | .51 | 2.23 | $27.40 |
| Demolition laborer | $13.40 | 1.05 | $14.45 | 1.11 | .12 | 4.44 | 1.26 | 2.54 | .43 | 1.88 | $26.20 |

**Paid Leave** is calculated based on two weeks paid vacation, one week sick leave, and seven paid holidays. Employer's matching portion of **FICA** is 7.65 percent. **FUTA** (Federal Unemployment) is .8 percent. **Worker's compensation** for the suspended ceilings trade was calculated using a national average of 11.90 percent. **Unemployment insurance** was calculated using a national average of 8.7 percent. **Health insurance** was calculated based on a projected national average for 2001 of $505 per employee (and family when applicable) per month. Employer pays 80 percent for a per month cost of $404 per employee. **Retirement** is based on a 401(k) retirement program with employer matching of 50 percent. Employee contributions to the 401(k) plan are an average of 6 percent of the true wage. **Liability insurance** is based on a national average of 12.9 percent.

## Suspended Ceiling Labor Productivity

| WORK DESCRIPTION | LABORER | COST PER HOUR | PRODUCTIVITY | UNIT PRICE |
|---|---|---|---|---|
| **Demolition** | | | | |
| remove 2' x 4' ceiling tiles | demolition laborer | $26.20 | .005 | $.13 sf |
| remove 2' x 4' suspended grid only | demolition laborer | $26.20 | .004 | $.10 sf |
| remove 2' x 4' suspended tiles & grid | demolition laborer | $26.20 | .009 | $.24 sf |
| remove 2' x 2' suspended tiles only | demolition laborer | $26.20 | .004 | $.10 sf |
| remove 2' x 2' grid only | demolition laborer | $26.20 | .004 | $.10 sf |
| remove 2' x 2' tiles & grid | demolition laborer | $26.20 | .004 | $.10 sf |
| remove 12" x 12" ceiling tiles only | demolition laborer | $26.20 | .010 | $.26 sf |
| remove 12" x 12" grid only | demolition laborer | $26.20 | .006 | $.16 sf |
| remove 12" x 12" tiles & grid | demolition laborer | $26.20 | .011 | $.29 sf |
| **Suspended ceiling installation crew** | | | | |
| install suspended ceiling | installer | $36.90 | | |
| install suspended ceiling | installer's helper | $27.40 | | |
| **install suspended ceiling** | **installation crew** | $32.20 | | |
| **Install 2' x 4' suspended ceiling** | | | | |
| grid only | installation crew | $32.20 | .013 | $.42 sf |
| grid and tiles | installation crew | $32.20 | .025 | $.81 sf |
| ceiling tiles only | installer's helper | $27.40 | .011 | $.30 sf |
| luminous panels | installer's helper | $27.40 | .010 | $.27 sf |
| **Install 12" x 12" concealed suspended ceiling** | | | | |
| grid only | installation crew | $32.20 | .020 | $.64 sf |
| grid and tiles | installation crew | $32.20 | .038 | $1.22 sf |
| tiles only | installation crew | $32.20 | .019 | $.61 sf |

# 37 ............... *Swimming Pools*

| Item Description | Unit | Remove | Replace | Total | |
|---|---|---|---|---|---|
| **Minimum charge for swimming pool work**<br>*Replace* Materials ......35.00    Labor .........48.00 | ea | — | $83.00 | $83.00 | ◄ **MINIMUM** |
| **Gunite swimming pool with plaster**<br>*Replace* Materials ......26.00    Labor .........9.80<br>*Remove* ..................    Labor .........6.42 | sf | $6.42 | $35.80 | $42.22 | ◄ **SWIMMING POOLS**<br>*Per square feet of walls and bottom of pool. Includes all equipment (average to high quality) and 6" x 6" tile border. Does not includes coping or deck.* |
| **Concrete swimming pool with vinyl liner**<br>*Replace* Materials ......18.00    Labor .........8.02<br>*Remove* ..................    Labor .........5.55 | sf | $5.55 | $26.02 | $31.57 | |
| **Galvanized steel swimming pool with vinyl liner**<br>*Replace* Materials ......15.50    Labor .........6.52<br>*Remove* ..................    Labor .........3.72 | sf | $3.72 | $22.02 | $25.74 | |
| **Aluminum swimming pool with vinyl liner**<br>*Replace* Materials ......15.70    Labor .........6.81<br>*Remove* ..................    Labor .........3.72 | sf | $3.72 | $22.51 | $26.23 | |
| **Fiberglass swimming pool**<br>*Replace* Materials ......24.10    Labor .........8.40<br>*Remove* ..................    Labor .........3.17 | sf | $3.17 | $32.50 | $35.67 | |
| **Brick coping**<br>*Replace* Materials ......14.00    Labor .........11.00<br>*Remove* ..................    Labor .........1.31 | lf | $1.31 | $25.00 | $26.31 | ◄ **COPING** |
| **Precast concrete coping**<br>*Replace* Materials ......12.50    Labor .........9.52<br>*Remove* ..................    Labor .........1.31 | lf | $1.31 | $22.02 | $23.33 | |
| **Flagstone coping**<br>*Replace* Materials ......15.20    Labor .........12.30<br>*Remove* ..................    Labor .........1.31 | lf | $1.31 | $27.50 | $28.81 | |
| **Remove coping for work, then reinstall**<br>*Replace* Materials ........ .72    Labor .........15.00 | lf | — | $15.72 | $15.72 | |
| **Swimming pool deck, concrete with epoxy aggregate surface**<br>*Replace* Materials ......2.24    Labor .........2.17<br>*Remove* ..................    Labor .........1.28 | sf | $1.28 | $4.41 | $5.69 | ◄ **DECK** |
| **Swimming pool deck, stamped and dyed conrete**<br>*Replace* Materials ......2.04    Labor .........1.93<br>*Remove* ..................    Labor .........1.28 | sf | $1.28 | $3.97 | $5.25 | |
| **Bond beam repair**<br>*Replace* Materials ......8.42    Labor .........51.70 | lf | — | $60.12 | $60.12 | ◄ **BOND BEAM REPAIR** |
| **Regrout tile swimming pool**<br>*Replace* Materials ........ .14    Labor .........1.16 | sf | — | $1.30 | $1.30 | ◄ **REGROUT TILE** |
| **Leak detection**<br>*Replace* Materials ......2.64    Labor .........198.00 | ea | — | $200.64 | $200.64 | ◄ **LEAK DETECTION** |

| Item Description | Unit | Remove | Replace | Total |
|---|---|---|---|---|
| **REPAIR LEAK ►** Repair pool leak in vinyl lining, underwater<br>*Replace* Materials.......11.00        Labor.........174.00 | ea | — | $185.00 | $185.00 |
| Repair pool leak with hydraulic cement, underwater<br>*Replace* Materials......18.00        Labor.........216.00 | ea | — | $234.00 | $234.00 |
| Remove rusted rebar & stain, patch with plaster, underwater<br>*Replace* Materials......32.00        Labor.........338.00 | ea | — | $370.00 | $370.00 |
| Repair plaster popoff, underwater<br>*Replace* Materials......14.00        Labor.........203.00 | ea | — | $217.00 | $217.00 |
| **REPLASTER ►** Replaster swimming pool<br>*Replace* Materials.......1.38        Labor...........1.84 | sf | — | $3.22 | $3.22 |
| **PAINT ►** Paint pool with rubber base paint<br>*Replace* Materials........ .67        Labor...........1.30 | sf | — | $1.97 | $1.97 |
| Paint pool with epoxy paint<br>*Replace* Materials........ .74        Labor...........1.69 | sf | — | $2.43 | $2.43 |
| **VINYL LINER ►** Replace vinyl liner<br>*Replace* Materials.......2.25        Labor...........1.06<br>*Remove* .....................        Labor........... .24 | sf | $.24 | $3.31 | $3.55 |
| **TILE BORDER ►** Tile border, 6" x 6"<br>*Replace* Materials.......6.84        Labor...........11.20<br>*Remove* .....................        Labor...........1.62 | lf | $1.62 | $18.04 | $19.66 |
| Tile border, 12" x 12"<br>*Replace* Materials.......8.90        Labor...........15.30<br>*Remove* .....................        Labor...........1.62 | lf | $1.62 | $24.20 | $25.82 |
| Remove tiles for work, then reinstall<br>*Replace* Materials........ .74        Labor.........30.50 | lf | — | $31.24 | $31.24 |
| **ACID WASH ►** Acid wash swimming pool plaster<br>*Replace* Materials........ .12        Labor........... .19 | sf | — | $.31 | $.31 |
| Minimum charge to acid wash swimming pool<br>*Replace* Materials.......17.40        Labor.........193.00 | ea | — | $210.40 | $210.40 |
| **DRAIN ►** Drain pool<br>*Replace* .....................        Labor.........203.00 | ea | — | $203.00 | $203.00 |
| Drain and clean pool<br>*Replace* Materials......15.00        Labor.........454.00 | ea | — | $469.00 | $469.00 |
| **SHOCK TREATMENT ►** Swimming pool chemical shock treatment<br>*Replace* Materials......30.00        Labor.........60.40 | ea | — | $90.40 | $90.40 |
| **OPEN POOL ►** Open swimming pool for the summer (cold climates)<br>*Replace* Materials......45.00        Labor.........157.00 | ea | — | $202.00 | $202.00 |
| **CLOSE POOL ►** Close swimming pool for the winter (cold climates)<br>*Replace* Materials......60.00        Labor.........242.00 | ea | — | $302.00 | $302.00 |
| **CAULK ►** Caulk expansion joint<br>*Replace* Materials.......2.00        Labor...........1.40 | lf | — | $3.40 | $3.40 |

# 38 ............................................... *Temporary*

| Item Description | | Unit | | | Total | |
|---|---|---|---|---|---|---|
| **Cover opening with single sheet of plywood**<br>Materials.................18.00   Labor.........28.20 | | ea | — | — | $46.20 | ◄ EMERGENCY BOARD UP<br>*Prices are for work done between 7:00 a.m. and 6:00 p.m. Monday through Friday. Add **25%** for emergency work between 6:00 p.m. and 10:00 p.m. Monday through Friday. Add **65%** for emergency work between 10:00 p.m. and 7:00 a.m. Monday through Friday, on weekends, or on holidays.* |
| **Cover opening with two sheets of plywood**<br>Materials...................36.00   Labor.........35.90 | | ea | — | — | $71.90 | |
| **Install temporary framing and cover opening**<br>Materials.......................80   Labor...........87 | | sf | — | — | $1.67 | |
| **Cover roof or wall with tarp**<br>Materials.......................54   Labor...........36 | | sf | — | — | $.90 | |
| **Cover roof or wall with plastic**<br>Materials.......................27   Labor...........36 | | sf | — | — | $.63 | |
| **Minimum charge for emergency board up**<br>Materials.................100.00   Labor.........79.00 | | ea | — | — | $179.00 | ◁ minimum |
| **Temporary electrical hookup**<br>Materials.................97.00   Labor.........54.90 | | ea | — | — | $151.90 | ◄ TEMPORARY POWER |
| **Temporary electrical, per week**<br>Materials...................84.00 | | wk | — | — | $84.00 | |
| **Temporary heating, per week**<br>Materials...................165.00 | | wk | — | — | $165.00 | ◄ TEMPORARY HEATING |
| **Scaffolding**<br>.............................. | Equipment...........18 | sf | — | — | $.18 | ◄ SCAFFOLDING<br>*Per week. Per sf of wall that scaffolding covers. 60" wide scaffolding attached with scissor braces.* |
| **Add for hook-end cat walk**<br>.............................. | Equipment...........95 | ea | — | — | $.95 | |
| **Add for tented scaffolding**<br>..............................   Labor...........20 | Equipment...........23 | sf | — | — | $.43 | ◁ tented scaffolding |
| **Scaffolding delivery, setup, and take down**<br>..............................   Labor...........20 | | sf | — | — | $.20 | ◁ setup and take down |
| **Minimum charge for scaffolding**<br>..............................   Labor.........39.50 | Equipment.........40.00 | ea | — | — | $79.50 | ◁ minimum |
| **Temporary 5' tall chain-link fence**<br>..............................   Labor...........4.66 | Equipment.........2.40 | lf | — | — | $7.06 | ◄ TEMPORARY CHAIN-LINK FENCE<br>*Per job. Up to 12 months.* |
| **Temporary 6' tall chain-link fence**<br>..............................   Labor...........4.86 | Equipment.........2.60 | lf | — | — | $7.46 | |
| **Minimum charge for chain-link fence**<br>..............................   Labor.........79.00 | Equipment.........130.00 | ea | — | — | $209.00 | ◁ minimum |
| **Security guard**<br>..............................   Labor.........13.50 | | hr | — | — | $13.50 | ◄ SECURITY GUARD<br>*Per hour.* |

| | Item Description | Unit | | | Total |
|---|---|---|---|---|---|
| **SECURITY GUARD** ▶<br>*continued* | Security guard with dog<br>.................................................... Labor............18.70 | hr | — | — | $18.70 |
| *minimum* ▷ | Minimum charge for security guard<br>.................................................... Labor.........270.00 | ea | — | — | $270.00 |
| **OFFICE TRAILER** ▶<br>*Per week.* | 8' x 32' office trailer<br>.................................................... Equipment...........48.00 | ea | — | — | $48.00 |
| **STORAGE TRAILER** ▶<br>*Per week.* | Storage trailer<br>.................................................... Equipment...........28.00 | ea | — | — | $28.00 |
| **PORTABLE TOILET** ▶<br>*Chemical. Per week.* | Portable toilet<br>.................................................... Equipment ...........24.00 | ea | — | — | $24.00 |
| **BARRICADES** ▶<br>*Per week.* | Folding reflective barricades<br>.................................................... Equipment.............4.00 | ea | — | — | $4.00 |
| | Folding reflective barricade with flashing light<br>.................................................... Equipment...........4.90 | ea | — | — | $4.90 |
| **TRAFFIC CONE** ▶<br>*Per week.* | 28" traffic cone<br>.................................................... Equipment ............ .40 | ea | — | — | $.40 |
| **SAFETY FENCE** ▶ | 4' tall orange plastic safety fence<br>Materials.......................41       Labor.............16 | lf | — | — | $.57 |
| | 5' tall orange plastic safety fence<br>Materials.......................62       Labor.............16 | lf | — | — | $.78 |
| **SAFETY TAPE** ▶ | Plastic "do not cross" barricade tape<br>Materials.......................03       Labor.............08 | lf | — | — | $.11 |

# TIME & MATERIAL CHARTS *(selected items)*

## Temporary Items Labor

| LABORER | BASE WAGE | PAID LEAVE | TRUE WAGE | FICA | FUTA | WORKER'S COMP. | UNEMPLOY. INSUR. | HEALTH INSUR. | RETIRE (401k) | LIABILITY INSUR. | COST PER HOUR |
|---|---|---|---|---|---|---|---|---|---|---|---|
| Carpenter | $21.50 | 1.76 | $24.36 | 1.86 | .19 | 4.56 | 2.12 | 2.54 | .73 | 3.17 | $39.50 |

**Paid Leave** is calculated based on two weeks paid vacation, one week sick leave, and seven paid holidays. Employer's matching portion of **FICA** is 7.65 percent. **FUTA** (Federal Unemployment) is .8 percent. **Worker's compensation** for carpentry work in the temporary trade was calculated using a national average of 18.71 percent. **Unemployment insurance** was calculated using a national average of 8.7 percent. **Health insurance** was calculated based on a projected national average for 2001 of $505 per employee (and family when applicable) per month. Employer pays 80 percent for a per month cost of $404 per employee. **Retirement** is based on a 401(k) retirement program with employer matching of 50 percent. Employee contributions to the 401(k) plan are an average of 6 percent of the true wage. **Liability insurance** is based on a national average of 12.9 percent.

## Temporary Items Labor Productivity

| WORK DESCRIPTION | LABORER | COST PER HOUR | PRODUCTIVITY | UNIT PRICE |
|---|---|---|---|---|
| **Temporary board up / fencing** | | | | |
| cover opening with single sheet of plywood | carpenter | $39.50 | .714 | $28.20 *ea* |
| over opening with two sheets of plywood | carpenter | $39.50 | .909 | $35.90 *ea* |
| install temporary framing and cover opening | carpenter | $39.50 | .022 | $.87 *sf* |
| cover roof or wall with tarp | carpenter | $39.50 | .009 | $.36 *sf* |
| cover roof or wall with plastic | carpenter | $39.50 | .009 | $.36 *sf* |
| install temporary 5' tall chain link fence | carpenter | $39.50 | .118 | $4.66 *lf* |
| install temporary 6' tall chain link fence | carpenter | $39.50 | .123 | $4.86 *lf* |

# 39 .................................................. *Tile*

*with cultured marble*

| Item Description | Unit | Remove | Replace | Total | |
|---|---|---|---|---|---|
| **Minimum charge for tile work** | ea | — | $122.10 | $122.10 | ◄ **MINIMUM** |
| *Replace* Materials......40.00        Labor .........82.10 | | | | | |
| **6′ tall tile bathtub surround, adhesive set on moisture-resistant drywall** | ea | $74.90 | $455.00 | $529.90 | ◄ **TILE TUB SURROUND** |
| *Replace* Materials ....260.00        Labor .........195.00 | | | | | *Both sides and one length of tub including trim tile and one tile soap dish.* |
| *Remove* ......................        Labor...........74.90 | | | | | |
| **6′ tall tile bathtub surround, adhesive set on tile backer board** | ea | $74.90 | $485.00 | $559.90 | ◁ **6′** |
| *Replace* Materials....290.00        Labor .........195.00 | | | | | |
| *Remove* ......................        Labor...........74.90 | | | | | |
| **6′ tall tile bathtub surround, mortar set** | ea | $93.50 | $595.00 | $688.50 | |
| *Replace* Materials.....310.00        Labor..........285.00 | | | | | |
| *Remove* ......................        Labor..........93.50 | | | | | |
| **7′ tall tile bathtub surround, adhesive set on moisture-resistant drywall** | ea | $77.00 | $536.00 | $613.00 | ◁ **7′** |
| *Replace* Materials....305.00        Labor..........231.00 | | | | | |
| *Remove* ......................        Labor ..........77.00 | | | | | |
| **7′ tall tile bathtub surround, adhesive set on tile backer board** | ea | $77.00 | $571.00 | $648.00 | |
| *Replace* Materials....340.00        Labor..........231.00 | | | | | |
| *Remove* ......................        Labor ..........77.00 | | | | | |
| **7′ tall tile bathtub surround, mortar set** | ea | $96.90 | $668.00 | $764.90 | |
| *Replace* Materials....360.00        Labor .........308.00 | | | | | |
| *Remove* ......................        Labor...........96.90 | | | | | |
| **8′ tall tile bathtub surround, adhesive set on moisture-resistant drywall** | ea | $79.40 | $609.00 | $688.40 | ◁ **8′** |
| *Replace* Materials ....345.00        Labor..........264.00 | | | | | |
| *Remove* ......................        Labor...........79.40 | | | | | |
| **8′ tall tile bathtub surround, adhesive set on tile backer board** | ea | $79.40 | $649.00 | $728.40 | |
| *Replace* Materials ....385.00        Labor..........264.00 | | | | | |
| *Remove* ......................        Labor...........79.40 | | | | | |
| **8′ tall tile bathtub surround, mortar set** | ea | $101.00 | $746.00 | $847.00 | |
| *Replace* Materials.....410.00        Labor .........336.00 | | | | | |
| *Remove* ......................        Labor..........101.00 | | | | | |
| **36″ x 36″ tile shower, adhesive set on tile backer board** | ea | $87.20 | $715.00 | $802.20 | ◄ **TILE SHOWER** |
| *Replace* Materials....430.00        Labor..........285.00 | | | | | *Includes walls, floor, all trim pieces, and one tile soap dish. Does not include shower pan, fixtures, door or any plumbing.* |
| *Remove* ......................        Labor...........87.20 | | | | | |
| **36″ x 36″ tile shower, mortar set** | ea | $96.90 | $791.00 | $887.90 | |
| *Replace* Materials.....455.00        Labor .........336.00 | | | | | |
| *Remove* ......................        Labor...........96.90 | | | | | |
| **Add for tile ceiling on 36″ x 36″ tile shower** | ea | — | $102.20 | $102.20 | |
| *Replace* Materials......70.00        Labor .........32.20 | | | | | |
| **36″ x 48″ tile shower, adhesive set on tile backer board** | ea | $90.40 | $816.00 | $906.40 | |
| *Replace* Materials....480.00        Labor .........336.00 | | | | | |
| *Remove* ......................        Labor ..........90.40 | | | | | |

| Item Description | Unit | Remove | Replace | Total |
|---|---|---|---|---|
| **TILE SHOWER** ► *continued* — **36" x 48" tile shower, mortar set** <br> *Replace* Materials....505.00 Labor.........370.00 <br> *Remove* ..................... Labor .........90.40 | ea | $90.40 | $875.00 | $965.40 |
| **Add for tile ceiling on 36" x 48" tile shower** <br> *Replace* Materials......80.00 Labor...........42.20 | ea | — | $122.20 | $122.20 |
| **TILE ACCESSORY** ► *Add to above prices for each additional accessory.* — **Add for tile soap holder or other accessory** <br> *Replace* Materials......29.00 Labor...........15.40 | ea | — | $44.40 | $44.40 |
| **CULTURED MARBLE** ► **TUB SURROUND** *Three-pieces, one length and two widths of tub.* — **Cultured marble tub surround** <br> *Replace* Materials....320.00 Labor.........142.00 <br> *Remove* ..................... Labor .........33.50 | ea | $33.50 | $462.00 | $495.50 |
| **TILE WINDOW SILL** ► **Tile window sill 4" thick wall** <br> *Replace* Materials........5.26 Labor............2.33 <br> *Remove* ..................... Labor ...........1.55 | lf | $1.55 | $7.59 | $9.14 |
| **Tile window sill 6" thick wall** <br> *Replace* Materials........5.64 Labor............2.33 <br> *Remove* ..................... Labor ...........1.55 | lf | $1.55 | $7.97 | $9.52 |
| **Tile window sill 8" thick wall** <br> *Replace* Materials........6.14 Labor............2.41 <br> *Remove* ..................... Labor ...........1.55 | lf | $1.55 | $8.55 | $10.10 |
| **CULTURED MARBLE** ► **WINDOW SILL** — **Cultured marble window sill 4" thick wall** <br> *Replace* Materials........5.44 Labor............1.96 <br> *Remove* ..................... Labor ............ .47 | lf | $.47 | $7.40 | $7.87 |
| **Cultured marble window sill 6" thick wall** <br> *Replace* Materials........6.93 Labor............1.96 <br> *Remove* ..................... Labor ............ .47 | lf | $.47 | $8.89 | $9.36 |
| **Cultured marble window sill 8" thick wall** <br> *Replace* Materials........9.37 Labor............2.00 <br> *Remove* ..................... Labor ............ .47 | lf | $.47 | $11.37 | $11.84 |
| **REGROUT TILE** ► **Regrout tile** <br> *Replace* Materials ........ .25 Labor ............1.48 | sf | — | $1.73 | $1.73 |
| **REPLACE TILE** ► *With an original tile furnished by owner.* — **Replace single tile** <br> *Replace* ..................... Labor .........34.30 | ea | — | $34.30 | $34.30 |

# TIME & MATERIAL CHARTS *(selected items)*

### Tile Labor

| LABORER | BASE WAGE | PAID LEAVE | TRUE WAGE | FICA | FUTA | WORKER'S COMP. | UNEMPLOY. INSUR. | HEALTH INSUR. | RETIRE (401K) | LIABILITY INSUR. | COST PER HOUR |
|---|---|---|---|---|---|---|---|---|---|---|---|
| Tile layer | $21.20 | 1.65 | $22.85 | 1.75 | .18 | 3.98 | 1.99 | 2.54 | .69 | 2.97 | $37.00 |
| Demolition laborer | $13.40 | 1.05 | $14.45 | 1.11 | .12 | 4.44 | 1.26 | 2.54 | .43 | 1.88 | $26.20 |

**Paid Leave** is calculated based on two weeks paid vacation, one week sick leave, and seven paid holidays. Employer's matching portion of **FICA** is 7.65 percent. **FUTA** (Federal Unemployment) is .8 percent. **Worker's compensation** for the tile trade was calculated using a national average of 17.41 percent. **Unemployment insurance** was calculated using a national average of 8.7 percent. **Health insurance** was calculated based on a projected national average for 2001 of $505 per employee (and family when applicable) per month. Employer pays 80 percent for a per month cost of $404 per employee. **Retirement** is based on a 401(k) retirement program with employer matching of 50 percent. Employee contributions to the 401(k) plan are an average of 6 percent of the true wage. **Liability insurance** is based on a national average of 12.9 percent.

# 40 .......... *Wall Coverings*

| Item Description | Unit | Remove | Replace | Total | |
|---|---|---|---|---|---|
| **Remove wallpaper, strippable**<br>*Remove* ..................... Labor ............. .44 | sf | $.44 | — | $.44 | ◄ **STRIP WALLPAPER**<br>Add **25%** for two layers, **36%** for three layers and **42%** for four layers. |
| **Remove wallpaper, non-strippable**<br>*Remove* ..................... Labor ............. .70 | sf | $.70 | — | $.70 | |
| **Minimum charge for wall covering work**<br>*Replace* Material ....... 31.00 Labor ........ 33.50 | sf | — | $64.50 | $64.50 | ◄ **MINIMUM** |
| **Wallpaper underliner**<br>*Replace* Material .......... .49 Labor ............. .44<br>*Remove* ..................... Labor ............. .44 | sf | $.44 | $.93 | $1.37 | ◄ **UNDERLINER**<br>Blank stock used to cover flaws in walls or over paneling. |
| **Grass cloth wallpaper, standard grade**<br>*Replace* Material ....... 1.55 Labor ............ 1.14<br>*Remove* ..................... Labor ............. .44 | sf | $.44 | $2.69 | $3.13 | ◄ **GRASS CLOTH**<br>Includes wall sizing and 21% waste. Add **$.30** per sf to patch small holes, gouges, and cracks. |
| **Grass cloth wallpaper, high grade**<br>*Replace* Material ....... 2.49 Labor ............ 1.14<br>*Remove* ..................... Labor ............. .44 | sf | $.44 | $3.63 | $4.07 | |
| **Wallpaper, standard grade**<br>*Replace* Material .......... .82 Labor ............. .87<br>*Remove* ..................... Labor ............. .44 | sf | $.44 | $1.69 | $2.13 | ◄ **PAPER**<br>From flat to high gloss papers. Includes wall sizing and 21% waste. Add **$.30** per sf to patch small holes, gouges, and cracks. |
| **Wallpaper, high grade**<br>*Replace* Material ....... 1.13 Labor ............. .87<br>*Remove* ..................... Labor ............. .44 | sf | $.44 | $2.00 | $2.44 | |
| **Vinyl-coated wallpaper, standard grade**<br>*Replace* Material ....... 1.04 Labor ............. .94<br>*Remove* ..................... Labor ............. .44 | sf | $.44 | $1.98 | $2.42 | ◄ **VINYL-COATED**<br>Vinyl with paper back. Includes wall sizing and 21% waste. Add **$.30** per sf to patch small holes, gouges, and cracks. |
| **Vinyl-coated wallpaper, high grade**<br>*Replace* Material ....... 1.38 Labor ............. .94<br>*Remove* ..................... Labor ............. .44 | sf | $.44 | $2.32 | $2.76 | |
| **Vinyl wallpaper, standard grade**<br>*Replace* Material ....... 1.11 Labor ............. .94<br>*Remove* ..................... Labor ............. .44 | sf | $.44 | $2.05 | $2.49 | ◄ **VINYL**<br>Seams overlapped, then cut. Includes wall sizing and 21% waste. Add **$.30** per sf to patch small holes, gouges, and cracks. |
| **Vinyl wallpaper, high grade**<br>*Replace* Material ....... 1.46 Labor ............. .94<br>*Remove* ..................... Labor ............. .44 | sf | $.44 | $2.40 | $2.84 | |
| **Foil wallpaper, standard grade**<br>*Replace* Material ....... 1.34 Labor ............. .90<br>*Remove* ..................... Labor ............. .44 | sf | $.44 | $2.24 | $2.68 | ◄ **FOIL**<br>Includes wall sizing and 21% waste. Add **$.30** per sf to patch small holes, gouges, and cracks. |
| **Foil wallpaper, high grade**<br>*Replace* Material ....... 1.69 Labor ............. .90<br>*Remove* ..................... Labor ............. .44 | sf | $.44 | $2.59 | $3.03 | |
| **Wallpaper border, standard grade**<br>*Replace* Material ....... 1.48 Labor ............. .77<br>*Remove* ..................... Labor ............. .34 | lf | $.34 | $2.25 | $2.59 | ◄ **BORDER**<br>All styles. Includes 21% waste. |

| Item Description | Unit | Remove | Replace | Total |
|---|---|---|---|---|
| **BORDER ▶** *continued* Use remove price when removing border only. | **Wallpaper border, high grade** | lf | $.34 | $2.82 | $3.16 |
| | *Replace* Material .........2.05   Labor ............ .77 | | | | |
| | *Remove* .....................   Labor ............ .34 | | | | |
| **ANAGLYPTA ▶** Brand name for a highly embossed wall or ceiling covering made from material similar to linoleum. Must be painted. Higher grades contain cotton fibers for extra strength and durability. Includes 21% waste. | **Anaglypta embossed wall or ceiling covering, standard grade** | sf | $.60 | $2.70 | $3.30 |
| | *Replace* Material .........1.19   Labor ............1.51 | | | | |
| | *Remove* .....................   Labor ............ .60 | | | | |
| | **Anaglypta embossed wall or ceiling covering, high grade** | sf | $.60 | $3.21 | $3.81 |
| | *Replace* Material .........1.70   Labor ............1.51 | | | | |
| | *Remove* .....................   Labor ............ .60 | | | | |
| | **Anaglypta embossed wall or ceiling covering, deluxe grade** | sf | $.60 | $3.40 | $4.00 |
| | *Replace* Material .........1.89   Labor ............1.51 | | | | |
| | *Remove* .....................   Labor ............ .60 | | | | |
| **LINCRUSTA ▶** Brand name for a highly embossed wall or ceiling covering made from material similar to linoleum. Lincrusta is typically much heavier than Anaglypta. Must be painted. Includes 21% waste. | **Lincrusta embossed wall or ceiling covering, standard grade** | sf | $.87 | $5.32 | $6.19 |
| | *Replace* Material .........3.44   Labor ............1.88 | | | | |
| | *Remove* .....................   Labor ............ .87 | | | | |
| | **Lincrusta embossed wall or ceiling covering, high grade** | sf | $.87 | $6.51 | $7.38 |
| | *Replace* Material .........4.63   Labor ............1.88 | | | | |
| | *Remove* .....................   Labor ............ .87 | | | | |
| | **Lincrusta embossed wall or ceiling covering, deluxe grade** | sf | $.87 | $7.60 | $8.47 |
| | *Replace* Material .........5.72   Labor ............1.88 | | | | |
| | *Remove* .....................   Labor ............ .87 | | | | |
| **ANAGLYPTA ▶** **FRIEZE** See Anaglypta above. Friezes are 12" to 21" wide. Includes 13% waste. | **Anaglypta embossed frieze, standard grade** | lf | $.50 | $5.10 | $5.60 |
| | *Replace* Material .........3.66   Labor ............1.44 | | | | |
| | *Remove* .....................   Labor ............ .50 | | | | |
| | **Anaglypta embossed frieze, high grade** | lf | $.50 | $5.58 | $6.08 |
| | *Replace* Material .........4.14   Labor ............1.44 | | | | |
| | *Remove* .....................   Labor ............ .50 | | | | |
| **LINCRUSTA ▶** **FRIEZE** See Lincrusta above. Friezes are approximately 21" wide. Includes 13% waste. | **Lincrusta embossed frieze, standard grade** | lf | $.70 | $6.05 | $6.75 |
| | *Replace* Material .........4.27   Labor ............1.78 | | | | |
| | *Remove* .....................   Labor ............ .70 | | | | |
| | **Lincrusta embossed frieze, high grade** | lf | $.70 | $7.08 | $7.78 |
| | *Replace* Material .........5.30   Labor ............1.78 | | | | |
| | *Remove* .....................   Labor ............ .70 | | | | |
| **ANAGLYPTA ▶** **PELMET** See Anaglypta above. Pelmets are narrower and often less ornate than friezes. Pelmets are from 4" to 7" wide. Includes 13% waste. | **Anaglypta embossed pelmet, standard grade** | lf | $.50 | $3.63 | $4.13 |
| | *Replace* Material .........2.29   Labor ............1.34 | | | | |
| | *Remove* .....................   Labor ............ .50 | | | | |
| | **Anaglypta embossed pelmet, high grade** | lf | $.50 | $4.60 | $5.10 |
| | *Replace* Material .........3.26   Labor ............1.34 | | | | |
| | *Remove* .....................   Labor ............ .50 | | | | |
| **ANAGLYPTA DADO ▶** See Anaglypta above. Dados are heavy, highly embossed wall panels installed as a wainscot. Includes 13% waste. | **Anaglypta embossed dado, standard grade** | lf | $3.38 | $21.32 | $24.70 |
| | *Replace* Material .........17.60   Labor ............3.72 | | | | |
| | *Remove* .....................   Labor ............3.38 | | | | |
| | ▶ Typical panels are about 22" wide and 36" tall. Five panels per box. | | | | |
| | **Anaglypta embossed dado, high grade** | lf | $3.38 | $25.52 | $28.90 |
| | *Replace* Material .........21.80   Labor ............3.72 | | | | |
| | *Remove* .....................   Labor ............3.38 | | | | |
| | ▶ Typical panels are about 24" wide and 40" tall. Five panels per box. | | | | |

# TIME & MATERIAL CHARTS (selected items)

## Wall Coverings Materials

Wallpaper materials were calculated based on double European size rolls with approximately 28 sf per single roll and 56 sf in a double roll. (Most manufacturers no longer make American size rolls which contained approximately 36 sf per single roll and 72 sf in a double roll.) Prices include sizing and glue application, even on pre-pasted rolls.

| DESCRIPTION | PRICE | | GROSS COVERAGE | WASTE | NET COVERAGE | UNIT PRICE | |
|---|---|---|---|---|---|---|---|
| **Minimum** | | | | | | | |
| for wall covering work | $31.00 | ea | 1 | 0% | 1 | $31.00 | ea |
| **Wallpaper underliner** | | | | | | | |
| blank stock | $21.80 | double roll | 56 | 21% | 44.24 | $.49 | sf |
| **Grass cloth wallpaper** | | | | | | | |
| standard grade | $68.40 | double roll | 56 | 21% | 44.24 | $1.55 | sf |
| high grade | $110.00 | double roll | 56 | 21% | 44.24 | $2.49 | sf |
| **Paper wallpaper** | | | | | | | |
| standard grade | $36.20 | double roll | 56 | 21% | 44.24 | $.82 | sf |
| high grade | $49.90 | double roll | 56 | 21% | 44.24 | $1.13 | sf |
| **Vinyl-coated wallpaper** | | | | | | | |
| standard grade | $46.20 | double roll | 56 | 21% | 44.24 | $1.04 | sf |
| high grade | $61.20 | double roll | 56 | 21% | 44.24 | $1.38 | sf |
| **Vinyl wallpaper** | | | | | | | |
| standard grade | $48.90 | double roll | 56 | 21% | 44.24 | $1.11 | sf |
| high grade | $64.40 | double roll | 56 | 21% | 44.24 | $1.46 | sf |
| **Foil wallpaper** | | | | | | | |
| standard grade | $59.40 | double roll | 56 | 21% | 44.24 | $1.34 | sf |
| high grade | $74.90 | double roll | 56 | 21% | 44.24 | $1.69 | sf |
| **Wallpaper border** | | | | | | | |
| standard grade | $35.00 | bolt | 30 | 21% | 23.70 | $1.48 | lf |
| high grade | $48.70 | bolt | 30 | 21% | 23.70 | $2.05 | lf |
| **Anaglypta embossed wall or ceiling covering** | | | | | | | |
| standard grade | $52.50 | double roll | 56 | 21% | 44.24 | $1.19 | sf |
| high grade | $75.30 | double roll | 56 | 21% | 44.24 | $1.70 | sf |
| deluxe grade | $83.50 | double roll | 56 | 21% | 44.24 | $1.89 | sf |
| **Lincrusta embossed wall or ceiling covering** | | | | | | | |
| standard grade | $152.00 | double roll | 56 | 21% | 44.24 | $3.44 | sf |
| high grade | $205.00 | double roll | 56 | 21% | 44.24 | $4.63 | sf |
| deluxe grade | $253.00 | double roll | 56 | 21% | 44.24 | $5.72 | sf |
| **Anaglypta embossed frieze** | | | | | | | |
| standard grade | $105.00 | bolt | 33 | 13% | 28.71 | $3.66 | lf |
| high grade | $119.00 | bolt | 33 | 13% | 28.71 | $4.14 | lf |
| **Lincrusta embossed frieze** | | | | | | | |
| standard grade | $124.00 | bolt | 33 | 12% | 29.04 | $4.27 | lf |
| high grade | $154.00 | bolt | 33 | 12% | 29.04 | $5.30 | lf |
| **Anaglypta embossed pelmet** | | | | | | | |
| standard grade | $65.80 | bolt | 33 | 13% | 28.71 | $2.29 | lf |
| high grade | $93.60 | bolt | 33 | 13% | 28.71 | $3.26 | lf |
| **Anaglypta embossed dado** (five panels per box) | | | | | | | |
| standard grade | $253.00 | box | 16 | 10% | 14.40 | $17.60 | lf |
| high grade | $314.00 | box | 16 | 10% | 14.40 | $21.80 | lf |

## Wall Coverings Labor

| LABORER | BASE WAGE | PAID LEAVE | TRUE WAGE | FICA | FUTA | WORKER'S COMP. | UNEMPLOY. INSUR. | HEALTH INSUR. | RETIRE (401K) | LIABILITY INSUR. | COST PER HOUR |
|---|---|---|---|---|---|---|---|---|---|---|---|
| Wallpaper hanger | $18.60 | 1.45 | $20.05 | 1.53 | .16 | 4.25 | 1.74 | 2.54 | .60 | 2.61 | $33.50 |

**Paid Leave** is calculated based on two weeks paid vacation, one week sick leave, and seven paid holidays. Employer's matching portion of **FICA** is 7.65 percent. **FUTA** (Federal Unemployment) is .8 percent. **Worker's compensation** for the wall coverings trade was calculated using a national average of 21.20 percent. **Unemployment insurance** was calculated using a national average of 8.7 percent. **Health insurance** was calculated based on a projected national average for 2001 of $505 per employee (and family when applicable) per month. Employer pays 80 percent for a per month cost of $404 per employee. **Retirement** is based on a 401(k) retirement program with employer matching of 50 percent. Employee contributions to the 401(k) plan are an average of 6 percent of the true wage. **Liability insurance** is based on a national average of 12.9 percent.

## Wall Coverings Labor Productivity

| WORK DESCRIPTION | LABORER | COST PER HOUR | PRODUCTIVITY | UNIT PRICE |
|---|---|---|---|---|
| **Remove wallpaper** | | | | |
| strippable | wallpaper hanger | $33.50 | .013 | $.44 sf |
| non-strippable | wallpaper hanger | $33.50 | .021 | $.70 sf |
| **Minimum** | | | | |
| for wall covering work | wallpaper hanger | $33.50 | 1.00 | $33.50 ea |
| **Install wallpaper** | | | | |
| underliner | wallpaper hanger | $33.50 | .013 | $.44 sf |
| grass cloth wallpaper | wallpaper hanger | $33.50 | .034 | $1.14 sf |
| paper wallpaper | wallpaper hanger | $33.50 | .026 | $.87 sf |
| vinyl-coated | wallpaper hanger | $33.50 | .028 | $.94 sf |
| vinyl | wallpaper hanger | $33.50 | .028 | $.94 sf |
| foil | wallpaper hanger | $33.50 | .027 | $.90 sf |
| **Install border** | | | | |
| all styles | wallpaper hanger | $33.50 | .023 | $.77 lf |
| **Install Anaglypta embossed wall or ceiling covering** | | | | |
| wall or ceiling | wallpaper hanger | $33.50 | .045 | $1.51 sf |
| **Install Lincrusta embossed wall or ceiling covering** | | | | |
| wall or ceiling | wallpaper hanger | $33.50 | .056 | $1.88 sf |
| **Install embossed frieze** | | | | |
| Anaglypta | wallpaper hanger | $33.50 | .043 | $1.44 lf |
| Lincrusta | wallpaper hanger | $33.50 | .053 | $1.78 lf |
| **Install Anaglypta embossed pelmet** | | | | |
| all grades | wallpaper hanger | $33.50 | .040 | $1.34 lf |
| **Install Anaglypta embossed dado** | | | | |
| all grades | wallpaper hanger | $33.50 | .111 | $3.72 lf |

NOTES:

end

# 41      *Water Extraction*

| Item Description | Unit | | | Total | |
|---|---|---|---|---|---|
| **Minimum charge for water extraction work** | ea | — | — | $140.70 | ◄ **MINIMUM** |
| *Replace* .......... Labor ........50.70   Equipment ........90.00 | | | | | |
| **Equipment delivery, setup, and take-home charge** | ea | — | — | $25.00 | ◄ **SETUP AND TAKE-HOME CHARGES** |
| *Replace* .......... .......... Equipment ........25.00 | | | | | |
| ► Per loss charge to deliver water extraction equipment, set the equipment up, and take the equipment home once the water is extracted and drying is complete. | | | | | |
| **Extract water from lightly soaked carpet** | sf | — | — | $.23 | ◄ **EXTRACT WATER** |
| *Replace* .......... Labor ........ .17   Equipment ........ .06 | | | | | |
| ► Carpet and pad are wet but water does not rise around feet as carpet is stepped on. | | | | | |
| **Extract water from typically wet carpet** | sf | — | — | $.31 | |
| *Replace* .......... Labor ........ .24   Equipment ........ .07 | | | | | |
| ► Water in carpet and pad rises around feet as carpet is stepped on. | | | | | |
| **Extract water from heavily soaked carpet** | sf | — | — | $.41 | |
| *Replace* .......... Labor ........ .34   Equipment ........ .07 | | | | | |
| ► Water is visible over the surface of the carpet mat. | | | | | |
| **Extract water from very heavily soaked carpet** | sf | — | — | $.57 | |
| *Replace* .......... Labor ........ .47   Equipment ........ .10 | | | | | |
| ► Standing water over the surface of the carpet. | | | | | |
| **Treat carpet with germicide** | sf | — | — | $.12 | ◄ **GERMICIDE AND MILDEWCIDE TREATMENT** *Treatments to kill germs and mildew in wet carpet.* |
| *Replace* Material ........ .02   Labor ........ .10 | | | | | |
| **Treat carpet with mildewcide** | sf | — | — | $.12 | |
| *Replace* Material ........ .02   Labor ........ .10 | | | | | |
| **Detach carpet, lift, and block for drying** | sf | — | — | $.14 | ◄ **DETACH, LIFT & BLOCK CARPET FOR DRYING** |
| *Replace* .......... Labor ........ .14 | | | | | |
| **Remove wet carpet** | sy | — | — | $2.70 | ◄ **REMOVE WET CARPET AND PAD** *See Flooring chapter, pages 257-258 for prices to tear-out dry carpet and pad.* |
| *Remove* .......... Labor ........2.70 | | | | | |
| **Remove wet carpet pad** | sf | — | — | $.17 | |
| *Remove* .......... Labor ........ .17 | | | | | |
| **Dehumidifier unit, 10 gallon daily capacity** | day | — | — | $38.90 | ◄ **DEHUMIDIFIERS** *Does not include delivery, setup and take-home (see above). Does include daily monitoring and adjustment.* |
| *Replace* .......... Labor ........13.90   Equipment ........25.00 | | | | | |
| **Dehumidifier unit, 19 gallon daily capacity** | day | — | — | $58.90 | |
| *Replace* .......... Labor ........13.90   Equipment ........45.00 | | | | | |
| **Dehumidifier unit, 24 gallon daily capacity** | day | — | — | $78.90 | |
| *Replace* .......... Labor ........13.90   Equipment ........65.00 | | | | | |
| **Drying fan** | day | — | — | $28.52 | ◄ **DRYING FAN** *Does not include delivery, setup and take-home (see above). Does include daily monitoring and adjustment.* |
| *Replace* .......... Labor ........3.52   Equipment ........25.00 | | | | | |

**EMERGENCY SERVUCE**

All prices are for work done between 7:00 a.m. and 6:00 p.m. Monday through Friday.

Add **25%** for emergency work between 6:00 p.m. and 10:00 p.m. Monday through Friday.

Add **65%** for emergency work between 10:00 p.m. and 7:00 a.m. Monday through Friday, on weekends, or on holidays.

| Item Description | | Unit | | | Total |
|---|---|---|---|---|---|
| **Hang and dry carpet in plant** | | sf | — | — | **$.25** |
| *Replace* ..................... Labor............ .17 | Equipment ............ .08 | | | | |
| **Hang and dry oriental rug in plant** | | sf | — | — | **$.39** |
| *Replace* ..................... Labor............ .27 | Equipment ............ .12 | | | | |
| **Minimum charge to hang and dry carpet in plant** | | sf | — | — | **$108.60** |
| *Replace* ..................... Labor ..........68.60 | Equipment..........40.00 | | | | |
| **Pad and block furniture, small room** | | ea | — | — | **$13.50** |
| *Replace* ..................... Labor...........13.50 | | | | | |
| **Pad and block furniture, average room** | | ea | — | — | **$18.90** |
| *Replace* ..................... Labor...........18.90 | | | | | |
| **Pad and block furniture, large room** | | ea | — | — | **$24.30** |
| *Replace* ..................... Labor...........24.30 | | | | | |
| **Pad and block furniture, very large room** | | ea | — | — | **$33.70** |
| *Replace* ..................... Labor ..........33.70 | | | | | |

**HANG & DRY CARPET IN PLANT** ▶ *Square foot price to haul carpet to plant, hang, and dry. Includes transport to and from plant. Does not include carpet removal (see page 257-258) or reinstallation (see page 257).*

**PAD AND BLOCK FURNITURE** ▶

# TIME & MATERIAL CHARTS (selected items)

## Water Extraction Materials

See **Water Extraction** material prices with the line items and other information in the **QuickFinder** column.

## Water Extraction Rental Equipment

| DESCRIPTION | UNIT PRICE |
|---|---|
| **Dehumidifier** | |
| 10 gallon capacity................................................................ | **$25.00** per day |
| 19 gallon capacity................................................................ | **$45.00** per day |
| 24 gallon capacity................................................................ | **$65.00** per day |
| **Drying fan** | |
| typical.................................................................................... | **$25.00** per day |

## Water Extraction Labor

| LABORER | BASE WAGE | PAID LEAVE | TRUE WAGE | FICA | FUTA | WORKER'S COMP. | UNEMPLOY. INSUR. | HEALTH INSUR. | RETIRE (401K) | LIABILITY INSUR. | COST PER HOUR |
|---|---|---|---|---|---|---|---|---|---|---|---|
| Water extractor | $19.40 | 1.51 | $20.91 | 1.60 | .17 | 3.41 | 1.82 | 2.54 | .63 | 2.72 | $33.80 |

**Paid Leave** is calculated based on two weeks paid vacation, one week sick leave, and seven paid holidays. Employer's matching portion of **FICA** is 7.65 percent. **FUTA** (Federal Unemployment) is .8 percent. **Worker's compensation** for the water extraction trade was calculated using a national average of 16.33 percent. **Unemployment insurance** was calculated using a national average of 8.7 percent. **Health insurance** was calculated based on a projected national average for 2001 of $505 per employee (and family when applicable) per month. Employer pays 80 percent for a per month cost of $404 per employee. **Retirement** is based on a 401(k) retirement program with employer matching of 50 percent. Employee contributions to the 401(k) plan are an average of 6 percent of the true wage. **Liability insurance** is based on a national average of 12.9 percent.

## Water Extraction Labor Productivity

| WORK DESCRIPTION | LABORER | COST PER HOUR | PRODUCTIVITY | UNIT PRICE |
|---|---|---|---|---|
| **Extract water** | | | | |
| from lightly soaked carpet | water extractor | $33.80 | .005 | $.17 sf |
| from very heavily soaked carpet | water extractor | $33.80 | .014 | $.47 sf |
| **Pad and block furniture** | | | | |
| small room | water extractor | $33.80 | .400 | $13.50 ea |
| very large room | water extractor | $33.80 | 1.00 | $33.70 ea |

# 42 Windows

| Item Description | Unit | small | average | large | very large | |
|---|---|---|---|---|---|---|
| **Remove window** | ea | $11.70 | $12.00 | $12.30 | $12.60 | ◀ DEMOLITION |
| *Materials* Small .........1.30  Average .......1.30  Large .......1.30  Very Large .......1.30 | | | | | | |
| *Labor* Small ...............10.40  Average ......10.70  Large ......11.00  Very Large ......11.30 | | | | | | |
| **Remove window for work then reinstall** | ea | $49.90 | $69.20 | $100.10 | $147.30 | ◀ REMOVE & REINSTALL |
| *Materials* Small .........1.30  Average ......1.30  Large .......1.30  Very Large .....1.30 | | | | | | |
| *Labor* Small ...............48.60  Average .....67.90  Large......98.80  Very Large ....146.00 | | | | | | |

| Item Description | Unit | all types | | | | |
|---|---|---|---|---|---|---|
| **Deduct for single-glazed window (all types)** | sf | – $4.10 | | | | ◀ OTHER OPTIONS |
| *Materials* All types ..- -4.10 | | | | | | |
| **Add for gray or bronze tinted glass (all window types)** | sf | $2.70 | | | | |
| *Materials* All types ......2.70 | | | | | | |
| **Add 8% for Low-E between panes (all window types)** | | | | | | |
| **Add 5% for argon fill between panes (all window types)** | | | | | | |
| **Add 11% for thermal break (aluminum windows only)** | | | | | | |

All windows in this chapter are double-glazed (insulated) units with clear glass. Use for all window types except skylights and roof windows. For information on Low-E and argon see page 501.

**RELATED ITEMS**

**Doors**
sliding patio ...................119

| Item Description | Unit | tempered | laminated | obscure | polished wire | |
|---|---|---|---|---|---|---|
| **Add for alternative glazing (all window types)** | sf | $7.20 | $4.70 | $.93 | $22.10 | ◁ other glass types |
| *Materials* Tempered .....7.20  Laminated .......4.70  Obscure ......... .93  Polished wire....22.10 | | | | | | |

| Item Description | Unit | 24" x 12" | 36" x 18" | 48" x 24" | 72" x 36" | |
|---|---|---|---|---|---|---|
| **Half-round aluminum window top** | ea | $207.10 | $248.10 | $302.90 | $446.00 | ◀ ALUMINUM  ◁ half-round |
| *Materials* 24" x 12"...168.00  36" x 18" ...209.00  48" x 24"...248.00  72" x 36" ....367.00 | | | | | | |
| *Labor* 24" x 12" ...........39.10  36" x 18" ...39.10  48" x 24" ...54.90  72" x 36" ......79.00 | | | | | | |

| Item Description | Unit | 36" x 15" | 48" x 16" | 60" x 19" | 90" x 20" | |
|---|---|---|---|---|---|---|
| **Half-elliptical aluminum window top** | ea | $359.10 | $394.10 | $443.90 | $645.00 | ◁ half-elliptical |
| *Materials* 36" x 15"..320.00  48" x 16" ...355.00  60" x 19" ...389.00  90" x 20" ...566.00 | | | | | | |
| *Labor* 36" x 15" ...........39.10  48" x 16" ...39.10  60" x 19" ...54.90  90" x 20" ......79.00 | | | | | | |

| Item Description | Unit | 20" x 20" | 30" x 30" | 40" x 40" | 48" x 48" | |
|---|---|---|---|---|---|---|
| **Round aluminum window** | ea | $378.10 | $452.10 | $531.90 | $604.00 | ◁ round |
| *Materials* 20" x 20" .339.00  30" x 30"...413.00  40" x 40"...477.00  48" x 48"...525.00 | | | | | | |
| *Labor* 20" x 20" ...........39.10  30" x 30" ...39.10  40" x 40" ...54.90  48" x 48" ......79.00 | | | | | | |

| Item Description | Unit | 15" x 24" | 24" x 36" | 25" x 40" | 30" x 48" | |
|---|---|---|---|---|---|---|
| **Elliptical aluminum window** | ea | $678.10 | $742.10 | $804.90 | $886.00 | ◁ elliptical |
| *Materials* 15" X 24 ...639.00  24" x 36"...703.00  25" x 40"...750.00  30" x 48"...807.00 | | | | | | |
| *Labor* 15" X 24" ...........39.10  24" x 36" ...39.10  25" x 40" ...54.90  30" x 48" ......79.00 | | | | | | |

| Item Description | Unit | 24" x 24" | 36" x 36" | | | |
|---|---|---|---|---|---|---|
| **Quarter round aluminum window** | ea | $314.10 | $434.10 | — | — | ◁ quarter-round |
| *Materials* 24" x 24" ..275.00  36" x 36" ...395.00 | | | | | | |
| *Labor* 24" x 24" ...........39.10  36" x 36" ...39.10 | | | | | | |

**ALUMINUM ▶**
*continued*
**casement ▷**

| Item Description | Unit | 36" tall | 48" tall | 60" tall |
|---|---|---|---|---|
| **18" wide aluminum casement window**<br>*Materials* 36" tall...320.00  48" tall...346.00  60" tall...398.00<br>*Labor* 36" tall.........39.10  48" tall.....39.10  60" tall......39.10 | ea | $359.10 | $385.10 | $437.10 |
| **24" wide aluminum casement window**<br>*Materials* 36" tall...345.00  48" tall...373.00  60" tall...422.00<br>*Labor* 36" tall.........39.10  48" tall.....39.10  60" tall......54.90 | ea | $384.10 | $412.10 | $476.90 |
| **30" wide aluminum casement window**<br>*Materials*....................  48" tall...404.00  60" tall...452.00<br>*Labor*.....................  48" tall.....54.90  60" tall......54.90 | ea | — | $458.90 | $506.90 |
| **36" wide aluminum casement window**<br>*Materials*....................  48" tall...480.00  60" tall...551.00<br>*Labor*.....................  48" tall.....54.90  60" tall......54.90 | ea | — | $534.90 | $605.90 |

**awning ▷**

### ALUMINUM

All aluminum windows are double-glazed, clear glass with white or bronze finish frames.

For mill-finish windows deduct **13%**.

All costs are for standard windows. Manufacturers' window sizes vary. For standard units round measurements to the nearest size. For custom sizes add **80%**.

| Item Description | Unit | 20" tall | 24" tall | 30" tall |
|---|---|---|---|---|
| **24" wide aluminum awning window**<br>*Materials* 20" tall...296.00  24" tall...333.00  30" tall...363.00<br>*Labor* 20" tall..........39.10  24" tall.....39.10  30" tall......39.10 | ea | $335.10 | $372.10 | $402.10 |
| **30" wide aluminum awning window**<br>*Materials* 20" tall...342.00  24" tall...375.00  30" tall...410.00<br>*Labor* 20" tall..........39.10  24" tall.....39.10  30" tall......39.10 | ea | $381.10 | $414.10 | $449.10 |
| **36" wide aluminum awning window**<br>*Materials*...................  24" tall...406.00  30" tall...456.00<br>*Labor*.....................  24" tall.....39.10  30" tall......39.10 | ea | — | $445.10 | $495.10 |
| **40" wide aluminum awning window**<br>*Materials*...................  24" tall...450.00  30" tall...508.00<br>*Labor*.....................  24" tall.....39.10  30" tall......39.10 | ea | — | $489.10 | $547.10 |

**double-hung ▷**

### GRILLES AND GRID

For aluminum grid between panes of glass or removable grilles outside of window add (per window):

Half-round ..............$18
Half-elliptical .........$29
Round....................$19
Elliptical ...............$25
Quarter-round..........$19
Casement ..............$24
Awning.................$24
Single-hung .........$19
Sliding.................$21
Fixed (picture) .......$23

| Item Description | Unit | 36" tall | 48" tall | 60" tall | 72" tall |
|---|---|---|---|---|---|
| **24" wide aluminum double-hung window**<br>*Materials* 36" tall....173.00  48" tall...193.00  60" tall....218.00  72" tall....244.00<br>*Labor* 36" tall..........39.10  48" tall.....39.10  60" tall.....39.10  72" tall.....39.10 | ea | $212.10 | $232.10 | $257.10 | $283.10 |
| **36" wide aluminum double-hung window**<br>*Materials* 36" tall....213.00  48" tall...238.00  60" tall....255.00  72" tall....279.00<br>*Labor* 36" tall..........39.10  48" tall.....39.10  60" tall.....39.10  72" tall......54.90 | ea | $252.10 | $277.10 | $294.10 | $333.90 |
| **42" wide aluminum double-hung window**<br>*Materials* 36" tall....234.00  48" tall...256.00  60" tall....279.00  72" tall....304.00<br>*Labor* 36" tall..........39.10  48" tall.....39.10  60" tall.....54.90  72" tall......54.90 | ea | $273.10 | $295.10 | $333.90 | $358.90 |
| **24" wide aluminum single-hung window**<br>*Materials* 36" tall....144.00  48" tall...164.00  60" tall....189.00  72" tall....215.00<br>*Labor* 36" tall..........39.10  48" tall.....39.10  60" tall.....39.10  72" tall......39.10 | ea | $183.10 | $203.10 | $228.10 | $254.10 |
| **36" wide aluminum single-hung window**<br>*Materials* 36" tall....184.00  48" tall...209.00  60" tall....226.00  72" tall....250.00<br>*Labor* 36" tall..........39.10  48" tall.....39.10  60" tall.....39.10  72" tall......54.90 | ea | $223.10 | $248.10 | $265.10 | $304.90 |
| **42" wide aluminum single-hung window**<br>*Materials* 36" tall....205.00  48" tall...227.00  60" tall....250.00  72" tall....275.00<br>*Labor* 36" tall..........39.10  48" tall.....39.10  60" tall.....54.90  72" tall......54.90 | ea | $244.10 | $266.10 | $304.90 | $329.90 |

| Item Description | Unit | 24" tall | 36" tall | 48" tall | 60" tall | |
|---|---|---|---|---|---|---|
| **36" wide aluminum sliding window** | ea | $101.40 | $108.10 | $134.90 | $166.10 | ◁ sliding |
| *Materials* 24" tall......62.30  36" tall......69.00  48" tall......95.80  60" tall ....127.00 | | | | | | |
| *Labor* 24" tall............39.10  36" tall......39.10  48" tall......39.10  60" tall......39.10 | | | | | | |
| **48" wide aluminum sliding window** | ea | $108.90 | $117.10 | $147.10 | $198.90 | |
| *Materials* 24" tall......69.80  36" tall......78.00  48" tall......108.00  60" tall....144.00 | | | | | | |
| *Labor* 24" tall............39.10  36" tall......39.10  48" tall......39.10  60" tall......54.90 | | | | | | |
| **60" wide aluminum sliding window** | ea | $115.40 | $124.10 | $172.90 | $211.90 | |
| *Materials* 24" tall......76.30  36" tall......85.00  48" tall......118.00  60" tall....157.00 | | | | | | |
| *Labor* 24" tall............39.10  36" tall......39.10  48" tall......54.90  60" tall......54.90 | | | | | | |
| **72" wide aluminum sliding window** | ea | $129.30 | $154.90 | $193.90 | $264.00 | |
| *Materials* 24" tall......90.20  36" tall......100.00  48" tall......139.00  60" tall....185.00 | | | | | | |
| *Labor* 24" tall............39.10  36" tall......54.90  48" tall......54.90  60" tall......79.00 | | | | | | |

**THERMAL BREAK**

Aluminum is an excellent conductor, which means heat and cold easily flow through it, reducing efficiency.

To cure this, a plastic or rubber spacer is introduced into the jamb to break the flow of hot or cold.

Add **11%** for each aluminum window with a thermal break.

| Item Description | Unit | 36" tall | 48" tall | 60" tall | 72" tall | |
|---|---|---|---|---|---|---|
| **24" wide aluminum fixed (picture) window** | ea | $127.10 | $167.10 | $191.10 | $203.10 | ◁ fixed (picture) |
| *Materials* 36" tall......88.00  48" tall....128.00  60" tall ....152.00  72" tall......164.00 | | | | | | |
| *Labor* 36" tall............39.10  48" tall......39.10  60" tall......39.10  72" tall......39.10 | | | | | | |
| **30" wide aluminum fixed (picture) window** | ea | $146.10 | $173.10 | $186.10 | $228.10 | |
| *Materials* 36" tall ...107.00  48" tall....134.00  60" tall ....147.00  72" tall......189.00 | | | | | | |
| *Labor* 36" tall............39.10  48" tall......39.10  60" tall......39.10  72" tall......39.10 | | | | | | |
| **36" wide aluminum fixed (picture) window** | ea | $154.10 | $192.10 | $195.10 | $274.90 | |
| *Materials* 36" tall ...115.00  48" tall....153.00  60" tall ....156.00  72" tall......220.00 | | | | | | |
| *Labor* 36" tall............39.10  48" tall......39.10  60" tall......39.10  72" tall......54.90 | | | | | | |
| **42" wide aluminum fixed (picture) window** | ea | $167.10 | $222.10 | $275.90 | $308.90 | |
| *Materials* 36" tall ...128.00  48" tall ...183.00  60" tall....221.00  72" tall ...254.00 | | | | | | |
| *Labor* 36" tall............39.10  48" tall......39.10  60" tall......54.90  72" tall......54.90 | | | | | | |
| **48" wide aluminum fixed (picture) window** | ea | $192.10 | $228.10 | $296.90 | $330.90 | |
| *Materials* 36" tall ...153.00  48" tall ...189.00  60" tall ...242.00  72" tall ...276.00 | | | | | | |
| *Labor* 36" tall............39.10  48" tall......39.10  60" tall......54.90  72" tall......54.90 | | | | | | |
| **60" wide aluminum fixed (picture) window** | ea | $195.10 | $250.90 | $281.90 | $381.00 | |
| *Materials* 36" tall ...156.00  48" tall....196.00  60" tall....227.00  72" tall ...302.00 | | | | | | |
| *Labor* 36" tall............39.10  48" tall......54.90  60" tall......54.90  72" tall......79.00 | | | | | | |
| **72" wide aluminum fixed (picture) window** | ea | $299.00 | $356.00 | $418.00 | $477.00 | |
| *Materials* 36" tall ...220.00  48" tall ...277.00  60" tall ...302.00  72" tall ...361.00 | | | | | | |
| *Labor* 36" tall............79.00  48" tall......79.00  60" tall......116.00  72" tall......116.00 | | | | | | |

**LOW-E AND ARGON**

Higher quality windows may have Low-E or argon gas or both.

**Low-E** A coating that increases heat retention in winter and reduces ultraviolet rays that fade carpet and upholstery. Also called high-performance glass and other brand names.

**Argon gas** An odorless gas that improves the window's energy efficiency when injected between panes of glass.

Argon is usually not available for windows with true divided lights.

See page 499 to add Low-E or argon to windows and page 506 to add to skylights and roof windows.

◀ **VINYL**

| Item Description | Unit | 24" x 12" | 36" x 18" | 48" x 24" | 72" x 36" | |
|---|---|---|---|---|---|---|
| **Half-round vinyl window top** | ea | $156.10 | $183.10 | $227.90 | $335.00 | ◁ half-round |
| *Materials* 24" x 12"....117.00  36" x 18" ...144.00  48" x 24" ....173.00  72" x 36"....256.00 | | | | | | |
| *Labor* 24" x 12" ............39.10  36" x 18"......39.10  48" x 24"......54.90  72" x 36"......79.00 | | | | | | |

| Item Description | Unit | 36" x 15" | 48" x 16" | 60" x 19" | 90" x 20" | |
|---|---|---|---|---|---|---|
| **Half-elliptical vinyl window top** | ea | $261.10 | $283.10 | $326.90 | $473.00 | ◁ half-elliptical |
| *Materials* 36" x 15".222.00  48" x 16"...244.00  60" x 19"....272.00  90" x 20"....394.00 | | | | | | |
| *Labor* 36" x 15 ............39.10  48" x 16"......39.10  60" x 19"......54.90  90" x 20"......79.00 | | | | | | |

| Item Description | Unit | 20" x 20" | 30" x 30" | 40" x 40" | 48" x 48" | |
|---|---|---|---|---|---|---|
| **Round vinyl window** | ea | $275.10 | $324.10 | $387.90 | $444.00 | ◁ round |
| *Materials* 20" x 20" .236.00  30" x 30" ......285.00  40" x 40" ....333.00  48" x 48"......365.00 | | | | | | |
| *Labor* 20" x 20" ............39.10  30" x 30"......39.10  40" x 40"......54.90  48" x 48"......79.00 | | | | | | |

| | Unit | 15" x 24" | 24" x 36" | 25" x 40" | 30" x 48" |
|---|---|---|---|---|---|
| **VINYL ▶** *continued* **elliptical ▷** **Elliptical vinyl window** | ea | $485.10 | $522.10 | $577.90 | $642.00 |
|     *Materials* 15" x 24" ..446.00  24" x 36" ...483.00  25" x 40"....523.00  30" x 48" ...563.00 | | | | | |
|     *Labor* 15" x 24" ...........39.10  24" x 36" .....39.10  25" x 40" .....54.90  30" x 48" ......79.00 | | | | | |

| | Unit | 24" x 24" | 36" x 36" | | |
|---|---|---|---|---|---|
| **quarter-round ▷** **Quarter-round vinyl window** | ea | $230.10 | $311.10 | | |
|     *Materials* 24" x 24" ...191.00  36" x 36" ...272.00 | | | | | |
|     *Labor* 24" x 24" ...........39.10  36" x 36" .....39.10 | | | | | |

| | Unit | 36" tall | 48" tall | 60" tall |
|---|---|---|---|---|
| **casement ▷** **18" wide vinyl casement window** | ea | $261.10 | $280.10 | $316.10 |
|     *Materials* 36" tall...222.00  48" tall....241.00  60" tall....277.00 | | | | |
|     *Labor* 36" tall...........39.10  48" tall.....39.10  60" tall......39.10 | | | | |
| **24" wide vinyl casement window** | ea | $279.10 | $299.10 | $349.90 |
|     *Materials* 36" tall ...240.00  48" tall...260.00  60" tall....295.00 | | | | |
|     *Labor* 36" tall...........39.10  48" tall.....39.10  60" tall .....54.90 | | | | |
| **30" wide vinyl casement window** | ea | — | $336.90 | $368.90 |
|     *Materials* .....................48" tall...282.00  60" tall ...314.00 | | | | |
|     *Labor* .........................48" tall....54.90  60" tall ....54.90 | | | | |
| **36" wide vinyl casement window (double)** | ea | — | $388.90 | $438.90 |
|     *Materials* .....................48" tall...334.00  60" tall ...384.00 | | | | |
|     *Labor* .........................48" tall....54.90  60" tall ....54.90 | | | | |

| | Unit | 20" tall | 24" tall | 30" tall |
|---|---|---|---|---|
| **awning ▷** **24" wide vinyl awning window** | ea | $245.10 | $270.10 | $293.10 |
|     *Materials* 20" tall...206.00  24" tall....231.00  30" tall ...254.00 | | | | |
|     *Labor* 20" tall...........39.10  24" tall.....39.10  30" tall......39.10 | | | | |
| **30" wide vinyl awning window** | ea | $278.10 | $300.10 | $325.10 |
|     *Materials* 20" tall...239.00  24" tall....261.00  30" tall...286.00 | | | | |
|     *Labor* 20" tall...........39.10  24" tall.....39.10  30" tall......39.10 | | | | |
| **36" wide vinyl awning window** | ea | — | $322.10 | $357.10 |
|     *Materials* .....................24" tall...283.00  30" tall ...318.00 | | | | |
|     *Labor* .........................24" tall.....39.10  30" tall....39.10 | | | | |
| **40" wide vinyl awning window** | ea | — | $353.10 | $393.10 |
|     *Materials* .....................24" tall...314.00  30" tall ...354.00 | | | | |
|     *Labor* .........................24" tall.....39.10  30" tall....39.10 | | | | |

| | Unit | 36" tall | 48" tall | 60" tall | 72" tall |
|---|---|---|---|---|---|
| **single-hung ▷** **24" wide vinyl single-hung window** | ea | $140.10 | $153.10 | $171.10 | $189.10 |
|     *Materials* 36" tall....101.00  48" tall ....114.00  60" tall ...132.00  72" tall...150.00 | | | | | |
|     *Labor* 36" tall...........39.10  48" tall.....39.10  60" tall.....39.10  72" tall......39.10 | | | | | |
| **36" wide vinyl single-hung window** | ea | $168.10 | $184.10 | $197.10 | $228.90 |
|     *Materials* 36" tall ...129.00  48" tall....145.00  60" tall....158.00  72" tall ....174.00 | | | | | |
|     *Labor* 36" tall...........39.10  48" tall.....39.10  60" tall.....39.10  72" tall .....54.90 | | | | | |
| **42" wide vinyl single-hung window** | ea | $182.10 | $198.10 | $228.90 | $245.90 |
|     *Materials* 36" tall ...143.00  48" tall....159.00  60" tall....174.00  72" tall ....191.00 | | | | | |
|     *Labor* 36" tall...........39.10  48" tall.....39.10  60" tall.....54.90  72" tall .....54.90 | | | | | |

---

### VINYL

All vinyl windows are double-glazed with clear glass.

All costs are for standard windows. Manufacturers' window sizes vary. For standard units round measurements to the nearest size. Add approximately **80%** for custom sizes.

Some manufacturers provide a less rigid, lower grade of windows for **15%** less.

---

### GRILLES AND GRID

For aluminum grid between panes or removable grilles outside of window add:

Half-round ..............$19
Half-elliptical.........$29
Round ......................$19
Elliptical ................$25
Quarter-round ........$19
Casement................$24
Awning ..................$24
Single-hung ...........$19
Sliding ..................$21
Fixed (picture).......$23

| Item Description | Unit | 24″ tall | 36″ tall | 48″ tall | 60″ tall | |
|---|---|---|---|---|---|---|
| **48″ wide vinyl sliding window** | ea | $145.10 | $168.10 | $186.10 | $213.10 | ◁ sliding |
| *Materials* 24″ tall....106.00 36″ tall....129.00 48″ tall....147.00 60″ tall....174.00 | | | | | | |
| *Labor* 24″ tall.........39.10 36″ tall...39.10 48″ tall.....39.10 60″ tall.....39.10 | | | | | | |
| **60″ wide vinyl sliding window** | ea | — | $184.10 | $208.10 | $262.90 | |
| *Materials* ............. 36″ tall....145.00 48″ tall....169.00 60″ tall....208.00 | | | | | | |
| *Labor* ............. 36″ tall...39.10 48″ tall...39.10 60″ tall....54.90 | | | | | | |
| **72″ wide vinyl sliding window** | ea | — | — | $247.90 | $279.90 | |
| *Materials* ............. 48″ tall....193.00 60″ tall....225.00 | | | | | | |
| *Labor* ............. 48″ tall...54.90 60″ tall....54.90 | | | | | | |

| Item Description | Unit | 36″ tall | 48″ tall | 60″ tall | 72″ tall | |
|---|---|---|---|---|---|---|
| **24″ wide vinyl fixed (picture) window** | ea | $101.30 | $127.10 | $145.10 | $153.10 | ◁ fixed (picture) |
| *Materials* 36″ tall.....62.20 48″ tall....88.00 60″ tall....106.00 72″ tall.....114.00 | | | | | | |
| *Labor* 36″ tall.........39.10 48″ tall...39.10 60″ tall.....39.10 72″ tall.....39.10 | | | | | | |
| **30″ wide vinyl fixed (picture) window** | ea | $113.70 | $132.10 | $142.10 | $171.10 | |
| *Materials* 36″ tall.....74.60 48″ tall....93.00 60″ tall....103.00 72″ tall.....132.00 | | | | | | |
| *Labor* 36″ tall.........39.10 48″ tall...39.10 60″ tall.....39.10 72″ tall.....39.10 | | | | | | |
| **36″ wide vinyl fixed (picture) window** | ea | $118.70 | $146.10 | $147.10 | $207.90 | |
| *Materials* 36″ tall.....79.60 48″ tall....107.00 60″ tall....108.00 72″ tall.....153.00 | | | | | | |
| *Labor* 36″ tall.........39.10 48″ tall...39.10 60″ tall.....39.10 72″ tall.....54.90 | | | | | | |
| **42″ wide vinyl fixed (picture) window** | ea | $141.10 | $184.10 | $232.90 | $258.90 | |
| *Materials* 36″ tall...102.00 48″ tall....145.00 60″ tall....178.00 72″ tall.....204.00 | | | | | | |
| *Labor* 36″ tall.........39.10 48″ tall...39.10 60″ tall.....54.90 72″ tall.....54.90 | | | | | | |
| **48″ wide vinyl fixed (picture) window** | ea | $146.10 | $171.10 | $223.90 | $247.90 | |
| *Materials* 36″ tall...107.00 48″ tall....132.00 60″ tall....169.00 72″ tall.....193.00 | | | | | | |
| *Labor* 36″ tall.........39.10 48″ tall...39.10 60″ tall.....54.90 72″ tall.....54.90 | | | | | | |
| **60″ wide vinyl fixed (picture) window** | ea | $147.10 | $191.90 | $213.90 | $289.00 | |
| *Materials* 36″ tall...108.00 48″ tall....137.00 60″ tall....159.00 72″ tall.....210.00 | | | | | | |
| *Labor* 36″ tall.........39.10 48″ tall...54.90 60″ tall.....54.90 72″ tall.....79.00 | | | | | | |
| **72″ wide vinyl fixed (picture) window** | ea | $232.00 | $272.00 | $326.00 | $367.00 | |
| *Materials* 36″ tall...153.00 48″ tall....193.00 60″ tall....210.00 72″ tall.....251.00 | | | | | | |
| *Labor* 36″ tall.........79.00 48″ tall...79.00 60″ tall.....116.00 72″ tall.....116.00 | | | | | | |

**RELATED ITEMS**

Doors
    sliding patio .................119

| Item Description | Unit | 24″ x 12″ | 36″ x 18″ | 48″ x 24″ | 60″ x 30″ | |
|---|---|---|---|---|---|---|
| **Half-round wood window top** | ea | $398.10 | $502.10 | $511.90 | $707.00 | ◀ WOOD ◁ half-round |
| *Materials* 24″ x 12″ ..359.00 36″ x 18″ ..463.00 48″ x 24″....457.00 60″ x 30″....628.00 | | | | | | |
| *Labor* 24″ x 12″ ..........39.10 36″ x 18″.....39.10 48″ x 24″ .....54.90 60″ x 30″......79.00 | | | | | | |

| Item Description | Unit | 36″ x 15″ | 48″ x 16″ | 60″ x 17″ | 72″ x 19″ | |
|---|---|---|---|---|---|---|
| **Half-elliptical wood window top** | ea | $601.10 | $658.10 | $718.90 | $874.00 | ◁ half-elliptical |
| *Materials* 36″ x 15″...562.00 48″ x 16″....619.00 60″ x 17″ ...664.00 72″ x 19″....795.00 | | | | | | |
| *Labor* 36″ x 15″ ..........39.10 48″ x 16″.....39.10 60″ x 17″ .....54.90 72″ x 19″......79.00 | | | | | | |

**Add 114% for true divided light, spoke pattern** (half-round or half-elliptical)

**Add $20 for 3 spoke hub grille** (half-round window)

| Item Description | Unit | 30″ x 30″ | 48″ x 48″ | | |
|---|---|---|---|---|---|
| **Round wood window** | ea | $938.10 | $1,069.10 | | ◁ round |
| *Materials* 30″ x 30″ .899.00 48″ x 48″.1030.00 | | | | | |
| *Labor* 30″ x 30″ ..........39.10 48″ x 48″ .....39.10 | | | | | |

**WOOD ▶**
*continued*

**elliptical ▷**

| Item Description | Unit | 25" x 30" | 30" x 36" | | |
|---|---|---|---|---|---|
| **Elliptical (oval) wood window** | ea | $1,079.10 | $1,209.10 | | |
| *Materials* 25" x 30" 1040.00  30" x 36"...1170.00 | | | | | |
| *Labor* 25" x 30"...........39.10  30" x 36".....39.10 | | | | | |
| Add $18 for 4-lite grille in round or elliptical window | | | | | |
| Add $23 for 9-lite grille in round or elliptical window | | | | | |
| Add $28 for sunburst grille in round or elliptical window | | | | | |

**quarter-round ▷**

| Item Description | Unit | 24" x 24" | 36" x 36" | | |
|---|---|---|---|---|---|
| **Quarter-round wood window** | ea | $480.10 | $559.10 | | |
| *Materials* 24" x 24" ..441.00  36" x 36" ...520.00 | | | | | |
| *Labor* 24" x 24" ...........39.10  36" x 36".....39.10 | | | | | |

| Item Description | Unit | all sizes | | | |
|---|---|---|---|---|---|
| **Add for single spoke grille in quarter-round window** | ea | $22.00 | | | |
| *Materials* All sizes.....22.00 | | | | | |
| **Add for double spoke grille in quarter-round window** | ea | $25.00 | | | |
| *Materials* All sizes.....25.00 | | | | | |
| **Add for single radial bar grille in quarter-round window** | ea | $29.00 | | | |
| *Materials* All sizes.....29.00 | | | | | |
| **Add for double radial bar grille in quarter-round window** | ea | $33.00 | | | |
| *Materials* All sizes.....33.00 | | | | | |

**casement ▷**

| Item Description | Unit | 36" tall | 48" tall | 60" tall | 72" tall |
|---|---|---|---|---|---|
| **18" wide wood casement window** | ea | $229.10 | $293.10 | $343.10 | $395.10 |
| *Materials* 36" tall ...190.00  48" tall...254.00  60" tall ...304.00  72" tall....356.00 | | | | | |
| *Labor* 36" tall ...........39.10  48" tall...39.10  60" tall.....39.10  72" tall......39.10 | | | | | |
| **24" wide wood casement window** | ea | $280.10 | $313.10 | $368.90 | $412.10 |
| *Materials* 36" tall...241.00  48" tall...274.00  60" tall...314.00  72" tall...373.00 | | | | | |
| *Labor* 36" tall...........39.10  48" tall...39.10  60" tall...54.90  72" tall......39.10 | | | | | |
| **30" wide wood casement window** | ea | — | $362.90 | $417.90 | $432.10 |
| *Materials* 36" tall........  48" tall...308.00  60" tall ...363.00  72" tall...393.00 | | | | | |
| *Labor* 36" tall ...............  48" tall...54.90  60" tall...54.90  72" tall......39.10 | | | | | |
| **36" wide wood casement window** | ea | — | $401.90 | $464.90 | $500.90 |
| *Materials* 36" tall........  48" tall ...347.00  60" tall...410.00  72" tall ...446.00 | | | | | |
| *Labor* 36" tall ...............  48" tall...54.90  60" tall...54.90  72" tall .....54.90 | | | | | |
| **Add 87% for authentic divided lites in casement window** | | | | | |
| **Add $13 for removable wood grille in casement window** | | | | | |
| **Add $12 for aluminum grille between panes in casement window** | | | | | |

### WOOD

All wood windows are double-glazed with clear glass. Interiors are natural wood and exteriors are primed wood or aluminum clad or vinyl clad.

Hardware on wood windows is bright brass, brushed brass, antique brass, or white.

All costs are for standard windows. Manufacturers' window sizes vary. For standard units, round to the nearest size. Add approximately **80%** for custom sizes.

**awning ▷**

| Item Description | Unit | 20" tall | 24" tall | 30" tall | |
|---|---|---|---|---|---|
| **24" wide wood awning window** | ea | $242.10 | $258.10 | $274.10 | |
| *Materials* 20" tall...203.00  24" tall....219.00  30" tall....235.00 | | | | | |
| *Labor* 20" tall ...........39.10  24" tall.....39.10  30" tall......39.10 | | | | | |
| **30" wide wood awning window** | ea | $252.10 | $267.10 | $297.90 | |
| *Materials* 20" tall...213.00  24" tall....228.00  30" tall....243.00 | | | | | |
| *Labor* 20" tall ...........39.10  24" tall.....39.10  30" tall....54.90 | | | | | |

| Item Description | Unit | 20" tall | 24" tall | 30" tall | |
|---|---|---|---|---|---|
| **36" wide wood awning window** | ea | $266.10 | $297.90 | $311.90 | |
| *Materials* 20" tall ...227.00  24" tall ...243.00  30" tall ....257.00 | | | | | |
| *Labor* 20" tall ..........39.10  24" tall ....54.90  30" tall ....54.90 | | | | | |
| **48" wide wood awning window** | ea | $310.10 | $333.90 | $365.90 | |
| *Materials* 20" tall ...271.00  24" tall ...279.00  30" tall .....311.00 | | | | | |
| *Labor* 20" tall ..........39.10  24" tall ....54.90  30" tall ....54.90 | | | | | |
| **Add 80% for authentic divided lites in awning window** | | | | | |
| **Add $14 for removable wood grille in awning window** | | | | | |
| **Add $13 for aluminum grille between panes in awning window** | | | | | |

| Item Description | Unit | 36" tall | 48" tall | 60" tall | 72" tall | |
|---|---|---|---|---|---|---|
| **24" wide wood double-hung window** | ea | $244.10 | $277.10 | $308.10 | $342.10 | ◁ double-hung |
| *Materials* 36" tall...205.00  48" tall ...238.00  60" tall ...269.00  72" tall ...303.00 | | | | | | |
| *Labor* 36" tall ..........39.10  48" tall ....39.10  60" tall .....39.10  72" tall......39.10 | | | | | | |
| **36" wide wood double-hung window** | ea | $289.10 | $326.10 | $365.10 | $423.90 | |
| *Materials* 36" tall...250.00  48" tall ...287.00  60" tall...326.00  72" tall...369.00 | | | | | | |
| *Labor* 36" tall ..........39.10  48" tall ....39.10  60" tall .....39.10  72" tall ....54.90 | | | | | | |
| **48" wide wood double-hung window** | ea | $357.10 | $357.10 | $422.90 | $479.90 | |
| *Materials* 36" tall....318.00  48" tall ...318.00  60" tall...368.00  72" tall...425.00 | | | | | | |
| *Labor* 36" tall ..........39.10  48" tall ....39.10  60" tall ....54.90  72" tall ....54.90 | | | | | | |
| **Add 105% for authentic divided lites in double-hung window** | | | | | | |
| **Add $14 for removable wood grille in double-hung window** | | | | | | |
| **Add $13 for aluminum grille between panes in double-hung window** | | | | | | |
| **24" wide wood single-hung window** | ea | $191.10 | $224.10 | $255.10 | $289.10 | ◁ single-hung |
| *Materials* 36" tall...152.00  48" tall ...185.00  60" tall ...216.00  72" tall ...250.00 | | | | | | |
| *Labor* 36" tall ..........39.10  48" tall ....39.10  60" tall .....39.10  72" tall......39.10 | | | | | | |
| **36" wide wood single-hung window** | ea | $236.10 | $273.10 | $312.10 | $370.90 | |
| *Materials* 36" tall....197.00  48" tall ...234.00  60" tall...273.00  72" tall ...316.00 | | | | | | |
| *Labor* 36" tall ..........39.10  48" tall ....39.10  60" tall .....39.10  72" tall ....54.90 | | | | | | |
| **40" wide wood single-hung window** | ea | $304.10 | $304.10 | $369.90 | $426.90 | |
| *Materials* 36" tall ...265.00  48" tall ...265.00  60" tall...315.00  72" tall...372.00 | | | | | | |
| *Labor* 36" tall ..........39.10  48" tall ....39.10  60" tall ....54.90  72" tall ....54.90 | | | | | | |
| **Add 105% for authentic divided lites in single-hung window** | | | | | | |
| **Add $14 for removable wood grille in single-hung window** | | | | | | |
| **Add $13 for aluminum grille between panes in single-hung window** | | | | | | |
| **Add 97% for segmented top in single-hung window** | | | | | | |

**RELATED ITEMS**

Doors
  sliding patio ..................119

| Item Description | Unit | 24" tall | 36" tall | 48" tall | 60" tall | |
|---|---|---|---|---|---|---|
| **48" wide wood sliding window** | ea | $338.10 | $361.10 | $418.10 | $473.10 | ◁ sliding |
| *Materials* 24" tall ...299.00  36" tall ...322.00  48" tall ...379.00  60" tall ...434.00 | | | | | | |
| *Labor* 24" tall ..........39.10  36" tall ....39.10  48" tall .......39.10  60" tall......39.10 | | | | | | |
| **60" wide wood sliding window** | ea | — | $423.10 | $474.10 | $552.90 | |
| *Materials* ...................  36" tall...384.00  48" tall....435.00  60" tall....498.00 | | | | | | |
| *Labor* ...................  36" tall ....39.10  48" tall......39.10  60" tall ....54.90 | | | | | | |

| Item Description | | | | | Unit | | 48" tall | 60" tall |
|---|---|---|---|---|---|---|---|---|
| **WOOD** ▶<br>continued<br>**sliding** ▷<br>continued | **72" wide wood sliding window** | | | | ea | | $545.90 | $607.90 |
| | Materials...... | ........ | 48" tall....491.00 | 60" tall....553.00 | | | | |
| | Labor............ | ........ | 48" tall ....54.90 | 60" tall.......... | | | | |
| | **Add 90% for authentic divided lites in sliding window** | | | | | | | |
| | **Add $14 for removable wood grille in sliding window** | | | | | | | |
| | **Add $13 for aluminum grille between panes in sliding window** | | | | | | | |

| Item Description | | | | | Unit | 36" tall | 48" tall | 60" tall | 72" tall |
|---|---|---|---|---|---|---|---|---|---|
| **fixed (picture)** ▷  | **24" wide wood fixed (picture) window** | | | | ea | $212.10 | $245.10 | $276.10 | $310.10 |
| | Materials 36" tall....173.00 | 48" tall...206.00 | 60" tall...237.00 | 72" tall....271.00 | | | | | |
| | Labor 36" tall ...........39.10 | 48" tall .....39.10 | 60" tall......39.10 | 72" tall......39.10 | | | | | |
| | **36" wide wood fixed (picture) window** | | | | ea | $257.10 | $294.10 | $333.10 | $391.90 |
| | Materials 36" tall....218.00 | 48" tall ...255.00 | 60" tall...294.00 | 72" tall....337.00 | | | | | |
| | Labor 36" tall ...........39.10 | 48" tall .....39.10 | 60" tall......39.10 | 72" tall ....54.90 | | | | | |
| | **48" wide wood fixed (picture) window** | | | | ea | $325.10 | $325.10 | $390.90 | $447.90 |
| | Materials 36" tall....286.00 | 48" tall ...286.00 | 60" tall ...336.00 | 72" tall....393.00 | | | | | |
| | Labor 36" tall ...........39.10 | 48" tall .....39.10 | 60" tall ....54.90 | 72" tall ....54.90 | | | | | |
| | **60" wide wood fixed (picture) window** | | | | ea | — | $394.90 | $445.90 | $533.00 |
| | Materials................. | 48" tall...340.00 | 60" tall....391.00 | 72" tall....454.00 | | | | | |
| | Labor..................... | 48" tall ....54.90 | 60" tall....54.90 | 72" tall......79.00 | | | | | |
| | **72" wide wood fixed (picture) window** | | | | ea | — | — | $526.00 | $588.00 |
| | Materials................. | ........ | 60" tall....447.00 | 72" tall....509.00 | | | | | |
| | Labor..................... | ........ | 60" tall....79.00 | 72" tall......79.00 | | | | | |
| | **Add 80% for authentic divided lites in fixed window** | | | | | | | | |
| | **Add $15 for removable wood grille in fixed window** | | | | | | | | |
| | **Add $14 for aluminum grille between panes in fixed window** | | | | | | | | |
| | **Add 97% for segmented top in fixed window** | | | | | | | | |

| Item Description | Unit | all types |
|---|---|---|
| **SKYLIGHT** ▶<br>**additional costs** ▷ | **Add for laminated glass over tempered glass in skylight or roof window**<br>Materials All types ....31.00 | ea | $31.00 |
| | **Add for Low-E in skylight or roof window**<br>Materials All types......8.00 | ea | $8.00 |
| | **Add for argon gas filled skylight or roof window**<br>Materials All types......7.00 | ea | $7.00 |
| | **Add or bronze or gray tint (all sizes)**<br>Materials All types.....12.00 | ea | $12.00 |
| | **Add for skylight or roof window installed on high-profile roof**<br>Materials All types....20.00 | ea | $20.00 |
| | **Add for skylight or roof window installed on low-slope roof (less than 4-12)**<br>Materials All types..258.00 | ea | $258.00 |
| | **Add for skylight or roof window installed on flat roof (less than 2-12)**<br>Materials All types....267.00 | ea | $267.00 |

*See "Low-E and Argon" on page 501. Skylight prices include flashing for roof with low-profile roofing such as asphalt shingles. For tile shingles, or ribbed metal roofing add for high-profile roof. Low-slope roof includes a curb and flat roof includes a special sloped curb.*

| Item Description | Unit | 24" x 24" | 24" x 48" | 30" x 30" | 48" x 48" | |
|---|---|---|---|---|---|---|
| **Single dome skylight** | ea | $160.00 | $214.00 | $192.10 | $383.00 | ◁ dome |
| *Materials* 24" x 24"....56.00  24" x 48"....110.00  30" x 30"......88.10  48" x 48"....279.00 | | | | | | |
| *Labor* 24" x 24"..........104.00  24" x 48"....104.00  30" x 30"....104.00  48" x 48"....104.00 | | | | | | |
| **Double dome skylight** | ea | $178.00 | $258.00 | $247.00 | $433.00 | |
| *Materials* 24" x 24"....74.00  24" x 48"....154.00  30" x 30"....143.00  48" x 48"....329.00 | | | | | | |
| *Labor* 24" x 24"..........104.00  24" x 48"....104.00  30" x 30"....104.00  48" x 48"....104.00 | | | | | | |
| **Triple dome skylight** | ea | $200.00 | $325.00 | $279.00 | $526.00 | |
| *Materials* 24" x 24"....96.00  24" x 48"....221.00  30" x 30"....175.00  48" x 48"....422.00 | | | | | | |
| *Labor* 24" x 24"..........104.00  24" x 48"....104.00  30" x 30"....104.00  48" x 48"....104.00 | | | | | | |
| **Single dome ventilating skylight** | ea | $227.00 | $340.00 | $294.00 | $691.00 | ◁ ventilating |
| *Materials* 24" x 24"...117.00  24" x 48"....230.00  30" x 30"....184.00  48" x 48"....581.00 | | | | | | |
| *Labor* 24" x 24"..........110.00  24" x 48"....110.00  30" x 30"....110.00  48" x 48"....110.00 | | | | | | |
| **Double dome ventilating skylight** | ea | $265.00 | $430.00 | $408.00 | $793.00 | |
| *Materials* 24" x 24"...155.00  24" x 48"....320.00  30" x 30"....298.00  48" x 48"....683.00 | | | | | | |
| *Labor* 24" x 24"..........110.00  24" x 48"....110.00  30" x 30"....110.00  48" x 48"....110.00 | | | | | | |
| **Triple dome ventilating skylight** | ea | $309.00 | $569.00 | $475.00 | $989.00 | |
| *Materials* 24" x 24"...199.00  24" x 48"....459.00  30" x 30"....365.00  48" x 48"....879.00 | | | | | | |
| *Labor* 24" x 24"..........110.00  24" x 48"....110.00  30" x 30"....110.00  48" x 48"....110.00 | | | | | | |

| Item Description | Unit | 28" long | 38" long | 48" long | 55" long | |
|---|---|---|---|---|---|---|
| **22" wide fixed skylight** | ea | $309.00 | $343.00 | $370.00 | $394.00 | ◁ fixed |
| *Materials* 28" long .202.00  38" long ...236.00  48" long....263.00  55" long....287.00 | | | | | | |
| *Labor* 28" long .........107.00  38" long....107.00  48" long....107.00  55" long....107.00 | | | | | | |
| **30" wide fixed skylight** | ea | — | $380.00 | — | $440.00 | |
| *Materials* ...............  38" long ...273.00  55" long ...333.00 | | | | | | |
| *Labor* ...................  38" long....107.00  55" long....107.00 | | | | | | |
| **44" wide fixed skylight** | ea | $404.00 | — | $484.00 | — | |
| *Materials* 28" long..297.00  48" long....377.00 | | | | | | |
| *Labor* 28" long .........107.00  48" long....107.00 | | | | | | |
| **22" wide fixed skylight with ventilation flap** | ea | $335.00 | $370.00 | $399.00 | $416.00 | ◁ fixed with vent flap |
| *Materials* 28" long.228.00  38" long ...263.00  48" long ...292.00  55" long ...309.00 | | | | | | |
| *Labor* 28" long .........107.00  38" long....107.00  48" long....107.00  55" long....107.00 | | | | | | |
| **30" wide fixed skylight with ventilation flap** | ea | — | $414.00 | — | $467.00 | |
| *Materials* ...............  38" long ...307.00  55" long ...360.00 | | | | | | |
| *Labor* ...................  38" long....107.00  55" long....107.00 | | | | | | |
| **44" wide fixed skylight with ventilation flap** | ea | $452.00 | — | $520.00 | — | |
| *Materials* 28" long..345.00  48" long ...413.00 | | | | | | |
| *Labor* 28" long .........107.00  48" long....107.00 | | | | | | |
| **22" wide ventilating skylight** | ea | $496.00 | $529.00 | $568.00 | $586.00 | ◁ ventilating |
| *Materials* 28" long .380.00  38" long ...413.00  48" long....452.00  55" long....470.00 | | | | | | |
| *Labor* 28" long .........116.00  38" long....116.00  48" long.....116.00  55" long.....116.00 | | | | | | |
| **30" wide ventilating skylight** | ea | — | $575.00 | — | $647.00 | |
| *Materials* ...............  38" long ...459.00  55" long ...531.00 | | | | | | |
| *Labor* ...................  38" long....116.00  55" long.....116.00 | | | | | | |
| **44" wide ventilating skylight** | ea | $600.00 | — | $705.00 | — | |
| *Materials* 28" long .484.00  48" long ...589.00 | | | | | | |
| *Labor* 28" long ..........116.00  48" long.....116.00 | | | | | | |

**RELATED ITEMS**

Doors
*sliding patio* ...................119

| Item Description | | Unit | 28" long | 38" long | 48" long | 55" long |
|---|---|---|---|---|---|---|
| **SKYLIGHTS ▶** *continued* roof window ▷ | **22" wide roof window** *Materials* 28" long...520.00   48" long....573.00 *Labor* 28" long.......116.00   48" long.....116.00 | ea | $636.00 | — | $689.00 | — |
| | **30" wide roof window** *Materials* .............. 38" long ...577.00   55" long....659.00 *Labor* .............. 38" long ....116.00   55" long.....116.00 | ea | — | $693.00 | — | $775.00 |
| | **44" wide roof window** *Materials* .............. 55" long....720.00 *Labor* .............. 55" long.....116.00 | ea | — | — | — | $836.00 |

| Item Description | | Unit | 28" long | 38" long | 48" long | 55" long |
|---|---|---|---|---|---|---|
| accessories ▷ | **Add for cord-operated roller shades** *Materials* 28" long....55.00  38" long.....55.00  48" long......55.00  55" long.....55.00 *Labor* 28" long...........32.90  38" long.....32.90  48" long......32.90  55" long......32.90 | ea | $87.90 | $87.90 | $87.90 | $87.90 |
| | **Add for motorized rod cord control for roller shades** *Materials* 28" long....170.00  38" long....170.00  48" long....170.00  55" long....170.00 | ea | $170.00 | $170.00 | $170.00 | $170.00 |
| | **Add for manually controlled Venetian blinds** *Materials* 28" long ...77.00  38" long .....91.00  48" long......96.00  55" long....122.00 | ea | $77.00 | $91.00 | $96.00 | $122.00 |
| | **Add for electrically controlled skylight system** *Materials* 28" long ..125.00  38" long....125.00  48" long....125.00  55" long....125.00 *Labor* 28" long...........79.00  38" long.....79.00  48" long......79.00  55" long......79.00 | ea | $204.00 | $204.00 | $204.00 | $204.00 |
| | **Add for electrically controlled window or skylight opener** *Materials* 28" long ..125.00  38" long....125.00  48" long....125.00  55" long....125.00 *Labor* 28" long...........54.90  38" long....54.90  48" long......54.90  55" long .....54.90 | ea | $179.90 | $179.90 | $179.90 | $179.90 |
| | **Add for infrared remote control system for opener** *Materials* 28" long..277.00  38" long ...277.00  48" long.....277.00  55" long....277.00 *Labor* 28" long...........43.80  38" long....43.80  48" long......43.80  55" long .....43.80 | ea | $320.80 | $320.80 | $320.80 | $320.80 |

| Item Description | | Unit | 24" tall | 36" tall | 48" tall | 60" tall |
|---|---|---|---|---|---|---|
| **STORM WINDOW ▶** aluminum ▷ | **24" wide aluminum storm window** *Materials* 24" tall .....58.90  36" tall .....85.90  48" tall .... 107.00  60" tall .... 120.00 *Labor* 24" tall............39.50  36" tall .....39.50  48" tall......39.50  60" tall......39.50 | ea | $98.40 | $125.40 | $146.50 | $159.50 |
| | **36" wide aluminum storm window** *Materials* 24" tall .....85.90  36" tall .... 113.00  48" tall .... 131.00  60" tall .... 151.00 *Labor* 24" tall............39.50  36" tall .....39.50  48" tall......39.50  60" tall......42.70 | ea | $125.40 | $152.50 | $170.50 | $193.70 |
| | **48" wide aluminum storm window** *Materials* 24" tall....107.00  36" tall .... 131.00  48" tall .... 157.00  60" tall.... 183.00 *Labor* 24" tall............39.50  36" tall .....39.50  48" tall......42.70  60" tall......42.70 | ea | $146.50 | $170.50 | $199.70 | $225.70 |
| | **60" wide aluminum storm window** *Materials* 24" tall....120.00  36" tall .... 151.00  48" tall .... 183.00  60" tall.... 213.00 *Labor* 24" tall............39.50  36" tall .....42.70  48" tall......42.70  60" tall......42.70 | ea | $159.50 | $193.70 | $225.70 | $255.70 |
| | **72" wide aluminum storm window** *Materials* 24" tall....131.00  36" tall .... 169.00  48" tall .... 207.00  60" tall.... 245.00 *Labor* 24" tall............39.50  36" tall .....42.70  48" tall......42.70  60" tall .....48.20 | ea | $170.50 | $211.70 | $249.70 | $293.20 |
| wood ▷ | **24" wide wood storm window** *Materials* 24" tall....72.30  36" tall .... 102.70  48" tall .... 119.00  60" tall.... 134.00 *Labor* 24" tall............39.50  36" tall .....39.50  48" tall......39.50  60" tall......39.50 | ea | $111.80 | $142.20 | $158.50 | $173.50 |

| Item Description | Unit | 24" tall | 36" tall | 48" tall | 60" tall |
|---|---|---|---|---|---|
| **36" wide wood storm window** | ea | $142.20 | $165.50 | $186.50 | $211.70 |
| *Materials* 24" tall....102.70  36" tall....126.00  48" tall ....147.00  60" tall....169.00 | | | | | |
| *Labor* 24" tall...........39.50  36" tall....39.50  48" tall......39.50  60" tall......42.70 | | | | | |
| **48" wide wood storm window** | ea | $158.50 | $186.50 | $217.70 | $246.70 |
| *Materials* 24" tall.....119.00  36" tall....147.00  48" tall ....175.00  60" tall ...204.00 | | | | | |
| *Labor* 24" tall...........39.50  36" tall....39.50  48" tall......42.70  60" tall......42.70 | | | | | |
| **60" wide wood storm window** | ea | $173.50 | $211.70 | $246.70 | $280.70 |
| *Materials* 24" tall....134.00  36" tall....169.00  48" tall ...204.00  60" tall ...238.00 | | | | | |
| *Labor* 24" tall...........39.50  36" tall....42.70  48" tall......42.70  60" tall......42.70 | | | | | |
| **72" wide wood storm window** | ea | $186.50 | $232.70 | $274.70 | $322.20 |
| *Materials* 24" tall ....147.00  36" tall....190.00  48" tall....232.00  60" tall ...274.00 | | | | | |
| *Labor* 24" tall...........39.50  36" tall....42.70  48" tall......42.70  60" tall ....48.20 | | | | | |
| **24" wide window screen** | ea | $14.84 | $16.94 | $18.54 | $21.94 |
| *Materials* 24" tall .......9.90  36" tall......12.00  48" tall......13.60  60" tall ....17.00 | | | | | |
| *Labor* 24" tall .........4.94  36" tall......4.94  48" tall.......4.94  60" tall......4.94 | | | | | |
| **36" wide window screen** | ea | $16.64 | $17.64 | $22.24 | $23.94 |
| *Materials* 24" tall ......11.70  36" tall......12.70  48" tall......17.30  60" tall......19.00 | | | | | |
| *Labor* 24" tall ..........4.94  36" tall......4.94  48" tall......4.94  60" tall......4.94 | | | | | |

◄ SCREEN

| Item Description | Unit | 1/8" thick | 3/16" thick | 1/4" thick | 3/8" thick |
|---|---|---|---|---|---|
| **Reglaze window with clear glass** | sf | $6.19 | $7.39 | $6.59 | $15.39 |
| *Materials* 1/8"..........3.70  3/16"......4.90  1/4"......4.10  3/8"......12.90 | | | | | |
| *Labor* 1/8"................2.49  3/16"......2.49  1/4"......2.49  3/8"........2.49 | | | | | |
| **Reglaze window with tempered glass** | sf | $8.59 | $9.69 | $10.09 | — |
| *Materials* 1/8"..........6.10  3/16"......7.20  1/4"......7.60 | | | | | |
| *Labor* 1/8"................2.49  3/16"......2.49  1/4"......2.49 | | | | | |
| **Reglaze window with laminated glass** | sf | — | — | $11.59 | $15.09 |
| *Materials* ..................1/4"......9.10  3/8"......12.60 | | | | | |
| *Labor* ........................1/4"......2.49  3/8".......2.49 | | | | | |
| **Reglaze window with polished wire glass** | sf | — | — | $26.59 | — |
| *Materials* ..................1/4"......24.10 | | | | | |
| *Labor* ........................1/4".......2.49 | | | | | |
| **Minimum charge for reglazing work** | ea | $70.50 | — | — | — |
| *Materials*..................31.00 | | | | | |
| *Labor* .........................39.50 | | | | | |

◄ REGLAZE

◁ minimum

| Item Description | Unit | all sizes | | | |
|---|---|---|---|---|---|
| **Rehang sash weight in antique double-hung window** | ea | $105.70 | | | |
| *Materials* All sizes .....16.00 | | | | | |
| *Labor* All sizes............89.70 | | | | | |
| **Refurbish antique double-hung window** | ea | $152.00 | | | |
| *Materials* All sizes.....28.00 | | | | | |
| *Labor* All sizes...........124.00 | | | | | |
| **Recondition antique wood window sash** | ea | $96.20 | | | |
| *Materials* All sizes .....14.00 | | | | | |
| *Labor* All sizes............82.20 | | | | | |

◄ REPAIR

**RELATED ITEMS**
Doors
*sliding patio* ..................119

NOTES: _____

_____ end

# TIME & MATERIAL CHARTS *(selected items)*

## Windows Materials

See **Windows** material prices with the line items and other information in the **QuickFinder** column.

## Windows Labor

| LABORER | BASE WAGE | PAID LEAVE | TRUE WAGE | FICA | FUTA | WORKER'S COMP. | UNEMPLOY. INSUR. | HEALTH INSUR. | RETIRE (401K) | LIABILITY INSUR. | COST PER HOUR |
|---|---|---|---|---|---|---|---|---|---|---|---|
| Installer | $22.60 | 1.76 | $24.36 | 1.86 | .19 | 4.56 | 2.12 | 2.54 | .73 | 3.17 | $39.50 |
| Demolition laborer | $13.40 | 1.05 | $14.45 | 1.11 | .12 | 4.44 | 1.26 | 2.54 | .43 | 1.88 | $26.20 |

**Paid Leave** is calculated based on two weeks paid vacation, one week sick leave, and seven paid holidays. Employer's matching portion of **FICA** is 7.65 percent. **FUTA** (Federal Unemployment) is .8 percent. **Worker's compensation** for the windows trade was calculated using a national average of 18.71 percent. **Unemployment insurance** was calculated using a national average of 8.7 percent. **Health insurance** was calculated based on a projected national average for 2001 of $505 per employee (and family when applicable) per month. Employer pays 80 percent for a per month cost of $404 per employee. **Retirement** is based on a 401(k) retirement program with employer matching of 50 percent. Employee contributions to the 401(k) plan are an average of 6 percent of the true wage. **Liability insurance** is based on a national average of 12.9 percent.

## Windows Labor Productivity

| WORK DESCRIPTION | LABORER | COST PER HOUR | PRODUCTIVITY | UNIT PRICE |
|---|---|---|---|---|
| **Remove window** | | | | |
| small (4 to 10 sf) | carpenter | $39.50 | .263 | $10.40 ea |
| average size (11 to 16 sf) | carpenter | $39.50 | .270 | $10.70 ea |
| large (17 to 29 sf) | carpenter | $39.50 | .278 | $11.00 ea |
| very large (30 sf and larger) | carpenter | $39.50 | .286 | $11.30 ea |
| **Remove window for work & reinstall** | | | | |
| small (4 to 10 sf) | carpenter | $39.50 | 1.23 | $48.60 ea |
| average size (11 to 16 sf) | carpenter | $39.50 | 1.72 | $67.90 ea |
| large (17 to 28 sf) | carpenter | $39.50 | 2.50 | $98.80 ea |
| very large (30 sf and larger) | carpenter | $39.50 | 3.70 | $146.00 ea |
| **Install window** | | | | |
| small (4 to 10 sf) | carpenter | $39.50 | .990 | $39.10 ea |
| average size (11 to 16 sf) | carpenter | $39.50 | 1.39 | $54.90 ea |
| large (17 to 28 sf) | carpenter | $39.50 | 2.00 | $79.00 ea |
| very large (30 sf and larger) | carpenter | $39.50 | 2.94 | $116.00 ea |
| **Install skylight or roof window** | | | | |
| dome ventilating | carpenter | $39.50 | 2.78 | $110.00 ea |
| fixed | carpenter | $39.50 | 2.70 | $107.00 ea |
| ventilating | carpenter | $39.50 | 2.94 | $116.00 ea |
| cord-operated roller shades | carpenter | $39.50 | .833 | $32.90 ea |
| electrically controlled system | carpenter | $39.50 | 2.00 | $79.00 ea |
| electrically controlled opener | carpenter | $39.50 | 1.39 | $54.90 ea |
| infrared remote control system for opener | carpenter | $39.50 | 1.11 | $43.80 ea |
| **Install storm window** | | | | |
| small (4 to 14 sf) | carpenter | $39.50 | 1.00 | $39.50 ea |
| average size (15 to 25 sf) | carpenter | $39.50 | 1.08 | $42.70 ea |
| large storm (26 sf and larger) | carpenter | $39.50 | 1.22 | $48.20 ea |
| **Reglaze window** | | | | |
| remove and replace glass | carpenter | $39.50 | .063 | $2.49 sf |
| **Repair antique double-hung window** | | | | |
| rehang sash weight | carpenter | $39.50 | 2.27 | $89.70 ea |
| refurbish | carpenter | $39.50 | 3.13 | $124.00 ea |
| recondition | carpenter | $39.50 | 2.08 | $82.20 ea |

# *mini price list* ............... **Manufactured Housing**

## SELECTED PRICES FROM THE *NATIONAL MANUFACTURED HOUSING ESTIMATOR*

This chapter contains some of the most common items found in manufactured housing. *It is not a complete price list.* A comprehensive costbook of manufactured housing costs is in the planning stages at *Craftsman Book Company.*

| Item Description | Unit | Remove | Replace | Total |
|---|---|---|---|---|
| **APPLIANCES** | | | | |
| **Clothes line** | | | | |
| **30-line, exterior** | ea | $6.88 | $153.30 | $160.18 |
| *Replace* Mat. .........122.00   Lab. ............31.30 | | | | |
| *Remove* ..................   Lab. ............6.88 | | | | |
| **7-line, exterior** | ea | $6.52 | $103.10 | $109.62 |
| *Replace* Mat. ..........73.00   Lab. ..........30.10 | | | | |
| *Remove* ..................   Lab. ............6.52 | | | | |
| **remove for work, then reinstall** | ea | — | $9.06 | $9.06 |
| *Replace* ..................   Lab. ............9.06 | | | | |
| **Sidewall exhaust ventilator** | | | | |
| **for 2" to 3" thick walls** | ea | $9.70 | $107.80 | $117.50 |
| *Replace* Mat...........50.00   Lab............57.80 | | | | |
| *Remove* ..................   Lab. ............9.70 | | | | |
| **for 2-3/4" to 4" thick walls** | ea | $9.70 | $109.80 | $119.50 |
| *Replace* Mat..........52.00   Lab............57.80 | | | | |
| *Remove* ..................   Lab. ............9.70 | | | | |
| **remove for work, then reinstall** | ea | — | $91.70 | $91.70 |
| *Replace* Mat...........2.00   Lab............89.70 | | | | |
| **CABINETS** | | | | |
| **Mobile-home type cabinets, average grade** | | | | |
| **lower units** | lf | $3.02 | $53.04 | $56.06 |
| *Replace* Mat. ..........47.00   Lab. ...........6.04 | | | | |
| *Remove* ..................   Lab. ............3.02 | | | | |
| **upper units** | lf | $3.02 | $36.98 | $40.00 |
| *Replace* Mat..........32.00   Lab. ...........4.98 | | | | |
| *Remove* ..................   Lab. ............3.02 | | | | |
| **lower island units** | lf | $3.02 | $73.55 | $76.57 |
| *Replace* Mat..........66.00   Lab. ...........7.55 | | | | |
| *Remove* ..................   Lab. ............3.02 | | | | |

◄ **CLOTHES LINE** *Steel posts, umbrella-style supports with vinyl-coated rayon lines.*

◄ **VENTILATOR** *Louvered inside grille, insulated outside door, approximately 9" x 9".*

◄ **CABINETS** *Mobile-home style*

| | Item Description | Unit | Remove | Replace | Total |
|---|---|---|---|---|---|
| **CABINETS ▶** *continued* | upper island units<br>*Replace* Mat. ..........57.00   Lab. ..........5.44<br>*Remove* ................   Lab. ..........3.02 | lf | $3.02 | $62.44 | $65.46 |
| | remove for work, then reinstall<br>*Replace* ..................   Lab. ..........6.95 | lf | — | $6.95 | $6.95 |

# DOORS

**ACCESS DOOR ▶** access door

| | Item Description | Unit | Remove | Replace | Total |
|---|---|---|---|---|---|
| | for water heater or furnace<br>*Replace* Mat. ..........44.20   Lab. ..........24.20<br>*Remove* ................   Lab. ..........14.40 | ea | $14.40 | $68.40 | $82.80 |
| | remove for work, then reinstall<br>*Replace* ..................   Lab. ..........30.20 | ea | — | $30.20 | $30.20 |

**ENTRY DOOR ▶** mobile-home type entry door, fiberglass

| | Item Description | Unit | Remove | Replace | Total |
|---|---|---|---|---|---|
| | flush<br>*Replace* Mat. ..........95.00   Lab. ..........22.70<br>*Remove* ................   Lab. ..........15.10 | ea | $15.10 | $117.70 | $132.80 |
| | flush with fixed lite<br>*Replace* Mat. ..........109.00   Lab. ..........22.70<br>*Remove* ................   Lab. ..........15.10 | ea | $15.10 | $131.70 | $146.80 |
| | flush with sliding window<br>*Replace* Mat. ..........120.00   Lab. ..........22.70<br>*Remove* ................   Lab. ..........15.10 | ea | $15.10 | $142.70 | $157.80 |
| | remove for work, then reinstall<br>*Replace* ..................   Lab. ..........31.70 | ea | — | $31.70 | $31.70 |

**COMBINATION DOOR ▶** mobile-home type combination entry door (with storm door)

| | Item Description | Unit | Remove | Replace | Total |
|---|---|---|---|---|---|
| | flush<br>*Replace* Mat. ..........124.00   Lab. ..........25.80<br>*Remove* ................   Lab. ..........18.10 | ea | $18.10 | $149.80 | $167.90 |
| | flush with fixed lite<br>*Replace* Mat. ..........142.00   Lab. ..........25.80<br>*Remove* ................   Lab. ..........18.10 | ea | $18.10 | $167.80 | $185.90 |
| | flush with sliding window<br>*Replace* Mat. ..........157.00   Lab. ..........25.80<br>*Remove* ................   Lab. ..........18.10 | ea | $18.10 | $182.80 | $200.90 |
| | remove for work, then reinstall<br>*Replace* ..................   Lab. ..........32.30 | ea | — | $32.30 | $32.30 |

# DOOR HARDWARE

**LOCKSET ▶** mobile-home type lockset

| | Item Description | Unit | Remove | Replace | Total |
|---|---|---|---|---|---|
| | interior passage<br>*Replace* Mat. ..........12.10   Lab. ..........11.70<br>*Remove* ................   Lab. ..........6.26 | ea | $6.26 | $23.80 | $30.06 |
| | interior privacy<br>*Replace* Mat. ..........14.00   Lab. ..........11.70<br>*Remove* ................   Lab. ..........6.26 | ea | $6.26 | $25.70 | $31.96 |
| | remove for work, then reinstall<br>*Replace* ..................   Lab. ..........13.60 | ea | — | $13.60 | $13.60 |

| Item Description | Unit | Remove | Replace | Total | |
|---|---|---|---|---|---|
| **mobile-home type entrance lockset** | | | | | ◄ ENTRANCE LOCKSET |
| **standard quality** | ea | $7.73 | $44.40 | $52.13 | |
| *Replace* Mat. .........27.60    Lab. ..........16.80 | | | | | |
| *Remove* .........................    Lab. ..........7.73 | | | | | |
| **remove for work, then reinstall** | ea | — | $22.30 | $22.30 | |
| *Replace* .........................    Lab. ..........22.30 | | | | | |
| **mobile-home type deadbolt** | | | | | ◄ DEADBOLT |
| **standard quality** | ea | $5.38 | $37.20 | $42.58 | |
| *Replace* Mat. .........18.00    Lab. ..........19.20 | | | | | |
| *Remove* .........................    Lab. ..........5.38 | | | | | |
| **remove for work, then reinstall** | ea | — | $22.70 | $22.70 | |
| *Replace* .........................    Lab. ..........22.70 | | | | | |

## ELECTRICAL

| Item Description | Unit | Remove | Replace | Total | |
|---|---|---|---|---|---|
| **Light fixture, mobile-home style** | | | | | ◄ LIGHT FIXTURE |
| **average quality** | ea | $11.10 | $29.40 | $40.50 | |
| *Replace* Mat. ..........12.00    Lab. ..........17.40 | | | | | |
| *Remove* .........................    Lab. ..........11.10 | | | | | |
| **high quality** | ea | $11.10 | $36.60 | $47.70 | |
| *Replace* Mat. .........19.20    Lab. ..........17.40 | | | | | |
| *Remove* .........................    Lab. ..........11.10 | | | | | |
| **remove for work, then reinstall** | ea | — | $18.70 | $18.70 | |
| *Replace* .........................    Lab. ..........18.70 | | | | | |

## FINISH CARPENTRY

| Item Description | Unit | Remove | Replace | Total | |
|---|---|---|---|---|---|
| **Casing (door or window)** | | | | | ◄ CASING |
| **2-1/2" prefinished plastic** | lf | $.44 | $1.40 | $1.88 | |
| *Replace* Mat. ............ .28    Lab. ...........1.12 | | | | | |
| *Remove* .........................    Lab. ............ .44 | | | | | |
| **Ceiling cove** | | | | | ◄ COVE |
| **3/4" prefinished plastic** | lf | $.44 | $1.40 | $1.88 | |
| *Replace* Mat. ............ .28    Lab. ...........1.12 | | | | | |
| *Remove* .........................    Lab. ............ .44 | | | | | |
| **Gimp molding** | | | | | ◄ GIMP MOLDING |
| **3/4" prefinished plastic** | lf | $.44 | $1.40 | $1.88 | |
| *Replace* Mat. ............ .28    Lab. ...........1.12 | | | | | |
| *Remove* .........................    Lab. ............ .44 | | | | | |
| **1" prefinished plastic** | lf | $.44 | $1.40 | $1.88 | |
| *Replace* Mat. ............ .28    Lab. ...........1.12 | | | | | |
| *Remove* .........................    Lab. ............ .44 | | | | | |
| **Outside corner trim** | | | | | ◄ OUTSIDE CORNER |
| **1" prefinished plastic** | lf | $.44 | $1.40 | $1.88 | |
| *Replace* Mat. ............ .28    Lab. ...........1.12 | | | | | |
| *Remove* .........................    Lab. ............ .44 | | | | | |

| Item Description | Unit | Remove | Replace | Total |
|---|---|---|---|---|
| **SHOE ▶ Shoe molding** | | | | |
| 3/4" prefinished plastic | lf | $.44 | $1.40 | $1.88 |
| *Replace* Mat. ....28  Lab. ....1.12 | | | | |
| *Remove* ........  Lab. ....44 | | | | |

# FOUNDATIONS, SETUP, & SITE PREP

| Item Description | Unit | Remove | Replace | Total |
|---|---|---|---|---|
| **ANCHOR ▶ Anchor** *Galvanized* | | | | |
| 30" auger type | ea | $3.60 | $22.10 | $25.70 |
| *Replace* Mat. ....10.00  Lab. ....12.10 | | | | |
| *Remove* ........  Lab. ....3.60 | | | | |
| 48" auger type | ea | $3.60 | $24.40 | $28.00 |
| *Replace* Mat. ....12.30  Lab. ....12.10 | | | | |
| *Remove* ........  Lab. ....3.60 | | | | |
| Slab type (includes concrete slab) | ea | $5.44 | $31.90 | $37.34 |
| *Replace* Mat. ....16.80  Lab. ....15.10 | | | | |
| *Remove* ........  Lab. ....5.44 | | | | |
| **JACK ▶ Jack, adjustable** | | | | |
| from 1'8" to 3' | ea | $3.02 | $41.06 | $44.08 |
| *Replace* Mat. ....32.00  Lab. ....9.06 | | | | |
| *Remove* ........  Lab. ....3.02 | | | | |
| from 3'1" to 5' | ea | $3.02 | $49.06 | $52.08 |
| *Replace* Mat. ....40.00  Lab. ....9.06 | | | | |
| *Remove* ........  Lab. ....3.02 | | | | |
| from 4'6" to 7'9" | ea | $3.02 | $61.06 | $64.08 |
| *Replace* Mat. ....52.00  Lab. ....9.06 | | | | |
| *Remove* ........  Lab. ....3.02 | | | | |
| remove for work, then reinstall | ea | — | $13.60 | $13.60 |
| *Replace* ........  Lab. ....13.60 | | | | |
| **SETUP ▶ Raise, setup, block, & level** *All materials furnished by manufacturer.* | | | | |
| single wide | ea | — | $544.00 | $544.00 |
| *Replace* Mat. ....  Lab. ....544.00 | | | | |
| double wide | ea | — | $725.00 | $725.00 |
| *Replace* Mat. ....  Lab. ....725.00 | | | | |
| triple wide | ea | — | $1,030.00 | $1,030.00 |
| *Replace* Mat. ....  Lab. ....1,030.00 | | | | |
| **RELEVEL ▶ Relevel** | | | | |
| single wide | ea | — | $185.00 | $185.00 |
| *Replace* Mat. ....34.00  Lab. ....151.00 | | | | |
| double wide | ea | — | $430.40 | $430.40 |
| *Replace* Mat. ....68.00  Lab. ....362.40 | | | | |
| triple wide | ea | — | $675.80 | $675.80 |
| *Replace* Mat. ....102.00  Lab. ....573.80 | | | | |
| **SITE PREP ▶ Site prep** | | | | |
| standard conditions | ea | — | $1,600.00 | $1,600.00 |
| *Replace* ........  Lab. ....1,600.00 | | | | |

| Item Description | Unit | Remove | Replace | Total | |
|---|---|---|---|---|---|
| **Tie-down strap** | | | | | ◀ **TIE-DOWN STRAP** Galvanized. Frame type includes adapter and is 6' long. Roof type is 37' long. |
| **frame type** *Replace* Mat. ..........9.25    Lab. ..........6.04 *Remove* ................    Lab. ..........4.38 | ea | $4.38 | $15.29 | $19.67 | |
| **roof type** *Replace* Mat. .........22.00    Lab. ..........7.55 *Remove* ................    Lab. ..........6.64 | ea | $6.64 | $29.55 | $36.19 | |
| **Utility hookup** | | | | | ◀ **UTILITY HOOKUP** |
| **sewer & water** *Replace* ...............680.00 | ea | — | $680.00 | $680.00 | |
| **electrical** *Replace* Mat. .........720.00 | ea | — | $720.00 | $720.00 | |

# HVAC

## Baseboard heater, mobile-home type, electric

| Item Description | Unit | Remove | Replace | Total | |
|---|---|---|---|---|---|
| **1,500 watt** *Replace* Mat. ..........9.10    Lab. ..........6.04 *Remove* ................    Lab. ..........3.02 | lf | $3.02 | $15.14 | $18.16 | ◀ **BASEBOARD HEATER** |
| **2,000 watt** *Replace* Mat. .........12.40    Lab. ..........6.04 *Remove* ................    Lab. ..........3.02 | lf | $3.02 | $18.44 | $21.46 | |
| **2,500 watt** *Replace* Mat. .........14.00    Lab. ..........6.04 *Remove* ................    Lab. ..........3.02 | lf | $3.02 | $20.04 | $23.06 | |
| **remove for work, then reinstall** *Replace* ................    Lab. ..........9.06 | lf | — | $9.06 | $9.06 | |

## Furnace, mobile-home type, gas or electric

| Item Description | Unit | Remove | Replace | Total | |
|---|---|---|---|---|---|
| **35,000 btu** *Replace* Mat. ........482.00    Lab. .........151.00 *Remove* ................    Lab. ..........37.80 | ea | $37.80 | $633.00 | $670.80 | ◀ **FURNACE** |
| **55,000 btu** *Replace* Mat. ........744.00    Lab. .........166.00 *Remove* ................    Lab. ..........37.80 | ea | $37.80 | $910.00 | $947.80 | |
| **70,000 btu** *Replace* Mat. ........839.00    Lab. .........181.00 *Remove* ................    Lab. ..........37.80 | ea | $37.80 | $1,020.00 | $1,057.80 | |
| **80,000 btu** *Replace* Mat. ........897.00    Lab. .........181.00 *Remove* ................    Lab. ..........37.80 | ea | $37.80 | $1,078.00 | $1,115.80 | |
| **100,000 btu** *Replace* Mat. ......1,010.00    Lab. .........181.00 *Remove* ................    Lab. ..........37.80 | ea | $37.80 | $1,191.00 | $1,228.80 | |
| **125,000 btu** *Replace* Mat. ......1,100.00    Lab. .........181.00 *Remove* ................    Lab. ..........37.80 | ea | $37.80 | $1,281.00 | $1,318.80 | |
| **remove for work, then reinstall** *Replace* ................    Lab. .........257.00 | ea | — | $257.00 | $257.00 | |

| Item Description | Unit | Remove | Replace | Total |
|---|---|---|---|---|
| **MOVING & TOWING** | | | | |
| TRANSPORT ▶ Transport fees | | | | |
| average, per section, per mile | ea | — | $2.34 | $2.34 |
| *Replace* ............... Lab. ...........2.34 | | | | |
| average, pilot car, per mile | ea | — | $.70 | $.70 |
| *Replace* ............... Lab. .............70 | | | | |
| **PLUMBING** | | | | |
| ELECTRIC WATER ▶ HEATER Water heater, mobile-home style, electric | | | | |
| 10 gallon | ea | $22.70 | $142.30 | $165.00 |
| *Replace* Mat. ...........97.00 Lab. ...........45.30 | | | | |
| *Remove* ............... Lab. ...........22.70 | | | | |
| 20 gallon | ea | $22.70 | $153.30 | $176.00 |
| *Replace* Mat. .........108.00 Lab. ...........45.30 | | | | |
| *Remove* ............... Lab. ...........22.70 | | | | |
| 30 gallon | ea | $22.70 | $182.30 | $205.00 |
| *Replace* Mat. ...........137.00 Lab. ...........45.30 | | | | |
| *Remove* ............... Lab. ...........22.70 | | | | |
| 40 gallon | ea | $22.70 | $195.30 | $218.00 |
| *Replace* Mat. .........150.00 Lab. ...........45.30 | | | | |
| *Remove* ............... Lab. ...........22.70 | | | | |
| 50 gallon | ea | $22.70 | $239.30 | $262.00 |
| *Replace* Mat. .........194.00 Lab. ...........45.30 | | | | |
| *Remove* ............... Lab. ...........22.70 | | | | |
| remove for work. then reinstall | ea | — | $57.40 | $57.40 |
| *Replace* Mat. ............... Lab. ...........57.40 | | | | |
| GAS WATER ▶ HEATER Water heater, mobile-home style, gas | | | | |
| 20 gallon | ea | $22.70 | $163.90 | $186.60 |
| *Replace* Mat. .........108.00 Lab. ...........55.90 | | | | |
| *Remove* ............... Lab. ...........22.70 | | | | |
| 30 gallon | ea | $22.70 | $187.90 | $210.60 |
| *Replace* Mat. ...........132.00 Lab. ...........55.90 | | | | |
| *Remove* ............... Lab. ...........22.70 | | | | |
| 40 gallon | ea | $22.70 | $210.90 | $233.60 |
| *Replace* Mat. ...........155.00 Lab. ...........55.90 | | | | |
| *Remove* ............... Lab. ...........22.70 | | | | |
| 50 gallon | ea | $22.70 | $244.90 | $267.60 |
| *Replace* Mat. .........189.00 Lab. ...........55.90 | | | | |
| *Remove* ............... Lab. ...........22.70 | | | | |
| remove for work. then reinstall | ea | — | $57.40 | $57.40 |
| *Replace* Mat. ............... Lab. ...........57.40 | | | | |
| **ROOFING** | | | | |
| DRIP EDGE ▶ Drip edge | | | | |
| aluminum | lf | $.12 | $1.20 | $1.32 |
| *Replace* Mat. .............29 Lab. .............91 | | | | |
| *Remove* ............... Lab. .............12 | | | | |

| Item Description | Unit | Remove | Replace | Total |
|---|---|---|---|---|
| galvanized | lf | $.12 | $1.17 | $1.29 |
|   *Replace* Mat. .............26    Lab. ..............91 | | | | |
|   *Remove* ...................    Lab. ..............12 | | | | |
| **Flashing** | | | | |
| aluminum, flexible | lf | $.12 | $1.95 | $2.07 |
|   *Replace* Mat. .............1.04    Lab. ..............91 | | | | |
|   *Remove* ...................    Lab. ..............12 | | | | |
| galvanized | lf | $.12 | $1.85 | $1.97 |
|   *Replace* Mat. .............94    Lab. ..............91 | | | | |
|   *Remove* ...................    Lab. ..............12 | | | | |
| **J-rail** | | | | |
| aluminum | lf | $.12 | $1.27 | $1.39 |
|   *Replace* Mat. .............36    Lab. ..............91 | | | | |
|   *Remove* ...................    Lab. ..............12 | | | | |
| **Roof coating** | | | | |
| complete roof (all types) | sf | — | $.34 | $.34 |
|   *Replace* Mat. .............16    Lab. ..............18 | | | | |
| seams and edges only | lf | — | $.47 | $.47 |
|   *Replace* Mat. .............20    Lab. ..............27 | | | | |
| **Roof repair** | | | | |
| patch | ea | — | $27.00 | $27.00 |
|   *Replace* Mat. .............4.30    Lab. ...........22.70 | | | | |
| replace section (per lf of 4' wide section) | lf | $.60 | $6.86 | $7.46 |
|   *Replace* Mat. .............3.84    Lab. .............3.02 | | | | |
|   *Remove* ...................    Lab. ..............60 | | | | |

## ROUGH CARPENTRY

| Item Description | Unit | Remove | Replace | Total |
|---|---|---|---|---|
| **Belt rail** | | | | |
| 1" x 2" | lf | $.30 | $.80 | $1.10 |
|   *Replace* Mat. .............20    Lab. ..............60 | | | | |
|   *Remove* ...................    Lab. ..............30 | | | | |
| 1" x 4" | lf | $.30 | $1.06 | $1.36 |
|   *Replace* Mat. .............30    Lab. ..............76 | | | | |
|   *Remove* ...................    Lab. ..............30 | | | | |
| **Belt rail including dado cut** | | | | |
| 1" x 2" | lf | $.45 | $1.41 | $1.86 |
|   *Replace* Mat. .............20    Lab. .............1.21 | | | | |
|   *Remove* ...................    Lab. ..............45 | | | | |
| 1" x 4" | lf | $.45 | $1.66 | $2.11 |
|   *Replace* Mat. .............30    Lab. .............1.36 | | | | |
|   *Remove* ...................    Lab. ..............45 | | | | |
| **Exterior wall, mobile home, with belt rail** | | | | |
| 2" x 2" | lf | $1.21 | $14.91 | $16.12 |
|   *Replace* Mat. .............5.85    Lab. .............9.06 | | | | |
|   *Remove* ...................    Lab. .............1.21 | | | | |
| 2" x 4" | lf | $1.21 | $18.70 | $19.91 |
|   *Replace* Mat. .............8.10    Lab. ...........10.60 | | | | |
|   *Remove* ...................    Lab. .............1.21 | | | | |

◄ FLASHING

◄ J-RAIL

◄ ROOF COATING

◄ BELT RAIL

◄ BELT RAIL WITH DADO

◄ EXTERIOR WALL

| | Item Description | Unit | Remove | Replace | Total |
|---|---|---|---|---|---|
| **EXTERIOR WALLS ▶** *continued* | **2" x 6"** | lf | $1.21 | $23.90 | $25.11 |
| | *Replace* Mat.............11.80 Lab. ...........12.10 | | | | |
| | *Remove* .................... Lab. ...........1.21 | | | | |
| **INTERIOR WALL ▶** | **Interior wall, mobile home** | | | | |
| | **2" x 2"** | lf | $1.06 | $11.24 | $12.30 |
| | *Replace* Mat.............5.20 Lab. ...........6.04 | | | | |
| | *Remove* .................... Lab. ...........1.06 | | | | |
| | **2" x 4"** | lf | $1.06 | $15.35 | $16.41 |
| | *Replace* Mat.............7.20 Lab. ...........8.15 | | | | |
| | *Remove* .................... Lab. ...........1.06 | | | | |
| | **2" x 6"** | lf | $1.06 | $18.96 | $20.02 |
| | *Replace* Mat............10.50 Lab. ...........8.46 | | | | |
| | *Remove* .................... Lab. ...........1.06 | | | | |
| **JOIST SYSTEM ▶** **2" X 6" PER JOIST** | **Joist system, mobile home, per joist, 2" x 6"** | | | | |
| | **10'** | ea | $3.62 | $15.40 | $19.02 |
| | *Replace* Mat.............9.03 Lab. ...........6.37 | | | | |
| | *Remove* .................... Lab. ...........3.62 | | | | |
| | **12'** | ea | $3.78 | $18.44 | $22.22 |
| | *Replace* Mat............10.80 Lab. ...........7.64 | | | | |
| | *Remove* .................... Lab. ...........3.78 | | | | |
| | **14'** | ea | $3.93 | $21.52 | $25.45 |
| | *Replace* Mat............12.60 Lab. ...........8.92 | | | | |
| | *Remove* .................... Lab. ...........3.93 | | | | |
| | **16'** | ea | $4.08 | $24.60 | $28.68 |
| | *Replace* Mat............14.40 Lab............10.20 | | | | |
| | *Remove* .................... Lab. ...........4.08 | | | | |
| **JOIST SYSTEM ▶** **2" X 8" PER JOIST** | **Joist system, mobile home, per joist, 2" x 8"** | | | | |
| | **10'** | ea | $3.78 | $16.49 | $20.27 |
| | *Replace* Mat............10.00 Lab. ...........6.49 | | | | |
| | *Remove* .................... Lab. ...........3.78 | | | | |
| | **12'** | ea | $3.93 | $19.70 | $23.63 |
| | *Replace* Mat............12.00 Lab. ...........7.70 | | | | |
| | *Remove* .................... Lab. ...........3.93 | | | | |
| | **14'** | ea | $4.08 | $23.06 | $27.14 |
| | *Replace* Mat............14.00 Lab. ...........9.06 | | | | |
| | *Remove* .................... Lab. ...........4.08 | | | | |
| | **16'** | ea | $4.23 | $26.50 | $30.73 |
| | *Replace* Mat............16.10 Lab............10.40 | | | | |
| | *Remove* .................... Lab. ...........4.23 | | | | |
| **JOIST SYSTEM ▶** **PER SF** | **Joist system, mobile home, per sf** | | | | |
| | **2" x 6", 16" on center** | sf | $.36 | $1.55 | $1.91 |
| | *Replace* Mat. .............92 Lab. ..............63 | | | | |
| | *Remove* .................... Lab. ..............36 | | | | |
| | **2" x 8", 16" on center** | sf | $.36 | $1.84 | $2.20 |
| | *Replace* Mat.............1.12 Lab. ..............72 | | | | |
| | *Remove* .................... Lab. ..............36 | | | | |
| | **2" x 6", 24" on center** | sf | $.30 | $1.20 | $1.50 |
| | *Replace* Mat. .............66 Lab. ..............54 | | | | |
| | *Remove* .................... Lab. ..............30 | | | | |

| Item Description | Unit | Remove | Replace | Total | |
|---|---|---|---|---|---|
| **2" x 8", 24" on center**<br>*Replace* Mat. .......... .80    Lab. .......... .48<br>*Remove* .................. Lab. .......... .30 | sf | $.30 | $1.28 | $1.58 | |
| **Rafter, mobile home, 2" x 8"** | | | | | ◄ **RAFTER, 2" x 8"**<br>**PER RAFTER** |
| **10'**<br>*Replace* Mat. ..........9.20   Lab. ..........9.06<br>*Remove* .................. Lab. ..........3.32 | lf | $3.32 | $18.26 | $21.58 | |
| **12'**<br>*Replace* Mat. ..........11.00   Lab. ..........9.66<br>*Remove* .................. Lab. ..........3.32 | lf | $3.32 | $20.66 | $23.98 | |
| **14'**<br>*Replace* Mat. ..........12.90   Lab. ..........10.30<br>*Remove* .................. Lab. ..........3.32 | lf | $3.32 | $23.20 | $26.52 | |
| **16'**<br>*Replace* Mat. ..........14.70   Lab. ..........11.50<br>*Remove* .................. Lab. ..........3.32 | lf | $3.32 | $26.20 | $29.52 | |
| **Truss, mobile home, bow roof** | | | | | ◄ **TRUSS, BOW**<br>**PER TRUSS** |
| **10'**<br>*Replace* Mat. ..........22.10   Lab. ..........10.60<br>*Remove* .................. Lab. ..........3.93 | lf | $3.93 | $32.70 | $36.63 | |
| **12'**<br>*Replace* Mat. ..........26.40   Lab. ..........11.50<br>*Remove* .................. Lab. ..........3.93 | lf | $3.93 | $37.90 | $41.83 | |
| **14'**<br>*Replace* Mat. ..........30.90   Lab. ..........12.40<br>*Remove* .................. Lab. ..........3.93 | lf | $3.93 | $43.30 | $47.23 | |
| **16'**<br>*Replace* Mat. ..........34.50   Lab. ..........13.60<br>*Remove* .................. Lab. ..........3.93 | lf | $3.93 | $48.10 | $52.03 | |
| **Truss, mobile home, gable roof** | | | | | ◄ **TRUSS, GABLE ROOF**<br>**PER TRUSS** |
| **10'**<br>*Replace* Mat. ..........23.00   Lab. ..........12.10<br>*Remove* .................. Lab. ..........3.93 | ea | $3.93 | $35.10 | $39.03 | |
| **12'**<br>*Replace* Mat. ..........27.60   Lab. ..........12.70<br>*Remove* .................. Lab. ..........3.93 | ea | $3.93 | $40.30 | $44.23 | |
| **14'**<br>*Replace* Mat. ..........32.20   Lab. ..........13.30<br>*Remove* .................. Lab. ..........3.93 | ea | $3.93 | $45.50 | $49.43 | |
| **16'**<br>*Replace* Mat. ..........36.80   Lab. ..........13.60<br>*Remove* .................. Lab. ..........3.93 | ea | $3.93 | $50.40 | $54.33 | |

# SIDING

## Horizontal lap siding, mobile home, all styles

◄ **LAP SIDING**

| Item Description | Unit | Remove | Replace | Total |
|---|---|---|---|---|
| **aluminum**<br>*Replace* Mat. .......... .38   Lab. .......... .42<br>*Remove* .................. Lab. .......... .30 | sf | $.30 | $.80 | $1.10 |

| Item Description | | | Unit | Remove | Replace | Total |
|---|---|---|---|---|---|---|
| **LAP SIDING** ▶ *continued* | **vinyl** | | sf | **$.30** | **$.79** | **$1.09** |
| | *Replace* Mat. ............37 | Lab. ..............42 | | | | |
| | *Remove* ..................... | Lab. ..............30 | | | | |
| **VERTICAL SIDING** ▶ | **Vertical siding, mobile-home style, all patterns** | | | | | |
| | **aluminum** | | sf | **$.30** | **$.96** | **$1.26** |
| | *Replace* Mat. ............54 | Lab. ..............42 | | | | |
| | *Remove* ..................... | Lab. ..............30 | | | | |
| **SHUTTERS, 9"** ▶ | **Shutters, mobile-home style, per pair, 9" wide** | | | | | |
| | **24" tall** | | ea | **$2.11** | **$31.04** | **$33.15** |
| | *Replace* Mat. ...........25.00 | Lab. ...........6.04 | | | | |
| | *Remove* ..................... | Lab. ...........2.11 | | | | |
| | **28" tall** | | ea | **$2.11** | **$32.04** | **$34.15** |
| | *Replace* Mat. ...........26.00 | Lab. ...........6.04 | | | | |
| | *Remove* ..................... | Lab. ...........2.11 | | | | |
| | **35" tall** | | ea | **$2.11** | **$33.54** | **$35.65** |
| | *Replace* Mat. ...........27.50 | Lab. ...........6.04 | | | | |
| | *Remove* ..................... | Lab. ...........2.11 | | | | |
| | **39" tall** | | ea | **$2.11** | **$34.54** | **$36.65** |
| | *Replace* Mat. ...........28.50 | Lab. ...........6.04 | | | | |
| | *Remove* ..................... | Lab. ...........2.11 | | | | |
| | **41" tall** | | ea | **$2.11** | **$35.54** | **$37.65** |
| | *Replace* Mat. ...........29.50 | Lab. ...........6.04 | | | | |
| | *Remove* ..................... | Lab. ...........2.11 | | | | |
| | **53" tall** | | ea | **$2.11** | **$38.04** | **$40.15** |
| | *Replace* Mat. ...........32.00 | Lab. ...........6.04 | | | | |
| | *Remove* ..................... | Lab. ...........2.11 | | | | |
| | **71" tall** | | ea | **$2.11** | **$44.04** | **$46.15** |
| | *Replace* Mat. ...........38.00 | Lab. ...........6.04 | | | | |
| | *Remove* ..................... | Lab. ...........2.11 | | | | |
| | **remove for work, then reinstall** | | ea | — | **$9.06** | **$9.06** |
| | *Replace* ..................... | Lab. ...........9.06 | | | | |
| **SHUTTERS, 12"** ▶ | **Shutters, mobile-home style, per pair, 12" wide** | | | | | |
| | **24" tall** | | ea | **$2.11** | **$34.55** | **$36.66** |
| | *Replace* Mat. ...........27.00 | Lab. ...........7.55 | | | | |
| | *Remove* ..................... | Lab. ...........2.11 | | | | |
| | **28" tall** | | ea | **$2.11** | **$36.55** | **$38.66** |
| | *Replace* Mat. ...........29.00 | Lab. ...........7.55 | | | | |
| | *Remove* ..................... | Lab. ...........2.11 | | | | |
| | **35" tall** | | ea | **$2.11** | **$38.55** | **$40.66** |
| | *Replace* Mat. ...........31.00 | Lab. ...........7.55 | | | | |
| | *Remove* ..................... | Lab. ...........2.11 | | | | |
| | **39" tall** | | ea | **$2.11** | **$39.55** | **$41.66** |
| | *Replace* Mat. ...........32.00 | Lab. ...........7.55 | | | | |
| | *Remove* ..................... | Lab. ...........2.11 | | | | |
| | **47" tall** | | ea | **$2.11** | **$41.55** | **$43.66** |
| | *Replace* Mat. ...........34.00 | Lab. ...........7.55 | | | | |
| | *Remove* ..................... | Lab. ...........2.11 | | | | |
| | **55" tall** | | ea | **$2.11** | **$44.55** | **$46.66** |
| | *Replace* Mat. ...........37.00 | Lab. ...........7.55 | | | | |
| | *Remove* ..................... | Lab. ...........2.11 | | | | |

| Item Description | Unit | Remove | Replace | Total |
|---|---|---|---|---|
| **63" tall** <br> *Replace* Mat. ..........39.00   Lab. ...........7.55 <br> *Remove* ..................   Lab. ............2.11 | ea | $2.11 | $46.55 | $48.66 |
| **71" tall** <br> *Replace* Mat. ..........41.00   Lab. ...........7.55 <br> *Remove* ..................   Lab. ............2.11 | ea | $2.11 | $48.55 | $50.66 |
| **80" tall** <br> *Replace* Mat. ..........42.00   Lab. ...........7.55 <br> *Remove* ..................   Lab. ............2.11 | ea | $2.11 | $49.55 | $51.66 |
| **remove for work, then reinstall** <br> *Replace* ..................   Lab. ............10.60 | ea | — | $10.60 | $10.60 |

# STEPS

◄ **REDWOOD STEPS**

## Redwood frame, steps, and side handrails (no landing)

| Item Description | Unit | Remove | Replace | Total |
|---|---|---|---|---|
| **24" high x 48" wide, 3 steps** <br> *Replace* Mat. ..........88.00   Lab. ...........189.00 <br> *Remove* ..................   Lab. ............11.20 | ea | $11.20 | $277.00 | $288.20 |
| **28" high x 48" wide, 4 steps** <br> *Replace* Mat. .........100.00   Lab. ..........193.00 <br> *Remove* ..................   Lab. ............11.20 | ea | $11.20 | $293.00 | $304.20 |
| **32" high x 48" wide, 4 steps** <br> *Replace* Mat. ..........118.00   Lab. ..........202.00 <br> *Remove* ..................   Lab. ............11.20 | ea | $11.20 | $320.00 | $331.20 |

## Redwood frame, steps, and railing, 48" x 48" landing

| Item Description | Unit | Remove | Replace | Total |
|---|---|---|---|---|
| **24" high x 48" wide, 3 steps** <br> *Replace* Mat. ..........112.00   Lab. ...........222.00 <br> *Remove* ..................   Lab. ............13.60 | ea | $13.60 | $334.00 | $347.60 |
| **28" high x 48" wide, 4 steps** <br> *Replace* Mat. ...........126.00   Lab. ..........227.00 <br> *Remove* ..................   Lab. ............13.60 | ea | $13.60 | $353.00 | $366.60 |
| **32" high x 48" wide, 4 steps** <br> *Replace* Mat. .........146.00   Lab. ..........240.00 <br> *Remove* ..................   Lab. ............13.60 | ea | $13.60 | $386.00 | $399.60 |

## Steel frame, steps, and side handrails (no landing)

◄ **STEEL STEPS**
*Steel frame and balustrade. Steps are made from 2" dimensional lumber.*

| Item Description | Unit | Remove | Replace | Total |
|---|---|---|---|---|
| **24" high x 48" wide, 3 steps** <br> *Replace* Mat. .........120.00   Lab. .........30.20 <br> *Remove* ..................   Lab. ............9.66 | ea | $9.66 | $150.20 | $159.86 |
| **28" high x 48" wide, 4 steps** <br> *Replace* Mat. .........140.00   Lab. .........30.20 <br> *Remove* ..................   Lab. ............9.66 | ea | $9.66 | $170.20 | $179.86 |
| **32" high x 48" wide, 4 steps** <br> *Replace* Mat. .........150.00   Lab. .........30.20 <br> *Remove* ..................   Lab. ............9.66 | ea | $9.66 | $180.20 | $189.86 |

## Steel frame and railing, wood steps with 27" x 36" landing

| Item Description | Unit | Remove | Replace | Total |
|---|---|---|---|---|
| **24" high x 36" wide, 2 steps** <br> *Replace* Mat. .........160.00   Lab. ............36.20 <br> *Remove* ..................   Lab. ............9.66 | ea | $9.66 | $196.20 | $205.86 |

| Item Description | Unit | Remove | Replace | Total |
|---|---|---|---|---|
| **STEEL STEPS ▶** *continued* | | | | |
| **28" high x 36" wide, 3 steps**<br>*Replace* Mat. .........185.00    Lab.............36.20<br>*Remove* .................    Lab. ............9.66 | ea | $9.66 | $221.20 | $230.86 |
| **32" high x 36" wide, 3 steps**<br>*Replace* Mat. .........190.00    Lab.............36.20<br>*Remove* .................    Lab. ............9.66 | ea | $9.66 | $226.20 | $235.86 |
| **Steel frame, steps, and railing, 27" x 72" landing** | | | | |
| **24" high x 72" wide, 3 steps**<br>*Replace* Mat. .........235.00    Lab.............36.80<br>*Remove* .................    Lab. ............9.66 | ea | $9.66 | $271.80 | $281.46 |
| **28" high x 72" wide, 4 steps**<br>*Replace* Mat. .........265.00    Lab.............36.80<br>*Remove* .................    Lab. ............9.66 | ea | $9.66 | $301.80 | $311.46 |
| **32" high x 72" wide, 4 steps**<br>*Replace* Mat. .........275.00    Lab.............36.80<br>*Remove* .................    Lab. ............9.66 | ea | $9.66 | $311.80 | $321.46 |
| **Steel frame and railing, wood steps with 4' x 5-1/2' landing** | | | | |
| **24" high x 48" wide, 2 steps**<br>*Replace* Mat. .........425.00    Lab.............58.90<br>*Remove* .................    Lab. ............13.60 | ea | $13.60 | $483.90 | $497.50 |
| **28" high x 48" wide, 3 steps**<br>*Replace* Mat. .........450.00    Lab.............58.90<br>*Remove* .................    Lab. ............13.60 | ea | $13.60 | $508.90 | $522.50 |
| **32" high x 48" wide, 3 steps**<br>*Replace* Mat. .........500.00    Lab.............58.90<br>*Remove* .................    Lab. ............13.60 | ea | $13.60 | $558.90 | $572.50 |
| **Steel frame and railing, wood steps with 9' x 5' landing** | | | | |
| **24" high x 36" wide, 2 steps**<br>*Replace* Mat. .........775.00    Lab.............60.40<br>*Remove* .................    Lab. ............13.60 | ea | $13.60 | $835.40 | $849.00 |
| **28" high x 36" wide, 3 steps**<br>*Replace* Mat. .........825.00    Lab.............60.40<br>*Remove* .................    Lab. ............13.60 | ea | $13.60 | $885.40 | $899.00 |
| **32" high x 36" wide, 3 steps**<br>*Replace* Mat. .........850.00    Lab.............60.40<br>*Remove* .................    Lab. ............13.60 | ea | $13.60 | $910.40 | $924.00 |

# SKIRTING

**ALUMINUM SKIRTING ▶**

**Aluminum skirting, solid with vented panels**

| Item Description | Unit | Remove | Replace | Total |
|---|---|---|---|---|
| **24" tall**<br>*Replace* Mat. .........3.43    Lab. ............1.66<br>*Remove* .................    Lab. ............ .60 | lf | $.60 | $5.09 | $5.69 |
| **28" tall**<br>*Replace* Mat. .........4.19    Lab. ............1.66<br>*Remove* .................    Lab. ............ .60 | lf | $.60 | $5.85 | $6.45 |
| **30" tall**<br>*Replace* Mat. .........4.27    Lab. ............1.66<br>*Remove* .................    Lab. ............ .60 | lf | $.60 | $5.93 | $6.53 |

| Item Description | Unit | Remove | Replace | Total |
|---|---|---|---|---|
| **36" tall** | lf | $.60 | $6.90 | $7.50 |
| *Replace* Mat............5.24 Lab. ............1.66 | | | | |
| *Remove* ..................... Lab. ............ .60 | | | | |
| **42" tall** | lf | $.60 | $8.51 | $9.11 |
| *Replace* Mat............6.85 Lab. ............1.66 | | | | |
| *Remove* ..................... Lab. ............ .60 | | | | |
| **add for access door** | ea | $3.02 | $63.60 | $66.62 |
| *Replace* Mat............44.00 Lab. ...........19.60 | | | | |
| *Remove* ..................... Lab. ............3.02 | | | | |

## Vinyl skirting, simulated rock

◄ **VINYL SIMULATED ROCK SKIRTING**

| Item Description | Unit | Remove | Replace | Total |
|---|---|---|---|---|
| **30" tall** | lf | $.60 | $9.76 | $10.36 |
| *Replace* Mat............8.10 Lab. ............1.66 | | | | |
| *Remove* ..................... Lab. ............ .60 | | | | |
| **36" tall** | lf | $.60 | $11.86 | $12.46 |
| *Replace* Mat...........10.20 Lab. ............1.66 | | | | |
| *Remove* ..................... Lab. ............ .60 | | | | |
| **48" tall** | lf | $.60 | $15.76 | $16.36 |
| *Replace* Mat...........14.10 Lab. ............1.66 | | | | |
| *Remove* ..................... Lab. ............ .60 | | | | |
| **add for access door** | ea | $3.02 | $65.60 | $68.62 |
| *Replace* Mat...........46.00 Lab. ...........19.60 | | | | |
| *Remove* ..................... Lab. ...........3.02 | | | | |

## Vinyl skirting, solid with vented panels

◄ **VINYL SKIRTING**

| Item Description | Unit | Remove | Replace | Total |
|---|---|---|---|---|
| **24" tall** | lf | $.60 | $4.78 | $5.38 |
| *Replace* Mat............3.12 Lab. ............1.66 | | | | |
| *Remove* ..................... Lab. ............ .60 | | | | |
| **28" tall** | lf | $.60 | $5.40 | $6.00 |
| *Replace* Mat............3.74 Lab. ............1.66 | | | | |
| *Remove* ..................... Lab. ............ .60 | | | | |
| **30" tall** | lf | $.60 | $5.47 | $6.07 |
| *Replace* Mat............3.81 Lab. ............1.66 | | | | |
| *Remove* ..................... Lab. ............ .60 | | | | |
| **36" tall** | lf | $.60 | $6.34 | $6.94 |
| *Replace* Mat............4.68 Lab. ............1.66 | | | | |
| *Remove* ..................... Lab. ............ .60 | | | | |
| **42" tall** | lf | $.60 | $7.76 | $8.36 |
| *Replace* Mat............6.10 Lab. ............1.66 | | | | |
| *Remove* ..................... Lab. ............ .60 | | | | |
| **add for access door** | ea | $3.02 | $59.60 | $62.62 |
| *Replace* Mat...........40.00 Lab. ...........19.60 | | | | |
| *Remove* ..................... Lab. ...........3.02 | | | | |

## Wood skirting, rough-sawn plywood

◄ **WOOD SKIRTING**

| Item Description | Unit | Remove | Replace | Total |
|---|---|---|---|---|
| **24" tall** | lf | $.60 | $3.84 | $4.44 |
| *Replace* Mat.............2.18 Lab. ............1.66 | | | | |
| *Remove* ..................... Lab. ............ .60 | | | | |
| **28" tall** | lf | $.60 | $4.28 | $4.88 |
| *Replace* Mat.............2.62 Lab. ............1.66 | | | | |
| *Remove* ..................... Lab. ............ .60 | | | | |

| Item Description | | | Unit | Remove | Replace | Total |
|---|---|---|---|---|---|---|
| **WOOD SKIRTING ▶** *continued* | **30" tall** | | lf | $.60 | $4.33 | $4.93 |
| | *Replace* Mat............2.67 | Lab. .............1.66 | | | | |
| | *Remove* ................ | Lab. ............. .60 | | | | |
| | **36" tall** | | lf | $.60 | $4.94 | $5.54 |
| | *Replace* Mat............3.28 | Lab. ............1.66 | | | | |
| | *Remove* ................ | Lab. ............. .60 | | | | |
| | **42" tall** | | lf | $.60 | $5.93 | $6.53 |
| | *Replace* Mat............4.27 | Lab. ............1.66 | | | | |
| | *Remove* ................ | Lab. ............. .60 | | | | |
| | **add for access door** | | ea | $3.02 | $47.60 | $50.62 |
| | *Replace* Mat............28.00 | Lab. ............19.60 | | | | |
| | *Remove* ................ | Lab. ............3.02 | | | | |

## Wood skirting, T1-11 or hardboard

| Item Description | | | Unit | Remove | Replace | Total |
|---|---|---|---|---|---|---|
| | **24" tall** | | lf | $.60 | $3.71 | $4.31 |
| | *Replace* Mat............2.05 | Lab. .............1.66 | | | | |
| | *Remove* ................ | Lab. ............. .60 | | | | |
| | **28" tall** | | lf | $.60 | $4.15 | $4.75 |
| | *Replace* Mat............2.49 | Lab. .............1.66 | | | | |
| | *Remove* ................ | Lab. ............. .60 | | | | |
| | **30" tall** | | lf | $.60 | $4.20 | $4.80 |
| | *Replace* Mat............2.54 | Lab. .............1.66 | | | | |
| | *Remove* ................ | Lab. ............. .60 | | | | |
| | **36" tall** | | lf | $.60 | $4.78 | $5.38 |
| | *Replace* Mat............3.12 | Lab. .............1.66 | | | | |
| | *Remove* ................ | Lab. ............. .60 | | | | |
| | **42" tall** | | lf | $.60 | $5.72 | $6.32 |
| | *Replace* Mat............4.06 | Lab. .............1.66 | | | | |
| | *Remove* ................ | Lab. ............. .60 | | | | |
| | **add for access door** | | ea | $3.02 | $46.20 | $49.22 |
| | *Replace* Mat............26.60 | Lab. ............19.60 | | | | |
| | *Remove* ................ | Lab. ............3.02 | | | | |

# WALL & CEILING PANELS

**CEILING PANEL ▶** ## Ceiling panel, drywall with textured finish

| Item Description | | | Unit | Remove | Replace | Total |
|---|---|---|---|---|---|---|
| | **3/8", no battens** | | sf | $.18 | $1.28 | $1.46 |
| | *Replace* Mat. ............ .52 | Lab. ............. .76 | | | | |
| | *Remove* ................ | Lab. ............. .18 | | | | |
| | **3/8" with battens** | | sf | $.18 | $1.45 | $1.63 |
| | *Replace* Mat. ............ .60 | Lab. ............. .85 | | | | |
| | *Remove* ................ | Lab. ............. .18 | | | | |

**WALL PANEL ▶** ## Wall panel, drywall

| Item Description | | | Unit | Remove | Replace | Total |
|---|---|---|---|---|---|---|
| | **1/2" with vinyl** | | sf | $.18 | $1.69 | $1.87 |
| | *Replace* Mat. ............ .88 | Lab. ............. .81 | | | | |
| | *Remove* ................ | Lab. ............. .18 | | | | |
| | **1/2" with wallpaper** | | sf | $.18 | $1.51 | $1.69 |
| | *Replace* Mat. ............ .70 | Lab. ............. .81 | | | | |
| | *Remove* ................ | Lab. ............. .18 | | | | |

| Item Description | Unit | Remove | Replace | Total | |
|---|---|---|---|---|---|
| **Ceiling and wall panel attachment** | | | | | ◄ **PANEL ATTACHMENT** |
| **batten** | lf | $.12 | $.63 | $.75 | |
| *Replace* Mat. ............ .15     Lab. ............. .48 | | | | | |
| *Remove* ..................     Lab. ............. .12 | | | | | |
| **screw with rosette** | ea | $.06 | $.36 | $.42 | |
| *Replace* Mat. ............ .21     Lab. ............. .15 | | | | | |
| *Remove* ..................     Lab. ............. .06 | | | | | |
| **screw with wing clips** | ea | $.06 | $.45 | $.51 | |
| *Replace* Mat. ............ .30     Lab. ............. .15 | | | | | |
| *Remove* ..................     Lab. ............. .06 | | | | | |

# WINDOWS

| Item Description | Unit | Remove | Replace | Total | |
|---|---|---|---|---|---|
| **Awning window, mobile home** | | | | | ◄ **AWNING WINDOW** |
| **14" x 27" with 2 lites** | ea | $9.06 | $83.60 | $92.66 | |
| *Replace* Mat. ............60.00     Lab. ............23.60 | | | | | |
| *Remove* ..................     Lab. ............9.06 | | | | | |
| **14" x 39" with 3 lites** | ea | $9.06 | $98.60 | $107.66 | |
| *Replace* Mat. ............75.00     Lab. ............23.60 | | | | | |
| *Remove* ..................     Lab. ............9.06 | | | | | |
| **24" x 27" with 2 lites** | ea | $9.06 | $98.60 | $107.66 | |
| *Replace* Mat. ............75.00     Lab. ............23.60 | | | | | |
| *Remove* ..................     Lab. ............9.06 | | | | | |
| **30" x 27" with 2 lites** | ea | $9.06 | $103.60 | $112.66 | |
| *Replace* Mat. ............80.00     Lab. ............23.60 | | | | | |
| *Remove* ..................     Lab. ............9.06 | | | | | |
| **30" x 39" with 3 lites** | ea | $9.06 | $118.60 | $127.66 | |
| *Replace* Mat. ............95.00     Lab. ............23.60 | | | | | |
| *Remove* ..................     Lab. ............9.06 | | | | | |
| **30" x 53" with 4 lites** | ea | $9.06 | $143.60 | $152.66 | |
| *Replace* Mat. ..........120.00     Lab. ............23.60 | | | | | |
| *Remove* ..................     Lab. ............9.06 | | | | | |
| **36" x 39" with 3 lites** | ea | $9.06 | $133.60 | $142.66 | |
| *Replace* Mat. ..........110.00     Lab. ............23.60 | | | | | |
| *Remove* ..................     Lab. ............9.06 | | | | | |
| **36" x 53" with 4 lites** | ea | $9.06 | $153.60 | $162.66 | |
| *Replace* Mat. ..........130.00     Lab. ............23.60 | | | | | |
| *Remove* ..................     Lab. ............9.06 | | | | | |
| **46" x 27" with 2 lites** | ea | $9.06 | $123.60 | $132.66 | |
| *Replace* Mat. ..........100.00     Lab. ............23.60 | | | | | |
| *Remove* ..................     Lab. ............9.06 | | | | | |
| **46" x 39" with 3 lites** | ea | $9.06 | $143.60 | $152.66 | |
| *Replace* Mat. ..........120.00     Lab. ............23.60 | | | | | |
| *Remove* ..................     Lab. ............9.06 | | | | | |
| **remove for work, then reinstall** | ea | — | $30.20 | $30.20 | |
| *Replace* ..................     Lab. ..........30.20 | | | | | |
| **Skylight, fixed, mobile home** | | | | | ◄ **SKYLIGHT** |
| **14" x 22"** | ea | $15.10 | $112.30 | $127.40 | |
| *Replace* Mat. ............59.40     Lab. ............52.90 | | | | | |
| *Remove* ..................     Lab. ............15.10 | | | | | |

| | Item Description | | Unit | Remove | Replace | Total |
|---|---|---|---|---|---|---|
| **SKYLIGHT** ▶ *continued* | **14" x 46"** Replace Mat. ........104.00  Lab. ..........52.90<br>Remove ................  Lab. ..........15.10 | | ea | $15.10 | $156.90 | $172.00 |
| | **22" x 22"** Replace Mat. ........68.40  Lab. ..........52.90<br>Remove ................  Lab. ..........15.10 | | ea | $15.10 | $121.30 | $136.40 |
| | **22" x 34"** Replace Mat. ........242.00  Lab. ..........52.90<br>Remove ................  Lab. ..........15.10 | | ea | $15.10 | $294.90 | $310.00 |
| | **remove for work, then reinstall** Replace ................  Lab. ..........66.40 | | ea | — | $66.40 | $66.40 |

### Skylight, ventilating, mobile home

| | Item Description | | Unit | Remove | Replace | Total |
|---|---|---|---|---|---|---|
| | **14" x 22"** Replace Mat. ........74.00  Lab. ..........66.40<br>Remove ................  Lab. ..........15.10 | | ea | $15.10 | $140.40 | $155.50 |
| | **14" x 46"** Replace Mat. ........119.00  Lab. ..........66.40<br>Remove ................  Lab. ..........15.10 | | ea | $15.10 | $185.40 | $200.50 |
| | **22" x 22"** Replace Mat. ........80.00  Lab. ..........66.40<br>Remove ................  Lab. ..........15.10 | | ea | $15.10 | $146.40 | $161.50 |
| | **22" x 34"** Replace Mat. ........277.00  Lab. ..........66.40<br>Remove ................  Lab. ..........15.10 | | ea | $15.10 | $343.40 | $358.50 |
| | **remove for work, then reinstall** Replace ................  Lab. ..........75.50 | | ea | — | $75.50 | $75.50 |

# TIME & MATERIAL CHARTS *(selected items)*

## Manufactured Housing Labor

| LABORER | BASE WAGE | PAID LEAVE | TRUE WAGE | FICA | FUTA | WORKER'S COMP. | UNEMPLOY. INSUR. | HEALTH INSUR. | RETIRE (401k) | LIABILITY INSUR. | COST PER HOUR |
|---|---|---|---|---|---|---|---|---|---|---|---|
| MH repair specialist | $17.00 | 1.33 | $18.33 | 1.40 | .15 | 3.30 | 1.59 | 2.54 | .55 | 2.38 | $30.20 |
| MH repair specialist's helper | $8.50 | .66 | $9.16 | .70 | .07 | 1.65 | .80 | 2.54 | .27 | 1.19 | $16.40 |

**Paid Leave** is calculated based on two weeks paid vacation, one week sick leave, and seven paid holidays. Employer's matching portion of **FICA** is 7.65 percent. **FUTA** (Federal Unemployment) is .8 percent. **Worker's compensation** was calculated using a national average of 17.99 percent for a manufactured housing repair professional. **Unemployment insurance** was calculated using a national average of 8.7 percent. **Health insurance** was calculated based on a projected national average for 2001 of $505 per employee (and family when applicable) per month. Employer pays 80 percent for a per month cost of $404 per employee. **Retirement** is based on a 401(k) retirement program with employer matching of 50 percent. Employee contributions to the 401(k) plan are an average of 6 percent of the true wage. **Liability insurance** is based on a national average of 12.9 percent.

# QuickCalculators

## QuickCalculators

QuickCalculators are designed to help you quickly calculate quantities and the surface areas of some basic room shapes. Pages 529-543 contain QuickCalculators that are designed to calculate quantities, and pages 544-549 contain QuickCalculators that are designed to calculate the surface area of rooms.

Instruction for each QuickCalculator sheet are contained on the left facing page.

The person who purchased this book or the person for whom this book was purchased may photo-copy or otherwise reproduce QuickCalculator pages so long as:

❶ the sheets are reproduced for that person's use only.

❷ the sheets are not reproduced for resale or as part of a package that is produced for resale.

❸ the sheets are not used in any promotional or advertising materials.

# USING THE BEARING WALL
## QuickCalculator

**A** Calculates the lineal feet of studs in a wall *before* adding for openings and corners.

The length of the wall (Answer 1) is converted into inches by multiplying it by 12.

The number of studs is calculated by dividing the wall length in inches by the stud centers (Answer 8), then adding 1 for the first stud.

The calculation should now be rounded *up*, then multiplied by the wall height (Answer 4).

**B** Calculates the lineal feet of studs typically added for openings and corners. The number of openings (Answer 6) is multiplied by 2.4 (the *average* additional studs typically needed for an opening). The number of corners (Answer 7) is multiplied by 2.6 (the *average* additional studs typically needed at corners). The studs for openings and corners are added together, then should be rounded *up*. The total additional studs is then multiplied by the wall height (Answer 1).

**C** Calculates the total lineal feet of lumber in the wall. The length of the wall (Answer 1) is multiplied by the number of plates (Answer 3). The lineal feet of plates is added to the lineal feet of studs (Sum A) and additional studs (Sum B).

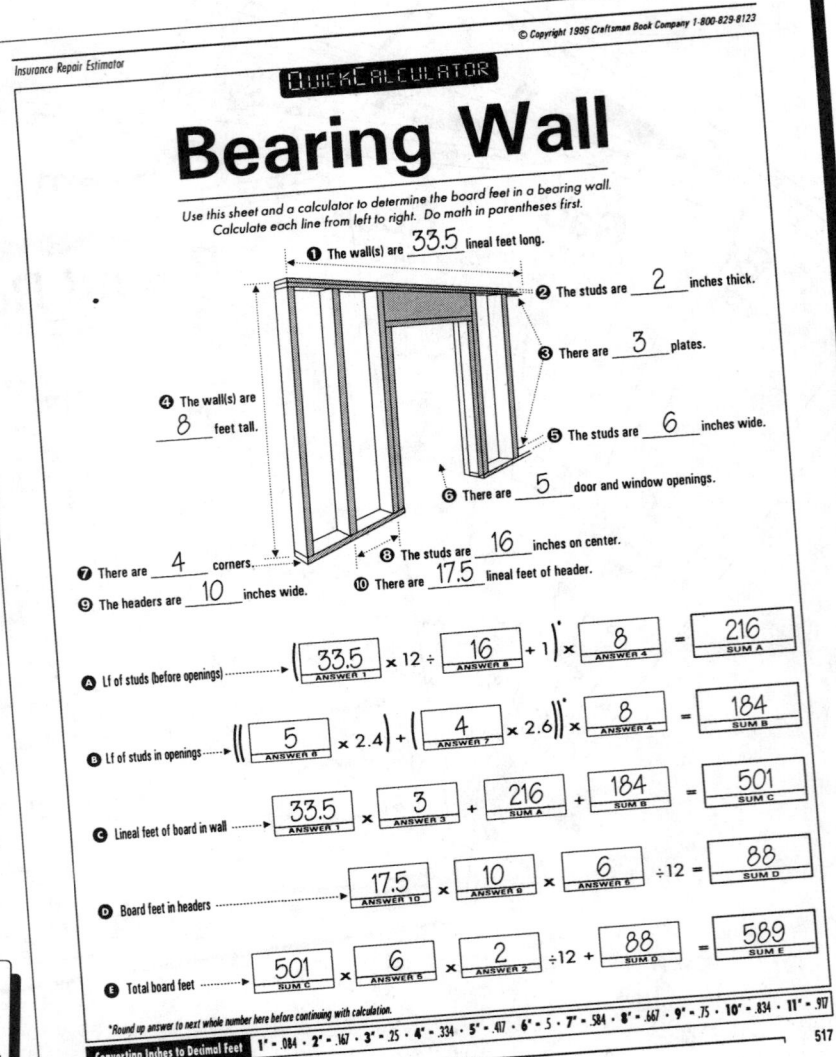

*Insurance Repair Estimator*

**QuickCalculator**

# Bearing Wall

Use this sheet and a calculator to determine the board feet in a bearing wall.
Calculate each line from left to right. Do math in parentheses first.

**1** The wall(s) are __33.5__ lineal feet long.

**2** The studs are __2__ inches thick.

**3** There are __3__ plates.

**4** The wall(s) are __8__ feet tall.

**5** The studs are __6__ inches wide.

**6** There are __5__ door and window openings.

**7** There are __4__ corners.

**8** The studs are __16__ inches on center.

**9** The headers are __10__ inches wide.

**10** There are __17.5__ lineal feet of header.

**A** Lf of studs (before openings) ───▶ $\left(\boxed{\underset{\text{ANSWER 1}}{33.5}} \times 12 \div \boxed{\underset{\text{ANSWER 8}}{16}} + 1\right)^* \times \boxed{\underset{\text{ANSWER 4}}{8}} = \boxed{\underset{\text{SUM A}}{216}}$

**B** Lf of studs in openings ───▶ $\left(\left(\boxed{\underset{\text{ANSWER 6}}{5}} \times 2.4\right) + \left(\boxed{\underset{\text{ANSWER 7}}{4}} \times 2.6\right)\right)^* \times \boxed{\underset{\text{ANSWER 4}}{8}} = \boxed{\underset{\text{SUM B}}{184}}$

**C** Lineal feet of board in wall ───▶ $\boxed{\underset{\text{ANSWER 1}}{33.5}} \times \boxed{\underset{\text{ANSWER 3}}{3}} + \boxed{\underset{\text{SUM A}}{216}} + \boxed{\underset{\text{SUM B}}{184}} = \boxed{\underset{\text{SUM C}}{501}}$

**D** Board feet in headers ───▶ $\boxed{\underset{\text{ANSWER 10}}{17.5}} \times \boxed{\underset{\text{ANSWER 9}}{10}} \times \boxed{\underset{\text{ANSWER 5}}{6}} \div 12 = \boxed{\underset{\text{SUM D}}{88}}$

**E** Total board feet ───▶ $\boxed{\underset{\text{SUM C}}{501}} \times \boxed{\underset{\text{ANSWER 5}}{6}} \times \boxed{\underset{\text{ANSWER 2}}{2}} \div 12 + \boxed{\underset{\text{SUM D}}{88}} = \boxed{\underset{\text{SUM E}}{589}}$

*Round up answer to next whole number here before continuing with calculation.*

**Converting Inches to Decimal Feet** | 1" - .084 · 2" - .167 · 3" - .25 · 4" - .334 · 5" - .417 · 6" - .5 · 7" - .584 · 8" - .667 · 9" - .75 · 10" - .834 · 11" - .917

517

**D** Calculates the board feet in the headers. The lineal feet of headers (Answer 10) is multiplied by the header width then multiplied by the wall thickness (Answer 5). This total is divided by 12 to convert to board feet.

**E** Calculates the total board feet in the wall. The lineal feet of board in the wall (Sum C) is multiplied by the wall width (Answer 5) then by the stud thickness (Answer 2). The total is divided by twelve to convert to board feet then added to the board feet in the headers (Sum D).

## QUICK FACTS

☞ See page 550 for more information about the geometric formulas used in this *QuickCalculator*. See page 414-415 for wall framing priced per board foot.

## QUICKCALCULATOR

# Bearing Wall

*Use this sheet and a calculator to determine the board feet in a bearing wall.
Calculate each line from left to right. Do math in parentheses first.*

❶ The wall(s) are _____ lineal feet long.

❷ The studs are _____ inches thick.

❸ There are _____ plates.

❹ The wall(s) are _____ feet tall.

❺ The studs are _____ inches wide.

❻ There are _____ door and window openings.

❼ There are _____ corners.

❽ The studs are _____ inches on center.

❾ The headers are _____ inches wide.

❿ There are _____ lineal feet of header.

Ⓐ Lf of studs (before openings) ········▶ ( [ANSWER 1] × 12 ÷ [ANSWER 8] + 1 )* × [ANSWER 4] = [SUM A]

Ⓑ Lf of studs in openings ······▶ (( [ANSWER 6] × 2.4) + ( [ANSWER 7] × 2.6))* × [ANSWER 4] = [SUM B]

Ⓒ Lineal feet of board in wall ········▶ [ANSWER 1] × [ANSWER 3] + [SUM A] + [SUM B] = [SUM C]

Ⓓ Board feet in headers ············▶ [ANSWER 10] × [ANSWER 9] × [ANSWER 5] ÷12 = [SUM D]

Ⓔ Total board feet ··········▶ [SUM C] × [ANSWER 5] × [ANSWER 2] ÷12 + [SUM D] = [SUM E]

*Round up answer to next whole number here before continuing with calculation.*

**Converting Inches to Decimal Feet** · **1"** = .084 · **2"** = .167 · **3"** = .25 · **4"** = .334 · **5"** = .417 · **6"** = .5 · **7"** = .584 · **8"** = .667 · **9"** = .75 · **10"** = .834 · **11"** = .917

# USING THE CONCRETE WALL & FOOTING QuickCalculator

**A** Calculates the cubic yards of footing by multiplying Answer 1 by 12 to convert the length of the footing to inches. The length in inches is then multiplied by the thickness (Answer 4) and by the width (Answer 5) to determine the cubic inches in the footing. The cubic inches are converted to cubic feet by dividing by 1,728. The cubic feet are then converted to cubic yards by dividing by 27.

**B** Calculates the cubic yards of foundation wall by multiplying Answer 2 by 12 to convert the length of the wall to inches. The length in inches is then multiplied by the thickness (Answer 1) and by the height (Answer 3) to determine the cubic inches in the wall. The cubic inches are converted to cubic feet by dividing by 1,728. The cubic feet are then converted to cubic yards by dividing by 27.

**C** Calculates the total cubic yards of concrete in the wall & footing by adding the cubic yards of footing (Sum A) to the cubic yards of foundation wall (Sum B).

© Copyright 1995 Craftsman Book Company 1-800-829-8123

*Insurance Repair Estimator*

**QuickCalculator**

# Concrete Wall & Footing

*Use this sheet and a calculator to determine the cubic yards of concrete in a foundation wall and footing. Calculate each line from left to right.*

① The wall is **8** inches thick.

② The wall & footing are **25.75** feet long.

③ The wall is **48** inches high.

④ The footing is **12** inches thick.

⑤ The footing is **24** inches wide.

**A** The cubic yards of footing → $\boxed{25.75}_{\text{ANSWER 2}} \times 12 \times \boxed{12}_{\text{ANSWER 4}} \times \boxed{24}_{\text{ANSWER 5}} \div 1{,}728 \div 27 = \boxed{1.91}_{\text{SUM A}}$

**B** The cubic yards of wall → $\boxed{25.75}_{\text{ANSWER 2}} \times 12 \times \boxed{8}_{\text{ANSWER 1}} \times \boxed{48}_{\text{ANSWER 3}} \div 1{,}728 \div 27 = \boxed{2.54}_{\text{SUM B}}$

**C** Total cubic yards of wall & footing → $\boxed{1.91}_{\text{SUM A}} + \boxed{2.54}_{\text{SUM B}} = \boxed{4.45}_{\text{SUM C}}$

**Converting Inches to Decimal Feet** | 1" = .084 • 2" = .167 • 3" = .25 • 4" = .334 • 5" = .417 • 6" = .5 • 7" = .584 • 8" = .667 • 9" = .75 • 10" = .834 • 11" = .917

519

## QUICK FACTS

☞ The sample *QuickCalculator* sheet shown above contains quantities that have been rounded. We suggest rounding to two decimal places. We also suggest rounding the final total (Sum C) *up* to the next 1/4 yards since this how concrete must usually be ordered. (In the example above the Sum C total of 4.45 should be rounded up to 4.5 cubic yards.) See pages 83–85 for concrete walls and footings per cubic yard.

☞ See page 550 for more information about the geometric formulas used in this *QuickCalculator*.

**QUICKCALCULATOR**

# Concrete Wall & Footing

*Use this sheet and a calculator to determine the cubic yards of concrete in a foundation wall and footing. Calculate each line from left to right.*

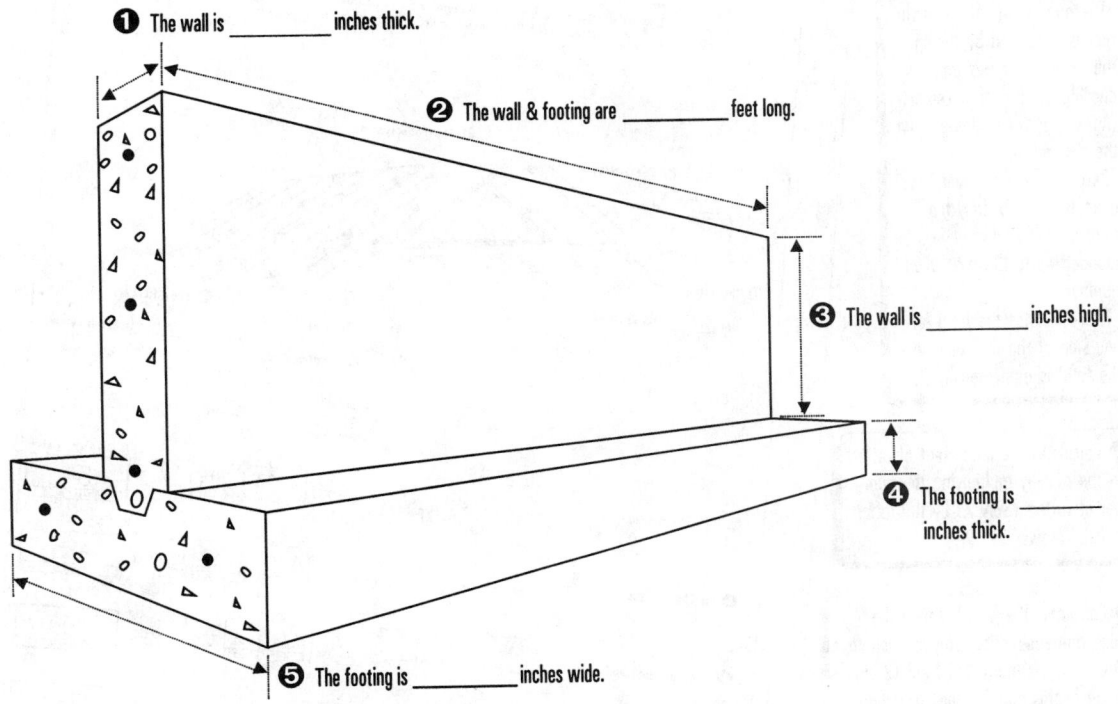

❶ The wall is _____ inches thick.

❷ The wall & footing are _____ feet long.

❸ The wall is _____ inches high.

❹ The footing is _____ inches thick.

❺ The footing is _____ inches wide.

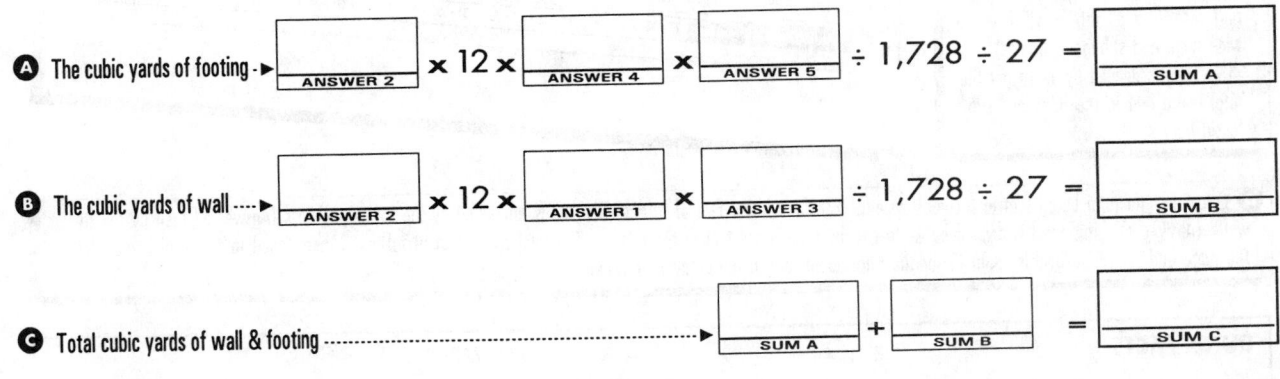

Ⓐ The cubic yards of footing ► [ ANSWER 2 ] × 12 × [ ANSWER 4 ] × [ ANSWER 5 ] ÷ 1,728 ÷ 27 = [ SUM A ]

Ⓑ The cubic yards of wall ···· ► [ ANSWER 2 ] × 12 × [ ANSWER 1 ] × [ ANSWER 3 ] ÷ 1,728 ÷ 27 = [ SUM B ]

Ⓒ Total cubic yards of wall & footing ························· ► [ SUM A ] + [ SUM B ] = [ SUM C ]

**Converting Inches to Decimal Feet**    **1"** - .084 • **2"** - .167 • **3"** - .25 • **4"** - .334 • **5"** - .417 • **6"** - .5 • **7"** - .584 • **8"** - .667 • **9"** - .75 • **10"** - .834 • **11"** - .917

# USING THE GABLE ROOF RAFTERS
## QuickCalculator

**A** Calculates the total number of rafters in the roof. The length of the roof (Answer 1) is converted into inches by multiplying it by 12.

The number of rafters in the roof is calculated by taking the length in inches and dividing by the rafter centers (Answer 4) then adding 1 for the first rafter.

Because you can never have a fraction of a rafter, the final answer should always be rounded *up* to the next *even* number.

This calculates the total for one side of the roof only so the total is multiplied by 2.

**B** Calculates the lineal feet of rafters in the roof by multiplying the number of rafters (Sum A) by the rafter length (Answer 2).

**C** Calculates the board feet in the ridge and sub-fascia. The roof length (Answer 1) is multiplied by 3 (2 sub-fascia boards and 1 ridge) to get the total lineal feet of sub-fascia and ridge. This total is multiplied by the rafter thickness (Answer 5), then by the rafter width (Answer 3) plus 2" (e.g. a roof with 2" x 8" rafters will have 10" wide ridge and sub-fascia boards). This total is divided by 12 to get the total board feet in the ridge and sub-fascia boards.

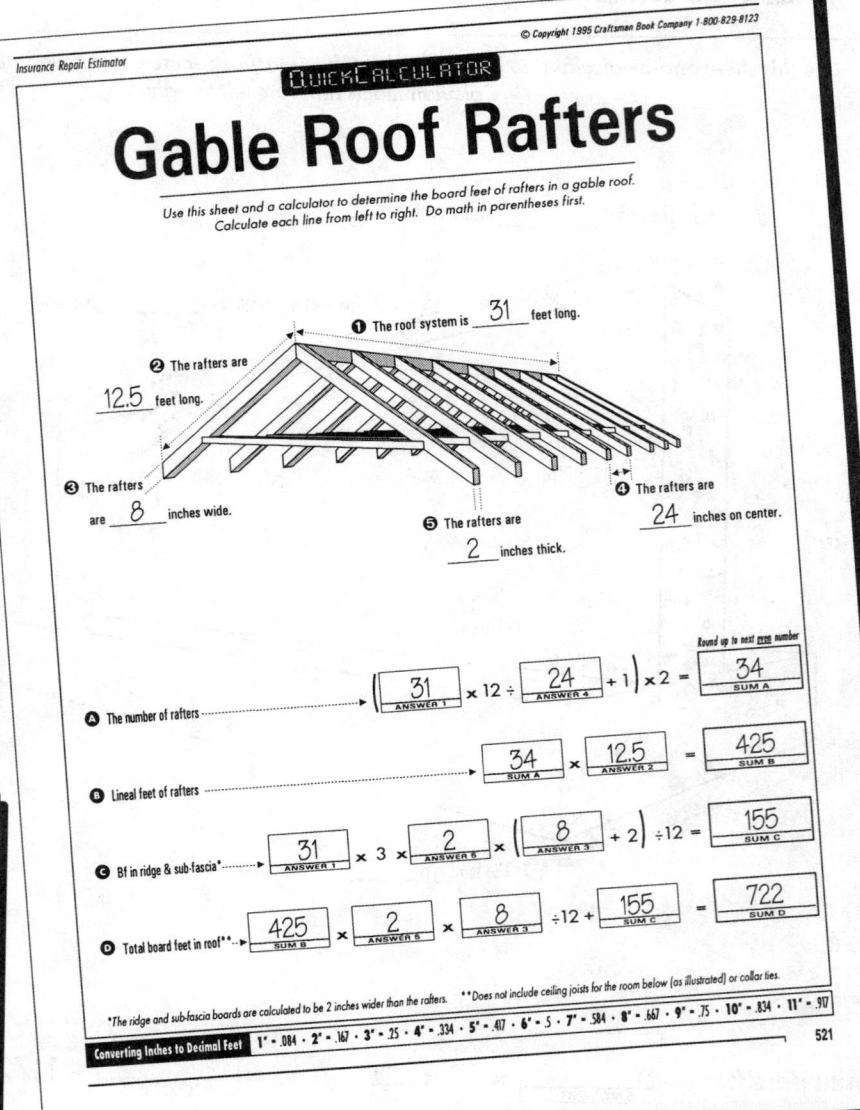

© Copyright 1995 Craftsman Book Company 1-800-829-8123

*Insurance Repair Estimator*

**QuickCalculator**

# Gable Roof Rafters

Use this sheet and a calculator to determine the board feet of rafters in a gable roof. Calculate each line from left to right. Do math in parentheses first.

❶ The roof system is __31__ feet long.

❷ The rafters are __12.5__ feet long.

❸ The rafters are __8__ inches wide.

❹ The rafters are __24__ inches on center.

❺ The rafters are __2__ inches thick.

Round up to next **even** number

**A** The number of rafters — $( \boxed{31}_{\text{ANSWER 1}} \times 12 \div \boxed{24}_{\text{ANSWER 4}} + 1 ) \times 2 = \boxed{34}_{\text{SUM A}}$

**B** Lineal feet of rafters — $\boxed{34}_{\text{SUM A}} \times \boxed{12.5}_{\text{ANSWER 2}} = \boxed{425}_{\text{SUM B}}$

**C** Bf in ridge & sub-fascia* — $\boxed{31}_{\text{ANSWER 1}} \times 3 \times \boxed{2}_{\text{ANSWER 5}} \times ( \boxed{8}_{\text{ANSWER 3}} + 2 ) \div 12 = \boxed{155}_{\text{SUM C}}$

**D** Total board feet in roof** — $\boxed{425}_{\text{SUM B}} \times \boxed{2}_{\text{ANSWER 5}} \times \boxed{8}_{\text{ANSWER 3}} \div 12 + \boxed{155}_{\text{SUM C}} = \boxed{722}_{\text{SUM D}}$

*The ridge and sub-fascia boards are calculated to be 2 inches wider than the rafters.   **Does not include ceiling joists for the room below (as illustrated) or collar ties.

**Converting Inches to Decimal Feet** | 1" - .084 · 2" - .167 · 3" - .25 · 4" - .334 · 5" - .417 · 6" - .5 · 7" - .584 · 8" - .667 · 9" - .75 · 10" - .834 · 11" - .917

521

**D** Calculates the total board feet in the roof system. The total lineal feet of rafters (Sum B) is multiplied by the rafter thickness (Answer 5) then by the rafter width (Answer 3). This total is divided by 12 to get the total board feet in the rafters. The total board feet of rafters is then added to the total board feet in the ridge and sub-fascia boards (Sum C) for the total board feet in the entire roof system.

## QUICK FACTS

☞ The sample *QuickCalculator* sheet shown above contains quantities that have been rounded. The total number of rafters should always be rounded up to the next even number. We also suggest rounding lineal feet and board feet to the nearest whole number.

☞ See page 550 for more information about the geometric formulas used in this *QuickCalculator*. See page 436 for rafter systems priced per board foot.

**QUICKCALCULATOR**

# Gable Roof Rafters

*Use this sheet and a calculator to determine the board feet of rafters in a gable roof.*
*Calculate each line from left to right. Do math in parentheses first.*

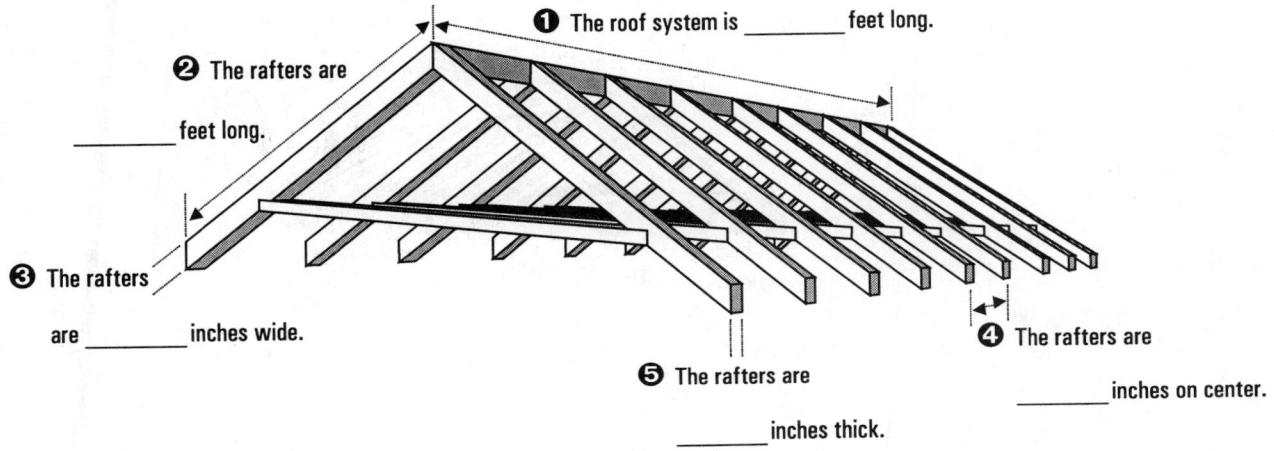

❶ The roof system is _____ feet long.

❷ The rafters are _____ feet long.

❸ The rafters are _____ inches wide.

❹ The rafters are _____ inches on center.

❺ The rafters are _____ inches thick.

**Ⓐ** The number of rafters ⋯⋯⋯⋯⋯▶ ( [ANSWER 1] × 12 ÷ [ANSWER 4] + 1 ) × 2 = [SUM A] *Round up to next even number*

**Ⓑ** Lineal feet of rafters ⋯⋯⋯⋯⋯▶ [SUM A] × [ANSWER 2] = [SUM B]

**Ⓒ** Bf in ridge & sub-fascia* ⋯⋯⋯▶ [ANSWER 1] × 3 × [ANSWER 5] × ( [ANSWER 3] + 2 ) ÷ 12 = [SUM C]

**Ⓓ** Total board feet in roof** ⋯⋯▶ [SUM B] × [ANSWER 5] × [ANSWER 3] ÷ 12 + [SUM C] = [SUM D]

*\*The ridge and sub-fascia boards are calculated to be 2 inches wider than the rafters.*   *\*\*Does not include ceiling joists for the room below (as illustrated) or collar ties.*

**Converting Inches to Decimal Feet**   **1"** = .084 • **2"** = .167 • **3"** = .25 • **4"** = .334 • **5"** = .417 • **6"** = .5 • **7"** = .584 • **8"** = .667 • **9"** = .75 • **10"** = .834 • **11"** = .917

# USING THE GABLE ROOF TRUSSES
## QuickCalculator

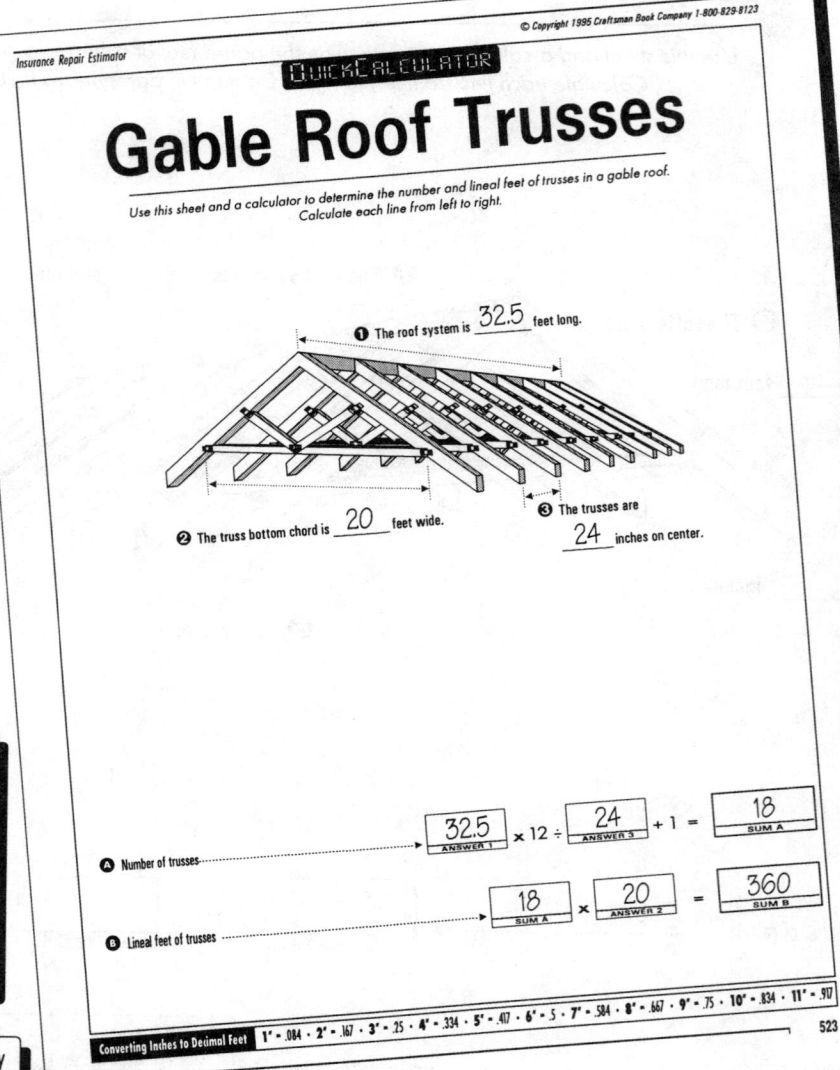

**A** Calculates the number of trusses in the roof by converting the length of the roof (Answer 1) into inches by multiplying it by 12.

The number of trusses is then calculated by taking this length in inches, dividing it by the truss centers (Answer 3), then adding 1 for the first truss.

**B** Calculates the lineal feet of trusses by multiplying the number of trusses (Sum A) by the length of the truss bottom chord (Answer 2).

## QUICK FACTS

☞ The sample *QuickCalculator* sheet shown above contains quantities that have been rounded. The total number of trusses should always be rounded up to the next whole number. We also suggest rounding lineal feet lineal feet to the nearest whole number.

☞ See page 550 for more information about the geometric formulas used in this *QuickCalculator*. See page 439 for truss systems priced per lineal foot.

**QUICKCALCULATOR**

# Gable Roof Trusses

*Use this sheet and a calculator to determine the number and lineal feet of trusses in a gable roof.*
*Calculate each line from left to right.*

❶ The roof system is _____ feet long.

❷ The truss bottom chord is _____ feet wide.

❸ The trusses are

_____ inches on center.

Round up to next whole number

Ⓐ Number of trusses- - - - - - - - - - - - - - - - - - - - - - - - - - ▶ | ANSWER 1 | × 12 ÷ | ANSWER 3 | + 1 = | SUM A |

Ⓑ Lineal feet of trusses - - - - - - - - - - - - - - - - - - - - ▶ | SUM A | × | ANSWER 2 | = | SUM B |

**Converting Inches to Decimal Feet** | **1"** = .084 • **2"** = .167 • **3"** = .25 • **4"** = .334 • **5"** = .417 • **6"** = .5 • **7"** = .584 • **8"** = .667 • **9"** = .75 • **10"** = .834 • **11"** = .917

# USING THE GABLE ROOFING QuickCalculator

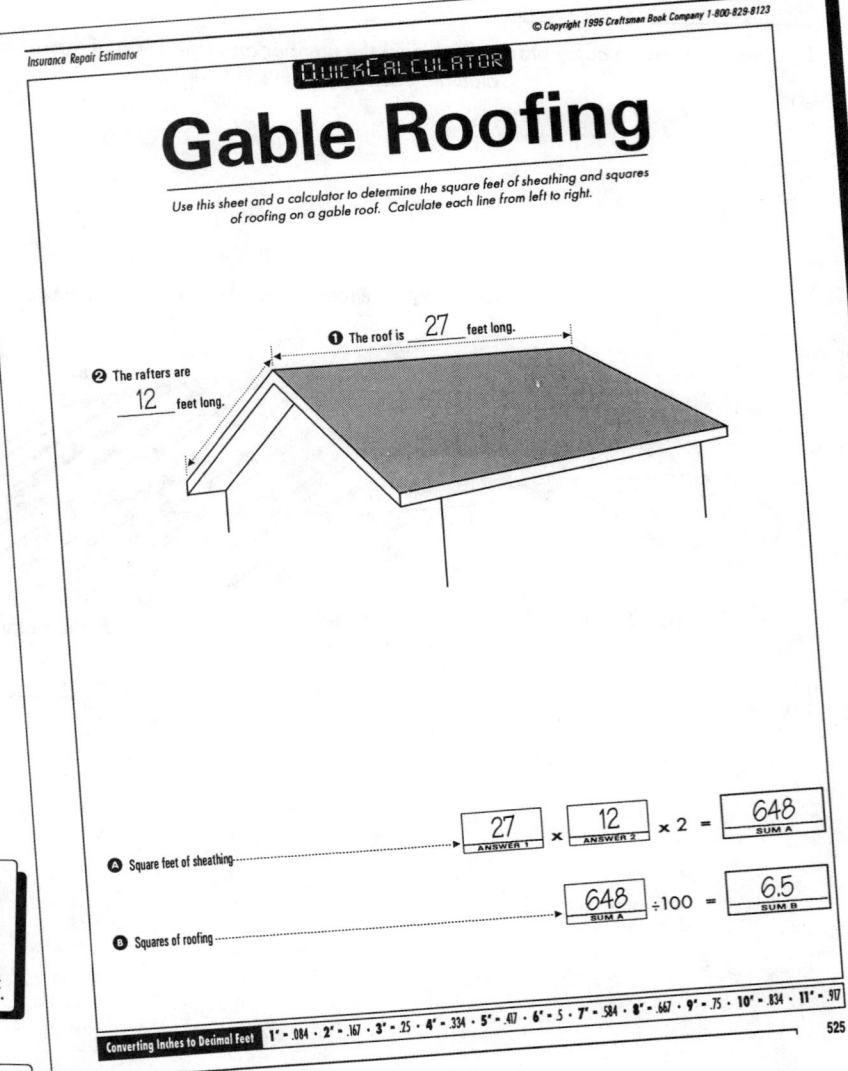

**A** Calculates the square feet of sheathing on the roof by multiplying the roof length (Answer 1) by the rafter length (Answer 2), then multiplying this total by 2 to calculate both sides of the roof.

**B** Calculates the squares of roofing by dividing the square feet of roof (Sum A) by 100.

## QUICK FACTS

☞ The sample *QuickCalculator* sheet shown above contains quantities that have been rounded. We suggest rounding sheathing to the nearest square foot and rounding squares *up* to the next 1/5 square for shakes, the next 1/4 square for wood shingles and clay tile, and the next 1/3 square for asphalt shingles.

☞ See page 550 for more information about the geometric formulas used in this *QuickCalculator*. Also see *Roofing* beginning on page 393.

**QuickCalculator**

# Gable Roofing

*Use this sheet and a calculator to determine the square feet of sheathing and squares of roofing on a gable roof. Calculate each line from left to right.*

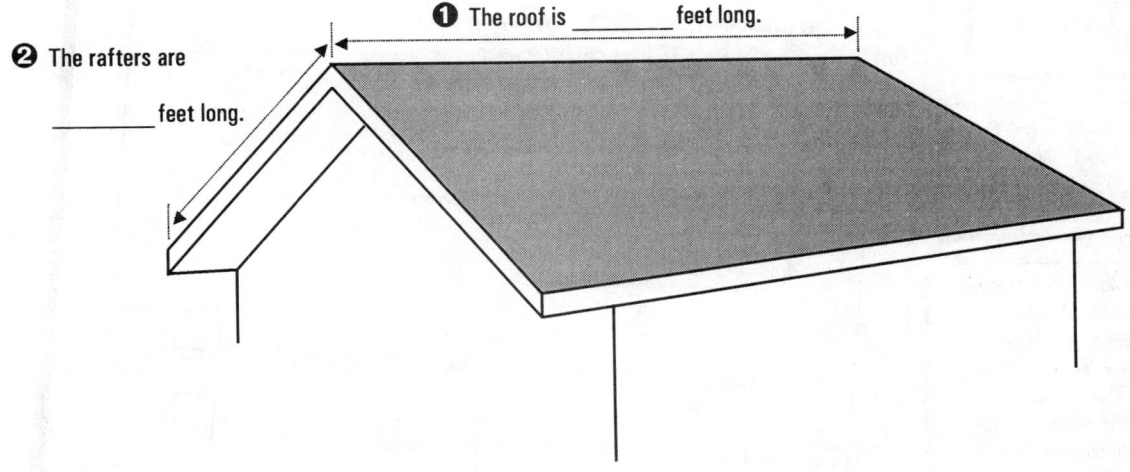

❶ The roof is _____ feet long.

❷ The rafters are _____ feet long.

Ⓐ Square feet of sheathing⋯⋯⋯⋯⋯➤ | ANSWER 1 | ✕ | ANSWER 2 | ✕ 2 = | SUM A |

Ⓑ Squares of roofing ⋯⋯⋯⋯⋯⋯➤ | SUM A | ÷100 = | SUM B |

**Converting Inches to Decimal Feet**   **1"** = .084 • **2"** = .167 • **3"** = .25 • **4"** = .334 • **5"** = .417 • **6"** = .5 • **7"** = .584 • **8"** = .667 • **9"** = .75 • **10"** = .834 • **11"** = .917

539

# USING THE JOIST SYSTEM
## QUICKCALCULATOR

**A** Calculates the total number of joists. The length of the joist system (Answer 1) is converted into inches by multiplying it by 12.
The number of joists is calculated by taking the joist system length in inches and dividing it by the joist centers (Answer 4) then adding 1 for the first joist.

**B** Calculates the lineal feet of joists by multiplying the number of joists (Sum A) by the joist length (Answer 2).

**C** Calculates the lineal feet in rim joists and in solid blocking. The length of the rim joist (Answer 1) is multiplied by 2 for rim joists on both sides of the joist system. The total lineal feet of rim joists are then added to the lineal feet of solid blocking (Answer 6).

**D** Calculates total lineal feet of lumber in the joist system by adding the lineal feet of joists (Sum B) to the lineal feet of rim joists and solid blocking (Sum C).

**E** Calculates the board feet in the joist system by multiplying the total lineal feet of joists (Sum D) by the joist thickness (Answer 5), then by the joist width (Answer 3). This total is then divided by 12.

© Copyright 1995 Craftsman Book Company 1-800-829-8123

Insurance Repair Estimator

**QUICKCALCULATOR**

# Joist System

*Use this sheet and a calculator to determine the lineal feet and board feet in a joist system. Calculate each line from left to right.*

① The joist system is ___25___ feet long.　② The joists are ___15___ feet long.

③ The joists are ___10___ inches wide.

④ The joists are ___24___ inches on center.

⑤ The joists are ___2___ inches thick.

⑥ There are ___25___ lineal feet of solid blocking in the joist system.

**Ⓐ** The number of joists —— $\boxed{25}_{\text{ANSWER 1}} \times 12 \div \boxed{24}_{\text{ANSWER 4}} + 1 = \boxed{14}_{\text{SUM A}}$ *Round up to next whole number*

**Ⓑ** The lineal feet of joists —— $\boxed{15}_{\text{ANSWER 2}} \times \boxed{14}_{\text{SUM A}} = \boxed{210}_{\text{SUM B}}$

**Ⓒ** The lineal feet of rim joists and blocking —— $\boxed{25}_{\text{ANSWER 1}} \times 2 + \boxed{25}_{\text{ANSWER 6}} = \boxed{75}_{\text{SUM C}}$

**Ⓓ** The total lineal feet of all joists and blocking —— $\boxed{210}_{\text{SUM B}} + \boxed{75}_{\text{SUM C}} = \boxed{285}_{\text{SUM D}}$

**Ⓔ** The total board feet in the joist system —— $\boxed{285}_{\text{SUM D}} \times \boxed{2}_{\text{ANSWER 5}} \times \boxed{10}_{\text{ANSWER 3}} \div 12 = \boxed{475}_{\text{SUM E}}$

**Converting Inches to Decimal Feet**　1" = .084 • 2" = .167 • 3" = .25 • 4" = .334 • 5" = .417 • 6" = .5 • 7" = .584 • 8" = .667 • 9" = .75 • 10" = .834 • 11" = .917　527

## QUICK FACTS

☞ The sample *QuickCalculator* sheet shown above contains quantities that have been rounded. The total number of joists should always be rounded *up* to the next whole number. We also suggest rounding lineal feet and board feet to the nearest whole number.

☞ See page 550 for more information about the geometric formulas used in this *QuickCalculator*. See page 432 for joist systems priced per board foot.

# QUICKCALCULATOR

# Joist System

*Use this sheet and a calculator to determine the lineal feet and board feet in a joist system.*
*Calculate each line from left to right.*

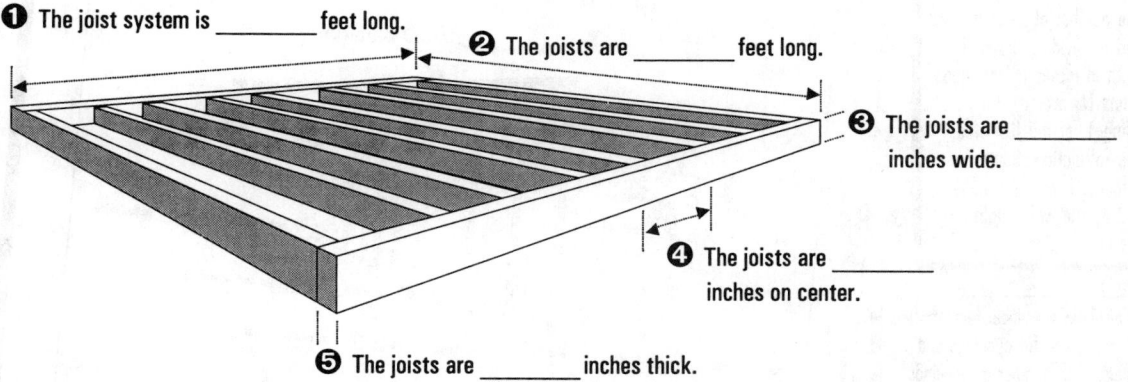

❶ The joist system is _____ feet long.

❷ The joists are _____ feet long.

❸ The joists are _____ inches wide.

❹ The joists are _____ inches on center.

❺ The joists are _____ inches thick.

❻ There are _____ lineal feet of solid blocking in the joist system.

---

Ⓐ The number of joists ┈┈┈┈┈┈┈┈➤ [ ANSWER 1 ] × 12 ÷ [ ANSWER 4 ] + 1 = [ SUM A ]   *Round up to next whole number*

Ⓑ The lineal feet of joists ┈┈┈┈┈┈┈➤ [ ANSWER 2 ] × [ SUM A ] = [ SUM B ]

Ⓒ The lineal feet of rim joists and blocking ┈┈┈┈➤ [ ANSWER 1 ] × 2 + [ ANSWER 6 ] = [ SUM C ]

Ⓓ The total lineal feet of all joists and blocking ┈┈┈┈┈➤ [ SUM B ] + [ SUM C ] = [ SUM D ]

Ⓔ The total board feet in the joist system ┈┈┈┈➤ [ SUM D ] × [ ANSWER 5 ] × [ ANSWER 3 ] ÷ 12 = [ SUM E ]

---

**Converting Inches to Decimal Feet** | 1" = .084 • 2" = .167 • 3" = .25 • 4" = .334 • 5" = .417 • 6" = .5 • 7" = .584 • 8" = .667 • 9" = .75 • 10" = .834 • 11" = .917

# USING THE NON-BEARING WALL QUICKCALCULATOR

**A** Calculates the lineal feet of studs in a wall *before* adding for openings and corners. The length of the wall (Answer 1) is converted into inches by multiplying it by 12. The number of studs is calculated by dividing the wall length in inches by the stud centers (Answer 8), then adding 1 for the first stud. The calculation should now be rounded *up*, then multiplied by the wall height (Answer 4).

**B** Calculates the lineal feet of studs typically added for openings and corners. The number of openings (Answer 6) is multiplied by 2.4 (the *average* additional studs typically needed for an opening). The number of corners (Answer 7) is multiplied by 2.6 (the *average* additional studs typically needed at corners). The studs for openings and corners are added together, then should be rounded *up*. The total additional studs is then multiplied by the wall height (Answer 1).

**C** Calculates the total lineal feet of lumber in the wall. The length of the wall (Answer 1) is multiplied by the number of plates (Answer 3). The lineal feet of plates is added to the lineal feet of studs (Sum A) and additional studs (Sum B).

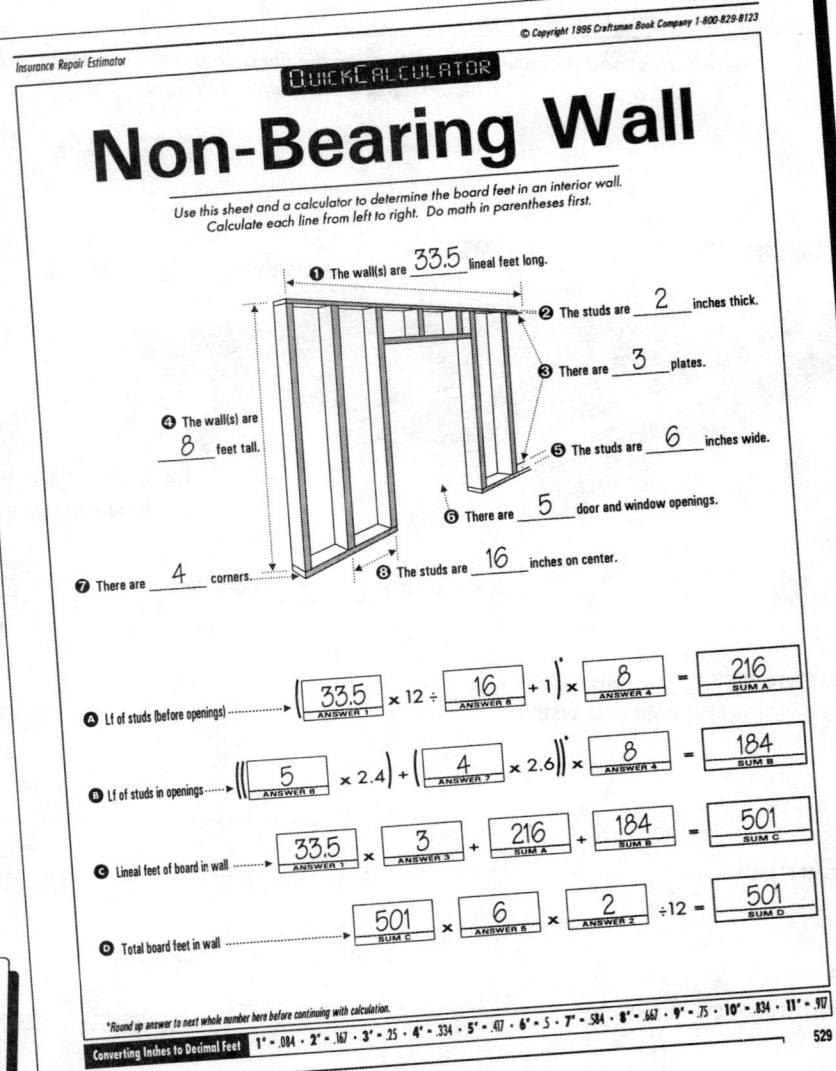

© Copyright 1995 Craftsman Book Company 1-800-829-8123

*Insurance Repair Estimator*

## QUICKCALCULATOR

# Non-Bearing Wall

*Use this sheet and a calculator to determine the board feet in an interior wall.*
*Calculate each line from left to right. Do math in parentheses first.*

❶ The wall(s) are **33.5** lineal feet long.

❷ The studs are **2** inches thick.

❸ There are **3** plates.

❹ The wall(s) are **8** feet tall.

❺ The studs are **6** inches wide.

❻ There are **5** door and window openings.

❼ There are **4** corners.

❽ The studs are **16** inches on center.

**A** Lf of studs (before openings) ——— ( **33.5** [ANSWER 1] × 12 ÷ **16** [ANSWER 8] + 1 )* × **8** [ANSWER 4] = **216** [SUM A]

**B** Lf of studs in openings ——— (( **5** [ANSWER 6] × 2.4) + ( **4** [ANSWER 7] × 2.6))* × **8** [ANSWER 4] = **184** [SUM B]

**C** Lineal feet of board in wall ——— **33.5** [ANSWER 1] × **3** [ANSWER 3] + **216** [SUM A] + **184** [SUM B] = **501** [SUM C]

**D** Total board feet in wall ——— **501** [SUM C] × **6** [ANSWER 5] × **2** [ANSWER 2] ÷ 12 = **501** [SUM D]

*Round up answer to next whole number here before continuing with calculation.

| Converting Inches to Decimal Feet | 1" = .084 · 2" = .167 · 3" = .25 · 4" = .334 · 5" = .417 · 6" = .5 · 7" = .584 · 8" = .667 · 9" = .75 · 10" = .834 · 11" = .917 |

529

**D** Calculates the total board feet in the wall. The lineal feet of board in the wall (Sum C) is multiplied by the wall width (Answer 5) then by the stud thickness (Answer 2). The total is divided by twelve to convert to board feet.

## QUICK FACTS

☞ The sample *QuickCalculator* sheet shown above contains quantities that have been rounded. When calculating Sum A and Sum B we suggest rounding the calculation *up* to the next whole number at the asterisk. Board feet and lineal feet should be rounded.

☞ See page 550 for more information about the geometric formulas used in this *QuickCalculator*. See page 414-415 for walls priced per board foot.

**QuickCalculator**

# Non-Bearing Wall

*Use this sheet and a calculator to determine the board feet in an interior wall.*
*Calculate each line from left to right. Do math in parentheses first.*

❶ The wall(s) are _____ lineal feet long.

❷ The studs are _____ inches thick.

❸ There are _____ plates.

❹ The wall(s) are _____ feet tall.

❺ The studs are _____ inches wide.

❻ There are _____ door and window openings.

❼ There are _____ corners.

❽ The studs are _____ inches on center.

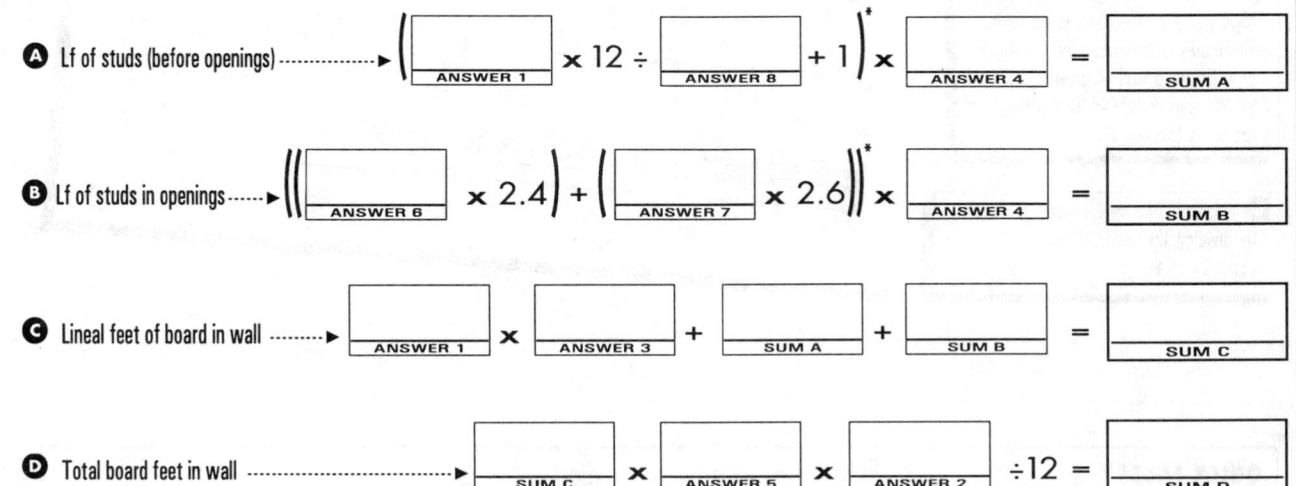

Ⓐ Lf of studs (before openings) ┈┈┈▶ ( [ANSWER 1] × 12 ÷ [ANSWER 8] + 1 )* × [ANSWER 4] = [SUM A]

Ⓑ Lf of studs in openings ┈┈┈▶ (( [ANSWER 6] × 2.4 ) + ( [ANSWER 7] × 2.6 ))* × [ANSWER 4] = [SUM B]

Ⓒ Lineal feet of board in wall ┈┈┈▶ [ANSWER 1] × [ANSWER 3] + [SUM A] + [SUM B] = [SUM C]

Ⓓ Total board feet in wall ┈┈┈┈┈┈┈▶ [SUM C] × [ANSWER 5] × [ANSWER 2] ÷12 = [SUM D]

*Round up answer to next whole number here before continuing with calculation.*

**Converting Inches to Decimal Feet**   **1"** = .084 • **2"** = .167 • **3"** = .25 • **4"** = .334 • **5"** = .417 • **6"** = .5 • **7"** = .584 • **8"** = .667 • **9"** = .75 • **10"** = .834 • **11"** = .917

# USING THE PRISMATIC ROOM
## QuickCalculator

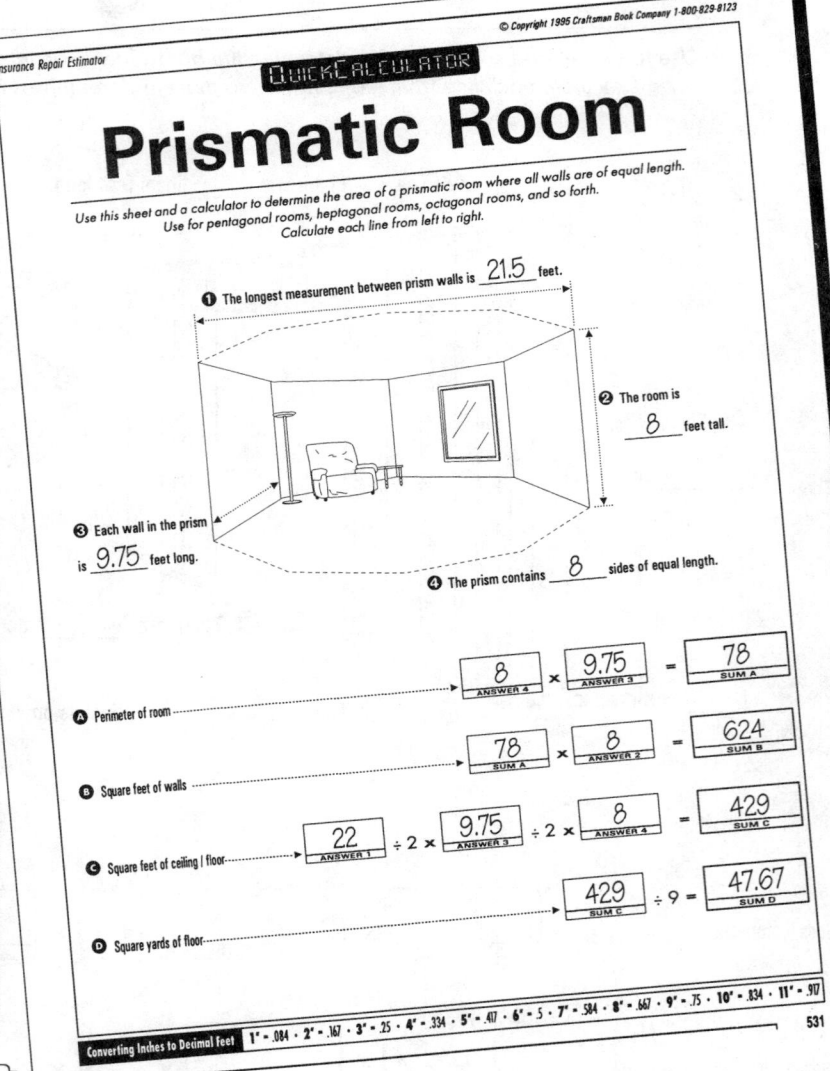

Insurance Repair Estimator

### QuickCalculator

# Prismatic Room

Use this sheet and a calculator to determine the area of a prismatic room where all walls are of equal length.
Use for pentagonal rooms, heptagonal rooms, octagonal rooms, and so forth.
Calculate each line from left to right.

❶ The longest measurement between prism walls is **21.5** feet.

❷ The room is **8** feet tall.

❸ Each wall in the prism is **9.75** feet long.

❹ The prism contains **8** sides of equal length.

Ⓐ Perimeter of room ............ $\boxed{8}_{\text{ANSWER 4}} \times \boxed{9.75}_{\text{ANSWER 3}} = \boxed{78}_{\text{SUM A}}$

Ⓑ Square feet of walls ............ $\boxed{78}_{\text{SUM A}} \times \boxed{8}_{\text{ANSWER 2}} = \boxed{624}_{\text{SUM B}}$

Ⓒ Square feet of ceiling / floor ............ $\boxed{22}_{\text{ANSWER 1}} \div 2 \times \boxed{9.75}_{\text{ANSWER 3}} \div 2 \times \boxed{8}_{\text{ANSWER 4}} = \boxed{429}_{\text{SUM C}}$

Ⓓ Square yards of floor ............ $\boxed{429}_{\text{SUM C}} \div 9 = \boxed{47.67}_{\text{SUM D}}$

Converting Inches to Decimal Feet | 1" = .084 • 2" = .167 • 3" = .25 • 4" = .334 • 5" = .417 • 6" = .5 • 7" = .584 • 8" = .667 • 9" = .75 • 10" = .834 • 11" = .917

531

---

Ⓐ Calculates the perimeter of the prism by multiplying the number of prism walls (Answer 4) by the length of the prism walls (Answer 3).

Ⓑ Calculates the square feet of walls by multiplying the perimeter of the room (Sum A) by the room height (Answer 2).

Ⓒ Calculates the square feet of ceiling / floor by taking the longest dimension between walls (Answer 1) and dividing by 2 to determine the radius. The radius is multiplied by the length of each prism wall (Answer 3), divided by two and multiplied by the height of the walls (Answer 2).

Ⓓ Calculates the square yards of flooring by dividing the square feet of floor (Sum C) by 9.

---

## QUICK FACTS

☞ The sample *QuickCalculator* sheet shown above contains quantities that have been rounded. We suggest rounding lineal feet to two decimal places then to the nearest inch when converting to inches. Square feet should probably be rounded to the nearest square foot and square yards should be rounded up to the nearest 1/3 or 1/4 yard.

☞ See page 550 for more information about the geometric formulas used in this *QuickCalculator*.

## ▬QUICKCALCULATOR▬

# Prismatic Room

*Use this sheet and a calculator to determine the area of a prismatic room where all walls are of equal length.*
*Use for pentagonal rooms, heptagonal rooms, octagonal rooms, and so forth.*
*Calculate each line from left to right.*

❶ The longest measurement between prism walls is _____ feet.

❷ The room is

_____ feet tall.

❸ Each wall in the prism

is _____ feet long.

❹ The prism contains _____ sides of equal length.

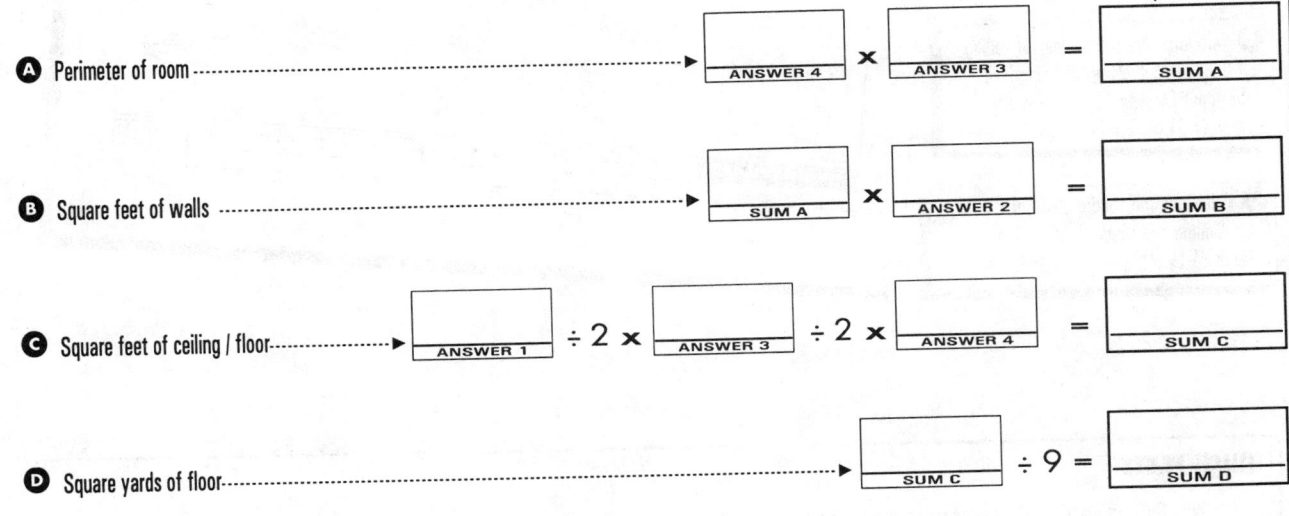

Ⓐ Perimeter of room ---------------------------------→ | ANSWER 4 | × | ANSWER 3 | = | SUM A |

Ⓑ Square feet of walls ----------------------------→ | SUM A | × | ANSWER 2 | = | SUM B |

Ⓒ Square feet of ceiling / floor-------------→ | ANSWER 1 | ÷ 2 × | ANSWER 3 | ÷ 2 × | ANSWER 4 | = | SUM C |

Ⓓ Square yards of floor-------------------------→ | SUM C | ÷ 9 = | SUM D |

**Converting Inches to Decimal Feet** | **1"** = .084 • **2"** = .167 • **3"** = .25 • **4"** = .334 • **5"** = .417 • **6"** = .5 • **7"** = .584 • **8"** = .667 • **9"** = .75 • **10"** = .834 • **11"** = .917

545

# USING THE RECTANGULAR ROOM QUICKCALCULATOR

**A** Calculates the perimeter of the room by adding the length (Answer 1) to the width (Answer 3) and multiplying by two.

**B** Calculates the square feet of walls by multiplying the perimeter of the room (Sum A) by the room height (Answer 2).

**C** Calculates the square feet of ceiling / floor by multiplying the length of the room (Answer 1) by the width (Answer 3).

**D** Calculates the square yards of flooring by dividing the square feet of floor (Sum C) by 9.

## QUICK FACTS

☞ The sample *QuickCalculator* sheet shown above contains quantities that have been rounded. We suggest rounding lineal feet to two decimal places then to the nearest inch when converting to inches. Square feet should probably be rounded to the nearest square foot and square yards should be rounded to the nearest 1/3 or 1/4 yard.

☞ See page 550 for more information about the geometric formulas used in this *QuickCalculator*.

## QuickCalculator

# Rectangular Room

*Use this sheet and a calculator to determine the area of a rectangular room.*
*Calculate each line from left to right.  Do math in parentheses first.*

❶ The room is _____ feet long.

❷ The room is _____ feet tall.

❸ The room is _____ feet wide.

Ⓐ Perimeter of room ·········· ( [ANSWER 1] + [ANSWER 3] ) x 2 = [SUM A]

Ⓑ Square feet of walls ·········· [SUM A] x [ANSWER 2] = [SUM B]

Ⓒ Square feet of ceiling / floor ·········· [ANSWER 1] x [ANSWER 3] = [SUM C]

Ⓓ Square yards of floor ·········· [SUM C] ÷ 9 = [SUM D]

| Converting Inches to Decimal Feet | **1"** = .084 • **2"** = .167 • **3"** = .25 • **4"** = .334 • **5"** = .417 • **6"** = .5 • **7"** = .584 • **8"** = .667 • **9"** = .75 • **10"** = .834 • **11"** = .917 |
|---|---|

# USING THE ROUND ROOM
## QuickCalculator

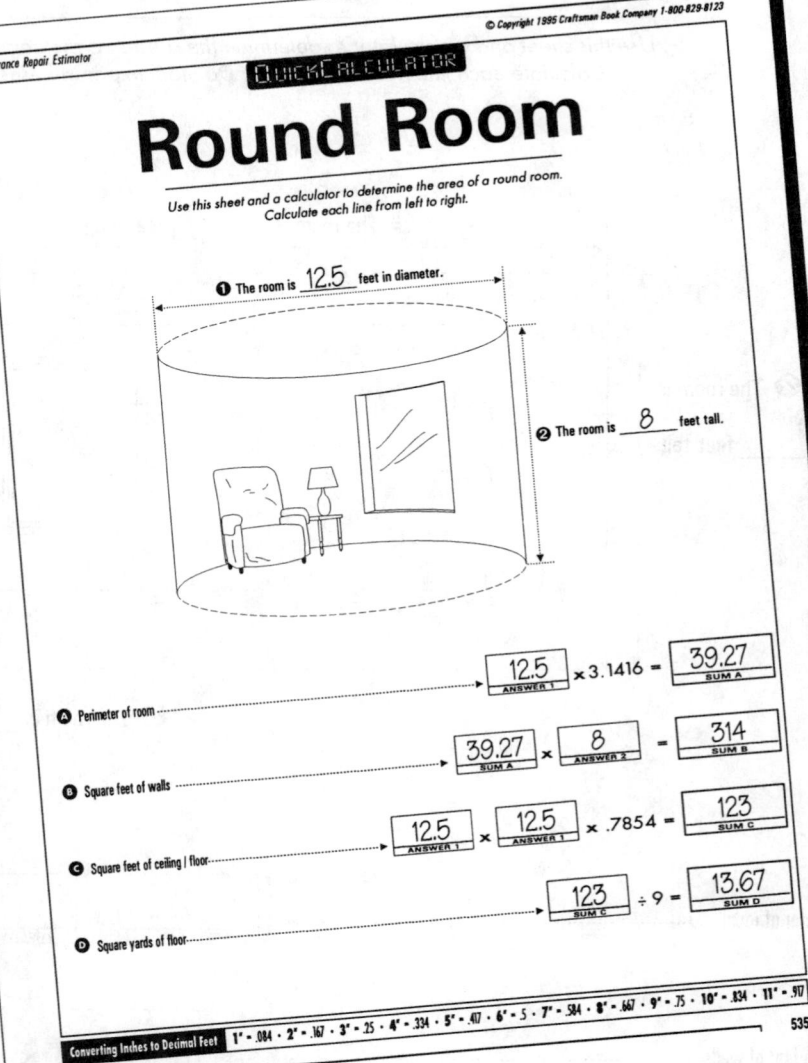

© Copyright 1995 Craftsman Book Company 1-800-829-8123

*Insurance Repair Estimator*

### QuickCalculator

# Round Room

*Use this sheet and a calculator to determine the area of a round room.*
*Calculate each line from left to right.*

❶ The room is __12.5__ feet in diameter.

❷ The room is __8__ feet tall.

**A** Perimeter of room ..... $\boxed{12.5}_{\text{ANSWER 1}} \times 3.1416 = \boxed{39.27}_{\text{SUM A}}$

**B** Square feet of walls ..... $\boxed{39.27}_{\text{SUM A}} \times \boxed{8}_{\text{ANSWER 2}} = \boxed{314}_{\text{SUM B}}$

**C** Square feet of ceiling / floor ..... $\boxed{12.5}_{\text{ANSWER 1}} \times \boxed{12.5}_{\text{ANSWER 1}} \times .7854 = \boxed{123}_{\text{SUM C}}$

**D** Square yards of floor ..... $\boxed{123}_{\text{SUM C}} \div 9 = \boxed{13.67}_{\text{SUM D}}$

Converting Inches to Decimal Feet   **1"** = .084 · **2"** = .167 · **3"** = .25 · **4"** = .334 · **5"** = .417 · **6"** = .5 · **7"** = .584 · **8"** = .667 · **9"** = .75 · **10"** = .834 · **11"** = .917

535

**A** Calculates the perimeter of the circle by multiplying the diameter (Answer 1) by Pi (3.1416).

**B** Calculates the square feet of walls by multiplying the perimeter of the room (Sum A) by the room height (Answer 2).

**C** Calculates the square feet of ceiling / floor by squaring the diameter (Answer 1 times Answer 1) and multiplying by .7854.

**D** Calculates the square yards of flooring by dividing the square feet of floor (Sum C) by 9.

### QUICK FACTS

☞ The sample *QuickCalculator* sheet shown above contains quantities that have been rounded. We suggest rounding lineal feet to two decimal places then to the nearest inch when converting to inches. Square feet should probably be rounded to the nearest square foot and square yards should be rounded to the nearest 1/3 or 1/4 yard.

☞ See page 550 for more information about the geometric formulas used in this *QuickCalculator*.

## QUICKCALCULATOR

# Round Room

*Use this sheet and a calculator to determine the area of a round room.*
*Calculate each line from left to right.*

❶ The room is _____ feet in diameter.

❷ The room is _____ feet tall.

**Ⓐ** Perimeter of room ┄┄┄┄┄┄┄┄┄┄┄┄┄┄┄┄┄➤ | ANSWER 1 | × 3.1416 = | SUM A |

**Ⓑ** Square feet of walls ┄┄┄┄┄┄┄┄┄┄┄┄┄➤ | SUM A | × | ANSWER 2 | = | SUM B |

**Ⓒ** Square feet of ceiling / floor ┄┄┄┄┄➤ | ANSWER 1 | × | ANSWER 1 | × .7854 = | SUM C |

**Ⓓ** Square yards of floor ┄┄┄┄┄┄┄┄┄┄┄┄┄➤ | SUM C | ÷ 9 = | SUM D |

**Converting Inches to Decimal Feet**    **1″** = .084 • **2″** = .167 • **3″** = .25 • **4″** = .334 • **5″** = .417 • **6″** = .5 • **7″** = .584 • **8″** = .667 • **9″** = .75 • **10″** = .834 • **11″** = .917

# QuickCalculator mathematics

## CIRCLE

*Area*

❶ = Pi x radius²

❷ = .7854 x diameter²

❸ = .0796 x perimeter²

*Perimeter*

❶ = Pi x diameter

## PARALLELOGRAM

*Area*

❶ = base x height

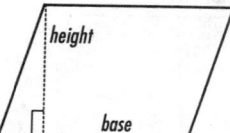

## PRISM

*Area*

❶ = sum of sides ÷ 2 x radius

## RECTANGLE

*Area*

❶ = length x width

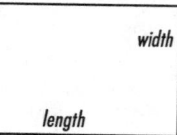

## TRAPEZOID

*Area*

❶ = base + top ÷ 2 x height

## TRIANGLE

*Area*

❶ = base x height ÷ 2

## PYTHAGOREAN THEORM

*Rafter length*

❶ rafter length² = rise² + run²

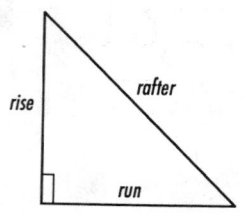

## CONVERSION FACTORS

| DIVIDE | BY | TO CONVERT TO |
|---|---|---|
| square inches | 144 | square feet |
| square inches | 144 | board feet |
| cubic inches | 1,728 | cubic feet |
| cubic inches | 46,656 | cubic yards |
| square feet | 9 | square yards |
| square feet | 100 | squares |
| cubic feet | 27 | cubic yards |
| feet | 16.5 | rods |
| rods | 40 | furlongs |
| feet | 5,280 | miles |
| meters | 1,609 | miles |
| yards | 1,760 | miles |

| MULTIPLY | BY | TO CONVERT TO |
|---|---|---|
| inches | 2.54 | centimeters |
| square inches | 6.4516 | square centimeters |
| square inches | .0069 | square feet |
| square feet | 9.29 | square centimeters |
| square feet | .0929 | square meters |
| square yards | .8361 | square meters |
| square meters | 1.1959 | square yards |
| centimeters | .3937 | inches |
| feet | .3048 | meters |
| meters | 3.281 | feet |
| yards | 91.44 | centimeters |
| yards | .9144 | meters |
| cubic feet | .0283 | cubic meters |
| cubic meters | 35.3145 | cubic feet |
| cubic meters | 1.3079 | cubic yards |
| cubic yards | .7646 | cubic meters |
| cubic inches | 16.3872 | cubic centimeters |
| cubic centimeters | .0610 | cubic inches |
| cubic meters | 1,000 | cubic liters |

# index

# Practical References for Builders

## Construction Forms & Contracts

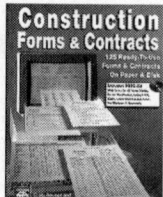

125 forms you can copy and use — or load into your computer (from the FREE disk enclosed). Then you can customize the forms to fit your company, fill them out, and print. Loads into *Word* for *Windows*™, *Lotus 1-2-3*, *WordPerfect*, *Works*, or *Excel* programs. You'll find forms covering accounting, estimating, fieldwork, contracts, and general office. Each form comes with complete instructions on when to use it and how to fill it out. These forms were designed, tested and used by contractors, and will help keep your business organized, profitable and out of legal, accounting and collection troubles. Includes a CD-ROM for *Windows*™ and Mac. **400 pages, 8¹/₂ x 11, $41.75**

## CD Estimator

If your computer has *Windows*™ and a CD-ROM drive, *CD Estimator* puts at your fingertips 85,000 construction costs for new construction, remodeling, renovation & insurance repair, electrical, plumbing, HVAC and painting. You'll also have the *National Estimator* program — a stand-alone estimating program for Windows that Remodeling magazine called a "computer wiz." Quarterly cost updates are available at no charge on the Internet. To help you create professional-looking estimates, the disk includes over 40 construction estimating and bidding forms in a format that's perfect for nearly any word processing or spreadsheet program for *Windows*™. And to top it off, a 70-minute interactive video teaches you how to use this CD-ROM to estimate construction costs. **CD Estimator is $68.50**

## Contractor's Guide to QuickBooks Pro 2000

This user-friendly manual walks you through QuickBooks Pro's detailed setup procedure and explains step-by-step how to create a first-rate accounting system. You'll learn in days, rather than weeks, how to use QuickBooks Pro to get your contracting business organized, with simple, fast accounting procedures. On the CD included with the book you'll find a QuickBooks Pro file preconfigured for a construction company (you drag it over onto your computer and plug in your own company's data). You'll also get a complete estimating program, including a database, and a job costing program that lets you export your estimates to QuickBooks Pro. It even includes many useful construction forms to use in your business. **304 pages, 8¹/₂ x 11, $44.50**

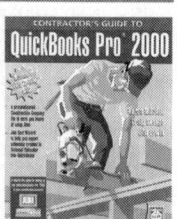

## National Construction Estimator

Current building costs for residential, commercial, and industrial construction. Estimated prices for every common building material. Provides manhours, recommended crew, and gives the labor cost for installation. Includes a CD-ROM with an electronic version of the book with *National Estimator*, a stand-alone *Windows*™ estimating program, plus an interactive multimedia video that shows how to use the disk to compile construction cost estimates. **616 pages, 8¹/₂ x 11, $47.50. Revised annually**

## Contracting in All 50 States

Every state has its own licensing requirements that you must meet to do business there. These are usually written exams, financial requirements, and letters of reference. This book shows how to get a building, mechanical or specialty contractor's license, qualify for DOT work, and register as an out-of-state corporation, for every state in the U.S. It lists addresses, phone numbers, application fees, requirements, where an exam is required, what's covered on the exam and how much weight each area of construction is given on the exam. You'll find just about everything you need to know in order to apply for your out-of-state license. **416 pages, 8¹/₂ x 11, $36.00**

## How to Succeed With Your Own Construction Business

Everything you need to start your own construction business: setting up the paperwork, finding the work, advertising, using contracts, dealing with lenders, estimating, scheduling, finding and keeping good employees, keeping the books, and coping with success. If you're considering starting your own construction business, all the knowledge, tips, and blank forms you need are here. **336 pages, 8¹/₂ x 11, $28.50**

## Contractor's Guide to the Building Code Revised

This new edition was written in collaboration with the International Conference of Building Officials, writers of the code. It explains in plain English exactly what the latest edition of the *Uniform Building Code* requires. Based on the 1997 code, it explains the changes and what they mean for the builder. Also covers the *Uniform Mechanical Code* and the *Uniform Plumbing Code*. Shows how to design and construct residential and light commercial buildings that'll pass inspection the first time. Suggests how to work with an inspector to minimize construction costs, what common building shortcuts are likely to be cited, and where exceptions may be granted. **320 pages, 8¹/₂ x 11, $39.00**

## National Painting Cost Estimator

A complete guide to estimating painting costs for just about any type of residential, commercial, or industrial painting, whether by brush, spray, or roller. Shows typical costs and bid prices for fast, medium, and slow work, including material costs per gallon; square feet covered per gallon; square feet covered per manhour; labor, material, overhead, and taxes per 100 square feet; and how much to add for profit. Includes a CD-ROM with an electronic version of the book with *National Estimator*, a stand-alone *Windows*™ estimating program, plus an interactive multimedia video that shows how to use the disk to compile construction cost estimates. **440 pages, 8¹/₂ x 11, $48.00. Revised annually**

## Troubleshooting Guide to Residential Construction

How to solve practically every construction problem - before it happens to you! With this book you'll learn from the mistakes other builders made as they faced 63 typical residential construction problems. Filled with clear photos and drawings that explain how to enhance your reputation as well as your bottom line by avoiding problems that plague most builders. Shows how to avoid, or fix, problems ranging from defective slabs, walls and ceilings, through roofing, plumbing & HVAC, to paint. **304 pages, 8¹/₂x 11, $32.50**

## Basic Engineering for Builders

If you've ever been stumped by an engineering problem on the job, yet wanted to avoid the expense of hiring a qualified engineer, you should have this book. Here you'll find engineering principles explained in non-technical language and practical methods for applying them on the job. With the help of this book you'll be able to understand engineering functions in the plans and how to meet the requirements, how to get permits issued without the help of an engineer, and anticipate requirements for concrete, steel, wood and masonry. See why you sometimes have to hire an engineer and what you can undertake yourself: surveying, concrete, lumber loads and stresses, steel, masonry, plumbing, and HVAC systems. This book is designed to help the builder save money by understanding engineering principles that you can incorporate into the jobs you bid. **400 pages, 8¹/₂ x 11, $34.00**

## Plumbing & HVAC Manhour Estimates

Hundreds of tested and proven manhours for installing just about any plumbing and HVAC component you're likely to use in residential, commercial, and industrial work. You'll find manhours for installing piping systems, specialties, fixtures and accessories, ducting systems, and HVAC equipment. If you estimate the price of plumbing, you shouldn't be without the reliable, proven manhours in this unique book. **224 pages, 5¹/₂ x 8¹/₂, $28.25**

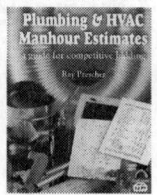

## Estimating with Microsoft *Excel*

Most builders estimate with *Excel* because it's easy to learn, quick to use, and can be customized to your style of estimating. Here you'll find step-by-step how to create your own customized automated spreadsheet estimating program for use with *Excel*. You'll learn how to use the magic of Excel in creating detail sheets, cost breakdown summaries, and linking. You can even create your own macros. Includes a CD-ROM that illustrates examples in the book and provides you with templates you can use to set up your own estimating system. **148 pages, 8¹/₂ x 11, $49.95**

## Construction Estimating Reference Data

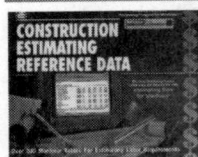

Provides the 300 most useful manhour tables for practically every item of construction. Labor requirements are listed for sitework, concrete work, masonry, steel, carpentry, thermal and moisture protection, doors and windows, finishes, mechanical and electrical. Each section details the work being estimated and gives appropriate crew size and equipment needed. Includes a CD-ROM with an electronic version of the book with *National Estimator*, a stand-alone *Windows*™ estimating program, plus an interactive multimedia video that shows how to use the disk to compile construction cost estimates. **432 pages, 11 x 8½, $39.50**

## Basic Lumber Engineering for Builders

Beam and lumber requirements for many jobs aren't always clear, especially with changing building codes and lumber products. Most of the time you rely on your own "rules of thumb" when figuring spans or lumber engineering. This book can help you fill the gap between what you can find in the building code span tables and what you need to pay a certified engineer to do. With its large, clear illustrations and examples, this book shows you how to figure stresses for pre-engineered wood or wood structural members, how to calculate loads, and how to design your own girders, joists and beams. Included FREE with the book — an easy-to-use limited version of NorthBridge Software's *Wood Beam Sizing* program. **272 pages, 8½ x 11, $38.00**

## Concrete Construction & Estimating

Explains how to estimate the quantity of labor and materials needed, plan the job, erect fiberglass, steel, or prefabricated forms, install shores and scaffolding, handle the concrete into place, set joints, finish and cure the concrete. Full of practical reference data, cost estimates, and examples. **571 pages, 5½ x 8½, $25.00**

## Building Contractor's Exam Preparation Guide

Passing today's contractor's exams can be a major task. This book shows you how to study, how questions are likely to be worded, and the kinds of choices usually given for answers. Includes sample questions from actual state, county, and city examinations, plus a sample exam to practice on. This book isn't a substitute for the study material that your testing board recommends, but it will help prepare you for the types of questions — and their correct answers — that are likely to appear on the actual exam. Knowing how to answer these questions, as well as what to expect from the exam, can greatly increase your chances of passing. **320 pages, 8½ x 11, $35.00**

## Contractor's Survival Manual

How to survive hard times and succeed during the up cycles. Shows what to do when the bills can't be paid, finding money and buying time, transferring debt, and all the alternatives to bankruptcy. Explains how to build profits, avoid problems in zoning and permits, taxes, time-keeping, and payroll. Unconventional advice on how to invest in inflation, get high appraisals, trade and postpone income, and stay hip-deep in profitable work. **160 pages, 8½ x 11, $22.25**

## Estimating Electrical Construction

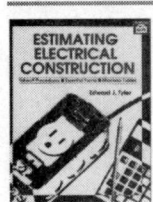

Like taking a class in how to estimate materials and labor for residential and commercial electrical construction. Written by an A.S.P.E. National Estimator of the Year, it teaches you how to use labor units, the plan take-off, and the bid summary to make an accurate estimate, how to deal with suppliers, use pricing sheets, and modify labor units. Provides extensive labor unit tables and blank forms for your next electrical job. **272 pages, 8½ x 11, $19.00**

## Estimating Excavation

How to calculate the amount of dirt you'll have to move and the cost of owning and operating the machines you'll do it with. Detailed, step-by-step instructions on how to assign bid prices to each part of the job, including labor and equipment costs. Also, the best ways to set up an organized and logical estimating system, take off from contour maps, estimate quantities in irregular areas, and figure your overhead. **448 pages, 8½ x 11, $39.50**

## Builder's Guide to Room Additions

How to tackle problems that are unique to additions, such as requirements for basement conversions, reinforcing ceiling joists for second-story conversions, handling problems in attic conversions, what's required for footings, foundations, and slabs, how to design the best bathroom for the space, and much more. Besides actual construction, you'll even find help in designing, planning, and estimating your room addition jobs. 3 **52 pages, 8½ x 11, $27.25**

## Home Inspection Handbook

Every area you need to check in a home inspection — especially in older homes. Twenty complete inspection checklists: building site, foundation and basement, structural, bathrooms, chimneys and flues, ceilings, interior & exterior finishes, electrical, plumbing, HVAC, insects, vermin and decay, and more. Also includes information on starting and running your own home inspection business. **324 pages, 5½ x 8½, $24.95**

## Steel-Frame House Construction

Framing with steel has obvious advantages over wood, yet building with steel requires new skills that can present challenges to the wood builder. This new book explains the secrets of steel framing techniques for building homes, whether pre-engineered or built stick by stick. It shows you the techniques, the tools, the materials, and how you can make it happen. Includes hundreds of photos and illustrations, plus a CD-ROM with steel framing details. **328 pages, 8½ x 11, $39.75**

## National Building Cost Manual

Square foot costs for residential, commercial, industrial, and farm buildings. Quickly work up a reliable budget estimate based on actual materials and design features, area, shape, wall height, number of floors, and support requirements. Includes all the important variables that can make any building unique from a cost standpoint. **240 pages, 8½ x 11, $23.00. Revised annually**

## Markup & Profit: A Contractor's Guide

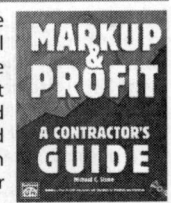

In order to succeed in a construction business, you have to be able to price your jobs to cover all labor, material and overhead expenses, and make a decent profit. The problem is knowing what markup to use. You don't want to lose jobs because you charge too much, and you don't want to work for free because you've charged too little. If you know how to calculate markup, you can apply it to your job costs to find the right sales price for your work. This book gives you tried and tested formulas, with step-by-step instructions and easy-to-follow examples, so you can easily figure the markup that's right for your business. Includes a CD-ROM with forms and checklists for your use. **320 pages, 8½ x 11, $32.50**

## National Electrical Estimator

This year's prices for installation of all common electrical work: conduit, wire, boxes, fixtures, switches, outlets, loadcenters, panelboards, raceway, duct, signal systems, and more. Provides material costs, manhours per unit, and total installed cost. Explains what you should know to estimate each part of an electrical system. Includes a CD-ROM with an electronic version of the book with *National Estimator*, a stand-alone *Windows*™ estimating program, plus an interactive multimedia video that shows how to use the disk to compile construction cost estimates. **520 pages, 8½ x 11, $47.75. Revised annually**

## Residential Plumbing Inspection

You never know what you'll find in a plumbing inspection. Corrosion between pipes, illegal traps, and even unsafe shut-off valves can be found in crawl spaces and attics of homes that appear on the surface to be built perfectly to code. This unique book is filled with illustrations and photographs of typical plumbing code violations you're likely to encounter during inspections. Then it explains what should be done to bring them to code. It covers all the areas: drainage systems, vents and venting, fixtures, water distribution, fuel gas piping, water heaters, vents and combustion, private wells and pumps, solar heating systems, and more. **90 pages, 8½ x 11, $49.95. Published by ITA**

## Roofing Construction & Estimating

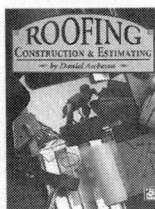

Installation, repair and estimating for nearly every type of roof covering available today in residential and commercial structures: asphalt shingles, roll roofing, wood shingles and shakes, clay tile, slate, metal, built-up, and elastomeric. Covers sheathing and underlayment techniques, as well as secrets for installing leakproof valleys. Many estimating tips help you minimize waste, as well as insure a profit on every job. Troubleshooting techniques help you identify the true source of most leaks. Over 300 large, clear illustrations help you find the answer to just about all your roofing questions. **432 pages, 8¹/₂ x 11, $35.00**

## Rough Framing Carpentry

If you'd like to make good money working outdoors as a framer, this is the book for you. Here you'll find shortcuts to laying out studs; speed cutting blocks, trimmers and plates by eye; quickly building and blocking rake walls; installing ceiling backing, ceiling joists, and truss joists; cutting and assembling hip trusses and California fills; arches and drop ceilings — all with production line procedures that save you time and help you make more money. Over 100 on-the-job photos of how to do it right and what can go wrong. **304 pages, 8¹/₂ x 11, $26.50**

## National Repair & Remodeling Estimator

The complete pricing guide for dwelling reconstruction costs. Reliable, specific data you can apply on every repair and remodeling job. Up-to-date material costs and labor figures based on thousands of jobs across the country. Provides recommended crew sizes; average production rates; exact material, equipment, and labor costs; a total unit cost and a total price including overhead and profit. Separate listings for high- and low-volume builders, so prices shown are specific for any size business. Estimating tips specific to repair and remodeling work to make your bids complete, realistic, and profitable. Includes a CD-ROM with an electronic version of the book with *National Estimator*, a stand-alone *Windows*™ estimating program, plus an interactive multimedia video that shows how to use the disk to compile construction cost estimates. **296 pages, 8¹/₂ x 11, $48.50. Revised annually**

## Residential Electrical Estimating

A fast, accurate pricing system proven on over 1000 residential jobs. Using the manhours provided, combined with material prices from your wholesaler, you quickly work up estimates based on degree of difficulty. These manhours come from a working electrical contractor's records — not some pricing agency. You'll find prices for every type of electrical job you're likely to estimate — from service entrances to ceiling fans. **320 pages, 8¹/₂ x 11, $29.00**

## Residential Structure & Framing

With this easy-to-understand guide you'll learn how to calculate loads, size joists and beams, and tackle many common structural problems facing residential contractors. It covers cantilevered floors, complex roof structures, tall window walls, and seismic and wind bracing. Plus, you'll learn field-proven production techniques for advanced wall, floor, and roof framing with both dimensional and engineered lumber. You'll find information on sizing joists and beams, framing with wood I-joists, supporting oversized dormers, unequal-pitched roofs, coffered ceilings, and more. Fully illustrated with lots of photos. **272 pages, 8¹/₂ x 11, $34.95. Published by JLC**

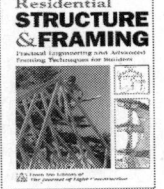

## Electrician's Exam Preparation Guide

Need help in passing the apprentice, journeyman, or master electrician's exam? This is a book of questions and answers based on actual electrician's exams over the last few years. Almost a thousand multiple-choice questions — exactly the type you'll find on the exam — cover every area of electrical installation: electrical drawings, services and systems, transformers, capacitors, distribution equipment, branch circuits, feeders, calculations, measuring and testing, and more. It gives you the correct answer, an explanation, and where to find it in the latest *NEC*. Also tells how to apply for the test, how best to study, and what to expect on examination day. **352 pages, 8¹/₂ x 11, $32.00**

## Finish Carpenter's Manual

Everything you need to know to be a finish carpenter: assessing a job before you begin, and tricks of the trade from a master finish carpenter. Easy-to-follow instructions for installing doors and windows, ceiling treatments (including fancy beams, corbels, cornices and moldings), wall treatments (including wainscoting and sheet paneling), and the finishing touches of chair, picture, and plate rails. Specialized interior work includes cabinetry and built-ins, stair finish work, and closets. Also covers exterior trims and porches. Includes manhour tables for finish work, and hundreds of illustrations and photos. **208 pages, 8¹/₂ x 11, $22.50**

## Carpentry Estimating

Simple, clear instructions to help you take off quantities and figure costs for all rough and finish carpentry. Provides checklists, manhour tables, and worksheets with calculation factors built in. Take the guesswork out of estimating carpentry so you get accurate labor and material costs every time. Includes FREE *National Estimator* software, with all the manhours in the book, plus the carpentry estimating worksheets in formats that work with *Word*, *Excel*, *WordPerfect*, and *MS Works* for *Windows*™. **336 pages, 8¹/₂ x 11, $35.50**

## Constructionary

A unique pocket-sized dictionary of up-to-date construction words and phrases in English-Spanish and Spanish-English. Here you'll find over 1000 construction terms and 70 commonly used on-the-job phrases. This dictionary includes phonetic pronunciation, tool section, commonly used sentences, and conversion tables. **170 pages, 4 x 7, $14.95**

## Contractor's Year-Round Tax Guide Revised

How to set up and run your construction business to minimize taxes: corporate tax strategy and how to use it to your advantage, and what you should be aware of in contracts with others. Covers tax shelters for builders, write-offs and investments that will reduce your taxes, accounting methods that are best for contractors, and what the I.R.S. allows and what it often questions. **192 pages, 8¹/₂ x 11, $26.50**

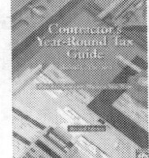

## Cost Records for Construction Estimating

How to organize and use cost information from jobs just completed to make more accurate estimates in the future. Explains how to keep the records you need to track costs for sitework, footings, foundations, framing, interior finish, siding and trim, masonry, and subcontract expense. Provides sample forms. **208 pages, 8¹/₂ x 11, $15.75**

## Kitchens & Baths

Practical, detailed solutions to every problem you're likely to approach when constructing or remodeling kitchens and baths. Over 50 articles from the *Journal of Light Construction* plus up-to-date reference material on codes, safety, space planning and construction methods for kitchens and bathrooms. Includes over 400 photos and illustrations. If you're looking for a complete reference on designing, remodeling, or constructing kitchens and baths, you should have this book. **256 pages, 8 x 11, $34.95**

## Painter's Handbook

Loaded with "how-to" information you'll use every day to get professional results on any job: the best way to prepare a surface for painting or repainting; selecting and using the right materials and tools (including airless spray); tips for repainting kitchens, bathrooms, cabinets, eaves and porches; how to match and blend colors; why coatings fail and what to do about it. Lists 30 profitable specialties in the painting business. **320 pages, 8¹/₂ x 11, $21.25**

## Professional Kitchen Design

Remodeling kitchens requires a "special" touch — one that blends artistic flair with function to create a kitchen with charm and personality as well as one that is easy to work in. Here you'll find how to make the best use of the space available in any kitchen design job, as well as tips and lessons on how to design one-wall, two-wall, L-shaped, U-shaped, peninsula and island kitchens. Also includes what you need to know to run a profitable kitchen design business. **176 pages, 8¹/₂ x 11, $24.50**

## Simplified Guide to Construction Law

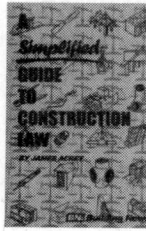

Here you'll find easy-to-read, paragraphed-sized samples of how the courts have viewed common areas of disagreement — and litigation — in the building industry. You'll read about legal problems that real builders have faced, and how the court ruled. This book will tell you what you need to know about contracts, torts, fraud, misrepresentation, warranty and strict liability, construction defects, indemnity, insurance, mechanics liens, bonds and bonding, statutes of limitation, arbitration, and more. These are simplified examples that illustrate not necessarily who is right and who is wrong — but who the law has sided with. **298 pages, 5¹/₂ x 8¹/₂, $29.95**

## Vest Pocket Guide to HVAC Electricity

This handy guide will be a constant source of useful information for anyone working with electrical systems for heating, ventilating, refrigeration, and air conditioning. Includes essential tables and diagrams for calculating and installing electrical systems for powering and controlling motors, fans, heating elements, compressors, transformers and every electrical part of an HVAC system. **304 pages, 3¹/₂ x 5¹/₂, $18.00**

## Wood-Frame House Construction

Step-by-step construction details, from the layout of the outer walls, excavation and formwork, to finish carpentry and painting. Contains all new, clear illustrations and explanations updated for construction in the '90s. Everything you need to know about framing, roofing, siding, interior finishings, floor covering and stairs — your complete book of wood-frame homebuilding. **320 pages, 8¹/₂ x 11, $25.50. Revised edition**

## Profits in Buying & Renovating Homes

Step-by-step instructions for selecting, repairing, improving, and selling highly profitable "fixer-uppers." Shows which price ranges offer the highest profit-to-investment ratios, which neighborhoods offer the best return, practical directions for repairs, and tips on dealing with buyers, sellers, and real estate agents. Shows you how to determine your profit before you buy, what "bargains" to avoid, and how to make simple, profitable, inexpensive upgrades. **304 pages, 8¹/₂ x 11, $19.75**

## National Building Assembly Costs

Complete assembly costs for all construction across the 16 CSI divisions. These prices include all the individual line items included in a typical construction assembly, added together to generate an assembly "unit" price. With unit price estimates from the assemblies section, and subcontractor unit prices from the line item cost information, you can put together an estimate for just about any project in minutes. It's far more accurate than a square foot cost estimate, yet takes a fraction of the time a stick-by-stick estimate takes. Includes a CD-ROM with estimating data you can use, and a demo version of WinEst LT, a powerful estimating program for light construction that includes the cost data from Craftsman's National Construction Estimator. **320 pages, 8¹/₂ x 11, $44.75**

## Roof Framing

Shows how to frame any type of roof in common use today, even if you've never framed a roof before. Includes using a pocket calculator to figure any common, hip, valley, or jack rafter length in seconds. Over 400 illustrations cover every measurement and every cut on each type of roof: gable, hip, Dutch, Tudor, gambrel, shed, gazebo, and more.
**480 pages, 5¹/₂ x 8¹/₂, $22.00**

---

# BUSINESS REPLY MAIL
FIRST CLASS MAIL PERMIT NO. 271 CARLSBAD, CA

POSTAGE WILL BE PAID BY ADDRESSEE

**Craftsman Book Company**
6058 Corte del Cedro
P.O. Box 6500
Carlsbad, CA 92018-9974

# BUSINESS REPLY MAIL
FIRST CLASS MAIL PERMIT NO. 271 CARLSBAD, CA

POSTAGE WILL BE PAID BY ADDRESSEE

**Craftsman Book Company**
6058 Corte del Cedro
P.O. Box 6500
Carlsbad, CA 92018-9974

# BUSINESS REPLY MAIL
FIRST CLASS MAIL PERMIT NO. 271 CARLSBAD, CA

POSTAGE WILL BE PAID BY ADDRESSEE

**Craftsman Book Company**
6058 Corte del Cedro
P.O. Box 6500
Carlsbad, CA 92018-9974